Stratigraphic Geology

A Series of Geology Texts

EDITORS: James Gilluly and A. O. Woodford

Stratigraphic Geology

by **MAURICE GIGNOUX**

Member of the Institute, Honorary Professor of the Faculty of Sciences, University of Grenoble, Grenoble, France

English translation from the Fourth French Edition, 1950
by **GWENDOLYN G. WOODFORD**

W. H. Freeman and Company

SAN FRANCISCO AND LONDON

Author's Preface
to the English Edition

The translation of a scientific work is relatively easy for one of the sciences called "exact"—mathematics, physics or chemistry—for there the technical terms may be defined precisely and they have exact equivalents in every language. Moreover, these sciences have neither regional nor personal peculiarities: physics in London differs in no way from physics in Paris or San Francisco; mathematical theorems are completely detached from the personalities of their creators, and in their statements there is nothing to indicate whether it be Pythagoras or Leibnitz.

Geologic syntheses, on the contrary, and the more or less symbolic language in which they are expressed, are colored by the "atmosphere" of an epoch, a country, a personality. Thus it is that a French geologist will freshen his outlook by assimilating German works which introduce him into a new world in which more and more abstract ideas are built up, one upon another —ideas often suggestive, explained by neologisms (craton, pluton, orthogeosyncline, diaphthoresis, geosuture, etc.), giving them an appearance of reality and precision. In British works, on the contrary, a Frenchman will find lessons in concrete realism and a keen critical spirit, not without humor; all expressed in simple, distinguished language which scorns barbarous and pretentious neologisms. Finally, in American treatises he will find models of clear and brief writing, aiming above all at efficiency, that is to say, inspired especially by the wish to be easily and quickly understood by the average reader for whom all the technical terms are carefully defined by extensive use of diagrammatic figures and well arranged pictures.

The American publisher of this translation has doubtless deemed that readers of English will have some interest in the work of a French geologist; of that I am naturally not qualified to judge. But I can, without reservation, very sincerely congratulate the translator of my French text. Of course the responsibility for this translation rests on the publisher, but the chapters of the English text which were sent to me permit me to admire the talent which the translator has shown in rendering in English the slightest shades of meaning of the often difficult original text.

Evidently, she was not constrained to use this "basic English" which some advocate as an international scientific language and of which one geologist has even given examples.* Nor have I sought to write a "basic French." For these too greatly simplified languages, impoverished and devoid of symbols, would give too diagrammatic and rigid an idea of our geologic theories and impart an illusory appearance of preciseness. There again, the translator has been able to render very exactly the words of the French text. For the considerable work involved in the translation of a scientific work of 700 pages, she deserves the admiration and gratitude of the author and his readers.

M. GIGNOUX

Grenoble, March, 1954.

* Alan Wood, *Proc. Geologists' Ass'n.,* London, 55 (1944), p. 99.

Translator's Note

Several geologic terms used in this book are different from those current in English-speaking countries. For example, Primary is used instead of Paleozoic and Lower Silurian instead of Ordovician.

In this translation geographical names are anglicized where custom dictates and spelled in accordance with either the London Times 1922 edition of the Bartholomew Atlas or the 1949 Rand-McNally Cosmopolitan World Atlas. Some French, German, and other foreign terms are retained where there is no English equivalent, but these are all defined in the text: e.g., *faluns, cargneules, vallums*. The French word *lacune* is in most places translated lacuna rather than the more usual discontinuity or hiatus. The author makes a distinction between a lacuna and a discontinuity, and the French text contains so many *lacunes* that the use of hiatuses would be almost unbearable. In captions for figures, *tableau* of the French text has been replaced by the weaker word chart, instead of the more literal "picture" suggested by the author. The author wished each chart to give its viewer a picture of the facies relationships.

Most sincere thanks are due to M. Gignoux for reading the translation of the Preface, Introduction, and Chapters 1 and 2, for suggestions that were useful in these and other chapters, and for a special preface that is the best reward a translator could desire; to Wendell P. Woodring, U.S. Geological Survey, Washington, D.C., who has read the whole manuscript and whose assistance has been invaluable; and to my husband, A. O. Woodford, Professor of Geology, Pomona College, without whose constant help and encouragement this work would never have been undertaken or completed.

Claremont, California   G. G. W.
December 30, 1954.

Preface
to the French Edition

Un fatto è come un sacco, che vuoto non si regge.
Perchè si regga, bisogna prima farci entrar dentro la ragione.

L. PIRANDELLO, SEI PERSONAGGI IN CERCA D'AUTORE

This book was originally conceived as a textbook, designed especially for students of our universities and technical institutes. As the title indicates, my wish was to rehabilitate stratigraphy by emphasizing its relationship to the other aspects of geology. Stratigraphy constitutes the central branch and the most individual of the geological sciences, but often seems difficult and unattractive for beginners, quite wrongly, I believe. In writing this work, I have thought then, not only of future geologists, but also of the readers who study geology to broaden their general culture. The stratigraphic syntheses represent logical constructions of a very special order, and it seems to me that one cannot be a complete naturalist if one has not learned how these constructions were developed.

From the immense number of stratigraphic observations made all over the world, I have kept especially those which could be grouped in general pictures. These are built up in accordance with some *guiding concepts,* thanks to which outcrops and facies are harmoniously arranged.

For each geological period, I have chosen one or several regions, the study of which could lead to a *stratigraphic synthesis.* The choice varies naturally according to the period. As far as possible, I have taken my examples from France, in order that on the whole my reader should acquire an adequate and detailed knowledge of the different natural regions of our own country. But, for the stratigraphy of the Cambrian and the Silurian, impossible to synthesize in France, I am forced to describe in detail the type series of England and of the Scandinavian and Baltic regions. The basis for the study of the Devonian was furnished by the Ardennes and the Rhenish *Schiefergebirge;* but to understand the important idea of an "Old Red Sandstone continent" I have been led to cast an eye on northern Europe and even on

North America. For the Permo-Carboniferous it was necessary to add to the classic regions of western Europe (France, Belgium, and England) a fairly detailed description of the marine series of Russia and to give a general survey of the "Continent of Gondwana." France, Germany, and England have furnished me, for the Triassic, Jurassic, and Cretaceous, synthetic pictures, of which the main features have long been classic. The description of the Tertiary is based first on these same countries, adding to them, for the Neogene, Italy and southeast Europe. Finally, for the Quaternary, we discuss principally the marine deposits of the western Mediterranean and the fluvioglacial formations of the Alps, northern Germany, and the Baltic regions.

In short, those of my readers who seek "instruction" in this work should first study the set of *"regional monographs"* for which I have named the chapter subheads. The guiding ideas which inspire each of these chapters will also interest professional geologists, in showing them how the interpretations of their observations may culminate in syntheses, in the reconstruction of what I have called·*sedimentary landscapes.* Stratigraphy, that is to say, the description of these successive panoramas, will then appear to them as a *harmonious succession of coherent geographies;* it will then truly deserve the name of Science. Moreover, these guiding ideas will help beginners to remember more easily the stratigraphic series of the classical regions; because one of the goals of teaching should be obviously to ease the role of memory.

Furthermore, encouraged by the indulgent favor with which the first three editions of this book have been received, I was led to make of it a *documented* tool for professional geologists. Distributed among the general pictures to which I have previously alluded there will be found a multitude of stratigraphic details, not synthesized, relating to the most diverse regions and particularly to those which, for each stage, show special facies or famous deposits. In particular, in connection with these details, I have given numerous *bibliographic references,* concerning which I must make some explanation.

First, I have not repeated any of the references already given in the classic but now antiquated treatises of A. de Lapparent and E. Haug; instead, I have cited many recent publications in which will be found the results of both the old fundamental work and those of later research.

These recent references are, of course, particularly numerous for our own country [France] and especially for timely questions or for subjects studied here in greatest detail (Brioverian of Brittany, Tertiary of the Paris Basin, Quaternary of the French Alps, etc.). Even from the teaching point of view these references will have the advantage of showing a science that is not dogmatic and ready made but rather in the course of development. The uncertainties and even the incoherencies, to which they bear witness, will very often develop in our young geologists the critical spirit and scepticism that are the sources of all scientific discovery.

Finally, it will be noted that the general works dealing with a given region are not repeated for each stage. Such general works will be found *via* the *alphabetical index,* which, for each region, refers to the pages where these works were cited. The same index will also serve for finding the maps that show the localities, often little known, discussed in the text. As many of my readers have assured me, these maps, placing the facts of stratigraphy in a geographic setting, are much more useful and instructive than sections or correlation tables, which may be reconstructed from the text without difficulty. Nevertheless, among the new figures which this fourth edition offers, I have included two large tables of the Tertiary of Acquitaine and the Nummulitic of the Paris and Anglo-Belgian Basins, tables that seem to me particularly suggestive. On the other hand, I have only rarely dared to draw those general paleogeographic maps so imprudently appreciated by beginners; for I hold it completely foolhardy to wish to trace, for example, the contours of Silurian or Devonian seas in France and western Europe.

Finally, if one recalls that the first edition of this work was issued in 1925, one may ask, what have been the geologic stages and regions in which knowledge has made the greatest progress between 1925 and 1949?

We must say first, that the great classical syntheses of western Europe have undergone only corrections of detail; nevertheless there will be found on each page, either in the text or in the bibliographic references, corrections or additions to the preceding edition. For these regions there are, for example, paragraphs relative to the Breton early Paleozoic, to the Parisian Montian, etc., which have been modified, witness to changes that are probably not yet finished, and which often indicate an elusory precision desired by the stratigraphic specialists in order to achieve synchronisms of detail (see, for example, p. 486). The chapter on the Quaternary has been notably enlarged and in the conclusion I allowed myself to develop some some new ideas that may be accepted or debated, but which will, I hope, cause reflection.

It is also necessary to give special treatment to the *Alps*. A relatively important place has been reserved for them. Their general tectonic description is the subject of quite a long section (pp. 286–298), for we find in them examples of a double synthesis, both stratigraphic and tectonic. Between 1925 and 1949 the geologic knowledge of the French Alps has made, and today is still making, great progress; that of the Swiss and eastern Alps, long fixed in too rigid dogmas, seems to have arrived at a turning point in its history, as we suggest in this fourth edition. Here we have preserved unchanged, lacking anything better and for ease of exposition, the classic but already somewhat shaken syntheses of P. Termier, E. Argand and R. Staub.

Among the regions outside of Europe we mention especially North Africa, where geology has made great progress. In the second edition we could already popularize the Paleozoic and the Jurassic of Morocco, which deserve to become as classic as those of the European type regions. The principal novelties of this fourth edition are especially concerned with the Tertiary (the question of the Sahelian; the Algerian-Tunisian and the Egyptian Nummulitic).

Finally, the documentation (with numerous bibliographic references) relative to the whole of the globe has been considerably extended in this edition.

In ending, I wish to thank the many colleagues who have helped me with their advice or with their publications; their names have been cited in the prefaces of previous editions and the list has become too long to be reproduced here.

Table of Contents

Chapter Ten

The Neogene

Chapter Eleven

The Quaternary

Introduction[1*]

I. The Materials of Stratigraphy (The Sediments)

Stratigraphy studies the beds of the earth's crust, the rocks, from the point of view of their chronological succession and their geographic distribution. Its indispensable prerequisite is, then, the knowledge of these rocks themselves; a study that can be made, up to a certain point, outside of time and space and, so to speak, in the drawers of collections. That is what petrographers and paleontologists do.

We shall assume the elementary knowledge of petrography (or lithology)[2] and of paleontology.[3] We shall depend in the same way on other works[4] for the knowledge of what are called, by general agreement, the geologic phenomena resulting from various agents of alteration or transportation (temperature, gravity, running water, glaciers, wind, waves, marine currents, etc.) which are working at the present time, and have always worked as they do today, to destroy, build, and model the surface of the globe.

We believe it useful to define here certain ideas concerning the sedimentary rocks; for we shall proceed to name and especially to classify these rocks in a particular way, in determining how the different types are assembled in sedimentary series. Each of these series will correspond to what we shall call a paleogeographic unit. It will be, if you like, a petrography of paleogeographic panoramas of ancient landscapes, as against what we have called the petrography of drawers or of specimens.

I. *Sediments and Facies*

As a matter of fact, sedimentary rocks interest stratigraphers in so far as they allow the reconstruction of the landscapes, that is, the local geographic conditions which prevailed at the time and at the place where they were formed. We refer to the combination of these conditions when we use the vague but useful word facies.

A. Continental Facies. The interpretation of rocks of continental origin will be relatively easy, since the phenomena of sedimentation which are taking place on the present continents are familiar to us.

Helped both by their mineral makeup and by the fossils they contain, we thus easily recognise: alluvium, gravels, sands or muds of ancient rivers; the

* See Reference Notes at the end of Chapter.

1

clayey or calcareous muds deposited in the beds of ancient lakes; the peats, lignites, and coal produced by the accumulation of vegetable debris in peat bogs or forest swamps; sands, feldspathic sandstones (arkoses) and gores (see p. 190), resulting from the disintegration of granitic rocks; the *terra rossa,* residue of the solution of limestones, often rich in iron (siderolithic facies of the Eocene, p. 493) and filling the fissures or alteration pockets of underlying rocks;[5] the sands and clays accumulated by running water in depressions, there progressively decalcified (impoverished) and oxidized by successive changes to terminate in varicolored sands and clays, often refractory;[6] lateritic or bauxitic clays,[7] clays with free aluminum hydroxide, which are formed by alteration of superficial rocks under certain climatic conditions; calcareous tufas or travertines, precipitated near springs or streams; the moraines built up by ancient glaciers; the eolian sediments of deserts, of sandy coasts (dunes) and of periglacial regions[8] (loess, p. 615).

But these continental series will be generally thin and localized, two reasons why there is little chance of finding them in the fossil state. In fact, when at a given moment in its history a region becomes continental, this period is often marked not by continental sediments but by an absence of sediments or, using a term that we shall define later, by a *lacuna of sedimentation.*

Actually, under climatic conditions analogous to those which prevail in our regions (neither deserts nor polar regions), the final result of the phenomena which occur on the continents is the carrying toward the sea of all the products of alteration and erosion of rocks. There are resting stages in that progress; momentarily the rivers build up alluvial plains; the lacustrine or swampy depressions fill up. But the common fate of all these stocks of debris is sooner or later to be removed toward the ocean, under the irresistible influence of peneplanation which tends to reduce to sea level all the continental surfaces.

Only under two conditions can thick and extensive accumulations of sediments be produced on continents (see Fig. 1):[9]

1. Certain regions of the continent may sink. They will be called *depressed troughs* when they correspond to clearly marked zones of dislocation bounded by faults; they will be *basins of subsidence*[10] when the depressions, having a large radius of curvature, are not crossed by cleancut dislocations. In both cases, these regions of subsidence evidently become zones calling for sedimentation.

If the continental area which is sinking remains limited, and small enough in proportion to surrounding regions that are not sinking, these latter, especially if they have a vigorous relief incessantly rejuvenated by uplift, will have an extent sufficient to nourish sedimentation capable of filling the trench faster than it can form and preventing the sea from penetrating to it. It is in this way that, since the end of the Tertiary, the Rhenish trench in the region of Heidelberg could be filled to the depth of several hundred meters with river alluvium, the base of which is well below sea level. Similarly, during the Oligocene (Middle Tertiary), the trenches of Limagne, Forez, and the Rhine between the Vosges and the Black Forest could be filled up with deposits, largely lacustrine, with thicknesses exceeding 1,000 m.

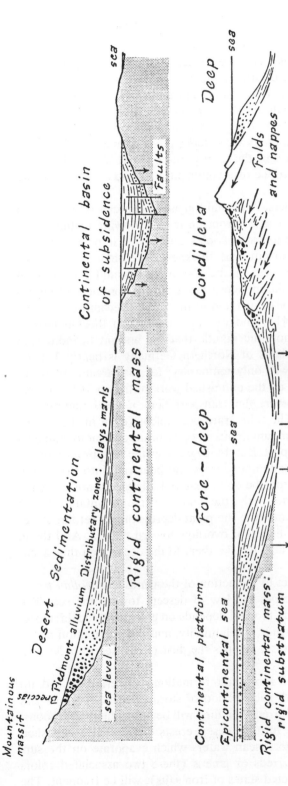

FIG. 1. *Wholly theoretical diagrams, illustrating different types of sedimentary series.*

ABOVE: The two cases in which thick sedimentary series can accumulate on continents. To the left: desert sedimentation; the sediments accumulate because they cannot be carried to the sea. To the right: a basin of subsidence, inviting continuous sedimentation.

BELOW: Marine sedimentary series; muddy, pelagic sediments are represented by lines (dashes), detrital facies by dots, organic facies by crosses, slumping by black triangles. To the left: edge of a stable continental structure: detrital, neritic, organic sedimentation; scanty deposit, very varied facies, lacunas, erosion by littoral currents, etc.; epicontinental or continental-platform type. To the right: geosynclinal chain in process of formation (orogene). A fore-deep at the edge of which terrigenous sediments from the continent may accumulate to great thickness; in the depths, on the other hand, relatively scanty pelagic and abyssal sediments are deposited. Farther to the right, a cordillera, bordered by very narrow neritic zones (sometimes with organic facies, not represented); here the sedimentation is fed by the narrow, emergent cordillera, with a relief constantly renewed by orogenic movements: mingling of slumping submarine breccias, coastal alluvium, etc., with pelagic sediments; Flysch type. Still farther to the right come other deeps and cordilleras.

IMPORTANT: See note 27.

If, however, the zone which is sinking is of great size compared to the emergent regions and to a weakened relief which surrounds it, the sedimentary materials furnished by these latter regions will be insufficient to fill up the depression as fast as it forms. This will become one of those epicontinental, marine basins, of which we shall speak later. This is the case of the Paris Basin which was, first in the Secondary and again in the Early Tertiary, a basin of marine subsidence with many vicissitudes (see explanation of Fig. 3).

2. Sometimes the agent causing the transportation and accumulation of sedimentary materials on the surface of a continent may lose its power before reaching the sea:

a) This is true of great glaciers. A glacial tongue or cap can transport and accumulate moraines only as far as its front, instead of flowing to the sea as a river. And in fact, the *glacial formations* play a relatively important role in stratigraphy because of their extent and thickness. We shall describe the ancient moraines formed at the end of the Carboniferous and the Permian (end of the Primary Era) over the immense extent of the Continent of Gondwana (see p. 238); we shall speak of them again in the Precambrian, at the beginning of the Primary (p. 41); and we shall see that in the Quaternary the average thickness of the morainic mantle that the ancient Scandinavian glaciers have left in the vast plains of Northern Germany is nearly 100 m. But there again, very often it was only temporary; for the streams of water which succeed the glaciers take up the unfinished work of transport to the sea.

b) In desert climates, however, the transportation of solid materials is under quite exceptional laws. The rains, rare but violent (even in the middle of the Sahara), falling on the mountainous massifs bring enormous amounts of alluvium into torrential transport. But, by degrees, as the temporary streams extend out farther from their mountain sources and penetrate into the desert, they evaporate and naturally drop the solid materials that they are carrying. These solids are deposited progressively, the coarser at the mountain margins (piedmont alluvium), the finest muds in the great depressions or settling zones that the floods are powerless to fill up or overflow toward the sea. And there, these deposits, finding no agent able to take them to the ocean, can thus accumulate to great thicknesses.[11]

They remain, however, subject to the action of the winds. But *eolian transportation,*[12] too, completely escapes the law of descent toward the sea. The accumulation of sand or dust due to wind depends on essentially local factors: the direction of the prevailing winds, the humidity, and the distribution of the vegetation which holds on the grassy steppes the dust (loess, see p. 615) torn from completely bare regions.

In such continental desert or sub-desert formations, materials picked up and moved again and again with each period of storms will be more or less thoroughly decalcified [13] and oxidized. The lime will be precipitated in lagoons, or it will be concentrated in the form of desert crusts (see p. 112) deposited by the rising circulation of subterranean waters which evaporate on the surface. Variegated colors, that is, reds or greens (these two associated colors correspond to the closely connected states of iron salts), will be frequent. The deposits formed in the lagoons or dry lakes will contain evaporation products: magnesian (dolomitic) limestones, gypsum, anhydrite, rock salt, and potassium salts. Moreover, fossils will be extremely rare and of small variety. Life is totally absent in the Dead Seas, and it is rare on the floor of the deserts.

All these different but associated or alternating rocks will thus constitute natural assemblages of sedimentary terrains to which we can apply the name of series of desert facies or, more briefly, *desert series.*

And actually, geologic history will show us many examples of very well marked sedimentary series, generally non-fossiliferous—conglomerates, arkoses, red sandstones, varicolored red and green marls, saline deposits, etc. The manner of formation of such sediments, sometimes several thousand meters thick, has long been, because of the almost complete absence of fossils, an enigma which has only been solved when the particular circumstances of desert sedimentation were realized. Let us take for example the Torridonian sandstone (p. 35), the Jotnian (p. 33), the Sparagmite (p. 90), dependents of the Precambrian, the Old Red Sandstone (Devonian, p. 109), the New Red Sandstones (Permian, p. 158, and Triassic, p. 278), the Karroo series (p. 241), and the red formations of the Jurassic, the Cretaceous and the North African Tertiary (pp. 373, 449, 531).

As the desert climate can only occur in the hearts of great continents, the desert series will only be found on ancient great continental masses, thus allowing us to reconstruct: a North Atlantic continent (Northeast of North America and northwest of Europe), a Sino-Siberian continent, or Angara, (p. 375), and a continent of Gondwana (p. 238).

B. Marine Facies.   If we were living in the center of Africa and our geologic explorations were carried on between the Saharan Atlas, the Gulf of Guinea, and the mountains of the Cape, we should be accustomed to seeing almost nothing but continental formations. But in the classic countries of Western Europe that we shall study, we shall be always at the edges of the continents, so that our stratigraphy will be essentially a stratigraphy of marine deposits. Very happily so, moreover, for fossils, so valuable to stratigraphers, are infinitely more abundant and more varied in the marine formations. That is true simply because the remains of living things have much more chance of becoming fossilized at the bottom of the sea than when exposed to destruction on continental land.

We shall distinguish three great groups of marine rocks: detrital, organic, and pelagic.[14]

1. *Detrital Rocks.*   These will be the rocks in which we can recognise, with the naked eye or with a lens, the debris of pre-existing rocks.[15] In order for such debris to be transported and assembled, the marine waters must have been agitated by waves or by littoral currents. Our detrital rocks will be then almost always relatively littoral formations, formed, for example, at a depth of less than 100 or 150 m.:[16] landslide breccias below cliffs, conglomerates, sandstones, sands, sandy muds, and sandy shales. A detrital rock naturally reflects the composition of the rocks of the nearby seacoast. And great accumulations of detrital sediments permit the postulation of the existence nearby

of emergent lands or mountain masses, capable of having nourished such a sedimentation, which we shall call, from this point of view, *terrigenous*.

2. *Organic* (Zoogenic) *Rocks.* Lacking this nourishment, even agitated waters cannot produce detrital sediments. On the other hand, in the shallower zones where the water, carrying neither sand nor mud, remains clear, organisms abound and their hard parts accumulate to form the rocks very improperly called zoogene.[17] Organisms, plant or animal, thus capable of building such rocks, will be called builders (e.g., reef builders). The most important of them will obviously be the sessile and colonial groups of coelenterates, especially the corals, reefs of which we find [18] in warm waters, in all geologic epochs. They will be accompanied by various hydrozoans (stromatoporids, for instance). In the Cambrian of the Primary an analogous role will fall on the archaeocyathids. The calareous algae have built important rocky masses in the Triassic (diplopore limestones, p. 266) and in the Tertiary (*Lithothamnium* limestones, Miocene). Also we must mention the extinct group of the *Rudistae* (attached pelecypods) which built true reefs in the tropical seas of the Upper Jurassic and Cretaceous; among the echinoderms there are moreover the crinoids, attached forms, that contributed to the formation of crinoidal limestone. As for organisms belonging to other groups, it is exceptional that they play a truly rock-building role: we may mention, for example, the bryozoans in the Lower Carboniferous (Waulsortian facies, p. 182), in the Permian (reefs of the Zechstein of Germany, p. 168), in the Upper Miocene of western Europe (Sarmatian, p. 588); the annelids (Scrpulite of the German Portlandian, p. 347; Ditrupa limestone of the Mediterranean Pliocene, studied by G. Checchia-Rispoli); the siliceous sponges (reefs of sponges of the Provençal Upper Cretaceous, p. 430), etc.

Except in the last case, the hard parts of all these building organisms are calcareous. The rocks which they build will be then white, reefy limestones, almost chemically pure, occasionally dolomitic (magnesian). Actually, in agitated marine waters, the porous limestones can precipitate magnesium and become dolomitized. Thus in the Red Sea, with a very strong salinity and high *p*H caused by the algae, there are examples of dolomitization up to 40%.[19]

3. *Pelagic Rocks.* These will be ancient, very fine muds, in which, neither with the naked eye nor with a hand lens (nor often even with a microscope), can we see any textural details.[20] They are produced, perhaps by the settling of very fine clay particles in suspension in calm waters, perhaps by the precipitation of dissolved or colloidal substances following mechanisms that we shall not study here. Their chemical composition may be quite variable and remains the only way of classifying them, since we see in them no mineralogical properties. They may be then, perhaps clayey muds, without lime, the *clays* (which become *shales* under the influence of orogenic pressures), perhaps muds composed of a mixture of lime and clay, or marls (producing calcareous shales), perhaps, lastly, pure calcareous muds, necessarily formed by precipitation, since the calcium carbonate is too soluble to be carried by the sea in the state of dust or fine powder, as are silicates and quartz. We

shall have, then, *dense limestone,* fine grained or "lithographic." The pure limestones, very fine grained, that are often found in the vicinity of coral reefs or in the lagoons of atolls (see examples of them in the Jurassic, p. 348), are often described as coral muds. These are probably not organic, detrital rocks, but the result of the precipitation of carbonate of lime from sea water.[21]

All these muddy sediments generally have a dark color,[22] black or gray-blue, due either to the organic matter (then the altered surfaces become whitish through alteration), or to a microscopic dust of iron minerals (pyrite, for example), which is transformed into dark red in the altered zones (type of bi-colored limestones).

While a detrital rock was, in general, a shallow sediment, or at least coastal, the depth at which pelagic rocks were formed varies greatly.

On the completely flat coasts, without cliffs, or again in the still waters of littoral lagoons, along the shores where the emerged lands do not contribute to the sea sufficient materials to nourish a detrital sedimentation, there may be pelagic sediments even at a very shallow depth. On the other hand, along abrupt shores, gullied by coastal torrents and bordered by violent littoral currents (such as the case of the Strait of Messina mentioned, note 16), detrital sedimentation can descend to greater depths and a pelagic sedimentation will take place only in the bottom of troughs or far from the shores. So, to estimate the depth of a pelagic sediment, our only indicators are the benthonic organisms which live on the bottom of the sea; for those which floated on the surface (pelagic organisms) or swam through the waters (nectonic) are apparently more or less indifferent to depth.

And this leads us to a few remarks on the distribution of faunas in the sea.

Distribution of Fossils in the Marine Sediments.   In a general way, marine life is concentrated in the shallow zones, in the littoral regions. That is strictly true for marine plants, which need light, and for herbivorous animals which live upon these plants. The carnivores can descend lower, as do the limivores (mud eaters), for which the bodies of pelagic micro-organisms (plankton), fallen to the bottom of the sea and mixed with mud, constitute a sufficient diet.

But for all living things, the renewal of oxygen is necessary. So, in the depths, the submarine currents will be sources of life. The muddy depths of the sea without currents will be almost lifeless. Thus, in the Mediterranean, when dredging in the blue muds that uniformly cover the sea floor from a depth of 100 m. a dredge will only occasionally bring up shells, even though thousands of organisms abound between 0 and 50 m.[23] We shall frequently encounter in geologic history such accumulations of clays, or blue or black marls, whose poverty of fossils makes the stratigrapher despair. But it needs only a current to bring the formation of a sandy layer in which shells immediately appear, in beds or nests, often very limited and very thin; these are the fossiliferous horizons. Often these horizons correspond to glauconitic or phosphatic beds, for glauconite and calcium phosphate are minerals which originate exactly on the bottoms swept by littoral currents. Glauconite, especially, is very easy to recognize even when it is more or less oxidized (red sands of the Breton Pliocene, tawny sands of the Miocene of the lower Pyrenees, ruddy facies of the Cretaceous of Vaucluse, p. 403). So, in the absence of shells, this mineral becomes actually a characteristic fossil of the marine facies, for it never occurs in continental sediments.[24]

So, a sediment rich in shells, or to use an expression familiarized by E. Haug, a *neritic* sediment (from the Greek word for shell), will always be a sediment of agitated waters, and usually shallow. These neritic facies have, for stratigraphers as for paleontologists, a very special interest because of the abundance of fossils. Such are: the *shell sands,* called *faluns* when they are composed almost entirely of shell fragments; the *shell sandstones,* called *gray-wackes* when they are clayey and have been in turn decalcified, so that shells are represented only by cavities showing the external mold and the internal mold of the fossil; the *lumachelles,* hardened calcareous-sandy muds where shells of pelecypods are embedded; the *bone beds,* where abound teeth or fragments of dermal skeletons of fish (pp. 109, 323),[25] and finally, the infinite variety of the *shelly limestones,* formed by the accumulation of minute remains of shells, mixed with a little clayey mud or sands and gravels (gravelly limestones) and passing insensibly into organic limestones or reefs, of which we have already spoken. These limestones will be named for the shells which predominate in them (*Cerithium* limestones, brachiopod limestones, nummu-litic limestones, etc.). We must mention especially the *calcaires à entroques* (crinoidal limestone, echinoderm breccias), formed by the accumulation of fragments of echinoderms, easily recognized by their crystalline cleavages (example: the "little granite," p. 182), the *tufas* or *molasse* limstones, white, chalky rocks remaining soft and easy to cut, and finally the *oolitic* limestones, where, in agitated waters, the precipitation of calcium carbonate dissolved in the sea water produces ooliths (sometimes ferruginous) which are formed in concentric layers, like almonds sugared in syrup. These oolitic facies, needing water very rich in calcium, often seem like satellites of the coral reefs, since in the quiet waters of the atoll lagoons we have seen lithographic limestones of the pelagic though shallow type formed in the same way by chemical precipitation.

This last example shows once more that a muddy sediment, with pelagic facies, is not necessarily deep, even, we may add, when it contains only the remains of pelagic animals; for the absence of benthonic fossils may often be explained by local conditions (absence of currents, for example).

So the *graptolitic shales* of the Silurian have long been considered as deposits of deep seas. It is probably true in certain cases among them, but very often we can be sure that it is a question of real littoral deposits, even lagoonal (p. 73). *Chalk* was formerly compared with the present globigerina ooze of the deep abyss, when in fact, judging from benthonic fossils that appear in it here and there, it must have been formed at quite medium depths, in general not exceeding 100 or 200 m. (see p. 393). The *black marls* with pyritic ammonites, so highly developed in the Jurassic (for example in the Paris Basin) and often characterized as of deep facies, must have been deposited under some tens of meters of water (see p. 324). Finally, *radiolarites,* siliceous rocks with pelagic radiolaria, which we find in the Carboniferous (p. 205) and in the Jurassic of the Alps (p. 357), have been compared to the radiolarian oozes of the present abyss. Such a comparison, perhaps true for certain rocks (L. Cayeux), is certainly not true of all (J. de Lapparent).[26]

In brief, so many rocks have, at first sight, the characteristics of coastal deposits, it is extremely difficult to prove that even a pelagic sediment is truly deep, bathyal. The deepest sedimentary series that we know of are perhaps the shales and shaley limestones with *Aptychus* of the Jurassic and the Mediterranean Cretaceous (p. 371), and also certain non-fossiliferous shales and clays of the Tertiary. And if these series contain sediments truly abyssal, they correspond doubtless only to some very thin beds (we shall return to this point later) that stratigraphers are still unable to define clearly.

II. *Sedimentation and Tectonics*[27]

We already suspect that there are movements of the earth (the study of which constitutes tectonics) which regulate the accumulation of sediments. From this point of view, we can distinguish two great groups of regions, the continental areas and the geosynclinal regions.

A. Continental Areas. These are stable regions, or more precisely, regions where the deep structure is formed by rocks folded long ago, which have become rigid. If as structural geologists often do, we compare the crust of the earth to a dress shirt, the continental areas would correspond to the starched portions, to the shirtfront of the garment. The orogenic stresses are shown there, sometimes by faults or vertical fractures, sometimes by deformations of very great radius of curvature (deep folds of E. Argand) which produce elevation or subsidence of vast areas, if these movements have a notable resultant in the course of a whole geologic period.

The uplifted areas become the emerged massifs, from which erosion, unceasingly renewed, will nourish the detrital sedimentation in the depressed regions which border them. Such depressed regions constitute the sunken troughs or basins of subsidence, sometimes lacustrine, sometimes marine, where sediments can accumulate to a thickness commensurate with the depth of the depression. On the other hand, the stable but submerged parts of these continental areas will be covered by shallow epicontinental seas, regions of weak neritic and organic sedimentation, ruled by the play of currents, which play the same role there as do rivers on the continents; this will be the continental shelf bordering the emergent continent.

B. Geosynclinal Regions. Here the substratum, still plastic, will react to the tectonic stresses by true folds, like waves rolling one after another. The crests of these waves will develop long and narrow emerged ranges (geanticlines or cordilleras) whose relief however will be strong, because supported by orogenic upheavals. Between the cordilleras, troughs (geosynclines proper) will be formed which will have, on the contrary, a tendency to become deeper.

In these regions, the sedimentary series will have very special characteristics. Slides and collapses, or the accumulation of subaerial or submarine debris along the abrupt sides of the cordilleras, will make breccias, sometimes in enormous blocks: this is the "Wildflysch" facies of the Swiss geologists (see p. 518). The erosion of the waves, the materials brought by the coastal torrents, and submarine currents will feed a terrigenous sedimentation (sands and clays), locally abundant but very irregularly distributed, able to get into even the deep-water zones. In waters so charged with materials in suspension, organic facies will only rarely develop. Finally because of the steepness of the coasts, the zone favorable to animal life, which is shown by neritic sediments, will be reduced to a narrow strip, instead of extending over vast surfaces as in the case of the continental platforms; that is, in such a sedimentary series, fossils will be rare. Shells will have been destroyed usually by the grinding action of the sandy currents. What we shall find especially will be trails and imprints left by algae or creeping animals (annelids, gastropods) on the muddy bottom.

Finally, in the calm waters of the deepest parts of the troughs, thin deposits of the deep pelagic type will be formed: calcareous muds with *Aptychus* and pelagic foraminifera, black clayey muds with radiolaria.

A special interest attaches to the transition zone between the two domains of the continental areas and the geosynclines. It is there that we are first going to find the maximum thicknesses of sediments (see pp. 402 and 453).[28] The sedimentary material supplied by the great emerged continents will find only temporary rest on the continental platforms. The erosion of the submarine currents, the play of the transgressions and regressions and the lacunas which accompany them, will constantly rearrange the sediments there (see p. 16). On the other hand, coming to regions already deep, through which we descend to the first geosynclinal trough, we find conditions analogous to those of the epicontinental basins of subsidence. The abundant detrital material coming from the neighboring continents will be captured as in a trap and will accumulate to great thickness without being exposed to rearrangement. Such zones, which will be especially interesting to stratigraphers because of the thickness and regularity of their sediments, we shall call *fore-deeps*.

Let us add finally that, if we can now study geosynclinal regions clear to their bottoms, it is because the continual succession of folding has finally transformed them into mountain ranges,[29] completely emerged and attacked in their turn by erosion. It is indeed the study of great folded chains which permits us to penetrate the mystery of geosynclinal sedimentation,[30] a mystery formerly well guarded, because the rarity of fossils as well as the tectonic complications made it a difficult study.

Thus in the *Alpine Chain,* of Tertiary age but whose history has not yet ended, we shall find fore-deep sedimentation represented in our subalpine chains, and a geosynclinal sedimentation in our internal zone of the French Alps. The irregular, but locally thick, sparsely fossiliferous accumulations of Tertiary shales and sandstones (with lenses of breccias, conglomerates or, contrarily, pelagic calcareous muds) of this last sedimentation are here called Flysch (see pp. 517 and 530). The contrast is striking between this thick and enigmatic Flysch, where the geologic stages are about 1,000 m.

thick, and the thin neritic series of the epicontinental type of the Paris Basin, for example, where the same stages are measured in meters or decameters.

The *Hercynian Chain,* formed near the end of the Primary, will also show us a fore-deep sedimentation, with its series, thick but still fossiliferous, of the Ardennes zone, the paradise of stratigraphers of the Primary (Devonian and Carboniferous). The Carboniferous Culm will correspond to the Tertiary Flysch and, following a Devonian analogue, is found again in the heart of the old chain in the Vosges, the Central Massif, Brittany and Devonshire.

Finally the *Caledonian Chain,* too, whose history ended at the dawn of the Devonian, will show us, in the Scandinavian Mountains and certain British regions (North Wales, Scotland) geosynclinal sedimentary series (Cambrian-Silurian) analogous to the Flysch and to the Culm, as opposed to the epicontinental series of the same stages which we shall study in the Counties of Central England and in the Baltic countries.

III. *Summary: The Great Types of Sedimentary Series*

We thus distinguish the following types of sedimentary series:

A. The Continental Series.   This series is generally greatly reduced, except in the cases of desert series and of sediments accumulated in the sunken troughs or continental basins of subsidence.

B. The Epicontinental Marine Series.   On the stable continental shelves, these series will remain generally thin but with infinite varieties of detail, where all the types of facies—neritic, organic, detrital—develop, governed by the play of submarine currents. This great variability of sediments, both in the vertical sense (time) and in the horizontal (space), together with the richness of faunas, will make it the realm par excellence of detailed stratigraphy. These series will thicken and become slightly less deep (and thus more monotonous) only in the epicontinental marine basins of subsidence, in the center of which muddy facies will predominate (example: Jurassic of the Germanic Basin, p. 345; Lias of the Causses, p. 366).

C. The Geosynclinal Series.   These have their successions of troughs and cordilleras, their Flysch facies, and their marginal series of fore-deeps, where the maximum thickness of the marine sedimentary series will be realized.

Thus, it is truly tectonics which governs stratigraphy, and the two branches of the geologic sciences are inseparable. A structural geologist who is not a stratigrapher is only a geometer, not a geologist; for he reasons about abstract surfaces and volumes, emptied of their history; and a stratigrapher who never concerned himself with tectonics would produce only a dead stratigraphy.

So we believed we should, in this book, allot an important place to the history of the Alpine Chain, in spite of the difficulties and the uncertainties that it still presents. We shall nevertheless find there clues to an understanding of the ancient Hercynian and Caledonian ranges. And stratigraphy will show us, moreover, that all the folded regions are not built in the same way as the Alps: in the Pyrenees and the mountains of Provence, lateral auxiliaries of the great Alpine Chain, we shall not find any geosynclinal stratigraphy on a scale comparable to that of the Alps.

II. The Stratigraphic Syntheses (The Concept of the Stage)

Stratigraphy is, we have said, the study of chronological succession and the geographic distribution of the rocks which constitute the earth's crust. Thus, a quarryman who notes the series of the beds that he exploits, a driller who indicates in his log the nature and thickness of the strata traversed, both contribute to stratigraphy. But as always, true scientific work begins only at the moment when, putting together two series of phenomena, we seek to find and express in a synthesis the relations between the two.

How then can scientific work be done in stratigraphy?

Rocks contain the remains of fossil animals or plants. We can study these remains and see if there is a relation between their anatomic structures and the rocks in which they are contained; that will be paleontology or paleobiology. We can also study the mechanism of the formation of rocks; that is lithology or petrography.

But to describe a series of terrains or, as they are called, geological sections, in many different parts of our globe, to compare these series, to try to synchronize one set by its relation to others, to see how they differ and to show these differences in both time and space at a glance, to group them harmoniously in a series of coherent pictures, free of contradictions: such is the proper sphere of stratigraphy.

So the true individuality of stratigraphy in the great assemblage of geologic sciences results from always interposing the geographic point of view; that is, the distribution in time and space of the facts with which these sciences are concerned. And its scientific character results precisely from the harmony that must exist simultaneously in this double framework of time and of space.

Lithologic and Paleontologic Concepts of the Stage

The first synthetic ideas in stratigraphy are derived naturally from the observations most easily made. In a quarry, a road cut, a ravine, what first strikes the observer is the nature of the outcropping rocks, their hardness, their color, their composition, their possibilities for industrial use: limestones, sandstones, marls, sands, chalk, conglomerates, etc. The first stratigraphic syntheses consisted in finding, at more and more distant points, a like succession of rocks and the most important of these rock successions were called *formations* or *stages*. There has long been recognized, for example, in all Northern Europe, the existence of a chalk formation, everywhere easily recognizable. The rocks of the Swabian Jura were first subdivided in a lower group, called Black Jura or Lias, composed of marls and black clayey limestones, a middle group containing layers of ferruginous rocks (Brown Jura) and an upper group with white limestones (White Jura). In the outskirts of Paris, the first stratigraphers observed long ago the existence of three superimposed stages of sands, which they called "lower, middle, and upper sands," separated by clayey or calcareous formations.

Such is the first period of the concept of the geologic stage.

Next, in studying the fossil animals and plants, it is quickly seen that each of the previously recognized lithologic stages has its own fauna and flora and this has allowed the recognition and definition of these stages by their characteristic fossils. Since they are different in successive stages, these faunas and floras were attributed first to successive creations (D'Orbigny), then to stages of evolution in a single continuous current of life. Be that as it may, at this moment, the paleontologic definition was added to the lithologic definition of the stage.

Facies and Provinces

Then it was seen at once that to compare these two definitions was a particularly suggestive operation. For identical species of marine animals having lived at the same time could have fallen on the bottom of the sea either on a sandy shore or in the muds of the open sea: they will be found then fossilized in sandstones or clays. And inversely, identical rocks could have been formed at very different epochs, which we recognize because they contain different faunas. Thus scientists were led to analyse more closely the conditions under which the rocks were formed, and to see in what degree these conditions reacted on the animal population: from that were derived the two ideas of facies and province.

We have already called *facies* the assemblage of characteristics resulting from geographic conditions, essentially local, which have determined the lithological nature of a sediment and the composition of the fauna or flora which this sediment contains: marine facies—beach, lagoon, coral reef, oceanic mud; lacustrine facies; desert dunes; etc. In a single epoch, the fauna changes with the facies, so that to appreciate exactly the relation of two successive faunas, it is necessary to look to the same facies.

Two sediments which have exactly the same fauna will be nearly contemporaneous, but the reciprocal is not always true: two sediments which are contemporaneous can nevertheless have different faunas, even if they also have absolutely identical facies. It depends then on general geographic conditions and it is said that these two sediments belong to two different provinces. There may be provinces of climatic origin: thus, a sandy beach of the English Atlantic Coast is not inhabited by the same fauna as a sandy beach of the Senegalese Atlantic. The facies, however, are the same, and it is reasonable to attribute these differences of fauna to the climate.

But in other cases the differences are due to facts of geographic isolation. Thus it would be possible to find on the two shores of the Atlantic, in Europe and in America, two sandy beaches where identical facies and climatic conditions might be realized. The faunas there would nevertheless be different, for, separated by the breadth of the Atlantic, which few animals can traverse, these two faunas have for ages evolved in divergent directions; and we have two purely geographical provinces.

The same for the present mammal faunas: the Arctic province is plainly a climatic province, while the Australian province is a geographic one.

Paleogeographic Concept of the Stage

We can now begin to see how the task of the stratigrapher grows. It is concerned with studying the different facies and provinces in each epoch, with grouping the sediments as we have done above in sedimentary series, each corresponding to one paleogeographic unit, to one landscape, and to deduce therefrom a complete view, clear and coherent, of the aspect of the whole earth in the epoch being considered. And these views should follow each other smoothly from one epoch to another. Thus understood, stratigraphy appears to us as a harmonious succession of coherent geographies. It is then truly a synthesis, truly a science, which like all others has, in some measure, its proofs.

We should not believe that the distribution of the facies and provinces of the same epoch are haphazard. It is absurd to suppose that saline deposits of evaporation could be formed in mid-ocean, or that fresh water lakes could exist in the middle of a desert with a hot, dry climate. A province of an inland sea should be separated from the open seas by continental barriers and, inversely, two seas which have exactly the same faunas should communicate. Finally, each of these succesive paleogeographic pictures should connect with the one which precedes it and the one which follows. When the sea invades a region previously emerged, we should be able to follow step by step the stages of this invasion. When a portion of the marine domain becomes isolated from the rest, this history should be read simultaneously on the contours of its shores and in the characteristic features of the successive faunas which inhabit it (example, Fig. 133, 134).

These facts find their most general and their most synthetic expression in the **law of correlation of facies,** formulated by Johannes Walther, which may be stated thus: *in a single sedimentary series, the variations of facies (horizontal) that are observed about a given point, reproduce in general the variations of facies of strata which follow vertically from the point; or, more briefly, facies vary in analogous manner both horizontally and vertically.*

This law, which is obviously only approximate, serves as a guiding thread to define sedimentary series and paleogeographic units. So, for example, the term Wealden Stage (p. 413) allows the grouping in a single sedimentary picture of a series of extremely varied rocks, the whole of which is characteristic of a single paleogeographic unit.[31] The same is true for the Old Red Sandstones of the Devonian (p. 109), for the New Red Sandstones of the Permo-Triassic (p. 158), etc.

Thus is born the paleogeographic concept of the stage.

For the first stratigraphers, the Upper Jurassic was white limestone, hard, excellent for fine building materials or lime. Later it was a list of characteristic fossils. Now, for us, it is (Figs. 78 & 85) the image of an immense sea, broken by cordilleras and deep troughs, covering the Mediterranean country, with a border of fringing reefs, holding central Europe like a scarf and from which the waves detached fine calcareous muds that are deposited out in the open sea. To the north of these reefs extend salt or fresh water lagoons, then continental plains. Still farther north, beyond the Boulonnais, was another and quite different sea, inhabited by other animals, without a border of reefs or calcareous muds.

A stage is, then, a stratigraphic synthesis, and the aim of this book is to try to make comprehensible, by precise examples, how these syntheses are established.

III. Definitions and Methods

Studying the rocks, fossils, geological phenomena, to place them in the double frame of space and time, stratigraphers naturally use the vocabulary and methods of petrographers, paleontologists and geographers.

But to these we must add some new definitions, relative both to the geographic viewpoint and to the chronological.

Continuity, Discontinuity, Lacunas

When two superposed formations follow each other without any interruption of sedimentation between them, they are said to be in stratigraphic continuity. But if, between these two formations, a period occured during which sedimentation was either nil [32] or, more likely, was replaced by erosion, it is said then that there has been a discontinuity, and this period corresponds to what is called a stratigraphic lacuna or, more briefly, a lacuna.

The existence of such lacunas is more or less easy to establish by observation. When the beds of the lower formation have been elevated, then truncated by erosion in such a way that the beds of the upper formation are deposited on the surface of truncation, the lacuna is quite visible, for it is then stressed by a discordance of stratification (see Fig. 4).

A discordance obviously gives a means of dating the dislocations and foldings which have preceded it: and stratigraphers customarily give the name of *chain* to all the foldings which were produced at about the same time (example; Hercynian Chain, Alpine Chain, etc.).[33]

When the lacuna corresponds only to a marked change in the facies, it is still generally easily recognizable. Thus when the deposits of two marine beds have been separated by a period of emersion, we often see intercalated between them the remains of continental deposits or at least an irregular surface of contact.

On the other hand, the lacunas most difficult to see will be those which are not accompanied by important changes in the facies. Such can be produced in marine beds by simple modifications of the rate of flow of currents. A slight increase in swiftness of these currents, the materials in suspension in the water remaining constant, suffices to insure that nothing is deposited on the bottom, and may even produce a weak erosion, following which new marine sediments being imposed upon the old, the lacuna may only be revealed by minute observations of detail.

So the lacuna is often underlain by *hard ground.* The lower bed, worn away and oxidized by currents, hardens and puts on a ferruginous, brown (rusty) crust, formed at the expense of the iron salts which the rock contains. If the sea is not too deep, this irregularly corroded rocky bottom is perforated by rock-boring molluscs (Pholads), the holes of which are filled by the upper bed. In the latter are often found rolled and broken fossil shells, coming from the lower bed (reworked fossils).

Geologists have now learned to recognize the hard grounds and prove thereby that the submarine lacunas are less rare and more important than was formerly believed, especially on the littoral shelves, furrowed by currents.[34]

Transgressions and Regressions

The extent of the old seas in each period is obviously one of the most important data for paleogeography and the distribution of facies. The study of the changes

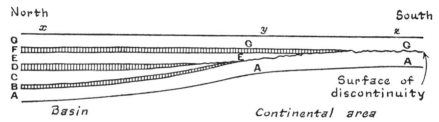

FIG. 2. *Theoretical representation of a regression, a lacuna, and a transgression.*

x—continuous sedimentation, without lacunas.
y—lacuna corresponding to stages B, C, D.
z—more important lacuna, corresponding to stages B, C, D, E, F.
Thus there was regression from south to north, then transgression from north to south.

of this distribution, commonly called the movements of the seas, has for a long time held the attention of stratigraphers.

When the sea invades a region formerly emerged, we say that there has been a transgression on this region and that the deposits brought by this new sea are transgressive. Inversely, when a region is abandoned by the sea, we say there is a regression.

Very often, during periods of emergence, few or no deposits are formed, for, as we have seen, sediments can accumulate on the continents only in exceptional circumstances and generally not on extensive surfaces. In other words, a period of emergence is often betrayed by a lacuna, as important as the emergence was prolonged. Thus frequently lacunas will follow regressions and precede transgressions.

The study of lacunas permits us to follow the parade of transgressions and regressions and to determine their sense. Thus, when in a specified region we

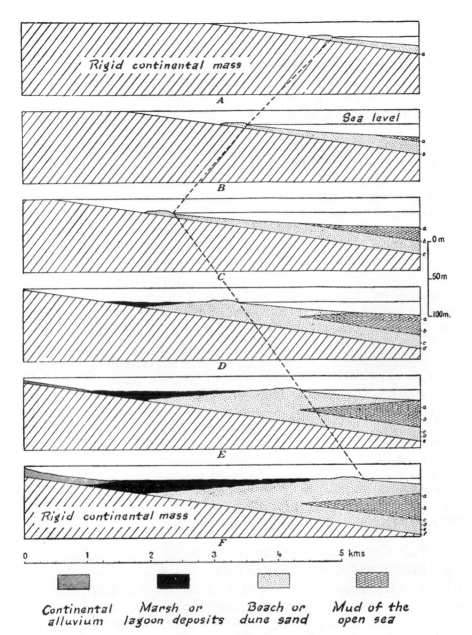

FIG. 3.   *Diagrammatic profiles showing that marine transgressions and re-gressions may result from a simple change of relative speed of sedimentation on the one hand and continental subsidence on the other hand.*

In these figures, the rigid continental mass is supposed to subside continuously: in the beginning (*A, B, C*), this subsidence is rapid enough and sedimentation slow enough for the sea to gain over the continent (transgression). Then (*D, E, F*) the subsidence moderates and the sedimentary materials increase, so that the shore recedes (regression). The broken line marks the transgression and regression. (Suggested by J. D. Sears, C. B. Hunt and T. A. Hendricks, *Transgressive and Regressive Cretaceous Deposits in Southern San Juan Basin, New Mexico*, U. S. Geol. Surv. Prof. Paper 193–F (1941).

17

find two marine series separated by a lacuna becoming more important as we go farther south, we deduce that this region has been the scene of a regression traveling from south to north, and followed by a transgression toward the south (see Fig. 2).

It must be noted that, during the lacuna and at the beginning of the invasion of the new transgressive sea, there could be erosion of the beds older than the lacuna. So, in Fig. 2, the beds B and C could very well have been laid down as far as *y*. The result is that, to know the meridional limit of the seas corresponding to these stages, we cannot depend only on the extent of these beds B and C. The position of the shores of these seas can only be determined if the littoral facies are found.

In other words, the extent of the marine deposits of a given age yield only the minimum size of the seas of that age, and to know the true contours of these seas, it will be necessary to find everywhere the *shore facies*. Because of failure to observe this rule, many old paleogeographic maps are inexact. Also the maps of facies or rather of facies grouped in natural regions, such as the synthetic maps established by E. Haug, are infinitely more exact and more interesting than the simple maps outlining old seas.

Sedimentary Cycle

Every series of marine formations which, in a given region, is bounded by two regressions, constitutes a sedimentary cycle. In reality this series necessarily begins with the deposit of littoral, coastal facies, corresponding to the coming of the sea.[35] It will continue with deeper-water formations, dating approximately the maximum of the transgression, and it will end finally with new littoral deposits, prelude to the regression.

Thus envisaged, the entire history of the sedimentation in the region considered can be conceived as a series of marine episodes, each of which is a sedimentary cycle, separated by lacunas or by continental formations. It is this periodic return which evokes the name of cycle.

The Great Paleogeographic Units: Basins and Continental Areas

Examining the successive maps of old seas, we see immediately that if the details of their contours change rapidly, nevertheless these contours often keep for long periods the same general appearance. Or, more precisely, we have the impression of a series of marine reservoirs that persist through numerous geological stages but which overflow or recede from the lands that border them. So, we can distinguish in the old seas two domains:

1. *Relatively permanent seas.* Since these seas could exist during long geologic periods without being filled up by the sediments that accumulated there, it must be admitted that the general results of the movements of the earth that affected their bottom is shown by increasing depth. This is true of the basins of subsidence, which we have already defined.

2. Surrounding these basins will extend regions sometimes submerged, sometimes emerged, according to the play of transgressions and regressions.

This will be the area of *continental platforms* which, as we already know, lend themselves particularly well to studies of detailed stratigraphy, because of their richness in marine faunas and the variety of their facies.

3. Finally, to this first region formed by basins and the continental platforms that surround them, and where these "epicontinental" seas (E. Haug) constitute, with the emerged continents, the continental areas, we have already contrasted the domain of *geosynclines,* the bottoms of which in the course of folding form troughs and mobile cordilleras. Their study will not be very instructive, from the viewpoint of detailed stratigraphy and in general will pose more problems than it will provide chronological landmarks.

So, in order to get our bearings somewhat in the infinite variety and the changing successions of paleogeographic contours that so often lead beginners astray, we should, with a single glance, embrace a long period of geologic time, in order to grasp what permanence these contours have. We shall take the basins as points of departure for a more detailed history of the movements of the seas.

Application of the Preceding Ideas to the Distinction of Stages

In the center of these basins there are generally only thick and monotonous successions of marine deposits, without sudden changes of facies. That means that the distinction of successive stages will often be difficult there and only possible if the usually impoverished faunas are improved by the facies becoming a little less deep. On the other hand, the borders of the continental shelves, domain of transgressions and regressions, by their lacunas, by the sudden variations of facies, and by their richer faunas, will allow the distinction of a detailed series of lithologic and paleontologic stages.

Likewise, it is not astonishing to find that many of the old stages or formations, defined long ago by their lithological facies, correspond to sedimentary cycles. So conceived, each stage begins with a transgression and ends with a regression (see Fig. 4).

It now remains for us to see if these stages, so defined regionally, have a general value and how they may agree with the divisions based on the faunas.

But, the larger the domain over which the sedimentary cycle, corresponding to a stage, is distinguishable, the greater the value of the stage, paleogeographically defined. And thus we are led to one of the greatest questions of stratigraphy: are the transgressions and regressions general, or is their history rather variable in different points of the same basin or from one basin to another?

In the first case, if we can really prove that a transgression is apparent at the same time over the whole extent of the basin, or even over the entire globe, that suggests inevitably the idea of an immense rising tide, the causes and effects of which are as unique as the sea itself. Briefly, this transgression would be due to a real movement of the surface of the sea (or of the seas), invading the continents which remained stable. For such general displacements of sea level, E. Suess has proposed the name *eustatic movements.* We shall examine, as we go along, the observations of facts on which this idea is based (pp. 455,

456, etc.), and we ought to find that frequently the movements of the seas do not seem to have had everywhere exactly the same history. So, to the eustatic movements, which must have existed, are added relative displacements of continental masses. A series of local stages will correspond to each regional history of these displacements. And it is paleontology alone that will permit us to find these stages in other regions and to establish the paleogeographic relations between them.

So we are led to our second question: are there reasons to believe that a stage conceived as a sedimentary series may be at the same time characterized by its fauna?

We can already, a priori, see the answer. Indeed, each lacuna or regression corresponds, not only to an often long period of time, but also to important

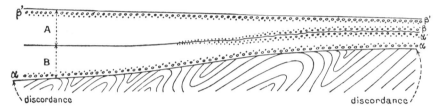

FIG. 4.   *Diagram showing two successive sedimentary cycles.*

A and B —Stages corresponding to two cycles.
α and β —Littoral or continental formations at the beginning of the transgressions.
α' and β' —Littoral or continental formations of the regressions.

To the left, beyond the region reached by the regression, sedimentation remained continuous and the stages are not paleogeographically distinct: there we have a basin, bordered by the region of the continental platform which is to the right.

changes in the configuration of the lands and the seas, and when the new sea comes, inaugurating a new sedimentary cycle, it will bring with it a new fauna. Moreover, since these changes of its fauna coincide with the migrations caused by the movements of the seas, it is ordinarily very difficult to recognize the part which is due to a true evolution of the species and that which results from migrations. From the stratigraphic point of view, that is of little importance. The essential thing is to note that at the beginning of each sedimentary cycle, there is generally found a renovation of the fauna. The paleogeographic stages will thus often coincide with the paleontologic stages. And so we shall understand how D'Orbigny, the true founder of stratigraphic paleontology, could, with good conscience and objectivity, be led to formulate his theory of the successive creations, each of which marked the beginning of a new stage.

IV. Nomenclature of the Stratigraphic Divisions

As seen above, the first groups that were distinguished in the series of terrains were regional and empirical: chalk, coarse limestone of Paris, London clay, etc. Then the need was felt for a nomenclature usable for all of the explored countries. So to these assemblages were given stage names, applicable to all the sediments deposited at the same epoch. It was agreed to call these stages after a locality where the sediments in question were easily seen, fossiliferous, and represented by a marine facies. In principle, and wherever possible, the names of these type localities were latinized (example: Lutetian, of Lutetia = Paris, for the coarse limestone).

Despite their forbidding appearance to beginners, these names of stages have the great advantage of recalling at once concrete facts: thus, in saying Dinantian, instead of saying only Lower Carboniferous, one evokes immediately a picture of the limestones of Dinant with their fauna and their characteristic facies, which recall, in their turn, a mass of stratigraphic facts.

For ease of description, these stages have been grouped in systems limited in such a way that each of them forms a natural unit, which is easily distinguished in the greatest possible number of regions (example: Carboniferous, Jurassic). In the same way, it has been agreed to unite several systems in great eras (Precambrian eras, Primary, Secondary, Tertiary, Quaternary).

Lacunas accompanied by discordance, that is, periods of formation of chains of mountains, furnish especially important division planes, since the geosynclinal regions, whose folding is completed, are then annexed to the continental areas, which constitutes a paleogeographic modification of the first order. Thus, in general, the Huronian orogeny will mark the boundary between the Precambrian eras and the Primary era, the Caledonian orogeny between the Silurian and the Devonian systems. The Hercynian orogeny plays a capital role in the countries where geological science originated. In France and more generally in central Europe, its foldings, surviving through the Upper Carboniferous and the Permian, caused the greatest division which was apparent, from the beginning of geological observations, between the vertical formations of the Primary and the horizontal formations of the Secondary (including the upper Permian). It is only later that paleontological arguments justified and made precise this distinction between the Primary and Secondary eras. As for the Alpine orogeny, where the principal folds began in the Tertiary, we can say that they are still in the process of formation. If the Pliocene formations bordering the Alps seem little affected by this folding, it is simply because the duration of geologic time elapsed since the beginning of the Pliocene has not been sufficient for these very slow orogenic phenomena in general to be translated into important deformations.

Inversely, the detailed study of the fauna or the flora has allowed the stages to be subdivided into paleontological zones, named from one or more characteristic species.[36] These zones are especially useful to stratigraphers who are engaged with a particular system and we shall mention them only in special cases.

Let us add that these divisions are all conventional and that consequently certain of them vary with authors or countries. But for the most part and thanks mainly to the world-wide circulation of the *Traité de Géologie* of A. de Lapparent, general agreement has been reached.

Quaternary or Pleistocene Era   200,000 yrs.*

Tertiary Era	Neogene system	{ Pliocene .... 6 Miocene 12	54,000,000 yrs.
	Paleogene or Nummu- litic system	{ Oligocene .... 16 Eocene 20	
Secondary Era	Cretaceous system	{ Upper Lower } 65	135,000,000 yrs.
	Jurassic system	{ Upper Middle } .. 35 Lower or Lias	
	Triassic system 35		
Primary Era	Permo-Carboniferous system	{ Permian .... 25 Carboniferous 85	360,000,000 yrs.
	Devonian system 50		
	Silurian system	{ Gothlandian Ordovician } ...130	
	Cambrian system 70		

Precambrian Eras   2,000,000,000 yrs.

* Since the publication of the French edition of this work, later study has slightly modified the values. Note by author.

Stage names will be given later. We present here only the list of the most important divisions, which we shall use from here on (see above). For each, we indicate its length in thousands or millions of years, calculated by modern geochemical methods (see L. Moret, *Précis de Géologie*, p. 17).

V. The Oldest Formations and the Question of the Archean

As we seek to recognize, in all parts of the globe, the oldest formations, we inevitably find, everywhere, that these are rocks called by petrographers *crystalline schists:* mica schists, gneisses, amphibolites, etc. These rocks are crystalline, for they contain crystals that have developed in place, and have not been derived from other pre-existing rocks; and they are at the same time stratified, by the arrangement of their elements.

This evidence led early geologists to suppose that these crystalline rocks were actually the first to be formed. For them it was the original crust of our earth, the first solid envelope, formed by cooling, at the surface of our liquid globe. The period of its formation thus constituted the oldest of the geologic eras, called *Archean* and characterized by a very special superficial sedimentation, of which nothing on the surface of the present earth can give us any idea.

But more careful observations have brought serious objections to this theory.

First, it is seen that in this alleged original crust are sometimes found intercalations of clearly sedimentary rocks, sandstones, limestones, shale, conglomerates, etc., more or less modified but still recognizable, and formed in every instance from the debris of older rocks. And especially, there have been discovered at certain points in these schistose complexes unquestionable fossils, whose geological age varies in different areas. Thus there are Primary schistose complexes in certain regions, Secondary in others. In other words, the crystalline schists have first been sedimentary rocks, like the others of any age, which after their deposition have become more or less crystalline.

To explain such a transformation, the petrographers had to turn to a new hypothesis. They now suppose that the crystalline schists are old sediments which, after their formation, descended to great depths below the earth's surface, to regions where the temperature, the pressure, and the proximity to rocks melted in the central hearth could cause the development of crystals. To these phenomena of transformation, the mechanism of which we need not elucidate, is given the name regional metamorphism or, simply, *metamorphism*.

We may conceive that this transformation might go as far as the complete making over of the old sediment, which would thus become entirely crystalline, losing all trace of its original stratification. Thus, for certain authors, granites may be the final stage of metamorphism. In fact, certain granitic massifs seem to be formed in place by complete digestion of a sedimentary mass. For this phenomenon, still very mysterious, a new word has naturally been coined, *anatexis;* and these granites of anatexis, cropping out in enormous massifs, are often termed deep granites. On the other hand, other granites, cropping out only in much more restricted massifs, seem to have been injected (in the liquid state) into a solid sedimentary covering that they could transform: the granitization is then shown by a network of veins or apophyses coming from a deep magma.[37]

In any case, and since the surface of the present earth shows us no analogous phenomenon, we can find metamorphic formations only in regions where slow burial of progressively accumulated sediments has occurred. Such is the case in the deepest geosynclinal troughs that we have defined above. Or again, and more precisely, we shall say that at a given moment in its history, such a region has passed through a geosynclinal phase, accompanied or not by metamorphism. And in order that the transformed sediments may become in turn accessible to our observation, a reverse movement is required, that is, folding must bring them near the surface and erosion must remove the sedimentary envelope which covered them.

Then, if our hypothesis is true, the regions of crystalline schists should present two characteristics: they will always be folded and they must have been covered, at some moment in their history, by a thick sedimentary coat. In fact, this is just what we observe, so that there is some presumption in favor of our theory.

Thus, crystalline schists confined in folded regions, far from all belonging

to the same Archean stage, will be of variable age, certainly older than the last
great folding of their respective chains, that is to say, as we shall see, pre-Cambrian in the Huronian orogeny, pre-Devonian in the Caledonian orogeny, pre-
Permian in the Hercynian orogeny, pre-Oligocene in the Alpine orogeny.[38] In
other words, there is not an Archean stage, but an Archean facies, a special
case of what we have called geosynclinal sedimentation.

So, whatever the old sediments may have been, they are now united in metamorphic complexes, unrecognizable and apparently azoic, although life may
certainly have been developed on our globe prior to the oldest fauna that we
know. And it is very likely that we shall never know more, either of the original
crust or of the first faunas.

From this viewpoint, the entire thickness of the sedimentary crust accessible
to our observation seems to us only a residue, accidentally spared by the two
causes of destruction which act on the two faces of the solid crust: destruction
by atmospheric agents above, remelting and metamorphism below. Thus suspended between these two infinities of destruction, infinite because they have
endless time, the long series of decipherable geologic stages is in reality only a
final episode, the final spared witness of a very long history forever effaced.

And on reflection, this destruction of deep beds by metamorphism seems to
us a necessary conclusion. Indeed the superficial sedimentary rocks are formed,
not only at the expense of other sedimentary rocks, but also at the expense of
igneous rocks (granites, lavas) risen from the depths: there is therefor a constant addition to the materials of which the outer crust is built. It necessarily
follows from this, to give equilibrium to this growth, that the crust be
destroyed, eaten away at its base.

We can say, then, when a certain volume of these eruptive rocks rises from
the depths and becomes incorporated in the surface crust, it is necessary that
a like volume of the surface sediments descend, perhaps sucked in, to the
depths. It is evidently in the geosynclinal troughs, in the orogenes (see note 29,
this chap.), that these descending movements are localized. Such is the starting
point of certain modern orogenic theories: theory of engulfing or of suction
(*Verschluckung*) formulated by Ampferer for the Alps, theory of orogenic
downbuckle proposed by Umbgrove and Vening Meinesz for the Indo-Pacific
orogeny. The earth's crust appears to us then, to be animated by an infinitely
slow boiling of magmatic currents (*Unterströmungen*), of ascending or
descending convection currents.[39]

Thus, a given mineral molecule, since the beginning of the life of our globe,
has described an incessant cycle, sometimes caught in the depth of a trough
and incorporated in a metamorphic or crystalline rock, sometimes elevated to
mountain heights, then torn away by atmospheric agents to be re-incorporated
in a new sediment. In comparison with this endless cycle, all our geologic
periods and the entire history of our chains of mountains seem to us only
passing episodes.

REFERENCE NOTES

1. Beginners are advised to run through this Introduction quickly, then return to it later; for the ideas that are here set forth are extremely theoretical and will reveal their full meaning only when the reading of the main work gives precise and varied examples.

2. See, for example, J. de Lapparent, *Leçons de Pétrographie, Paris, Masson* (1923).

3. M. Boule and J. Piveteau, *Les Fossiles,* Paris, Masson (1935); L. Moret, *Manuel de Paléontologie animale,* Paris, Masson (1948), *Manuel de Paléontologie végétale,* Paris, Masson (1943).

4. E. Raguin, *Géologie appliquée,* Paris, Masson (1934); E. Haug, *Traité de Géologie,* vol. 1, Paris, A. Colin; E. de Martonne, *Traité de géographie physique,* Paris, A. Colin; L. Bertrand, *Les anciennes mers de France,* Paris, Flammarion. All the general ideas helpful for reading the present work are set forth in L. Moret, *Précis de Géologie,* Paris, Masson (1948).

5. Carried to the sea, these red formations may color the marine, coastal deposits: example, "red Argovian" of the Alps, p. 359.

6. Example, Wealden facies of the Lower Cretaceous of the Anglo-Parisian Basin, p. 411, Lower Eocene of the Franco-Belgian Basin, p. 478, and of the valley of the Rhône, (p. 493).

7. Cretaceous of Provence, p. 429, Carboniferous of Scotland, p. 177.

8. A. Cailleux, *Les actions éoliennes périglaciares en Europe,* Thèse, Paris (1942), Mém. Soc. géol. France, n. s., t. 21, no. 46.

9. One will find something of a commentary on this figure in the interesting article of J. Tercier, *Dépôts marins actuels et séries géologiques,* Eclogae geol. Helvetiae, 32 (1939), where the present marine sediments of the Indo-Malayan Archipelago and of the Antilles are studied.

10. Anglo-Latin term recently naturalized into French and put into use by P. Pruvost (work cited in chap. 5, note 6); it is very useful indeed to evoke at the same time the idea of a slow and continued subsidence and the resultant call for sedimentation.

11. These will be still further increased if, by chance, we have to deal with a sinking zone.

12. See pp. 42, 112, 272, 278, some examples of peculiarities by which sediments of aeolian origin are recognized.

13. Of course, dust transported by the wind and not by water will not be decalcified, so loess contains a notable proportion of calcium carbonate.

14. Analogous distinctions can also be made for the continental facies, but there they have no interest for us.

15. This definition will not seem precise to petrographers, but it is nonetheless useful for the field geologist.

16. This is not an absolute rule. Thus, in the Pliocene of the Strait of Messina, a region where deep and very violent currents still rule along the abrupt coasts, I know of coarse gravels in which abound valves of *Pachylasma giganteum,* a cirripede which in the present Mediterranean Sea scarcely rises above a depth of 200 meters (see M. Gignoux, thesis cited in chap. 10, note 7, pp. 60 and 564). Very recently A. Heim has drawn attention to the importance of the phenomena of sedimentation or erosion due to these swift submarine currents, whose existence can be recognized even at great depths; see Arnold Heim, *Problemas de erosion submarine y sedimentacion pelagica del presente y del pasado,* Rev. Mus. La Plata, n. s. sect. Geol., t. 4 (1946).

17. Etymologically, these terms zoogene and terrigene are evidently badly constructed; thus, zoogene means that which produces animals and not produced by animals. Nevertheless, they are sanctioned by long usage and everyone understands their significance. We believe it useless then to invent new words to replace them. On the contrary, for the adjective corralligene, it is easier to substitute the more correct corallian (or, in English, coral used as an adjective).

18. H. T. Stearns, "An Interpretation of Coral-reef Hypotheses," Amer. Jour. of Sci. (1946), p. 245.

19. A. Rivière, *Observations nouvelles sur le mécanisme de dolomitisation des sédiments calcaires* C. R. Acad. Sci. (Nov. 6, 1939); *L'eau de mer et les sédiments calcaires,* C. R. somm. Soc. Géol. France (Mar. 4, 1940).

20. Naturally we exclude the secondary minerals which may have been formed in the sediments after their deposition, by metamorphism or metasomatism. Petrographers can easily distinguish the detrital minerals coming from pre-existing rocks. Let us note in addition that we here use the term mud in its common meaning and not in the restricted sense (*vase*—very fine sediments rich in colloidal organic matter) that J. Bourcart has recently given it. Bourcart has well demonstrated the special properties of these muds *sensu stricto.* See J. Bourcart and C. Francis-Boeuf, *La Vase,* Paris, Hermann (1942).

21. On this subject, see the article of A. Heim cited in Note 16, and a very suggestive note of L. Royer, *Au sujet d'une précipitation de carbonate de calcium observée dans la Mer Morte,* C. R. Acad. Sci. t. 221 (1945), p. 221.

22. Except the pure lithographic limestones, which may be pure white.

23. We cannot too highly recommend to geologists the study of the magnificent work of A. F. Marion, *Esquisse d'une topographie zoologique du Golfe de Marseille. Considérations sur les faunes profondes de la Mediterranée,* Ann. Musée Hist. Nat. Marseille, Zoologie, t. 1 (1883). See also L. Dangeard, *Observations de Géologie sous-marine et d'Océanographie rélatives a la Manche,* Ann. Inst. Océanographique n. s., t. 6, Paris (1928).

24. Nevertheless, this classic idea has recently been questioned. According to E. Wayne Galliher, Bull. Geol. Soc. Am., 46 (1935), p. 1351, glauconite could be derived from transformation of biotite in alkaline waters, marine or brackish. On this subject see H. H. Renz, *Die subalpine Molasse zwischen Aare und Rhein,* Eclogae geol. Helvetiae, 30, no. 1 (1937), p. 113.

25. Some very interesting observations in the lagoons of Tunisia have been described by H. Heldt, A. Rivière, P. Bellaire, *Origine possible des bone beds,* C. R. Acad. Sci., t. 225 (1948), p. 882.

26. H. Grünau has just described some wood of fossil conifers in the Alpine radiolarites. (See chap. 7, note 140).

27. Note 1 and Fig. 1 apply especially to this paragraph. The figure is designed to illustrate the phenomena of sedimentation which takes place in a relatively brief time (that of external dynamics) and in the legend we have continued to use the language of classic tectonics. If, on the contrary, one wished to discuss this figure in the light of orogenic phenomena, incomparably slower, and in which all rocks can flow, it would be necessary to use the language of flow tectonics (see M. Gignoux, reference cited note 39). Then the continental foundations can no longer be described as rigid but only as stable and quiet. They are opposed, thus, to the geosynclinal or orogenic regions, activated by convection currents of deep origin. On the surface, the zones of descending currents correspond to the suction or to troughs, the zones of ascending currents correspond to swellings or cordilleras. On the flanks of these cordilleras, rocks flow superficially by gravity.

28. On this subject, see the interesting article of R. Laffitte, *La formation et l'épaisseur des sédiments dans l'Aurès (Algérie),* Archives du Muséum d'Hist. nat., vol. du Tricentenaire, 6 sér., t. 12 (1935).

29. Also our expression of geosynclinal regions, which includes the troughs and the cordilleras which separate them, has recently been replaced in the terminology of many foreign geologists (Kober, Staub, etc.) by the term orogenes.

30. We shall speak of this again à *propos* of the Jurassic (p. 351), then of the Alpine Flysch (p. 517). Let us remark in passing how much the scheme that we give here (Fig. 1) of the geosynclinal sedimentation has advanced from the explanation that was formerly given of the geosynclinal great trough where the thickness of the sediments increased regularly from the edges to the bottom (see for example Fig. 36 of the *Traité de Géologie* of E. Haug).

31. It is precisely for the Wealden that the law of correlation of facies was clearly formulated by J. F. Kirkaldy (work cited in chap. 8, note 57).

32. This extremely rare limiting case of exact equilibrium between deposition and erosion is eminently unstable.

33. This chronological concept of the mountain chain is different than the purely geographic concept. Chains, for geologists, unite branches, subdivisions and massifs, which would be separate chains for the geographers.

34. A. Bigot, *Les surfaces d'usure et les remaniements dans le Jurassique de Basse-Normandie,* Bull. Soc. Géol. France, 5 sér., t. 10 (1940), p. 165.

35. The coarsest of these deposits are naturally the oldest, remains of coastal plains or of littoral strands. Also usually the beginning of a transgression is marked by a basal conglomerate. We shall see examples of them continually.

36. Since faunas and floras vary with facies and provinces, a succession of paleontological zones or, as it is called a scale of characteristic species, is often valuable only for a single facies or a single province. One of the problems most often faced by the stratigrapher is precisely that of establishing synchronisms between several of these scales.

37. See E. Raguin, *Géologie du granite* Paris, Masson (1946). We call attention also to the particularly original and interesting study of H. H. Read, "Meditations on Granite," Proc. Geologists Assn., 54 (1943), and 55 (1944). Finally, specialists in plutonic petrogenesis will find numerous recent bibliographic references in an article by L. Glangeaud, Revue scientif. (December, 1947).

38. To tell the truth, the later crystalloblastic (*cristallophylliens*) complexes are much less metamorphic. Thus in the Alps, the only region of Europe where there are metamorphic terrains (the *schistes lustres*) of the Secondary and perhaps partly of the Tertiary age, there are only shales and limestones in which metamorphic minerals have developed. Nowhere is there true gneiss. That doubtless happens, because in this chain, whose history is not yet finished, the folding and subsequent erosion have not yet been sufficient to bring to the surface the formations which descended into the deepest zones.

39. See M. Gignoux, *Méditations sur la théorie de la tectonique d'écoulement par gravité,* Trav. Lab. Géol. Univ. Grenoble, t. 27 (1948).

Chapter One

Precambrian Formations

The oldest formations on the whole globe that can be distinguished by their fauna are called Cambrian. For the moment it is enough to know that this fauna is sufficiently rich in abundant specimens of well defined species so that it can be recognized without question.

In formations underlying the Cambrian, traces of organisms have been found in several regions, but they are very rare and everywhere almost unrecognizable; up to the present, no distinctive characteristics have been recognized in them.[1] We are, then, unable to establish for these formations any chronological classification having a general application. So we have adopted for the title of this chapter the noncommittal expression "Precambrian Formations." [2]

The term Archean is often used for these old formations when, as is frequently the case, they are metamorphic (mica schists, gneisses, amphibolites) and the term Precambrian (or Algonkian) when they are not. But we already know that the degree of metamorphism of a rock is only a facies distinction and does not mean a definite age. This subdivision may have a local value, the Archean rocks being normally older than the Precambrian rocks which are contiguous to them, but it has no general chronological significance.[3]

However that may be, the Precambrian formations can naturally only be recognized and described with certainty in the regions where the Cambrian fauna is known. It is to such regions that we shall confine our study.

I. The Canadian Shield

Let us go first to the Great Lakes region of North America[4] (Fig. 5).

At the north there is the slightly undulating Canadian plain, where the old moraines of the great Quaternary glaciers form the most important minor elements of the topography. The lakes themselves and Hudson Bay do not add greatly to the relief, since the deepest of these depressions is no more than 200 m. Everywhere under the recent deposits—moraines, lacustrine clays and river alluvium—outcrops of bed rock are made up of ancient rocks: granites

A = Atikokan; B = Little Belt Mts.; C = Grand Canyon of the Colorado;
K = Keweenaw Peninsula; Ki = Keewatin; P = Potsdam
-------- Approximate southern limit of the Canadian Shield

FIG. 5. *Structural map of North America.*

and micaceous or other schists whose bedding planes have been bent and
folded, then eroded and leveled.

South of the Great Lakes all these folded formations disappear at depth
under a covering of horizontal Primary strata, the lowest of which contain a
Cambrian fauna. These horizontal beds must originally have advanced much
further to the north than today, for it is easy to show that their northern limit
is an erosion boundary, a scarp, and it is from under this scarp that the Canadian plain pushes out indefinitely to the north. Suess has proposed the name
line of glint for this boundary;[5] often the waters coming from the north are
stopped against it; thus, the Great Lakes are aligned at its foot.

Thus the line of glint may be followed from the Atlantic shores, approximately along the course of the lower Saint Lawrence, successively by Lake
Ontario, Lake Huron, Lake Superior, Lake Winnipeg, Lake Athabasca, Slave
Lake, and Bear Lake to the Arctic Sea near the mouth of the Mackenzie River
(see Fig. 5).

All the country north of this line constitutes the Canadian Shield, according to Suess; for it is a vast and slightly convex pedestal which supports the whole framework of North America. The folded, eroded rocks of which it is composed are certainly Precambrian, since on the south edge of the Shield we find them covered by the horizontal Cambrian.

The largest part of the Shield is made up of the granites or gneisses and mica schists generally called Laurentian. Sedimentary rocks form only relatively narrow bands, striking SW-NE (approximately parallel to the course of the Saint Lawrence), which indicates the general direction of these very old Precambrian folds.

The stratigraphy of these formations is very difficult, because of their dislocations and metamorphism; we seek to distinguish in them lithological assemblages, often separated from each other by discordances, and it is upon this that we take our stand to establish stages. These so-called stages have then only a local validity, since the classifications proposed vary with authors and regions.[6]

M. E. Wilson (Jour. Geol., 26, 1918) has clearly shown that the adoption of the same names of stages for different regions could only cause confusion and would in no way imply synchronism.

Here is, for example, the type series selected by Lawson in the region of the Great Lakes, the area best studied:

Algonkian (*Keweenawan* formation[7])
        Great unconformity
Archean   *Huronian*, with intrusive granites (and gneiss) called *Algoman*.
        Great unconformity
      Ontarian (*Keewatin*[8] formation), with granites (and gneiss) called *Laurentian*.

The *Ontarian* especially is formed of more or less metamorphosed lava flows and tuffs, but detrital sedimentary rocks are also found in it; very important iron deposits are worked there, which seem to be precipitation deposits. It is in these beds in relation with the Laurentian granites that we find the Eozoon, formerly considered organic, but whose purely mineral nature is now recognized.[9]

To the east, near the Saint Lawrence, limestone facies predominate (Grenville series), a fact which suggests the participation of rock-forming organisms.[10]

The *Huronian* begins with glacial conglomerates (see later, p. 41); it continues with various detrital formations, sometimes granitized.

It is probably at this level that the limestones of Steeprock Lake (near Lake Atikokan, a hundred miles west of Lake Superior) should be placed, where *Atikokania* are found in great abundance, enigmatic organisms similar to the *Archeocyathidae* (see p. 46) or the sponges.

The iron ores of the Huronian, very important industrially, are, according to Cayeux,[11] of sedimentary origin and analogous to the Silurian oolithic ores of Normandy or the Jurassic of Lorraine: this investigator points out the presence of the remains of echinoderms.

The *Algonkian* (or *Keweenawan*) is rarely granitized;[12] it contains the finest known deposits of native copper, in connection with igneous extrusions.

As may be seen from the diagram (Fig. 6), Lawson's classification emphasizes periodic granitization and metamorphism, but many authors contest its
generality. We have mentioned it here, for it gives good evidence of the long
duration and the complexity of Precambrian times, during which at least two

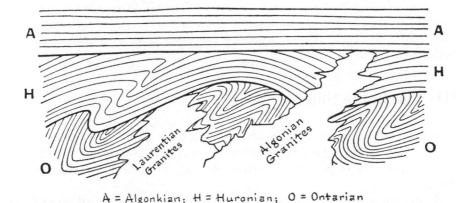

A = Algonkian; H = Huronian; O = Ontarian

FIG. 6. *Diagram of Precambrian formations and their granitic intrusions
in the region of the Great Lakes of North America (Canadian Shield) (after
F. D. Adams, modified). For* Algonian, *read* Algoman.

great orogenic periods occurred, each accompanied by the emplacement of
granitic massifs with metamorphism and followed by a period of erosion.

There are in addition, within the Huronian and the Algonkian, other less
important unconformities, that we have omitted for the sake of simplicity.

II. The Grand Canyon of the Colorado

South of the line of glint, the Precambrian formations of the Canadian Shield
disappear into the depths beneath the horizontal Paleozoic. They reappear,
more or less well defined, in certain American chains; a single example of this
out-cropping will receive our attention, that of the Grand Canyon.

Between the folded chains of the Rocky Mountains and the Pacific Sierras
(see Fig. 5) lies a region of high plateaus where great expanses of horizontal
Primary (Paleozoic) or Secondary (Mesozoic) formations crop out. These are
the deserts of Utah and Colorado, but the Colorado River has made a cut in
them deep enough to expose the Precambrian formations. The base of the
celebrated Grand Canyon gorge shows us the following sequence:

Cambrian horizontal, beginning with a basal conglomerate.

Precambrian { *Algonkian:* inclined beds of marl and sandstone with fossil debris.
              Archean: much-folded gneiss.

As we can see, the existence of Precambrian formations is here indisputable
and as in the Great Lakes region, a lower metamorphic stage (Archean) and

an upper nonmetamorphic stage (Algonkian) can be distinguished among them; but we cannot say that these stages are the equivalent of the formations with the same names in Canada.

It is there and a little farther north in Montana (Belt beds: see Fig. 5) that the most remains of Precambrian animals are found (Algonkian): these are not merely fragments, from which it is usually impossible to define true recognizable genera, but they are sufficient to show us the diversity which this fauna must have had (coelenterates, trilobites and other large crustaceans, gastropods, worms).

III. The Baltic Shield

Some structural elements entirely analogous to those we have just described in North America are found in northern Europe. The two areas are roughly symmetrical with respect to a north-south axis through the middle of the Atlantic.

So the Baltic Shield corresponds to the Canadian Shield.[13] All around the Baltic stretch vast plains, where very old rocks, folded, metamorphosed and eroded, appear everywhere under cover of moraines or Recent alluvium. To the west, south and east, the Baltic Shield also disappears under a covering of horizontal Cambrian or Silurian strata, whose scarp-forming margin is likewise a line of glint. As in America, it is marked by a series of lakes.

The boundary of the Shield starts with the Archangel Gulf and passes through Lakes Onega and Ladoga and along the Gulf of Finland to the Baltic Sea. The shallow North-Baltic Basin, which can be classified as epicontinental, is thus analogous to Hudson Bay. Then our boundary passes north of the islands of Oeland and Gotland, leaves Scania to the south, rejoins the Norwegian coast at Stavanger and turns toward the northeast, passing between the Swedish shore of the Baltic and the Scandinavian Mountains, along a whole series of little glint lakes[14] until it terminates at Varangerfjord, where it enters the Arctic Sea (see Fig. 9).

Moreover, the structural scheme of the Baltic Shield, that is, the Precambrian folded and eroded formations, covered by the horizontal Cambrian or other Primary strata (see Fig. 10), extends far to the southeast over the greater part of Russia; the Shield there is only masked by a Primary cover: this immense region is called the Russian Platform.[15]

Analogies with America are found in the similar make-up of the Baltic formations; these have been studied especially in Finland.[16] An extremely varied series of more or less crystalline or metamorphic rocks is found there, in which unconformities and succeeding granitizations have made possible the distinction of a series of stages:

1. Archean.   These are almost everywhere very metamorphic and granitized rocks. We can distinguish a lower or Svionian group and an upper or Bothnian group in which the sediments are sometimes less metamorphosed, a kind of phyllite, in which, under the name of *Corycium enigmaticum,* carbonaceous impressions attributed to Algae (?) have been described. The Archean, thus defined, is ended by an important period of folding which gave birth to a chain of mountains called the Svecofennides.[17]

2. Precambrian. Formerly three successive stages were distinguished here: the *Ladogian,* the *Kalevian,* more metamorphic, and the *Jatulian,* which is the least metamorphic. This last even contains, on the banks of the Shunga River in Russian Karelia (northwest shore of Lake Onega), a bed of anthracite called shungite which reaches a thickness of 2 m. and appears to be the oldest known combustible rock. In beds of dolomitic limestone, traces of organisms related to the tabulate corals, called *Carelozoon jatulicum*[18] are also found. But Wegmann has recently shown[19] that these Jatulian sediments were affected by granitization; according to this geologist, they represent the epicontinental shallow and less metamorphosed equivalent of a geosynclinal series corresponding to the Ladogian and Kalevian. The whole, to which the name Karelian stage is applied, was finally granitized and folded, forming a new chain of mountains, the Karelides. Certain granites, and in particular the special, celebrated type called Rapakivi,[20] were not affected by the folding; they are, then, post-tectonic. Wegmann could thus emphasize the analogies between the Precambrian history of the Karelides and the Tertiary history of the Alpine Chain; in both cases we find an epicontinental series, not metamorphic, deposited on the borders of the foreland, a geosynclinal and metamorphic series in the axis of the chain itself, and finally granitic intrusions later than the main folding.

3. Jotnian. These are the red sandstones, probably of continental origin, for which it is agreed to reserve a place apart, above the Precambrian proper. They are really later than all the granites and are not folded; we can consider them to have been formed during the period of erosion and continental sedimentation which followed the raising of the Karelides, and in the course of which the entire Baltic Shield was reduced to the state of a peneplain (called Subjotnian) before it was reached by the marine transgressions of the Cambrian.[21]

Probably these Jotnian sandstones originally covered most of the Baltic Shield; at present only scattered fragments remain, sometimes preserved in small depressed troughs. The type region of these sandstones is situated southwest of Lake Onega, where they form extensive outcrops; they are known also on the Finnish Coast of the Gulf of Bothnia, northwest of Helsinki (Helsingfors) and on the shores of the Kola peninsula.[22] Analogous formations are found on the west edge of the Shield in Sweden, southeast of Lake Vätern, and in Dalecarlia, where they are called sandstones of Dala or of the Dalarne; finally, a little farther northwest, they may be compared to the celebrated sparagmite; but since this sparagmitic region was involved in the Caledonian folding of the Scandinavian chain, we shall discuss it later when we study the Primary rocks of these mountains.

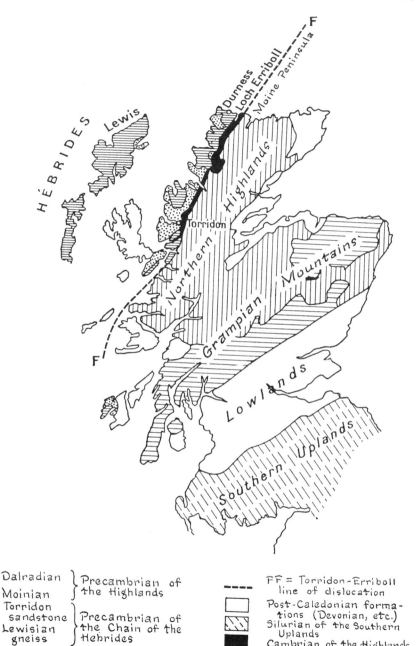

FIG. 7. *Diagrammatic geologic map of the Caledonian Massifs of Scotland (after J. W. Gregory, simplified).*

IV. The Chain of the Hebrides

The northwest extremity of Scotland is traversed by a great line of dislocation (see Fig. 7), which, starting from Loch Erriboll near Durness, is directed to the southwest, passing near Torridon. We shall call it the Torridon-Erriboll line and shall examine its significance later.

This line separates two regions with very different structures: to the east there are only gneisses, called the Eastern Gneisses, of which we shall speak again; to the west there are three distinct formations: the Western Gneisses, sandstones without fossils, and Cambrian fossiliferous rocks (see Fig. 8).

The Western Gneisses are developed especially in the Hebrides and particularly in the Island of Lewis: so they are called the Lewisian gneiss; like all metamorphic rocks, they naturally are much folded.

The sandstones without fossils, reaching a thickness of 6,000 m., form great outcrops near Torridon: this celebrated Torridonian sandstone is commonly feldspathic (arkose), more or less reddish and very coarse, especially in the north. British petrographers believe that these sandstones mainly represent continental formations, probably desert, resulting from the destruction of highlands which must have extended especially to the north over the present location of the Atlantic. They would thus be analogous to the Old Red Sandstone which we shall discuss later. These sediments, not at all metamorphic, are tilted rather than folded, and they unconformably overlie the Lewisian gneiss.

Finally this Torridonian is, in its turn, overlaid unconformably by the fossiliferous Cambrian of the Durness band (which we shall study later).

Consequently the Lewisian and Torridonian formations are Precambrian. We may, if we like, compare them respectively with the Archean and Algonkian of America, understanding that this does not imply any strict synchronism. But we should especially emphasize the close analogy which exists between the Torridonian and the Jotnian.

All this domain west of the Torridon-Erriboll line we shall call the Chain of the Hebrides.

It has long been recognized that the Chain of the Hebrides is continued with the same elements and the same structure, in the Lofoten Islands and in some of the promontories which face them as far as Varangerfjord. We shall see later (p. 90) that non-fossiliferous Norwegian rocks correlated with the Lewisian gneiss and the Cambrian of Durness are in reality of a very debatable age.

V. Other European Regions

The Baltic Shield and the Chain of the Hebrides are the only two European regions that offer a real stratigraphic interest; that is because the Cambrian there, being horizontal or only slightly folded, can be easily separated from older formations.

Everywhere else, however, the Cambrian is folded. It is even often metamorphosed and granitized (even as more recent formations); so that the upper limit of Precambrian formations, judged sometimes by unconformities, sometimes by the degree of metamorphism, sometimes by the absence of fossils, usually becomes very difficult to define. In such regions the study of formations, which by agreement are attached to the Precambrian, are hardly

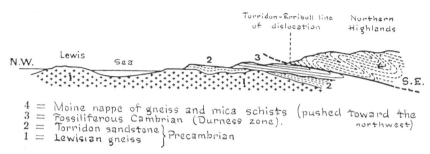

4 = Moine nappe of gneiss and mica schists (pushed toward the
3 = Fossiliferous Cambrian (Durness zone).   northwest)
2 = Torridon sandstone ⎱ Precambrian
1 = Lewisian gneiss   ⎰

FIG. 8. *Theoretical section showing the stratigraphic relation between Precambrian and Cambrian formations in northwestern Scotland (compare map, Fig. 7).*

instructive from our point of view; so we shall confine ourselves to a rapid review of the most extensive and the most classic outcrops.

a. *British Isles*[23]

All the north of Scotland is composed of an immense massif of old rocks: these are the Highlands of Scotland,[24] the southern part of which is often designated as the Grampian Mountains (see the map, Fig. 7, and the section, Fig. 8). At the southeast this massif is bounded by a great bordering fault, which separates it from the Lowlands, a trough filled by the Devonian and the Carboniferous. To the northwest it extends as far as the Torridon-Erriboll line of dislocation, of which we have just spoken. Along this line the gneisses of the Highlands, here called Eastern Gneisses, are superimposed on the Cambrian of the Durness band, which we shall study later. It was long believed that these Eastern Gneisses were post-Cambrian, Silurian. But today it is known that this Torridon-Erriboll line represents the outcrop of an almost horizontal surface of displacement, dipping slightly to the ESE, along which the Eastern Gneisses have been pushed over the Cambrian of the Durness band. So that it is impossible to be certain about the stratigraphic relationship of these gneisses to the Cambrian of Durness or to the Torridonian or the Lewisian. It has been agreed to make a separate stage of it, called the Moinian (after the peninsula of Moine at the north of Scotland); and a whole complex of formations is included under this name. In general they are very metamorphic rocks (gneisses, mica schists, quartzites, etc.), which make up the greater part of the Highlands. Towards the southeast appear less metamorphic formations (mica schists, phyllites, quartzites, limestones, etc.), which compose the Dalradian stage (name taken from the old kingdom of Dalriada, in the north of Ireland, whose inhabitants colonized Scotland).[25] The tectonics of this whole area being very complicated and still debated, we do not know exactly the stratigraphic relationships of the Moinian and the Dalradian; most British geologists agree that the Dalradian is more recent than the Moinian.

In the same way the position of the Moinian-Dalradian complex in relation to the Cambrian has long been argued; some authors (Geikie, followed by Haug, etc.) thought this complex might represent a geosynclinal and metamorphic series of Cambrian-Silurian age; in fact, the Highlands extend to the northeast through the Scandinavian Mountains, where, in an analogous metamorphic series, the Cambrian and the Silurian are certainly represented (see pp. 52 and 88). At present, however, British geologists are unanimous in putting the Moinian and Dalradian in the Precambrian, because it has been discovered that certain rocks of the Moinian, in the form of rounded pebbles, are to be found in the Torridonian conglomerates.[26]

Gregory and Barrett (work cited, note 10) believed they could find a detailed parallel between the Precambrian formations of Canada and Scotland as follows:

Algonkian (Keweenawan)		....	Torridonian
Huronian	.... ⎫	....	Upper Dalradian
	⎧ Keewatin ⎭		
Ontarian	⎪ Grenville	....	Lower Dalradian
	⎨ Coutchiching Gneiss	....	Moine Gneisses
	⎩ Laurentian Gneiss	....	Lewisian Gneiss

We shall keep in mind especially the great analogies of the Algonkian with the Torridonian.

In Wales and its eastern neighbors (The Wrekin, Longmynd, Malvern Hills, etc., see the map, Fig. 17), the Cambrian lies unconformably on very different rocks. In the Wrekin these are especially volcanic rocks, for which the name Uriconian stage has been devised. (This word stems from *Uriconium,* a Roman city, whose name is the source of the present term Wrekin).[27] In the Longmynd these rocks are mostly schists, sandstones, and conglomerates (Longmyndian stage).[28] Special mention should be made of Charnwood Forest (Leicestershire)[29] to the northeast of Birmingham. There, old rocks, folded in the direction NW-SE ("Charnian" direction), appear beneath the Carboniferous or the Triassic. This is the Charnian stage, generally attributed to the Precambrian.

b. *Armorican Massif (Brittany)*

The study of the Precambrian of this massif is inseparable from the study of the Cambrian, for the distinction between these two formations poses difficult problems, not yet completely solved and which we shall discuss in detail later in connection with the Cambrian.

For the moment, let us be satisfied with remarking that the framework of the massif is formed: 1st, by crystalline (granitic) rocks of different ages, the oldest of which are certainly Precambrian but most of which were emplaced in the Devonian or Lower Carboniferous; 2nd, by gneisses and mica schists which seem to be almost everywhere Archean; 3rd, by ancient shales, very little metamorphosed, phyllites, quartz-phyllites and sandstones, which are grouped under the name of *Brioverian* (p. 55). Very characteristic layers are sometimes interbedded in it, which have long been considered as authentic representatives of the Precambrian; as, for example, the famous conglomerates of Gourin and the cherts of Lamballe celebrated for their *Radiolaria* fauna; but recent research has brought in question the age of these beds, which some geologists now tend to make younger and to classify in the Cambrian, as we shall see.

Thus, on the map, Fig. 11 (p. 56), where all these old formations, granites, crystalline schists and Brioverian, have been combined, certain zones attributed to the Brioverian should perhaps be made younger. This is the case in central Brittany (Gourin and Lamballe zones) and in the region of Morlaix-Paimpol, where we shall see that the formations formerly considered Brioverian and Silurian represent more likely, according to Pruvost and his collaborators, a complex that is mostly Dinantian.

c. *Massif Central of France*

The old formations pose the same problems here as in Brittany.

The fossiliferous Cambrian has been recognized only in the extreme south, in the Montagne-Noire area, which we shall study carefully later. For the moment, let us note that A. Michel-Lévy and M. Thoral [30] have demonstrated the Precambrian age of the crystalline or metamorphic rocks which constitute the axial zone of this Montagne-Noire, as well as the neighboring small massifs of Devèze and Meudic, north of Graissessac; for there the fossiliferous Lower Cambrian overlies these rocks in discordance. But in other parts of this same Montagne-Noire, it has been recognized ever since the early studies of Bergeron that the Cambrian and Silurian, affected by regional metamorphism, pass into metamorphic rocks.

However, in the western part of the massif, in the Limousin and as far as the pass of Poitou, immense areas are made up of old schists, relatively little metamorphosed, analogous to the Brioverian of Brittany and still considered Precambrian (stage x of geological maps). But M. Roque [31] has pointed out at Génis, south of Saint-Yrieix, lenses of dolomite and crinoidal limestone and suggests the possibility of the Cambrian or Silurian. Going still further, G. Mathieu [32] notes that this "Brioverian" west of the Massif Central is an extension of that which he studied in the Vendée; and he finds lithologic horizons (quartzites, conglomerates, graphitic schists, etc.) in it, analogous to those he identified in the Vendée as determining Cambro-Silurian bands in the midst of the Precambrian.

Finally, in northern Auvergne, we shall find a fossiliferous Dinantian lying in discordance on the folded and eroded gneisses; while in the extreme north of the massif, around Morvan, this same Dinantian is penetrated by granitic injections which there cause a slight contact metamorphism.

Such are the facts that a stratigrapher can accept.

We deduce from them, first that the gneisses and mica schists which play the principal role in the old framework of the Massif Central may be of different ages. In reaction against the old theory of the Archean, some geologists have been led to assign them to a much later period; thus it is that in the Mountains of Lyonnais, A. Michel-Lévy (Lyon sheet at 1/80,000) has proposed the recognition even of metamorphic Devonian, a hypothesis which does not seem to have been accepted. Others, on the contrary (J. Jung),[33] think that, except in the south, the gneisses and mica schists are certainly Precambrian, even the deep granites (granites of anatexis, see p. 24) which there represent the last stage of regional metamorphism; on the contrary, the granites which inject the Dinantian in the north part of the Massif seem to us like shallow injection granites.

These problems are completely outside our field and belong to the petrographers who study the origins of metamorphic rocks and to whose work we are content to refer.[34] Let us note, especially, that the new classifications and nomenclatures proposed for crystalline rocks by J. Jung and M. Roques have provided the basis for field surveys and have been adopted in the most recently published geologic maps.

d. *The Vosges*

Here, also, the evolution of ideas has followed a similar course. Although the Cambrian cannot be recognized with certainty, and although certain granites are surely Carboniferous, J. Jung[35] believes he can conclude that the gneisses and mica schists of this Massif are Precambrian; likewise, following the ideas of his predecessors, he still attributes to the Precambrian the classic shales of Villé, slightly metamorphosed sediments which crop out between Barr and Saales (see map, Fig. 30).

More recently J. Jung[36] has applied to the Vosges his classification of the zones of metamorphism, deduced from his studies in the Massif Central. South of a northern zone, thus marked by the schists of Villé (zone of upper mica schists), he sees the Precambrian become more and more metamorphic; thus the schists of Lubine, representing the zone of lower mica schists, are followed by the gneisses of Sainte-Marie-aux-Mines, then the anatexites, represented by the gneisses of Trois-Epis, of Gérardmer and of Remiremont, and pass finally into the anatectic granites of Hohneck and of Ballon d'Alsace, which are contrasted to the intrusive (*granites superficiels*) injected into the Devono-Dinantian of Grand Ballon, which we shall study later.

e. *Bohemian Massif*

Without discussing the granitic or metamorphic rocks which play a primordial role in this massif and certain of which are Precambrian (Archean), we shall mention a well-known series of slightly metamorphic formations, shaly or sandy, which are unconformably overlain by a generally fossiliferous Cambrian. Developed especially in the heart of Czechoslovakia (Prague-Plzen area), in a complex of classic Primary formations which we shall study later under the name of Barrandian, these Precambrian sediments are generally called Algonkian; their stratigraphy has been described in detail [37] and geologic maps picture them with precision.

f. *Other Primary European Massifs*

Finally, examples of the Precambrian must still exist in a generally very metamorphic facies in most of the other European Primary massifs; we are reasonably sure of this for those massifs where the Cambrian has been recognized with certainty (Scandinavian Mountains, Rhenish Massifs, Spain, Sardinia, etc.); we can only suspect it for those where the oldest fossiliferous sediments are later than the Cambrian. We shall have occasion to look again at some of these massifs in connection with the Silurian, the Devonian or even the Carboniferous.

VI. Conclusions (The Huronian Chain; Precambrian Glaciers)

From the preceding discussion, we can see how fragmentary is our knowledge of the history of Precambrian time.[38]

To judge from the complicated structure of the Canadian and Baltic Shields, the only Precambrian regions of which we do know a little, we are led to believe that its history is longer and more complex than that of the Primary, Secondary, and Tertiary Eras combined. For merely during its latest episodes, the only ones that we can decipher, we can discern the rise and erosion of several successive mountain chains.

Of all these foldings, the most interesting are the latest, those which immediately preceded the Cambrian period; they are in fact the only ones in which we can recognize the approximate synchronism of one region with another, realizing that we have no other method of dating the older folding.

So, wherever sediments with a Cambrian fauna unconformably overlie the more ancient folded formations, we shall say, by definition, that we are in the domain of the *Huronian Chain*.[39]

It may be that the Cambrian itself or still more recent sediments have been affected by later movements (Caledonian, Hercynian, Alpine); in this case, the features of the Huronian architecture have been to some extent effaced by more recent orogenic movements; their reconstruction then becomes more difficult and less interesting.

We shall reserve then the name of Huronian Chain for the domains in which the Cambrian has remained horizontal; these are ancient platforms long fixed and practically undeformed since the beginning of the Cambrian.

The most typical examples of these old platforms are:

1st. The *Canadian Shield,* described above.

2nd. The *Chain of the Hebrides,* which appears as the edge of a platform, sinking towards the east under its covering of Cambrian[40] and abruptly cut off at the west by the subsidence that gave birth to the Atlantic.

3rd. The *Baltic Shield,* set in a border of horizontal Cambrian.

4th. A *Siberian Shield,* still rather poorly defined. The existence of a very old platform has long been recognized, occupying almost all of northern Asia and extending as far south as the district of Irkutsk, where E. Suess believed he found an old Asiatic ridge. But it has since been recognized that the structure of this immense northern Asia was much more complicated and that it included many old platforms which we shall not describe here.[41]

The Precambrian sediments have been carefully studied in China, however, where Grabau[42] has distinguished, above a more or less crystalline Archean, some slightly metamorphic formations, analogous to the Algonkian of America and to the Torridonian and Jotnian of Europe; and for them he proposes the name *Sinian.* We even find there structures attributed to fossil algae (*Collenia*).[43]

Between South Africa and the Sahara, the Precambrian formations crop out over immense distances and have been the subject of numerous routine researches, on which we cannot dwell; we shall only refer briefly, further on (p. 63), to this Saharan Shield.

We shall likewise merely mention the old platforms of India, Australia, Guiana, and Brazil.

These very old mountain chains, the most recent of which is the Huronian Chain, must have nourished glaciers. For we can recognize in many regions, in the Precambrian sediments, conglomerates with striated blocks, enclosed in a clayey matrix, which certainly represent old moraines; English speaking geologists generally call them *tillites* (see p. 241).

The most typical outcrops are found in the basal conglomerates of the Huronian in the Great Lakes region of North America: they are not local accidents, for they extend for more than 1,000 km. Schuchert even believed he could distinguish several successive glacial periods. That shows clearly that the Canadian platform was covered by a very extensive continental glaciation, recalling those which developed in the Quaternary. At Cobalt (Province of Quebec) we even recognize old laminated clays not unlike the seasonal varves of Quaternary glacial clays (see page 614).[44] Eskola also described them in the Lagodian of Finland.[45]

Previously, metamorphic tillites had been pointed out in the Precambrian of Wyoming.[46]

In China, tillites, attributed first to the Cambrian, are covered by 700 m. of Precambrian Sinian limestones with *Collenia,* which are overlain in turn by the fossiliferous Cambrian.[47]

Finally, Precambrian glacial formations are also recognised in the Varangerfjord of Norway (see p. 90), at Spitzbergen, in northeast Greenland, in Siberia (near the mouth of the Lena), in Australia and in South Africa.[48]

These old moraines have been especially studied in the Belgian Congo by M. Robert; he considers that, at least on the African continent, these glacial formations may be all contemporaneous and date from the end of the Precambrian. Thus he uses them to date the ancient series of Katanga, where the glacial and fluvio-glacial conglomerates (300 m. thick) are found above the schisto-dolomite system and under the Kundelungu system (3,000 m.), which would correspond to the Cambrian-Silurian-Devonian.[49]

But, by way of compensation, in the conglomerates of the Jotnian and in the Torridonian sandstone faceted pebbles fashioned by aeolian erosion have been found, which suggest periods of desert climate.[50]

We see then that, contrary to earlier opinion, the temperature during these first phases of the history of the earth must not have remained uniformly high. From that date there is proof of the alternations of hot and cold periods (or the juxtapositions of hot and cold regions) as we shall find them in more recent times. So that even in these remote epochs, the oldest concerning which geologists can gather any information, the physical aspect of the earth's crust may have differed in no essential from that of our earth of today.

In spite of everything, this immense Precambrian period, in the present state of our knowledge, offers little of interest from the point of view of stratigraphic syntheses; however, it does pose many important tectonic and especially petrographic problems, the study of which demands specialized knowledge— particularly physical and chemical rather than that of the naturalist. And this is so true that a few years ago among geologists of the whole world an *International Association for the Study of the Precambrian* was organized. Curiously, it is only for the study of the Quaternary, which is intimately related to Prehistory and to Physical Geography, that we find a similar International Association.

With the Cambrian, however, we shall enter the true domain of stratigraphic geology, which we shall not leave until the Quaternary.

REFERENCE NOTES

1. See P. E. Raymond, "Pre-cambrian life," Bull. Geol. Soc. Amer., 46, no. 3 (1934), Washington (1935).

2. The Committee on Stratigraphic Nomenclature of the Geol. Survey of the U.S.A. has just made a similar decision.

3. Note moreover that in the formations called "Archean" we do not yet have any decisive proof of the existence of fossils. See J. E. Hawley, "An Evaluation of the Evidence of Life in the Archean," Jour. of Geol., 34, no. 5 (1926).

4. For all that concerns North America we shall refer once for all to the *Textbook of Geology* of Pirsson and Schuchert, 2nd edition, New York (1924), and to the work of E. Blackwelder, *United States of North America, Handbuch der regionalen Geologie,* Heidelberg (1912). Definitions of all the names of stages, formations, and zones used in the U.S.A., accompanied by brief descriptions, will be found in M. Grace Wilmarth, *Lexicon of Geological Names of the United States,* Geol. Surv. U.S.A., Bull. 896 (1938).

5. The word "glint," of Russian origin, was used by Suess thus to designate cliffs due to erosion; where the beds are inclined or where there is a succession of scarps due to hard beds, the term "cuesta" or "côte" is used.

6. See the publications of the 12th *International Geological Congress in Canada,* 1913; the articles of F. D. Adams and of A. P. Coleman in *Problems of American Geology,* Yale Univ. Press (1915);—A. C. Lawson, "Correlation of the Precambrian

Rocks of the Region of the Great Lakes," Univ. of Calif. Publications, Bull. of the Dept. of Geol. Science, 10 (1916), and "The Classification and Correlation of the Precambrian Rocks," ibid., 19 (1930);—E. Steidtmann, "Summaries of Precambrian Literature," Jour. of Geol., 28–29 (1920–21).

7. Named from a peninsula on the south shore of Lake Superior.

8. Named from a locality near the Lake of the Woods in Canada.

9. A. Rothpletz, *Ueber Cryptozoon, Eozoon und Atikokania,* Abhandl. d. K. Bayerischen Akad. d. Wiss., Math. Phys. Klasse, Band 28, Abhandl. 4, Munich (1916).

10. The age of this Grenville series has been much debated; it has often been attributed to the Huronian; see T. Quirke, "Correlation of Huronian and Grenville Rocks," Jour. of Geol., 32 (1924), and T. Quirke and W. H. Collins, *The Disappearance of the Huronian,* Geol. Surv. of Canada, Mem. No. 160 (1930). But we will leave it in the Ontarian, conforming to the opinion of Lawson and that of J. W. Gregory and B. H. Barrett, "The Stratigraphical Position of the Keewatin," Jour. of Geol., 35 (1927).

11. Cf. L. Cayeux, C. R. Acad Sc., t. 43, 1911, pp. 910 and 1188.

12. The granites have recently been named *"Killarnian."*

13. For all that concerns the Baltic and Scandinavian regions, see the publications (*Guides géologiques*) of the 11th *Congrès géologique international* in Sweden (1910), and Högbom's *Fennoskandia, Handbuch der regionalen Geologie* (1913).

14. In reality the structure of the line of glint is more complex here, for the scarp is formed at certain points by the fronts of thrusts [*nappes*] emerging from the Scandinavian Mountains (see Fig. 19).

15. On the structural units of these regions, see the synthesis of S. von Bubnoff, *Geologie von Europa, 1. Bd, Einführung, Osteuropa, Baltischer Schild,* Berlin (1926), and especially A. D. Arkhangelsky, N. S. Schatski, etc., *Abrégé de la Géologie structurale et de l'Histoire géologique de l'U.S.S.R.,* published in 1937 by the Acadamy of Sciences of the U.S.S.R.; I heartily thank M. Roger for having been kind enough to send me the French translation of this work, made under his direction at the *Centre de Documentation de géologique et paléontologique* of the *Muséum national d'Histoire naturelle.*

16. See J. S. Sederholm, *Prequaternary Rocks of Finland,* Bull. commission géol. Finlande, No. 91 (1930);—F. von Wolff, *Das Präkambrium Finnlands,* Geol. Rundschau, 23 (1932);—T. W. Gevers, *Comparative Notes on the Precambrian of Fennoscandia and South Africa,* Bull. Comm. Geol. Finlande, No. 119 (1937);—also, this Precambrian of Finland is especially interesting and unique in the world for the study of the phenomena of granitization and metamorphism, clearly and substantially summarized by E. Raguin, *A propos d'observations récentes sur le metamorphisme dans les chaînes de montagnes,* Revue gén. des Sci. (31 March, 1932), and J. de Lapparent, *Courses géologiques en Finland,* Bull. Soc. géol. France, 5 sér., 2 (1932).

17. One will find a discussion of the Precambrian stages and a map of the Precambrian chains in H. G. Backlund, *Die Umgrenzung der Svecofenniden,* Bull. geol. Inst. Univ. Upsala, 27 (1937).

18. A. T. Metzger, *Die jatulischen Bildungen von Suojärvi in Ostfinnland,* Bull. Comm. Geol. Finlande, No. 64 (1924).

19. C. E. Wegmann, *Sur un problème de la stratigraphie du Précambrien,* C. R. Soc. géol. France (Nov. 5, 1928).

20. Name which means "rotten stone"; for on the surface these granites are often very altered.

21. The role of the Jotnian sandstones in relation to the old Precambrian chains is then exactly analogous to that of the Devonian Old Red Sandstones in relation to the Caledonian chain and to that of the Permian New Red Sandstones in relation to the Hercynian chain.

22. S. von Bubnoff, *Die Halbinsel Kola,* Geol. Rundschau, 28 (1937).

23. For everything concerning the British Isles, I refer once and for all to the three following fundamental volumes by numerous collaborators: *Handbook of the Geology of Great Britain, Handbook of the Geology of Ireland,* London, T. Murby (1929), and *Geology in the Field,* The Jubilee volume of the Geologists Association (1910). I point out especially the excellent work of L. Dudley Stamp, *An Introduction to Stratigraphy*

(*British Isles*), London, T. Murby, 2nd edit. (1934), which suggests ideas similar to those which guide us here.

24. See J. Phemister, *Scotland: the Northern Highlands, British Regional Geology,* Geol. Surv. and Mus., 2nd ed. (1948); H. H. Read and A. G. Macgregor, *The Grampian Highlands* (ibid.).

25. The term *Dalradian,* incorrect, was proposed by Geikie as more euphonious.

26. This argument does not seem absolutely decisive; it proves only that certain parts of the Moinian are Precambrian; but this conclusion does not inevitably extend to the whole of the Moinian-Dalradian complex.

27. See F. H. Edmunds and K. P. Oakley, "The Central English District," *British regional Geology,* Geol. Surv. and Mus. (1947), p. 6.

28. See R. W. Pocock, T. H. Whitehead, etc., "Geology of the Country around Shrewsbury," *British regional Geology,* Geol. Surv. and Mus. (1938).

29. W. Watts and H. Gregory, "Report of the Field Meeting in Charnwood Forest," Proc. Geol. Assoc., 48 (1937).

30. A. Michel-Lévy, *Existence de formations antécambriennes dans la Montagne Noire (Hérault),* C. R. Acad. des Sc. (18 April 1932);—J. Blayac, A. Michel-Lévy and M. Thoral, *Sur un conglomérat de base dans le Cambrien des Monts de Lacaune et sur l'âge antécambrien des formations granitiques du Mendic, près de Graissessac (Hérault)* (ibid., 29 Jan. 1934).

31. M. Roques, *Découverte de calcaires à entroques et de roches eruptives basiques dans les schistes metamorphiques de Genis (Dordogne),* C. R. Acad. Sci., t. 206 (1938), p. 1581.

32. Article cited note 31, Chap. 2.

33. J. Jung, *Remarques sur les relations du cycle cristallophyllien et de sa couverture paléozoïque dans le Massif central,* C. R. somm. Soc. géol. France (1939), p. 32;— *Géologie de l'Auvergne et de ses confins bourbonnais et limousins,* Mém. Carte géol. France (1946), 372 p., 135 fig., 14 pl. phot.

34. J. Jung and M. Roques, *Les schistes cristallins du Massif central,* Bull. Carte géol. France, No. 197, t. 39 (1938);—M. Roques, *Les schistes cristallins de la partie Sud-Ouest du Massif central de la France,* Bull. Soc. géol. France, 4 sér., t. 30 (1930)— The attempts at tectonic syntheses, such as those of A. Demay, seem obviously a little rash, based as they are on so uncertain a stratigraphy.

35. J. Jung, *Contribution à la Géologie des Vosges hercyniennes d'Alsace,* Mém. Serv. Carte géol. d'Alsace et de Lorraine, No. 2 (1927).

36. J. Jung, *Sur l'existence et le rôle des migmatites dans le terrain cristallophyllien des Vosges,* C. R. somm. Soc. géol. France (Dec. 21, 1936).

37. R. Kettner, *Versuch einer stratigraphischen Einteilung des böhmischen Algonkiums,* Geolog. Rundschau, 8 (1917).—This article contains a small, very clear geologic map of the Barrandian.

38. R. Ruedemann, *The Existence and Configuration of Precambrian Continents,* New York State Museum, Bull. Nos. 239–240 (1922).

39. The name "Huronian Chain" was originated by Marcel Bertrand with a little different meaning; this geologist had in fact called the folds, formed between the Archean and the Precambrian of Canada and in the zone of the Hebrides, "Huronian folds." But there is no reason for these folds to be contemporaneous, for the names of stages have only a strictly local value.

40. In this chain, where it approaches the Torridon-Erriboll line, one sees the Cambrian affected by the dislocations which accompany this line: thus, face to face with the Caledonian folding of the Eastern Gneisses, this Cambrian acts exactly as the Cambrian of the west border of the Baltic Shield in relation to the Caledonian folding of the Scandinavian Mountains.

41. See E. Argand on this subject, *La Tectonique de l'Asie,* Congrès. géol. internat., Belgique (1922), p. 183 and Fig. 8. D. Mouchketov, *Les données nouvelles sur la Géologie de l'Asie centrale, du Caucase, de l'Oural et de la Sibérie,* Bull. Soc. géol. France, 5 sér., t. 1 (1931), p. 260, and especially the work of Arkhangelski, cited note 15, this chap.

42. A. W. Grabau, "The Sinian System," Bull. géol. Soc. China, 1, Peking (1922);— *Stratigraphy of China, Part I: Paleozoic and Older*, Geol. Surv. China, Peking (1923–1924). P. Teilhard de Chardin, *Les intervalles épiarchéens et épisiniens en Chine*, Bull. Soc. géol. Chine, 17 (1937). J. S. Lee, *The Geology of China*, 528 p., 93 Figs., London, T. Murby (1939). T. K. Huang, *On Major Tectonic Forms of China*, Nat. geol. Surv. China, Geol., sér. A, No. 20, Pehpei, Chung King (Dec. 1945).

43. Analogous structures have been described under the same name in the old limestones extending from the Sahara as far as the Belgian Congo; but there, and contrary to the belief of certain Belgian geologists, the French Sahara specialists attribute them to the Cambrian and not to the Precambrian.

44. L. W. Collet, *Varves anciennes et récentes*, C. R. Congrès inter. Geogr., Paris (1931), Vol. 2.

45. P. Eskola, "Conditions During the Earliest Geological Times, as Indicated by the Archean Rocks," Ann. Acad. Sci. Fennicae, series A. vol. 36, No. 4, Helsinki (1932).

46. E. Blackwelder, "Precambrian Geology of the Medicine Bow Mountains," Bull. Geol. Soc. of Amer. 37 (1927).

47. Y. C. Sun, "Cambrian, Ordovician and Silurian of China," C. R. 14e Congrès géol. internat., fasc. 2, Madrid (1927).

48. A general focusing of the question of old glaciations has been given by A. P. Coleman, *Ice Ages—Recent and Ancient*, New York, Macmillan (1926), a work treating more especially of North America. Refer also to the summary table set up by Werner Beetz (Neues Jahrbuch f. Min., 56 Beilage-Band, Abt. B, p. 468) for all the evidence, more or less doubtful, of old glaciations.

49. M. Robert, *Contribution à la Géologie du Katanga; le système du Kundelungu et le système schisto-dolomitique*, 2e partie, Mém. Inst. roy. colonial belge, sect. Sc. nat. médic., vol. 6 (1941); —*Les traces de glaciation et les périodes climatiques glaciaires au Katanga et en Afrique australe*, Bull. Soc. belge Géol., vol. 56 (1947). In the first of these articles a complete reconsideration of all publications relative to Precambrian glacial formations will be found.

50. For all that deals with old climates, we refer once for all to the works of Dacqué, *Grundlagen und Methoden der Paläogeographie*, p. 397, and especially of W. Köppen and A. Wegener, *Die Klimate der geologischen Vorzeit*, Berlin (1924), followed by *"Ergänzungen und Berechtigungen,"* Bornträger, Berlin (1940).

Chapter Two

The Cambrian

The Cambrian formations[1] are easily recognised by their fauna, which clearly mark three successive stages: Lower = Georgian, Middle = Acadian, and Upper = Potsdamian. We shall define them in detail in this chapter.

I. The Cambrian Fauna

Most of the zoological groups are represented only by forms without much stratigraphic interest. They are either very rare or poorly preserved, or else are not sufficiently different from post-Cambrian forms. This is true of the foraminifera, some sponges, the medusas, echinoderms (cystids, crinoids), pelecypods, gastropods, and worms. Study of these groups offers only paleontologic interest. It shows that all the principal types of invertebrates are already represented, but by forms with archaic characteristics. Attention should be called especially to the very curious deposit of the Burgess shale in the Selkirk Mountains (British Columbia), where Walcott has described the imprints of worms, holothurians, etc., even showing details of the soft parts (cilia, digestive canal, etc.).[2]

At least 1,500 species of invertebrates are known in the Cambrian, all marine, of which 60% are trilobites and 30% brachiopods. But the most important groups, from the stratigraphic point of view, are the following:

1. *Archaeocyathids*

Their systematic position is doubtful. They are classified sometimes as sponges, sometimes as corals. In any case, they are reef-building organisms, like the corals. They are always found in zoogenic limestones, similar to those which later were produced by the true corals. They seem to be characteristic of the upper Georgian in the most diverse regions: Scotland, Cotentin, Silesia, the Montagne-Noire, Spain, Morocco, Turkestan, the Altai, the Punjab, the Urals, Siberia,[3] North China, California, New York State, Labrador, Australia, and

46

the Antarctic. Particularly in Australia, *Archaeocyathus*—limestones, about 100 m. thick, extend for distances of more than 500 km. These are the most extensive Paleozoic reefs known. These limestones also play an important morphological role in the Moroccan Atlas and Anti-Atlas.

If we assume, as we sometimes do, that the archaeocyathid facies required the same conditions for development as the coral facies, we should deduce that these different regions had a relatively warm climate in the Cambrian, but this is a very doubtful hypothesis.[4] Some authors even think that the porous skeletal structure of these archaeocyathids gives evidence that they lived in relatively cold water, poor in calcium.

2. Brachiopods

These can scarcely be used as characteristic fossils in the Cambrian; but they have a certain practical importance, none the less, because of their relative abundance. We shall frequently refer to the inarticulates such as *Lingula* and *Obolus*. These are fossils from sandy, littoral facies, indicating old beaches.

3. Trilobites

Numerous genera and species of these are known and are distributed through all kinds of facies, sandy or shaly. Most of the genera are peculiar to the Cambrian: *Olenellus, Paradoxides, Olenoides, Olenus, Sao, Ellipsocephalus, Conocoryphe, Dikellocephalus;* only a few continue into the Silurian: *Agnostus, Ogygia.*

Certain *genera* can be used to characterize stages, and their geographic distribution has likewise made it possible to distinguish two provinces, especially clear in the Middle and Upper Cambrian. The one called the *Pacific* province includes almost all of North America (see p. 65) and extends to Argentina, Australia, and China. These Pacific faunas seem to have migrated by way of the Arctic seas as far as Nova Zembla, where a Norwegian expedition in 1921 discovered Cambrian Trilobites and Brachiopods of the Pacific type.[5] The other, or *Atlantic* province includes Europe, Morocco, and the Atlantic Coast of North America.

The following trilobite genera are the basis of the definition of these two provinces and the three stages:[6]

	Atlantic Province	Pacific Province
Potsdamian	*Olenus*	Not *Olenus*, but *Dikellocephalus.*
Acadian	*Paradoxides*	Not *Paradoxides*, but *Olenoides, Ptychoparia*, etc.
Georgian	*Olenellus*[7]	*Olenellus*

Proceeding to the species, we can say that certain ones have a much more limited stratigraphic distribution. Many of them allow the definition of paleontologic zones. Thus, in Scandinavia especially, about fifteen zones can be recognized, several of which are found in Wales and even on the Atlantic Coast of North America.

II. Grouping of Facies in Natural Regions (Geosynclinal and Continental Areas of the Cambrian)

We have just seen that in certain regions (Huronian zone or Chain), folding occurred just before the Cambrian. The old mountain chains thus formed either remained emerged during the Cambrian, or were progressively leveled off by erosion and invaded by Cambrian seas. As a result the Cambrian in these regions will be, first, discordant on its substratum, second, frequently incomplete, and, finally, represented by coarse, sandy, shallow-water deposits derived from neighboring continents. We have agreed (p. 9) that in the Cambrian paleogeography these regions play the role of continental areas, whether they remained emerged or were covered by shallow seas, defined as epicontinental seas.

On the other hand, in other regions there was no folding before the Cambrian and neither was there emergence. In such regions, the Cambrian is complete, continuous, without lacunas and usually represented by relatively deep-water facies of shale or fine-grained sandstone. We shall see that these formations are often found to be very thick (several thousand meters), which proves that the sea floor sank as fast as the sediments accumulated. Also these formations are frequently metamorphic (see p. 23). We have defined these regions where the sediments are characteristically continuous, very thick and metamorphic, as geosynclinal regions, as opposed to the formations of continental areas.

In addition, the geosynclinal regions appear unstable in comparison to the continental areas, which are stable. And indeed, we almost always find that sooner or later these regions, having played a geosynclinal role during a longer or shorter period, end by folding in their turn, and thus are transformed into chains of mountains. Sediments of continental areas, however, remain horizontal.

This is admittedly only schematic, a mental image, better still an expository process; and it is often impossible to classify a region, at a given moment in its history, in the category of geosynclines or in that of continental areas. But this conception, which will be completed and made precise in what follows (for we shall seek to apply it to all periods), from now on allows us to group rationally (as E. Haug has done) the multitude of observations gathered on the Cambrian facies.[8]

III. The Facies of the Cambrian in Europe (and in Morocco)

Let us distinguish here the following natural regions:

1. *A border zone of the Baltic Shield.* Here the horizontal Cambrian lies

in discordance on the older, folded formations. We are in a typical continental area.

2. *A border zone of the Chain of the Hebrides.* The Cambrian has the same characteristics here.

3. *A Northern European geosynclinal zone.* This zone is divided into two arms by the Baltic Shield. It includes one arm formed by the Scandinavian Chain,[9] and a second made up of the Ardennes, Franconia, Silesia, and Poland (Lysa Gora). In these countries, the Cambrian seems concordant with the older formations. Wales should be added here, where there is indeed a discordance between the Precambrian and the Cambrian. But that region has, from the beginning of the Cambrian, taken on a geosynclinal character. Everywhere in this zone, the Cambrian has been folded, either in the Upper Silurian or in the Carboniferous.

4. *A Middle European zone.* This zone is very poorly defined and includes Brittany and Bohemia. There is sometimes a discordance at the base of the Cambrian, which is often quite incomplete. Nevertheless these regions later became geosynclinal in character and were folded at the end of the Carboniferous.

5. *A Mediterranean geosynclinal zone.* This was without doubt very extensive. The Cambrian is surely known in the Montagne-Noire, Sardinia, Spain, and Morocco. Moreover in southern Morocco, everything indicates that there is a neighboring, very old rigid mass, the Saharan Shield, which, on the other side of the immense European and Mediterranean domain, represents a kind of symmetry with the Baltic Shield.

Thus, region 2 and even more region 1 show typical characteristics of continental areas; regions 3 (except Wales) and 5, the typical characteristics of geosynclines. Region 4 and Wales have mixed characteristics.

1. *Border Zone of the Baltic Shield*

The central region of the shield was perhaps not entirely covered by the Cambrian seas. In any case, on all sides the Cambrian border shows facies becoming more littoral as we approach this central region. Toward the south, in Scania, the region around Christiania (= Oslo), and the Baltic countries[10], the Cambrian has been most thoroughly studied.

The principal Cambro-Silurian remnants of this region (see Fig. 9) are all localized in the sunken troughs of the Baltic Shield; and, thanks to this location, they have escaped erosion and been preserved. The beds there are almost horizontal, except in the part north of the Oslo Basin and in Jämtland, where they first show the effects of the Caledonian folding of the Scandinavian Chain.

A. The section of the Oslo region[11] shows a classic type of this Baltic Cambrian. The facies there are no longer wholly littoral.

At the base, there are sandstones with *Eophyton* (animal traces), overlain by shales and glauconitic sandstones with *Olenellus* (subgenus *Holmia*), indicating the Georgian (30–50 m. thick). Then comes a shaly assemblage called the alum shales, no more than 75 m. thick. At their base, these shales

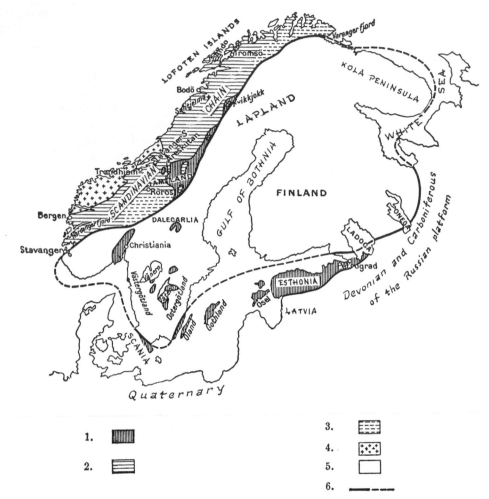

FIG. 9. *Structural map of the Baltic Shield and of the Scandinavian Chain showing the distribution of the Cambrian-Silurian facies. (After Högbom and Holtedahl). Several countries and cities are represented by their old names.*

1. Cambrian-Silurian (eastern facies) of the border of the Baltic Shield. (N. B. West of Areskutan, a fragment appears as a "window" under the overthrust formations of the Scandinavian Chain; see Fig. 20).
2. Cambrian-Silurian (western facies) of the Scandinavian Chain, according to some authors partially Precambrian. (N. B. In Lapland and Jämtland there are outliers thrust over the domain of the eastern facies; see Fig. 19).
3. Regions of Sparagmite to the south and Varanger sandstone to the north (Precambrian?, Silurian?).
4. Precambrian gneiss of western Norway.
5. Precambrian formations of the Baltic Shield.
6. Approximate limit of the Baltic Shield.

contain *Paradoxides,* characteristic of the Acadian. At the summit appears *Olenus* of the Potsdamian. It is there that the 15 zones of trilobites, mentioned above, are distinguishable. This series ends with shales with *Dictyonema flabelliforme* (a graptolite, see p. 73) which is considered the extreme base of the Silurian.[12]

B. Approaching the central region of the Shield, on the shores of the Gulf of Finland, where the cliffs offer magnificent natural sections, we find a Cambrian section very different from that of Oslo.[13]

On the granites and gneisses lie, first, sandstones and conglomerates without fossils (60 to 80 m.), overlain by the celebrated blue clay of Leningrad, whose thickness (67 m. at Reval [Tallinn], 100 or even 300 m. in the bore holes at Leningrad) seems to increase rapidly toward the east. These sediments are perhaps continental, and at all events coastal, and their age is disputed. They have indeed no equivalents in the Cambrian series of Oslo. Also, they occasionally resemble the Jotnian (Precambrian).

In any case, several meters of the *Eophyton* sandstone, whose base contains

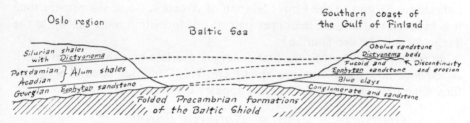

FIG. 10. *Diagrammatic section showing variations of the facies of the Cambrian on the south border of the Baltic Shield.*

some *Olenellus,* come next. These represent the Georgian.[14] The fucoid sandstone (impressions of algae) 10 to 15 m. thick is separated by a lacuna of sedimentation from the basal Silurian, represented by sandstone with *Obolus,* which includes shaly intercalations with *Dictyonema.*[15]

Rüger believes that the Acadian and Potsdamian are missing in this series, but that they must have been deposited, for he finds evidences of these stages in rounded cobbles in the sandstone with *Obolus.*

It is very striking to note, however, the absence here of the shales with trilobites, so characteristic of the Cambrian of Oslo, and the substitution for them of more littoral sandy facies or lacunas. The Cambrian has become more and more epicontinental. East of Leningrad, there may even have been a vast emerged land in the Cambrian corresponding to most of the Russian platform.[16] Thus, these variations of facies are arranged in a harmonious way in relation to the great structural features which we have used to synthesize the Cambrian paleogeography (see Fig. 10).

Let us remember finally that all this Cambrian is perfectly horizontal and not at all metamorphic. The sandstones there unmistakably recall our Tertiary Parisian sandstones and the resemblance of the blue clay of Leningrad to the plastic clay of Paris greatly surprises those who know these very old formations only in our country [France].

2. *Border Zone of the Chain of the Hebrides*

As we have already seen (p. 35 and Figs. 7 and 8), the Cambrian crops out in northwest Scotland, in the form of a thin band bounded at the east by the Torridon-Erriboll line of dislocation. In the west, the Cambrian lies in discordance either on the Lewisian gneiss or the Torridonian sandstone.

This transgressive Cambrian begins with a basal conglomerate which is overlain by sandstones or quartzites; the lower beds of sandstone are riddled with tubular cavities (pipes) attributed to worms (*Scolytus*), from which comes their name of Pipe-Rock or *Scolytus* sandstone. But this sandy formation also supplies some *Olenellus* (s. str.), which classifies it as Georgian.

Above the sandstones comes the complex of the Durness limestones (500 m. thick), more or less dolomitic. Here are found *Archaeocyathus* (upper Georgian) and poor fragments of *Paradoxides,* so that the Acadian must be represented. The Potsdamian fauna is not found, but instead the brachiopods indicate similarities to the Lower Silurian of America. So at the present time it is believed that at least the upper part of this formation must belong to the Tremadocian (Lower Silurian).

As we have seen (p. 36) the limestones are overlain by a thrust sheet which superposes the Eastern Gneisses upon them. This Cambrian band of Scotland, thus separating two gneissic regions, appears completely isolated.

3. *Geosynclinal Zone of Northern Europe*

We already know that, according to E. Haug, two branches can be distinguished here: a northern (Scandinavian Mountains) and a southern (Rhenish Massif, Saxony, Thuringia, Poland), separated by the Baltic Shield and by the Welsh zone. These branches deserve special study.

A. Northern Branch: Scandinavian Mountains. This chain is formed of very greatly folded and more or less metamorphic rocks of Precambrian to Silurian age. We shall describe it later. We shall be satisfied for the moment to note that Cambrian fossils are found here in certain places. A first group of beds is found in the south, northeast of Hardangerfjord: Cambrian *Hyolithes* (*Torelella*)[18] at the foot of the Haalingskarven, and *Dictyonema flabelliforme* (extreme base of the Silurian) southeast of Mount Haarteigen; farther north, at Torneträsk (south of Tromsö), Moberg has discovered various Cambrian fossils in the *Hyolithes* zone (see map, Fig. 9).

In this Precambrian to Silurian geosynclinal series of the Scandinavian Mountains, the Cambrian is poorly defined, although we are sure of its presence. Also, as we have seen above (p. 36), Haug was led to believe that this geosyncline must be prolonged in Scotland by the Grampian Mountains, and that the non-fossiliferous rocks, more or less metamorphic, which make up these mountains, must also include the Cambrian. However, we have accepted here the opinion of British geologists who believe that the Moinian and the Dalradian of Scotland are older than the Cambrian. Let us note that everywhere along the southern border of the Highlands, fragments of inarticulate brachiopods have been discovered, which could indicate the existence here of a questionable Cambrian, perhaps far distant extension of that of the Scandinavian Mountains.

B. Wales and Neighboring Regions. Neither in the southern Uplands nor in the Lake District are formations found older than the Ordovician (see Fig. 15). To find the Cambrian again, it is necessary to go as far south as Wales: the region, indeed, that gave its name to the system. The Welsh Cambrian can be subdivided in the following way (Fig. 17):

First, a great anticlinal dome, that of Harlech, situated in North Wales and matched, north of the synclinal zone of Snowdon, by other anticlinal outcrops which extend along the coast across from Anglesey. Second, another anticlinal nucleus, in reality divided into two parts, near St. David's in the south. Third, some isolated outcrops east of Wales: The Wrekin (with the classic locality of Comley), Lickey Hill (southwest of Birmingham), Nuneaton (east of Birmingham), Malvern Hills, etc.

1. In the first two groups of outcrops, this Cambrian has its Welsh facies, with typical geosynclinal character: very thick accumulations of shales and sandstones, sometimes coarse.

The most classic series is that of the anticline of St. David's.[19] There conglomerates lie unconformably on the Precambrian, and are succeeded by sandstones and shales with fragments of *Olenellus* (subgenera *Holmia* and *Callavia*). This is therefore the Georgian (500 m. thick). The Acadian (800 m.) is represented by finer sandstones and black shales in which 5 zones of paradoxids can be distinguished. Next come the *Lingula* flags (about 1,500 m.), again a more littoral formation of old beach deposits. Doubtless they correspond to the Potsdamian, but no *Olenus* fauna has been found in them.

About the same succession of rocks, with the same thickness (more than 3,000 meters), has been found in the region of Harlech; but here the *Lingula* flags contain *Olenus,* which confirms their Potsdamian age.

2. In the outcrops of the third group, the Cambrian is less thick (for example, 200 or 400 m. total), more littoral, but also more fossiliferous,[20] with calcareous intercalations and lacunas. This is the type called Shropshire or Midlands (Central Counties). The most constant element is made up of the quartzites of the Lower Cambrian overlain by an *Olenus* zone and a *Protolenus* zone, an American trilobite unknown farther north, but which we shall find again in Central Europe. The overlying Middle Cambrian, always characterized by its paradoxids, and the Upper Cambrian are frequently incomplete. We find here, then, a zone less geosynclinal in character, where perhaps the distant influence of the Baltic Shield is felt. We shall see the same thing in the Silurian.

C. Southern Branch. The general structure of the Ardennes will be studied later (p. 115). We shall merely mention here that in the midst of the Devonian, which constitutes the largest part of it, several small massifs appear, which are described as Cambro-Silurian (see the map, Fig. 23). In fact, the Cambrian and Silurian are sometimes hard to distinguish here because of

tectonic difficulties and the great scarcity of fossils. The oldest truly characteristic fossils known here date from the Lower Silurian (*Dictyonema flabelliforme* zone). It is without any decisive paleontological evidence that a thick
series of fine grained, little metamorphosed rocks (phyllites or quarzitic sandstones), containing non-diagnostic impressions (*Oldhamia*), are assigned to
the Cambrian. Excellent slates and coticules (very fine-grained siliceous rocks
used for whet-stones) are worked there.

Thus defined, this Cambrian, the oldest formation found in the Ardennes,
was divided into stages based only on lithological facies, whose individuality
has been the subject of long discussions, because of the tectonic complications.

Indeed, in the whole of the Hercynian orogeny, which has affected the
Devonian and the Carboniferous, the Cambro-Silurian massifs play the role
of anticlinal belts, but in the very interior of these massifs the Cambrian and
Silurian, usually folded before the Devonian (Caledonian folds) are far from
showing an anticlinal structure. This is especially clear in the massif of Rocroy,
which forms a broad arch (Hercynian orogeny) completely surrounded by
the Lower Devonian. The Caledonian tectonics are easy to reconstruct here,
but, according to Waterlot, the arch corresponds, in the Cambrian, to a great
recumbent syncline, complicated by thrust slices pushed from south to north.[21]

In this Rocroy Massif,[22] almost entirely composed of Cambrian, the stratigraphic succession is the easiest (or the least difficult) to reconstruct. So,
adopting the earlier ideas of Belgian geologists, Waterlot distinguishes the
following:

1. At the base, a Devillian stage, the type of which is composed of generally greenish rocks (*Oldhamia radiata* shales and quartzites) in the environs
of Deville. The violet platy rocks of Fumay would be a contemporaneous
equivalent of it, differing from the Devillian shales only by metamorphic
phenomena.

2. At the top, a Revinian stage, its lower part composed of the slaty, black
shales of Revin, its upper part corresponding to an eruptive and quartzitic
zone, at the top of which appears *Dictyonema flabelliforme* var. *sociale,* characteristic of the Tremadoc (base of the Silurian).[23]

In Franconia, opposite the northwest extremity of the great Hercynian
massif of Bohemia (see map Fig. 28), Cambrian faunas have recently been
discovered by Wurm[24] in sandstone and more or less quartzitic shales. The
genera *Paradoxides, Ptychoparia, Conocoryphe,* etc. indicate the Middle Cambrian.

Farther east, in Silesia, along the northeastern border of the Sudeten Moun-
tains, Richter[25] has described a fauna of the Lower Cambrian, north of Görlitz.
In this same region M. Schwartzbach[26] recently studied the Cambrian of the
Oberlausitz and the Bober-Katzbach range. Curiously, it begins with 10 to
500 m. of archaeocyathid limestone, a calcareous facies unknown in Central
Europe and recalling that of the upper Georgian of the Montagne-Noire and
Sardinia. This Lower Cambrian or Georgian is characterized by its trilobites,
Olenellus (subgenus *Holmia*) at the base, *Protolenus* at the top. These genera,
unknown in Scandinavia, are found in Morocco, Poland, Siberia, Korea and

Canada, that is in the Atlantic province, at the boundary of the Lower and Middle Cambrian.

Finally, still farther east, we find a very interesting Cambrian in the Central Polish Massif. This is the name of a small Hercynian massif located 200 km. south of Warsaw, between the towns of Kielce and Sandomierz, on the Vistula. It culminates at 600 m. in the Mountains of the Sacred Cross[27] (Swiety Krzyz) or Lysa Gora,[28] isolated in the middle of the Polish plains. There, a very thick series (1,500 to 2,000 m.) of shales and sandstones of the Flysch facies (see p. 11) shows the three stages of the Cambrian, well defined paleontologically.[29] As in Silesia, the Georgian contains *Olenellus* at the base and *Protolenus* at the top. The Acadian is defined by the abundance of *Paradoxides,* and the Potsdamian likewise contains trilobites, with Scandinavian affinities.

4. *The Middle European Zone*

A. The Armorican Massif. This Hercynian massif of Primary formations, which geologists often call Brittany for brevity, in reality comprises not only Brittany proper, but also the Vendée south of the Lower Loire, and part of Lower Normandy (the Norman Bocage and Cotentin Peninsula). Its skeletal framework is formed of granitic or schistose rocks and especially of old, slightly metamorphosed shales (phyllites), in the midst of which synclinal bands (synclinoria) of well dated Primary formations (Silurian to Carboniferous) extend from west to east. The most important is the great axial synclinorium, dilated at its two extremities in the basins of Laval and Brest-Chateaulin. In the south are the long synclines of Segré, Angers (or of St. Julien-de-Vouvantes), and Ancenis. To the north, in Normandy, the correlations are more difficult, but here we may distinguish the synclines of Mortain, Granville-Fougères (or bocaine zone), Coutance-Urville (or the Brèche au Diable), May, Saint-Sauveur-le-Vicomte, and Néhou. Finally, in Brittany, the Dinantian syncline of Morlaix extends from Brest to Paimpol.

The old schists of the skeletal structure are certainly in great part Precambrian. But the oldest bed that we can easily identify in the whole massif is that of the Armorican sandstones of the Silurian (Arenig stage). Relatively characteristic Cambrian faunas have been discovered at only a very few isolated points. Except at these places, it is impossible to determine the boundary between the Cambrian and the Precambrian formations. So, as first suggested by C. Barrois,[30] it has long been customary to group all these old formations under the name of Brioverian.

In the absence of any characteristic fossil, the stratigraphy of this Brioverian can be attempted only according to lithologic facies. Consequently the attention of Breton geologists has been naturally drawn to certain lithologic zones, distinguished in the monotonous shaly series: conglomerates, cherts, calcareous lenses. In particular, limestones being rare in Brittany, the smallest beds of lime rock were long ago discovered and exploited. If we add that all the Primary of Brittany is greatly folded, with its beds stretched and overturned, and that in this country of low relief, damp and covered with vegetation, the

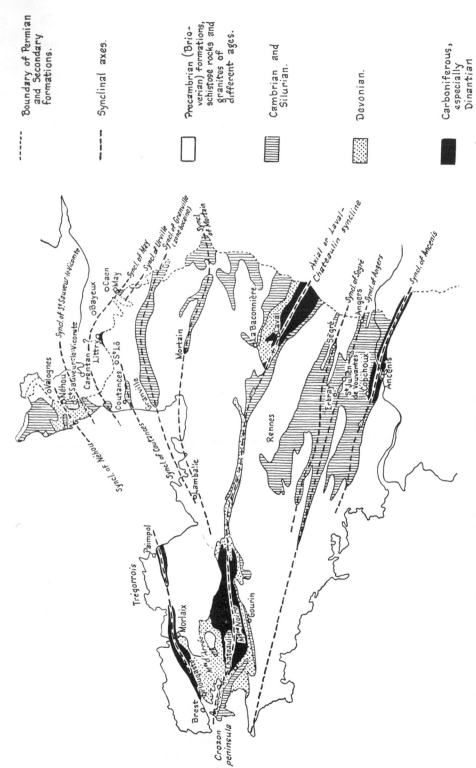

Legend (top, read vertically):

Boundary of Permian and Secondary formations.

Synclinal axes.

Precambrian (Brio-verian) formations, schistose rocks and granites of different ages.

Cambrian and Silurian.

Devonian.

Carboniferous, especially Dinantian

Map labels:

Syncl. of St Sauveur-le-Vicomte
Syncl. of May
Syncl. of Urville
Syncl. of Granville (zone bocaine)
Syncl. of Mortain
Axial or Laval-Chateaulin syncline
Syncl. of Segré
Syncl. of Angers
Syncl. of Ancenis
Syncl. of Néhou
Syncl. of Coutances
oValognes
Néhou
St Sauveur-le-Vicomte
oBayeux
oCaen
oMay
Carentan
Littry
oSt Lô
Coutances
Granville
Mortain
La Baconnière
Laval
Ségré
Angers
Craon
St Julien de Vouvantes
Copchoux
Ancenis
Rennes
Lamballe
Paimpol
Trégorrois
Morlaix
Mts d'Arrée
Chateaulin
Mne Noire
Gourin
Brest
Douguastel
Crozon peninsula

FIG. 11.   *Diagrammatic geologic map of the Armorican Massif.*

56

visible geologic sections are reduced to quarries and road cuts, we can understand how difficult and uncertain are stratigraphic syntheses. We shall nevertheless discuss them in some detail, as an example of the somewhat special methods used. Thus, the beds of conglomerates which earlier bore an exaggerated importance, are nevertheless interesting, because they often allow us to recognize the order of the stratigraphic successions. Indeed, the stratified rocks which occur as pebbles in a puddingstone are surely older than the puddingstone itself.

We shall study the Brioverian and the Cambrian successively in Normandy, Brittany and the Vendée.[31]

1. *Normandy*.[32] The May section, the most classic of all Normandy, is visible on the banks of the Laize, tributary of the Orne, south of Caen. Over the vertical Brioverian quartzitic phyllites of Saint-Lô a reddish conglomerate lies unconformably, the Rocreux conglomerate,[33] or purple conglomerate of early geologists. It is overlain by purple shales, containing lenses of a limestone, called Laize-la-Ville marble, then by feldspathic sandstones. On top comes the Armorican sandstone, which we shall describe later as representing the base of the Silurian in the region.

It has long been recognized that the beds contained between this "Cadomian" unconformity (from the Latin name of Caen) and the Armorican sandstone may represent the Cambrian. Recent paleontological discoveries have confirmed this.

In fact, this conglomerate and these purple shales are found, easily recognizable, in the Cotentin. And there, at Carteret, where the axis of the Néhou syncline ends at the coast, A. Bigot has discovered, in the reefy, calcareous lenses intercalated in the purple shales, the only fossils of the Armorican Massif truly characteristic of the Cambrian.[34] These are first, archaeocyathids, at the present time everywhere considered as of upper Georgian age. There are also some fragments of trilobites, which were first assigned to the genus *Ptychoparia* of the Acadian, but E. S. Cobbold [35] has made a new genus for them: *Bigotina,* belonging to the group of *Protolenus* of the upper Georgian.

We may agree, with Bigot, that the marbles of Laize, of the May section, are equivalent to the limestones of Carteret, and therefore of upper Georgian age, and in that case that the Cambrian begins with the conglomerates of Rocreux (and Cherbourg). The Cadomian unconformity would mark the Precambrian-Cambrian boundary and the red color of the Norman Cambrian would give evidence of continental facies, or at the very least of continental contributions. The deep reddening of the Brioverian quartzitic-phyllites of May, under the purple conglomerates, would result from the continental alteration undergone by the sub-Cambrian pencplain leveling the Cadomian folds.

2. *Brittany*. Cambrian fossils here are found only in the little massif of the Coëvrons, situated north of Sillé-le-Guillaume, near the Jurassic margins of the Paris Basin, between the Laval and Mortain synclines. The relief of this little synclinal massif is due to its belt of Armorican sandstones, which lie on beds whose succession from bottom to top is described as follows:

a. First, there are soft shales, called Brioverian, causing the depression which surrounds the massif, and containing, near the top, the purple conglomerate of Sillé, comparable to the Rocreux puddingstone.

b. Then come sandstones and quartz-phyllites with *Lingulella* and lenses of limestone, in which F. Dangeard [36] has recognised in concretions algae identical to those in the Carteret limestones, described by H. M. Derville.[37] Moreover, shale comparable to the purple shales of May are found at the top.

c. These shales are overlain first by the Sainte-Suzanne sandstone, with *Dinobolus,* then by thick, volcanic formations (porphyritic lavas and tuffs).[38] Above these are sandstones and psammites in which Oehlert long ago noted *Lingulella* (*Thomasina*) *criei,* which he compared to those in the *Lingula* flags of the English Upper Cambrian.[39]

d. Finally, this Coëvrons series is crowned by Armorican sandstones (Ordovician, Arenig stage).

Let us note, however, that the significance of these so-called Cambrian faunules of Coëvrons has been questioned by M. Thoral and M. Pelletier.[40] According to them, the *Dinobolus* and the *Thomasina* are found in the Montagne-Noire, in the *Lingula* sandstones of the Ordovician (Arenig stage). Thus, there would be no fossils here truly characteristic of the Cambrian, and only the lower part (purple conglomerate, sandstones and quartz-phyllites with calcareous lenses, and purple shale) of the Coëvrons section could be compared to this stage.

Moreover, leaving this Coëvrons section and going east, toward central Brittany, C. Barrois and P. Pruvost [41] tried to follow the continuity of the purple conglomerate of Sillé, and so were led to see here the extension of the celebrated Gourin conglomerate, long recognized on the southern slope of the Breton Montagne-Noire. This conglomerate marks the base of a Gourin series described earlier by C. Barrois, composed mostly of shales and quartz-phyllites, with some calcareous lenses, for example the Saint-Thurial limestones[42] south of Rennes. According to C. Barrois and P. Pruvost, this Gourin series could thus be followed more than 200 km. between Finisterre and l'Ille-et-Vilaine, where, joining the Coëvrons section, it would be of Lower or Middle Cambrian age. And these geologists could say that "half of the Brioverian of the Breton maps thus belongs to the Cambrian." [43]

But still in central Brittany, the Lamballe series of C. Barrois would remain Precambrian, or at least Lower Cambrian, according to G. Mathieu. It contains an intercalation of siliceous rocks, the famous Lamballe cherts, in which L. Cayeux has described a fauna made up of radiolaria, which would thus be the oldest fossils known in France. The cherts are found as pebbles in the Gourin conglomerate, which surely proves that this Lamballe series is older than the Gourin series.

Finally, according to these same geologists, the oldest part of this Breton Precambrian is represented by the schistose series of Lanvollon, with amphibolites, gneisses, and even granites. Here the intercalated Cesson conglomerate[44] contains pebbles of granite which show derivation from the granites of the Precambrian.[45]

Another attack against the Breton Brioverian was launched near the north shores of the peninsula.[46] North of Morlaix, this Brioverian contains lenses of a Dourdu limestone, which, in accordance with its microfauna and a section of coral (*Carcinophyllum*) was attributed to the Dinantian by Y. Milon, an opinion corroborated by P. Pruvost and his collaborators. Moreover, one of them, P. Corsin,[47] believed he could attribute an Upper Devonian to Dinantian age to the plant remains collected in the Taulé sandstones (Finistère) of the Trégorrois, formerly ascribed to the Armorican sandstones. Thus a whole vast region of northern Brittany, from le Conquet as far as Jersey, passing through Morlaix, Trégorrois and Paimpol, which formerly seemed Brioverian and Silurian, would become a great Devono-Dinantian synclinal basin, with a great development of volcanic formations. This is the interpretation of the new 1 = 320,000 Brest-Lorient sheet of the *Service de la Carte géol. de France*. Moreover, this Devono-Dinantian contains some layers of carbonaceous and siliceous rocks. But these cherts or Lydian stones are assigned not to the Lamballe cherts but to the Lydian stones so often included in western Europe in the Culm facies of the Dinantian. Indeed, because of these different features, this Breton Devono-Dinantian reminds us very much of that in the Vosges, for instance, which we shall describe later.

3. *Vendée*.   Our knowledge of the Vendée is more easily summarized, for it is the result of the work of a single geologist, G. Mathieu.[48] Before Mathieu, all that immense extent of old formations was uniformly ascribed to the Brioverian, with the exception of two small Carboniferous synclines (Chantonnay and Angers) and a minute trail of Devonian limestones (Ville-Dé-d'Ardin limestones). Guided by lithological analogies, G. Mathieu has been able to distinguish narrow bands of Cambro-Silurian distributed among eight compressed synclines. Later, by a happy chance, he discovered in a shaly horizon of this Silurian (which we shall mention again later) a little pelecypod fauna (*Nucula, Leda, Ctenodonta*) and two fragments of *Calymene,* which confirmed their Ordovician age.[49]

But, beneath the Silurian, the boundary between the Cambrian and the Precambrian is completely uncertain. The oldest member is represented by amphibolites, comparable to the Lanvollon series of Brittany. Then comes a thick slaty series, in which there are scarcely any exact points of reference. G. Mathieu discovered in it some radiolarian cherts, which he compared to those of Lamballe and out of which he made his Lower Cambrian (Georgian).[50] Representing the Gourin conglomerate, there are only some brecciated intercalations in the shales (Saint-Fulgent breccias). And the series ends with the purple shales of Chantonnay, containing only local beds of conglomerate (Sigournais conglomerate). G. Mathieu believes these last to be the equivalents of the Montfort conglomerate and purple shales of the Rennes region. These conglomerates and shales, that he attributes to the Upper Cambrian (Potsdamian), would thus be more recent than the members given the same names in the May section.

On the whole, we see how delicate is the use of points of reference that we have evoked first for this old Breton Primary (conglomerates, limestones, cherts). It is not surprising to find the stratigraphic and tectonic problems which are posed here in the Hercynian tectonics comparable to those which have been so difficult to solve in the Secondary and Tertiary formations of the internal zones of the French Alps.[51]

B. The Bohemian Massif. Such is the name applied to an immense massif of old formations, subordinate to the Hercynian chain, whose roughly quadrilateral form stands out clearly on the map (Fig. 28).

Granite and crystalline schists, formerly referred to the Archean but many of which are doubtless more recent, form the principal framework of the massif, and especially the chains which encircle it: the Ore Mountains (= Erzgebirge = Zelezné hory), the Sudeten Mountains or Giants' Mountains (= Riesengebirge = Krknoše), Moravian-Czech Massif, Bohemian Forest (= Böhmerwald = Sumava). But in the interior of the massif itself, in the center of the quadrilateral, subsidence has allowed the preservation of the most recent formations.

Thus, a wide band of Cretaceous lies along the southwest border of the Sudeten Mountains. On the southeast border of the Ore Mountains extensive Tertiary outcrops are found with recent volcanic rocks, followed by a truncated band of Carboniferous farther southeast. Finally, in the heart of Bohemia, highly folded bands of Primary fossiliferous formations extend in the Variscan direction (SW-NE, see p. 162); this is Barrande's Region of Old Shales, a series of formations which Czech geologists now call Barrandian,[52] in honor of the French geologist who, from 1846 to 1884, published a whole series of studies on the "Silurian of Bohemia," which are still indispensable for the recognition of Primary faunas. A magnificent sequence is found there, ranging from the Precambrian (see p. 39) to the Devonian.

The Cambrian outcrops are found in two areas: one, very extensive, to the southeast, in the neighborhood of Příbram; the other very limited, in the northwest, northeast of Plzen:

1. At the southeast are the Brdy Mountains (Brdské hřebeny).[53] The Cambrian, invariably transgressive and discordant on the Precambrian, begins there with conglomerates, graywackes and the Příbram sandstones, 1,200 m. thick, but containing no fossils. Above come the very fossiliferous Jince shales (100–150 m.). Finally 350 m. of barren sandstones and conglomerates, overlain by volcanic rocks,[54] at the top of the Cambrian.

2. To the northwest lies the region of Skreje and Tejřovice,[55] where the Cambrian series is much thinner and undoubtedly deposited in a little lateral gulf.[56] It too begins with conglomerates and sandstones, at the top of which, in the Tejřovice sandstones, Pompeckj [57] believed he found *Olenellus,* indicating Lower Cambrian. But Kettner has since discovered paradoxids there. Above comes the classic fossiliferous layer of the Skreje shales, overlain by conglomerates and volcanic rocks.

All the fossils collected in Bohemia and coming from either the Jince or the Skreje shales are unquestionably Acadian, easily determined by the abundance of paradoxids, accompanied by other trilobites (*Conocoryphe, Ellipsocephalus, Agnostus, Sao,*[58] etc.), and cystids, etc. Barrande called this rich fauna the "primordial fauna"; for at that time the *Olenellus* fauna of the Lower Cambrian in Northern Europe and America was not yet known. The paradoxid fauna of Bohemia is consequently "primordial" only for that country.

In fact no Georgian fossils have been found there. The Czech geologists now attribute the thick series of conglomerates and Přibram sandstones (which are, moreover, possibly continental) to the Lower Cambrian only for cartographic convenience. For the same reason the barren beds which overlie the fossiliferous Acadian strata are attributed to the Upper Cambrian.

Finally the Silurian covers the whole area in transgression; so the Cambrian of Bohemia is well defined stratigraphically.

5. *Mediterranean Geosynclinal Zone*

The fossiliferous Cambrian here is recognized in Spain,[59] where only the paradoxid fauna has been found, in the Montagne-Noire, in Sardinia and in Morocco. We shall discuss only the last three regions.

A. La Montagne-Noire. In its broadest sense, this name is applied by geologists to a promontory of old formations which pushes south from the Massif Central; it is almost entirely separated therefrom by a gulf of more recent formations, the Jurassic plateaus of the Causses, followed to the west of Saint-Affrique by extensive Permian outcrops.

The skeletal structure of this *Montagne-Noire* (*s. l.*) is composed of an axial zone of crystalline or metamorphic rocks, whose highest parts reach an altitude of 1,000 to 1,200 m. At the west there is the "Montagne-Noire" of local usage and on the east the summits of Espinouse and Caroux. Along the southern flank of this axial zone a wide band of very fossiliferous formations extends from west to east. It is to this region, made classic by Bergeron's studies, that, conforming to an old usage, we shall reserve the name of *Montagne-Noire*. The capital of this privileged little domain of the French Paleozoic is the village of Cabrières. The north slope of the axial zone also shows extensive outcrops of Primary formations which were not explored for a long time; these are the Lacaune Mountains, recently studied by Thoral.[60]

The Cambrian is present along the north and northwest margins of the axial zone, beginning with mylonitized conglomerates lying on schistose formations whose Precambrian age is thereby demonstrated (see p. 38). But the most interesting and most fossiliferous Cambrian outcrops are on the south slope, in the Montagne-Noire proper, where Thoral's researches have accurately determined the stratigraphic succession.[61]

1. The Georgian begins with the Marcory sandstones, which Bergeron classified as Potsdamian, but which are, instead, the oldest sedimentary formation of the region,[62] either on the south margin or in the Lacaune Mountains.[63] In its upper part, specimens of *Olenopsis* have recently been discovered. In America (Atlantic province) this genus characterizes the upper Georgian. Above these sandstones come thick archaeocyathid limestones, whose stratigraphic position has been much disputed. Bergeron considered them Georgian. Thereafter they were long believed to overlie paradoxid shales. But re-

cently Thoral [64] has recognized that this is a question of an abnormal, tectonic superposition and he has collected trilobite faunules in these limestones, including in particular, according to Cobbold, the genus *Micmacca,* which characterizes the upper Georgian in Canada, Shropshire, and Morocco.

2. The Acadian made up of calcareous shales has long been recognized; for it contains the "primordial fauna" with *Paradoxides,* with two paleontologic levels, the lower with *P. rouvillei,* the higher with *P. mediterraneus.* There are also many cystids.

3. The Potsdamian is represented by shaly sandstones, long considered "azoic," but in which Thoral [65] has discovered trilobite faunules characteristic of the Upper Cambrian.

B. Sardinia.[66]   In the old Corsican-Sardinian Massif, the Cambrian is found only in the Iglesiente. Paradoxids and archaeocyathids have long been known there, but the tectonics are very complicated, so the stratigraphy has been much debated. According to the important monograph of Novarese,[67] who has redrawn the geologic map, the Cambrian, whose substratum is unknown, shows *Paradoxides* shales at its base, archaeocyathid limestones in the middle, and sandstones with *Paradoxides* and *Olenopsis* at the top. So this author decided to classify all the Sardinian Cambrian as Acadian, because of the *Paradoxides.* But the genus *Olenopsis,* founded by Bornemann on specimens from Sardinia, has lately been found everywhere in the upper Georgian; finally, Novarese mentioned also *Dictyonema,* discovered by Taricco, but he assumes that this genus would have begun, in Sardinia, at the base of the Middle Cambrian.

As usual, it is paleontological stratigraphy which straightens out the tectonics. New researches by Minucci[68] have led him to propose the following succession:

1. A sandy lower series with *Olenopsis,* no doubt representing the Georgian. At its top, in dolomitic lenses, appear archaeocyathids, at the same horizon as in the Montagne-Noire and Morocco.

2. More or less dolomitic limestones with archaeocyathids, several hundred meters thick and mineralized by granitic injections ("metalliferous" limestones).

3. Shales with *Paradoxides,* representing the Acadian; but the series must rise into the Potsdamian, for, at the top, *Dictyonema* characteristic of the Tremadoc (base of the Silurian) appears. Thus, here as in many other regions, the Tremadoc is naturally attached to the Cambrian and a transgression separates it from the true Silurian beginning with the Arenig stage (see p. 98).

This Sardinian Cambrian seems perfectly analogous to that of the Montagne-Noire, Morocco, and Silesia, as Schwartzbach recognized.[69]

C. Morocco.   Following the heroic period of the first Moroccan pioneers (L. Gentil, A. Brives, P. Lemoine), recent explorations[70] in this country have revealed the existence of a very complete Primary series which should become classic. The outcrops of these Primary formations are distributed in the following natural regions (see Fig. 12):

1. In the north, the *Rif Zone:* this is a section of the Mediterranean chain

(Alpine, s. 1.), whose great folds date from the Tertiary. It is prolonged by littoral chains of the Algerian Tell. The poorly known Primary plays an unimportant role.

2. The *Moroccan Meseta:* this is a region of plateaus, comparable to the Iberian Meseta (see p. 161) or to the French Hercynian massifs. The Primary core, often hidden under horizontal or slightly folded sediments of the Secondary or Tertiary, seems nevertheless to be very extensive.

3. The *Djebilet,* Primary hills where the old core of the Meseta reappears at the north margin of the great Basin of Marrakech.

4. The *Atlas Chain,* folded in the Tertiary, but where the Primary core

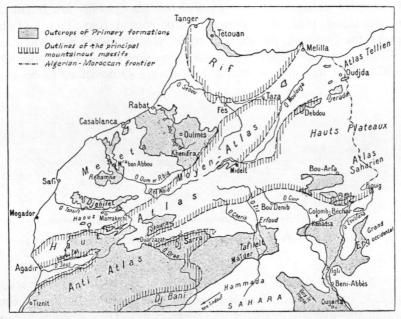

FIG. 12. *Diagrammatic map of the Primary outcrops of Morocco (by L. Moret, completed with the assistance of N. Menchikoff).*

composes the central part of the massifs, making this range comparable to the Pyrenees. The Great Atlas, with the highest summits (4,173 m.), is flanked on the north by the Middle Atlas range and on the south by the Anti-Atlas and is prolonged by the Djebel Sarro.

5. Finally, for an understanding of the geology of southern Morocco, we must mention here the Saharan Shield, still not entirely known.[71] Its ancient (Precambrian) rigid mass appears especially in the crystalline massif of Hoggar (= Ahaggar): around it Cambrian-Devonian horizontal sediments, including beds of hard sandstones, form a series of cliffs, like halos, called "Tassilis" and similar to the glint cliffs which encircle the Baltic Shield (see p. 29).

The Moroccan Cambrian accumulated in a vast geosyncline, recalling that of the Caledonian trough of northern Europe, where the Flysch facies prevailed (see p. 11). It has been affected locally (Great Atlas) by granitic injections, with local metamorphic effects. Approaching the Saharan Shield, it is reduced and assumes the littoral facies of organic limestones.

1. In the *Meseta* and *Djebilet,* the series is principally shaly or sandy-shaly; the substratum nowhere appears and the only faunas known are Acadian (*Paradoxides, Conocoryphe, Ptychoparia*). Still, in the Djebilet the beginning of thin beds of limestone with archaeocyathids is seen in these shales, indicating, as always, the upper Georgian.[72]

2. In the *High Atlas* the Cambrian becomes very thick (1,000 m.). It begins with thick sandstones and conglomerates in the upper part of which thick lenses of dolomitic limestones with archaeocyathids are intercalated. These limestones play an important morphological role. This assemblage represents the Georgian; for above it come Acadian shales with *Paradoxides* and *Ellipsocephalus.* Finally non-fossiliferous shales and sandstones (Potsdamian?) effect a transition to the fossiliferous Ordovician, to be studied later.

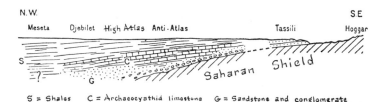

S = Shales   C = Archaeocyathid limestone   G = Sandstone and conglomerate

FIG. 13.   *Diagram of the Cambrian facies in Morocco (by L. Moret).*

3. In the *Anti-Atlas* and *Djebel Sarro,*[73] the Precambrian basement is widely exposed; it is composed of crystalline and metamorphic rocks (Archean) unconformably overlain by quartzites (Algonkian?). The Cambrian lies above another unconformity. It begins with conglomerates and sandstones (with intercalations of andesitic and rhyolitic flows and tuffs) at the top of which Bondon and Neltner have recently found *Protolenus* and *Micmacca* faunas, trilobites which are characteristic of the top of the Georgian in Shropshire (Comley) and in the Atlantic Provinces of Canada (New Brunswick). Next comes the shaly series with paradoxids, always overlying enormous calcareous lentils with archaeocyathids. The Cambrian ends with non-fossiliferous shales and sandstones, gradational into the Silurian.

4. Far to the south, in the Mauritanian Sahara, dolomites with stromatoliths (problematical, concretionary organisms), found everywhere under the Ordovician sandstones, may correspond to a littoral and very reduced Cambrian, surrounding the Saharan Shield and similar to that which borders the Baltic Shield. Analogous formations are found at certain points around the Hoggar, at the base of the sandy cliffs of the internal Tassili.[74]

IV. Cambrian Facies of North America [75]

The Cambrian facies in North America lend themselves to an organization similar to that proposed for Europe. In fact, the Canadian Shield here plays a role in the history of Cambrian times, identical to that of the Baltic Shield in Europe (see Figs. 5 and 14).

1. *Marginal Zone of the Canadian Shield*

The Cambrian is here neritic, thin, and incomplete. These are typical characteristics of continental areas.

On the margin of the shield itself are found only sandstones generally assigned to the Upper Cambrian or Potsdamian. These are the Potsdam sandstones, with their characteristic trilobitic fauna, especially the genus *Dikellocephalus,* for we are now in the Pacific province.

To find the Acadian, we need to go far beyond the Shield, across the Rocky Mountains, to the High Plateaus. Then we may see it in the celebrated chasm of the Grand Canyon of the Colorado; there, unconformably above the tilted Algonkian lie *Olenoides* and *Ptychoparia* sandstones of the Acadian (Pacific province), topped by sandstones and *Dikellocephalus* shales of the Potsdamian. This whole assemblage, moreover, is scarcely more than 300 m. thick.

2. *Geosynclinal Zone of the Pacific Chains*

Farther west, in ranges near the Pacific coast, we find the Cambrian wholly altered. All the stages are present, including the Georgian, which is concordant with the Algonkian; they have more shaly facies and reach an enormous thickness (up to 2,500 m.); moreover they are folded. It is indeed the geosynclinal type. The Georgian, Acadian, and Potsdamian are represented by characteristic trilobite faunas of the Pacific province, of which this is the type.

3. *Geosynclinal Zone of the Appalachians*

Analogous features are observed east of the Canadian Shield. We find another geosynclinal zone, folded at the end of the Primary and to-day occupied by the Appalachian Mountains. The Cambrian reaches a thickness of 4,000 m. and the three successive faunas of the Pacific province are present. Communication with the zone of the Pacific Chain is established through the southern part of North America, thus circling around the Canadian Shield; for the Central States have been reached only by the Potsdamian transgression.

4. *The Atlantic Zone*

Here the Cambrian is found all along the coast from Labrador to the state of New York. It lies unconformably on Precambrian formations and is very fossiliferous in places. Here are found the type localities of the three stages:

Georgian (Georgia, on the shores of Lake Champlain), Acadian (Acadia =
Nova Scotia) and Potsdamian (Potsdam, N. Y.). The Georgian contains
Olenellus and ends with archaeocyathid limestones; *Paradoxides* is found in
the Acadian and *Olenus* in the Potsdamian. This is indeed the Atlantic prov-
ince; there must have been an arm of the sea extending from Europe to
America along which the Cambrian faunas spread.

Curiously enough, in the Lower Cambrian the distribution of the various
sub-genera of *Olenellus* presents a certain symmetry on either side of the
Atlantic. Indeed, *Olenellus s.s.* is found only on the northern shores of this
sea: that is, on one side in Scotland, on the other in Newfoundland, while
the sub-genera *Holmia* and *Callavia* are confined to the southern shores of
the arm of the sea, on one side in Wales, Shropshire, and the Baltic countries,
on the other side south of New Brunswick. So it is the arm of the sea itself

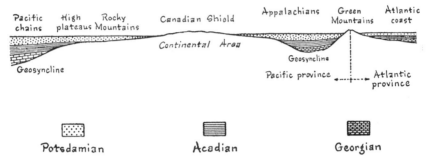

FIG. 14. *Diagram of the different types of the Cambrian in North America*
(*after Walcott, very much simplified; compare map Fig. 5*).

that separates the littoral faunas of these two sub-provinces of the Atlantic
domain.

In the Middle and Upper Cambrian, the separation of the two great Atlantic and Pacific provinces may be due, according to the hypothesis of early
American geologists and E. Haug, to the existence of an emerged chain, that
of the Green Mountains, which extended, north of the Appalachians, between
the Hudson River and Lake Champlain on the west and the Connecticut
River on the east. This chain is formed of ancient crystalline and metamorphic
rocks and the Cambrian seas do not appear to have covered it.

REFERENCE NOTES

1. Name taken from Cambria: Wales.

2. For a general résumé, see C. D. Walcott, "Evidences of Primitive Life," Smith-
sonian report for 1915, 20 p., 18 pl. (1916).

3. A. G. Volodgin, *The Archaeocyathinae of Siberia,* Editions de Géologie de l'Ad-
ministration principale de recherches géologiques, Moscow-Leningrad (1931).

4. The attempt made by Dacqué to deduce the position of the Cambrian poles from
the distribution of the archaeocyathids would seem very risky. See, instead, the little
map on which P. Range tried to show the location of the Cambrian deposits of glacial

(?) origin: P. Range, *Ueber die kambrische Eiszeit,* Zeitschr. Deutschen geol. Ges., 88 (1936).

5. See O. Holtedahl, "An Upper Cambrian Fauna of Pacific Type in the European Arctic Region," Amer. Jour. of Sci. (May, 1922); M. E. Janisevsky, *Matériaux pour la connaissance de la faune paléozoïque de la Nouvelle-Zemble,* Travaux du Musée géol. et mineral. Pierre-le-Grand, t. V (1926).

6. Before the discovery of the *Olenellus* fauna, these three stages were called *Annelidian, Paradoxidian* and *Olenidian.*

7. This large, old genus *Olenellus* is now sub-divided in several sub-genera (*Olenellus s.s., Callavia, Holmia,* etc.) constituting the family of mesonacids, which are essentially characteristic of the lower Cambrian and from which, with no known intermediates, the paradoxids of the Middle Cambrian are derived.

8. One will see very interesting attempts at synthesis of the Cambrian paleogeography made by Born in the textbook of W. Salomon, *Grundzüge der Geologie,* Band II (1926), but it seems to us a little daring to attempt to map cartographically the extent of the seas of different stages of the Cambrian in Europe. Let us note finally the synthetic maps of facies, relative to all the Primary systems, accompanying the recent article of A. Demay, *Contribution à la synthèse de la Chaîne hercynienne d'Europe,* Revue de Géogr. phys. et de Géol. dynamique, 7 (1934).

9. And as we shall see, extending perhaps into the Grampian Mountains and into Ireland.

10. Let us cite these recent works: A. H. Westergard, *Sveriges Olenidskiffer* (with an English résumé: *The Olenus Shale of Sweden*), Sveriges Geologiska Undersökning, No. 18, Stockholm (1922); L. Rüger, *Paläogeographische Untersuchungen im baltischen Cambrium unter Berücksichtigung Schwedens,* Centralblatt f. Min. (1923); B. Frosterus, *Ueber die Kambrischen Sedimente der Karelischen Landenge,* Bull. Comm. géol. Finlande, no. 75 (1925); T. Strand, "The Cambrian Beds of the Mjösen district in Norway," Norsk. geol. Tidsskrift, 10 (1929).

11. See the excellent survey by O. Holtedahl and various collaborators: "The Geology of the Oslo District, and the Adjacent Sparagmite District," Proc. Geologists' Assn., Vol. 45 (1934), p. 314.

12. Certain authors attach it, however, to the Cambrian (see p. 80).

13. B. A. Nekrassow, *Eophyton-, Ischora (Fucoïden)- und Obolus-Sandsteine des Leningrader Gebietes,* C. R. Soc. Natur. Moscou, 46, sect. géol. [2], 16 (1938), in Russian with a German résumé.

14. A. Opik, *Studien über das estnische Unterkambrium (Estonium),* Publ. geol. Inst. Univ. Tartu, no. 15 (1929).

15. This discovery proved the Silurian age of these sandstones, formerly attributed to the Cambrian.

16. L. von zur Mühlen, *Einige Neue Tiefbohrungen im Gebiete der Russischen Tafel,* Zeitschr. deutschen geol. Ges., 93 (1941); see paleogeographic map, p. 225.

17. On the Cambrian-Silurian paleogeography of England, see O. T. Jones, "On the Evolution of a Geosyncline," Quart. Jour. Geol. Soc. London, Anniversary address, vol. 94, part 2 (1938).

18. Small tubular shells that are close to the pteropods, pelagic mollusks.

19. A recent monograph on this classic region by several collaborators appeared in the Proceedings of the Geologists' Association, vol. 41 (1930), part 3.

20. V. C. Illing, "The Paradoxidian Fauna of a Part of the Stockingford Shales," Quart. Jour. Geol. Soc., vol. 71 (1915); E. S. Cobbold, "The Stratigraphy and Geological Structure of the Cambrian Area of Comley (Shropshire)," id., vol. 83 (1927); C. J. Stubblefield, "A New Upper Cambrian Section in South Shropshire," Summary of Progress of the Geol. Survey of Great Britain (1929).

21. The study of the Caledonian tectonics would involve us too deeply. We shall refer to the work of G. Waterlot, *L'évolution de l'Ardenne au cours des diverses phases des plissements calédoniens et hercyniens,* Bull. Soc. géol. France, 5 sér. t. 15 (1945); very ingeniously, the author tries to compare the Caledonian foldings with the paleogeographic history of the Cambrian and Silurian.

22. G. Waterlot, *Structure du massif cambrien de Rocroy,* C. R. Acad. Sci. (11 Jan., 1937), *Sur la stratigraphie et la tectonique du massif cambrien de Rocroy,* Bull. Carte géol. France, t. 39 (1937), no. 195 (1938).

23. The stratigraphic synthesis of Waterlot has been discussed by R. Anthoine, *Contribution à l'étude du massif cambrien de Rócroy,* Mém. Acad. roy. Belgique, C. R. Sci. 12, no. 4 (1940); but a new observation by G. Waterlot, C. R. Acad. Sc., 226 (1948), p. 349, presents an important argument against the interpretations of Anthoine. Let us cite also a note of F. Tanazacq, *Découverte d'un horizon fossilifère en Ardenne française,* C. R. Acad. Sc. (28 Nov., 1938); this author, having collected some *D. flabelliforme* in beds that he places at the base (?) of the Revinian, proposes to class all the Revinian in the Tremadoc; only the Devillien would belong to the Cambrian, *s. s.*

24. A. Wurm, *Ueber ein Vorkommen von Mittelkambrium im Bayerischen Frankenwald bei Wildenstein südlich Presseck,* Neues Jahrb. f. Min., Beil. Band 52 (1925); *Ueber neuentdeckte Kambrische Faunen in Deutschland,* C. R. Congr. géol. internat. Espagne, 1926, Madrid (1927); *Ueber eine neue mittelcambrische Fauna aus dem bayrischen Frankenwald und ihre Bedeutung für die Stratigraphie des älteren Paläozoicums,* Neues Jahrb. f. Min., Beil. Band 59 (1928).

25. Richter, *Eine cambrische Fauna im Niederschlesichen Schiefergebirge,* Geol. Centralblatt (1923).

26. M. Schwartzbach, *Neue Trilobiten aus dem Cambrium der Oberlausitz,* Zentralbl. f. Min. (1933); *Das Cambrium der Oberlausitz,* Abhandl. Naturforsch. Ges. zu Görlitz, H. 2, Bd. 32; *Das Bober-Katzbach-Gebirge im Rahmen des europäischen Paläozoikums,* Zeitschr. deutsch. geol. Ges., 92 (1940), p. 164.

27. S. Lencewicz, *Le Massif Hercynien des Lysogory (Sainte-Croix) et ses enveloppes,* Congr. intern. Geogr., Varsovie (1934), Excurs. B.3.

28. This is the "Mont-Chauve" musically depicted by Moussorgsky's symphonic poem.

29. J. Czarnocki, *Le Cambrien et la faune cambrienne de la partie moyenne du Massif de Swiety Krzyz,* C. R. Congr. géol. internat. Espagne, 1926, Madrid (1927).

30. And in particular, the quartzitic phyllites of Saint-Lô, of which the Latin name is Brioveria.

31. See the very clear and interesting synthesis presented by G. Mathieu, *Le problème du Précambrien dans l'Ouest de la France,* La Revue scientifique, no. 3241 (Feb. 1945).

32. A. Bigot, *La Basse Normandie, esquisse géologique et morphologique,* Librairie générale du Calvados, Caen (1942).

33. Locality situated on the north flank of the Urville syncline.

34. The fossils of Carteret are presented in A. Bigot, *Sur les calcaires cambriens de la region de Carteret et leur faune,* Bull. Soc. géol. Normandie, 7 sér., t. 8 (1925).

35. E. S. Cobbold, Ann. and Magaz. Nat. Hist. (1) XV, p. 381 (1935).

36. F. Dangeard, *Observations sur les calcaires cambriens des Coëvrons,* Bull. Soc. linnéenne Normandie, 8 sér., t. 7, p. 93, Caen (1934).

37. H. Derville, *Les recifs en coupole du Cambrien de Carteret,* Bull. Soc. géol. France, 5 sér., t. 3, p. 603 (1933).

38. Formerly much worked for road ballast; for these are the best materials that can be found this close to Paris.

39. These fossils have been restudied and presented by C. Barrois and P. Pruvost (work cited note 41).

40. M. Thoral and M. Pelletier, *A propos du cambrien armoricain,* C. R. Soc. géol. France (1948), p. 117; conclusions discussed by A. Bigot, ibid., p. 156.

41. C. Barrois and P. Pruvost, *Des relations stratigraphiques des couches cambriennes de la Bretagne avec celles du Maine,* Ann. Soc. géol. Nord, t. 56 (1931).

42. C. Barrois and P. Pruvost, *Le calcaire de Saint-Thurial,* Ann. Soc. géol. Nord, t. 54, p. 142 (1929). This limestone is classed then in the Cambrian, although it encloses a micro-fauna very similar to that of the limestones of Dourdu (see further on) and which has been related to the Dinantian by Y. Milon, *Recherches sur les calcaires paléozoïques et le Briovérien de Bretagne,* Thèse sc. Rennes (1928). M. Thoral and M. Pelletier also think that this limestone is certainly much more recent than the Cambrian.

43. But this opinion does not seem to be unanimously accepted. See P. R. Giot, *Sur le Briovérien au Sud des Montagnes-Noires (Finistère et Morbihan)*, C. R. Soc. géol. France (1944), p. 179; this geologist claims that in this region where the type locality of Gourin is found, the conglomerates of Gourin are Precambrian and not Cambrian. Let us recall also the views of L. Dangeard and C. Batard, *Sur les poudingues intercalés dans les schistes briovériens au Nord des Coëvrons (Mayenne et Sarthe) et sur la nature des mouvements cadomiens*, C. R. Acad. Sc. (June 24, 1935); they compare the purple Montfort conglomerates (which become 500 m. thick at Montfort, west of Rennes) and leave them in the Precambrian, like the conglomerates of Gourin. This Montfort conglomerate is overlain by purple schists; also, through analogy to the May section, it formerly made the base of the Cambrian; G. Mathieu, however, believes it much more recent than all the other conglomerates and sees in it a lateral equivalent of the sandstones of Sainte-Suzanne-des Coëvrons (Upper Cambrian).

44. At the bottom of the bay of Saint-Brieuc.

45. Most of the Breton granites are, however, much more recent, and sometimes certainly Carboniferous. We recall again the very interesting summary of G. Mathieu, *Essai sur les granites du Massif Armoricain*, La Revue scientifique, No. 3228 (Jan. 1944). The age of the granites here is determined both by the metamorphism that they have exerted on the neighboring sediments, and by the age of the strata (sandstones, conglomerates) that contain their pebbles or altered mineral constituents (micas). This is a good example of the mutual help which petrographic and stratigraphic studies should give each other.

46. P. Pruvost, G. Waterlot and P. Comte, *Le Bassin Carbonifère de Morlaix*, Bull. Serv. Carte géol. France, no. 212 (1943).

47. P. Corsin, *Les plantes fossiles du Grès de Taulé (Finistère)*, Ann. Soc. géol. Nord, t. 63, p. 82.

48. G. Mathieu, *Recherches géologiques sur les terrains paléozoïques de la région vendéenne*, Thèse Sc. Lille (1937).

49. G. Mathieu, *Sur la faune ordovicienne de Réaumur*, Bull. Soc. géol. France, 5 sér. t. 11 (1941), p. 3.

50. On this subject we find a little audacious the suggestion of L. Bertrand (*Histoire géologique du sol français*, t. II, p. 66 and 76) who, comparing these black jaspers to the Lydian stone of the Devonian-Dinantian of the region of Morlaix, is thus led to attribute all the Brioverian of the Vendée to a Devonian-Dinantian in the midst of which the Cambrian-Silurian bands of G. Mathieu would correspond, not to synclines but to anticlines.

51. And nevertheless, it is an obligation for geologists, who have the painful duty of preparing geologic maps, to reach some stratigraphic syntheses at any cost. They are unfortunately forbidden to leave any blank spaces in their maps.

52. R. Kettner, *Paléogéographie des formations entrant dans la composition du Barrandien*, C. R. Congrès. géol. internat. en Espagne en 1926, Madrid (1927); *L'évolution tectonique du Barrandien*, Bull. Soc. géol. France, 5 sér., t. 7 (1937) (with a geologic map of the whole); P. Kettner and B. Boucek, *Tableaux synoptiques des formations du Barrandien*, Trav. Inst. Géol. Pal. Univ. Charles, Prague (1936).

53. R. Kettner and O. Kodym, *Coupes géologiques du Barrandien, 1ʳᵉ partie, Brdské hřebeny*, Knihovna státního géol. ústavu Ceskosl. Rep., svazek II, Prague (1922).

54. F. Slavik, *L'activité volcanique dans le Barrandien*, Bull. Soc. géol. France, 5 sér., t. 7 (1937), p. 527.

55. R. Kettner, *La géologie du Cambrien de Skreje et de Tejřovice*, Sbornik statniho geol. ustava Ceskosl. Rep. svazek III, Prague (1923).

56. R. Kettner, *Transgressions et régressions de la mer du Silurien inf. dans la Bohême*, (Bull. internat. Acad. Sc. Bohême (1921).

57. J. F. Pompeckj, *Die Fauna des Kambriums von Tejřovice und Skrej in Böhmen*, Jahrb. d. k. k. Reichsanst., Wien (1895).

58. This genus, peculiar to Bohemia, has often been used to define a Bohemian Province. Its individuality seems less and less clear (see Pompeckj's article).

59. P. H. Sampelayo, *El sistema cambriano*, Explic. del nueva maps geol. de España,

Madrid (1934). P. Comte, *La série cambrienne et silurienne du Léon (Espagne)*, C. R. Acad. Sc. (Feb. 22, 1937).

60. M. Thoral, *Contribution à l'étude géologique des Monts de Lacaune et des terrains cambriens et ordoviciens de la Montagne-Noire*, Bull. Service Carte géol. France, t. 38, no. 192, 308 p., 52 fig., 5 pl., 1 carte au 1/200,000 (1935). *Contribution à l'étude paléontologique de l'Ordovicien inférieur de la Montagne-Noire et révision sommaire de la faune cambrienne de la Montagne-Noire*, Montpellier, Imprimerie de la Charité (1935).

61. Concerning the tectonics of this region, see the ingenious synthesis ventured by B. Gèze in a series of Notes to the C. R. de l'Acad. des Sc. (1944), t. 218, pp. 160 (with map and synthetic sections), 238, 324 and 366.

62. J. Blayac and M. Thoral, *Contribution à l'étude du Géorgien de la Montagne-Noire*, Bull. Soc. géol. France, 5 sér., t. I (1931); E. S. Cobbold, *Le genre Olenopsis en France*, ibid.

63. M. Thoral, *Existence du Géorgien dans les monts de Lacaune*, C. R. Acad. Sc. (Jan. 16, 1933).

64. M. Thoral, *Age des Calcaires à Archaeocyathus de la Montagne-Noire*, C. R. Acad. Sc. (Dec. 26, 1934).

65. M. Thoral, *Découverte de Nouveaux gisements fossilifères dans le Potsdamien et l'Arenig inf. de la Montagne-Noire*, C. R. Acad. Sc. (Mar. 13, 1933).

66. A complete geological bibliography of this country will be found in fasc. 4 of t. 41 (1922) of Bollettino della Soc. geol. italiana, Pisa (1923).

67. V. Novarese, *Contributo alla Geologia dell'Iglesiente. La serie paleozoica*, Boll. del R. Ufficio geol. d'Italia, vol. 49 (1924); M. Gortani, *La serie paleozoica nelle Alpi carniche e nella Sardegna*, C. R. Congrès. géol. Internat. en Espagne, 1926, Madrid (1927).

68. E. Minucci, *Le condizioni del Paleozoico nel Sulcis orientale (Sardegna)*, Boll. Soc. geol. ital., 54 (1935), p. 75.

69. M. Schwartzbach, *Das Normalprofil des sardinischen Cambriums*, Zentralbl. f. Min., B (1939), pp. 49–59.

70. First, the work of J. Barthoux, J. Bourcart, F. Daguin, P. Fallot, G. Lecointre, L. Moret, L. Neltner, E. Roch, P. Russo, H. Termier, etc. A résumé of the works relating to the Primary of Morocco up to 1930 will be found in L. Moret, *Recherches géologiques dans l'Atlas de marrakeck,* Notes et memoires du Service des Mines et de la Carte geol. du Maroc, 1931. An excellent summary of the general structure of Morocco was given by P. Despujols, *Note sur l'industrie minière au Maroc*, Congrès. de l'Afrique du N., Rabat (1930). See especially the monumental work of H. Termier, *Etudes géologiques sur le Maroc Central et le Moyen-Atlas septentrional* Service Mines et Carte géol. Maroc, Notes et Mém. No. 33 (1936), 1423 p., 26 tabl., 63 fig., 61 pl.

71. See the schematic maps attached to the brief description of the assemblage by R. Furon, C. Kilian, N. Menchikoff, *La géologie du Sahara,* Revue générale des Sc. (Feb. 28, 1935).

72. L. Neltner and N. Poctey, C. R. Acad. Sc., t. 224, p. 352 (1947).

73. J. Bondon, L. Clariond, and L. Neltner, *Une nouvelle coupe du Djebel Sarro (Maroc saharien)*, C. R. Acad., des Sc. (Feb. 5, 1934). J. Bondon and L. Neltner, *Sur la série cambrienne des plateaux du Draa (Sud-marocain) et la présence du Géorgien dans cette série* (Id., July 10, 1933). L. Clariond, *La série paléozoïque du territoire du Tafilelt (Maroc)*, (Id. June 25, 1934). L. Neltner, *Sur le Cambrien du Sud-marocain, essai paléogéographique*, C. R. Soc. géol. France (Mar. 18, 1935).

74. C. Kilian, *Essai de synthèse de la Géologie du Sahara Sud-constantinois et du Sahara central,* C. R. du Congrès géol. internat. en Belgique en 1922, Liége (1925). See also article referred to in Note 71.

75. We cite only the following recent synthesis: B. F. Howell, etc., *Correlations of the Cambrian Formations of North America*, Bull. Geol. Soc. Amer., 55 (1944), p. 999.

76. Actually, recent researches seem to have modified this conception; many of these metamorphic complexes formerly believed to be very old are now revealed to be of Cambro-Silurian age.

Chapter Three

The Silurian

I. Boundaries and Subdivisions

The name, Silurian, was proposed in 1835 by Murchison for a group of formations in Wales and especially in Shropshire, an area formerly peopled by the Silurian tribe.

A. *Lower Boundary*

This boundary is purely paleontological and conventional; for in the European countries where the Cambrian and Silurian are most typical, no paleogeographic event of general value occurred at any place (except Bohemia). Thus, this boundary varies greatly with different authors.

In certain countries, classic for these two systems, for example in Scandinavia, the transition from one to the other occurs in the following manner: above the Potsdamian with its *Olenus* fauna, comes a shale stratum containing the oldest graptolites, *Dictyonema* (= *Dictyograptus*) *flabelliforme;* and overlying this bed, there are shales containing genera of trilobites (*Euloma, Niobe, Ceratopyge*), many of which are unknown in the Cambrian. So, some authorities place the system boundary between the *Dictyonema* shales which they attach to the Cambrian and the *Euloma-Niobe* horizon, which they make the base of the Silurian.

But in certain other regions, still more classic, at Tremadoc (Wales) for instance, according to Fearnsides the *Niobe* fauna is found below the *Dictyonema* shales. The only solution is to combine these two paleontological horizons in a single stage, which will be called the Tremadocian, or transition beds between the Cambrian and Silurian. In Wales and Shropshire, the Tremadocian is connected, naturally enough, with the Cambrian rather than the Silurian (see p. 80); this is the opinion accepted by British geologists. We shall follow the traditional custom of French geologists, which makes the Tremadocian the base of the Silurian.

71

B. *Upper Boundary; The Downtonian*

At the end of the Silurian, however, a very important paleogeographic event took place in the vast expanses of Northern Europe. This was the rise of the Caledonian Chain, withdrawing from the marine empire huge domains which became continental and on which the Devonian is represented, as we shall see, by the very special facies of the "Old Red Sandstone."

Thus, in general, the break between Silurian and Devonian is clearly shown. But, to be explicit, we shall be forced to seek a more precise definition.

The boundary formations between the Silurian and Devonian have been most carefully studied in Shropshire (England) and in the Ardennes.

1. In England, there are transition beds called Downtonian (see p. 109), in which beds with marine shells alternate with beds containing lagoonal faunas (fish and eurypterids) of the Old Red Sandstone. Because of these marine intercalations, English geologists generally attribute this Downtonian to the Silurian.

2. In the Ardennes, a very clear line is marked by a great discordance (the Caledonian discordance), above which the Devonian naturally begins. This Ardennes Devonian starts with a basal conglomerate (Fépin conglomerate), then continues with shales with marine faunas (Mondrepuis shales), which constitute the lower Gedinnian, first stage of the system (see p. 117).

But a comparative study of these two regions has recently shown[1] that the Mondrepuis shales are the exact equivalent of the English Downtonian. If, then, we wish to accept as the boundary of the Silurian and the Devonian the great discordance so long known in the Ardennes, we must put the Downtonian in the Devonian and not in the Silurian. That is what we shall do here, even while recalling that in northern Europe this Downtonian is characteristic of the transition beds between the two systems.

Finally, the Silurian is more naturally allied to the Cambrian than to the Devonian. Many geologists, therefore, have considered the Cambrian as simply a division of a Silurian *sensu lato;* the Scandinavians still do.

C. *Subdivisions*

Study of central England is going to show us that there the early recognition of local paleogeographic modifications, which came before more general ones at the end of the Silurian, made possible a division of the system into two great stages: at the base, the Ordovician, so called after an ancient tribe of Wales, and at the top, the Gothlandian, named from the Isle of Gothland (Baltic).[2] In other countries, it is ordinarily only the fauna which, in comparison with that of Britain, makes possible the recognition of this subdivision.

II. The Silurian Fauna

From the Silurian on, fossils become extremely abundant and varied; we may say that all the great groups of marine animals are represented. It is impossible to discuss all of them here. Completely excluding the paleontologic aspects, we shall confine ourselves to noting the organisms which play a preponderant role in the formation of the sediments and to those which serve to define the facies or to furnish the most important guide fossils.

A. *Reef-building Coelenterates*

The development of calcareous reefs is especially marked in the Gothlandian, and several groups of coelenterates participated.

1. There are first the corals proper, represented by the group of tetracorals, which flourished to the end of the Primary (genera *Cyathophyllum, Gonio-phyllum, Zaphrentis,* etc.).

2. Next come some forms related to the present alcyonarians; these are the *Heliolitides.*

3. The *Tabulata,* a poorly defined group confined to Primary sediments, whose affinity with living types is uncertain, were very abundant in the Silurian (*Favosites, Halysites*).

4. Finally, the stromatoporids, a kind of crust-covered hydrozoan, played an important part in the building of reefy, calcareous masses.

The development of these reefs[3] seems to be almost entirely independent of their geographic location; they are found equally in the southern hemisphere (Australia) and in the most northern parts of the northern hemisphere (Grinnell land, north of Siberia). If we concede, as seems probable but not proven, that these faunal associations indicate a temperature comparable to that necessary for present reefs, we can deduce that there must have been relatively warm periods in the Silurian.

The Island of Gothland itself, which we have taken as the type for the Gothlandian stage, furnishes beautiful examples of Silurian reefs.

B. *Graptolites*

Probably some of these animals belong to a group of coelenterates peculiar to the Primary, being pelagic with a float-bladder and having filaments where polyps are found. Others must have lived attached to floating algae. In any case, they usually are found in fine-grained shales, often coaly and black, called graptolite shales, for very often they contain no other fossils. Such sediments are sometimes defined as deep-water facies or even bathyal facies; we have such examples today, as well as for many similar facies (especially facies with radiolaria—radiolarites, cherts, etc.—which often are associated with graptolite shales).[4] It seems actually that these sediments may have formed at shallow depths but in tranquil waters where only the fine muds held in suspension in sea water were deposited, along with the remains of animals floating therein, to the exclusion of terrigenous debris brought directly from the neighboring emerged land. Instead of deep-water facies it would be better to define this as a deep or shallow pelagic facies as contrasted to the terrigenous facies. R. Hundt even believes that graptolitic shales, in which no other fossils are found, were sometimes deposited in the lagoons of inland seas (similar to the Black Sea, certain Baltic basins, the Sulu Sea, etc.), without currents, with depths contaminated by the release of hydrogen sulphide under reducing conditions. The results include the frequency of pyrite and the richness of organic materials which are shown by carbonaceous (ampelites) or even bituminous facies.[5]

Like all pelagic animals, certain species of the graptolites have a wide geographic distribution. Moreover, the species are very numerous and follow one another rapidly in time. Therefore the fossils are eminently suited for the definition of paleontologic zones. Thus, in Scania, 15 graptolite zones can be distinguished in the Ordovician and 16 in the Gothlandian. Many of these zones are also found in Scotland, France, and even in America and Australia.

The oldest graptolites have very special forms, reticulated and fan shaped (dendroids). The genus *Dictyonema* only is found at the extreme base of the Ordovician (*Dictyonema flabelliforme* bed, Tremadocian stage). In the rest of the Ordovician, the predominant genera have cups on two sides (*Diplograptus*) or are even branched (*Didymograptus*) or enlarged in leaf form (*Phyllograptus*). In the Gothlandian especially there are species with linear filaments with cups on one side (*Monograptus*).[6]

After the Silurian, the only graptolites are rare dendroids, so that the Silurian may be called the age of graptolites.

C. *Echinoderms*

The crinoids, or sea lilies, are important because of their abundance. Many belong to special groups that had their maximum development in the Gothlandian. In fact, it seems that the submarine fields of crinoids flourished especially in relatively shallow waters rich in lime, a condition found on the submarine shelves around the coral reefs. Indeed the *calcaires à entroques,* formed there in the Silurian, were composed almost completely of crinoidal remains.

The sea urchins are always only interesting rarities.

In the Silurian, however, and especially in the Gothlandian, the special group of cystids peculiar to the Primary reach their greatest richness (genera *Echinosphaerites, Pleurocystites,* etc.).[7]

D. *Brachiopods*

These are among the most abundant and the most widely distributed fossils of the Silurian. They are found especially in rather littoral facies, which, for this reason, the British call shelly facies. They too furnish many genera and characteristic species, which we shall have occasion to note later. Among the most widely distributed genera are: *Spirifer, Orthis, Chonetes, Atrypa, Pentamerus,* etc.

E. *Trilobites*

The same is true of the trilobites. However, the Silurian marks the end of their prosperity, because from the Gothlandian on they become less numerous. The most characteristic genera are: *Trinucleus,* whose species have served to establish numerous paleontologic zones in the Ordovician, particularly in Northern Europe; *Calymene,* often found coiled, a characteristic shared by no

Cambrian trilobite; *Asaphus* and *Illaenus,* which reach a great size; *Phacops, Dalmanites,* etc.

These trilobites are found in greatly varied facies. Many must have been diggers and limivores (mud-eaters), and lived on muddy bottoms;[8] they are found in the shales. But others must have lived on sandy or coral bottoms close to shore, for there are also sandstones and limestones with trilobites.

F. Mollusks

The gastropods and pelecypods are generally of little value in stratigraphy; an exception must be made for a lamellibranch, *Cardiola interrupta,* that is extremely widespread in the Gothlandian and characteristic of that stage. It has a very thin shell and is found, as is usual in such cases, in beds or nodules of fine-grained clayey limestones intercalated in the graptolitic shales.

The cephalopods are especially abundant in the moderately deep-water facies, in shales or particularly in calcareous muds. The nautiloids, represented by *Orthoceras, Cyrtoceras, Trochoceras, Lituites,* etc., also reach their maximum in the Silurian. Finally, the group of ammonoids make their first appearance here. Impressions which may be attributed to the genus *Agoniatites* were noted in the upper Silurian by Kellerwald, near Cassel. Other genera appeared in the Carnic Alps, in the beds with *Tornoceras inexpectatum* and *Anarcestes praecursor* (expressive names of species), which we shall assign to the extreme top of the Silurian.

The conularia, frequent in certain sandy formations, are at present considered as probably sessile mollusca, having no connection with other known groups.[9]

III. The Type-Series of the Silurian in Britain

The Silurian of Britain deserves somewhat detailed study, for it is there that the types of stages are located; moreover, thanks to the fine research of numerous geologists, the succession of beds has been very precisely established there over extensive areas, across several facies. So the British Silurian offers a magnificent example of stratigraphic synthesis.

A. Silurian Outcrops: the Caledonian Massifs

All of Britain is dependent upon the Caledonian Chain, formed at the end of the Silurian, except the two extremities of the island: that is, northwest Scotland, which is part of the Huronian Chain (see p. 40), and the Cornish Peninsula, which rises from the Hercynian Chain. To study the Silurian here, we must describe the history of the Caledonian Chain immediately preceding its folding, when its site was occupied by a deep sea, which we shall call the "Caledonian trough."

The present outcrops of the Silurian thus constitute a series of Caledonian Massifs, as follows (Fig. 15):

1. The Massif of the Scottish Highlands, comprising the Grampian Mountains. There, neither the Cambrian nor the Silurian is paleontologically dated. But, as we have already seen (p. 37) it is possible that the Silurian may be represented in this complex of ancient rocks, particularly in the Dalradian, near the southern boundary.

2. The Scottish Southern Uplands, a folded Silurian country, immediately south of the trough of the Lowlands.

3. The Lake District.

4. Wales,[10] with its eastern annexes, formed by isolated outcrops of ancient rocks which appear here and there through the horizontal cover of Devonian or more recent formations.

In all these areas the usual direction of the Caledonian folds is SW-NE. But along the southeast border of Wales, these folds take the form of an arc approximately parallel to the boundary of the massif. Near Haverfordwest they are W-E, then they bend to the SW-NE in the region of Llandovery and become almost S-N in northern Wales (see Fig. 17).

B. *Silurian Facies*

These are extremely varied. They may be grouped in four principal types:

1. Facies of black, clayey, graptolitic shales, often accompanied by beds of radiolarian cherts. These are the deepest-water deposits or at least the most pelagic. Generally they are not very thick.

2. Facies of sandy shales, sandstones, conglomerates—the type geologists usually call Flysch (see p. 11). These predominantly terrigenous sediments may be rather shallow-water, even though accumulating enormous thicknesses, sometimes several thousand meters. Also, as British geologists have noted, these accumulations presuppose a continual sinking of the base; the facies is in this sense geosynclinal. Fossils are never very numerous here, but to the graptolites of the preceding facies, trilobites and sometimes brachiopods are added.

3. Volcanic facies, formed by the accumulation of ash, tuffs, and lavas; such deposits are sometimes very thick. They show us that the Caledonian trough was in some epochs studded with submarine or aerial volcanoes, forming archipelagos similar to the present day Islands of Japan.

4. Shelly facies, more or less calcareous. These are the coastal facies of the littoral platforms. Here are found the finest fossil beds, where limestone-building coelenterates are mixed with brachiopods and trilobites. There are practically no graptolites. These formations are generally not thick and correspond to zones where the base remained relatively stable or affected only by variable movements that had little effect.

C. *Stage Nomenclature*

The first division into stages was established in southeast Wales and in Shropshire. The facies there are very littoral and varied, so that a series of clearly individualized lithological formations appears. Each formation then became the basis for a stage, usually designated by the same place name as the forma-

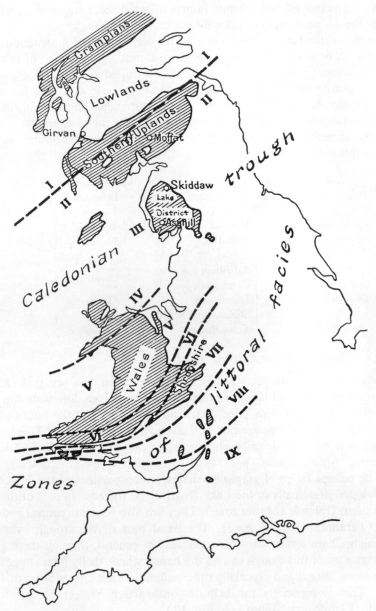

FIG. 15. *Diagrammatic map of the British Caledonian massifs.*

Ruled: Pre-Silurian and Silurian formations.
Blank: Post-Silurian formations.
         Roman numerals indicate the zones of Silurian facies (especially Upper
         Silurian) corresponding to those shown in the table, Fig. 16.

tion. Rich brachiopod and trilobite faunas allowed these stages to be followed through the whole domain of littoral facies.

Then in Scotland and in the Lake District very thick and monotonous series of the Flysch or graptolitic shale types were found. A succession of numerous graptolite zones[11] was established here, also grouped in stages. The precision and wide distribution of these zones has led to their use as a basis for classification. Finally, harmony between the deep-water stages and the littoral stages has been established in the regions where these two facies alternate.

Finally, therefore, the correlation between the two nomenclatures is established as follows:

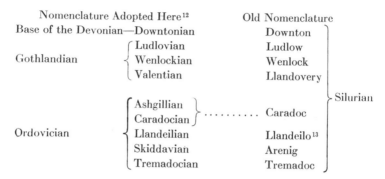

D. *General Distribution of Facies*

If we seek to distribute these facies in natural areas, we see that they are grouped in great parallel bands, in the whole assemblage, following the direction of the Caledonian folds (Fig. 15). Thus the history of the future chain is already expressed in the geography of the sea where it will rise.[14] This is a concordance that we shall describe elsewhere for the Hercynian Chain (p. 187) and for the Alpine Chain (p. 351).

1. The pelagic facies of graptolite shales or geosynclines of the Flysch type are developed principally in the Lake District and the eastern part of the Scottish Southern Uplands (Moffat zone). They are also found in central and north Wales (Tarannon-Conway zone). The axial part of the trough, where the Caledonian Chain arose, must have passed, in general, through these points.

2. Southeast of this trough extend the bands where shelly facies appear, becoming more littoral and especially differentiated in the Upper Silurian (O. T. Jones). This is especially the belt of southeastern Wales: Haverfordwest, Llandeilo, Llandovery, Builth (see Fig. 17).

3. Farther southeast comes the zone of Shropshire. The principal outcrops are those of the regions of Ludlow, Downton and Wenlock, and the areas of Caradoc and Shelve, separated by the Longmynd Precambrian anticline. We shall connect to this the two isolated Silurian islets which appear near Birmingham, of which the best known is at Dudley.

4. Still more to the southeast, other isolated Silurian massifs are found on the north shore of the Bristol Channel; Woolhope, the Malvern Hills, May Hill, and Usk.

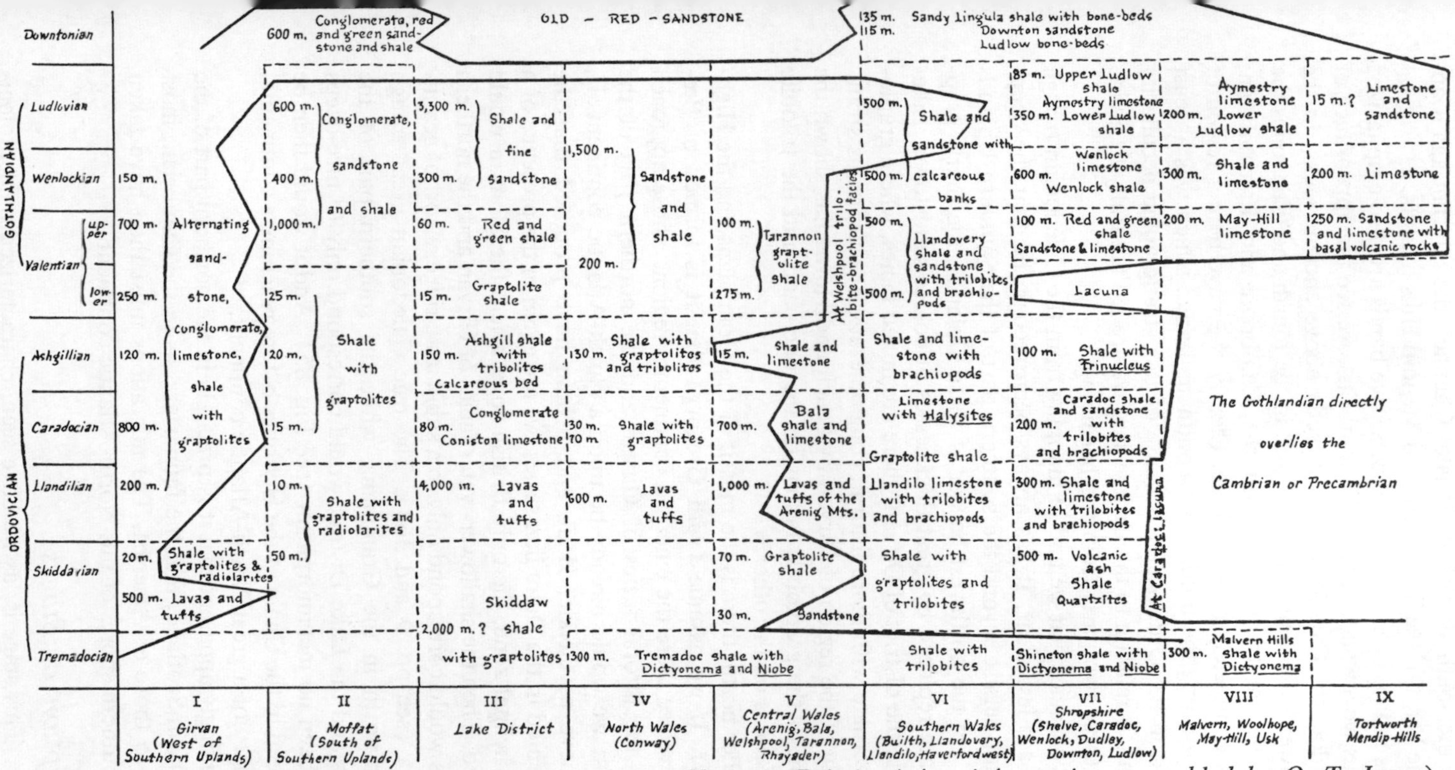

FIG. 16. *Diagram of Silurian facies in the Caledonian Chain in Britain (after information assembled by O. T. Jones).*

The two heavy lines separate the littoral marine facies from the abyssal pelagic facies on one side and from the purely continental facies on the other side; this separation is of necessity very diagrammatic.

Compare with the maps, Figs. 15 and 17, for the location of the zones designated by roman numerals I–IX.

This diagram shows that after the very extensive sea of the Cambrian-Tremadocian, the abyssal graptolite facies were localized in the Caledonian trough between southern Scotland and northern Wales. Notice the thinness of graptolite pelagic sediments compared to the thickness of the contemporaneous sandy-shaly beds of Flysch facies. This trough was bordered by continental platforms with littoral facies and lacunas (Gothlandian transgression toward the southeast).

In the upper Ludlovian the graptolite facies have disappeared, the trough is filled up and the Caledonian folds add it to the Old Red Sandstone continent. Lagoonal-marine transition beds (Downtonian) are preserved, especially on the site of the two basins (Scottish and Welsh) where the continental sedimentation of the Old Red Sandstone was concentrated.

79

5. Finally, on the south side of the Bristol Channel, the Silurian again appears, forming the heart of the Tortworth and Mendip Hills massifs.

The differences in facies between these successive bands are also emphasized by the fact that, as we advance toward the southeast, we see the appearance of lacunas. At Caradoc, the Caradocian lies directly above ancient rocks; in the third zone, the lower Valentian is missing, and in the fourth and fifth zones the upper Valentian lies in transgression on the Cambrian and Precambrian; the Ordovician is completely missing there. Clearly, we have here a region of littoral platforms forming the border of a continental area, which was at least partially emergent in the Ordovician. Because of this stratigraphic peculiarity of the Gothlandian in relation to the Ordovician, we are led naturally to divide the Silurian into these two parts from the beginning.

The variations of facies that we find in mapping from the Caledonian trough to the northwest are less clear. It has always been recognized that the deep-water facies do not persist beyond the southern part of the Southern Uplands (Moffat region). On the northwest border of these Uplands, the marly graptolitic sediments are replaced by great thicknesses of coarse sandstones. Likewise in the west, in the district of Girvan, there are mixed facies, where graptolitic sediments alternate with more littoral, conglomeratic or calcareous strata. The detailed study of the region of Girvan by Peach and Horne has shown the exact synchronism of the graptolitic faunas on the one hand and the trilobite and brachiopod faunas on the other.

Then, still further north, there is the massif of the Grampians and the Highlands (see p. 36). If we assume (with Gregory) that it is formed of Precambrian rocks, we see there the emerged continental region, whose approach was indicated by the littoral facies of Girvan and the northern part of the Southern Uplands: we would already be upon a North-Atlantic continent. If, however, we believe as Geikie, Haug and Frödin have proposed that the Silurian is represented in the Dalradian series, we are again in the presence of a Caledonian geosynclinal zone, the only British zone where the Silurian would be metamorphosed. Then the shallower-water facies of Girvan and the northern Southern Uplands would correspond only to a submarine ridge, a sort of geanticline or cordillera (see pp. 9 and 364). The true Caledonian great trough would lie further north in the Grampians, while the southern part of the Southern Uplands and the Lake District would correspond only to fore-deeps where there had been no metamorphism (see Fig. 85). And it would then be necessary to proceed to the Chain of the Hebrides before reaching a continental region, the boundary of a great North-Atlantic continent.

In fact, it is strikingly apparent that it is precisely in the northern part of the Caledonian trough, in Scotland, that the faunas are, as in the Cambrian, most markedly similar to those of America. The migrations must then have taken place along the southern shores of this North-Atlantic continent.

E. *Description of Stages*

1. Tremadocian. This stage is, as we have seen, characterized paleontologically by the appearance of the first graptolites, the *Dictyonema,* and certain

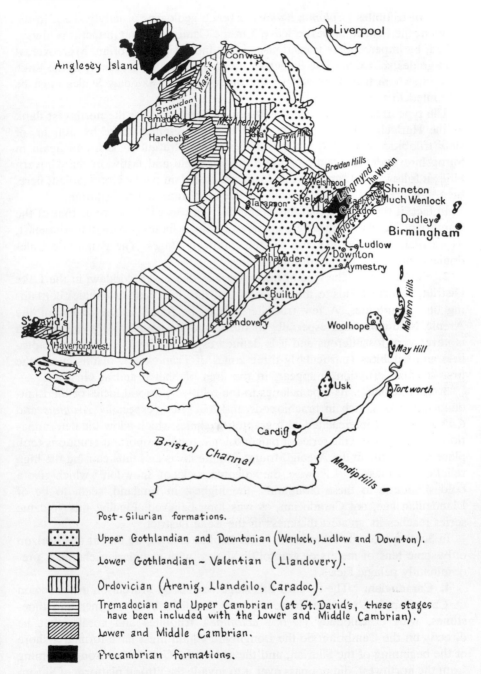

FIG. 17. *Geologic map of the Caledonian Massif of Wales (after Jones, Fearnside, and the maps of the Geological Survey).*

genera of trilobites (*Euloma, Niobe*). French geologists usually place it in the Silurian; the British, however, leave it in the Cambrian. And in fact it is always linked, by imperceptible transitions, to the underlying Cambrian. Moreover, it even grades sometimes into higher strata of the Silurian, especially in the Lake District, where the lower part of the thick series of Skiddaw Shales must be attributed to the Tremadoc.

The type area for the stage was taken at Tremadoc, on the northwest flank of the Harlech anticline (see p. 53). It is represented there by 300 m. of slaty trilobitic shales and a clayey *Dictyonema* stratum. It is found again in Shropshire under the name of the Shineton shale and lastly, in the Malvern Hills, it follows the Cambrian and is directly overlain by the Gothlandian; here, then, it is attached stratigraphically to the Cambrian, not the Silurian.

In fact, it seems clear that the Tremadoc sea was as extensive as that of the Cambrian. Nowhere have we evidence of shores limiting it on the southeast, as we shall see to be the case for the following stages. The graptolitic Caledonian trough was not yet distinguishable.

2. Skiddavian. The type of this stage was chosen at Skiddaw, in the Lake District; it corresponds to the upper part of the thick Skiddaw shales containing only graptolites. A few trilobites are to be found in the region of the Arenig Mountains and especially in the Llandeilo country. But this horizon is never very fossiliferous and it is defined especially by its species of graptolites and trilobites (particularly three zones of *Trinucleus*). In this epoch the first volcanic eruptions[15] appear, in the area of Shelve and at Girvan.

3. Llandeilian. Its type belongs to the relatively littoral facies of the Llandeilo limestones, rich in brachiopods and trilobites (especially *Asaphus* and *Calymene*), but intercalated with graptolitic shales which allow the determination of their place in the series of paleontologic zones. Important eruptions took place at this time in the Arenig Mountains, the lavas and tuffs causing the high relief of this massif.[16] Likewise, the volcanic rocks of Snowdon[17] which give a bold silhouette to these mountains, the highest in England, seem to be of Llandeilian age, not Caradocian, as was long believed. Finally, this volcanic series reaches its greatest thickness in the Lake District.

In Scotland, on the other hand, in the Moffat district, we find at this horizon only some tens of meters of graptolitic shales, with radiolarian cherts, a predominantly pelagic facies.

4. Caradocian. The type for this stage was set by Murchison in the region of Caer Caradoc,[18] where there are very fossiliferous sandstones and limestones, with brachiopods (*Orthis actoniae*) trilobites and corals, that lie directly on the Cambrian. So the Longmynd Chain must have formed a shore at the beginning of the Silurian, and the sea of the Caledonian trough, coming from the northwest, did not pass over it to invade the littoral platform of Shropshire until the Caradocian (Fig. 18).

But farther west, we find deeper-water facies. In southern Wales and at Bala,[19] there are thick graptolitic shales with still some limestone intercalations, for example, the very fossiliferous Bala limestone, from which comes the name

Bala series, sometimes given to this stage. Lastly, at Conway[20] and at Moffat in Scotland, only thin beds of graptolitic shales remain. But at Girvan, the facies again become littoral, the sediments thick and varied.

5. Ashgillian. This stage was established for the Ashgill shales (in the Lake District) which contain a rather special trilobite fauna (genera *Cheirurus, Lichas, Encrinurus*).[21] Graptolites found here indicate almost everywhere equivalence to beds formerly assigned to the Caradoc.

6. Valentian.[22] Valentia was an old province of southern Scotland; this name calls to mind black graptolitic shales, not thick, which are also found in the Lake District where 14 paleontologic zones can be distinguished.

The corresponding strata in Central Wales are the Tarannon shales (which

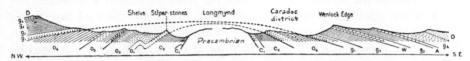

FIG. 18. *Semi-diagrammatic section across Shropshire (compare with map, Fig. 17), showing the variations of the Silurian facies (Caradocian transgressive east of Longmynd, Gothlandian limestones of the east lost in the shales of the west), and the discordance of the Gothlandian on the Ordovician formations (after Lapworth and Watts, generalized).*

Devonian	D = Downtonian and Old Red Sandstone.
Gothlandian	g_4 = Upper Ludlovian: upper Ludlow shales and sandstones.
	g_3 = Lower Ludlovian: lower Ludlow shales (A = Aymestry limestone).
	g_2 = Wenlockian: Wenlock shales (W = Wenlock limestone).
	g_1 = Upper Valentian: upper Llandovery conglomerates, sandstones, and limestones.
Ordovician	o_4 = Caradocian: Caradoc sandstones and shales with *Trinucleus*.
	o_3 = Llandeilian: shales and limestones.
	o_2 = Upper Skiddavian: shales and sandstones of the upper Arenig.
	o_1 = Lower Skiddavian: basal sandstone of the Arenig (Stiper quartzites).
Cambrian	c_2 = Tremadocian and Upper Cambrian: Shineton shales.
	c_1 = Middle and Lower Cambrian: sandstones.

sometimes serve to name the upper part of the stage). These shales are very thick, yet contain very few graptolites.

Beyond Welshpool the shelly facies appear. And it is these which are found in the shales and sandstones of Llandovery,[23] the old name given to the very fossiliferous stage (*Pentamerus,* corals) all along the border of southern Wales as far as Haverfordwest.

Farther southeast, the lower part of the stage is missing, so that in Shropshire the Valentian lies discordantly on the Ordovician, and then in the Malvern Hills, at May Hill and at Tortworth, on the Cambrian and Precambrian. This stratigraphic independence, which shows clearly in the table (Fig. 16), was, as we have said, the starting point for the break established between Ordovician and the Gothlandian.

7. Wenlockian and Ludlovian.

a. *Type-Facies, littoral.* The classic development of these stages is observed at Wenlock, on the eastern edge of the Welsh Massif: the facies there are called calcareous though in reality they are composed of an alternation of shales and massive calcareous layers, respectively translated in the topography as monoclinal "combes" (little valleys) and calcareous ridges. Such is the Wenlock Edge (or Wenlock scarp, see Figs. 17 and 18), which runs parallel to the southeast border of the Longmynd anticline;[24] such also are the calcareous ridges which, like arcs, surround the isolated massifs of Woolhope and May Hill.

The series begins there with the Woolhope limestone, quite localized, ending in shales at the northwest; then come the Wenlock shales, with numerous brachiopods, trilobites and *Cardiola interrupta*. Above, the Wenlock limestone, the most important and most continuous horizon, is celebrated for the beauty of its fossils, especially in the little exposure at Dudley (Dudley limestone),[25] which has enriched collections all over the world (trilobites, tabulata, etc.). In particular, the *Calymene blumenbachi* are so numerous that they are popularly called "Dudley crickets (locusts)" and have become a kind of local coat of arms.[26] In the most laminated or best stratified zones of this Wenlock limestone, we find, from place to place, lenses of varying size (from 3 to 15 m. long, from 2 to 6 m. thick) of compact, unstratified limestone called "crog-balls," "self-lumps," "ballstones"; these are miniature-reefs born of the luxuriant development on the muddy bottom of calcareous reef organisms growing around an initial solid support.

The Ludlovian at the base includes the lower Ludlow shales in which appear, together with marine faunas, the first fragments of eurypterids (see p. 107). Finally, there is a last calcareous band, the Aymestry limestone, at the top of which are some shaly banks containing the last graptolites. And in the upper Ludlow shales, already a little sandy, there is scarcely anything but trilobites and brachiopods remaining.

b. *Graptolite Facies.* These are developed in Central and North Wales, and especially in the Lake District, where the two stages reach a thickness of 4,000 m. They are extremely monotonous shales where only graptolite faunas make subdivision possible.[27] Six zones are distinguished in the Wenlockian, five in the Ludlovian. Moreover, the upper Ludlovian, always more littoral, contains no graptolites; it is the end of the history of the Caledonian trough (see Fig. 16).

To show more clearly the homogeneity of these graptolitic facies and the important break caused by their disappearance, many authors combine the Wenlockian and the lower Ludlovian in a single stage, Salopian,[28] the top of which, by definition, corresponds to the last graptolitic faunas; the upper Ludlovian is then combined with the Downton (s. l.), to form a Downtonian still belonging to the Silurian: such for example is the classification adopted by O. T. Jones, in 1917, in the work "The British Isles."[29]

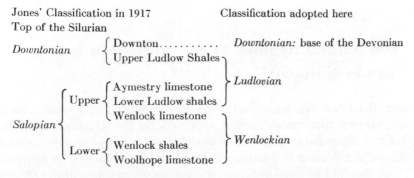

F. *Conclusions*

This stratigraphic history of the Caledonian Chain suggests instructive comparisons with that of the Alpine Chain (to be studied later). The Secondary and lower Tertiary of the Alps corresponds to the Silurian of England. The Alpine fore-deep, with its great accumulations of Secondary shales and its Tertiary Flysch, is similar to the Caledonian graptolitic trough. The pelagic Caledonian graptolites play exactly the same rôle in stratigraphic syntheses as the ammonites play in the Alps. The littoral calcareous facies bordering the Caledonian trough represent the sub-Alpine and Jura facies bordering the Alps (the Wenlock Edge is comparable to the sub-Alpine scarp, see Fig. 93), and their synchronism with the deep facies, shales or Flysch, poses analogous problems in the two chains.[30]

It will suffice to compare the tables on pages 79 and 120, to see the similarities between the Caledonian and Hercynian Chains. The history of the Devonian in the Ardennes, at the north margin of the Hercynian Chain, is revealed as analogous to the Silurian history of the southeast margin of Wales. To the Condroz zone, which was the shore of the lower Devonian sea and was overflowed by the transgressive sea of the middle Devonian, should be compared the Longmynd Massif, bordered by the Carodocian sea.

The paleogeographic units which this analysis of the English Silurian, that is, the Caledonian Trough and its margins in Shropshire, has permitted us to define, still seem to us as only details in the face of Europe in the Silurian. Already, however, Britain gives us glimpses of other units. While the upper Silurian is always littoral or missing east of Shropshire (central counties), deep wells in the extreme southeast of the island (Chilham, Kent, northwest of Folkstone) have disclosed a pelagic Gothlandian, represented by graptolite shales. There, then, is the beginning of another domain which we shall see extended into the Rhenish massifs, though for the present we are satisfied with a synthetic study which only suggests the place of British Silurian paleogeography in a more general European setting.

IV. The Natural Regions of the Silurian in Europe (and in Morocco) [31]

Between the Cambrian and Silurian no important chain of mountains was formed; no new continental domain appeared. So the structural features on which Cambrian paleogeography was modeled will continue to serve as starting points, and the Silurian will have, on the whole, facies analogous to those of the Cambrian. Still we need not study the border of the Chain of the Hebrides, since only Cambrian (Durness band) and no Silurian is found there.[32]

So we shall find as in the Cambrian:

1. A *border zone of the Baltic Shield* (Scandinavia and the Baltic countries).

2. A *geosynclinal zone of Northern Europe,* with a northern branch (Scandinavian Mountains, Anglo-Caledonian Massifs) and a southern branch (Rhenish Massif, Harz, Thuringia, Saxony, Poland).

3. A *Middle European zone* (Brittany and Bohemia).

4. A *Mediterranean geosynclinal zone* (Montagne-Noire, Pyrenees, Spain, Carnic Alps, Sardinia, Morocco, etc.).

I. *Border Zone of the Baltic Shield*

The variations of the Silurian facies are here entirely classic; as we cannot describe them in detail, we must be satisfied with the following suggestions concerning the diverse regions named on the map (Fig. 9).

In a general way, we shall find here facies becoming proportionally more littoral (more calcareous) as we more nearly approach the central region of the Shield, that is, near Finland.

A. Ordovician.

1. *Littoral calcareous facies.* This facies is developed in the eastern part of the Silurian band of Jämtland, in Dalecarlia, in Västergötland and Ostergötland and the Island of Oeland. No Ordovician is found in Gothland but it is found with its calcareous facies in Esthonia as far as Lake Ladoga; of all these regions, the most classic are Västergötland and Esthonia.

In these facies, the Tremadocian, beginning with conglomerates and sandstones with *Obolus,* sometimes directly transgressive on the Precambrian (see p. 51 and Fig. 10), is fully characterized by a bed of *Dictyonema* shales several meters thick, overlain by limestones or sandstones with *Ceratopyge* (*Euloma-Niobe* fauna), though sometimes the calcareous or sandy facies usurp the whole stage.

The orthocerid limestones which constitute the most important member of the Ordovician (40–50 m. thick) correspond to the Skiddavian and Llandeilian. In spite of their richness in nautiloids, these are not deep-sea formations. They are also called vaginate limestones, a name suggesting the orthocerids (*Endoceras*) of the vaginate group, or even *Asaphus* beds, because of the abundance of this genus of trilobite.

The top of these limestones corresponds approximately to the Caradocian. In the lower part we can distinguish the cystid limestone or echinospherite limestone, with the classic species *Echinosphaerites aurantium,*[33] and in the upper part, the *Chasmops macrurus* limestone (trilobite). In these alternating calcareous complexes, at Kuckers in Esthonia,[34] there is a bed of bituminous shale (kuckersite), from which important quantities of hydrocarbons are obtained by distillation.[35]

Finally, the Ashgillian is represented by the *Trinucleus* shales and the brachiopod shales, about 30 m. thick. But in Dalecarlia even these upper beds become calcareous.

2. *Shaly, pelagic facies.* This facies is especially clear in Scania; from there it extends into the Oslo Basin, where it passes by intercalations into the calcareous facies. It is the same in the west part of Jämtland.

It is a monotonous series of black shales, a continuation of the alum-bearing shales of the Cambrian, in which the horizons (14 zones) can only be distinguished by graptolites. Despite the notably pelagic facies, it is not thick, 200 to 400 m. at the most. The beds are naturally little folded; in this sense, this is not a geosynclinal type.

B. Gothlandian. The limits of distribution of the two types, pelagic and coastal, are not the same as in the Ordovician. At the beginning of the Gothlandian, the shaly facies seem to have invaded several domains (Dalecarlia, Väster– and Ostergötland) which in the Ordovician belonged to calcareous facies.

1. The *graptolite shale facies* is usually typically realized in Scania: Moberg distinguished there 16 graptolite zones (200 to 300 m.). The upper beds, where *Cardiola interrupta* is associated with *Monograptus colonus,* are sometimes called *Cardiola* shales (800 m.). Then come 100 m. of the Downtonian type of sandstones, which we classify as Devonian.

In the Oslo Basin, as in the Ordovician, a sort of composite type is found, where in beds of 400 to 600 m. graptolite shales alternate with brachiopod or even coral limestones. The same is true in the western part of the Jämtland band, where pentamerid, coral, and crinoidal limestones are covered with graptolite shales.

In Västergötland, Ostergötland and Dalecarlia, the Ordovician limestones are overlain by 100 m. of graptolite shales, which correspond only to the base of the Scania shales. Immediately above come sandstones of the Downton type. The emergence must have begun much sooner there than in Scania, which is natural since it is nearer to the center of the Shield.

2. The *typical calcareous facies* is represented in Esthonia and Gothland, from which the stage name is derived. There are magnificent coral reefs there, but the details of the stratigraphy are much disputed. In Esthonia absolutely identical facies are found, with lacunas; thus all the lower Llandovery is missing. At the top are found beds with eurypterid and placoderms alternating

with strata containing a clearly marine fauna; it is possible that the Downtonian facies began in the Silurian.

C. Conclusions. For the whole period we can summarize these facts as follows:

1. The shaly, pelagic facies are exclusively predominant in Scania.

2. The regions of Jämtland and Lakes Vänern and Vätern show a composite facies.

3. Littoral, calcareous facies predominate in Dalecarlia and especially in Gothland and Esthonia.

It is scarcely necessary to note the analogy between this series of facies and that which we described in Britain. Scania corresponds to the Lake District, Esthonia and Gothland to Shropshire. But this analogy is not complete, for all this Baltic Silurian is deposited around a relatively stable rigid mass and has not since been folded; we are there outside of the Northern European geosyncline, which we shall now take up.

2. *Northern European Geosyncline*

A. Northern Branch.

1. *The Scandinavian Mountains.* The stratigraphy of the Scandinavian mountains is still the subject of discussion. This whole chain is, in fact, made up of very thick, much folded, frequently metamorphosed formations.

We are sure that the Cambrian is represented in it and also the Silurian.

In 1882, Reusch noted in mica schists near Bergen some Silurian fossils: trilobites, graptolites, *Halysites*. This discovery was of great historical importance for it proved that crystalline schists were not of necessity Archean. Later, in complexes of more or less metamorphosed formations that crop out over great areas east of the Trondhjem Fjord (the region called the Trondhjem syncline), badly preserved fossils (brachiopods, cephalopods, gastropods, crinoids, trilobites, graptolites) were found indicating the upper Ordovician and Gothlandian. Finally, farther north in the vicinity of Sulitjelma, banks of Silurian crinoidal limestone appeared in a complex of schists injected by granites and gabbros.

This Silurian of the Scandinavian Mountains resembles nothing that we have described at the eastern base of the chain, in Jämtland, on the border of the Baltic Shield. It corresponds to what the Scandinavian geologists call the west facies of their Silurian (= Cambrian plus Silurian), which contrasts with the eastern facies developed especially east of the eastern boundary of the chain (see Fig. 9). Nowhere do we find a clearer contrast between a geosynclinal (western) type and an area of continental (eastern) type.

The contrast between these two types is still more accented by the absence of the usual transition zones. For the contact of the two zones, where they meet, is not a normal contact, but rather a thrust surface. The contents of the Scandinavian geosyncline are overturned upon the border of the Baltic Shield (its fore-land) so that displaced fragments of the Cambro-Silurian west facies lie on top of the Cambro-Silurian east facies.[36]

The Scandinavian geologists agree on the facts that we have presented. But

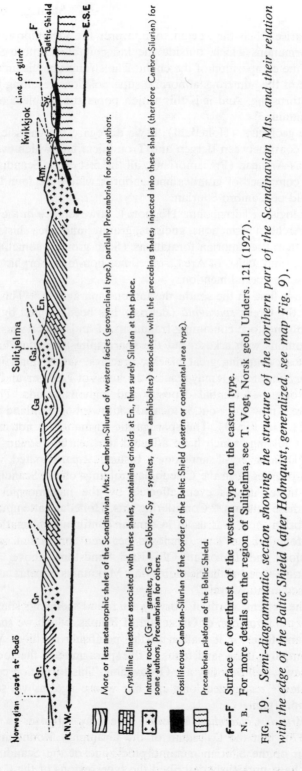

More or less metamorphic shales of the Scandinavian Mts.: Cambrian-Silurian of western facies (geosynclinal type), partially Precambrian for some authors.

Crystalline limestones associated with these shales, containing crinoids at En, thus surely Silurian at that place.

Intrusive rocks (Gr = granites, Ga = Gabbros, Sy = syenites, Am = amphibolites) associated with the preceding shales; injected into these shales (therefore Cambro-Silurian) for some authors, Precambrian for others.

Fossilliferous Cambrian-Silurian of the border of the Baltic Shield (eastern or continental-area type).

Precambrian platform of the Baltic Shield.

f—F   Surface of overthrust of the western type on the eastern type.

N. B.   For more details on the region of Sulitjelma, see T. Vogt, Norsk geol. Unders. 121 (1927).

FIG. 19.   Semi-diagrammatic section showing the structure of the northern part of the Scandinavian Mts. and their relation with the edge of the Baltic Shield (after Holmquist, generalized, see map Fig. 9).

89

differences arise when they begin to interpret the metamorphic or non-fossiliferous formations which, outside the indisputable Cambro-Silurian, enter
largely into the composition of the chain. The stratigraphy is indeed very difficult because of the numerous abnormal superpositions resulting from the phenomena of thrusting. And it is this which poses the problem of the Scandinavian Mountains.[37]

For some geologists (Holtedahl), if we disregard the gneissic massif which
borders the coast between Bergen and Trondhjem and which everyone agrees
to consider as Archean (Precambrian), all the rest of the Scandinavian Mountains, there composed of granites and gabbros which are found in the thrust
blocks, would be Cambro-Silurian.

Other geologists (Törnebohm, Högbom), however, see in the Scandinavian
Mountains Archean formations, gneisses, granites and mica shists, quite widely
distributed, then Precambrian formations (Seve group), sometimes metamorphic (gneisses and schists of Are), sometimes non-metamorphic. Among these
last, two deserve special mention:

1st. There is first, in the south, the famous sparagmite.[38] This name, which
comes from the Greek *sparagma* (debris), has been applied by Scandinavian
geologists to sandstone containing fragments of feldspar crystals. It is thus almost synonomous with arkose; but the sparagmite formation has in addition
conglomerates containing great blocks, breccias, sandy quartzites, and even
beds of clayey limestone. It may reach a thickness of 1,500 m. and is probably of
continental origin—torrential deposits and lagoonal muds. The sparagmite
region, where it now crops out, is located southwest of Jämtland and northwest
of Dalecarlia (see Fig. 9). The sparagmitic formation is not involved in the
Precambrian foldings which have affected the nearby Jotnian sandstones of
Dalecarlia (Dala or Trysil sandstone). Instead, it participated, with the Cambrian which overlies it, in the Caledonian foldings of the Scandinavian mountains and, there, it was even affected by the metamorphism which accompanied these foldings.[39] Considering this, Holtedahl attempted to attach it
to the Cambrian; but, as is usual in similar continental formations, no fossils
have been found there. Thus, enclosed between continental sparagmite formations below and Devonian Old Red Sandstone above, the Cambro-
Silurian marine series of the Scandinavian Mountains appears as a clearly defined great sedimentary cycle.

2nd. In the extreme north of Norway are found sediments similar to sparagmite: this is the formation of Gaisa and of Raipas, which we shall simply call
Varanger sandstone for it makes up the peninsula north of Varangerfjord.
Högbom compares these sandstones to the sparagmite or the Jotnian;[40] Holtedahl,[41] however, believes they are Ordovician. This formation contains glacial
conglomerates,[42] recognized long ago but whose age, as we see it, remains
somewhat uncertain.

2. *The British Caledonian Massifs.* We may suppose, as we have indicated (p. 37), that the Dalradian of the Grampian Mountains represents a
prolongation of the Silurian metamorphic zone of the Scandinavian Mountains.[43] We have previously described the type regions of the Caledonian geo-

syncline in the Southern Uplands of Scotland, the Lake District and Wales.
This geosyncline certainly extended into Ireland, where Ordovician fossils are
recognized in a complex and much folded series.

Finally, we have shown that the southeastern zones of Wales, Shropshire
and the Central Counties mark the southern border of the Caledonian trough
and that these regions, distant extensions of the Baltic Shield, bound the
southern branch of the North European geosyncline.

B. Southern Branch.   The most western evidences of this may be seen in the
Gothlandian graptolite shales that have been found in the sub-soil of Kent, in
southeastern England (p. 85), by deep drilling.[44] Similar shales have been

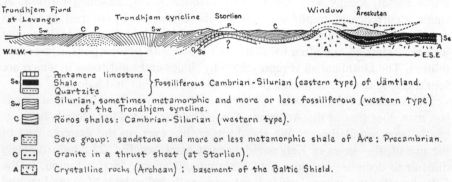

FIG. 20.   *Semi-diagrammatic section showing the structure of the Scandinavian Chain at the latitude of the Trondhjem syncline (after Högbom,
slightly simplified; see map, Fig. 9).*

N. B.   The interpretation of Högbom, given above, has recently been questioned.
Allowing first that P and G represent metamorphic facies (with granitic injections) of
the Cambrian-Silurian, then there is not necessarily a window at Storlien, which
would greatly reduce the length of the displacements. Frödin even thinks that the
mass of the Are shales forming the mountain of Areskutan is rooted and that the
series Se does not go beneath these shales: Areskutan would then be a structure with
fan-shaped roots and the thrusts would be reduced to unglued scales; at the same time
there would be, for the Cambrian-Silurian, a lateral or very rapid vertical transition
of the eastern, non-metamorphic type to the western type.

found not far away, in French wells at Caffier (Boulonnais), and at Liévin in
the Pas-de-Calais.

From there we join the known outcrops of Silurian in the Rhenish Massif,
Saxony, Thuringia and Poland (Lysa-Gora). The Silurian has common features in all these regions: it is of the geosynclinal type and is concordant with
the Cambrian, from which it is not easily separated. On the other hand, it is
discordant with the Devonian (except in Lysa-Gora, the only place where
there was at that period a tendency to emergence).

However, none of these regions is classic and we shall not insist upon this
point.

In the *Ardennes,* the Silurian contributes, with the Cambrian, to the framework of ancient massifs, called Cambro-Silurian, fragments of the Caledonian
Chain which we shall enumerate later (p. 115 and Fig. 23). But the detailed

stratigraphy is very difficult, because of tectonic complications, rarity of fossils, and uniformity of facies.[45]

The Tremadocian, called Salmian by Belgian geologists, is made up of very thick, variegated phyllites which, around Vieilsalm (Stavelot Massif), are well dated by *Dictyonema flabelliforme*. An obolid (*Lingulella*) is also found there. Beds of similar facies exist in the Rocroy Massif (where *D. flabelliforme* has been mentioned near Deville) and in Brabant (where the same fossil has just been discovered).[46]

The following stages are recognized only in Brabant and in the Silurian zone of Condroz (or Sambre-et-Meuse band). The Arenig[47] is represented by graptolitic shales, locally very fossiliferous (*Homalonotus, Illaenus, Orthis*). A single occurrence of graptolites indicates the Llandeilo. In contrast, the Caradoc, beginning sometimes (as in Shropshire) with a slight discordance[48] is quite well characterized and often fossiliferous (*Trinucleus,* brachiopods, some graptolites). The Gothlandian is represented by shales and sandstones in which are found graptolites characteristic of the English Valentian and Salopian.

The Silurian of the *Rhenish Schiefergebirge* deserves the designation classic less than does that of the Ardennes. Some Ordovician trilobite fossils have recently been found there.[49] We should note, however, in the extreme east of the massif, the series of Kellerwald (near Cassel, see Fig. 28) unfortunately difficult to decipher because of tectonic complications. In this region, in the Gilsa limestones (upper Gothlandian) apparently below beds of graptolites and so probably Silurian, there have been discovered poorly preserved and doubtful remains of the oldest ammonoids known (*Agoniatites?*).

In the *Harz,* the very complicated and much discussed tectonics (Kosmatt has described the thrust nappes, see p. 128) has given rise to various stratigraphic mistakes.[50]

Thuringia gives the most complete series of the German Silurian. Contrary to the beliefs of some geologists, the Ordovician does not seem to be transgressive, for the *Euloma-Niobe* zone has been found as far as the southern part of Thuringia. Consequently there is still no lacuna between the Cambrian and the Silurian, as we shall see further south in Bohemia. At the top of the Thuringian Tremadoc, represented by sandy quartzites with *Obolus,* begin[51] the facies of shale or sandstone with phycodes, so named after questionable impressions. The upper part of the quartzites with phycodes and the base of the Griffelschiefer (shales with minute cylindrical partings) which overlie them, correspond, according to Schmidt,[52] to the Arenig. This shaly, graptolite facies continues in the Llandeilo. It is momentarily interrupted in the Caradoc by more detrital beds with *Echinosphaerites*. Likewise the usual facies of the graptolite alum-bearing shales of the Gothlandian contains an intercalation of ochreous limestone (Ockerkalk) with *Orthoceras*.

In the *Polish Central Massif* (Lysa Gora, see p. 55) a somewhat similar series is found. The early publications by Gürich and the more recent ones of Czarnocki and Samsonowicz (Bull. Surv. géol. Poland, 1923) have demonstrated there a Silurian passing to the Cambrian by beds whose fauna corresponds to the *Euloma* and *Niobe* horizon (Tremadocian). But very interestingly, the Ordovician shows here great similarity to that of the Baltic regions. *Asaphus* and *Endoceras vaginatum* limestones are found which correspond exactly to the vaginate limestones of Esthonia (Skiddavian and Llandeilian). They are overlain also by limestones with cystids (Caradocian). But the top of the Ordovician is missing and the Gothlandian, composed of graptolite shales, is transgressive and discordant on the Cambro-Silurian series; on the other hand, it sometimes grades into the marine Devonian through semi-lagoonal beds analogous to the Downtonian.

As we see, the Silurian of Lysa Gora, with its northern affinities, already reflects the distant influences of the Baltic Shield, playing the part of a continental platform.

Further southeast, in the high valley of the Dneister (Volhynia and Podolia),[53] the Silurian is found supported against the crystalline core of Podolia. This stratigraphy has long been uncertain. Above arkoses and motley shales (sometimes compared to the Leningrad blue clays of the Lower Cambrian), lies a fossiliferous Ordovician, very sandy, then a Gothlandian with limestone beds with corals and brachiopods.[54]

3. *The Middle European Zone*

Brittany and Bohemia are classified here.

The Silurian fauna is quite different here from that of northern Europe, and, according to Barrande, a Bohemian province[55] is often contrasted to a northern European province. This difference is particularly apparent in the benthonic animals that lived on the sea bottoms (trilobites, brachiopods, certain cephalopods), although paleontologic zones of pelagic graptolites similar to those in Scotland may be found in Bohemia. So it is difficult to say whether the separation of the two provinces was due to an emerged land or to a deep sea. We do not know just what happened in the intermediate regions of Cornwall (where only a few Silurian fossils have been found) and the southern part of the Rhenish Massif.

Moreover, this Bohemian fauna is found in the Mediterranean zone in southern Europe. But in Brittany and Bohemia, the outstanding fact is the discontinuity that exists between the Cambrian and Silurian, a discontinuity that defines our middle European zone.

a. The Armorican Massif. The Silurian is found in all the synclinal zones enumerated above (see p. 55) and this system, recognized with certainty by its lithologic facies or its fossils, sometimes occupies quite large areas. While anticlinal regions, made up of granitic or metamorphic rocks, have a monotonous relief and make a less fertile land, the synclinal zones, made up of successions of sandy, shaly, and limey beds very unevenly resistant to erosion, show a much more varied topography and a more fertile aspect (the Devonian and Carboniferous contribute to this in large part, as we shall see).

The *Breton Silurian* is composed, from bottom to top, of the following members, easily recognized in the classic May section (Fig. 21):

1. *The Armorican sandstones.* These lie transgressively on the oldest formations. Traces of animal (*Bilobites*) tracks are frequently detected but fos-

sils are very rare, a few *Lingula,* pelecypods and trilobites. They are compared with the Arenig, so there must have been a lacuna corresponding to the Tremadoc, in Brittany. Note, moreover, that the thickness of these sandstones diminishes from the north (500 m.) to the south (50 m.). In the south, they seem to be partially replaced by shaly facies where Peneau[56] has recently noted some graptolites of the lower Arenig[57] near Angers. These east-west bands of Armorican sandstones play a large part in the morphology, for they correspond to so many jutting and infertile ridges.

2. The *Shales of Angers.*   The following member is made up of very thick, fissile shales (200 to 500 m.), making well cultivated lowlands. These shales are exploited in numerous quarries around Angers and make excellent slates,

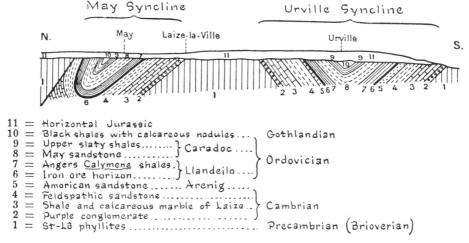

11 = Horizontal Jurassic
10 = Black shales with calcareous nodules... } Gothlandian
 9 = Upper slaty shales........} Caradoc....
 8 = May sandstone...........}
 7 = Angers Calymene shales.} } Ordovician
 6 = Iron ore horizon........} Llandeilo....}
 5 = Amorican sandstone....... Arenig.....
 4 = Feldspathic sandstone...................}
 3 = Shale and calcareous marble of Laize..} Cambrian
 2 = Purple conglomerate...................}
 1 = St-Lô phyllites .... Precambrian (Brioverian)

FIG. 21.   *Section of Precambrian, Cambrian and Silurian formations at May, near Caen (compare Fig. 11). Section about 15 kilometers long.*

N. B.   After a section by A. Bigot, modified according to more recent works by the same author. Notice the absence of Armorican sandstone in the May syncline, and the thinness of the same on the north flank of the Urville syncline. This section is intended especially to explain the stratigraphy of the region: actually the tectonics of the Urville syncline are much more complicated.

for they contain no lime. At the base are found the famous iron ores of Normandy, exploited especially south of Caen. These are sedimentary, oolithic ores, in regular beds, whose exploitation is easy, but whose iron content is small.

The shales of Angers contain many trilobites ("crayfish" of the workers) and are often called shales with *Calymene.* They represent the Llandeilo, for there are graptolites at their base indicating the extreme top of the Arenig.

3. *May sandstones.*   This is a second sandy formation, whose morphologic role is similar to that of the Armorican sandstones. They are also called Conularid sandstones, for they contain these fossils in abundance; *Homalonolus,* a trilobite characteristic of sandy facies, is also found there. In the midst of the sandstone is a shaly intercalation with the same trilobites (especially *Calymene*

tristani) as the shales of Angers. The lower May sandstones with this intercalation still belong to the Llandeilo; the Upper May sandstones are attributed to the Caradoc.

4. The *upper slaty shales.* This member, which ends the Ordovician, is not continuous. It is sometimes replaced by nonfossiliferous sandstones, continuing the May sandstone facies, or by limestones containing *Orthis actoniae,* a species characteristic of the Caradoc.

5. The *Gothlandian,* sometimes reaching a thickness of 500 m., generally begins with sandstones, but is especially represented by coaly black shales (ampelite) with graptolites (9 zones, according to Kerforne),[58] and contains, especially at the top, beds or nodules of limestones with *Cardiola interrupta* and orthocerids. This is the usual facies of this stage in most of Europe.

Such is the type-series of the Breton Silurian, a series long considered classic. There are, however, in the Armorican Massif, two regions where recent research has modified our ideas on the distribution of the Silurian. They are:

1. The Region of *Morlaix.* This is the eastern terminus of a great syncline coming from the roadstead of Brest, through Trégorrois. There, the recent work by P. Pruvost and his collaborators, verifying certain previous suggestions of Y. Milon, has shown (see work cited Chap. II, note 46) that formations previously attributed to the Silurian (for example, to the Armorican sandstones) or to the Brioverian should be associated with the Devonian (for example, with the Plougastel quartzites) or with the Dinantian. P. Pruvost has even been able to say that "the Silurian does not exist in Brittany north of a Brest-Dinan line." So the little Silurian syncline of Morlaix, which shows on old maps, has been replaced by the great Devono-Dinantian Brest-Morlaix syncline (see the schematic map, Fig. 11).

2. *The Vendée.* We already know (see p. 59) that in this vast area, where old maps place all the ancient Primary formations in the Brioverian, G. Mathieu was able to distinguish limited Cambro-Silurian synclines. The sandstones of La Châtaigneraie represent the Armorican sandstones and the shales of La Meilleraie correspond to the shales of Angers. The Ordovician age of the shales of La Meilleraie has been confirmed by the discovery of the little faunule cited on p. 59.

But nothing is known in the Vendée that can be likened to the Breton Gothlandian.

b. Bohemia. The Silurian of Bohemia[59] (see p. 60 and Fig. 28) is very fossiliferous and made famous by the fine studies of Barrande, who made of it his stages D (Ordovician) and E and F (Gothlandian), the Cambrian being represented by B and C.

We know already that there is a lacuna between the Cambrian and Silurian, since this last stage is everywhere transgressive, so it is not surprising to find that the Tremadoc shows a very irregular development and several successive transgressions, which have been studied in detail by R. Kettner.

The transgressive Ordovician[60] begins then with beds of conglomerates, shales with *Dictyonema,* and sandstones with linguloids representing the Tremadoc, at the top of which, in 1920, the characteristic *Euloma-Niobe* fauna was discovered. The Bohemian sea of the Tremadoc thus must have communicated with the Baltic Sea. Then come trilobite sandstones, alternating with graptolite shales; this is the Arenig. To the Llandeilo correspond trilobite and graptolite shales, then quartzites with *Dalmania socialis, Asaphus* and *Trinucleus goldfussi.* The Caradoc is shaly-sandy, always rich in trilobites, and it ends with quartzites. But a lacuna separates the Ordovician from the Gothlandian, so that there is a clear break, both lithologic and faunal, between these two stages.

The Gothlandian is composed particularly of graptolite shales with nodules or beds of limestone with *Cardiola interrupta* and orthocerids. Toward the top, the limestones predominate and become more littoral (crinoids). Finally, the Silurian ends with gray crystalline limestones containing an extremely rich and varied fauna, widely distributed in all collections: *Phacops,* calymenids, nautiloids, *Pentamerus knighti, Orthis, Strophomena rhomboidalis, Halysites,* and *Favosites.* Above come beds containing eurypterids of the Old Red Sandstone facies. But, remarkably, these beds are in their turn overlain by marine beds with a clearly Silurian fauna, containing, in particular, the last known graptolites (*Monograptus hercynicus*). So, unlike what takes place in the east, in Lysa Gora, the transition from the Silurian to the Devonian is made by marine beds. And thus there is perfect continuity between the two systems, whose boundary has been and still is much discussed.

Barrande had been greatly intrigued by noting, at certain points, beds with a Gothlandian fauna which seemed to him intercalated in massifs with an Ordovician fauna. He thus supposed that the Gothlandian fauna had first appeared locally in isolated colonies in the Ordovician, to become definitively prevalent only later, in the Gothlandian. It has since been found that these colonies were in reality masses of truly Gothlandian beds, appearing in the Ordovician due to faults or faulted folds.[61]

4. *Mediterranean Zone*

This composes all of Europe south of the Breton-Rhenish Massif-Bohemia zone. Many massifs of ancient rocks are found there, like the French Massif Central. But these rocks are in general metamorphic, non-fossiliferous and their age cannot be specified. So indisputable Silurian outcrops are rather rare and in general poorly known. We may cite the Montagne-Noire, the central and eastern Pyrenees, the coastal chain of Catalonia, different regions of the old Iberian Massif (Meseta), Algeria, Morocco and the littoral Algerian chains, the Eastern Alps (region of Salzburg and Carnic Alps), Sardinia, Isle of Elba, the Apuane Alps,[62] and the Balkans.

Special mention must be made of the Maures-Esterel Massif, extending along the Mediterranean coast between Toulon and Cannes. It is made up of quite varied rocks: small granitic massifs, gneisses, mica schists, shales and quartzites slightly metamorphic, recalling the Brioverian of Brittany. But recently, J. Schoeller[63] has discovered in it, at Chapelle du Mont-Fénouillet near Hyères (Var), in black shales with quartzitic beds, some graptolite remnants, their species indeterminable, but probably indicating the lower Gothlandian.

Similar discoveries are being made on the Algerian coast in the Primary Massif of Grande Kabylie (see Fig. 107), a large part of which is made up of crystalline schists[64] with some granitic spots. In the slightly metamorphic shaly complexes, two occurrences of Silurian fossils have just been discovered.

One is located on the north slope of Djurdjura, that is, near the south edge of the old massif. A. Lambert, H. and G. Termier (C. R. Acad. Sc., 226, 1948, p. 824) have recognized there a fauna of *Orthis actoniae* and cystids similar to that of the Caradoc of the Montagne-Noire. The other, which A. Barbier, H. and G. Termier (ibid., p. 1385) attribute to the Llanvirnian stage (intermediary between the Arenig and the Llandeilo, see note 12) was found, however, on the north edge of the same massif, near Tizi-Ouzou. It is possible then that a good part of these old shales are Silurian.

But it is only in the Eastern Alps, the Montagne-Noire, Sardinia and Morocco that a somewhat detailed stratigraphy can be made out. On the whole, the faunas are related to the Bohemian province rather than that of northern Europe. Finally, there is often an unbroken succession from Cambrian to Silurian and from Silurian to Devonian.

a. The Montagne-Noire.[65] The Silurian shows here a certain similarity to that of Brittany and Bohemia, but the Tremadoc is surely represented, for there is a continuous passage from the Cambrian. The fossils are numerous so that the parallelism with Wales can be made out without difficulty.

1. *Tremadoc.* It begins with green micaceous sandstone containing the trilobite genus *Euloma,* characteristic of this stage. Then come sandy shales and graywackes with *Orthis* and various trilobites.

2. *Arenig.*[66] Its base is composed of sandy shales with trilobites (*Miquelina miqueli*) and graptolites that identify the *Dictograptus* zone of the English lower Arenig. Above are sandstones with linguloids and *Bilobites,* long compared to the Armorican sandstones, but passing sometimes (near Cabrières) into *Didymograptus* shales. The facies called Boutoury shales and shale with *Calymene,* which also contain *Phyllograptus* should be placed here also. And another celebrated facies especially developed at the top of this middle Arenig is the "shales with cakes" so called because they contain calcareous nodules enclosing impressions left by giant trilobites (up to 50 cm.), represented in collections all over the world. They were formerly attributed to the genus *Asaphus,* but in reality they are great asaphids, belonging to different genera (*Niobe, Megalaspis,* etc.). According to their graptolites (*Phyllograptus* and *Didymograptus*) these "shales with cakes" extend no higher than the middle Arenig.[67]

3. *Llandeilo.* Contrary to what was believed for a time,[68] this stage does not exist in the Montagne-Noire, nor does the upper Arenig. Thoral has shown that there was a lacuna locally accompanied by folding (called Taconic), for the upper Ordovician or the Devonian lies discordantly on the middle Arenig.[69]

4. *Caradoc.* It begins with sandstones with *Trinucleus* (called Glauzy sand-

stones), quartzites, and arkoses indicating a transgression, as in Wales. Then come limestones rich in cystids and shales with *Orthis* (*Nicolella*) *actoniae,* a brachiopod characteristic of this stage, with graptolites of the English lower Caradocian.

5. *Gothlandian.* Here are found the usual facies of carbonaceous shales with graptolites (*Monograptus priodon*) with calcareous beds or nodules[70] with *Cardiola interrupta.* But the stage ends with very fossiliferous calcareous beds with *Slava bohemica* (a pelecypod) which are reminiscent in every way of the terminal Silurian beds of Bohemia. Naturally there is no longer the slightest trace of the Old Red Sandstone. As to the species of graptolites, recently studied, they range between the lower Llandovery and the middle Ludlovian.[71] The Downtonian seems to be missing.

b. The Carnic Alps.[72] The Cambrian is not found here at all and the oldest faunas date from the Caradocian, well represented by shales with brachiopods and cystids. The Gothlandian[73] shows a shaly facies with graptolites in which are found species characteristic of the Llandovery, Wenlock, and lower Ludlow of England, and a calcareous facies. At the top of these Gothlandian limestones with orthocerids with Silurian affinities some rare goniatites are associated, the oldest known (*Tornoceras inexpectatum, Beloceras, Anarcestes, Aphyllites*). Some authors would place these beds in the Devonian, but according to Gortani they are really still Gothlandian.

c. Sardinia. The Silurian, transgressive on a Cambrian previously folded and eroded, begins with shales in which the earliest faunas (*Trinucleus, Asaphus*) date from the Skiddavian and are followed by a Caradocian equally shaly and very fossiliferous (*Orthis actoniae*). The Gothlandian has its regular facies of shales with graptolites[74] (with species characteristic of the Llandovery and Wenlock) in which are intercalated very fossiliferous, calcareous lenses with *Orthoceras* and *Cardiola interrupta.* This Wenlock of Sardinia contains a special fauna of giant *Monograptus* which, curiously, are found in the Wenlock of the Basque Pyrenees and of Morocco.[75]

d. Morocco.[76] In the Moroccan Meseta, the western part of which has been carefully studied by G. Lecointre, and the central and eastern part by H. Termier, a thick series of shales, more or less micaceous or sandy, which has yielded fossils especially in the eastern region (*Trinucleus ornatus*), is assigned to the Ordovician. The Gothlandian, however, is everywhere very fossiliferous. It has its usual facies of shales with graptolites (characteristic species of all the English stages) with calcareous nodules with orthocerids and *Cardiola.*

The Djebilet show an analogous series, where shales which are probably Ordovician contain thin lenses of crinoidal limestone and are overlain by Gothlandian with graptolites (species of the Llandovery and base of the Wenlock).

The Silurian reappears in the High Atlas. It passes there into the Cambrian through a thick shaly series (the Cambro-Ordovician of Moroccan geologists) in which it is impossible to trace the boundary of the two systems, for the fossils (*Trinucleus* and conularids in the Primary massif of the Skouras country) (E. Roch) appear only at the top and clearly indicate an upper Ordovician age. There is likewise a progressive transition to the graptolite shales of the Gothlandian, long known here (L. Gentil).

In the Anti-Atlas, the Ordovician becomes a little sandier and shows characteristic trilobite faunas (*Acidaspis buchi, Illaenus, Trinucleus, Asaphus*).[77] There has even been noted recently the *Calymene tristani* of the shales of Angers.[78]

Far to the southeast, in the Tafilet, then in Ougarta (see Fig. 12), the approach of the Saharan Shield is evidenced by a series of sandy facies in the Ordovician, sometimes with oolitic iron ores (as in Normandy). The thick Ougarta sandstones (1,000 m.) seem surely to be Cambro-Silurian; quite recently, at the top, *Calymene tristani*[79] was discovered. But above, the Gothlandian preserves its pelagic facies of thick black shales with graptolites, always with limestone lenses with orthocerids and *Cardiola*.

Finally, we have already said (p. 64) that a similar series is found in the heart of the Sahara, where the crystalline schists of the Saharan Shield stand out in the Hoggar Mountains. In fact, around them, the lower Tassili sandstones (C. Kilian) overlain by Gothlandian[80] shales with graptolites should correspond to the Ougarta sandstones and like them be Cambro-Ordovician.

REFERENCE NOTES

1. On these questions, see: Ch. Barrois, P. Pruvost and C. Dubois, *Sur les couches de passage du Silurien au Dévonien dans le Bassin houiller du Pas-de-Calais,* C. R. Acad. Sc. (Nov. 11, 1918); M. LeRiche, *La limite entre le Silurien et le Dévonien,* Bull. Soc. belge Géol., t. 32, 1922, Brussels (1923); L. Dudley Stamp, "The Base of the Devonian, with Special Reference to the Welch Borderland," Geol. Mag., vol. 60, nos. 708–711, London (1923).

2. At the present time, many British geologists prefer not to use the term Gothlandian, which they deem not precise enough. They replace it by that of Silurian, used in a restricted sense. They distinguish, thus, in the lower part of the Primary, the three systems, Cambrian, Ordovician, and Silurian.

3. M. Lecompte, *Quelques types de "récifs" siluriens et dévoniens de l'Amérique du Nord: essai de comparaison avec les récifs coralliens actuels,* Bull. Mus. r. Hist. nat. Belgique, t. 14, no. 39 (1938).

4. A discussion on the depth significance of graptolitic muds will be found following a communication from W. R. B. King, "The Upper Ordovician Rocks of the Southwestern Berwyn Hills," Quarterly Jour. geol. Soc. 79 (1923). This problem has also been studied by L. Cayeux, *Le Gothlandien du sondage de Danneville (Calvados) et son milieu générateur,* Livre jubilaire du Centenaire de la Soc. géol. de France (1930).

5. R. Hundt, *Silurische Graptolitenmeere und rezente äquivalente; ein biologischer und morphologiscer Vergleich,* Geologie der Meer und Binnengewässer, Bd. 2, H. 3 (1938). The works of this author have sometimes been criticized, Neues Jahrb. f. Min., Ref., III (1941), p. 525.

6. For the determination of graptolites, refer to the two following works: G. Waterlot, *Les Graptolithes du Maroc; première partie: généralités sur les Graptolithes,* Serv. géol. Maroc, Notes et Mémoires, Mém. No. 63 (1945); R. Ruedemann, *Graptolites of North America,* Geol. Soc. America, Mem. 19 (1947), 652 p., 92 pl.

7. J. Chauvel, *Recherches sur les Cystoïdes et les Carpoïdes armoricains,* Mém. Soc. géol. et min. Bretagne, 4 (1941), 286 p., 101 fig., 7 pl.

8. Mlle. G. Delpey, *Les Bios des schistes à Calymènes,* C. R. somm. Soc. Biogéogr., no. 162–163 (1942).

9. J. Kowalski, *Les Conulaires; quelques observations sur leur structure anatomique,* Bull. Soc. Sc. nat. Ouest de la France, 5 sér., t. 5 (1935). H. and G. Termier, C. R. Soc. géol France, 1947, p. 337, compare them to the "Vermidiens."

10. B. Smith and T. Neville George, *North Wales,* British regional Geology, Geol. Surv., London (1935).

11. See Miss G. Elles, "The Graptolite Faunas of the British Isles," Proc. Geologists' Assoc., Vol. 33 (1922). Later, this same author made a list of the characteristic species of each zone in vol. 72 (1925) of the Geological Magazine. An excellent elementary survey is found in the manual, *Outlines of Paleontology,* of H. H. Swinnerton, London (1923). See also, R. Hundt, *Die Graptolithen des deutschen Silurs,* 18 plates, Max Weg, Leipzig (1924).

12. Note that the Ashgillian, based especially on rather poorly characteristic trilobite faunule (see p. 83) and on the grouping of two zones of graptolites, could without inconvenience be omitted and united with the Caradocian.

Moreover, note that British geologists now accept an intermediate stage between the Arenig and Llandeilo, Llanvirnian (from Llanvirn, near St. David's), grouping the two zones of graptolites which form respectively the top of the Arenig and the base of the Llandeilo.

13. Sometimes written "Llandilo."

14. See the very interesting paleogeographic maps illustrating the article of T. Jones, cited Note 17, Chap. II.

15. Already the Tremadocian in the vicinity of Harlech contains some ash and lavas.

16. For these volcanic rocks Sedgwick created the stage name Arenig; after him, it was extended to the fossiliferous (Skiddavian) formations below these rocks. Then the discovery of several graptolites in the series of tuffs showed that it belonged to the Llandeilo. So Sedgwick's true "Arenig" is in reality contemporary with the Llandeilo and for the Arenig of authors it is preferable to choose the name Skiddavian, which is unequivocal.

17. A. Howel Williams, "The Geology of Snowdon (North Wales)," Quart. Jour. geol. Soc. 83 (1927).

18. Caradoc is the name of a chief of the Silurian tribe which inhabited this country. (Caer: house). He fought the Romans, a Welch Vercingetorix.

19. See G. L. Elles, "The Bala Country, its Structure and Rock Succession," Quart. Jour. geol. Soc., 78 (1922).

20. A. Bryn Davies, "The Ordovician Rocks of the Trefriw District (North Wales)," Quart. Jor. geol. Soc. London, 92, 2, no. 365 (1936).

21. This fauna, with American affinities (see p. 80), lived in Scotland after the beginning of the Ordovician; it is only in the Ordovician that it spread throughout Britain, as far as Southern Wales.

22. See O. T. Jones, "The Valentian Series," Quart. Journ. geol. Soc. 77 (1921); "The Llandoverian Graptolite Succession in Britain," Bull. Mus. r. Hist. nat. Belgique, 23, no. 22 (1947).

23. O. T. Jones, "The Geology of the Llandovery District," Quart. Jour. geol. Soc., 81 (1925).

24. For a recent description of this classic region, see T. Das Gupta, "The Salopian Graptolite Shales of the Long Mountain and Similar Rocks of the Wenlock Edge," Proc. Geologists' Ass., 43 (1932).

25. A. J. Butler, "The Stratigraphy of the Wenlock Limestone of Dudley," Quart. Jour. geol. Soc. London, 95 (1939). R. W. Pocock and T. H. Whitehead, "Geology of the Country around Dudley," Mem. geol. Surv. and Mus. (1947)

26. Like the Ceratites of the Triassic in Wurtemberg or the present lavarets of Lake Annecy.

27. Miss G. L. Elles, "Upper Silurian Graptolite Zones," Geol. Magaz., 81, London (1944), p. 275.

28. Salop is a synonym of Shrop (Shropshire).

29. This work, part of a collection published in Germany under the name of *Handbuch der regionalen Geologie,* is now replaced by the two volumes mentioned in Note 23, Chap. I.

30. If we concede, as we have indicated above (p. 37), that the Dalradian series of the Scotch Highlands includes the metamorphic Silurian, we would have the equivalent of the great Alpine trough, where the Secondary and lower Tertiary are equally metamorphic (*schistes lustrés*), while the littoral facies of the Girvan zone (north of the Southern Uplands) would correspond to the Briançonnais Cordillera of the Alps, and the geosynclinal but not metamorphic facies of the southern part of the Southern Uplands, of the Lake District and of Northwest Wales, would represent the Alpine foredeep (see Fig. 85).

31. For the American Silurian, which we shall not discuss here, see the summary by E. O. Ulrich and R. S. Bassler, *American Silurian Formations,* Maryland Geol. Survey, Silurian (1923).

32. As noted (p. 52), it is always probable that the upper part of the Durness limestones belongs to the Tremadocian.

33. K. Orviku, *Die Rassenvariationen bei Echinosphaerites aurantium Gyll., und ihre stratigraphische Verbreitung im estnischen Ordovicium,* Publ. Inst. geol. Univ. Tartu, no. 8 (1927).

34. A. Opik, *Brachiopoda Protremata der estländischen ordovizischen Kukruse-Stufe,* ibid., no. 20 (1930), an article containing a general survey of the Ordovician of Esthonia.

35. K. Andrée, *Der estländische Brennschiefer, sein Vorkommen, seine Gewinnung und Verwendung,* Brennstoff-Chemie, Bd. 16, Essen (1935).

36. Study of the Jurassic of the French Alps will show similar facts, on one hand between the Dauphinois and Briançonnais facies of the Jurassic, and on the other hand, between these last and the *schistes lustrés*. We could even say that the nappe of the *schistes lustrés* in the Briançonnais seems a little like the thrusts of the Areskutan (see later) in the Scandinavian Mountains, and thus are the subject of similar discussions.

37. O. Holtedahl, "The Scandinavian 'Mountain Problem'," Quart. Jour. Geol. Soc., 76 (1921). G. Frödin, "On the Analogies Between the Scottish and Scandinavian Portions of the Caledonian Mountain Range," Bull. geol. Inst. Univ. Upsala, 18 (1922). G. Frödin, *Ueber die Geologie der zentralschwedischen Hochgebirge,* ibid.; this article contains a map and cuts of the classic region of the Areskutan thrusts (see Fig. 20). Finally, the important work of Von Bubnoff, *Geologie von Europa II,* Berlin (1930), in which these new ideas are explained in detail.

38. On the sparagmite, see work by O. Holtedahl, in the Norsk. geol. Tidssk., vol. 6, Oslo, 1920 (with an English summary). The same author has given a very valuable summary in the article cited note 11, Chap. II.

39. T. F. W. Barth, "Progressive Metamorphism of Sparagmites Rocks," Norsk. geol. Tidssk. 18 (1938).

40. In this interpretation, the Varanger sandstones become analogous to the Torridon sandstones. That is why it is sometimes supposed that the gneissic Lofoten region and the Varanger sandstone zone represent the extension of the Chain of the Hebrides, constituted of Lewisian gneiss and Torridon sandstones (see p. 35).

41. O. Holtedahl, "On the Paleozoic Formations of Finmarken," Amer. Jour. Sc. (1919).

42. See an article by O. Holtedahl in Amer. Jour. Sc. (1922).

43. This hypothesis was recently developed by Frödin in the article cited, note 37, this chap.

44. S. W. Wooldridge and D. L. Linton, "Some Episodes in the Structural Evolution of S. E. England Considered in Relation to the Concealed Boundary of Meso-Europa," Proc. Geologists' Ass., 49 (1938), part 3. This article, illustrated with numerous maps, contains a very interesting study of the Primary platform of S. E. England and its Jurassic and Cretaceous covering.

45. E. Maillieux, *Remarques sur l'Ordovicien de la Belgique,* Bull. Soc. belge de Géol., 36 (1926); *Remarques sur le Gothlandien de la Belgique* (id.). These articles contain a general revision of the Belgian Silurian faunas. See also Waterlot's study, note 21, Chap. II.

46. M. Lecompte, *Existence du Trémadocien dans le Massif du Brabant,* Bull. Acad. r. Belgique, Cl. Sc. 5 sér., t. 34 (1948).

47. A revision of the Arenig and Llandeilo of Belgium will be found in E. Maillieux, *L'Ordovicien de Sart-Bernard,* Mém. Mus. r. Hist, nat. Belgique, Mém. no. 86 (1939).

48. P. Michot, *Une discordance à la base du Carodocien dans la bande silurienne de Sambre-et-Meuse,* Bull. Cl. Sc. Acad. r. Belgique (June, 1931).

49. R. and E. Richter, *Der Herscheider Schiefer, ein zweites Vorkommen von Ordovicium in Rheinischen Schiefergebirge und ihre Beziehungen zu den wiedergefundenen Dayin-Schichten,* Senckenbergiana 19, Frankfurt a. M. (1937).

50. A table of the stratigraphic series of the Silurian and Devonian of the Harz is given by F. Dahlgrün, *Analogien und Unterschiede im geologischen Bau des Ober- und Unterharz,* Zeitschr. deutschen geol. Ges., Abh., 79 (1927).

51. R. Hundt, *Graptolithen aus den Phycoden-Schichten Ost-Thüringens,* Beitr. z. Geol. v. Thüringen, 5, Jena (1940).

52. W. Schmidt, *Graptolithen aus dem Phycodenquarzit Thüringens,* Zeitschr. deutschen geol. Ges., 1 (1937), p. 177.

53. T. Vascautzanu, *Les formations siluriennes de la rive roumaine du Dniestr; contributions à la connaissance du Paléozoïque du basin moldo-podolique,* Ann. Inst. géol. Roumania, 15 (1930). Z. Sujkowski, *Le Silurien de Volhynie d'après le sondage de Bocianowka,* Bull. Inst. géol. Pologne, no. 12 (1939). L. Lungershausen and O. Nikiforova, "On the Stratigraphical Relation of Silurian Beds of Podolia to Analogous Beds of Some Other Districts of Western Europa," C. R. Acad. Sc. USSR (1942), 34, no. 2.

54. R. Kozlowski, *Les Brachiopodes gothlandiens de la Podolia polonaise,* Palaeont. polonica, 1 (1929).

55. Already more or less differentiated in the Cambrian (see note 58, Chap. II).

56. J. Peneau, *Etude sur L'Ordovicien inférieur (Arénigien-grés armoricain) et sa faune, spécialement en Anjou,* Bull. Soc. Et. Sc. Angers, t. 74–76 (1944–46), p. 37–106, 8 pl.

57. In three successive Notes, C. R. somm. Soc. géol. France (Mar. 1, Mar. 15, Dec. 20, 1943), devoted to the graptolite faunas of the Breton Ordovician, A. Philippot believes he has proved that species which characterize several different horizons in England, here are found together.

58. L. Glémarec, *Etude de la faune graptolitique des Ampélites de Poligné (Ille-et-Vilaine),* Bull. Soc. géol. et min. de Bretagne, 10 (1929).

59. See articles by Kettner and Kodym (notes 52, 53, and 56, Chap. II). A complete bibliography will be found in F. Heritsch, *Das Silur von Böhmen (Sammelreferat über neuere Arbeiten),* Geol. Rundschau, 19 (1928). Note especially J. Perner and O. Kodym, "On the Zonal Division and Correlation of the Silurian of Bohemia," Amer. Jour. of Science, 4 (1922).

60. B. Bouček, *Stratigraphie et parallélisme de l'Ordovicien inférieur de la Bohême,* Bull. Soc. géol. France, 5 sér., t. 7 (1937). J. Koliha, *Sur le Trémadocien et sur l'Arénigien inférieur en Bohême* (ibid.).

61. J. Perner, *Les "Colonies de Barrande,"* Bull. Soc. géol. France, 5 sér., t. 7 (1937). We shall find at the boundary of the Cretaceous and the Tertiary (Petites Pyrénées) "colonies" apparently similar but whose origin is completely different.

62. A little massif north of Pisa, formed especially of Triassic and quite distinct from the Apennine. M. Gortani, Rendiconti R. Acad. Sc. Ist. Bologna (1933) noted Gothlandian graptolite shales there.

63. J. Schoeller, *Sur la présence de Graptolithes dans les schistes métamorphiques du Massif des Maures,* C. R. somm. Soc. géol. France (May 16, 1938).

64. L. Royer, *Les terrains cristophylliens des massifs d'Alger et de la Grande-Kabylie,* Bull. Serv. Carte géol. Algérie, 5 sér., Pétrographie, no. 2 (1937).

65. See the works of M. Thoral, cited notes 60, 62, 63, 64 and 65, Chap. II.

66. M. Thoral, *Stratigraphie et faciès de l'Arenig languedocien,* Ann. Univ. Lyon, Sc. Nat., section C, fasc. 2 (1941).

67. M. Thoral, *Age et faune des schistes ordoviciens de Cabrières (Hérault) dits "schistes à Asaphus,"* C. R. Acad. Sc. Nov. 9 (1936); *Cycles géologiques et formations*

noduliféres de la Montagne-Noire, Nouvelles Archives du Muséum d'Hist. nat. de Lyon, fasc. 1 (1946), magnificent photographs of these giant Trilobites.

68. J. Blayac and Mlle. Chaubet, *Découverte paléontologique dans le sous-étage Llandeilo de l'Ordovicien de la Montagne-Noire,* C. R. Acad. Sc. (Jan. 7, 1935).

69. M. Thoral and B. Gèze, *Orogénie et vulcanisme calédoniens sur le versant méridional de la Montagne-Noire,* C. R. Acad. Sc. (1939), t. 209, p. 891. There was, then, emergence there after the lower Ordovician. The lacuna becomes more important toward the north, toward the axial zone. The Caradoc is transgressive there upon the Georgian.

70. Some limestones formerly attributed to the Georgian are in reality Gothlandian or Devonian, which causes notable changes in the tectonic interpretations. See M. Thoral, *Sur l'âge des formations paléozoïques des environs de Caunes-Minervois (Aude),* C. R. Soc. géol. France (Nov. 20, 1938). M. Thoral and B. Gèze, *Sur la structure de la région occidentale du versant méridional de la Montagne-Noire (Aude-Hérault),* C. R. Acad. Sc. (Jan. 16, 1939).

71. Mlle. M. C. Chaubet, *Contribution à l'étude géologique du Gothlandien du versant méridional de la Montagne-Noire,* Travaux Lab. géol. Univ., Montpellier (1937).

72. H. R. von Gärtner, *Geologie der Zentralcarnischen Alpen,* Denkschr. Akad. Wiss. Wien, Math. Nat. Kl., 102 (1931). F. Heritsch, *Die Karnischen Alpen,* herausgeg. von d. geol. Inst. Univ. Graz (1936), p. 205. For the Primary of the Carnic Alps and of Sardinia, see the valuable summary by M. Gortani in the article cited note 67, Chap. II.

73. F. Heritsch, *Zur Stratigraphie des Gothlandiums der Karnischen Alpen,* Zentralbl. f. Min., Abt. B (1936), p. 503. A complete list of works on the graptolites of the Alps appears in R. Hundt, *Das Silur der Ostalpen im Vergleich mit dem ostthüringisch-frankenwäldisch-vogtländischen Silur,* Zentralbl. f. Min., Abt. B (1941), no. 8, but the work of this author has been sharply criticized by F. Heritsch and I. Peltzmann, ibid. (1942), no. 9, p. 271.

74. M. Gortani, *Successione di faune a Graptoliti nei dintorni di Goni (Sardegna),* Rendic. R. Accad. Lincei, Cl. Sc. fis., mat. e nat., 19, ser. 6 (1934).

75. G. Waterlot, Bul. Serv. Carte. géol. France, no. 216, p. 255, and C. R. Acad. Sc., 226 (1948), p. 681.

76. For the definition of the different regions of outcrops and the bibliography see p. 62 and Fig. 12, and in addition: G. Choubert, H. and G. Termier, *Sur la stratigraphie de l'Ordovicien marocain,* C. R. somm. Soc. géol. France (1947), p. 335.

77. A. Bigot and J. Dubois, *Sur la présence de l'Ordovicien dans l'Anti-Atlas marocain,* C. R. Acad. Sc. (August 3, 1931). E. Segaud and H. Termier, *Sur l'Ordovicien du Djebel Tachilla,* C. R. Soc. géol. France (Feb. 6, 1933).

78. H. Termier and E. Segaud, C. R. Soc. géol. France (Feb. 19, 1934).

79. N. Menchikof, *La série primaire de la Sahoura et des Chaînes d'Ougarta,* Bull. du Serv. de la Carte géol. d'Algérie (1933).

80. C. Kilian, *D'une association de Graptolithes observée dans le Gothlandien de Tiounkenin (Emmidir, Sahara central),* C. R. Soc. géol. France (April 24, 1933).

Chapter Four

The Devonian

The name Devonian was originated in 1839 by Murchison and Sedgwick to designate the marine, fossiliferous formations of Devonshire. Actually, in all of southern England, south of a line passing through Bristol channel, leaving the Mendip Hills on the north and projected 20 km. north of London (data taken from wells), the Devonian is marine. But its subdivisions there are difficult to define so the types of the Devonian stages have been taken elsewhere, in the Rhenish *Schiefergebirge* and in the Franco-Belgian Ardennes which is an extension of it to the west.

These stages are the following:

Devonian
- Upper
  - Fammenian (from la Famenne, Belgium).
  - Frasnian (from Frasne, Belgium).
- Middle
  - Givetian (from Givet, Ardennes).
  - Eifelian (from the Eifel).
- Lower
  - Coblenzian (from Coblenz).
    - Emsian (from Ems, Ger.)
    - Siegenian (from Siegen, Ger.)
  - Gedinnian (from Gedinne, Belgium).

On the other hand, in all of Central and Northern England, north of the line described above, the Devonian is represented by formations with a very special fauna and facies, long since called Old Red Sandstone, to distinguish it from the New Red Sandstone which has a certain similarity of facies but which is of Permian and Triassic age. As we shall soon see, this Old Red Sandstone is continental or lagoonal, and probably of desert origin.

I. General Characteristics of the Devonian Fauna

We shall mention only the organisms most interesting from the point of view of stratigraphy or in the origin of the sediments.[1]

A. *Coelenterates*

The corals in the Devonian continue to play a very important role as reef builders.[2] Coral limestones are abundant in Europe, especially in the Middle Devonian. All these corals are of course tetracorals, belonging to many genera, with the help of which Wedekind tried to define 7 successive zones in the coral facies of the Middle Devonian. The genus *Calceola* is especially important, with the classic species *C. sandalina.* This small simple coral (that is, reduced to a single calyx, not colonial) is especially abundant in the Eifelian; and like many simple corals, it seems to have been able to live in deeper, muddier zones than the colonial forms. It is found, therefore, not only in limestones but also in shales. The Eifelian very commonly is represented by facies of shales and limestones with *Calceola.* Moreover *Calceola sandalina* extends even into the Givetian stage where it is represented by special mutations in which the angle at the top of the flat face of the calyx is more or less open.[3]

Stromatoporids are abundantly present in the coral facies, as in the Silurian.

Tabulates[4] likewise persist, but many are different from the Silurian forms. *Halysites* have disappeared; instead *Pleurodictyum* appears, whose classic species, *P. problematicum* is especially characteristic of the Coblenzian.

Graptolites are almost extinct. All the forms with simple threads, called graptoloids, have disappeared. Only the reticulate forms, called dendroids, still persist, such as the *Dictyonema.*

B. *Echinoderms*

The echinoids, cystids and blastoids play only a secondary role.[5] The last two groups are, however, on the way to extinction. Crinoids,[6] on the other hand, are very abundant and their remains have built the crinoidal limestone that is found, almost everywhere, in the same kinds of facies as in the Silurian. Finally we shall see that the asteroids, or star fish, seldom preserved elsewhere, are abundant in the shales of the Hunsrück.

C. *Brachiopods*[7]

These are extremely abundant everywhere, with great variety of forms. Many of them (and especially the genera *Spirifer, Orthis, Athyris, Atrypa*) furnish characteristic fossils: for example, *Spirifer cultrijugatus,* which in a large part of Europe characterizes a very constant zone at the base of the Eifelian. In the Upper Devonian, *Spirifer verneuili* is found almost everywhere.

Finally, the two genera *Stringocephalus* and *Uncites* deserve special mention, for they are characteristic of the Devonian. *S. burtini,* a very large form, is restricted to the Givetian stage where it is associated with *Uncites gryphus,* a genus with a well developed beak, characteristic of brachiopods of reefy facies.

D. *Mollusks*

The gastropods and pelecypods supply scarcely any interesting information.

Among the pelecypods,[8] the family of aviculids, with primitive characteristics, is abundantly represented by widely varied species. Many genera and species are characteristic. In the Middle Devonian the megalodontids (genera *Megalodus* and *Mecynodus*), with a very thick and strongly hinged shell, also appear and they become especially abundant in the Triassic.

For the gastropods, we find the continuation of the pleurotomariids and bellerophontids, as well as the great development of certain capulids (*Platyceras, Hercynella,* etc.) in the Hercynian facies (see p. 128) of the Lower Devonian in central Europe and eastern United States.

Cephalopods are especially important. They are represented by the two groups of nautiloids and ammonoids.

Nautiloids continue their Silurian aspects. True orthocerids have disappeared but more highly developed forms follow them, with differentiated apertures, such as *Gomphoceras* and *Phragmoceras*. Along with these straight forms are found forms which are curved (*Cyrtoceras*) or coiled (*Gyroceras*).

But they begin to yield ground to ammonoids.[9] These last have perhaps already appeared in the Silurian (see p. 75), but it is not until the beginning of the Middle Devonian that they become sufficiently numerous to establish paleontologic zones. They are in general unornamented forms, found most frequently in relatively deep-water facies. So, we have either goniatite limestones, fine grained rocks, often light colored with rose or green veinlets (red and brown flecked marble of the Mediterranean regions), which make them resemble certain cephalopod limestones of the Secondary, or we may have marls or marly limestones with pyritized goniatites, that remind us at once of the marls with pyritized ammonites of the Jurassic or Cretaceous.

These ammonoids, mostly pelagic, like the graptolites, have a wide geographic distribution and have been used to define stages and sub-stages (see Fig. 27) and establish zones.

According to the classic treatise of E. Haug, the oldest ammonoid known is an *Agoniatites* of the Silurian in the region of Cassel (Kellerwald, eastern extremity of the Rhenish *Schiefergebirge*). But in reality, these are very badly preserved fossils in a series of very complicated structures (see p. 92). Then, in the Carnic Alps, we have found that *Tornoceras inexpectatum* and *Anarcestes praecursor* appear in beds formerly attributed, for that reason, to the Gedinnian, but which Gortani now prefers to leave in the Silurian, in consideration of the rest of the fauna (see p. 98).

And it is only in the Hunsrück shales (Upper Coblenzian) that we shall find, with *Agoniatites fidelis,* the first unquestionably Devonian form.

Next, in the Middle Devonian, ammonoids become frequent, especially *Agoniatites* and *Anarcestes,* which latter do not extend beyond the lower part of the Middle Devonian (*Anarcestes* stage), while the upper part is characterized by *Maeneceras* and *Parodiceras*. Finally, in the Frasnian, the fauna is renovated, with the appearance of the genus *Gephyroceras* (*Mantioceras*), characteristic of this stage. *G. intumescens* is found everywhere in Europe and America.

Clymenia or intrasiphonate goniatites must be specially mentioned. In

Europe, they are essentially characteristic of the upper Famennian, where limestones with *Clymenia* exist in the Rhenish Schiefergebirge, the Montagne-Noire, the Pyrenees, etc. In America, they are known as early as the Frasnian. Perhaps then the sudden arrival of this group in Europe may be due to an immigration.

In certain regions (Germany, Morocco), ammonoids make possible the distinction of as many as 13 paleontological zones in the Upper Devonian.

E. *Crustaceans*

Trilobites, so plentiful in the Silurian, now lose much of their importance. The best represented family is that of the phacopids, with the genera *Dalmanites* and *Phacops,* which persist into the Lower Carboniferous, and *Cryphaeus,* essentially characteristic of the Devonian.

On the other hand, the Devonian saw the flowering of a special group of giant crustaceans, the eurypterids (*Eurypterus* and *Pterygotus*). Known in America from the Cambrian,[10] they appear sporadically in Europe in the upper Ordovician (Bohemia), the Llandovery and Wenlock. But they become really plentiful only in the Devonian where they characterize the lagoonal beds of the Old Red Sandstone. As they are found before the Devonian in marine beds, then in the Carboniferous in lacustrine beds, it has been inferred that these great crustaceans were originally marine and they progressively adapted themselves first to brackish and then to fresh waters.[11]

Lastly, let us note in the Upper Devonian of certain regions (Rhenish Schiefergebirge) the abundance particularly of the cypridines (genus *Entomis*), small ostracod crustaceans with horned, bivalve shells, impressions of which are seen by the thousands in certain shaly facies called cypridine shales.

F. *Fish*[12]

Only three groups play a relatively important role in the Devonian.

1. The selacians, a group of sharks and rays, inhabited the seas. The skeleton being cartilaginous, usually only bony spines are found, from which many genera have been described, though they have no stratigraphic significance.

2. The ganoids or group of sturgeons had rhombic bony scales, which improve their chances for preservation. They are mostly marine, but the genus *Holoptychius,* belonging to an isolated group (crossopterygians) is very frequent in the facies of the Old Red Sandstone, especially in the upper part (*Holoptychius* sandstone).

3. The armoured fish or placoderms (genera *Cephalaspis, Pteraspis,* etc.), already seen in the Upper Silurian, also characterize the facies of the Old Red Sandstone. Their history is exactly the same as that of the eurypterids which they accompany.

4. Finally, the dipnoans are represented in the Old Red Sandstone by *Dipterus.*

In summary, from the standpoint of facies, we see that the corals, the crinoids and certain brachiopods characterize the littoral or organic facies;

cephalopods associated with some simple brachiopods are everywhere wide-spread in the deep-water facies; finally placoderms and eurypterids are characteristic of the Old Red Sandstone.

From the stratigraphic standpoint, the brachiopods and the ammonoids are in general most useful.

II. Distribution of Devonian Facies in Europe

Toward the end of the Silurian an event of capital importance occurred in Europe. This was the Caledonian folding, of which we have spoken earlier. Let us repeat that it extended over almost all of Ireland (except the south) and Britain (except Cornwall), the Scandinavian Chain, the Ardennes, the Rhenish Schiefergebirge, the Harz and the northern appendages of the Bohemian Massif (Fichtelgebirge, Thuringia, Lower Silesia), excluding the central part of this massif. The mountain chains thus formed just before the Devonian were added to the domain of the Huronian Chain, thus considerably enlarging the great North Atlantic continent.

Britain (except Cornwall) and Scandinavia have scarcely been folded since, so that the Devonian there remains horizontal or undulating and is represented only by subcontinental facies. For these regions we shall reserve the name Caledonian Chain. On the other hand, Cornwall, the Ardennes, the Rhenish Schiefergebirge, the Harz and Thuringia, later, at the end of the Carboniferous, are involved in the Hercynian folding, so that, although included in the Caledonian Chain, it is this last folding which stamped upon them their present architectural form. Moreover, this phase of the Hercynian folding was preceded, in these regions, by a geosynclinal phase, so that the Devonian of the Ardennes and especially of the Rhenish Schiefergebirge is not at all of the epicontinental type, but is, instead, of relatively deep-water facies and very thick.

Finally, south of the Caledonian domain, extends country where the oldest folding that can be accurately determined dates only from the end of the Primary (Hercynian Chain) or from the Tertiary (Alpine Chain). This is the Mediterranean geosyncline, where the Devonian often has a deep-water facies in harmony with both the Silurian and the Carboniferous.

In summary, we can now distinguish the following natural regions in western Europe, for the Devonian facies:[13]

1. *The Region of the Old Red Sandstone*

This includes all the British Isles except the south (see p. 103), all the Scandinavian peninsula and the Baltic countries, which under the name of Baltic Shield have long been attached to the continents. Here the Devonian, with continental facies, sometimes lagoonal, has remained almost horizontal.

2. *The Region of the Ardennes, or Shaly, Sandy Facies*

This is the zone of the edge of the continent. Here the Devonian is plainly marine, sometimes of deep-water facies, but the sandy detrital facies indicates the proximity of the continent. Cornwall, the Ardennes and the old massifs of Germany are typical regions of this facies. The Devonian here lies in discordance on the Silurian and is itself folded (Hercynian Chain). For simplification we shall add to it Bohemia and Brittany, which take us outside of the Caledonian domain proper and there is no general discordance between the Silurian and the Devonian; but nevertheless, in Brittany, the Caledonian folds seem to have had repercussions, for the Devonian is often incomplete at the base.

3. *The Region of Mediterranean Facies*

Here the Devonian is generally of deep-water and muddy facies, often metamorphic and always folded (Hercynian and Alpine Chains). Cephalopod limestones are frequent and there is often continuity of sedimentation with the Silurian and the Carboniferous. The type region in France is the Montagne-Noire. We shall add to it the Pyrenees, the Massif Central and, further away, the Vosges on one side and the Carnic Alps, Sardinia, and Morocco, on the other.

4. *Eastern Europe*

Finally, we shall describe separately the Devonian of eastern Europe, which shows the passage from a geosynclinal type (Ural) to the type characteristic of a continental area (Russian platform).

III. The Facies of the Old Red Sandstone

1. *The Transition Beds to the Silurian: the Downtonian*

The replacement of the marine beds of the Silurian by the continental facies of the Devonian was not, naturally, an instantaneous and abrupt phenomenon. So, at the boundary of the two systems, we discover an alternation of lagoonal beds, containing placoderms and eurypterids of the Old Red Sandstone type, and beds still marine, containing brachiopods and mollusks, which furnish the last traces of the Caledonian sea. Frequent intercalations of "bone beds," thin layers containing the comminuted remains of fish and crustaceans killed in masses by the abrupt invasions of the sea into lagoons, mark catastrophic episodes of this struggle between the marine and lagoonal domains, as for example when a lagoon situated below sea level is suddenly invaded by marine waters.[14]

The Downtonian stage was proposed for these transition beds, which, as we have seen above (p. 72), should be joined to the Devonian. But it is worthy of a separate study for it shows a very different paleontology and a sea still covering, at least temporarily, a good part of the lands which later become the Old Red Sandstone continent.

Paleontologically, the Downtonian is distinguished from the Old Red Sandstone proper, not only by its intercalations of a marine fauna, but also by the character of its lagoonal fauna: the presence of special fish (*Thelodus, Birkenia, Lanarkia, Cephalaspis murchisoni*) and the absence of the genus *Pteraspis* and of *Cephalaspis lyelli,* which only appear above it.

The type locality of the Downtonian has been taken in the region of Downton Castle, near Ludlow (Shropshire), on the border of the Welsh Massif. There, it includes the following series:

1. At the base, the Ludlow bone-bed, with *Pterygotus,* overlying the shales of the upper Ludlow, which are still Silurian.

2. Fifteen meters of Downton Castle sandstone, with *Lingula* and placoderm bone-beds.

3. Thirty-five meters of sandy shale with *Lingula* and marine mollusks, also containing bone-beds with *Pterygotus.* It is in these shales, often called the Temeside shales, that a marine fauna is found identical with that of the Mondrepuis shales in the Ardennes which was discussed earlier (p. 72).

4. Thick, red, lagoonal marls (Red Marls), at the base of which are still found the last scattered *Lingula.* They mark the final retreat of the sea and are distinguished from the Old Red Sandstone only by the predominance of clayey facies.

An equivalent of the Downtonian of Shropshire[15] is found in the great Devonian region of the Scottish Lowlands, at the base of the Old Red Sandstone; this is again a sandstone with marine mollusks and lagoonal animals among which are some very curious fish (*Birkenia, Lanarkia*).

Likewise, similar sediments are seen on the edges of the Baltic Shield, where, from Scania to Esthonia, they overlie the Silurian described previously (p. 87). This Baltic Downtonian is attached to the Silurian by Scandinavian geologists. Indeed, for example, in the classic region of Oslo,[16] the top of the marine Silurian passes in continuity into very thick red sandstones (900 m.), at the base of which appears a lower Downtonian placoderm fauna. On the island of Jelo, at the entrance of the Oslo Fjord, Kiaer recently discovered (see p. 127 of work cited note 16, this chap.) species of the Middle Downtonian, in the upper part of these sandstones.

These lagoonal formations of the Downtonian are found south of the Baltic Shield as far as Lysa-Gora (Poland) where they separate the marine Silurian from a marine Devonian; for there, the Devonian sea regained the upper hand and recovered momentarily the lost ground (see p. 130).

2. *Geographic Distribution of the Old Red Sandstone Proper*

Its domain extends over all of northwest Europe: that is, Ireland, Scotland, England (except the Cornish peninsula), Scandinavia and all of northwest Russia as far as the White Sea. This corresponds to the Caledonian Chain and the Baltic Shield, or in other words, to the regions that, at the end of the Silurian, were already a part of the continental domain or were being annexed to it.

The most extensive outcrops of the Old Red Sandstone may be grouped as follows (see Fig. 22): 1st, the south coast of Ireland; 2nd, south and southeastern Wales; 3rd, the northeastern extremity of the southern Scottish

Uplands (Cheviot Mts.); 4th, the two borders of the Lowland trough; 5th, the northeast extremity of the Highlands with the Orkney Islands; 6th, some very small outcrops on the Scandinavian coast, in the ancient massif north of Bergen; 7th, a diminutive remnant of sandstone with plants discovered in 1913 by Goldschmidt and interesting because of its location right in the middle of the Scandinavian Chain, south of Röros; 8th, finally, a wide band which spreads out south of the Gulf of Finland in Livonia and, tapering, continues south of Lakes Ladoga and Onega to the White Sea.

These boundaries of outcrops are obviously only erosion boundaries and the formation may very well originally have extended over the whole of the Caledonian and Baltic areas (as the fragment of Röros proves). In fact some isolated blocks of Old Red Sandstone with *Osteolepis* (placoderm) have recently[17] been pointed out in Schleswig-Holstein. Finally, to the north, some Old Red Sandstone is found on Spitzbergen (with *Pteraspis* and *Cephalaspis*), on Bear Island (with *Holoptychius*), and in Greenland.[18]

3. *Conditions of Formation*

The name Old Red Sandstone is applied in these regions to an extremely thick formation, sometimes reaching several thousand meters and made up of alternating conglomerates, more or less coarse, sometimes feldspathic sandstones (arkoses), and clays or shales. All these sediments are generally brightly colored, red or yellow, with the green or violet zones customary in such cases.

The fauna is very special and monotonous, of an impoverished type. Ordinarily it is composed exclusively of eurypterids and fish, belonging to some particular groups: placoderms, some ganoids and dipnoans. There have been found, as great rarities, a pelecypod related to the anodontans or present fresh water mussels (*Archanodon = Amnigenia*), an isopod (*Praearcturus*), a phyllopod (*Estheria*), some myriapods (*Kampecaris, Archidesmus*). Lastly, plants are fairly frequent, forming the oldest flora that we know with any accuracy.[19] The stems do not show any clear annual rings; moreover, very rich floras are known as far as the polar regions (Bear Island and Ellesmere Land), which seems to prove either that there were no differentiated climatic zones or that the poles did not occupy their present positions.

The early British geologists believed, with Geikie, that these formations, so different from the Devonian with a marine fauna which develops further south, were lacustrine; thus Geikie reconstructed in Britain several large Devonian lakes. But on the southern edge of the domain of the Old Red Sandstone, it has been proved, as we shall see, that these sandstones in some way become mixed with the marine Devonian, that is, they contain intercalations with normal marine faunas. The lacustrine hypothesis was rejected then and this Old Red Sandstone was considered a sort of "transgressive facies" of the Devonian sea.

Today, particularly because of the influence of J. Walther, geologists are almost unanimous in seeing in this formation continental deposits, of more or less desert origin.

We could compare this continent of Old Red Sandstone to the vast zone that today extends from the Atlantic shore south of Morocco across the Sahara and Libyan deserts as far as Mesopotamia. There, vast expanses, subject to eolian accumulations alone, are buried under thick dunes of red or yellow sands, with cross bedding, with rounded and frosted grains, characteristics different from those of fluviatile sands but like those which the English petrographers found in their Devonian sandstones. All around the mountainous desert massifs, the downpour of storms, rare but violent, gives rise to

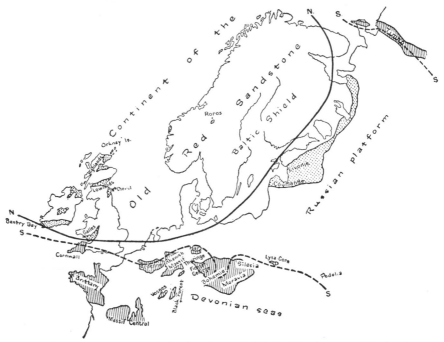

FIG. 22.   *Diagrammatic map of the Continent of Old Red Sandstone and its border zone.*
Dotted: Principal actual outcrops of Old Red Sandstone.
Ruled: Hercynian Massifs (marine Devonian).
N-N   Northern limit of the marine advance over the Continent of Old Red Sandstone.
S-S   Southern limit of the intercalations of Old Red Sandstone in the marine Devonian of middle Europe.
N. B.   This map shows only the Old Red Sandstone proper, exclusive of the Downtonian.

formidable accumulations of torrential conglomerate deposits; further on, these waters, reaching closed depressions, form temporary lakes or chotts (salt lakes) and deposit marls in them, to which dust brought by the wind is later added. Often even salt beds (gypsum and rock-salt) are formed in these chotts, such as those observed in the Old Red Sandstone of the Baltic countries. We sometimes see intercalated in the Red Marls of the Lower Devonian of Wales and in the Upper Devonian of the Scottish Lowlands, irregular beds of reddish limestones, concretionary and more or less brecciated. These "cornstones" [20] are doubtless analogous to the calcareous crusts of present-day dry countries. In certain Devonian marls even isolated calcareous concretions ("roots") are found that Evans compares to the calcareous concretions or "puppets" of the steppe loess. Finally, vegetable life is concentrated either in isolated oases or in limited regions of desert zones (Tchad), which explains the presence of plant beds in this Devonian of Northern Europe.

To make clear the various aspects which the Old Red Sandstone continent should present, some authors have also evoked the present deserts in the plateaus of Bolivia or of southern Australia, with their immense temporary lakes, reduced to almost nothing during periods of dryness.

This interpretation explains very well the various peculiarities of the Old Red Sandstone, its color, the extreme variability of its grain from marls to conglomerates containing large blocks, the irregularity of its stratification, its great thickness and its wide distribution,[21] and finally its very special and impoverished fauna.

Animal life in these lagoons of variable salinity is evidently only possible for specially adapted creatures such as the eurypterids and placoderms for which we know no present day equivalents. But for other fish, the comparison with their living counterparts is very significant. Thus the Devonian genus *Dipterus* is closely related to the present dipnoids, for instance to the genus *Neoceratodus* which lives in the temporary lakes of the Australian deserts (those to which we have just referred) and is able, thanks to its pulmonary breathing, to continue to live enveloped in mud during dry periods. In the same way the *Holoptychius* belong to a group of ganoids (the crossopterygians) represented today by the polypters of Lake Tchad. Finally, the phyllopod *Estheria,* found in the Old Red Sandstone, and which we find again in the Permo-Triassic lagoons, is biologically related to the *Artemia* which still lives in the steppe lagoons of Asiatic Russia.

4. *Stratigraphy of the Old Red Sandstone*

The extreme diversity, due to essentially local conditions, of the sediments formed on the continent of the Old Red Sandstone, makes its stratigraphy almost indecipherable. There are no marine fossils in it and the only chronological standards having general value are furnished by the floras[22] and the lagoonal faunas. Above the Downtonian, whose paleontologic characteristics we have defined earlier, the British geologists distinguish a Lower Old Red Sandstone,[23] characterized by *Cephalaspis lyelli* and the appearance of the genus *Pteraspis,* and an Upper Old Red Sandstone where *Holoptychius* appears.

In Wales and its southern border, the two subdivisions are, in general, concordant. The Lower is especially made up of red marls (1,000 m. thick), for which a Caledonian stage was established; but the Upper is sometimes transgressive and, for example, at Tortworth and in the Mendip Hills (see Fig. 17), lies directly on the Silurian.

In the Scottish Lowlands, where the lower division reaches a thickness of 3,700 m., it is covered discordantly by the upper division.

Lastly, in northeast Scotland and the Orkneys the series seems to be divided in two parts by a discordance. But the lower part contains a peculiar flora and fish fauna,[24] different from those of typical Lower Old Red Sandstone. Therefore, a Middle Old Red Sandstone or Orcadian stage has been devised for this portion, which is more than 3,000 m. thick. The Lower Devonian is missing.

5. *The Southern Shores of the Continent of Old Red Sandstone*

On the southern edge of this continent (see Fig. 22) marine intercalations naturally appear in the Old Red Sandstone.[25] As we have seen, this evidence formerly led to the belief that the entire sandstone series was marine.

The first evidence of it is seen at the southwestern extremity of Ireland, at the foot of Bantry Bay. There, red sandstones (Coomhola grits) attributed to the Upper Devonian contain *Avicula* and some other marine pelecypods.

This evidence is still clearer in the extreme southwest of Wales, in the county of Pembroke. Intercalations are seen in the upper Old Red Sandstone, of sandstones, shales, and even limestones with normal marine fauna: crinoids, lingulids, rhynchonellids, bellerophontids, and various pelecypods.

Finally this mixed Devonian type is still better characterized in the wide zone of Old Red Sandstone which, between Livonia and the White Sea, girdles the southeast Baltic Shield. There, in the middle part of this formation marine intercalations are most extensive. We shall see (p. 140) that this transgression is of the Frasnian age.

These lenses of marine facies in the Old Red Sandstone thus mark the northern limit of the temporary incursions of the sea on the continent (see Fig. 22).

Inversely, it is possible to find, fairly far south, in the marine deposits of the Devonian, the last lenses of Old Red Sandstone with their characteristic fish.

So also the marine Devonian of northern Devonshire contains at different levels beds with plants and placoderms (*Pteraspis*). Likewise the deep wells around London have shown sometimes marine Upper Devonian with *Spirifer verneuili* and *Rhynchonella cuboides,* sometimes Upper Old Red Sandstone with *Holoptychius.*

We shall describe later (p. 119) the last traces of the Old Red Sandstone facies in the Boulonnais and the Ardennes. In the German part of the Rhenish Massif, in the region of the Lenne River (southern Westphalia), the Lenne shales of the marine Middle Devonian contain intercalations with plants and *Amnigenia,* a fresh water pelecypod.

In Bohemia, the marine Devonian series is terminated by beds with plants of the top of the Middle Devonian. Finally, in Poland (Lysa-Gora), at the base of the Devonian, in the Middle Devonian and in the Upper Devonian, are intercalated true sandstones with placoderms of the classic type, which we shall find again at Moscow in the Middle Devonian.

It is naturally due to this confusion of facies in this border zone that we can be sure of the synchronism of the Old Red Sandstone with the marine

Devonian of the south. And the reconstruction of this continent of Old Red Sandstone, with the diversity of its sediments and its mobile fringe of ancient shores, seems to us a fine example of the stratigraphic synthesis.[26] We shall presently see this continent projected as far as North America.

IV. The Hercynian Massifs of Central Europe

We shall first study in detail the Ardennes, which will serve as a type. We shall describe its extension toward the northwest in the Boulonnais and the Cornish peninsula, then toward the east in the German Rhenish Massifs; continuing in this direction until we reach Bohemia. Finally we shall end with Brittany, which occupies a place apart.

1. The Ardennes

Because of the fine studies of Gosselet and the Belgian geologists, the Ardennes has long been the classic land of the Devonian in France and Belgium[27] and it may be taken as a starting point for a division into stages.

For geologists, the name Ardennes (s. l.) designates the whole of a Primary massif, the western branch of the great Rhenish Schiefergebirge (see Fig. 28), remnant of the Hercynian Chain. This Ardennes massif is thus bounded on almost every side by Secondary or Tertiary horizontal formations and slightly elongated in the shape of a crescent: on the north, the Primary formations disappear under the Tertiary Belgian plain; on the west, the folds are lost under the chalk of northern France; on the south, they are buried under the Jurassic or Cretaceous on the edge of the Paris Basin; on the east, the Jurassic and Triassic Gulf of Luxemburg almost completely separates the Ardennes from the rest of the Rhenish Schiefergebirge.

The crescent shape of the Ardennes reflects the direction of the Hercynian folds. These, in fact, describe a slight concavity toward the north; at the west they are directed WNW, while in the east they are inflected towards ENE. We can distinguish the following elements in it from south to north (Fig. 23 and 24):

1st. The anticlinal area of the Ardennes proper, formed by broad outcrops of Lower Devonian, under which from place to place appear Cambro-Silurian cores.[28] These are the anticlines of Rocroy, Givonne, Serpont, Stavelot-Spa. The almost exclusively siliceous nature of these formations (Cambro-Silurian shales, Lower Devonian sandstones, and conglomerates) makes a natural wooded region here, not very fertile, monotonous plateaus with few valleys. This is the Ardennes of the geographers.

Thanks to the alignment of the Cambro-Silurian Massifs, this anticlinal area of the Ardennes may be subdivided thus, from south to north: *a*, the Givonne anticline; *b*, the complicated syncline or "synclinorium" of the Eifel, very narrow toward the Meuse but rapidly widening toward the east, where it is marked out by the outcrops of Witry (top of the Lower Devonian and not Middle Devonian as the map shows, Fig. 23) and by numerous bands of

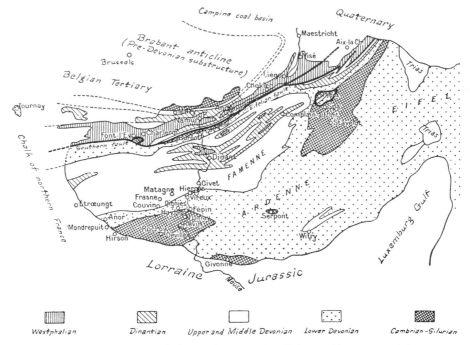

FIG. 23.   *Geologic map of the Ardennes Massif (very diagrammatic).*

Middle and Upper Devonian, of which only one was diagrammed in the Eifel; *c*, the Ardennes anticline proper, whose axis is defined by the Massifs of Rocroy, Serpont, and Stavelot (see Fig. 26).

2nd. On the north is the wide Dinant syncline. It is surrounded by a belt of Middle and Upper Devonian and the center is occupied by elongated bands of Carboniferous following several secondary synclines. The alternation of the shaly rocks (Upper Devonian, Middle Carboniferous) and limestones (Middle Devonian, Lower Carboniferous) give more variety to the relief and greater richness to the soil. This is the Dinant Basin.

3rd. This basin is bordered on the north by a more arid zone where sandy and quartzose formations again predominate. It is the natural region of Condroz. There, in fact, the Silurian reappears, forming a narrow band, extending from east to west and known as the Silurian band of Condroz or of Sambre-Meuse.

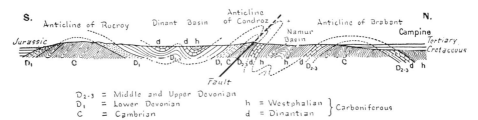

FIG. 24.   *N-S section from the Ardennes to Brabant, through the valley of the Meuse (very diagrammatic: compare map, Fig. 23).*

A narrow zone of Lower Devonian lies along its southern edge, while along its northern border is found only Middle or Upper Devonian. The band of Condroz has, thus, the appearance of an anticline, but one whose whole northern flank has been cut off along a great fault or a thrust surface of the great thrust of Condroz,[29] which will be studied later.[30]

4th. North of the zone of Condroz, the Lower Devonian is completely missing. A thin band of Middle and Upper Devonian precedes a great syncline filled with Carboniferous, the Namur Basin. This is the beginning of the great Belgian plain, for the Carboniferous soon disappears under the horizontal cloak of Tertiary formations.[31]

5th. Nevertheless, valleys dug in the plain allow us to see, from time to time, the ancient basement. We know also that north of the Namur Basin there is an anticlinal area which exposes the Silurian, bordered on the south by the Devonian: this is the Massif of Brabant.

A. The Section of the Devonian on the southern edge of the Dinant syncline, in the Meuse Valley. The old Ardennes Chain was completely leveled and reduced to a peneplain. But in a relatively recent epoch, this peneplain was warped and elevated, so that powerful streams, like the Meuse, have dug deep gorges in it. Along its steep banks, between the emergence from the Cambro-Silurian Massif of Rocroy and entrance into the Carboniferous Dinant Basin, we can see[32] almost without interruption the following succession, all the names of which have become classic:

Gedinnian. Lying discordantly on the Cambrian, there is first a basal conglomerate, the Fépin conglomerate, followed by the Haybes arkoses, formed at the expense of a granulitic massif unknown in outcrop, probably situated farther north and hidden under Primary terrain. These arkoses alternate with the Mondrepuis shales containing the first marine fossils. Then come shales, often green or red, such as the variegated shales of Oignies, overlain by the green shales of Saint-Hubert [33] where placoderms have been found as far as this southern edge of the Dinant syncline (P. Pruvost).[34] The whole assemblage of the Mondrepuis shales is well dated by the marine fauna, with *Spirifer sulcatus,* and it constitutes the Gedinnian stage.[35]

Further west, under the Secondary, their equivalents are found in the pits and wells of the Pas-de-Calais. The marine horizon of Mondrepuis is represented here by the Liévin shales, whose fauna has long been well known. They are overlain by beds with eurypterids[36] which are equivalent to the Oignies stage.

Finally, this mixed Gedinnian facies of the Ardennes and Pas-de-Calais extends as far as the subsurface of southeast England. A well in Buckinghamshire[37] revealed at the base of the Old Red Sandstone a complex in which beds with placoderms are associated with shales containing the marine fauna of Mondrepuis. This is the Downtonian which, as we have said earlier (p. 72), is thus shown to be contemporaneous with the Gedinnian.

Coblenzian. This stage starts with the Anor sandstone, followed by the Montigny graywacke. The latter is surrounded by the shaly horizons which are developed farther east in Belgium, giving it the deep-water facies of the

Neufchâteau phyllites; this is also the Houffalize beds (see Fig. 26) of the Belgian geologists. These horizons are very fossiliferous: *Homalonotus, Bellerophon, Pleurotomaria, Avicula,* and characteristic brachiopods (*Spirifer primaevus, Leptaena murchisoni* and especially the genus *Rensselaeria,* the type of which is American). All this makes up the lower Coblenzian for which there is now a tendency to make an independent stage under the name of Siegenian (see later).[38]

Above come the sandstones and shales of Vireux, with *Spirifer hercyniae.* They are followed by some beds of red shale (shales of Winenne) passing in the upper part into the celebrated Hierges graywacke,[39] very fossiliferous[40] (*Spirifer arduennensis, Athyris undata, A. concentrica, Phacops potieri*). This is the Burnot bed of the Belgian geologists, so named after a classic locality which will be discussed later. This upper Coblenzian is also called Emsian.[41]

Eifelian. This stage is represented by its typical facies, of shales with calcareous lentils called Couvin shales, where *Calceola sandalina, Spirifer cultrijugatus, S. speciosus* and the usual fauna of the stage are found. This is the Couvinian of the Belgian geologists.[42]

Givetian.[43] Here is the type locality. These are the Givet limestones forming the escarpments which dominate this town. They contain a coral fauna (*Cyathophyllum, Favosites,* stromatoporids), with gastropods, *Megalodus,* and many characteristic brachiopods: *Uncites gryphus, Stringocephalus burtini, Atrypa reticularis,* etc.

Frasnian.[44] This stage begins with the shales and limestones of Frasne,[45] where lentils of organic limestone[46] similar to the Givet limestones are intercalated between marly beds. The whole is very fossiliferous with *Spirifer verneuili, Athyris concentrica, Atrypa reticularis, Rhynchonella cuboides, Orthis striatula,* etc. But the shaly masses indicate an increase of depth, for ammonoids (*Gephyroceras intumescens*) appear here and become abundant, in the state of pyritic internal molds, in the upper beds, called Matagne shales.[47] The maximum depth of the Devonian sea in the Ardennes is here.

Famennian. The Famennian also shows its true type, the shales of Famenne, with deep facies containing *Spirifer verneuili.*

To sum up, in this section the transgressive Lower Devonian has a facies still sandy and coarse; the Middle Devonian is especially calcareous and more or less organic and the Upper Devonian has shaly and deep-water facies.

B. Variations of facies in the rest of the Ardennes.[48]

1. *Toward the South.* In the longitude of the Meuse, the Devonian is no longer south of the Rocroy anticline, for there the Silurian disappears directly under the Jurassic. But farther east, south of the Serpont Massif and in the region of Witry, that is to say, in the Eifel synclinorium, modifications of interesting facies in the Devonian are found. Here, in fact, the Gedinnian and Coblenzian have lost their littoral sandy facies. These are the deepest-water shales, reaching a thickness of 9,000 m. according to Fourmarier (example, the Neufchâteau phyllites), in which red intercalations still mark the extension of the Winenne red shales and the Oignies variegated shales.

2. *Toward the North.* Going down the Meuse, on the other hand, we shall see the Devonian becoming more littoral or continental and especially incomplete at the base. Already in the Dinant Basin itself, detailed studies show that the Middle and Upper Devonian acquire more littoral facies as one goes farther north.[49]

a) On the northern margin of the Dinant syncline (that is, along the southern border of the Silurian band of Condroz) the equivalents of beds which we have just described on the southern margin are found again but with a more littoral facies. The clearly marine horizon of Mondrepuis has disappeared and the Gedinnian is represented only by sandy shales, the Fooz psammites, extending the variegated shales of Oignies and Saint-Hubert. In the Siegenian, above the Anor sandstones, the Montigny graywacke is replaced by sandstones and red shales which continue in the lower part of the Emsian. And above all, the top of this last stage (Winenne and Hierges beds) is represented by a thick formation of red shales, sandstones, and conglomerates, called the Burnot beds. Here we have obviously reached the edge of the basin of sedimentation of the Lower Devonian which we do not find further north.[50]

Above the Burnotian, however, comes a marine Eifelian with calceolas, only slightly less thick and showing beds of conglomerate and red shale at its base. The Givetian and Frasnian, likewise less thick, have nevertheless kept their normal marine facies. Finally, in the Famennian, the upper part of the shales of Famenne is replaced by the psammites of Condroz. The base of this sandy formation (psammites of Esneux and Montfort) is still marine, with *Spirifer verneuili,* but the top (psammites of Evieux) contains the flora[51] and the fish fauna[52] characteristic of the Upper Old Red Sandstone; *S. verneuili* always reappears in thin, uppermost beds (macignos of Ouffet). This is the beginning of the marine transgression which will develop with the base of Carboniferous.

b) When we enter the Namur Basin, after having passed over the Silurian band of Condroz and the line of thrusting on its northern border, we suddenly find a very different Devonian. The Gedinnian and Coblenzian are completely missing and the Devonian begins with a basal conglomerate (Nannine conglomerate) directly overlain by the sandstones and Calceola shales of the Eifelian, which has become much thinner (50 m.). The Givetian, very thin (50 to 100 m.), shows some sandy layers. Finally the Upper Devonian remains similar to that on the northern border of the Dinant Basin, but with an equally reduced thickness.

c) Lastly, in the northern part of the Namur syncline, on the border of Brabant, the Eifelian itself is missing and the Devonian begins with a basal conglomerate (Alvaux conglomerate) covered by Givetian limestones with *Stringocephalus*. At the same time a new non-marine episode appears at the top of the Givetian and the base of the Frasnian: there are the red rocks of Mazy[53] where marine beds with *Spirifer verneuili* are found.

As the table (Fig. 25) shows, these variations of facies are harmoniously grouped, if the Ardennes is represented at the extreme southern edge of the great desert continent on which lay the lagoons of the Old Red Sandstone. In the Lower Devonian, the sea, becoming ever deeper toward the south, still occupied only the region which has since become the Dinant Basin; thus this transgressive sea, crossing the Condroz zone, in the Middle Devonian, occupied the Namur Basin and finally, in the Upper Devonian, reached as far as the Brabant Massif.

The contrast between these two types of the Devonian, the Namur Basin type and the Dinant Basin type, is clearly apparent for, as we shall see (p.

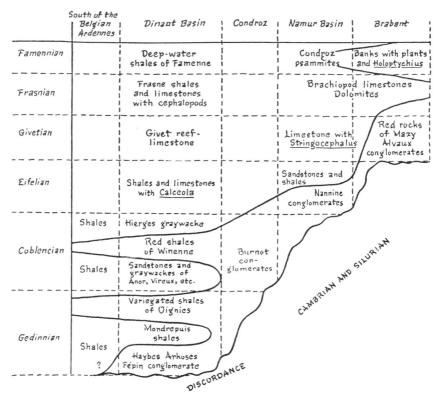

FIG. 25. *Diagram of the variations of Devonian facies in the Ardennes (partially after M. Leriche).*

────── Southern limits of the conglomerate facies (littoral belt) and of the red beds (Old Red Sandstone type).

N. B. Note that the limestone of Givet is not always reef limestone.

187), the great thrust of Condroz has brought together these two sedimentary areas which in the Devonian, before the folding, must have been relatively distant from each other.

Finally, we see that the tectonic directions of the future Hercynian Chain are already expressed, from the Devonian on, in the paleogeography of the region where it will originate. The British Caledonian Chain showed us a first example of such a parallelism, which we shall find again in the history of the Alpine Chain during the Secondary.

2. *The Boulonnais*

The Primary terrains of the Ardennes disappear toward the west under the broad Cretaceous plains of northern France, where pits and wells of the Pas-de-Calais (region of Liévin, see p. 117) have exposed them. Later, a solitary outcrop, not extensive but very interesting, comes to light in the Boulonnais, showing both Devonian and Carboniferous.

Tectonically, the Boulonnais lies north of the prolongation of the Silurian axis of Condroz. It belongs, then, to the Namur Basin and in fact the Devonian is there, as in this Basin, incomplete at the base and relatively littoral.

The *Givetian* marks the beginning of the Devonian transgression; the basal conglomerate is called the Caffiers conglomerate; then come some beds of green psammites with plant remains in which P. Corsin[54] has recently discovered some determinable plants, probably of lower Givetian age. Above these the Blacourt limestone contains the Givetian marine fauna with organic facies.

The *Frasnian* begins with the Ferques limestone, equally littoral, rich in brachiopods.

Above come beds with very different facies. These are alternating red shales and sandstones, recalling the Condroz psammites and announcing the Old Red Sandstone facies. This complex has been classified in the Famennian up to the present. But recently P. Corsin[55] has found in it *Gephyroceras intumescens,* which shows that the base of this series of beds, the Fiennes psammites, should still be included in the Frasnian. Therefore, the Famennian is represented only by the upper bed, called the Ste-Godeleine sandstone, about 50 m. thick.

3. *The Cornish Peninsula*

We include here not only Cornwall proper, but also Devonshire. The Devonian there has two principal areas of outcrops: one comprises Cornwall and southern Devon, the other northern Devon and western Somerset.

As we have already said, the Devonian is there marine and the very name of the system has been taken from this country. But it has been much folded by the Hercynian movements and even has injections of granitic rocks. There are thick accumulations of shales and sandstones in which the stratigraphy has long remained rather confused. More and more, however, we have come to recognize it as similar to that of the Ardennes;[56] in the whole assemblage, the facies become more littoral, more sandy in the north. We shall merely mention two facts:

1st. On the south coast of Devon, near Torquay, and equally on the northern coast of Cornwall, are found shales containing calcareous lenses with cephalopods, among them clymenids which we shall find again only in the eastern part of the Rhenish Massif.

2nd. On the other hand we recall that in the northern zone of outcrops in northern Devon, alternating with marine beds, appear some layers with Old Red Sandstone facies, with their characteristic fish. Recently Leriche (see note 52, this chap.) has shown that these continental episodes are placed at exactly

the same stratigraphic levels as in the Ardennes. Thus the Foreland grits of
northern Devon and western Somerset, with their fauna of *Pteraspis and
Cephalaspis* (Lower Old Red Sandstone) correspond to the psammites of Fooz
of the northern border of the Dinant syncline, and they are prolonged in
southern Devon by the Dartmouth slates which are the equivalent of the shales
of Oignies and Saint-Hubert of the southern border of the same Dinant syncline. At a higher level, the Hangman grits of Devon are contemporary with the
Burnot beds of the Ardennes Massif. Finally the Pickwelldown sandstones of
Devon, which contain the *Holoptychius* fauna of the Upper Old Red Sandstone, mark, in the marine Famennian, a last continental episode at the same
epoch as the psammites and red shales of Condroz (psammites of Evieux).

4. *The Rhenish Massifs of Germany*[57]

These form the extension of the Ardennes toward the east, incompletely separated by the Jurassic and Triassic Gulf of Luxembourg. The Hercynian folds
have there the same general direction as in the eastern Ardennes, that is,
SW-NE. The Devonian, 5,000 to 10,000 m. thick, constitutes almost the whole
of these massifs, and it is very difficult to establish, in this homogeneous mass,
subdivisions into natural regions.

Following Wedekind and von Bubnoff, we shall distinguish, beginning in
the south, the following structural units (see maps, Fig. 28 and especially Fig.
26):

1st. The *Hunsrück* and *Taunus Massifs*, composed of the Lower Devonian.
Along their southern edge there are also outcrops of quartzitic rocks or phyllites of doubtful age (Cambrian?) but almost surely pre-Devonian; this would
be the extreme edge of an ancient massif buried under the encroaching areas
of the Saar (Triassic, Permian) and the Mainz Basin (Tertiary).

2nd. The *Hesse synclinorium*, composed especially of Middle and Upper
Devonian with even some Carboniferous synclines (Culm, see p. 188) at the
eastern extremity. There, however, the structure is complicated: on the northern border, in Hörre and the Kellerwald, appear anticlinal bands of ancient
formations (Silurian) where the stratigraphy is still poorly known (see p.
92).

3rd. *The Siegerland block*, made up of Lower Devonian (especially Siegenian) and having played in certain epochs the role of shoals in the Devonian
paleogeography.

4th. The *Eifel-Sauerland synclinorium*, the western part of which we have
already studied, set in the Belgian Ardennes between the anticlines of Givonne
and Serpont; in the Sauerland we have the Middle and Upper Devonian with
some synclines of Culm.

5th. Lastly, on the north, the *coal basin of Westphalia* (or of the Ruhr)
which does not interest us at the moment.

In the whole massif, the zones of facies of the Devonian are arranged parallel
to these structural directions, but with numerous irregularities. Toward the
northwest, we shall find, as in the Ardennes, littoral facies indicating the
approach of the Old Red Sandstone continent. To the southeast the succession

of facies is much more complicated than in the Ardennes; that is due to the role played by the Siegerland block and further south by an emerged land which perhaps existed south of the Taunus.

a. Gedinnian. This stage is not well understood. On the southern edge of the Taunus, we can classify as lower Gedinnian the shales showing a marine fauna[58] similar to that of the Mondrepuis shales in the Ardennes. And the upper Gedinnian would be represented in the same region by the variegated phyllites of the Taunus and by the *Hermeskeilschichten,* equivalent in age and facies to the variegated shales of Oignies and Saint-Hubert in the Ardennes.

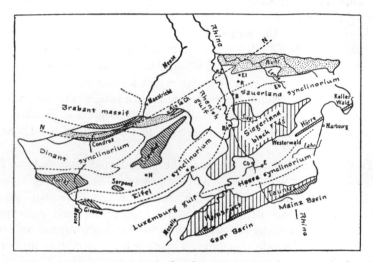

FIG. 26. *Diagrammatic map of the large structural units of the Rhenish Schiefergebirge (inspired by von Bubnoff).*

Close ruled: Cambrian-Silurian Massifs.
Dotted: Coal basins.
NN   North of this line the Givetian is transgressive directly on the Cam-
               brian-Silurian (after H. Breddin).

B = Bergisch; Bn = Bonn; C = Cologne; Cb = Coblenz; E = Ems; Eb = Ebbe Mts.;
El = Elberfeld; H = Houffalize; P = Prüm; R = Remscheid; Ra = Ratingen; S =
Siegen.

Likewise in the Sauerland, the base of the Devonian in the region of the Ebbe Range (see map, Fig. 26) is formed by variegated beds, the *Bunte Ebbeschichten* (600 m. thick), which may represent an Old Red Sandstone facies of the Lower Devonian. On the other hand, the age of the Verse beds (Sauerland) where Fuchs[59] has described a marine fauna near that of the Mondrepuis shales, is very debatable; according to Richter they are superposed on the Siegenian.

b. The Coblenzian. This is the type area for the Coblenzian, which deserves a more detailed study.[60] It is, moreover, very thick and has quite varied facies. We shall divide it into: Siegenian and Emsian.

1. *Siegenian.*[61] α) In the Siegerland and north of the Eifel, this stage is

typically represented by the celebrated Siegen beds, extensions of the analogous facies of the Ardennes. They are in fact graywackes, sandstones and shales, several thousand meters thick (10,000 m., according to Richter) and extremely fossiliferous. The genus *Rensselaria* and *Spirifer primaevus* are found there. These beds are subdivided into three members, equivalents of which have been found in the Ardennes by Asselberghs: lower Siegenian, represented by light colored phyllites (*Tonschiefer*) with sandy intercalations which develop toward the north; middle Siegenian, composed of calcareous graywackes and streaked sandy shales, the facies called *Rauhflaserschichten,* very fossiliferous (Seifen fauna); upper Siegenian or *Hersdorferschichten,* muddy shales with plaques of sandstone.

β) At the north of the Siegerland, that is in Sauerland and especially in Bergischesland or the Oberbergishes (hills of Bergisch, see map Fig. 26), this thick complex of Siegen beds is modified:[62] certain beds disappear or are replaced by a more littoral facies (quartzites) or a subcontinental facies (variegated beds). Thus the Bunte Ebbeschichten, appearing in the anticlinal region of the Ebbe Range, are covered directly by the transgressive Emsian. All this indicates, as in the Ardennes, the approach to the Old Red Sandstone continent.

γ) To the south of the Siegerland in the Taunus and Hunsrück we find the Siegenian again, but with entirely different facies. The stage begins with the classic Taunus quartzites, a very thick series of white sandstones with shaly beds that are somewhat fossiliferous (especially brachiopods and pelecypods).[63] These hard, siliceous rocks are responsible for the high, rugged and infertile relief of the Taunus Massif; sometimes it is made the type of a Taunusian stage, correlative of the Anor sandstones. Then come deep facies, identical to the Neufchateau phyllites that were noted in the southern Ardennes, and called here the Hunsrück shales (Hunsrückian stage),[64] black, fine grained, slightly bituminous. They contain almost no brachiopods, but in place of them many trilobites and some ammonoids (*Agoniatites*) and pyritized imprints of starfish and ophiuroids. This is the lateral equivalent of the Montigny graywacke of the Ardennes. But in reality the only distinction between the Taunusian and Hunsrückian is due to a difference of facies and depth (Kayser). Indeed, in the sandy, more littoral beds which are intercalated in the Hunsrück shales we find the Taunusian brachiopod fauna and thus it is probable that Hunsrück shales are in part contemporaneous with the Taunus quartzites (Wedekind).

Finally, a very special type is developed in the Kellerwald and the region of Marburg. Beneath the Emsian are found organic limestones several meters thick probably representing the Siegenian, under a facies called Hercynian, for it was first described in the Harz. We shall refer to it again when we study that region.

2. *Emsian.* This stage, so named after the little town of Ems on the Lahn, a little east of Coblenz, shows its typical development in the Hesse synclinorium (and also in the Eifel). There, it corresponds to the Coblenz graywackes, celebrated for their richness in fossils; and so the name of Coblenzian stage is sometimes restricted to it.[65] These have long been divided into the *Untere*

Koblenzschichten (up to 1,000 m. thick) with *Spirifer hercyniae, S. arduennensis, Pleurodictyum problematicum,* etc., the *Koblenzquartzit* and the *Obere Koblenzschichten* always containing *S. arduennensis* with many forms of the Lower Devonian. In the upper part of these last beds forms occasionally appear which will be abundant in the base of the Middle Devonian (*Spirifer speciosus, S. cultrijugatus*); this is the equivalent of the Hierges graywacke.

In the extreme north of the Rhenish Massif, however, that is, in Sauerland and Bergischesland, the Emsian is transgressive and incomplete at its base. It begins with a conglomerate and red shales called the *Rimmerschichten,* probably equivalent to the Coblenz quartzite. Above come the *Remscheiderschichten,*[66] volcanic tuffs, red shales and graywackes, very fossiliferous (special pelecypods), doubtless contemporary with the Obere Koblenzschichten. Thus it is only in the upper Emsian that the sea extended north of the Siegerland block.

c. Eifelian-Givetian. As in the Ardennes, the Middle Devonian is characterized by the reduction of sandy, detrital facies and the appearance of calcareous facies. We can distinguish three principal types.

1. *Normal or Eifel type.* In the Eifel, the lower limit of the Eifelian is marked by a sandy-calcareous zone where the large *Spirifer cultrijugatus* (*cultrijugatus*-beds) abound; then begins the great series of shales and limestones with *Calceola,* very fossiliferous in the Eifel, from which the stage name is taken. Above comes the Givetian. At the base, it is sometimes littoral and organic. This is the crinoid zone where some special forms of *Calceola* (see above) are still found but where *Stringocephalus burtini* already appears. It is the latter genus which will really characterize the whole Givetian, called by German geologists *Stringocephalen-Schichten.* The base is made up of limestone with corals and stromatoporids alternating with more marly beds. At the top the calcareous masses (*Massenkalk*) prevail, sometimes dolomitic representing true reefs.

Crossing the Rhine, we see new facies appear. Conforming to the general rule, the deep-water facies develop to the southeast and the littoral facies to the northwest.

2. *Deep-water type* or shales with *Tentaculites.* This facies is developed all over the east and south, that is, in the eastern extremity of Sauerland, in Kellerwald, and in the Hesse synclinorium. So in the Lahn region, the whole Middle Devonian is sometimes represented by a thick series of shales showing innumerable impressions of little shells of pteropods (?), smooth (stylioline) or annulated (tentaculite), eminently pelagic facies, in which neritic faunas have almost completely disappeared. Ammonoids are sometimes fairly frequent and have allowed Wedekind [67] to distinguish 4 or 5 zones of goniatites in this Middle Devonian.

3. *Littoral or Lenne type.* This is found in the extreme northwest of the massif, that is, on the northern edge of Sauerland, between the Lenne and the Rhine and thus in the region closest to the continent of Old Red Sandstone. Here the thick Lenne shales correspond to the Eifelian and lower Givetian. Intercalations of shales and red sandstones appear in it;[68] plant remains are

associated with marine faunas; there has even been found, in the region of Elberfeld (see map, Fig. 26), *Amnigenia rhenana,* a fresh water pelecypod already noted in the Old Red Sandstone of Ireland and which we shall find in the lacustrine Middle Devonian of North America. Finally, in the northwest angle of Sauerland, the whole Lower Devonian seems to be missing as well as the Eifelian. There the Givetian begins with conglomerates containing huge blocks of Cambro-Silurian rocks which cannot be of distant origin.[69] We cannot see the substratum of these conglomerates but we can assume that we have arrived at the northern edge of the basin of sedimentation that, in the Lower and Middle Devonian, comprised the whole Rhenish Massif, in prolongation of the Dinant Basin. Also, the line of demarcation of the typical Dinant Basin and Namur Basin, so clearly marked in Belgium by the Silurian band of Condroz, would thus extend beyond the Rhine, reappearing in the northwest extremity of the Sauerland (see Fig. 26).

On the other hand, from the upper Givetian on, the sea takes over. The upper shales of the Lenne are indeed covered by upper beds with *Stringocephalus* but the facies is always deeper in the southeast than in the northwest.

d. Frasnian.[70]   Variations of analogous facies are found here. In most of the Rhenish Massif, in this period, facies with cephalopods, somewhat marly limestones, or even marls with pyritic goniatites (example, Büdesheim shales, near Prüm, in the Eifel) predominate, that is, facies that we shall find again in the Mediterranean Devonian.

The genus *Manticoceras* is characteristic of the stage, which the Germans, for this reason, call *Manticoceras* stage or again *Intumescens* stage from the name of a species, *M. (Gephyroceras) intumescens,* frequent at this horizon all over Europe. Wedekind could distinguish 4 successive zones of ammonoids in the Frasnian. But in detail, this sea with goniatites is varied by numerous shoals,[71] along which marly facies are replaced by sandy or calcareous, sometimes even reefy facies. These limestones are especially developed in the northwest part of the Sauerland, for example in the vicinity of Elberfeld, where they are very fossiliferous and similar to rocks of the same facies of the Ardennes Frasnian.

e. Famennian.   Almost everywhere the facies become deeper-water and consequently more uniform. Nevertheless we always find the influence of the northern continent, bringing the red clays, and of the shoals of the Siegerland block, producing sands.

So in the northwestern part of the Sauerland, the stage begins with beds which are often variegated and sandy showing the proximity of the coast, the cypridine shales, in which imprints of small ostracods (genus *Entomis*) often provide the only fossils.[72] But toward the east, this lower Famennian is represented by the deep facies of pyritic limestones and shales with goniatites, characterized by the genus *Cheiloceras*. This is the *Cheiloceras* stage, equivalent to the lower Famennian, which Wedekind subdivided into two paleontologic zones.

Higher, in the whole of eastern Sauerland, in the Kellerwald and the whole central area of the Hesse synclinorium, the very uniform type of limestones

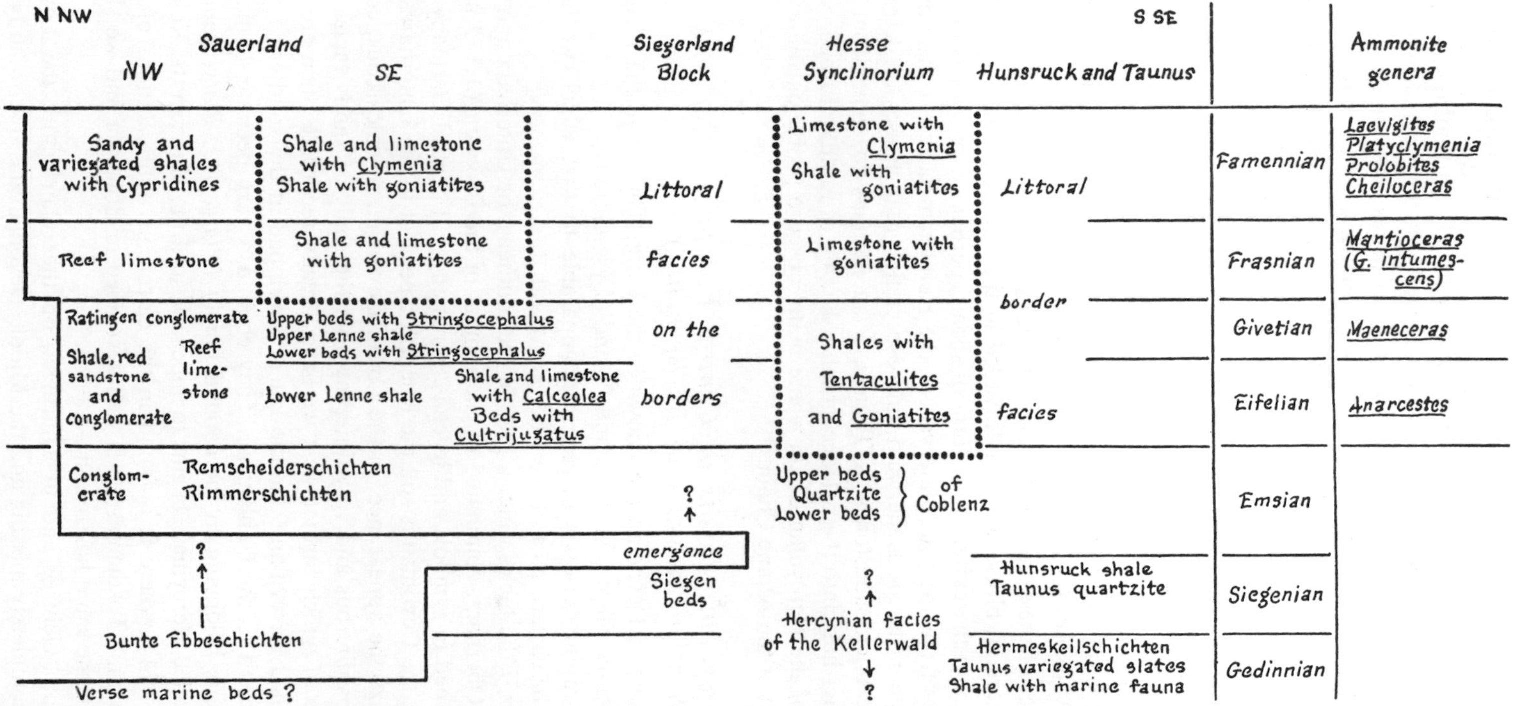

FIG. 27. *Diagrammatic chart of the Devonian facies in the Rhenish Schiefergebirge.*

To the left of the heavy line, continental (or lacustrine) facies, corresponding to the edge of the Old Red Sandstone Continent. Above the heavy broken line, the deepest-water facies of the eastern part of the massif and of the Hesse synclinorium.

with *Clymenia*[73] of the upper Famennian appears. Their marbling in pink almonds (*Kramenzelkalke*) reminds us of the red and brown marble of the Mediterranean Devonian. This is still a deep-water facies containing successive ammonoid genera, *Prolobites, Platyclemenia, Laevigites,* which make possible 3 subdivisions.[74] Moreover on the edge of this deep sea, particularly in north-western Sauerland, shoals remain with sandy-shaly facies with cypridines and even conglomerates.[75]

Like the Middle Devonian, this Rhenish Famennian contains volcanic tuffs (*Schalsteine*) and diabase flows.

f. Conclusions. Thus, while the study of the Franco-Belgian Ardennes shows only a very simple paleogeographic picture, that of the southern border of the continent of Old Red Sandstone with its changing fringe of ancient shores, the Rhenish Massif of Germany, reveals other peculiarities. We find there first the approaches of the same northern continent, of which a projecting promontory, the Siegerland block, was only invaded in the course of the Lower Devonian, to remain thereafter in the form of shoals, perhaps even an island. But other elements from the south intervened: the Hercynian facies of the Lower Devonian appears in the Kellerwald, and especially great masses of detritus, shown by the thick sandstones of Taunus, seem perhaps to come from the south. We enter here into the paleogeographic domain of middle Europe, right to the heart of the Hercynian Chain where many obscure problems still exist, as in the heart of the Alpine Chain.[76]

5. Hercynian Massifs of Central Europe (Harz, Bohemian Massif and its Branches)

Classic outcrops of Devonian are known in the Harz, Thuringia, the Fichtel-Gebirge, Bohemia, Silesia, Moravia and Poland (Lysa-Gora).

The stratigraphic series is in general comparable to that which we have described in the eastern part of the Rhenish Massif.

In the Harz,[77] the facies differ a little in the southeast or Unterharz and the northwest or Oberharz, dominated by the summit of the Brocken (1,172 m.), which, enveloped in symbols and legends, commands all central Germany. In the Oberharz, the Devonian is still the Rhenish type. But in the Unterharz, we must emphasize the appearance, in the Lower Devonian, of calcareous, coral facies, very fossiliferous and very different from the shaly or sandy facies the predominance of which farther west we have already recorded. Such are the limestones called Hercynian[78] (of the Harz) developed in the southern Harz, which correspond to the Coblenzian. They contain a very peculiar fauna of large gastropods belonging to the capulid family (*Platyceras, Platyostoma*). This fauna, called Hercynian, begins to appear west of the Harz, in the Kellerwald (see p. 124), where it is found in the calcareous intercalations of the Lower Devonian.[79] To the east, it is well developed in Bohemia and we shall find it again in the same horizon in America.

In the Fichtel-Gebirge and in Thuringia, on the other hand, the Lower Devonian is completely missing and the Middle Devonian lies discordantly on the Silurian. In lower Silesia[80] (regions of Saltzbrunn and Glatz), the lacuna is

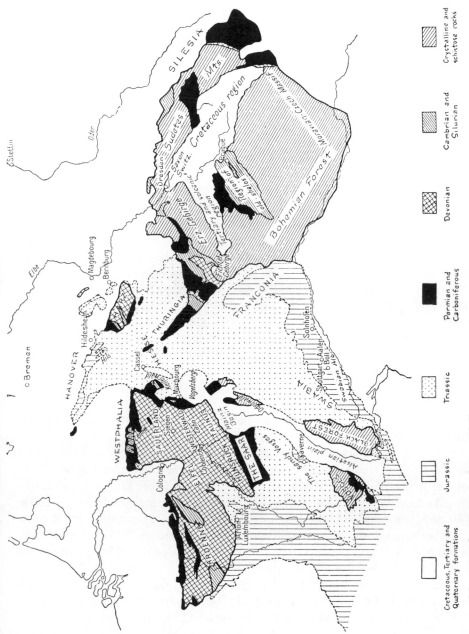

FIG. 28. *Geologic map of central Europe.*

Legend:

Cretaceous, Tertiary and Quaternary formations

Jurassic

Triassic

Permian and Carboniferous

Devonian

Cambrian and Silurian

Crystalline and schistose rocks

129

still more important, for the Upper Devonian, beginning with basal conglomerates, directly overlies crystalline rocks.

Finally, in Bohemia, in the classic region called Barrandian (see p. 60) the Devonian crops out only in a restricted area, between Prague and Beraun, but it contains very rich faunas long ago studied by Barrande. Then the Lower Devonian, which follows the Gothlandian in continuity, assumes the Hercynian facies: these are the famous, very fossiliferous Konjeprus limestones. They are covered by a Middle Devonian of deeper-water facies, with cephalopods. The limestones of Mneniany (or of Branick) and shales with tentaculites represent the Eifelian there and the Hostim shales (or Srbsko) the Givetian with *Stringocephalus burtini*. The series ends with plant beds, with a flora clearly older than the *Archaeopteris* flora of the Upper Devonian, so we may assume that this last stage is missing.

But in Moravia, northeast of Brno, little Devonian islets cropping out in the middle of the Carboniferous show a completely different type.[81] The series seems to begin here with the Givetian. There are beds with stringocephales, overlain by beds with *Calceola sandalina,* but containing a Givetian mutation of this species (see p. 105). Above, non-fossiliferous sandy-shaly beds pass in continuity to the Carboniferous, so the Upper Devonian must be represented.

Farther east, in the central Polish Massif (Sainte-Croix Mts., see pp. 55, 92), Volhynia, and Podolia, the Lower Devonian is very interesting, for we find here, as in the Ardennes, the boundary between two facies domains. In the northern part of the massif, that is in the Lysa Gora proper, and in Volhynia, beds with marine facies (with, however, no trace of Hercynian, calcareous facies) alternate with others of Old Red Sandstone facies. In the southern part (near Kielce) and in Podolia, there is nothing but Old Red Sandstone facies.

According to Czarnocki,[82] the succession of beds in the Lysa Gora (north facies) are established as follows:

Following the Gothlandian graptolite shales comes the Niewachlow graywacke (200 m.) with brachiopods, representing the middle and upper Ludlovian. Above, but without discordance, comes the lower Gedinnian (Downtonian) beginning with red shales and the conglomerate of Miedzania Gora (40 m.), comparable to the Fépin conglomerate and continuing with Rzepin beds, variegated shales and sandstones with calcareous beds, containing a fauna of brachiopods[83] and trilobites similar to that of the Mondrepuis shales or of the Verse beds of the Sauerland.

The upper Gedinnian (150 m.) is represented by the Klonow beds, without fossils, but with facies so typical of the Old Red Sandstone (English Dittonian) that they were formerly attributed by Siemiradzki to the variegated sandstone of the Triassic.

The Siegenian corresponds to a lacuna of sedimentation.

In the lower Emsian (Barcza beds, 140 m.) the Old Red Sandstone facies still predominates but with some sandy intercalations with a marine fauna analogous to that of the same horizon in Belgium.

The middle Emsian (175 m.) is shown by the *Spirifer* sandstones with some red beds reminiscent of Remscheid beds in the Sauerland.

The upper Emsian (190 m.) is clearly marine, with dense sandstones with brachiopods and marine mollusks.

To the lower Eifelian may be assigned the shales with marine fauna of Bukowa Gora (140 m.) overlain again by 100 m. of variegated sandstones.

And it is only above these that the decisively marine series of the Eifelian transgression commences, which deposited very characteristic thick dolomites on the whole Polish massif.

In the southern region on the other hand (Kielce facies) and in Podolia, all the Lower Devonian is of the Old Red Sandstone type or sandstone with placoderms, lying in discordance on ancient (Cambrian) rocks, which is, moreover, difficult to synchronize with the marine beds of the northern facies. But, leaving the Lysa Gora and progressing southward, we see the marine Gedinnian of the north reduced little by little to 1 or 2 m. Czarnocki thinks then that in the domain of the southern facies, there is a complete lacuna of the Gedinnian and even of the Siegenian.

The analogy of this Polish Lower Devonian with that of the Ardennes and the Sauerland is truly striking. But while in the Ardennes the Old Red Sandstone facies appear toward the north, bordering the North Atlantic continent, here it is to south (vicinity of Kielce and Podolia) that they develop, on the margin of a Podolian rigid mass, a distant extension of the shoals of Siegerland and separated from the North Atlantic continent by a kind of subsiding sill (North trough of Stille, note 76, this chap.), at the eastern extremity of which were accumulated great thicknesses of beds with marine facies of the Lysa Gora and Volhynia.

6. *The Armorican Massif*

The Devonian here occupies broad areas only in the Basins of Laval and Chateaulin. But there are also other small isolated outcrops of it, especially marked by the calcareous ridges (very rare rocks in Brittany, see p. 64) in the synclines of Ancenis, Angers, Nehou and in the Vendée. This Devonian has, moreover, in these different regions, rather different characteristics which make comparison difficult. Numerous works, well summarized by L. Bertrand (work cited note 50, chap. 2), have followed the old studies made especially by Barrois, Oehlert, and Kerforne.[84]

The Devonian series is complete only in the western part of the great Laval-Chateaulin syncline, with which we begin our study.

Chateaulin Basin.[85]   The best known example of the Lower Devonian is here represented by the Plougastel quartzites, which, projecting as a headland in the roadstead of Brest, play an important orographic role in all western Brittany: they compose the crests of the Arrée mountains on the north side of the Chateaulin Basin and, on its south side, the southern part of the Black Mountain. They are generally attributed to the Gedinnian, for at their base, in shales and sandstones passing in continuity into the Gothlandian shales, is found a mixed fauna in which the Devonian *Homolonotus* is associated with Silurian forms. Above come sandstones with *Orthis monnieri,* a brachiopod that is characteristic of the lower Coblenzian or Siegenian everywhere in Brittany. But on the northern edge of the Chateaulin Basin, the Lower Devonian is transgressive, for there is no Silurian, and the Lanfains quartzites of Lower Devonian age (Coblenzian) lie directly on the Brioverian phyllites.

Then, shaly-sandy beds with *Phacops potieri, Spirifer arduennensis, S. paradoxus,* with some calcareous lentils, pass in continuity from Lower to Middle Devonian. But the latter shows here none of the development of calcareous facies which were described in the Ardennes. This is the Rhenish type, the Porsguen shales with tentaculites and even goniatites (*Agoniatites, Anarcestes*). *Spirifer cultrijugatus* has been found, however, and even in the Crozon peninsula (Brest roadstead), the presence of *Calceola sandalina*[86] confirms the Eifelian age of the base of these shales; while the top, with *Rhynchonella cuboides, Tornoceras* and cypridines, rises to the Upper Devonian.

Laval Basin.[87] The series begins here, as in the Chateaulin Basin, with sandy facies predominating at the base but it ends with La Baconnière limestones (near Laval), corresponding to the lower Coblenzian (Siegenian) and with shales and sandstones of Sablé, containing faunas of the Siegenian and Eifelian (J. Pillet, C. R. Soc. géol. France, 1948, p. 141). The absence of the Givetian and Upper Devonian may be due perhaps to tectonic stretching, or to erosion which preceded the beginning of the Carboniferous sedimentation.

Syncline of Angers (or of Saint-Julien-de-Vouvantes).[88]

The Lower Devonian begins here only with the sandstones with *Orthis monnieri.* With this local form, valueless for comparison with other regions, other species are also associated which, common to the Ardennes, suggest the probability of lower Hunsrückian age. The transgression thus would not begin here until the upper Siegenian. Above, the Vern limestones, similar to those of La Baconnière (Laval Basin), with *Homalonotus gervillei* and *Leptaena murchisoni,* should still be classified as Siegenian. And this stage ends with the shales, calcareous shales and graywackes of Angers, with *Spirifer primaevus.*

The limestones of Angers and Erbray with *Spirifer paradoxus and Phaecops potieri* certainly correspond to the Emsian. We also note here the appearance of *Calceola sandalina.*

The Middle Devonian. It is represented by the shales and limestones of St.-Julien-de-Vouvantes, with *Spirifer elegans, Atrypa reticularis,* etc., certainly of Eifelian age. The Givetian is unknown.

Upper Devonian. The oldest visible member is made up of shales and tentaculite limestones which can be attributed to the Frasnian and perhaps even to the lower Famennian (*Cheiloceras* zone), for in Finisterre (Chateaulin Basin) analogous shales with the same tentaculites contain *Cheiloceras.*

Then there was certainly a lacuna of sedimentation. For the beds which overlie in slight discordance these tentaculite limestones contain an entirely new fauna. These are shales with nodules with *Laevigites, Wocklumeria,* and *Clymenia.* Thus they correspond to the very top of the Rhenish Famennian and even (*Wocklumeria*) to the base of the Carboniferous.

Ancenis Syncline.[89]   The Devonian is found here only in narrow bands pinched between the Silurian and Carboniferous. Nothing older than the Eifelian is found, represented by shales of Liré (near Ancenis) with *Phacops potieri* and *Pleurodictyum problematicum*[90] and by limestones which have provided Mlle. Le Maître with Eifelian faunas (not Givetian) even having affinities with those of the upper Coblenzian limestones of the eastern Alps

	NÉHOU	LAVAL-CHATEAULIN	ANGERS	ANCENIS
Famennian		Bathyal black shales with goniatites and cypridines	Shales with cypridines of Saint-Julian-de-Vouvantes	
Frasnian		Shales with Rhynchonella cuboides	Shales and limestones with Tentaculites	Copchoux limestone with Rhynchonella cuboides
Givetian		Shales	Unknown	Limestone with Stringocephalus
Eifelian		Deep-water shales of Porsguen with Spirifer cultrijugatus	Shales and limestones of Saint-Julien-de-Vouvantes	Shales of Liré (near Ancenis) with Pleurodictyum problematicum
Coblencian	Néhou shales and limestone Sandstone with Orthis monnieri	Limestone of La Baconnière (near Laval) Sandstone with Orthis monnieri	Erbray limestone Sandstone with Orthis monnieri	
Gedinnian	Shales and quartzites	Plougastel quartzites Shales passing into the Silurian		

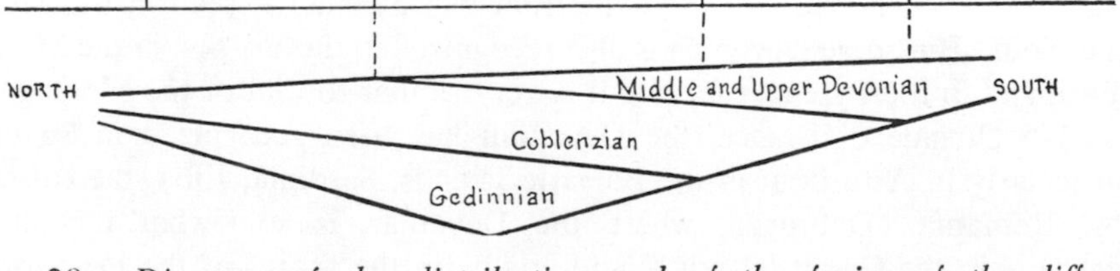

FIG. 29. *Diagram of the distribution and of the facies of the different Devonian stages in Brittany.*

and especially with those of the Mneniany (Bohemia) limestones. In any case, as in the Angers and Chateaulin Basins, the Devonian ends with cypridine shales of the Rhenish type.

Vendée.[91]   Doubtless because of a series of tectonic movements, the Devonian is here represented only by narrow calcareous lentils, of which the most interesting is that of the marbles of Ville-dé-d'Ardin which appear under the Jurassic at the southern threshold of the Armorican Massif and become buried under the Carboniferous of the Chatonnay-Vouvant Basin. In these limestones, rich in corals and stromatoporids, G. Mathieu has recently noted *Stringocephalus burtini,* which demonstrates its Givetian age.

Cotentin.[92]   Here, as in the southern part of the Chateaulin Basin, there seems to be continuous passage between the Gothlandian shales and the Devonian, beginning with shales with *Grammysia* which A. Bigot classifies as Gedinnian. Above is found the classic horizon of Siegenian sandstone with *Orthis monnieri,* followed by the shales and limestones of Nehon with an upper Coblenzian fauna (Emsian) with *Athyris undata, Leptaena murchisoni, Cryphaeus,* etc. The Middle and Upper Devonian are unknown.

V. Mediterranean Zone

As in the Silurian, we cover here all of southern Europe, south of the zone of Brittany, the Rhenish Massif and Bohemia. This area is characterized by the fact that the Devonian is generally continuous with the Silurian on one side and the Carboniferous on the other. We are, however, beyond the influence of the Caledonian folding, which affected various parts of the central European zone.

The geosynclinal regime does not end here until toward the middle of the Carboniferous at the earliest. That is to say, the Devonian of this Mediterranean area is always much folded, sometimes even granitized and more or less metamorphic. It is, then, not impossible that it may have been incorporated in the schistose series of ancient massifs (Hercynian) where it remains completely unrecognizable. So the outcrops recognized as Devonian in this zone must be shown as islets, spared by metamorphism and quite insufficient to account for what should actually be there, the Devonian sediments before their metamorphism and folding.

The best French type of the Mediterranean Devonian is seen in the Montagne-Noire. But some Devonian is also recognized in the Vosges, in the Massif Central and in the Pyrenees (where it is very similar to that of the Montagne-Noire).[93] Outside of France, the Devonian has been recognized in Spain[94] (particularly in Asturias), in the Balearic Islands, Sardinia, Elba, the eastern Alps, Romania (Dobrogea, where the Devonian is somewhat metamorphosed),[95] in the Greek Islands,[96] and finally on the shores of the Bosphorus and in Morocco. Of all these regions, we shall take as examples only the Vosges, the French Massif Central (especially Montagne-Noire), the Carnic Alps, Sardinia, and Morocco.

1. *The Vosges*

In the Hercynian Massif of the Vosges,[97] the era of greatest folding and of granitization ended just before the Westphalian, for the non-metamorphic Carboniferous sediments there lie discordantly on all the older formations. These latter comprise an assemblage where fossils are very rare, the tectonics highly complicated, and the stratigraphy still uncertain. We can describe it as follows (see Fig. 30):

1st. Some gneisses, probably very old (Precambrian).

2nd. Some granitic rocks of varying ages, some of which are certainly pre-Devonian, for they are found in pebbles in Devonian conglomerates; others are post-Devonian or even post-Dinantian, for they are injected in and metamorphose the Devonian or Dinantian sediments.

3rd. Ancient schists, localized, as we have seen (p. 39) in a unique band between Barr and Saales. A southern zone is formed there by the Villé shales,

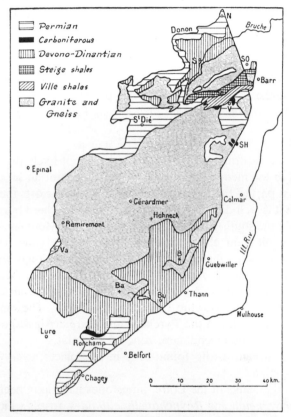

FIG. 30. *Diagrammatic geologic map of the Hercynian Vosges.*

The Secondary and Tertiary are left white. N = Nideck; S = Schirmeck; SO = Sainte-Odile; St = Steige; V = Villé; SH = Saint-Hippolyte; Va = Val d'Ajol; B = Grand Ballon; Ba = Ballon d'Alsace; Bu = Bourbach.

sericitized and tourmaline-bearing, which may be classified as Precambrian, though without good reason. They are bordered on the north by the zone of the Steige shales, slightly metamorphic and resembling either the Cambrian phyllites of the Ardennes or the phycod shales of the Lower Silurian of Thuringia.

4th. A very complex and greatly folded series of formations of great variety, which are grouped under the name of Devono-Dinantian, because fossils dating from these two ages have been found in them. But, beyond the fossiliferous strata, it is difficult to make out what is Devonian, what Dinantian. These formations crop out in two regions, thus comprising two Devono-Dinantian Massifs.

a) On the north, there is the Massif of the Bruche, from the name of the river which crosses it. This is a thick series of shales, graywackes (sandstones with eruptive materials), volcanic tuffs, sandstones, marbles, breccias, conglomerates, etc. For a long time, near Schirmeck, either in shales or marbles, coral faunas of the Eifelian and Givetian (*Stringocephalus, Calceola sandalina,* stromatoporids, crinoids) have been recognized in it and recently plant remains with Devonian affinities have been found.[98] But, as we shall see later, some Dinantian fossils appear at certain places.

b) On the south, the Grand Ballon Massif, which contains the highest point of the Vosges (Ballon de Guebwiller), for the most part is certainly Carboniferous (Dinantian). But, at its southern extremity, at Chagey, southwest of Belfort, the shales have yielded a typical Famennian fauna,[99] *Spirifer verneuili, Orthis striatula, Phacops trinucleus, P. (Cyrtosymbole) bergicus.*

2. The French Massif Central

Let us repeat that contrary to former opinion it is not likely that the Devonian is represented in the metamorphic state in the Precambrian series which comprise the largest part of the Massif. The Devonian then exists there only in two regions, where it is well dated by fossils, one on the southern border of Morvan and the other in the southern end of the Massif, in the Montagne-Noire. It has, moreover, very different characteristics in these widely separated domains, with no relation between them. The northern domain belongs with the Vosges and Brittany (A. Demay, J. Jung). As in those two regions, the Devonian and Dinantian are hard to distinguish from each other in the absence of fossils and we may thus speak of Devono-Dinantian complexes. The southern domain, on the other hand, bound to the Pyrenees and Carnic Alps, shows us the true Mediterranean type, the Paleodinaric zone of Kossmat.

a. South of Morvan, fossils, found only in two places, everywhere indicate the Upper Devonian.

At Diou, on the banks of the Loire, limestones have long been known, containing *Spirifer verneuili* and *Rhynchonella cuboides,* fossils which indicate the Frasnian age. Near Bourbon-Lancy (Saône-et-Loire), A. Michel-Lévy discovered shales with cypridines and *Clymenia* demonstrating the existence of a Famennian quite similar to that of the Rhenish Massifs. Finally, it is possible that the andesitic complex that we shall describe later (p. 197), at the base of the fossiliferous Dinantian around Vichy, may really be Devonian because of its resemblance to the Upper Devonian of Bourbon-Lancy; but there are no fossils.

b. In the Montagne-Noire, there is an excellent representation of the Mediterranean type of the Devonian. After the lacunas of sedimentation that we have mentioned (p. 97) toward the end of the Ordovician, due, as in Wales, to a preliminary phase (called Taconic) of the Caledonian folds,[100] came the terminal phase (called Ardennian) of this Caledonian orogeny. So the Devonian often begins with very compact sandstones standing out sharply in the topography and locally called the "quartzose wall." But this Devonian is complete and from the Gedinnian the facies are much deeper than in the north. The tectonics are very complicated but the abundance of fossils helps us to identify clearly almost all the classic stages.

1st. The Lower Devonian is represented by sandstones and dolomites in which M. Thoral [101] has recently discovered *Spirifer* cf. *sulcatus*.

2nd. The Eifelian has the organic, calcareous facies which forms great dry plateaus, often in nappes thrust over the Carboniferous shales. There are found trilobites (*Phacops potieri, Bronteus*), *Spirifer cultrijugatus* characteristic of the base of the Eifelian, the calceolas of this stage, and above all very numerous corals.

3rd. The Givetian is also represented by limestones, but fine grained, muddy and with a deep-water fauna. Around Cabrières, they form numerous small overlapping scales, rising above the Carboniferous shales, especially in the Peak of Bissons, where they are very fossiliferous, from which their name of white limestones of the Peak. The fauna is composed of goniatites (*Fornoceras, Maeneceras*). It is thus very different from the Givet limestone, but the discovery of an example of *Stringocephalus burtini* confirms its parallelism with the Givetian stage.

4th. The Upper Devonian is also calcareous but the red, greenish or violet tints, already apparent in the Givetian, here are frequent. This is the essentially Mediterranean facies of Griotte Marbles, widely exploited in the Pyrenees, a facies which corresponds, as in the Secondary (see p. 359), to deep-water muddy sediments, or at any rate pelagic, with which are mixed contributions of red earth coming from neighboring emerged regions. The fauna[102] is composed almost entirely of goniatites, often pyritic in the more marly banks. *Gephyroceras intumescens* indicates the Frasnian; *Cheiloceras,* the lower Famennian, etc. At the top of the series appears a *Clymenia* characteristic of the upper Famennian.

3. *Eastern Alps and Sardinia*

In the **Carnic Alps,**[103] especially on the Italian slope, the entire Devonian is represented by very fossiliferous limestone facies, for example in the region of Volaia (Gail valley, Fig. 64). There the Lower and Middle Devonian are in the state of reefy limestones, sometimes dolomitic and unstratified, whose thickness exceeds 1000 m. and whose fauna recalls that of the Hercynian facies of the Harz and Bohemia. The Lower Devonian, beginning with a characteristic layer of silicified corals, everywhere contains brachiopods (*Spirifer princeps,* the genus *Karpinskya*) and gastropods. In the Middle Devonian, made up of limestones with corals and stromatoporids, we can distinguish an Eifelian, represented by limestones with large pentamerids (without calceolas) and the Givetian, well characterized by *Stringocephalus burtini.* In the Upper Devonian are gray siliceous reticulated limestones. The Frasnian contains brachiopods (rhynchonellids of the *cuboides* group) while in the Famennian deeper-water facies with *Clymenia* appear.

But on the Austrian slope, the Devonian is profoundly modified; the preceding limestones pass laterally into a comprehensive thin series[104] of reticulated pink and gray limestones (long confused with the analogous facies of the Silurian) which, according to their goniatite faunas, encompass all the Middle and Upper Devonian.[105]

Farther east, a Devonian similar to that of the Carnic Alps, always with Bohemian affinities, extends into the Karawanken and as far as Styria, in the vicinity of Graz.[106]

Finally, in **Sardinia,** Devonian stratigraphy is still a matter of uncertainty. The existence of very important Caledonian folds, with a lacuna of the whole Lower and Middle Devonian, has long been agreed upon. M. Gortani thinks, however, that here, as in the northern Carnic Alps, there is a comprehensive series of such a kind that the whole Devonian would be represented by reticulated limestones in continuity of sedimentation with the Silurian at the base, non-fossiliferous in its lower part and at the top containing *Clymenia.*

4. *Morocco*

Because of the richness of its faunas, the extent of its outcrops and the diversity of its facies, the Devonian of Morocco deserves to become classic.[107]

In the Moroccan Meseta, the Devonian, following in continuity the Silurian, shows three subdivisions with characteristic faunas. The Lower Devonian is represented by shales with calcareous lenses in the west (G. Lecointre), by quartzose graywackes in the center and east. It contains especially trilobites (*Phacops, Cryphaeus, Dalmania*) but in the southwestern part (Rehamna) it assumes more neritic and reefy facies. This indicates the approach of an emerged region which we shall soon find in the Djebilet. In the Middle Devonian, organic limestones with corals and stromatoporids predominate in the west, while in the center and the east are found shales with goniatites. In the Upper Devonian these deep-water facies (with *Mantioceras intumescens*) persist in the same region, while in the coastal region of the west, a more detrital and even subcontinental facies is found, with plant remains (*Archaeocalamites*), trilobites and dwarf brachiopods. But even there, the Devonian is quite complete, for the upper beds include the fauna of the Etroengt zone of the base of the Carboniferous.[108]

The Djebilet, on the other hand, must have had a very different history. Indeed, it is agreed that only a transgressive Upper Devonian is represented there by the limestones and quartzites with corals, crinoids and *Spirifer verneuili.*[109]

In the High Atlas, we find, as in the Meseta, a Devonian passing in continuity to the Gothlandian and probably complete, but the rarity of fossiliferous strata will not allow a precise stratigraphy. In the western part of the Marrakech Atlas, brownish calcareous shales containing *Spirifer paradoxus-hercyniae,* with sandstones and conglomerates, certainly represent the Lower Devonian. The system ends with quartzites and limestones with corals and crinoids of the Upper Devonian. In the west and in the country of Skoura the only faunas known up to the present time belong to the Eifelian, here a deep-water facies with shales rich in goniatite faunas (E. Roch).

In the Anti-Atlas, only the Lower Devonian, in the Djebel Sarron, is yet known, with black limestones with *Phacops,* corals and crinoids (see chap. 2, note 73).

In the northwestern Sahara, the Devonian, recently studied by Menchikoff,[110] proves to be complete and remarkably fossiliferous. The Lower Devonian, which succeeds the Gothlandian in continuity, is still quite detrital: there are sandstones with trilobites, *Spirifer primaevus* and *S. rousseaui.* In the Middle Devonian, the depth increases; sandstones and limestones with *Calceola sandalina* are accompanied by shales and limestones with goniatites. Finally, the Upper Devonian remains sandy and neritic only in the west (Tindouf region, with *Spirifer verneuili*). Moreover, everywhere, in Maider, the Tafilelt, the Saoura Basin, and the Colomb-Béchar region (Djebel Grouz), it is represented by limestones and shales with goniatites and *Clymenia,* often pyritic, and recognized for a long time (E. Haug).

To sum up, while in the Lower Devonian, the facies remain everywhere more or less neritic (with perhaps even emergence in the Djebilet), on the other hand in the Middle and especially the Upper Devonian, a very important paleogeographic feature appears: this is a great trough, marked by deep-water facies of shales and limestones with goniatites and *Clymenia,*[111] which extends over all central Morocco (central and eastern Meseta, country of Skoura), and into the northwestern Sahara. To the west, this trough was probably bordered by emerged lands, the approach of which is announced by neritic facies of the Upper Devonian of Tindouf and the western Meseta. We do not know its eastern boundaries. On the south, it certainly stops at the edge of the Sahara Shield (Haggar, see above). On the north, H. Termier[112] sees its extension as far as the Mediterranean regions, through the cephalopod facies of Montagne-Noire, Sardinia, the western Alps, and possibly still farther in the Rhenish Famennian. And we shall find later this same paleogeographic unity during the Lower Carboniferous.

Thus, in the Mediterranean regions, everywhere that the Devonian has not been rendered unrecognizable by the metamorphism of the Hercynian or Alpine geosynclines, we find it with similar characteristics: predominance of limestone facies, more or less organic in the Lower or Middle Devonian, but sandy and pelagic in the Upper Devonian, with goniatites and *Clymenia,* that extend, as we have said, as far as the Sahara.

This Mediterranean type contrasts then, in its general effect, with the shaly-sandy or Ardennes type, and this is natural, for it is evident the greater the separation from the continent of the Old Red Sandstone, the more predominant should be the muddy, pelagic or organic sediments formed, more or less in place, and not directly at the expense of emerged lands.

To find again a great development of sandy sediments, we must go into the heart of the Sahara (sandstone of the external Tassilis of Hoggar, described by C. Kilian) and into the Libyan Desert. There we arrive at the edges of another great continent, the continent of Gondwana, which we shall study in detail in the chapter on the Permo-Carboniferous.

VI. The Marine Devonian of Eastern Europe

Russian Platform and The Urals

The Devonian crops out in eastern Europe in five different regions.

1. The Baltic States. Between Courland and the White Sea is the region of the edge of the Baltic Shield. We already know (see p. 114), that the Devonian is represented there by the Old Red Sandstone with marine intercalations and is, in the north, transgressive directly on the Precambrian formations of the Baltic Shield.

The series begins with lower Baltic sandstones, with facies of Old Red Sandstone containing saline beds. The fish fauna shows that it is not Lower Devonian. So it may be assumed that these beds are almost contemporaneous with the Orcadian of northeastern Scotland (see p. 114). But, at the top, appear the fish genera *Asterolepis* and *Bothriolepis,* characteristic of the upper Old Red Sandstone. Then come limestones, dolomitic and marly, with *Spirifer verneuili* and *S. murilis*.[113] This marine transgression occurred then, not in the Middle Devonian as formerly believed, but in the Upper Devonian (Frasnian). Above, the series of the upper Baltic sandstones begins with gypsiferous marls in which the genus *Holoptychius* appears, characterizing the Old Red Sandstone, and ends with beds half marine, half continental. The top of the Devonian, immediately eroded in the Permian, is missing in the Baltic States and is only found again farther east in Russia.

2. Central Russia.[114] Here, in the region of Orel and Voronezh, south of the Carboniferous aureole of Moscow (see p. 209), a slight undulation in the canopy of the undisturbed sedimentary rocks covering the Russian platform brings the Devonian to the surface. But this Devonian series, essentially calcareous and marine, 300 m. thick, studied by Venjukov, belongs entirely to the Upper Devonian, according to the new ideas of Nalivkine, and can be subdivided as follows:

Frasnian. Limestones, marls, and sandstones of the Semiluk stage, with *Spirifer verneuili* ($= S.$ *disjunctus*) and *Rhynchonella cuboides,* and the Voronezh stage;[115] above comes the Evlanov stage, where we find coral limestones and marly limestones in which *Manticoceras intumescens,* an ammonoid characteristic of the Frasnian, has been noted.

Famennian. In the stages of Elezk (containing *Atrypa reticularis* and *Athyris concentrica*), and of Lebedjansk, the limestones become dolomitic, indicating a tendency to lagoonal facies. Finally the limestones of the Malevka-Muraevna stage contain a transition fauna of the Devonian and Carboniferous (see p. 210).

But recently, in Moscow itself, that is to say, north of this outcrop of Upper Devonian, a deep well,[116] after having cut through marine Upper Devonian, similar to that we have just described, penetrated a thick series (785 m.) of Old Red Sandstone facies, with fish bones. This is undoubtedly a continental Middle Devonian, here lying directly on the crystalline rocks.

On the whole, this Devonian of central Russia still remains comparable to that of the Baltic States. But the replacement of the continental facies of the upper Baltic sandstones by marine facies shows that we are already farther from the zones of the ancient, mobile shores which bordered the continent of Old Red Sandstone on the south.

3. The Timan. This is a branch of the Hercynian Chain that is to the Urals about what the Jura is to the Alps. So the Devonian here is folded.

Originally, this region must have been part of the continent of Old Red Sandstone but the lower Baltic sandstones are no longer found at its base.[117] Above the old metamorphic rocks, the series begins with beds with *Rhynchonella cuboides* and *R. meyendorfi* which perhaps still belong to the top of the Middle Devonian. Then come the famous bituminous shales of Domanik, deep-water facies with ammonoids whose fauna (especially *Manti-*

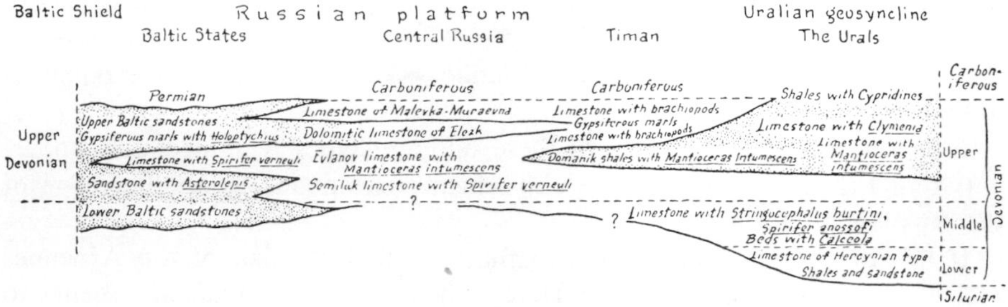

FIG. 31. *Diagram of the Devonian facies between the Baltic Shield and the Urals, showing the relation between the three types of Devonian.*

1st. Baltic type or type of the Old Red Sandstone Continent.
2nd. Type of the Russian platform or of the continental area with transgression and littoral facies.
3rd. Type of the Uralian geosyncline with deep-water facies.

The gray tone indicates: on the left, the Old Red Sandstone facies; on the right, pelagic facies with cephalopods.

coceras intumescens) clearly indicate the Frasnian. And the Devonian ends with limestones with *Spirifer*,[118] at the top of which (Famennian) gypsiferous marls are intercalated.

4. The Urals. Here we reach a geosynclinal region, which, moreover, must connect with the Mediterranean geosyncline by the Kirghiz steppes, Turkestan, Asia Minor, the shores of the Bosphorus, and Dobrogea (see p. 134); this completes the geosynclinal belt which surrounds the continental area of the Old Red Sandstone.

The Devonian of the Urals is, indeed, continuous and concordant with the Silurian (metamorphic, however) and with the Carboniferous. It is extremely folded (Hercynian Chain) and presents an uninterrupted series of marine deposits where the facies are of deeper-water than in other Russian areas.

The Lower Devonian is composed of shales and limestones of the Hercynian type (see p. 128), with faunas similar to those of Bohemia. Then come sandstones and variegated marls, without fossils, which alone perhaps show the distant influences of the continent of Old Red Sandstone (as the shales of Oignies, see p. 119). Above are shales and limestones with *Calceola*, indicating the Eifelian, then limestones and shales bearing the fauna of *Spirifer anossofi*. *Stringocephalus burtini* is also found there, which establishes the Givetian age of this fauna. Corresponding to the Upper Devonian are facies with cephalopods which greatly resemble those of the eastern Rhenish Massif:[119] clayey limestones with *Gephyroceras intumescens* (Frasnian) overlain by limestones with *Clymenia* (Famennian) and shales with cypridines, passing into the Carboniferous.

5. Podolia, or the region of the Dniester. Here the Devonian appears as a prolongation of that of the Lysa Gora (see p. 131); we are, then, on the southwest border of the Russian platform. The Lower Devonian presents a mixed type, where marine beds alternate with beds of sandstone containing fish of the Old Red Sandstone type.[120] More recently, marine faunas of the Middle Devonian have been found;[121] but the Upper Devonian is unknown.

Conclusions. The synthesis of these different types is immediately apparent from Fig. 31, except for Podolia which corresponds to another edge of the Russian platform.

If this diagram is compared with that of the Devonian of the Ardennes (see Fig. 25), the zone of the Hercynian Massifs of Ardennes seems to occupy about the place taken here by the Timan-Ural region.

It is equally instructive to compare this diagram of an episode of the pre-Carboniferous history of the Urals and Timan, which are Hercynian Chains, with the diagram of Fig. 16 which represents the pre-Devonian history of the British Caledonian chains. We see that the Urals seem to correspond approximately to Scotland and the Lake District, and the Timan to Shropshire.

Finally, a comparison with the Jurassic and Cretaceous history of the Alpine Chain in France shows the Urals corresponding to the Alps and the Timan to the Jura and sub-Alpine Chains.

It is to evoke such comparisons that we make use of the concepts of geosynclines and continental areas, ideas whose deep meaning and interest we now begin to perceive.

VII. The Devonian in Central and Eastern North America [122]

Disregarding completely the Devonian of the Rocky Mountains and Pacific Chains, whose description might be the subject of an elementary synthesis, we shall discuss only central and eastern America, that is, in effect, the border of the Canadian Shield (see p. 28).

The Devonian outcrops, from the point of view of the history of the seas and faunas,[123] may be grouped as follows (Fig. 32):

1. *The Atlantic Region:* This includes all the country located east of the lower course of the Saint Lawrence. The Devonian has outcrops in the Gaspé Peninsula, Nova Scotia, New Brunswick (Canada) and in Maine (U. S.).

2. *The Appalachian Region,* including the Appalachian Plateau and Chains, where the Devonian forms narrow bands running SW–NE, which blend into the great outcrops of New York State.

3. *The Interior or Central Region.* The Devonian, slightly undulant, crops out in the region of the Great Lakes, that is, south of Lake Ontario (in this direction it is united to the Devonian of the preceding region) in Ohio and Indiana. Much more is found further north, at the southern end of Hudson Bay (James Bay). On the other hand, in the south, thin bands border the ancient massifs of the Cincinnati and Nashville domes, and the Ozark Mountains south of St. Louis. This is called the Mississippi Basin.[124]

4. *The Region of the Northwest* where, directly bordering the Canadian Shield, the Devonian forms a wide band, which runs without interruption from the mouth of the Mackenzie River as far as Manitoba (west of Lake Winnipeg). Farther southeast, an isolated strip is found in Iowa.

In all this vast domain, studies of American paleontologists and stratigraphers have led to correlating the faunal provinces and the movements of the seas, so that the American Devonian provides a beautiful example of stratigraphic synthesis.

From the double viewpoint of faunas and lithologic formations, three successive groups can be recognized, which are about equivalent to the Lower, Middle, and Upper Devonian of Europe. Here is the list of formations which have been distinguished and whose types were established in New York State. The approximate European equivalents, according to E. Haug, are indicated.

Upper Devonian	Chemung sandstone (marine)—Catskill sandstone (lagoonal)		Famennian
	Portage Shale and sandstone		
	Genesee shale		Frasnian
	Tully limestone		
Middle Devonian	Hamilton	Hamilton shale	Givetian
		Marcellus shale	
	Onondaga limestone		Eifelian
Lower Devonian	Oriskany sandstone		Coblenzian
	Helderberg limestone		Gedinnian

A. *Lower Devonian*

This is recognized with certainty only in the first three of the regions we have just listed. It is divided into two stages, whose types are established in eastern New York State: at the base is the Helderberg limestone (from the Helderberg Mountains north of New York); at the top, the Oriskany sandstone.[125]

The extent of these two stages is very different. The Helderberg limestones are developed especially in the east and so are found in the Atlantic region, particularly in Gaspé. They are the thickest limestones in Gaspé (500 m.) containing the Oriskany fauna at the top, so the two stages blend here into

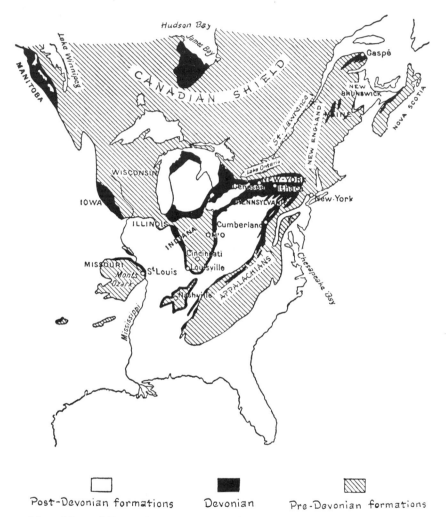

Post-Devonian formations   Devonian   Pre-Devonian formations

FIG. 32. *Map of Devonian outcrops in the central and eastern parts of North America.*

one limestone formation. This Helderberg stage is much thinner in Pennsylvania[126] (200 m.) and in eastern New York (100 m.) where it does not seem to extend farther west than the Helderberg Mountains. On the other hand, west of this same crest, the Oriskany becomes distinct, for it is transgressive and represented by its typical sandy facies, facies corresponding to its transgressiveness. The sea invades the northeastern part of the interior region and extends as far as Lake Ontario. Likewise, in the Appalachians, the Oriskany sandstone is easily recognized. The region of Cumberland (Md.) shows a typical development of it (about 100 m.).

This distribution of the two stages of the Lower Devonian would suffice to show us that the transgressive Devonian sea must have attacked the American Continent from the east, coming from the Atlantic. And certainly the faunas have close affinities with those of Europe; the fossils of the Helderberg limestone greatly resemble those of the European Lower Devonian of calcareous facies, that is, the type that we have called Hercynian. Here we find again the special gastropods of the Harz and Bohemian limestones (see pp. 128, 130), while the Oriskany sandstone contains the more littoral fauna of the Coblenzian with *Pleurodictyum,* with the brachiopod genus *Rensselaeria,* which we have noted (p. 118) in the Siegenian of Europe. These affinities are especially marked in the eastern part of the American basins, that is, in the limestones of Gaspé where several Rhenish forms (as *Spirifer primaevus*) have been found that have not penetrated further in America. Thus, it must be recognized, not only that there was a marine connection between Europe and the American Atlantic region, but also that there must have existed a coast uniting the two continents, along which the littoral faunas could spread. There we return to the southern coast of the North-Atlantic Continent.

Beside these two gulfs of the Lower Devonian (Atlantic region, Appalachian Gulf and the northeast part of the interior region) there is a third, coming from the lower Mississippi and reaching as far as the vicinity of St. Louis. There, it is difficult to define the respective boundaries of the Helderberg and the Oriskany. We only know that this gulf of the Lower Devonian must have been closed at the north and that it did not communicate with the interior basin. The faunas there are similar to those of the preceding regions and so originated in the Atlantic domain.[127]

B. *Middle Devonian*

Two great stages are distinguished, well differentiated especially in the Appalachian Basin (Penn.). These are the Onondaga limestone at the base and the Hamilton shale at the top.[128]

In the Atlantic region, this Middle Devonian is poorly characterized and doubtless represented, in part, by the upper zones, with few fossils, of the Gaspé limestone or by lagoonal sandstone which we shall soon discuss.

In the Appalachian region and that of the interior, the Onondaga stage is well characterized and very transgressive. A wide communication was established between these two regions so that the Onondaga limestone, often lying directly over the ancient rocks, extends from New York to the Mississippi. Sometimes there are true coral reefs, for example, those which crop out in the rapids of the Ohio River near Louisville. The fauna here always shows European affinities, with a *Spirifer* (*S. acuminatus*) almost identical to *S. cultrijugatus.* The sea extends as far north as the southern shore of the Hudson Sea where, at James Bay, there are vast outcrops of limestone with

Spirifer mucronatus. The interior basin, however, must have been closed toward the south, not extending beyond St. Louis, and having no connection with the Gulf of the lower Mississippi.

Finally in the northwest, in Manitoba and the Mackenzie region, great dolomitic outcrops of the Middle Devonian are found. But there, we have a completely different fauna, with *Stringocephalus burtini,* which doubtless migrated from Europe via northern Asia. This difference of faunas shows that an emerged barrier, extending over Wisconsin and Missouri, must have separated this Northwestern sea from the interior basin. And it was, then, from the north, by the Hudson Sea, that the new Onondaga fauna reached the central region, mingling there with the descendants of the Oriskanian fauna migrating earlier from the east.[129]

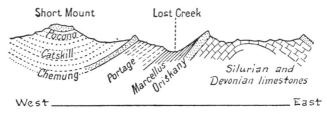

FIG. 33. *Diagrammatic transverse section of the Appalachians at the latitude of Washington, showing the morphologic role of the different beds of the Devonian.*

Folded in regular anticlines and synclines, these alternations of hard sandstones (especially the Oriskany, Chemug, and Pocono, or lower Dinantian, sandstones) and soft shales (particularly the Marcellus shale) produce long and narrow, very deep longitudinal slopes or combes, while the sandy-marly complexes of the Portage and the Catskill produce gentle slopes. This is the type of the so-called Appalachian style of morphology.

See the suggestive aerial photograph reproduced in E. de Martonne, *Géographie aérienne,* Albin Michel, Paris (1948), pl. VII, and the explanatory structure section.

The Hamilton stage is represented in Pennsylvania and the Appalachians by very thick shales (500 to 1,000 m.), the base of which, called Marcellus shale, contains a goniatite fauna with Eifelian affinities according to E. Haug, preferably of the top of the Givetian according to Wedekind. But this stage remains calcareous and thinner in the Mississippi Basin. In Ohio, it is represented by Columbus and Delaware limestones overlain by the Olentangy shales, sometimes assigned to the top of the Middle Devonian,[130] sometimes to the base of the Upper Devonian.[131] At this epoch, there is a great transgression in this basin, in which the Hamilton often lies directly on the ancient rocks. Thus the interior basin communicated, through the lower Mississippi, with the Gulf of Mexico and thereby new littoral faunas appear, coming from the south.

During this time, the northwest region is always occupied by the sea and isolated by the Wisconsin-Missouri barrier, which must have been broken somewhat toward the end of the Hamilton, for the beginning of faunal exchanges is recorded at this epoch.

C. *Upper Devonian*

In the central regions, there is almost the same distribution as in the Middle Devonian, except in southwest Missouri where there is transgression. But the fauna is changed.

Indeed, the Wisconsin-Missouri barrier is submerged and through it, from the Northwestern sea, comes a Frasnian fauna with European and Asiatic relationships with *Rhynchonella cuboides* and *Gephyroceras intumescens*. This new fauna appears first in Iowa, then in New York, invading all the interior basin joined to the Appalachian Basin.

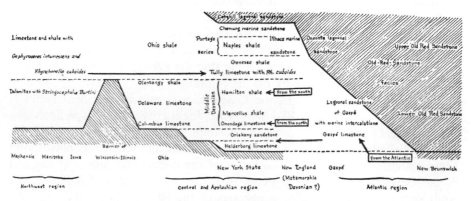

FIG. 34. *Diagram of the Devonian facies in the northern United States and Canada, showing the marine transgressions and the connections between the different basins. The arrows indicate the direction of the migrations of the marine faunas (principally after information from Chamberlin and Salisbury.)*

The facies are quite variable and have been studied especially in Pennsylvania and New York.

In these regions, the series begins with a thin calcareous bed called Tully limestone,[132] containing *Rhynchonella cuboides* and consequently marking the arrival of the new fauna. Above come black bituminous shales (of Genesee),[133] only 10 m. thick on the shores of Lake Erie but reaching 100 m. in Pennsylvania. Finally, the principal part of the Upper Devonian is formed by shales and sandstones called Portage,[134] which reach 500 m. thickness. At this period, deep-water shaly facies are developed in the center of the gulf, that come from the west and extend to the northern part of New York State. This is the Naples shale containing the oldest known clymenia (*Acanthoclymenia neapolitana*) which here occurs together with *Gephyroceras intumescens* and is of Frasnian age. On the edge of the gulf, however, are deposited sandstones, either still marine (Ithaca facies) or lagoonal (Oneonta facies).

At the end of the Devonian,[135] the sandy facies become general. They are, in the west, very thick, marine sandstones called Chemung sandstone (Famennian) with *Spirifer verneuili*. In the east, on the other hand, are thick, red, lagoonal beds (Catskill sandstone) identical with the Old Red Sandstone.[136]

D. *The Old Red Sandstone Continent in America*

We have already shown several times that the Baltic Shield and the Canadian Shield must have occupied, during the Primary, the two extremities of a vast continental area, the North Atlantic continent.

We can thus expect to find in America on the surface or the border of this continent, the same Old Red Sandstone as in Europe. But actually, they are nowhere found with as great a homogeneity and continuity as in Britain.

Particularly, it is only in New Brunswick, in a thick series of sandstones, clays, and red conglomerates, that we have been able, with the help of the fish faunas, to find the two British subdivisions of lower and upper Old Red Sandstone. In Nova Scotia we know only that the *Pteraspis* fauna of the lower Old Red Sandstone lies directly on the Silurian.

Still farther west, in Gaspé, the Gaspé sandstone with lagoonal facies is equivalent to the upper Old Red Sandstone, for it covers the Gaspé limestone with marine faunas of the Lower and perhaps Middle Devonian. Finally, still farther west, the Oneonta and Catskill sandstones, in New York, correspond to an extreme advance to the southwest of the continental facies, at the end of the Devonian. Thus they represent, for the central states of America, the equivalent of the upper Baltic sandstones of the Russian platform.

Considering all that we know of the conditions of formation of this Old Red Sandstone, we can conclude that in the Devonian a vast, more or less desert zone extended over all the North Atlantic continent. And the similarity of formations over such great areas would thus be explained by a similarity of geographic and climatic conditions.[137]

REFERENCE NOTES

1. See the very interesting summarizing tables given by R. Wedekind in the classic Treatise of Salomon, cited Chap. 2, note 8.

2. See the study of LeCompte, cited Chap. 3, note 3.

3. See R. Richter, Neues Jahrb. f. Min. (1916), p. 31; and F. Lotze, Senckenbergiana, 10 (1928). H. and G. Termier, *Etude sur Calceola sandalina Linné,* Rev. scientif., no. 3291 (Feb. 15, 1948), 32 fig.

4. M. LeCompte, *Les Tabulés du Dévonien moyen et supérieur du bord Sud du Bassin de Dinant,* Mém. Mus. r. Hist. nat. Belgique, mém. no. 90 (1939).

5. Except in America, where the blastoids reach their maximum development in the Devonian.

6. J. M. Clark, *The Devonian Crinoids* of the State of New York, Albany (1923).

7. E. Maillieux, *Répartition des Brachiopodes dans la Dévonien de l'Ardenne,* Bull. Mus. r. Hist. nat. Belgique, 17 (1941), no. 30; *Répartition des Spiriferidae et des Spiriferinidae dans le Dévonien de l'Ardenne,* ibid., no. 17; *Les Brachiopodes de l'Emsien de l'Ardenne,* Mém. mus. r. Hist. nat. Belgique, no. 96 (1941).

8. E. Maillieux, *Les Lamellibranches du Dévonien inférieur de l'Ardenne*, Mém. Mus. r. Hist. nat. Belgique, no. 81 (1937).

9. A. K. Miller, *Devonian Ammonoids of America*, Geol. Soc. America, Special Paper no. 14, 262 p., 39 pl. (1938).

10. Perhaps we should even include in this group the remains of large crustaceans described under the name of *Beltina danai* in the Precambrian (Belt beds) in America (see p. 37).

11. Such, at least, is the classic opinion still held by such specialists as Clarke and Ruedemann. Very recently, however, J. F. Pompeckj (*Palaeontologische Zeitsch.* V, 3, p. 319) claims, with good enough reason, that the Silurian eurypterids were continental and that their remains were accidentally swept into the sea. Finally, see R. Ruedemann, Amer. Journ. of Science (1924), p. 227.

12. J. A. Moy-Thomas, *Palaeozoic Fishes*, Methuen's Monographs on Biological Subjects, 149 p., 32 figs., New York (1939). He noted the discovery in 1939, in the Indian Ocean, of a living representative of the fossil group of coelacanths (crossopterygians).

13. Only the first of which is clearly distinguished. For the others, attempts to synthesize Hercynian Europe (Kober, Kossmat, Von Bubnoff, Demay) are still unsatisfactory, and their explanation would entail regional tectonic descriptions beyond the compass of this book.

14. See p. 8. We shall later find analogous bone-beds formed under the same paleogeographic circumstances, at the end of the lagoonal Triassic and the marine lower Jurassic; and just as the Downtonian is classified either in the Silurian or Devonian, we shall see the Rhetian attributed either to the Triassic or Jurassic (p. 323).

15. The classic sections of the Devonian of this region were the subject of a recent study by T. Robertson, "The Highest Silurian Rocks of the Wenlock District," Summary of progress of the Geol. Survey of Great Britain (1927).

16. On the Downtonian of Norway, see a very important publication containing much new data on the fauna of fishes: J. Kiaer, "The Downtonian Fauna of Norway," Videnskapselskapets Skrifter (1924), Oslo. Note also J. P. Lehman, *Les Poissons du Downtonien de la Scanie*, Mém. Diplôme Et. sup. Fac. Sc. Univ. Paris. no. 664 (1937).

17. W. Haack, *Die Gesteinsscholle von Schobull bei Husum; ein Devonvorkommen in Schleswig-Holstein*, Zeitsch. deutschen geol. Ges., Abh., 78 (1926).

18. L. Koch, *Geologie von Grönland*, Geologie der Erde, Berlin (1935). H. Bütler, *Die Mächtigkeit der kaledonischen molasse in Ostgrönland*, Mitt. naturf. Ges. Schaffhausen, 12. Heft (1935), no. 3.

19. See the publications of Kidston and Lang in the late years of the *Trans. Roy. Soc. Edinburgh*, and the résumés given by A. C. Seward, "The Earlier Records of Plant Life," Quart. Journ. Geol. Soc., 79 (1923), and by P. Bertrand, *Observations sur l'évolution de la flore pendant la période dévonienne et sur la première flore houillère*, Ann. Soc. Geol. du Nord, 58 (1933). Also bibliographic information will be found in the monograph cited note 51, this chap. Finally a list of all the known Devonian plants, with their geographic distribution and bibliography is given by K. Mägdefrau, *Die Flora des Oberdevons im östlichen Thüringer Wald*, Beihefte z. bot. Centralbl., 56 (1936), Abt. B.

20. Which produce, however, relatively fertile soils on account of the sands and clays of the Old Red Sandstone; whence their name "corn stones."

21. All that we have said applies equally to the Torridon, Jatulian and especially the Jotnian sandstones, whose facies remind us very much of those of the Old Red Sandstone, to such a degree that certain geologists have proposed that the Jotnian sandstone of the Kola Peninsula (p. 33) and even the Varanger sandstone (p. 90) be classified as Devonian.

22. We have recently been able to use the floras to establish a synchronism between the Old Red Sandstone and the marine Devonian. On this subject, see an article by R. Kräusel, Neues Jahrb. f. Min., Referate, Abt. B (1926), 1, p. 301.

23. This is the Dittonian stage, following the Downtonian. See W. W. King, "The Downtonian and Dittonian Strata of Great Britain and Northwestern Europe," Quart. Journ. geol. Soc. London, 90, part 4, no. 360, p. 526 (1934).

24. T. S. Westoll, "The Old Red Sandstone Fishes of the North of Scotland, Particu-

larly of Orkney and Shetland," Proc. Geologists' Assn., 48 (1937); this article contains interesting stratigraphic and biologic considerations.

25. We omit here the Downtonian which has been studied separately.

26. This shows also how dangerous is the task of tracing exact contours of the distribution of lands and seas. The maps of facies are infinitely more valuable for the synthetic ideas that they suggest.

27. On the geology of Belgium in general, see E. Maillieux, *Terrains, roches et fossiles de la Belgique,* 2nd edition, work published through the efforts of the Musée roy. d'Hist. nat. at Brussels; P. Fourmarier, *Vue d'ensemble sur la Géologie de la Belgique,* Ann. Soc. géol. Belgique Mem. (1934); and finally the guide books published on the occasion of the Internatl. Geological Congress in Belgium, in 1922. For the Primary, E. Maillieux and F. Demanet, *L'échelle stratigraphique des terrains primaires de la Belgique,* Bull. Soc. belge Géol., 38 (1928). Finally A. Hacquaert has made a complete list, with short analyses, of all the Belgian geological works appearing between 1939 and 1944, "Natural Sciences in Belgium During the War, Geology," pp. 105–163, Naturw. Tijdschr. Gand (1946).

28. Remember that, in these massifs, the Cambrian and Silurian were affected by the pre-Devonian folding. This Caledonian orogeny has recently been studied by Waterlot (cited Chap. 2, note 21).

29. Thus the name "Condroz Anticline," used in Fig. 24 for greater brevity, is not generally used by Belgian geologists.

30. By very ingenious, indirect reasoning, P. Fourmarier tried to define the original extent of this thrust surface: P. Fourmarier, *Quelques résultats de l' étude de la schistosité dans la bande silurienne de Sambre-Meuse,* Bull. Soc. géol. Belgique, t. 63 (1939).

31. This tectonic glimpse, sufficient for the moment, will be completed later (p. 180).

32. Local details in E. Asselberghs, *Le Dévonien inférieur de la feuille Givet (Ardennes) au 1/80,000,* Bull. Serv. Carte géol. France, no. 199, t. (1939).

33. Locality situated a little north of the Serpont Massif.

34. See also M. Leriche, *Les Pteraspis du Dévonien de la Belgique,* Bull. Soc. belge Géol., 33 (1923).

35. E. Asselberghs, *L'Eodévonien de l'Ardenne et des régions voisines,* Mém. Inst. géol. Univ. Louvain, 14 (1946), 598 p., 9 pl., 1 colored map. This important monograph synthesizes the numerous previous publications of the author, but we do not agree when he attributes a marine origin to the whole Gedinnian, even to the red beds with *Pteraspis* (p. 560), while later acknowledging (p. 562) that these placoderm faunas could have been lagoonal.

36. R. Dehée, *Découverte de Pterygotus anglicus à Liévin,* Ann. Soc. géol. du Nord, 52 (1927).

37. P. Pruvost, *Découverte de la faune marine gédinnienne de l'Ardenne et de l'Artois dans le Comté de Buckingham,* Ann. Soc. géol. du Nord, 58 (1933).

38. E. Maillieux, *Le Siegénien de l'Ardenne et ses faunes,* Bull. Mus. r. Hist. nat. Belgique, 16, no. 5 (1940).

39. These graywackes of the Ardennes, like those of Coblenz, are very fine, decalcified sandstones in which calcareous fossils have been dissolved and are represented by empty spaces. We shall see later (p. 136) that this same term graywacke also serves to designate somewhat different rocks.

40. This graywacke was formerly attached to the Eifelian; in fact, *Calceola sandalina* and *Spirifer cultrijugatus* were noted in it. But the *Calceola* is found sporadically in the upper Coblenzian of the Eifel while as for the *Spirifer,* it is not *S. cultrijugatus* but its Coblenzian mutation, *S. auriculatus.*

41. E. Asselberghs, *Emsien et Koblenzschichten en Ardenne, dans l'Osling et dans l'Eifel,* Mém. Inst. géol. Univ. Louvain, 13 (1941).

42. E. Maillieux, *Le Couvinien de l'Ardenne et ses faunes,* Mém. Mus. r. Hist. nat. Belgique, no. 83 (1938).

43. E. Maillieux, *Documents pour servir à l'étude du Givétien de l'Ardenne,* Bull. Mus. r. Hist. nat. Belgique, 16 (1940).

44. L. Dubrul, *La stratigraphie et les variations de faciès du Frasnien en Belgique,* Bull. Soc. belge de Géol., 62 (1938–39).

45. E. Maillieux, *Contribution à la connaissance du Frasnien moyen* (*assise de Frasnes*) *de la Belgique,* Bull. Mus. r. Hist. nat. Belgique, 16 (1940).

46. M. Lecompte, *Contribution à la connaissance des "récifs" du Frasnien de l'Ardenne,* Mém. Inst. géol. Univ. Louvain, 10 (1936).

47. E. Maillieux, *La faune des schistes de Matagne* (*Frasnien supérieur*), Mém. Mus. r. Hist. nat. Belgique, no. 77 (1936).

48. For a very detailed description of this Lower Devonian of the Ardennes and its parallelism to that of the Rhenish region, see the table published by E. Maillieux, *Un aspect nouveau du Dévonien inf. de l'Ardenne,* Bull. Mus. r. Hist. nat. Belgique, t. 8, no. 17 (1932).

49. J. Van Tuijn, *Le Couvinien et la partie supérieure de l'Eodévonien du bord oriental du synclinorium de Dinant entre l'Ourthe et Ferrières,* Mém. Inst. géol. Univ. Louvain, 4 (1927).

50. Let us note, however, that, by very ingenious indirect reasoning, to explain which would take us too far, P. Fourmarier (work cited, note 30, this chap.) was recently led to believe that, beyond an emerged region composed of the Silurian band of Condroz, the Lower Devonian must have been deposited in the Namur Basin. Its absence in this Basin at the present time would be due to erosion which preceded the transgression of the Middle Devonian.

51. H. Ledoux-Marcelle, *Sur les flores du Dévonien de la Belgique,* Bull. Soc. belge de Géol., t. 37 (1927); t. 40 (1931); t. 50 (1942); bibliography of Devonian floras. F. Stockmans, *Végétaux éodévoniens de la Belgique,* Mém. Mus. r. Hist. nat. Belgique, no. 93 (1940). E. Asselberghs, *L'extension verticale des espèces végétales dans l'Eodévonien de la Belgique,* Bull. Mus. r. Hist. nat. Belgique 18, no. 52 (1942) corrects some stratigraphic identifications of the preceding work.

52. See the very important article of M. Leriche, *Les Poissons famenniens de la Belgique; les faciès du Famennien dans la région gallo-belge. Les relations entre les formations marines et les formations continentales du Dévonien supérieur sur la bordure méridionale du Continent Nord-Atlantique,* Mém. Acad. r. de Belgique, Sc., 2 sér., 10 (1931).

53. E. Asselberghs, *Le Dévonien du bord Nord du Bassin de Namur,* Mém. Inst. géol. Univ. Louvain, 10 (1936). The red rocks of Mazy, whose age has been much debated, are here classified as Givetian.

54. C. R. Acad. Sc. (Sept. 11, 1933).

55. Ann. Soc. géol. du Nord, séance du June 6, 1928.

56. See, for example, E. Asselberghs, "Correlation between the Meadfoot Beds of Devonshire and the Siegenian of the Ardennes," Geolog. Magazine (1921), p. 165 and J. W. Evans, *La Corrélation des roches dévoniennes britanniques,* Livre jubilaire Soc. géol. Belgique (1926), p. 10. An excellent summary in H. Dewey, *South-West England,* 2nd edit. (1948), British regional Geology, Geol. Surv. and Mus.

57. See first the remarkable syntheses of the Rhenish Devonian given by Wedekind, in Salomon, *Grundzüge der Geologie,* Stuttgart (1926) and by von Bubnoff, *Geologie von Europa* II, 1, Berlin (1930). M. Asselberghs has very kindly given me some information. On more recent works, many accounts (maps, diagram of facies, p. 613) will be found in the C. R. of the excursions of the German Geological Society at Cassel, in 1936 (Zeitschr. deutschen geol. Ges., 88, 1936). Likewise, on the occasion of an excursion of British geologists, a very clear résumé (structural map, p. 49) was published by R. Tilmann, etc., "Contributions to the Geology of the Rhenisch Schiefergebirge," Proc. Geologists Ass., 49 (1938), part I.

58. A. Fuchs, *Die unteren Gedinneschichten der Gegend von Wiesbaden,* Jahrb. Nass. Ver. f. Naturk., Jahrb. 80, pp. 74–86; *Sedimentations- und Faunenfolgen im Unter- und Mitteldevon des Rheinischen Schiefergebirges,* Zeitschr. deutschen geol. Ges., 85 (1933), p. 455; this article describes the variations of facies from south to north analogous to those of the Ardennes.

59. A. Fuchs, *Ueber die Beziehungen des sauerländischen Faciesgebiets zur belgischen*

Nord und Südfacies und ihre Bedeutung für das Alter der Verseschichten, Jahrb. preuss. geol. Landesanst., 13 (1933), p. 839.

60. See the important memoir of J. Spriesterbach, *Die Oberkoblenzschichten des Bergischen Landes und Sauerlandes,* Jahrb. preuss. geol. Landesanst. zu Berlin, 45 (1924). Local accounts in O. Follmann, *Die Koblenzschichten am Mittelrhein und im Moselgebiet,* Verhandl. d. Naturhist. Ver. d. preuss. Rheinlande und Westfalens (1921–22).

61. W. Henke, *Beiträge zur Klärung der Stratigraphie und Tektonik der Siegener Schichten zwischen Sieg und Rhein,* Verh. Naturh. Ver. preuss. Rheinlande u. Westfalens, 86 (1930); *Verbreitung und Ausbildung der Siegener Schichten in der Osteifel,* Geol. Rundschau, 24 (1933). G. Dahmer, *Die Fauna der Seifener Schichten (Siegenstufe),* Abh. preuss. geol. Landesanst., N.F., 147 (1931).

62. W. Schriel, *Das Unterdevon im südlichen Sauerlande und Oberbergisch,* Festschr. z. 60. Geburtstag von Hans Stille, F. Enke, Stuttgart (1936).

63. Kegel, Abhandl. preuss. geol. Landesanst., n. F., H. 6 (1913).

64. S. Simpson, *Das Devon der Südost-Eifel zwischen Nette und Alf; Stratigraphie und Tektonik mit einem Beitrag zur Hunsrückschiefer-Frage,* Abhandl. Senckenberg. Naturf. Ges., 447 (1940), 81 p., 10 tabl., 3 fig.

65. See E. Asselberghs, *Siegenien, Siegenerschichten, Hunsrückschiefer et Taunusquartzit,* Bull. Soc. belge de Géol., 36 (1926). The term Coblenzian was, in fact, employed by Belgian geologists in numerous different usages: E. Mallieux, *Pourquoi le terme Coblencien devrait disparaître de la nomenclature géologique,* ibid., 30 (1920).

66. From the little town of Remscheid (see map, Fig. 26).

67. R. Wedekind, *Genera der Paläoammonoïdea (Goniatiten),* Paläontographica, 62 (1917).

68. See for example the diagram given on p. 6 of H. Breddin and M. Richter, *Exkursionsführer durch das Oberbergische,* Ber. uber die Versammlungen des Niederrheinischen geol. Ver. (1922). The most recent works are those of R. Thienhaus, *Der Faziesverhältnisse im Südwestteil der Attendorfer Mulde und ihre Bedeutung für die Stratigraphie des bergisch-sauerländischen Mitteldevons,* Abh. Reichsamts Bodenforsch., 199 (1940) and J. Spriesterbach, *Lenneschiefer (Stratigraphie, Fazies und Fauna),* ibid., 203 (1942), p. 7–219, 10 fig., 10 pl.

69. H. Breddin, *Die Mitteldevonischen Konglomerate des Schwarzbachtales bei Ratingen und ihre stratigraphische Bedeutung,* Zeitschr. deutschen geol. Ges., Abhandl., 78 (1926). W. Paeckelmann, *Die Konglomerate des oberen Mitteldevons im Schwarzbachtale bei Ratingen und ihre belgischen Æquivalente,* ibid., Monatsber., 80, 128. For the Middle Devonian facies in the eastern part of the Sauerland, see F. Lotze, *Das Mitteldevon des Wennetals nordlich der Elsper Mulde,* Abhandl. preuss. geol. Landesanst., n. F., Heft 104 (1928).

70. O. Schindewolf, *Versuch einer Paläogeographie des europäischen Oberdevonmeeres,* Zeitschr. deutschen geol. Ges., 73 (1921); its paleogeographic map is obviously, as the author himself admits, quite hypothetical, especially concerning France.

71. See H. Schmidt, *Schwellen- und Beckenfazies im Oberrheinischen Paläozoicum,* Zeitschr. deutsch. geol. Ges., 77 (1925), Monatsber.

72. Recently the attempt has been made to utilize these cypridines for detailed stratigraphy. See H. Matern, *Die Ostracoden des Oberdevons,* Abhandl. preussischen geol. Landesanst., n. F., 118 (1929).

73. R. Wedekind and W. Helmbrecht, *Monographie der Clymenien des Rheinischen Schiefergebirges,* Abhandl. Ges. d. Wiss. zu Göttingen, n. F., 10 (1914).

74. We shall agree to attribute the upper zone with *Wocklumeria* to the base of the Carboniferous.

75. H. Weber, *Das Oberdevon der Attendorn-Elsper Doppelmulde,* Zeitschr. deutsch. geol. Ges., 86 (1934).

76. H. Stille, *Die subvariscische Vortiefe,* Zeitschr. deutsch. geol. Ges., 91 (1939), p. 537.

77. On the geology of the Harz in general, see Dahlgrün, Erdmannsdörfer, Schriel, *"Harz,"* Sammlung geol. Fuhrer, 29–30, Berlin (1925). For the much debated tectonics: F. Kossmat, *Das Problem der Gross-Ueberschiebungen im variskischen Gebirge Deutsch*

lands, Centralbl. f. Min. (1931), Abt. B. no. 11. F. Dahlgrün, *Ueber die Grundlagen einer tektonischen Gliederung des Harzes*, Zeitschr. deutsch. geol. Ges., 91 (1939), p. 537. This article is preceded by several others in which the "nappe" theories of Kossmat are discussed at length. For the Devonian of the Harz, see the article of Dahlgrün cited note 50, chap. 3.

78. Fr. Drevermann, *Bemerkungen zu den neueren Arbeiten über das Hercyn des Rheinischen Schiefergebirges*, Geol. Rundschau, 6 (1915).

79. This similarity of facies between the Kellerwald and the Unterharz is found, according to Kossmat, in the great lines of the Hercynian tectonic structure. This is the "Taunus-Kellerwald-Unterharz zone" of this geologist, which, in the Harz, would be thrust over the "Ardennes-Sauerland-Oberharz zone" where the Devonian has Rhenish facies. See F. Kossmat, *Das karbonische Faltengebirge von Mitteleuropa*, Congrès de Heerlen, work cited note 3, chap. 5.

80. E. Bederke, *Das Devon in Schlesien und das Alter der Sudetenfaltung*, Fortschr. d. Geol. u. Pal., H. 7 (1924).

81. See two articles of R. Kettner, with English summaries, in the Bull. du Service géol. de la République tchécoslovaque (1932).

82. J. Czarnocki, *Ueberblick der Stratigraphie und Paläogeographie des Unterdevons im polnischen Mittelgebirge*, Bull. Service geol. Pologne, vol. 8, livre 4, Warsaw (1937).

83. See work by Kozlovski, cited note 54, chap. 3.

84. F. Kerforne, *Les variations de faciès du Dévonien dans le Massif armoricain*, Bull. Soc. géol. France, 4 sér., 19 (1919).

85. Mlle. A. Renaud, *Le Dévonien du synclinorium médian Brest-Laval*, Mem. Soc. géol. et min. Bretagne, 8 (1942). P. Pruvost and G. Waterlot, *Structure du flanc septentrional du bassin de Châteaulin au Sud de Quintin (feuille de Saint-Brieuc au 1/80,000)*, Bull. Serv. Carte géol. France, no. 203 (1940). P. Pruvost and D. Le Maître, *Observations sur la région orientale du bassin de Châteaulin*, ibid., no. 212 (1943).

86. L. Collin, Bull. Soc. géol. et min. Bretagne, 9 (1928).

87. Mlle. D. Le Maître, *Etude de la faune des calcaires dévoniens de Bois-Roux (Ille-et-Vilaine)*, Bull. Soc. géol. et min. Bretagne 9 (1928).

88. J. Peneau, *Etudes stratigraphiques et paléontologiques dans le Sud-Est du Massif armoricain (synclinal de Saint-Julien de Vouvantes)*, Bull. Soc. Sc. nat. de l'Ouest de la France, 4 sér., 8 (1929).

89. Mlle. D. Le Maître, *Etudes sur la faune des calcaires dévoniens du Bassin d'Ancenis*, Mém. Soc. géol. du Nord, 12 (1934); this contains a full bibliography of the Devonian. J. Peneau, *Etudes sur le Dévonien de la Basse-Loire*, Bull. Soc. géol. nat. de l'Ouest de la France, 5 sér. I (1931).

90. This genus, well known in the Coblenz graywackes, persists even into the Carboniferous.

91. See work by G. Mathieu, cited note 48, chap. 2.

92. See work by A. Bigot, cited note 32, chap. 2.

93. Nevertheless, in the Basque country the Famennien assumes a facies very different from the deep-water facies that we shall study in the Montagne-Noire. These are sandstones and graywackes with a littoral fauna, with *Spirifer verneuili*. Thus, there should be, at this epoch, an emerged land west of the Pyrenees. See especially J. W. Laverdière, *Contribution à l'étude des terrains paléozoiques des Pyrénées occidentales*, Mém. Soc. géol. du Nord, 10, mém. no. 5 (1931). Farther west, in the Cantabrian Chain, A. Comte has described in Léon, a thick Devonian series (1,800 m.), complete and continuous, of the Ardennes-Rhenish type, especially beginning with a Gedinnian fauna analogous to that of the Mondrepuis shale. See A. Comte, *Sur le Gédinnien de la chaine cantabrique*, C. R. Soc. géol. France (June 7, 1937); *Les faciès du Dévonien supérieur dans la Cordillère cantabrique*, C. R. Acad. Sc. (May 16, 1938).

94. See W. Müller, *Die Fauna der Frasne-Stufe bei Almaden in der Sierra Morena*, Senckenbergiana, 6 (1924).

95. See I. P. Voitesti, *Aperçu général sur la Géologie de la Roumanie*, Ann. des Mines de Roumanie, IV (1921); a recent regional bibliography will be found here. For the Dobrogea specially, restatement and bibliography in J. L. Wilser, *Die stratigraphische und tektonische Stellung der Dobrudscha*, Geol. Rundschau, 19 (1928).

96. See the Communication de A. Ktenas to the International Geological Congress in Belgium in 1922.

97. The whole bibliography will be found in the important article of J. Jung, cited note 35, chap. 1.

98. G. Dubois, *Sur la subdivision stratigraphique du complexe schisto-grauwackeux des Vosges*, C. R. Acad. Sc. (Jan. 16, 1933).

99. E. Asselberghs, *Sur l'existence du Famennien (Néodévonien) à Chagey (Belfort)*, Bull. Soc. géol. France, 4 sér., 26 (1926).

100. M. Thoral, *Ordovicien supérieur, Gothlandien et orogénèse calédonienne en Languedoc*, Bull. Soc. Et. sc. de l'Aude (1943).

101. M. Thoral, *Age et faune des dolomies dévoniennes de la Montagne-Noire (Herault)*, C. R. somm. Soc. géol. France (Nov. 15, 1937).

102. Cephalopods revised by Schindewolf (work cited note 70, this chap.).

103. See article by M. Gortani, cited note 67, chap. 2.

104. M. Gortani, *La serie devoniana comprensiva nelle Alpi carniche e nella Sardegna*, Rendiconti R. Accad. Sc. Inst. Bologna (1933).

105. See article by von Gärtner, cited note 72, chap. 3.

106. F. Heritsch, *Geologie der Steiermark*, Graz, 1921.

107. For the regional description and bibliography, see pp. 62 and 98. The Primary of Morocco has been synthesized in the important work by H. Termier, cited note 70, chap. 2.

108. L. Neltner, C. R. Soc. géol. France (1929), p. 40.

109. E. Roch, *Etudes géologiques dans la région méridionale du Maroc occidental*, Mém. Serv. Carte géol. Maroc (1930).

110. N. Menchikoff, *Recherches géologiques et morphologiques dans le N du Sahara occidental*, Revue de Géogr. phys. et de Géol. dynamique, 3 (1930). H. Termier, *Sur le Dévonien du Tafilelt*, C. R. Acad. Sc. (July 29, 1929). H. Termier et L. Clariond, *Sur le Dévonien du Tafilelt et du Haïder*, C. R. Soc. géol. France (Nov. 5, 1934). N. Menchikoff, ibid. (April 23, 1934 and Feb. 4, 1935). L. Clariond, Leca et H. Termier, Bull. Soc. géol. France (1933), p. 139.

111. These cephalopods here show the same succession of characteristic genera and species as in the Rhenish Devonian. In particular, the genera *Anarcestes, Manticoceras, Cheiloceras, Platyclymenia, Laevigites* are found.

112. H. Termier, *Sur un trait paléogéographique important du Dévonien et du Carbonifère de la province européenne*, C. R. Soc. géol. France (Mar. 16, 1931).

113. All the classic treatises point out the presence here of *Spirifer anossofi*, a species which we shall find to be characteristic of the Middle Devonian of the Ural. But Nalivkine (Leningrad) has recently shown that the form designated by this name in the Baltic States (and also in central Russia and Timan) was quite distinct from the species in the Urals. This correction leads to a complete change of Devonian stratigraphy in these regions. Von Bubnoff (work cited note 15, chap. 1) had already drawn attention to this question; and I have been kindly advised on this Devonian of the Baltic States by MM. Leriche (Brussels) and Dalinkevicius (Kaunas).

114. W. Gross, *Ueber das Devon der russischen Tafel*, Geol. Rundschau, 31 (1940). R. M. Pistrak, *Paléogéographie du Dévonien du Bassin de Moscou et des régions voisines*, C. R. Soc. Nat. Moscou, n.s., 46, sect. geol. (3), 16; Russian with English summary.

115. It is in the Voronej, Evlanov and Elezk stages that *Spirifer anossofi* of the Middle Devonian of the Urals was incorrectly noted.

116. L. von zur Mühlen, *Einige neue Tiefbohrungen im Gebiete der russischen Tafel und ihre Bedeutung für die Paläogeographie und Erdölgeologie*, Zeitschr. deutsch. geol. Ges., 93 (1941).

117. Nevertheless, in a well 180 km. west of Oufa (see L. von zur Mühlen, work cited note 116, this chap.) some very littoral beds, with marine plants and fossils of Givetian age, were found lying on the crystalline rocks. This Middle Devonian thus appears as intermediary between the marine type of the Urals and the continental type of the lower Baltic sandstone.

118. There *Sp. anossofi* has also been noted in the upper beds in the zone with *M. intumescens,* which would indicate tectonic complications.

119. E. Perna, Mém. Com. géol. St. Petersburg, 99 (1915) even found several zones of cephalopods of the Rhenish Famennian.

120. See the article by M. Leriche, cited note 52, this chap.

121. See E. Kayser, *Lehrbuch der Geologie,* 6th and 7th editions, Stuttgart (1923); the Russian Devonian is very briefly and clearly synthesized, as it is in the work by von Bubnoff, *Geologie von Europa,* I, Berlin (1926).

122. G. A. Cooper, etc., "Correlation of the Devonian Sedimentary Formations of North America," Bull. Geol. Soc. America, 53 (1942), p. 1729.

123. The cephalopod faunas, long neglected, have been revised by A. K. Miller, work cited note 9, this chap.

124. For this region, see E. B. Branson, V. O. Tansey, G. A. Stewart, *The Devonian of Missouri,* Missouri Bur. Geol. and Mines, ser. 2, 17 (1922).

125. P. H. Price, J. H. C. Martens, etc., *Oriskany Sand Symposium,* Appalachian Geol. Soc., 110 p., 26 sect., 7 maps, Charleston (1937).

126. C. K. Swartz and F. M. Swartz, "Early Devonian and Late Silurian Formations of Southeastern Pennsylvania," Bull. Geol. Soc. America, 52 (1941).

127. Chamberlin and Salisbury consider that the communication between the Atlantic and our second region (Appalachian and Interior Basins) was not directly via the northwest, but through a strait coming from the Atlantic and passing through the present location of Chesapeake Bay. They believe, in fact, that in New England a barrier of ancient rocks must have existed, analogous to the barrier of the Green Mts. in the Cambrian (see p. 66). But little is known yet of these crystalline and metamorphic formations of New England. They may be composed of metamorphosed marine Devonian and the Devonian sea could well have occupied the location of this massif.

128. B. Willard, "The Onondaga Formation in Pennsylvania," Journ. Geol., 44 (1936); "Hamilton Correlations," Amer. Journ. Sc., 5 ser., 33 (1937). C. Campbell, "New Albany Shale," Bull. Geol. Soc. America, 57 (1946).

129. For, according to Chamberlin and Salisbury, the Chesapeake Strait must have been closed in the Onondaga epoch, so there was no longer any communication between the Appalachian region (and the interior) and the Atlantic.

130. C. R. Stauffer, "The Fauna of the Typical Olentangy Shale," Journ. of Geol., 46 (1938).

131. R. C. Baker, "The Age and Fossils of the Olentangy Shale of Central Ohio," Amer. Journ. Sc. (Feb., 1942).

132. G. A. Cooper and J. S. Williams, "Tully Formation of New York," Bull. Geol. Soc. America, 46, no. 5, 1933. Washington (1935).

133. W. L. Grossman, "Stratigraphy of the Genesee Group of New York," Bull. Geol. Soc. America, 55 (1944), p. 41–75, 4 fig., 2 pl.

134. B. Willard, "Portage Group in Pennsylvania," Bull. Geol. Soc. America, 46, 1934, New York (1935); a study of the variations of facies from east to west.

135. G. H. Chadwick, "Faunal Differentiation in the Upper Devonian," Bull. Geol. Soc. of America, 46, no. 2, 1933, New York (1935).

136. J. Barrell, "The Upper Devonian Delta of the Appalachian Geosyncline," Amer. Journ. Sc., 36 (1913).

137. Similar analogies between Europe and America are found again in the Carboniferous (see p. 234).

Chapter Five

The Permo-Carboniferous

I. Generalities

1. *The Permo-Carboniferous System in Western Europe; its Subdivisions*

Though this system corresponds to two periods, the Carboniferous and the Permian, there is, from many points of view, an advantage in studying them together and it was to this end that E. Haug proposed the name Anthracolithic[1] which does not seem to have found favor.

The great variety of facies of the Permo-Carboniferous in Europe and the harmonious way in which they can be grouped make of this system, seen as a whole, a magnificent illustration of stratigraphic synthesis.

There were in Europe, at the end of the Devonian, two great natural regions: to the north, the region of Old Red Sandstone, an immense continental mass, in part desert, dotted with lagoons, extending over all of Britain, except the Cornish peninsula, undoubtedly occupying the location of the North Sea and approaching Brabant, and including next, all the Scandinavian and Baltic countries. To the south, there was the immense domain of the Mesogean sea,[2] a distant ancestor of the present Mediterranean, with its marine deposits of varying depth facies, and its numerous islands.

A. The Carboniferous Limestone. At the beginning of the Carboniferous, a great transgression took place. The sea invaded all of Britain and marine formations, principally calcareous, succeeded the Old Red Sandstone. Thus a new stratigraphic entity comes to be defined: this is the Carboniferous limestone of the early geologists, now comprising the Dinantian stage.[3] This calcareous facies prevails in the Ardennes Massif and in almost all of Britain; thus it appears to us as linked to the continental platforms lying along the southern border of the Old Red Sandstone continent. Organic sedimentation prevailed there over terrigenous deposits or pelagic sedimentation. The facies are naturally neritic and the stratigraphic subdivisions are based on zones of corals (especially in Britain) or brachiopods (especially in northern France or Belgium). So a lower Dinantian or Tournaisian is distinguished and an upper Dinantian or Visean.

The shores of this sea of Carboniferous limestone are known only in northern Scotland, where we shall see the calcareous facies replaced by lagoonal beds with carbonaceous beds or gypsum.

To the south, however, in the immense Mesogean area, the Dinantian is very different:

a) In the Rhenish Massifs where the Devonian ended with pelagic beds with cephalopods, similar facies persist in the Dinantian, which is represented by shales with goniatites, and it is these latter which permit a detailed stratigraphy.

b) In Brittany, on the other hand, and in Devon, the Vosges (and the southern part of the Rhenish Massif), the French Massif Central, etc., terrigenous, shaly-sandy facies of the Flysch type prevail (see p. 10). This thick sedimentation was fed by emerged lands whose history and distribution are still largely unknown. This terrigenous Dinantian is, moreover, in part continental or lagoonal. It contains strata with plant remains but also thick marine beds. To these thick sandy-shaly accumulations of Flysch has been given the name Culm facies.[4] This somewhat inexact term of German origin (Culm or Kulm), is thus used to contrast the calcareous facies of the Dinantian to the sandy-shaly facies of the same stage, whether pelagic shales with cephalopods or delta sediments, torrential or lacustrine with carbonaceous layers.

B. The Productive Coal Measures.[5]   The individuality of this Dinantian is emphasized by important paleogeographic changes which marked its end. In fact, in all the countries of western Europe previously occupied by the sea, where the Carboniferous limestone was deposited, a continental or subcontinental regime appears. We can see there, either regions of accentuated relief, in the process of erosion (for a good part of the Hercynian foldings date from this epoch, see p. 161), or lacustrine basins of sedimentation, or finally broad coastal plains where beds of mud with marine shells (especially at the beginning) alternate with beds containing only lacustrine or continental fossils. And in particular, all these formations contain coal beds: fresh water coal (limnic coal basins) formed in lakes or marshes, marine coal (paralic basins) in the swampy coastal plains which were encroaching on the continent.

The problem of the formation of the coal will not be considered here: it is, however, treated in a number of recent works.[6] We shall be satisfied to call attention to a tentative, little known evaluation of the length of time of formation of the coal beds. A like problem has been worked on by geologists who studied the Silesian coal basin.[7] As a starting point, we can recognize (with Von Bulow and R. Dubois) that in the peat-bogs of present plains, the annual increase in thickness of the peat bed is of the order of .5 to 1 mm. Then the coal formation of this peat is accompanied by a compression, so that (according to Gothan) 1 m. of coal corresponds to 5 m. of peat, perhaps about 10,000 years. In the Silesian Basin, the thickest bed (12 m.) would correspond to 120,000 years; and the total thickness of all the beds of coal in the basin, reaching 272 m., perhaps about 3 million years.

On the other hand, in the west part of the basin (at Hindenburg) is a group of beds comprising a total of 28 m. of coal, separated by 200 m. of barren beds. To the east (at Niemce), 32 km. away, this whole group is reduced to a single bed of coal 12 m. thick. Recognizing that the rate of sedimentation of coal would have been one-fifth as great in the east as in the west, that of the barren beds would be 1 m. in 1,600 years. The total thickness of sterile deposits of the Silesian Coal Measures being 6,500 m., it would mean about 10 million years for the sterile beds, or a total of 13 million years. This figure, obviously very hypothetical, would fit in well with the estimates given on p. 22 for the whole Carboniferous (85 million years).

We should not believe, however, that this coal formation, which has given its name to the system, represents a single and unique episode in the history of the globe; its value is only relative. First the total thickness of the coal beds in comparison with the sterile strata of the coal formation that includes them is very small, of the order of 1 to 100. And in particular the importance of this episode results from the fact that it was localized in civilized areas, where geology originated and developed, western Europe and North America. As always, a local geographic phenomenon was the starting point for the establishment of the stage.

The subterranean work necessitated by the mining of coal [8] has made possible the precise determination of the coal bed stratigraphy down to the last detail and with a certainty not attained in any other formation. The synchronism of the coal beds is now established with a precision of the order of a few meters, over the large area reaching from Silesia to Britain.

For this, naturally, the floras and continental faunas are the center of attention; first the plants, then, more recently, freshwater pelecypods. In addition, horizons with marine faunas are still found in certain regions, especially at the base of the coal measures, where, in turn, the strata of coal are sometimes, as in Belgium, unexploitable; to these "coal measures without coal" of the early Belgian geologists, the name Namurian stage is now given.

On the whole, all these numerous subdivisions, based on plants, freshwater pelecypods and intercalations of marine faunas, may be divided into two great stages: at the base, the Westphalian (from the Ruhr Basin in Westphalia) including the Namurian[9] at its base, and at the top the Stephanian (from the St. Etienne Basin).

C. The New Red Sandstone.   The sandstones, black shales, and coal beds of the productive coal measures are overlain in western Europe by very different rocks. These are conglomerates, arkoses, sandstones or shales, in general brightly colored, red, green or violet, to which was long ago given the name New Red Sandstone as contrasted to the Old Red Sandstone of the Devonian which it greatly resembles. This is the *Rothliegende* of German geologists. No clearly marine fossil is found there and its special characteristics may be explained, as in the Devonian, in terms of more or less arid continents, with scattered lagoons and sedimentary basins. So the passage

from the regime of the Coal Measures to that of the red sandstone resulted
from a climatic change.[10] The wooded plains favored by a humid climate
were followed by vast dry stretches whose aridity produced important deposits of evaporites, gypsum and various salts.[11]

In some areas, however, for example at Autun, there is a transition zone
between the two regimes marked by beds of an intermediate character, especially shaly, but often still sandy or black and rich in plant remains or organic

FIG. 35. *Diagrammatic map of the Carboniferous and Permian seas in
Europe.*

	(Northwestern region after Stille; southeastern region after Wilser).
———————	Maximum extent toward the north and west of the clearly marine Mesogean facies with fusulines and cephalopods in the Middle and Upper Carboniferous and the Permian.
- - - - - - -	Limit of the Zechstein sea in western Europe.
Stippled:	Carboniferous outcrops in Russia.

materials (bituminous shales). This is the Autunian stage, distinguished from
the Stephanian by its flora. The New Red Sandstone proper, whose extent
is much greater than that of the preceding shales and which covers immense
surfaces in Germany, becomes the type of the Saxonian stage.

D. The Zechstein Sea. At the end of the Permian epoch a final geographic modification occurred. A great interior sea spread over all northern
Germany and Britain, in which were deposited dolomitic limestones, a common facies in deposits of concentrated waters. It is this rock, very different

from those of the preceding stages, and overlain by thick, saline formations, that the German geologists have called Zechstein; it is the magnesian limestone of the British. All this upper Permian complex corresponds to the Thuringian stage, for it reaches its most typical development in Thuringia. There the impoverished marine fauna of a more or less lagoonal inland sea is found; this German Zechstein sea (Figs. 35 and 51) was in fact only a distant tributary of the open sea which then covered Russia and the Mediterranean countries, as we shall see.

This sea ended on the west in the Palatinate, north of Wissemburg, so there is no marine Permian in France. Thus the Thuringian stage here corresponds to the upper part of the red sandstone and becomes impossible to distinguish since the guide zone established by the marine Zechstein is missing.

2. *The Marine Facies of the Permo-Carboniferous*

The Dinantian sea covered almost the whole of Europe. But from the Westphalian on, it is necessary, in order to find a continuous succession of clearly marine sediments, to go to the regions we still have to mention, the Russian arm of the sea and the Mediterranean regions.[12]

A. The Russian Arm of the Sea. All over central and northern Russia, including the Urals, the Carboniferous and the Permian are represented almost entirely by marine beds, extremely fossiliferous, with faunas no longer impoverished but normal. The study of the stratigraphic succession is easy here, for outside the Urals, over the whole immense Russian Platform, the sediments lie horizontally. Thus in Russia, it has been possible to define a series of successive marine faunas. The parallelism between these marine stages and the continental stages of western Europe is rather difficult to show accurately. It may be established especially in the intermediate regions, located at the boundary of the two domains, as the Donetz Basin (see p. 211). The table below shows approximately these relations:[13]

	W. Europe Facies	*Russian Marine Facies*[14]
Permian	⌠ Thuringian	Kazanian
	⟨ Saxonian	Kungurian
	⌡ Autunian	Artinskian
Carboniferous	⌠ Stephanian	Uralian
	⎥ Westphalian ⎰ Upper = Westphalian (s. str.) . .	Moscovian
	⎥ ⎱ Lower = Namurian	Namurian
	⌡ Dinantian ⎰ Visean ⎱	Dinantian
	⎱ Tournaisian ⎰	

B. The Mediterranean Regions. Through Asia Minor, the Russian arm of the sea connected with the Mesogean sea, of which it was only a tributary, where the same faunas are found as in Russia. But in all the Mediterranean regions, the Carboniferous and Permian are folded and sometimes metamorphic. Their recognizable outcrops are far distant from each other and isolated. It can only be said that the domain of this Mesogean sea must have been quite reduced in Europe. The Carnic Alps mark its extreme northern advance. In Asia, on the other hand, the Persian and Himalayan Chains were included. There the Permian and Carboniferous are represented by thick marine beds.

3. *The Hercynian Chain*[15]

Under the name of the Hercynian folding are grouped the orogenic phenomena which were produced during the Permo-Carboniferous. But to apply the name Hercynian Chain to all the regions where folding of this age could be recognized, would result in too broad and inaccurate a definition. Indeed, in many of these regions, there has been more recent folding, in particular at the middle or end of the Tertiary (Alpine folding) and it is naturally to the latter that the principal features of the present structure are due. The Hercynian folding there is difficult to distinguish. To take examples in France, the Primary massifs of the Alps and Pyrenees were folded in the Hercynian epoch and it is sometimes (but not always) possible to reconstruct the appearance of the Hercynian folds. Thus we may speak of the Hercynian Massifs incorporated in the Alpine Chain, but we should not include these regions in the Hercynian Chain.

We shall reserve this latter name for the Primary massifs folded during the course of the Permo-Carboniferous, which have not been folded since and where, in consequence the Secondary formations, preserved around their margins or on their crests, have remained almost horizontal. It should be mentioned that this definition does not exclude massifs that show traces of earlier folding, such as the Caledonian (for example, the Ardennes).

So understood, the Hercynian Chain extends over a great part of Europe and the cover of Secondary formations allows us to distinguish a certain number of massifs. These are, in Britain, the Cornish Peninsula (with part of Devon, see p. 120); in France, Brittany, the Massif Central (where only the southeast edge has undergone the counter blow of Alpine folding), the Vosges and the Ardennes; this last massif extends into Belgium and Germany and is in reality the western extremity of the great Rhenish Schiefergebirge. In central Europe (see map Fig. 28) all the Primary massifs are part of the Hercynian Chain: the Black Forest with its northern extension, the Odenwald, the small isolated Harz Massif, and the great Bohemian Massif with its appendages (Fichtel-Gebirge, Thuringia). Finally in the Mediterranean regions, there are two tabular blocks which escaped the Alpine folding, the Iberian Meseta and the Moroccan Meseta (mesa, meseta = plateau). Aside from this last exception the Hercynian Chain is located between the Caledonian Chain on the north and the Alpine Chain to the south.

The distinction between these folded Hercynian Massifs and their borders of horizontal Secondary formations, a distinction so general and so striking in all the European countries where geology originated, has very naturally led to placing here the great break between the Primary and the Secondary.[16]

In all this vast domain, the Hercynian folding is not everywhere exactly contemporaneous and an accurate knowledge of the exact dates of folding is very important practically and theoretically in defining the stages of the Carboniferous. We shall return then to regional descriptions. Let us note that, in western and central Europe, the principal phase of folding[17] is usually at the base or at the top of the Westphalian. This fact suggests why the Dinantian marked the end of the marine regime in regions which have been progressively occupied, from the beginning of the Westphalian, by mountain chains or continental plains.

Moreover, the unity of the Hercynian Chain stands out still more vividly, if we make a survey of the directions of folds,[18] which, although not everywhere contemporaneous, nevertheless are shaped according to the same guiding lines. This is very natural, for we usually see, in a region previously folded, that the new folds, called *posthumous folds,* follow directions more or less parallel with the earlier ones.

In the extreme western part of Europe, the Hercynian folds are aligned NW–SE. This is the direction, called Armorican,[19] which is observed in Cornwall, Brittany, and the western parts of the Ardennes and of the Massif Central. In central Europe, on the other hand, the Hercynian folds in general are directed SW–NE, following the direction called Variscan or Hercynian, so named after the Harz.[20] This is the case in the eastern part of the Ardennes, the Rhenish Schiefergebirge, the Hercynian Massifs of central Europe and the eastern part of the French Massif Central. The junction of these two directions is made either progressively by a concavity turned toward the north (the Ardennes) or by an abrupt (?) change of direction (Massif Central).

4. *Continental Flora and Fauna of the Permo-Carboniferous*

The study of these fossils is of capital importance, since most of the coaly and Permian deposits of central and western Europe contain only continental plants and animals.

A. The Flora.[21]   Because of the great number of plant species known in the Coal Measures, one may be tempted to believe that the coal epoch was a unique episode in the history of the plant world, an unequaled epoch of prosperity and richness. This is not at all probable, for the abundance of evidence on the Carboniferous flora is due chiefly to the fact that in the best explored regions of the globe, the assemblage of geographic conditions and the phenomena of sedimentation have allowed, in that particular place and at that particular period, both the development of an abundant vegetation and its burial under conditions particularly favorable to its preservation. The poverty of vegetation in the Devonian and Permo-Triassic in the same regions, a poverty due to the predominance of a clearly marine regime or else a desert and arid one, again accentuates by contrast the obvious richness of the Carboniferous flora. But it is evident that the predecessors and successors of the coal plants must have been developed in other regions with as much variety and luxuriousness.

Moreover, in spite of this apparent richness, due to quite local circumstances, we probably do not know all the aspects of the Carboniferous flora.

It seems to be well established that, in the Franco-Belgian Basin at least, the beds of coal were formed on the sites of ancient coastal plains where the ground level was near the mean sea level. In present-day nature their counterparts are the coastal swamps along the Gulf of Mexico or the forests of mangrove trees of tropical coasts. The thick beds of coal correspond then to the moments when the subsidence of the land was just sufficient to counterbalance the accumulation of plant remains, the sterile marine beds to the times when too rapid subsidence drowned the vegetation. On the other hand an upheaval or the contribution of alluvium gave a continental fauna to the sterile beds. These numerous alternations in various combinations are found in all the coal basins. The old soils with roots in place that are found in the footwalls of all these coal beds indicate that the coal plants actually lived *in place*[22] in the coastal plains. The vegetative aspects of these plants also show adaptations to this special mode of life.

The fact that the coal flora remains essentially the same when we consider the entirely lacustrine basins (Massif Central) seems to demonstrate that even in these basins the geographic conditions must have been very much the same.

Thus, it is especially the vegetation of the swampy plains, coastal, lagoonal, or lacustrine, that we have learned to know from the thousands of plant fossils taken from the coal mines. The other assemblages of floras which must have existed at the same period remain little known.

In the genesis of the coal beds, the principal role goes uncontested to the remains of arborescent plants. These were *Lycopodiaces* (lepidodendrons and sigillarias), great trees 25 to 30 m. high, whose terminal leafy branches resembled our present lycopods.[23] Their trunks, branches and roots have formed about four-fifths of the coal beds mined in northern France. There were also giant horsetails or calamites[24] reaching 8 to 12 m. in height, conifers[25] (*Walchia*) similar to our araucaria (monkey-puzzle) and *Cordaites* or primitive gymnosperms (cones were replaced by loose inflorescences), great trees 30 to 40 m. high which, in the St. Etienne Basin, for example, played a very large part in the formation of the coal.

In the shales associated with the coal beds, innumerable impressions of fern leaves are found, which by the variety of their venation furnish paleobotanists with most of their characteristic species. Some were trees, direct ancestors of the arboreal ferns of the present day, others were lianas (*Mariopteris*), etc. They bore either spores, as do present ferns, or seeds (pteridosperms). The latter, although they had leaves similar to our contemporary ferns, must actually be classified between the vascular cryptogams and the gymnosperms.

Needless to say the specific determination of these plants, of which in general only isolated fragments are found, is extremely delicate and can scarcely be attempted except by specialists.

Also the stratigraphic utilization[26] of this flora is very difficult. In addition, many of the characteristic species are isolated one from another and do not represent successive mutations of the same branch. So, we might ask if the

Smooth Sigillaria — Channeled Sigillaria *(brackets over the FLORAS column)*

	FRESHWATER FAUNAS	BRITAIN	FRANCO-BELGIAN BASIN	SAAR	ST. ETIENNE	GARD	FLORAS
Stephanian	*Anthracomya stephaniensis*			Upper Ottweiler Beds	St. Etienne Stage	Grand Combe Series	*Cordaites lingulatus*
	Anthracomya prolifera and *Leaia baentschi*			Lower Ottweiler Beds	Rive-de-Gier Stage	Bessèges Series	*Pecopteris lamurensis*
	D Estheria cebennensis	Upper Coal Measures		La Houve Beds		Molières Series	*P. lamurensis* *Mizoneura ovata*
Upper Westphalian	*C Anthracomya phillipsi* *Estheria simoni*	Upper Middle Coal Measures	Bruay Beds	Sulzbach Beds			*Neuropteris tenuifolia* *Linopteris obliqua*
	B Anthracomya pulcra *Carbonicola similis*	Lower Middle Coal Measures	Anzin Beds	St. Ingbert Beds			*Alethopteris davreuxi* *Lonchopteris bricei*
	A Anthracomya williamsoni *Carbonicola robusta*	Lower Coal Measures	Vicoigne Beds				*Alethopteris lonchitica* *Neuropteris schlehani*
Lower Westphalian or Namurian	Very rare	Millstone Grit	Flines Beds / Bruille Beds				*Pecopteris aspera* *Adiantites oblongifolius*

Continental paleontologic zones in some European coal basins (after P. Bertrand and P. Pruvost). The double line corresponds to a stratum with a marine fauna called Rimbeau band in France, Petit-Buison band in Belgium and Mansfield marine band in Britain. In the Saar a bed of claystone is found at this level. The genus *Carbonicola* entirely disappears above this horizon. The heavy line corresponds to the marine band of Poissonnière in France, of Quaregnon in Belgium and of Gin Mine in Britain.

The upper Westphalian (or Westphalian, s. str.) is divided into four parts, which the paleobotanists designate by the letters A, B, C, D.

N.B. In previous publications, *Anthracomya prolifera* Waterlot was, wrongly according to Trueman and Waterlot, included in an English species, *A. calcifera.*

164

successions of floras are not simply successions of plant associations, determined by local geographic modifications and having no general chronological value. Thus, it is when restricted to the study of one single basin that paleobotany gives the more precise results and provides precious landmarks to the worker.

Nevertheless, we shall have to recognize the special floral characteristics of the Dinantian,[27] Westphalian, and Stephanian stages; in the two last stages, 14 plant zones have been distinguished. The Permian flora, well characterized as an assemblage, can hardly be subdivided.

Most of the characteristic forms are chosen from the ferns; some are mentioned in the tables on pp. 164 and 200. Let us cite, in addition, *Callipteris,* whose appearance in abundance marks the beginning of the Permian.

Lepidodendrons are especially abundant in the Westphalian, but they were represented by special genera as early as the Devonian. Sigillarias with grooved bark characterize the Westphalian and lower Stephanian and those with smooth bark, the Stephanian and Permian.

B. The Continental Fauna. This is extremely interesting from the purely paleontologic point of view and certain groups (vertebrates in the Permian, freshwater mollusks in the Carboniferous) can even be used in stratigraphy to define paleontologic zones.

The reptiles are represented by the two groups of the prosaurians and theromorphs.[28]

The prosaurians, known only in the Permian, resemble somewhat present-day lizards, but had more primitive characteristics. We shall mention *Proterosaurus* of the Permian of Thuringia and *Mesosaurus,* a kind of large lizard adapted for swimming, which lived, during the Permian, in the rivers and lagoons of the Continent of Gondwana (see pp. 241 and 246).

The theromorphs were much larger animals and included a multitude of diversely adapted forms. During the Permian and Carboniferous, on the continents, they played the role filled today by mammals. Most of them were found in the Karroo (Permian) formation of South Africa (see p. 241): *Dicynodon,* so named because of its powerful canine teeth; and *Pareiasaurus* which reached 3 m. in length and which has also been found in Russia (p. 240). A few were known in western Europe: *Palaeohatteria,* of the Permian in the Saar, which was for a long time wrongly considered as the direct ancestor of *Hatteria,* the present-day lizards of New Zealand with primitive characteristics; and *Haptodus* and *Stereorachis* of the Permian of Autun.

The amphibians all belong to the particular, extinct group of the stegocephalians. Appearing as early as the Upper Devonian, with *Ichtyostega* which has just been found in eastern Greenland, they are very abundant in the Carboniferous and Permian. *Protriton,* whose gill-breathing larvae are called *Branchiosaurus,* is very abundant in the Stephanian of Commentry and the bituminous shales of the Permian of Autun (*P. petrolei*) and resemble salamanders. *Actinodon,* of the Autun Permian, has the appearance of a small crocodile. *Sauravus,* of the Stephanian of Blanzy, had a long tail like a lizard. *Archegosaurus,* $1\frac{1}{2}$ m. in length, is frequent in the Permian of Germany.

Fish[29] are numerous but they are selachians, dipnoids, or ganoids. There are no bony fishes.

Insects are extremely abundant, for certain facies of the Coal Measures shales are exactly right for the preservation of their impressions. They are especially forms close to present-day primitive forms of orthoptera (cockroaches) and neuroptera (dragonflies). Some dragonflies of the Carboniferous of Commentry reach a gigantic size (.7 m. wing-spread), which has often led, without any decisive reason, to the supposition that the atmosphere must have been more dense than it is today.

Besides insects and some crustaceans (*Leaia, Estheria*), the only continental animals which are useful in Carboniferous stratigraphy are freshwater pelecypods or Naiadids.[30] They are represented by the genera *Carbonicola, Anthracomya* and *Naiadites,* similar respectively to living unios, anodontas and dreissensias. P. Pruvost was one of the first to show that they could serve as guide species.[31]

5. *Marine Fauna of the Permo-Carboniferous*

Three groups are of very special stratigraphic importance, the fusulinids (protozoa), brachiopods and ammonoids.

A. Fusulinids. These large foraminifers, with a shell rolled in spindle form, are strictly characteristic of the Carboniferous and Permian. They are widespread in the Russian arm of the sea and also in the whole Mesogean sea. They lived only in the open sea of normal salinity and at relatively shallow depths, where they built, almost by themselves, purely fusuline limestones. In short, they play in the Carboniferous exactly the same part as the nummulites and alveolines play in the Tertiary.

It has thus been possible in many regions to try to distinguish paleontologic zones defined by species of fusulinids. We shall limit ourselves here to naming the principal characteristic genera, which appear successively and then persist all together, except perhaps *Schwagerina* and *Fusulina* (s. str.).

Fusulinella[32] appeared in the Dinantian, *Fusulina* in the Moscovian, *Schwagerina* in the Uralian. Finally, *Doliolina, Neoschwagerina* and *Sumatrina* seem to have appeared as early as the beginning of the Permian (J. Gubler).[33]

All these genera are easily recognized in thin sections and so provide valuable stratigraphic criteria. The Carboniferous forms are universally widespread, and we shall speak of them again in considering different regions. The Permian forms are especially abundant in the Far East where they have been the subject of much important stratigraphic work.[34] They were long believed to be peculiar to the far eastern domain, but actually are found much farther west, in Afghanistan,[35] the islands of the Aegean Sea and even in Sicily and Tunisia.[36]

B. Brachiopods. The Devonian genera persist and provide numerous characteristic species, examples of which we shall cite later (p. 181). Here we shall mention two genera peculiar to the Permo-Carboniferous.

The genus *Richthofenia*, accompanied by some others (*Lyttonia, Prorichthofenia, Geyerella, Scachinella*), represents a small group of aberrant brachiopods,[37] living in coral reefs and very deformed. The lower valve has taken the form of a deep cup, so that the shell is similar to a rudist or a coral. It appears in the Uralian in China and in the Salt Range, and in the Permian spreads farther west (eastern Alps, Sicily, Texas), but is always confined to the tropical province.

Productus is a genus whose attaching peduncle has disappeared but whose long spines anchor the shell in the mud.[38] There are numerous characteristic species, littoral or deep-water, of which we shall give examples later for the Carboniferous. In the Permian *P. horridus* is found everywhere in the Zechstein.

C. Cephalopods. E. Haug was among the first to show that successive zones of ammonoids could be defined in the Permo-Carboniferous, zones applicable in America as well as in Europe. Since then, the stratigraphic use of goniatites has been greatly perfected, especially in the stages and countries where the cephalopod-bearing strata are well developed and fossiliferous. This is especially true for the Namurian of England (Bisat),[40] for the Dinantian-Namurian of Germany (Schmidt),[41] and for the Franco-Belgian Dinantian (Delépine).[42] The most precise guides are given by well defined species. Thus, E. Haug recognized in Europe and America the general presence of a *Pericyclus princeps* zone in the Tournaisian and a *Glyphioceras striatum* zone in the Visean. The genera, however, are often understood differently by different authorities or are based on theoretical characteristics difficult to recognize in the species. Nevertheless, unable here to go into details, we shall be limited to giving an idea of the evolution of the principal genera, following Delépine for the Dinantian and Bisat for the Namurian.

At the extreme base of the Dinantian, the transition beds to the Devonian in the Franco-Belgian Basin (Etroeungt horizon or Strunian) still contain a *Cymaclymenia*. Delépine therefore makes it parallel to the *Wocklumeria* zone that the German geologists usually place at the top of their Devonian (see p. 181).

Above, the lower Tournaisian, lacking goniatites in the Franco-Belgian Basin, in Germany contains *Gattendorfia* and *Aganides*. The upper Tournaisian is everywhere characterized by *Pericyclus* (*P. princeps*) and *Munsteroceras*.

In the Visean, we already find representatives of all the phyla of Carboniferous ammonoids and the predominance of the different branches in successive epochs furnishes the basis for a division into zones. Thus the lower Visean is characterized (especially in England) by the flowering of *Beyrichoceras*, a genus still poorly defined, apparently derived from *Munsteroceras*. At the same time, *Pericyclus* persists and *Glyphioceras* (= *Goniatites*, s. str.) and *Nomismoceras* appear. The upper Visean is essentially characterized by the flowering of *Nomismoceras* and especially *Glyphioceras* (*G. striatum*).

The lower Westphalian or Namurian[43] sees the succession of *Eumorphoceras,* then *Homoceras,* lateral branches derived from the beyrichoceratids. Lastly *Reticuloceras,* a descendant of *Homoceras,* appears in the upper Namurian (Chokier bed).

The base of the upper Westphalian is well characterized by *Gastrioceras,* derived from *Homoceras,* while at the top *Anthracoceras* is found, extending perhaps into the Stephanian. Finally, in America, the genus *Schistoceras* seems contemporary with the Stephanian.

In the Permian, the cephalopod zones have naturally been studied especially in the countries where the formation is marine, that is, in Russia and in North America.[44] We shall only say that the Carboniferous genera have, for the most part, completely disappeared and in their place appear new genera belonging to the families of the prolecanitids (already present in the Dinantian), the medlicottids and even the ceratitids, which will flourish in the Triassic.

Keeping to the stages in which the ammonoids can be utilized with some precision in stratigraphy, we can draw up the following table:[45]

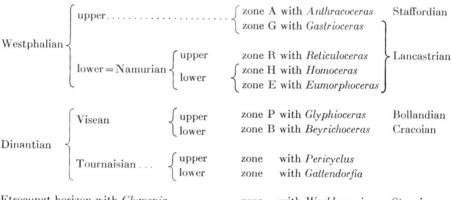

Westphalian	upper		zone A with *Anthracoceras*	Staffordian
			zone G with *Gastrioceras*	
	lower = Namurian	upper	zone R with *Reticuloceras*	Lancastrian
		lower	zone H with *Homoceras*	
			zone E with *Eumorphoceras*	
Dinantian	Visean	upper	zone P with *Glyphioceras*	Bollandian
		lower	zone B with *Beyrichoceras*	Cracoian
	Tournaisian	upper	zone with *Pericyclus*	
		lower	zone with *Gattendorfia*	

Etroeungt horizon with *Clymenia* . . . . zone with *Wocklumeria*   Strunian

D. Other Groups. The coelenterates continue the Devonian forms; thus in the reefs so highly developed in the French Dinantian tabulate corals (*Chaetetes*), tetracorals (*Cyathaxonia, Zaphrentis, Amplexus, Lithostrotion*), and stromatoporids are found. British geologists were able to distinguish in the Dinantian a whole succession of paleontologic zones defined by the corals (see p. 170).

The crinoids have almost everywhere produced crinoidal limestones, often associated with reefy facies. The echinoids are always relatively rare although the group of palechinids here reaches its maximum development, especially in North America.[46] The family of the cidarids appears with *Miocidaris*. The cystoids have disappeared, but the blastoids, which will not survive the Primary, are represented by prolific forms (*Pentremites florealis* of the Dinantian). Beautiful echinoderm faunas, belonging to these different groups, have been described from the Permian of Timor.

Certain genera of bryozoa (*Fenestella*) are very abundant in the German[47] and Franco-Belgian Dinantian, where they characterize a special facies (Waulsortian, see later), and also in the German Zechstein.[48]

Among the pelecypods, note especially *Aviculopecten,*[49] very frequent in the muddy facies; *Schizodus,* ancestor of the trigonias of the Secondary: forms of the littoral facies penetrating as far as the bottom of the interior Zechstein sea; and *Posidonomya,* whose thin shells become very large in the shaly facies of the Dinantian (*P. becheri*).

The gastropods have abundant representatives in *Bellerophon*[50] and *Euomphalus* (Bellerophon limestones of the eastern Alps).

Finally, the trilobites are now dying out. They are practically reduced to the two genera *Griffithides* and *Phillipsia*. *Phillipsia gemmulifera* is one species often noted in the Dinantian.[51]

II. The Carboniferous of Western Europe

1. *Britain*

British geologists have long distinguished, in the Carboniferous of their country, three successive formations. The Carboniferous limestone, in which marine facies predominate, lies at the base. Then comes the Millstone Grit,[52] a sandy formation of beach or estuary, semi-continental, in which fossils are very rare. Last are the Coal Measures or the productive Carboniferous proper.

But these different formations are very unevenly developed in different regions. And a deeper study of the faunas and floras and the paleontologic zones to which they give definition, has shown that the boundaries of these formations were, in detail, the boundaries of facies, without general chronologic value.

It is nevertheless convenient to preserve this old nomenclature as stage names, if we note that these different stages are sometimes represented by facies in little agreement with their names. For instance, we shall see that in Scotland the principal coal beds are contained in the Carboniferous limestone, in which there is no limestone.

Let us say at once that on the whole the Carboniferous limestone corresponds to the Dinantian (Lower Carboniferous) with its two sub-stages, Tournasian at the base, Visean at the top; the Millstone Grit is equivalent to the Namurian and the Coal Measures represent the upper Westphalian (Upper Carboniferous).

A. Carboniferous Limestone.   By reason of the extent of its outcrops and the diversity of its facies, Britain is the classic country for the study of the Lower Carboniferous in western Europe.

Detailed stratigraphy remained uncertain for a long period, but during the last thirty years the British paleontologists have studied with admirable precision the distribution of fossil species in the different horizons. In particular the corals, frequent everywhere in these calcareous facies, have made it possible to define a succession of paleontologic zones which, contrary to what could have been expected of these animals, by repute worthless fossils, seem to be found everywhere in Britain and can even be compared with the subdivisions of the Franco-Belgian Dinantian (see table, p. 181).[54] We emphasize this because it is the best example we could find of coral zones.[55]

To understand the variety of facies of this stage, we have to group, follow-

Coral Zones	Goniatite Zones	Lithologic Formations	English Nomenclature	French Nomenclature
				St. Etienne ⎫ Stephanian
				Rive-de-Gier ⎭
		Upper Coal Measures (transition beds)	Morganian	La Houve D ⎫ Upper Westphalian
		Middle Coal Measures		Bruay C ⎬
	G	Lower Coal Measures	Ammanian	Anzin B
				Vicoigne A ⎭
	R	Millstone Grit	Namurian	Flines ⎫ Lower Westphalian =
	H			Bruille ⎬ Namurian
	E			
	P	Bowland Shales		
	B	Carboniferous Limestone	Avonian	Visean ⎫ Dinantian
D				Tournaisian ⎭
S				
C				
Z				Strunian = z. of Etroeungt
K				

Coral zone brackets: Namurian (above D); Visean = D, S, C; Tournaisian = Z, K.

STRATIGRAPHIC CLASSIFICATION OF THE ENGLISH CARBONIFEROUS[53] N.B. For the definition of the zones of Goniatites, see p. 168, for that of coral zones, see p. 172.

ing Vaughan, the different outcrops in natural regions in the following way (see Fig. 36):

1. The Devon province.

2. The province of southwest England, comprising the Mendip Hills, the vicinity of Bristol, the Forest of Dean, the belt bordering the coal basin of south Wales and finally the Clee Hills.

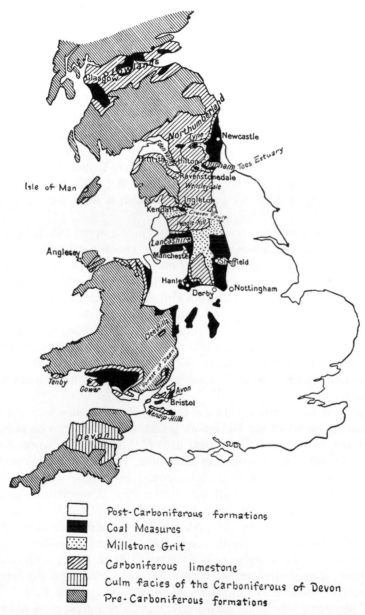

Post-Carboniferous formations
Coal Measures
Millstone Grit
Carboniferous limestone
Culm facies of the Carboniferous of Devon
Pre-Carboniferous formations

FIG. 36.   *Diagrammatic map of the Carboniferous outcrops in Britain.*

Only the most important outcrops are shown, especially for the Millstone Grit.

3. North Wales province.

4. South Pennine province or the Midlands, including the great mass of Carboniferous limestone between Manchester and Derby.

5. Central Pennine province, corresponding to the part of the Pennine Chain which extends north of the Lancashire coal basin (near Pendle) as far as the Craven fault.

6. North Pennine province, which, north of the preceding, continues to about the Tyne Valley.

7. The Northern province, composed of Northumberland and the Scottish Lowlands.

In each of these provinces, there is a type of the Lower Carboniferous characterized by different peculiarities.

a. *Devon province.* This merits a place quite to itself. As in the Devonian, the detailed knowledge of the Carboniferous is poor. There are thick accumulations of shales, sometimes sandy with Flysch facies, much folded, sometimes metamorphic with granite intrusions (Hercynian Chain). It is assuredly not the type of continental area known everywhere else in Britain. We already know that the name of Culm is given to this marine, shaly Dinantian, that is also found in Germany and the Vosges, to distinguish it from the Carboniferous limestone.

The oldest Carboniferous faunas are found in the upper Pilton beds (north of Devon) and indicate lowest Dinantian age (zone K = Strunian). This is actually black shale passing in continuity into the marine Devonian. It is sometimes assumed, without any decisive reason, that there was, at least in this region, a lacuna,[56] because the Codden Hill beds, which lie above the preceding beds, contain *Prolecanites* and must be assigned to the upper Visean. There are likewise some beds of radiolarites, a facies unknown elsewhere in Britain, but very frequent in the Culm of the continent. Finally, beside these Codden Hill beds, below or above according to different authors,[57] black limestones and shales contain *Posidonomya becheri,* a form common in the Culm facies.

b. *Southwestern province.* This is the only British region with a complete and continuous series of the Dinantian. Beautiful sections can be seen in the gorges of the lower Avon river, near Bristol.[58] Hence the name Avonian, often used by the British instead of Dinantian. It is there that Vaughn has defined the paleontologic zones, characterized by corals, which have since served as a starting point for all the stratigraphy of the British Dinantian. These zones are usually designated by the letters K.Z.C.S.D, initials of the generic names of corals or brachiopods which have served to define them.

1st. In the vicinity of Bristol, above the Old Red Sandstone, the Carboniferous begins with a shaly-sandy complex (100 m. thick) with calcareous intercalations. The shales are not deep-water (*Modiola*) and the limestones contain corals (*Kleistopora*) characteristic of the lowest zone K.[59]

2nd. Then come limestones exclusively, especially a great mass of crinoidal limestone. This is zone Z with *Zaphrentis* (120 m.).

3rd. Zone C with *Caninia* or *Syringothyris*[60] is represented by crinoidal dolomites with oolitic layers. The boundary between the Tournaisian and the Visean goes through about the middle of this zone.

4th. Next the black limestones, sometimes brecciated or oolitic and with shale intercalations, correspond to Zone S, with *Seminula*[61] (260 m.).

5th. Finally the series ends with 130 m. of coral limestone with shaly beds. This is Zone D, with *Dibunophyllum,* which passes into the Millstone Grit.

As may be seen, these subdivisions are indicated only by faunas. We can only point out that the base and especially the top are not exclusively calcareous, but rather shaly, the significance of which will be seen later.

In the rest of the southwestern province, the facies remains calcareous, as at Bristol, but the thickness varies greatly and conversely to that of the Millstone Grit which overlies the limestone. Thus, the Carboniferous limestone, 700 m. thick near Bristol, reaches 900 m. in the Mendip Hills and 1,000 m. in the Gower Peninsula. But its thickness decreases to 360 m. at Tenby, 180 m. in the Forest of Dean and 30 m. in the Clee Hills. So, the marine limestones are reduced toward the northwest to be replaced by sandstones having the deltaic facies of the Millstone Grit, but not contemporary with these latter strata. They are called Cornbrook sandstones and may reach 300 m. in thickness. Because of intercalations of variegated marls, they remind us curiously of the Old Red Sandstone type. This Visean regression (see Fig. 37), is explained by assuming that an emerged land must have extended from the center of Wales as far as Ireland, thus occupying the present location of Saint George Channel. British geologists call it Saint George Land. It extended to the east by way of a narrow isthmus called the Midlands Barrier. As we shall see later (Fig. 40) it persisted into the Westphalian in the shape of a long emergent zone dominating the Carboniferous lagoons and extending from Ireland through Britain to Brabant.

c. *North Wales province.* Here the oldest marine beds, whose basal conglomerate lies on the Silurian, belong, according to their fauna, to the Visean. This is, then, the north border of the Welch Massif (St. George Land), emergent in the Tournaisian and here only covered by the Visean sea. The same is true in Anglesea and the Isle of Man. This is the domain of this Visean transgression (see Fig. 37) which defines the North Wales province.

d. *South Pennine province.* East of the old massifs of Wales and the Lake District comes a wide band of Carboniferous formations, ranging N-S. On its borders are found the coal basins of Sheffield and Lancashire in the south, of Newcastle in the north. This band may be loosely compared to a N-S anticline, whose axis is formed of Carboniferous limestone with a girdle of Millstone Grit. It is called the Pennine Chain. This so-called chain is in reality flat country, cut by faults and sometimes even by extreme but localized folding. It is a little like the French tabular Jura, from the tectonic aspect. It is the true country of Carboniferous limestone, which forms here important heights, from which its old name of Mountain Limestone was derived.

This formation crops out in two areas separated by a band of Millstone Grit;

the one to the south, between the Sheffield and Lancashire basins, is the South Pennine province, the other, to the north, extends from the vicinity of Pendle into Northumberland and so belongs to our next province.

In the South Pennine province, nowhere do we find the basement of the Carboniferous limestone, or even its base. We may agree with Kendall [62] that the marine Tournaisian must exist at great depth for we shall find it again a little farther north in the Pennine Chain. In any case, only limestones of the upper Visean are known (zone D, here immoderately developed). The top is very shaly with chert beds that contain sponges. This is the beginning of a

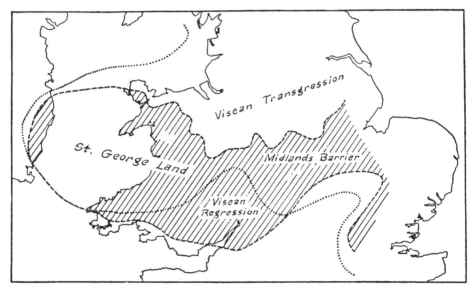

FIG. 37.   *Map showing the extent of the seas in the Tournaisian and Visean around St. George Land, the region remaining emergent throughout the Dinantian.* (*After* The Central England District, *cited note 27, chap. 1.*)

Ruled: The region emergent in the upper Visean (zone *D*).
....   Indicates the ancient shores in the lower Tournaisian (zone *Z*).

facies already indicated in the southwest and, as we shall see, more fully developed towards the north.

e. *Central Pennine province.*   There, in the Pennine Chain proper, the basement is still not visible, though Wilmore has shown that the series extends at least as far as zone Z. So the Tournaisian is surely represented as in southwest Britain. Then, farther northwest, the Carboniferous of this province rests against the southern border of the Lake Massif. Garwood has noted Tournaisian forms there, in the vicinity of Kendal.[63]

But the most interesting region[64] in this province is that which extends between the Craven fault and Pendleside in the Craven lowlands, for there the transition beds between the Visean and Namurian contain cephalopod faunas.

The terminal bed of Carboniferous limestone, here called Pendleside limestone (100 m.) contains *Beyrichoceras* especially at Cracoe, north of Pendle Hill. This is the Cracoian stage of Bisat (see p. 168), equivalent of the lower Visean. Above come very thick shales (up to 400 m.) with sandy or calcareous beds. Formerly called the Pendleside shales, they are now designated rather as Bowland shales, for they are especially fossiliferous in the Bowland Forest, south of Ingleton. This is zone P or the Bollandian stage of Bisat, characterized by its upper Visean *Glyphioceras*. Pelecypods of the shaly facies, *Aviculopecten papyraceus* and especially *Posidonomya becheri* (from which comes the name zone P), are found there in abundance, but the top of the shaly series already contains the *Eumorphoceras* characteristic of the extreme base of the Namurian.

And it is only above this that the Millstone Grit facies commences, thus beginning here a little above the base of the Namurian.

f. *North Pennine province.*[65] This province differs from the preceding one

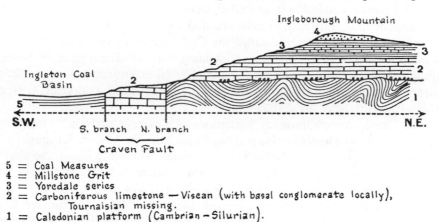

5 = Coal Measures
4 = Millstone Grit
3 = Yoredale series
2 = Carboniferous limestone — Visean (with basal conglomerate locally),
    Tournaisian missing.
1 = Caledonian platform (Cambrian – Silurian).

FIG. 38. *Diagrammatic section of the Carboniferous at Ingleborough (Yorkshire) (after Goodchild).*

by the absence of the Tournaisian. This fact may first be verified in the south along the Craven fault, in the celebrated section of Ingleborough Mountain, northeast of Ingleton. This fault bounds the little coal basin of Ingleton on the north, east of which it extends across the Pennine Chain. The southern or depressed block (Craven Lowlands) is made up of the plateaus of Carboniferous limestones of the preceding province. But north of the fault (Craven Highlands) the old rocks (Cambrian and Silurian) crop out in a little isolated massif. On them lies a basal conglomerate overlain by Visean fossiliferous limestones;[66] there is, therefore, here a Visean transgression. Above, the upper part of the Carboniferous limestone is represented by a thick series of shales and limestones in which are found the *Posidonomya becheri* of the Pendleside beds, but without goniatites. These shaly upper beds (here 280 m. thick) are highly developed in all the northern part of the Pennine Chain, especially in Wensleydale or Yoredale (dale=enclosed valley). They are called Yoredale beds and may be considered as a more littoral facies, with brachiopods and corals, of the Bowland shales, and hence at the boundary between the Visean and Namurian. They are as always overlain by Millstone Grit.

g. *Northern province.* In the extreme southwest of this zone, at Ravenstonedale, a very early Tournaisian fauna is known, indicating that the transgression began very early. Nevertheless, the marine influences do not begin until the lower Visean.

The principal characteristic of this province consists however in profound modifications of facies.[67] Three successive formations are distinguished in it.

1st. At the base lie the Calciferous sandstones. They begin with "cement stones" (120 m. thick), formed of reddish sandstone and green or black shales with thin beds of dolomitic limestone, exploited for cement. There is even gypsum in the vicinity of Glasgow. The fauna is generally continental or lacustrine, with *Spirorbis* (discussed later). This is the Tournaisian. Above comes the Fell Sandstone (30 m.), containing little beds of shale and even of coal. Plants are found in it, as well as fresh water pelecypods and some rare brachiopods indicating marine influence and dating it as lower Visean.

2nd. Next comes the series called the Carbonaceous group (700 m.). This is made up of sandstone and shale containing thin calcareous beds. In Northumberland, it contains numerous thick coal beds, extensively mined. In Scotland, at this horizon are the celebrated bituminous shales (oil shales), from which oil is extracted by distillation.[68]

3rd. Finally come calcareous formations (Calcareous division) which correspond to a more clearly marine regime, dating from the Visean, for these beds are generally correlated with the Yoredale series. There are also some shales and even coal beds that can be mined to some extent in Northumberland but particularly in Scotland, where they are associated with iron minerals.

Conclusions. Figure 39 summarizes all these data. In it, we can see how the Dinantian transgression, beginning in the geosynclinal region of Devon, spread over the continent of Old Red Sandstone. This continent was irregular and the sea first invaded the most depressed parts, especially the southwestern basin, certain massifs being submerged only in the Visean. In this shallow sea, without detrital contributions, the crinoidal or coral facies of the Carboniferous limestone were developed. Scotland, however, was near the shore of the continuously emergent continent, the North Atlantic continent. The lagoonal facies of the cement stones with its variegated sandstones and shales, its dolomitic intercalations and its gypsum beds, resembles the Permian feature for feature. These two episodes were evidently caused by similar paleogeographic and climatic circumstances.

The upper Dinantian was the time of maximum marine influences. The sea of the Carboniferous limestone extended its coral depths even into Scotland, bordered by swampy forests, while in central England the calcareous facies weakened to make place for the muddy and more pelagic type of the Yoredale and especially the Pendleside shales.

Finally, the Dinantian ends with the estuarine deposits of the Millstone Grit.

We shall not study the Dinantian of Ireland. We note only the development there of special reefy facies with bryozoa unknown in the rest of Britain but which we shall find again, under the name of Waulsortian, in the Franco-Belgian Basin. In addition, in the north and northwest a shaly facies with subcontinental beds appears, as in Scotland. Thus here we again approach the ancient shores of the North Atlantic continent.

B. Millstone Grit. This is a simple facies, essentially Namurian, but which may begin or end earlier or later. Thus in the Gower Peninsula (south Wales) shales intercalated in the lower beds of Millstone Grit contain goniatites (*Glyphioceras*) of the upper Visean.

In Central and northern England is the true Millstone Grit, represented by arkoses. The rock is extraordinarily like the Torridon sandstone (see p. 35) according to the studies of Gilligan. But the freshness of the rocks, in particular of the feldspars and pegmatite fragments, does not permit the theory that the Millstone Grit was formed at the expense of the Torridon sandstone; rather, it is evident that these two rocks had a common origin and that they resulted from the destruction of the same mountainous massif, situated probably to the north and now covered by the waters of the Atlantic. There must have been, in this massif, enormous outcrops of pegmatites and near Glasgow, thick beds of kaolinic clays are found; in Ayrshire, in the base of the Millstone Grit, there are even bauxitic clays (fire clays) and J. de Lapparent[70] concludes from this, with reason, that the climatic conditions must have been similar to those of the Upper Cretaceous of Provence, in which we shall study these bauxitic facies.

This Millstone Grit sometimes contains marine intercalations with faunas of brachiopods, corals and, more rarely, goniatites,[71] indicating the Namurian, plant beds whose flora is likewise that of the Namurian,[72] and even thin layers of coal. Thus this formation is compared to great deltas extending along the border of the North Atlantic continent, the sands of which have covered the organic depths of the Carboniferous limestone sea. It is in the Pennine Chain that the Millstone Grit, like the Carboniferous limestone, reaches its greatest thickness (nearly 1,000 m.). This must have been then an area of subsidence.

In the southwest province, the arkoses of the true Millstone Grit are no longer found; but we find instead quartzitic sandstones and conglomerates the elements of which probably were derived from the center of the Welsh Massif or St. George Land, which then must have formed an island or peninsula south of the continent and probably extended as far as Brabant (see Fig. 40).[73]

C. The Coal Measures. This is naturally the most important division of the Carboniferous from the industrial standpoint. Maps (Figs. 36 and 40) give an idea of the distribution of the principal British coal basins. But we shall be satisfied here with some general observations, for we shall find as good examples of this formation in France.

The Coal Measures are principally shales and sandstones with beds of coal. British geologists seem unanimous in thinking that their coals were formed in place (autochtonous theory) in the forest-swamps of coastal plains. The total thickness reaches 2,500 m. in Wales, but is quite variable, for the subsidences were localized in certain zones. One can even demonstrate discontinuities and

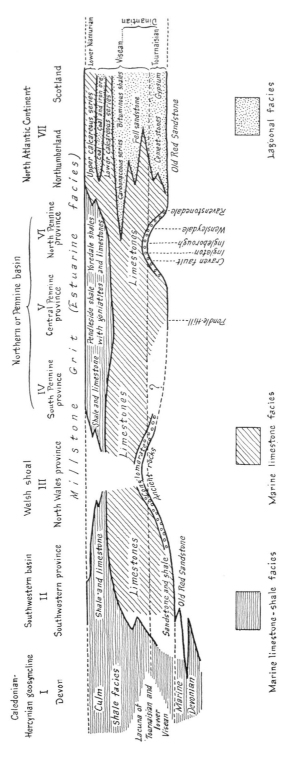

FIG. 39. *Diagram showing the distribution of facies of the Dinantian in Britain in the different provinces.*

The marine invasion progresses, on the whole, from the south (from the Devon geosyncline) toward the north (toward the North Atlantic continent), with irregularities due to transverse shoals, in particular, the shoal (or emerged region) of Wales or "St. George Land," prolonged to the east by the narrow "Barrier of the Midlands" (see Fig. 37), separating the southwestern basins from those of the North.

178

discordances in the coal series. Thus even in England there was an expression of the influence of those preliminary Hercynian foldings (called "Mercian" by British geologists) which we shall describe later in the Franco-Belgian Basin where they also started in the same part of the Carboniferous (see p. 186).

a. The lower series or Lower Coal Measures is remarkable for the frequence of shaly intercalations with a marine fauna. Even goniatites are found,

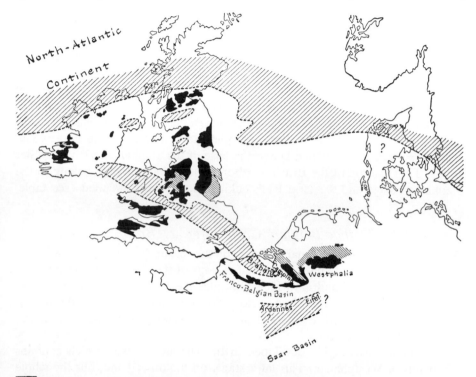

Coal basins cropping out or known at depth.

Their probable prolongation at depth.

Elevations dominating the swampy coal plains; especially the North Atlantic Continent and the long zone formed by St. George Land, the barrier of the Midlands, and Brabant.

FIG. 40.   *Map of the coal basins of northwestern Europe (after van Waterschoot).*

especially abundant in calcareous nodules or "coal balls." Some beds of very hard siliceous sandstone, or gannister, are utilized in the manufacture of siliceous bricks or paving stones. There is in general little coal at this horizon. These Lower Coal Measures are, of course, defined by their flora and fresh water fauna.[74] This may be called the *Carbonicola* zone, for this genus of naiadids is abundant in it (*C. ovalis*) (see p. 164).

b. The middle series or Middle Coal Measures contains, in general, more important coal beds. *Carbonicola* disappears during this period but *Naiadites* continues, specially represented by *N. modiolaris*.

c. Finally, the upper series or Upper Coal Measures becomes poorer in coal. Red rocks and lagoonal facies, similar to those of the "Cement Stones," are frequent here and already announce the beginning of desert conditions which will prevail everywhere in the Permo-Triassic (New Red Sandstone). There are frequent intercalations of limestone with *Spirorbis,* a tubicular annelid similar to present marine serpulids, which fastened on fern leaves or shells of naiadids as serpulids today grow on marine algae. The paleontologists are agreed then to consider *Spirorbis* as lacustrine or lagoonal. We have already seen it appear in Scotland in the Dinantian, also introduced in a lagoonal facies. These thin calcareous beds, very fine grained, often have a very wide and regular extent. They must have been formed by chemical precipitation in lagoons.

Finally, at the top of the Upper Coal Measures, the flora is modified and the lacustrine fauna is characterized by *Anthracomya tenuis* and *Leaia baentschi.* This was the Radstockian stage which some British geologists[75] correlate with the Westphalian D. But, according to Jongmans,[76] the flora would indicate both the Westphalian D and the base of the Stephanian (Rive-de-Gier zone). Thus the top of the British Carboniferous would already belong to the Stephanian stage and the term Radstockian should be abandoned (see table, p. 170).

2. The Franco-Belgian Carboniferous Basin

We already know the regional location of this basin (see Figs. 23 and 24). The Carboniferous is found in the axial regions of the Dinant and Namur synclines. The zone of Condroz, which separates the two synclines, is no longer differentiated in the Carboniferous, so there must have been a wide arm of the sea passing between the massifs of the Ardennes proper and of Brabant, probably partly emergent.

The Dinantian is highly developed in the Dinant syncline, which contains thin bands of Westphalian. This later stage, on the other hand, fills the whole Namur syncline, where all the exploitation is concentrated and which thus constitutes the Franco-Belgian Coal Basin. Between Namur and Andenne, along the little valley of the Samson, there is a higher raised area, so the Namur syncline is there drained of its coal contents (see Fig. 23). Thus this interruption separates the Liége Basin,[77] extending into Germany as far as Aix-la-Chapelle, from the Hainaut Basin which extends into France.

A. Stratigraphy. This can be summed up in two words: the Dinantian (Carboniferous limestone) and the lower Westphalian or Namurian (shales and sandstones) are marine and sterile; the upper Westphalian is productive, but still contains marine intercalations at its base; the Stephanian is unknown. So there is great similarity to Britain.

a. *Dinantian.* The detailed stratigraphy of the Franco-Belgian Dinantian has been the subject of recent studies by Delépine and Carpentier,[78] who have been able to find in it the paleontologic zones defined in Britain. However, as the corals have not yet been studied sufficiently, the brachiopod zones are commonly used, so, according to Delépine and Vaughan, the parallelism of the two paleontologic scales is established as given below. The nomenclature of the beds which represent each zone in the central part of the Dinant Basin has been added.[79]

ENGLISH CORAL ZONES	FRANCO-BELGIAN BRACHIOPOD ZONES	CENTER OF THE DINANT BASIN	
Zone D with *Dibunophyllum*..	*Productus giganteus*...	Black limestone & shale / Great breccia	
Zone S with *Seminula*.......	*Productus cora*.......	Cherty limestone / Oolitic limestone	Visean
Zone C with *Syringothyris*...	*Productus sublaevis*... / *Spirifer konincki*.....	Black marble of Dinant / Black limestone / "*Petit granite*"	
Zone Z with *Zaphreutis*......	*Spirifer tornacensis*...	Calcareous shales / Crinoid limestone	Tournaisian
Zone K with *Kleistopora*.....	*Spirifer strunianus* ...	Shale / Limestone of Etroeungt	

The lowest of these formations deserves special mention. It is known especially in the localities of Etroeungt in France and Comblain-au-Pont in Belgium (Dinant Basin, see Fig. 23).[80] Delépine has noted *Kleistopora* in it, which confirms its parallelism with the lower English zone. And, in addition, it shows characteristics intermediate between those of the Devonian and the Carboniferous. The *Spirifer tornacensis* and *Productus* of the Carboniferous make their appearance here, but *Spirifer verneuili* and *Orthis striatula* of the Devonian still persist, represented by mutations. Finally Delépine[81] has described in it a specimen clearly determinable as *Clymenia camerata,* a form which, in Germany, is characteristic of the *Wocklumeria* zone that German geologists place at the top of the Devonian (see p. 128). It is a case then of true transition beds between the two systems and, unlike what is found in almost all of Britain, this passage is effected here, as in Germany, in a continuous series of marine beds.

As to the Dinantian proper, it shows extremely varied facies which have long prevented a precise description of the stratigraphy. These variations are especially marked for the middle members, the upper Tournaisian and the lower Visean.

In the central part of the Dinant Basin, where the stratigraphic series is indicated in the table above, the black limestone and Dinant marble represent, at this horizon, muddy sediments, fine grained limestones with cephalopods and large spiny *Productus* of the clayey bottoms. But, turning to the north, on entering the Namur Basin, we see the *"Petit Granite,"* which is a limestone with large crinoidal plates, enormously developed at the expense of black limestone, while the black marble of Dinant is replaced by oolitic or crinoidal limestones.

Likewise to the south, on the southern border of the Dinant Basin, approaching the Ardennes, we see, at the boundary of the Tournaisian and Visean, the appearance of reefs in which bryozoans (*Fenestella*) abound. This is the Waulsortian facies, which was formerly considered an intermediary

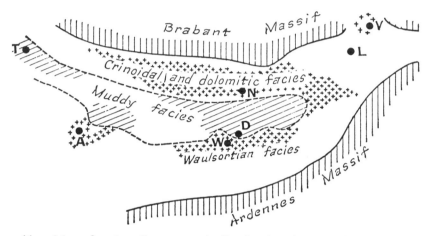

FIG. 41. *Map showing diagrammatically the distribution of the Carboniferous Limestone facies (particularly at the boundary between the Tournaisian and the Visean) in the Franco-Belgian Basin (after Delépine and Carpentier, simplified).*

T = Tournai; A = Avesnes; W = Waulsort; D = Dinant; N = Namur; L = Liége; V = Visé.

stage between the Tournaisian and Visean. The type of this facies[82] is the blue-veined limestone, formed by networks of fenestellids, which cemented the calcareous muds and constituted a favorable habitat for a very special fauna of mollusks. The only common coral is *Amplexus coralloides*. This Waulsortian, which we have already seen in Ireland, is found again in Brittany, in the Laval Basin, and near Vichy, in the Massif Central.

Finally, the bed known as the "Great Breccia" deserves special mention, for it has been the subject of much discussion.[83] It is a sedimentary breccia, sometimes with red cement, and represents ancient, partially submarine debris, for F. Bourguignon has noted goniatites[84] in it. Thus, there must have been, during the Dinantian, shoals and even emerged regions bordering the Dinant Basin, between the massifs of the Ardennes and Brabant.

The map (Fig. 41) summarizes the distribution of these facies.[85] It shows that the zone of muddy facies is found in the center of an arm of the sea, doubtless shallow, but in course of subsidence, as the great thickness of the Dinantian bears witness. The muddy belt is bordered by littoral, epicontinental facies which develop on the periphery of the two great anticlinal areas of the Ardennes and Brabant, which must have been, at least temporarily, partially emerged (see Fig. 40). In fact, between Namur and Liége, the Visean is transgressive on the Brabant margin, as it is also, farther east, on the edge of the Rhenish Massif north of Liége, east of Aix-la-Chapelle and north of Cologne (Ratingen).[86]

Finally, a sensational discovery was recently made[87] and confirmed during an excursion of the Geological Society of Belgium.[88] The discovery established the complete absence of the Dinantian and even of the base of the Namurian in the little Massif of Herve, cut by the valley of the Berwinne at Val-Dieu, southeast of Visé. There, the Namurian, well dated by a fossiliferous horizon, lies directly on Famennian sandstone, equally fossiliferous, separated only by a thin bed of gravel. As R. Marlière has so aptly remarked, we have there a curious and instructive example of an extremely important lacuna that is not made conspicuous by a discordance, nor by a basal conglomerate, nor even by gullying.

The types of the two sub-stages, Tournaisian and Visean, were chosen at Tournai and Visé, outside the great development of the Dinantian. Quarries in these two localities have provided many fossils, but the stratigraphic relations in these two regions are unfortunately not clear. Near Tournai, only the Tournaisian is visible, represented by calcareous or shaly facies, muddy and similar to those of the central part of the Dinant Basin and corresponding to the two zones with *Spirifer tornacensis* ($=$ of Tournai) and *S. konincki.* The Visé limestone, with *Productus giganteus* and *P. semireticularis,* corresponds to the *Dibunophyllum* zone and is overlain by black shales (ampelites) with cherts and goniatites (*Glyphioceras diadema*) which make these shales approximately equivalent to the Pendleside beds of England. The Devonian crops out nearby but it seems to be separated from the Visé limestone by a fault so that it was not definitely known whether the Tournaisian existed at depth. And now F. Charles[89] has reported an outcrop of lower, marine Tournaisian (*Spiriferellina acuta* zone). Finally, contrary to earlier belief, there is neither lacuna nor discordance between the Dinantian and the Namurian.[90]

Likewise, the Tournaisian has recently been discovered in the Boulonnais, where, in the vicinity of the Devonian, only formations classified in the Visean were known, which led to the belief that the Tournaisian is missing. Delépine and Pruvost[91] have recently shown that its apparent absence was due to local dislocations. The Dinantian series is complete there, represented by well-exploited dolomites and limestone marbles.[92] The distribution of the different paleologic zones is established in simplified form, as follows:

Visean	Zone of *Productus giganteus*	Napoleon marble
	Zone of *Productus cora*	Marble of Haut-Banc
	Zone of *Productus sublaevis*	Huré dolomite
Tournaisian	Zone of *Spirifer konincki*	
	Zone of *Spirifer tornacensis*	Calcareous shales of the Vallée Heureuse

Basal gravels (small transgression)

Upper Devonian ...   Fiennes psammites.

b. *Marine Lower Westphalian or Namurian.*[93]   Two successive formations are distinguished here.

1st. At the base, the Chokier ampelite. This is black shale with nodules (balls) remarkable for their goniatite fauna,[94] containing, in particular, *Eumorphoceras* and *Homoceras* which are characteristic of the English zones E and H.

As we have said, beds equivalent to this Chokier ampelite are seen at Visé, above the Visé limestone. Finally, this formation is found in the coal basin of northern France where it is called the Bruille ampelite.

2nd. At the top, the Andenne sandstone, a formation similar in every aspect to the English Millstone Grit. Its equivalent in northern France is known as the bed of Flines. It contains marine fossils, composed of productids, in general not very characteristic,[95] but also some goniatites which belong to the genus *Reticuloceras,* allowing this bed to be correlated with zone R of England. The flora is that of the stage with *Pecopteris aspera.*

As may be seen, this Namurian, marine and sterile, constitutes a very well individualized ensemble between the Carboniferous limestone and the productive Coal Measures. The Belgian geologists used to call it the "Houiller sans houille" (Coal Measures without coal).[96]

c. *Upper Westphalian.*   These are the productive Coal Measures. They are made up of alternating sandstones and shales. There are marine beds, containing even goniatites whose shells were doubtless brought by currents to the edges of the coastal plains. The calcareous fauna is completely missing, so there is no affinity with the Moscovian of Russia. The fresh water beds contain naiadids. Finally coal beds are very numerous, with thicknesses varying from 10 cm. to 1.6 m.

Each coal bed lies on a footwall that is generally clayey, fissile, but with conchoidal fractures, for the stratification has disappeared. It is the ancient plant soil, altered by the subterranean parts of the Carboniferous plants, roots of which, in fact, are found still in place. Above the coal comes the roof, generally sandy, well stratified, showing that the Carboniferous forest was killed in place by the invasion of ancient marine beaches or buried under estuary alluvium.[97] The lithologic nature of the footwall and roof are however quite variable, and clayey roofs may be found as well as sandy footwalls. But the stratification, always clear in the roof, confused or absent in the footwall, allows the top and bottom of a coal bed to be distinguished. Thus we may discover immediately if a bed is overturned, naturally a very important point in clarifying the tectonics of beds traversed by borings.

As a whole, this Franco-Belgian upper Westphalian contains enough coal beds to deserve the name of productive Coal Measures. However, its lower

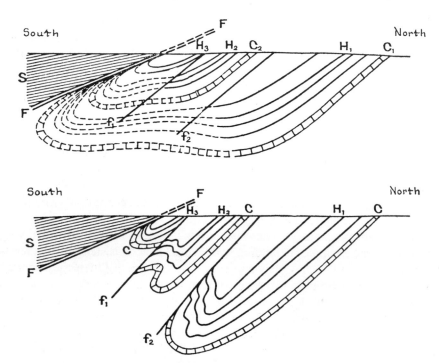

FIG. 42.   *Diagrammatic sections showing the stratigraphy of the productive Coal Measures of northern France.*

FORMER INTERPRETATION: C_1 and C_2 were considered as two successive horizons: thus H_1, H_2, H_3 are superposed. Mining operations had not penetrated into the deep zones, indicated by broken lines, and the direction of the beds was hypothetical.

NEW INTERPRETATION OF CH. BARROIS: C_1 and C_2, which have the same fauna, are contemporaneous (C); H_1, H_2, H_3 are also contemporaneous and the tectonic structure is deduced from these facts.

$H_1 = $ *maigres* coal; $H_2 = $ *demi-grasses* coal; $H_3 = $ *grasses* coal (see text for explanation). C_1, $C_2 = $ limestone horizons with a marine fauna. S = Silurian-Devonian of the band of Condroz; F = Great fault; f_1, $f_2 = $ secondary faults. The *morts-terrains* are imagined to be removed.

part still contains marine intercalations, is relatively poor in coal beds and is called *"Houiller maigre."*

The detailed stratigraphy of these Coal Measures is of course very important for the conduct of mining operations.

It was formerly believed that these coal beds, poor in fixed carbon (about 85% C) but rich in hydrocarbons and for that reason called fat, were the shallowest; next came the semi-fat coals (90%), and finally the "weak" coals (92%). But, as we shall see, it was recognized that the superposition of these different varieties of coal were only apparent and resulted from tectonic dislocations (see Fig. 42). There was not actually any necessary relation between the stratigraphic level and the composition of a coal.

It was necessary then to represent the stratigraphy of the Coal Measures starting with new data. This was done in France by the geologists of the "Institute de la Houille" at Lille (Ch. Barrois, P. Pruvost, P. Bertrand), in Belgium by A. Renier and X. Stainier, in Holland by the "Bureau of Geologic and Mining Studies" at Heerlen (W. J. Jongmans) and in Westphalia by P. Kukuk and R. Bärtling, etc.[98]

In such a series of sandstones and shales (Flysch facies), as monotonous in the whole as it is varied in detail, lithologic considerations are of little help. It is very difficult to know how to relate the coal beds of one pit to those of another, though some conglomerates could be used as horizon markers.

But only paleontologic studies have helped to reach precise comparisons, often verified subsequently by mining operations. For this, we may refer:

1st. To the floras, whose succession is diagrammed on page 164;

2nd. To fresh water faunas (pelecypods and crustaceans), of which the principal zones are indicated in the same table;[99]

3rd. To marine faunas.[100] These last are localized in marine horizons, very thin, but in some examples extending with remarkable consistency from Westphalia as far as the Pas-de-Calais and even into Britain.[101] Often they contain only *Lingula,* valuable only for distinction of facies, but sometimes goniatites are found, *Gastrioceras* at the base, *Anthracoceras* above. Two of these horizons are especially important. The lower (called "Katharina bed" in Westphalia, "Gin Mine" in Staffordshire) is characterized by *Gastrioceras katharinae,* the upper (called "Aegir" in Westphalia, "Bay Mine" in Britain) contains *Anthracoceras aegiranum.*[102]

Finally, the beds defined by these horizon guides have been given names taken from mine pits and indicated in the following table.

UPPER WESTPHALIAN	NORTHERN FRANCE	BELGIUM	WESTPHALIA
D. Missing			
C. Bed of............	Bruay	Flénu	Upper coals with long flame
Marine horizon of....	Rimbert	Petit Buisson	Aegir
B. Bed of............	Anzin	Upper Charleroi	{ Lower coals with long flame / Gas coals
Marine horizon of....	Poissonnière	Quaregnon	Katharina
A. Bed of............	Vicoigne	{ Lower Charleroi / Chatelet	{ Fat coals / Weak coals

B. Tectonics. The Franco-Belgian Basin, and the Ardennes as well, belong to the Hercynian Chain. The Dinantian and Westphalian, which are concordant with each other, are here folded, so that the Hercynian folds are necessarily post-Westphalian. But they began during the Westphalian. For, as

P. Pruvost has shown,[103] these folds are more accentuated in the lower beds of the Coal Measures than in the upper, which may be explained by assuming that they were produced during the course of the Carboniferous sedimentation. This also explains the curious Roucourt conglomerate, whose age was long debated, but which was recently shown to belong to the Bruay strata. It represents a true piedmont alluvium formed on the edge of a cordillera of the Condroz, already emerged during this epoch.[104]

Of course, the principal phase of Hercynian folding and thrusting is certainly post-Westphalian. Finally, as the Stephanian and Permian are missing, it is quite difficult to assign an upper age limit to the folding. But, to judge by neighboring regions (Saar Basin, see p. 191), the folding had probably ended before the end of the Permian and perhaps is of Permian-Autunian age.

Above this folded Hercynian mass, come horizontal formations of the Secondary and Tertiary. In Belgium, they form only isolated remnants on the Carboniferous. But toward the west, all the Hercynian basement finally disap-

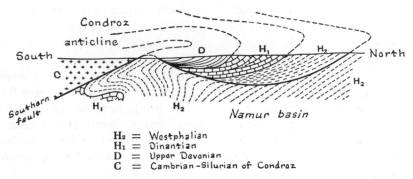

H_2 = Westphalian
H_1 = Dinantian
D = Upper Devonian
C = Cambrian-Silurian of Condroz

FIG. 43. *Very diagrammatic N-S section of the thrust remnant of Fontaine-l'Evêque (or of la Tombe), near Charleroi (after Briart, simplified).*

pears under the chalk. The miners call this horizontal covering which traverses the pits, *morts-terrains*. To understand the tectonics of the basin, we must imagine these strata removed.

In France, the coal basin, which corresponds to the Namur syncline, is sharply bounded on the south by a great dislocation which brings up much older formations. This is the Great Fault (see Fig. 23); in Hainaut, where the basin passes into Belgium, it is called the fault of the Midi. It can be followed with no uncertainty as far as between Namur and Charleroi, where it is connected with one of the numerous dislocations which displace the Silurian band of Condroz. There it is called the fault zone of Sambre-Meuse, which crosses about the middle of the valley of the Samson. Then, farther east, it appears again as the Eifelian fault, forming the south edge of the Namur syncline, here forming the Liége Basin. Its German extension reaches Aix-la-Chapelle.

The single fact of seeing the fault of the Midi pass to the east into a faulted anticlinal zone warns us that it is a question whether it is a true fault or a fold-fault or even a true overthrust, produced by tangential, sub-horizontal movements. And, in fact, north of this great fault, both in Belgium and France, displaced masses, *lambeaux de recouvrement,* are found above the coal basin. Fig. 43 shows how, in these *lambeaux,* the presence of coal in the mine pits below the Devonian can be explained.

Finally, if, as is not unreasonable to believe, the surface of the great fault can become sub-horizontal, we should expect to see the coal assemblage reappear south of the fault, in certain elevated areas, below the ancient formations which have been pushed over it. These breaks in the displaced mass, allowing its substratum to appear, are called windows. Such, according to Fourmarier,[105] is the Theux window in the Liége country where, south of the Eifelian fault, pits have shown the subterranean extension of the Coal Measures of the Liége Basin under the Devonian. On the whole, the maximum width of this great Condroz displacement has been estimated by Fourmarier[106] as 40 km.

In detail, still other complications intervene. There are secondary faults, many of which are parallel to each other on the north side of the great fault, which they accompany, so to speak. To each block bounded by these faults corresponds a zone in which coal can be mined and which thus constitutes a small secondary basin. So we can understand the multiplicity of these basins, all designated by local names (see Fig. 42).[107]

C. Extension of the Franco-Belgian Basin to the North: The Campine. North of the Namur syncline, which corresponds to the Franco-Belgian Basin, a slow elevation of the Hercynian substratum brings new outcrops of ancient rocks. This is the wide anticline of Brabant, almost entirely buried under the *morts-terrains.* These latter certainly cover its north flank as far as the North Sea, so that the ancient core of northern Belgium and Holland is disclosed only through deep drilling.[108]

These drillings have multiplied the past few years and have shown us, on the edge of the Brabant anticline, another body of the Coal Measures buried beneath the plains. So the little Dutch town of Heerlen is now becoming a mining center.[109]

D. Eastern Extension of the Franco-Belgian Basin; The Ruhr.[110]   After an interruption due to the plain of the Rhine, the Carboniferous reappears in Germany on the northern edge of the Sauerland (see Fig. 26). This is the Basin of the Ruhr or of Westphalia.[111]

The coal deposits here have the same general appearance as in the Franco-Belgian Basin. The greatest difference is that, in the Dinantian, the limestone[112] facies is confined to the extreme north border. Everywhere else this Dinantian, following the marine Devonian[113] in continuity, is represented by thick accumulation of shales and sandstone with widely variable facies.[114] Black shales with *Posidonomya becheri* and with goniatites (with the aid of which Schmidt was able to define cephalopod zones which had previously been in question, p. 168), chert beds with radiolarians (lydian stone), sandstones and graywackes and lentils of conglomerate. This is the Culm, a term applied here, as Paeckelmann has recently noted, to a typical Flysch facies, which is also continued in the Westphalian. Thus ends the history of the Hercynian Chain, as the Tertiary Flysch of the Alps will mark the end of the sedimentary history of the Alpine Chain.

The Westphalian, very thick and very productive, has here furnished the stage type.[115] It is, even in detail, identical with that of the Franco-Belgian Basin.

The Stephanian is missing, as in northern France. To find it again toward the east, we should have to go into Bohemia and Silesia, where we observe in concordant superposition both the Westphalian and the Stephanian, with rich floras, which furnish a valuable standard for the stratigraphic succession of these floras.[116] But here, at the eastern extremity of this long series of coal basins, we approach the marine facies which we shall describe later in Russia (Moscovian and Uralian). In fact, M. Schwartzbach[117] has recently discovered, in the upper Silesian Coal Basin, a succession of 10 marine horizons. Their number is reduced however in the west part of the basin, showing that the seas which momentarily invaded the Carboniferous lagoons and advanced as far as Britain must certainly have come from the east, from the Russian seas.

3. *The Saar-Lorraine Basin*

We have described above (see p. 122) the Devonian Massif of Hunsrück, separated from the Ardennes by the Secondary Gulf of Luxemburg. To the south, this Hunsrück disappears along a system of great faults, so that it is bordered by a wide Permian zone, extending in the Variscan direction, that is to say, SW-NE. Farther south, the coal deposits of the Saar Basin, following a band in the same direction, crop out below this Permian bed and, under the *morts-terrains,* extend at depth into Lorraine.[118]

A. Stratigraphy. Neither the substratum of the Carboniferous nor even the Lower Carboniferous is known. The oldest beds that have been reached are, as shown by their flora, more recent than the base of the Westphalian. Two complexes have long been distinguished in the Coal Measures of the Saar; at the base, the beds of Saarbruck and at the top the Ottweiler beds. Indeed the lithologic facies alone allow this subdivision.

The beds of Saarbruck are formed of dark colored shales and sandstones, of the usual Coal Measures type, with numerous and fine beds of coal—fat coal (*Fettkohlen*) at the base, flaming coal (*Flammkohlen*) at the top. The lower boundary of the Ottweiler beds is very well marked by a constant bed of uninterrupted coarse-cobble conglomerate, the Holz conglomerate (named from the village indicated on the map, Fig. 44), whose thickness, however, may vary from 3 to 200 m. Above, the Ottweiler stage is composed of sandstones and shales, frequently red or green colored; it is a sort of variegated Coal Measures, already suggesting the Permian. The upper stage contains only thin beds of poor coal (*Magerkohlen*), also called dry long-flame coal, and is generally neglected. Above, in perfect continuity, comes the lower Permian or Autunian.

On the whole, there are in these Saar-Lorraine Coal Measures, 6,000 m. thick, 88 beds of coal having a total thickness of 92 m. The exploited beds have an average thickness of 3 to 4 m.

Finally, the Saarbruck strata contain 5 beds (from a few cm. to 1 m. thick) of a very peculiar rock, known as claystone, which is almost never found in the coal basin of the north. This is a clayey rock, very compact, with conchoidal or parallelipipedic fractures, very fine grained. It is refractory and has the composition of aluminum silicate, with minute amounts of potassium and sodium. Finally, it contains a crystallized mineral (leverriérite) which we cannot study here. In short, the appearance of this rock is so characteristic that it has been recognized and named by miners. Similar rocks are also found in the coal basins of the Massif Central, called *gores blancs* by the workmen. And this name suggests their mode of formation. In fact, we know that in the dialect of central France, the word *gore* designates the sands resulting from the superficial alteration of crystalline rocks. And claystone, which seems peculiar to lacustrine basins, results from the scattering of the clayey muds coming from the leaching of the *gores*. In any case, from the stratigraphic point of view, the beds of claystone are often regular and uninterrupted enough to serve as horizon guides in exploitation. Thus the beds of St. Ingbert and Sulzbach, described later, are always separated by a bed of claystone which defines their boundaries.

But, of course, it is only the study of the flora and fauna which will allow us to find here the classic stages of the Coal Measures. Let us note in advance that, unlike the external Franco-Belgian-Westphalian Basin, here there is no trace of marine facies. All this formidable thickness of the Coal Measures was deposited, not on a coastal plain, but in a sinking lacustrine depression. Like the coal basins of the Vosges and Massif Central, the Saar Basin is found right in the heart of the young Hercynian Chain, in process of formation (internal basins). The only paleontologic scales applicable here are those of plants and freshwater faunas (pelecypods and crustaceans). These have made it possible to establish the following table, in which the names of beds are taken from the localities where they are exploited or crop out (see map, Fig. 44).

The Saar Basin has then for us stratigraphers the great interest of showing us a continuous Coal Measures series from the Westphalian to the Stephanian.

Kusel Beds...					Lower Autunian
Ottweiler Beds	weak coals	Breitenbach Beds (200 m.).....	Avaize	C	Stephanian
		Potzberg Beds (1,000 m.)	St. Etienne	B	
		Sarrelouis Beds (550 m.).......	Rive-de-Gier	A	
Holz conglomerate (3 to 200 m.)					
	flaming coal	La Houve Beds (2,000 m.).....	Molières	D	
Saarbruck Beds					Westphalian
	fat coal	Sulzbach Beds (600 m.)........	Bruay	C	
		St. Ingbert Beds (450 m.)......	Anzin	B	
			Vicoigne	A	

In the Northern Basin, the top of the Westphalian is missing. We shall do no better in the St. Etienne Basin, where the series begins with the Rive-de-Gier strata, base of the Stephanian. In the Gard Basin, however, recent studies of P. Bertrand and P. Pruvost point out, under the classic Stephanian, strata (Molières) completely representing the upper Westphalian. But these latter are incomparably more highly developed in the Saar-Lorraine Basin, at La Houve, and the name La Houve beds has thus been adopted as the type of this upper Westphalian (stage D, see table p. 164).

During the last war, a new stratigraphic study of the Saar Basin was made by H. Bode.[119] His conclusions agree with those of French geologists. Still, the Geisheck beds, intermediate between the flaming and the fat coals, the latter classified in Westphalian D, are attributed to Westphalian C. We note that, based on the abrupt change of flora between the La Houve and Sarrelouis beds, he believes with his predecessors (see later) in a lacuna of sedimentation between the Westphalian and Stephanian, a lacuna which would be underlain by the Holz conglomerate, which is connected with the base of Stephanian A.

B. Tectonics.   As we said in the beginning, the Coal Measures of the Saar appear between the old Massifs of Hunsrück and the Vosges, in the middle of a wide synclinal region filled with Permian and Triassic. If the Coal Measures crop out here, it is in consequence of an anticlinal uplift. This Saar Basin is then in reality, a vault or rather a complex anticlinal region, in which recent studies have distinguished two main anticlines.

1. *The Saar anticline* has its axis well marked by the oldest beds (Sulzbach and St. Ingbert) which crop out between Frankenholz and Saarbruck (see map, Fig. 44). This constitutes the Saar Basin proper, seat of the oldest mining operations, since the beds are not concealed under the *morts-terrains*. This anticline is, however, strongly unsymmetrical and bent towards the southeast. It even passes into a faulted fold, with stretching or suppression of the inverse flank, which the normal flank sometimes overlaps with a true overthrust (see section No. 1, Fig. 45). This fracture line, long known as the Great Southern Fault, marks the end of all the old exploitations in this direction. Its interpretation has only recently become precise, because of numerous transverse or oblique faults which are often superposed and culminate in a detailed structure too complicated to be described here. Finally, in the southwest part of the Saar valley, the Coal Measures disappear under the *morts-terrains,* but drill holes and mine workings allow us to find the extension of our anticline. The map (Fig. 44) shows that its axis passes near Forbach, where it becomes much more regular and more deeply buried (see sections 3 and 4, Fig. 45).

2. The second anticline may be called, according to P. Pruvost, the Lorraine anticline, for it gives rise to the Lorraine exploitations (concessions of Saar-Moselle, Petite-Rosselle, La Houve). In a way it takes the place of the first one. Northeast of the Saar Valley it is indicated only by insignificant undulations in the northwest flank of the great Saar anticline. Then, in proportion as this latter is buried and becomes weaker, the Lorraine anticline is

distinguished in a new festoon. It also becomes unsymmetrical, even passing
into a fold-fault (section 3). Thanks to this anticline the productive beds,
nearing the surface, can be exploited at Petite-Rosselle. It extends still farther
southwest, very clearly outlined (section 4), in the mines of La Houve and
Merlebach. But, in this direction, the thickness of the *morts-terrains* increases
rapidly.

The age of these dislocations can be established in detail, thanks to the coal
stratigraphy, and it is one of the best examples of the help that stratigraphy
can supply to the tectonic history of a region, or more pompously in modern

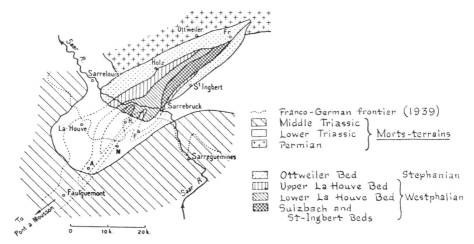

FIG. 44.   *Diagrammatic geologic map of the coal basin of the Saar and of
Lorraine (after P. Pruvost).*

The lines bounding the outcrops of the different stages of the Carboniferous have
been extended in broken lines beneath the cover of *morts-terrains* southwest of the
Saar. These lines are extremely diagrammatic. No account is taken of the numerous
faults which complicate them, in particular bringing up the Stephanian directly
north of Sarrebruck.

Notice that on the axis of the Saar anticline, the transgressive Stephanian directly
covers the lower members of the lower Westphalian.

Fr = Frankenholz; R = Petite-Rosselle; F = Forbach; M = Merlebach; A = St.-Avold.

language, to its embryotectonics. First, it is probable that in the depths of the
basin the Dinantian, if we could reach it, would be shown as very folded and
even granitized, as we shall see in the other internal basins of the Vosges and
Massif Central where the principal period of the Hercynian orogeny is located
between the Dinantian and Westphalian, that is to say approximately in the
Namurian. Then the folding continued in the Saar, so that the Holz conglomerate is often discordant and transgressive on its Westphalian substratum.
At St. Ingbert, exactly on the culminating point of the Saar anticline, it lies
directly on the Sulzbach bed. So, at the boundary of the Westphalian and
Stephanian, other steps are marked in the continuity of the folding. The Saar
anticline in this epoch plays the role of those cordilleras that we shall describe

in the history of the Alpine Chain. Finally, another important step corresponds to the end of the Autunian. This last stage is indeed concordant with the Stephanian, but, on the other hand, discordant with the great continuous Saxonian-Triassic-Jurassic series, in which no longer are found any traces of true orogenic movements.

But nevertheless the deformation of the ground continues. In fact, the map (Fig. 44) shows that, in the extension of the Saar-Lorraine anticlinal region itself, the Lower Triassic outcrops advance in a promontory toward the southwest, in the direction of Faulquemont. There is the indication of an anticlinal undulation, certainly post-Triassic, probably much more recent (perhaps Ter-

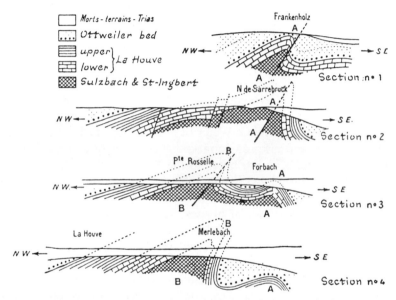

FIG. 45. *Four transverse sections of the coal basin of the Saar and of Lorraine (by P. Pruvost).*

A = Saar anticline; B = Lorraine anticline.

The names of localities allow these sections to be located in reference to the map of Fig. 44.

tiary). Thanks to this posthumous fold,[120] distinct descendant of the Hercynian folds, there is hope of reaching the Coal Measures by drilling in the region of Pont-à-Mousson. And this prediction, due to Nicklès, has actually been realized, but the coal beds so found are still at too great depths for profitable mining.

4. *The Carboniferous in Brittany*[121]

With Brittany, we enter upon a series of regions where the exclusively continental Coal Measures have taken the type of the internal basins of the Hercynian Chain, the type defined in connection with the Saar. But, while we do not know the Dinantian in the Saar, we do find it again in Brittany. It is a very thick, shaly-sandy series (Culm or Flysch facies), containing now plants, now marine fossils. These are especially abundant in calcareous lentils, of which we shall speak again. This Dinantian, locally granitized, is thus immediately anterior to the great Hercynian folding. It is discordantly covered by the continental Coal Measures, forming very small basins, which lie on any earlier formation and in which the floras have sometimes made possible the identification of the Westphalian and Stephanian, as in the Saar.

But because of the intensity of the folding, scarcity of outcrops and absence of underground workings, the stratigraphy can not be defined as in the great classic basins.

A. Dinantian.   This is represented in the following regions (see p. 55 and Fig. 11), from north to south:

1. *Northern Brittany and Cotentin.*   We have already seen that along the northern shore of Brittany, recent research has shown that the beds formerly classified as Brioverian are probably younger and should be reclassified as Dinantian of the Culm facies, seeming also to grade into the Devonian, as in Devon. This is so in the Carboniferous basin of Morlaix (shown on the map, Fig. 11), for which we refer back to the discussion on p. 59.

In addition, P. Pruvost and G. Waterlot[122] have restudied the non-fossiliferous red sandstones and arkoses, long known, especially at Erguy and Cape Frehel, but which had been attributed to the Brioverian, the Cambrian, or the Permian. Through ingenious stratigraphic considerations, these geologists conclude that we have here Red Coal Measures, which facies would thus indicate the proximity of continental masses, subordinate to the North Atlantic continent.

And A. Bigot[123] likens to them the red sandstone outcrop in the Cotentin south of Coutances, overlain by a transgressive Visean. In fact, at Montmartin, we know there are Culm shales containing a lentil of Régneville limestone in which G. Delépine has recognized *Davisiella comoides,* a large productid characteristic of the lower Visean.

2. *The Great Axial Syncline of Châteaulin-Laval.*   There, shales with plants of the Culm predominate. Associated with Devonian shales, they make the great, fertile depression of the Châteaulin Basin. Along its northern edge, at Plouyé near Huelgoat (north of Gourin, see map, Fig. 11), Barrois has noted beds with *Spirifer striatus.* But in this basin the most interesting calcareous lentil is that of St. Ségal, immediately north of Châteaulin, containing *Productus latissimus,* of the top of the Visean.

The faunas are richest in the Laval Basin. We have first, in the narrow strip which connects the Châteaulin and Laval Basins, near St. Germain-sur-Ille (north of Rennes), the Quenon limestone of the lower Visean, in which appear the Waulsortian facies (see p. 182). Farther east the outcrops of Culm shales, sandstone, and conglomerates, transgressive over miscellaneous older formations, are highly developed in the Laval Basin proper. There the brachiopod and coral faunas of the Laval limestones (Waulsortian facies) and of the Sablé limestones (southeast of Laval, on the edge of the Armorican Massif) have made it possible for Delépine to connect the Dinantian stratigraphy of Brittany with the British zones C, S and D, as shown in the table below:

Laval shales $\begin{cases} \text{Shales with plants of the Culm}\ldots\ldots\ldots\ldots \text{D}_{2\text{-}3} \\ \text{Calcareous beds}\ldots\ldots\ldots\ldots\ldots\ldots\ldots \text{D}_1 \end{cases}$

Visean

Sablé limestone $\begin{cases} \text{Laval limestone}\ldots\ldots\ldots\ldots\ldots\ldots\ldots \text{S}_2 \\ \text{Graywacke with echinoids}\ldots\ldots\ldots\ldots \text{C}_2\text{-S}_1 \end{cases}$

Sandstones and shales with plants and *Productus burlingtonensis*[121]$\ldots\ldots$

Blaviérite[125]$\ldots\ldots\ldots\ldots\ldots\ldots\ldots\ldots\ldots\ldots\ldots\ldots\ldots\ldots\ldots$

Tournaisian

3. *Angers Syncline.* Near this village are outcrops of graywackes with plant remains that Péneau (work cited note 88, chap. 4) assigns to the extreme base of the Tournaisian.

4. *Ancenis Syncline.* Here only the Culm with marine pelecypods and plants, recently restudied by Carpentier,[126] is found. According to Delépine[127] the flora is of upper Visean age, indicating a Visean transgression on the Devonian with *Spirifer verneuili.*

B. Coal Measures (Westphalian and Stephanian). The Coal Measures of Brittany are exclusively continental. They contain some beds of coal, but have never been extensively mined, so the flora is in general little known. We mention only the following coal basins:

1. The Littry Basin (see map, Fig. 11) in Calvados, generally classified as Stephanian.[128]

2. The three small coal basins in southern Finisterre (Quimper, Kergogne, Cap Sizun), studied by Piquenard.[129] Sandstones and shales lying directly on the ancient formations (and not on the Dinantian) contain a Stephanian flora.

3. *The Coal Basin of Saint-Pierre-la-Cour,* northeast of Rennes, is near the western end of the Dinantian Basin of Laval. According to its flora, it belongs to the Stephanian and P. Pruvost has noted in it *Anthracomya prolifera,* a pelecypod characteristic of the Rive-de-Gier stratum (see the note for the chart on p. 164, concerning this species).

4. *The Ancenis Basin* is the most important. In it, above the Culm with Dinantian plants, Westphalian and Stephanian floras are present.

5. Finally, in the Vendée, the small, aligned Basins of *Chantonnay-Faymoreau-Vouvant* (map, Fig. 11) have recently been studied by G. Mathieu.[130] The floras allow the identification of the Namurian, upper Wesphalian, and lower and middle Stephanian stages.

5. *The Carboniferous in the Vosges*[131]

Here again we find basins of the internal type. The Dinantian is enfolded, with the Devonian, in the great folds of the Hercynian Chain. It is even locally granitized (A. Michel-Lévy, J. Jung). On the other hand, the Coal Measures, entirely continental, little folded and not at all metamorphic, constitute small basins lying on miscellaneous earlier formations so that they are thoroughly well defined.

A. Dinantian.   We already know that it is found in the two great Devono-Dinantian Massifs of the Hercynian Vosges (see p. 134 and Fig. 30).

1. In the *Massif of Bruche,* it seems to play a role of little importance. It is always the Culm facies, with *Posidonomya* shales and chert beds with radiolaria, discovered and studied by J. de Lapparent and recalling the lydian stone of Devon and the Rhenish Massif. More recently sandy beds with plants have furnished P. Corsin and G. Dubois[132] determinable plants, characteristic of the Dinantian.

2. In the *Grand Ballon Massif,* the Culm occupies enormous areas. It is formed of quite varied beds, sometimes granitized and very rich in volcanic products, lava flows, dikes or tuffs. Fine fossiliferous strata, long recognized, exist in the region of Thann and Bourbach, in particular near the farm of la Boutique.[133] The fauna, rich and varied, is composed of corals, echinoderms, brachiopods, pelecypods, gastropods, and even a goniatite. According to Delépine, who has recently revised it (results not published), it belongs with *Productus hemisphaericus* strata of the lower Visean. The floras lead to the same conclusion.[134]

B. The Westphalian and Stephanian.   They lie discordantly on all the older folded formations. They do not contain intrusive granites and have not been metamorphosed. Finally, they are little folded or only faulted and have been preserved only in small sunken basins. The most important of these basins is that of Val-de-Villé, forming a great depression which penetrates to the heart of the chain. The Stephanian here lies directly on the, gneiss or ancient shales (shales of Villé = Cambrian?) and passes gradually into the Permian.[135]

On the other hand, the insignificant productive remnants around St. Hippolyte have shown a Westphalian flora.

All these basins are now considered exhausted.

By contrast, at the extreme southern border of the Vosges, between Belfort and Lure, the Ronchamp Basin shows a fine development of the Stephanian, actively exploited to a depth of 1,000 m.

Recent studies of G. Mathieu[136] have established the relation of this coal of Ronchamp with the Devono-Dinantian of the Vosges.

1. The substratum of the coal beds is formed by Culm, whose base is certainly Devonian (strata near Chagey, see p. 136) and whose top, with coal streaks and eruptive rocks, may be attributed to the Tournaisian.

2. Next, above a basal green puddingstone, witness of orogenic movements, comes the transition formation of early geologists, with micro-diorites, shales and green graywackes which may be assigned to the Namurian; at any rate, the Westphalian is certainly missing.

3. In fact, the productive Coal Measures are discordant on this Namurian. Their basal part, composed of sandstones and "talcose" conglomerates, contain the Mourière *faisceau* with a flora which can be classified as lower Stephanian (Rive-de-Gier bed). Above comes the productive Ronchamp

faisceau, whose flora, revised by G. Mathieu, is made up of a mixture of lower and middle Stephanian species (St. Etienne bed).

Thus, through the appearance of orogenic phenomena in the Namurian (or Visean) and especially by the complete absence of the Westphalian, this Ronchamp basin is entirely different from those of the Ardennes and Saar. It is the type that we shall find again in the Massif Central.

6. *The Carboniferous of the French Massif Central*

The Carboniferous of the Massif Central is very similar to that we have just described in the Vosges.

Here again, the principal phase of the Hercynian folding took place between the Dinantian and the productive Coal Measures. The granitic intrusions ended only in the course of the Dinantian and affected the Tournaisian and perhaps even the base of the Visean.[137]

As for the productive Coal Measures, they are usually, throughout the Massif Central, considered to be Stephanian. But recent studies of P. Bertrand and P. Pruvost have shown that in the south (Gard), at least, the coal series began with the top of the upper Westphalian.

A. Dinantian.[138]   Through reaction against the old idea of an Archean stage, we already know (see p. 38) that some geologists supposed that the Devono-Dinantian could, at least in certain regions (Lyonnais Mts. for example), be included in the schistose series, but this opinion is generally abandoned today. In any case, wherever Dinantian fossils have been discovered, this well-dated Dinantian is found lying in transgression on folded and eroded gneisses and micaschists. It has everywhere the Culm facies: great thicknesses of shales and sandstones with rare calcareous lentils (Regny limestone, near Roanne) or beds of radiolarian lydian stone, discovered by A. Michel-Lévy, and especially, as in the Vosges, a great display of acid volcanic rocks, lava flows, and tuffs.

The fossiliferous strata are all (with the exception of the Montagne-Noire, studied later) localized in the northern part of the massif: Morvan, Beaujolais, the vicinity of Vichy and Gannat and even in the Creuse, south of Montluçon. The southernmost examples are the sandstone and conglomerate noted by A. Demay[139] near Boën (Forez), non-fossiliferous, but which by their lithologic facies seem clearly Visean.

The most complete series is that of the classic region of L'Ardoisière, near Vichy, recently restudied by Chichery. It includes, from bottom to top:

a) An andesitic complex, with calcareous lenses, without fossils, perhaps in part Devonian.

b) The shaly-sandy stage of L'Ardoisière, very thick, with indeterminable plants, but similar to the Tournaisian of Bourbon-Lancy (with *Spirifer tornacensis*).

c) The stage of graywackes and conglomerates (600 to 700 m.) with Visean faunas of *Productus cora* and *P. hemisphaericus,* indicating the upper part of the middle Visean (at the boundary between the British zones S[2] and D[1]).

d) The stage of anthraciferous tuffs, with beds of coal, and containing *P. latissimus* and *P. giganteus,* discovered by Chichery and characterizing zone D^2 of the upper Visean.

West of the Allier, this Culm is reduced to stage *d,* transgressive over the crystalline rocks. Likewise on the eastern border of the massif, in Beaujolais, the floras, studied especially at Fuissé, indicate the Visean, according to Delépine.

In the Montagne-Noire, it was believed until recently, following the old studies of Bergeron, that the Dinantian, in continuity with the Devonian, began with a Tournaisian with *Spirifer tornacensis.* But the beds at the base (10 to 20 m.) of this Dinantian, characterized by lydian stone and phosphate nodules, already contain, according to recent study,[140] a goniatite fauna (*Pericyclus, Aganides, Nomismoceras*) indicating the base of the Visean; the continuity with the Devonian would be, then, only apparent. At any rate, we find here, cropping out over great areas, very thick black shales (300 m. at least), of Culm facies, sometimes containing plant debris, sometimes *Posidonomya becheri* and calcareous lentils with brachiopods or faunas of *Productus cora* and *P. giganteus,* indicating that the series rises as far as the top of the Visean. Stratigraphic study is, however, made very difficult by very intense folding, with true nappes, though these were formed previous to the Coal Measures (Stephanian) of the small Basins of Neffiès and Graissessac.

It was therefore after the Visean and probably during the Namurian that the great Hercynian folds were produced. Definitely emergent, the Massif Central constituted a mountainous region, the depressions of which were to become, in Coal Measures time, internal basins.

B. The Productive Coal Measures. It is thus on a chain young and probably already attacked by erosion that the sediments composing the productive Coal Measures were deposited. They were shales, sandstones and conglomerates, with beds of coal. No marine fossil is ever found, only pelecypods and fresh water crustaceans (*Estheria*), fish, insects (very abundant at Commentry) and especially plants.

The distribution of these sediments in small isolated basins (Fig. 46), the dip of the beds, very steep near the edges, diminishing toward the centers, formerly led to the belief that these coal basins resulted from the filling up of ancient, deep lakes by torrents descending from neighboring mountains. The coal would have been then a plant alluvium (allochtonous theory). But today we tend more and more to apply to the Massif Central the ideas developed on the subject of the northern coal basin. The coal must have been formed, at least in part, in place in the swampy forests, the floor of which was sinking at some points. And it is precisely the continuation of these phenomena of subsidence along the same zones which allowed the enormous accumulation of coaly sediments in so many local basins.

Thus the localization and the form of these basins would be due to tectonic causes. Actually, the folding continued after the Stephanian. Each basin is transformed today into a syncline, very narrow and broken by faulted folds. The dip of the coal and the sterile beds near the borders is certainly of tectonic origin, not sedimentary.

It is difficult to give the exact date at which these posthumous folds were completed. They may have been partly Permian and partly much more recent. For on the southeast edge of the massif, in the neighborhood of the great Tertiary folds of southern France (Pyrenees-Provençal zone), we know, thanks to the works of Termier and Friedel on the Basin of Alès, of Depéret

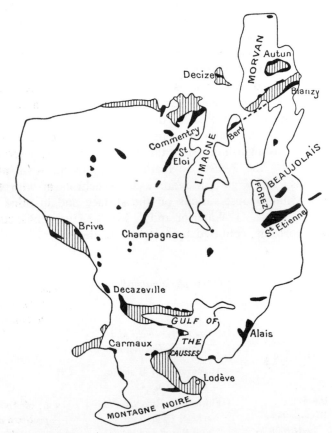

FIG. 46. *Diagrammatic map of the French Massif Central, showing the extent of the Primary formation, the coal basins (in black) and the Permian (ruled lines). (Partly after A. de Lapparent).*

N. B. At Bert, only the Permian, not the Carboniferous, crops out.

and Nicklès on the border of the Montagne-Noire, that the horizontal displacements (example: Cevennes fault) were produced during the Tertiary.

At any rate, these posthumous folds almost exactly fit the directions of the Hercynian folds, Armorican direction in the west, Variscan direction in the east (see p. 162). Such is the orientation of the coal basins in the Massif Central.

The map (Fig. 46) makes evident the peculiar alignment of the coal basins following each other from NNE to SSW, between Moulins and Decazeville and especially from St. Eloi to Champagnac. All together they constitute what has been called the great coal furrow. We can in fact imagine that this zone was, in the Stephanian, a great depressed trough, separating the Armorican and Variscan parts of the massif [141] and playing, in this epoch, a role similar to that played by the Rhenish trough, for example, in the Tertiary (and still being played today). And the end of the filling up of this channel was marked by an abrupt tightening of its borders, folding its contents in overlapping and overridden scales.

We shall study, as examples, two of the most important basins of the Massif Central, those of St. Etienne and Gard.[142]

a) *The St. Etienne Basin.* This is a great syncline, crushed and faulted, which runs from SW to NE, separating the Lyonnais Mts. on the northwest from the little Massif of Mont-Pilat to the southeast.

The stratigraphy of the Carboniferous was first studied here by Grand-Eury, who tried to distinguish in it a certain number of stages based on floras. Next, P. Bertrand [143] and P. Pruvost made a study of the fossil plants and freshwater faunas, which gave a more exact synchronism with the other basins. Finally, detailed observations on the surface and in mine galleries, carried out by A. Bonte, G. Waterlot and J. Maistre,[144] established the succession of coal horizons, confused by tectonic accidents.

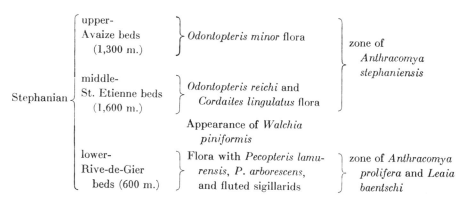

The lower Stephanian is found only at Rive-de-Gier, a locality between St. Etienne and the Rhône, at the northeast extremity of the Carboniferous outcrops. The coal series is in fact transgressive toward the southwest.

The middle Stephanian, or St. Etienne beds proper, is introduced by the mosaic conglomerate of Grand'Croix, with a rhyolitic lava flow. In the middle of this unit, not at its base as formerly believed, is intercalated the conglomerate of Saint-Chamond (locality between St. Etienne and Rive-de-Gier).

The upper Stephanian corresponds to the Avaize beds. Its lower part is made up of the thick (500 m.) Montrambert beds, containing bituminous shales with fish scales. At the top it passes concordantly into red beds (called

the "Botanical Garden") which, according to the flora, already belong to
the base of the Autunian.

In total, this coal series is 3,500 m. thick and contains about twenty coal
beds. So, we see that in this limnic basin, purely lacustrine, in the mid-con-
tinent, the phenomena of subsidence have as great importance as in the
coastal plains of the Franco-Belgian Basin (paralic). However, we never
find the series complete in the same section; the zone of subsidence is displaced even during the course of the filling up of the basin. We have already
shown that the lower series (Rive-de-Gier) is found only in the northeast,
while the upper series of Avaize, toward the southwest, lies directly on
the crystalline floor.

Tectonics.[145]   The section (Fig. 47) clearly shows the crushing of the
syncline under the influence of pressure coming from the southeast. The
boundary fault, which puts an end to exploitation in that direction, is very

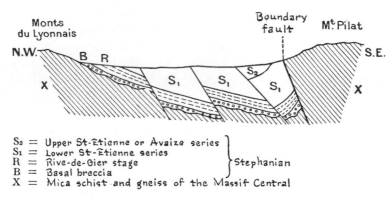

FIG. 47.   *Diagrammatic section of the St. Etienne basin (after Grüner,
modified)*.

probably, as in the northern basin, a fold-fault. Other secondary dislocation
surfaces determine, as in the Namur Basin, successive blocks, deeper and
deeper toward the southeast; thus J. de Maistre has recently demonstrated
that the fault of the *Puits de la Loire* would give a vertical throw of 500 m.

Notice, finally, that the St. Etienne Basin continues along the left bank
of the Rhone, in the Lower Dauphiné,[146] where wells have found coal under
a thick covering of *morts-terrains* (especially Miocene and Oligocene). Unfortunately these coal beds are too thin and too deep to justify even attempts
at exploitation.

b).   *The Gard Coal Basin or Basin of Alès*.   This basin is one of the most
complicated and at the same time one of the best studied. So, its description
will give us an example, worthy of becoming classic, of a double stratigraphic
and tectonic synthesis.[147]

This basin is located along the southeast edge of the Massif Central. On
this border, the *morts-terrains* (Triassic and Jurassic) usually directly overlie the schistose formations, so the Coal Measures outcrops are very limited.

They are distributed in two gulf-like basins open to the southeast, the Grand-'Combe Basin at the southwest and the Bessèges Basin at the northeast, separated by the promontory of mica schists of Rouvergue. To this whole assemblage is given the name Basin of Alès, from the most important town of the vicinity.[148]

The stratigraphic series, as it appears from the studies of P. Bertrand (floras) and P. Pruvost (lacustrine faunas), includes the units indicated in the table following.

But, if the distribution of these different series is examined in mine workings and outcrops (see Fig. 48 and 49), it is immediately apparent that there are numerous abnormal superpositions.

All the western outcrops and in particular the great extent of the Coal Measures of the Grand'Combe Basin, belong to the middle Stephanian (h^2), lying directly in the west on ancient formations through the medium of thick basal breccias, without any intercalation of lower Stephanian. On the other hand, the lower Stephanian and the upper Westphalian (h^1) appear in the eastern part, but instead of being beneath the middle Stephanian of Grand-'Combe, they are above it. This superposition is clearly seen in the Sainte-Barbe Mountain, where a little window, excavated by erosion across the lower Stephanian, lets us see the middle Stephanian below, which thus extends at depth under this mountain. The Ricard bore, the bottom of which has cut through a Ricard *faisceau* with a flora identical to that of the Pradel *faisceau,* verifies this superposition.

NAMES OF STAGES	FLORAS	LACUSTRINE FAUNAS	LOCAL NAMES IN THE ALES BASIN
Middle Stephanian = St. Etienne stage	zone of *Cordaites lingulatus*	zone of *Anthracomya stephaniensis*	Series of Grand'Combe (*faisceaux* of Champclauson, Grand-Baume, and Ricard-Pradel-Feljas) ....h^2
Lower Stephanian = Rive-de-Gier stage	zone of *Pecopteris lamurensis*	zone of *Leaia baentschi* and *Anthracomya prolifera*	Bessèges and Saint Jean de Valériscle series...h^{1c}
			Series of Sainte-Barbe and upper Molières..h^{1b}
Upper Westphalian = La Houve stage	zone of *P. lamurensis* and *Mixoneura flexuosa*	zone of *Estheria cebennensis*	Molières anthracites and Gagnières sterile beds ....h^{1a}

In the Bessèges Basin, we are led to identical conclusions. Here the autochthonous middle Stephanian (h^2) lying normally on the mica schists is covered directly by a layer of beds belonging to the Bessèges series (h^{1c}),

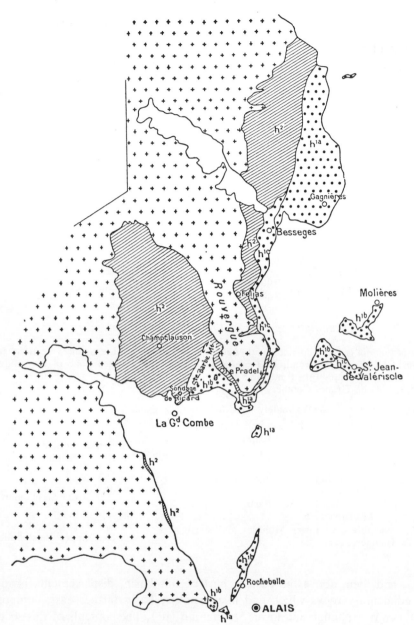

FIG. 48. *Geologic map of the Gard coal basin (after the Alais sheet of the geologic map of France, 1/80,000)*.

White: *Morts-terrains*.
Crosses: Schistose formations of the Massif Central.
Ruled: h^2 = middle Stephanian.
Dotted: h^1 = lower Stephanian (h^{1c}, h^{1b})
               and upper Westphalian (h^{1a}).
Scale: Approximately 1/200,000. More detailed legend as in Fig. 49.

N. B.   According to information on the section (Fig. 49), but contrary to that indicated on this map, the scale of Ste. Barbe Mountain includes not only h^{1b} (Ste. Barbe assemblage) but also h^{1c} (Bessèges assemblage) which, like the border of the Bessèges basin, is thrust directly over h^2.

the top of the lower Stephanian. Toward the east, this sheet pinches out rapidly at depth, for the Parran Pits, at Gagnières, have not crossed them and have reached directly, at the bottom, beds with the Feljas flora (h^2). Next, above this first sheet, a whole new assemblage appears, composed first of the Gagnières series (upper Westphalian, h^{1a}), then, in normal superposition the upper Molières series (h^{1b}) (that is, the same layer which farther southwest formed Sainte-Barbe Mountain), and last the St. Jean-de-Valériscle series (h^{1c}) with a flora identical to that of Bessèges.

To summarize, everything occurs as if there had been, above the mica schists, a first autochthonous coal basin, composed only of middle Stephanian

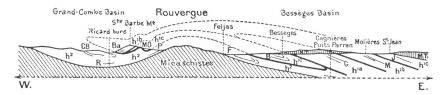

FIG. 49. *Diagrammatic section of the Gard coal basin.*

This section is built up and synthesized by imagining all the detailed sections published by Marcel Bertrand, P. Termier, G. Friedel projected on one plane, modified according to unpublished information kindly given by M. Livet, engineer for the Mines of the Grand' Combe.

Horizontal scale: approximately 1/65,000; heights exaggerated.

MT = morts-terrains (Triassic and Jurassic)
GB = assemblage of Grand-Baume .... ⎫ h^2 = middle
R,P,F = assemblage from the bore-holes of Ricard, ⎬   Stephanian
     Pradel and Feljas .... ⎭

B,J,MD = assemblage of Bessèges, St. Jean and
     Mas-Dieu .... h^{1c} ⎫
Ba,M = assemblages of Ste. Barbe and upper   ⎬ = lower Stephanian
     Molières .... h^{1b} ⎭

G = assemblage of lower Molières and sterile
     Gagnières .... h^{1a} ⎱ = upper Westphalian

(h^2), and then, above the eastern part of this basin, displacements brought in sedimentary rocks which had filled another basin farther east, composed of upper Westphalian and lower Stephanian (h^1). The contents of this second basin are then comparable to a vast covering nappe, now broken up by erosion or hidden under the *morts-terrains*. A first fragment of this nappe, entirely isolated from the root zone, forms the Sainte-Barbe Mountain. Another, larger, constitutes the whole region of Gagnières, Bessèges, and St. Jean-de-Valériscle. Its base here is formed by the thick series of the Gagnières sterile beds (h^{1a}). The Sanguinet bore, northeast of Molières, which went to a depth of 1,700 m. and passed through more than 900 m. thickness of this series, did not reach its base.[149] We do not know if the autochthonous h^2 extends at greater depth as far as this region.

7. *The Carboniferous of the Pyrenees*

This Carboniferous is very similar to that of the Montagne-Noire. Moreover, an intermediary landmark between these two regions is provided by the small Primary Massif of Monthoumet which forms the framework of the Corbières and in which is found Culm with plants.

In the Pyrenees, the Dinantian begins with black shale with phosphate nodules and beds of radiolarite, usually classified as Tournaisian. Delépine,[150] who discovered in these nodules, exploited in Ariège, a goniatite (*Prolecanites*, sub-genus *Merocanites*) characteristic of the lower Visean, recognizes a lacuna. He considers that the sea did not reach here until the beginning of the Visean. This Culm facies, with intercalations of plant-bearing sandstones, is followed by shale with calcareous beds containing faunas of the upper Visean (*Productus latissimus, Glyphioceras*). The depth facies are deeper than in the Montagne-Noire, for goniatites predominate over brachiopods (Dalloni). In fact, the marine facies here persist particularly late. For in the Basque Pyrenees, southeast of St.-Jean-Pied-de-Port, Delépine has determined, in the terminal Culm beds, *Eumorphoceras bisulcatum,* a species characteristic of the lower Namurian. And the celebrated fauna of Mondette, in Ariège south of St-Girons, is placed at almost the same horizon. Formerly assigned by Haug to the Artinskian, this fauna was noted in all the classic treatises as the single representative of the marine Permian in France. According to the revisions of Delépine,[151] a *Glyphioceras* fauna is involved, indicating a horizon close to the boundary between the Visean and Namurian.

This persistence of the marine facies announces the approach of the Mediterranean type of the Carboniferous which, characterized by seas with fusilines, appears in the Asturias.

Nevertheless, in the Pyrenees, we find again purely continental Coal Measures, of the type of the internal basins of the Hercynian Chain. Discordant on the Dinantian, very folded and sometimes granitized,[152] these Coal Measures lie on various old formations. They are localized in very small basins, none of which is exploited, but which have provided floras spaced between the middle Westphalian and the upper Stephanian.[153]

8. *The Carboniferous of the French Alps, the Swiss Alps and Provence*

A. French Alps. The study of the Carboniferous of the French Alps, necessary to the understanding of the structure of the chain, has a very special interest from the stratigraphic viewpoint.[154] As often happens in the folded chains, the facies are arranged, in fact, following bands approximately parallel to the direction of the folds, that is, of the chain. Crossing the Alps, from the Rhône valley to Italy, we find, thus, three successive zones[155] in which the Carboniferous crops out with different characteristics (Figs. 50, 60 and 62).

a) *External zone, or the Crystalline Hercynian Massif.* The westernmost outcrops of the Alpine Carboniferous appear in synclines in massifs of ancient rocks,[156] generally very metamorphic (granites, micaschists, phyllites, rarely cipolines), whose age cannot be precisely determined. Their ages may range from Cambrian to Dinantian, but we shall merely call them pre-coal. In fact, the Coal Measures, the oldest dated formation in the French Alps, are discordant on these ancient rocks (phase of the principal Hercynian folding). These Coal Measures, however, were folded before the deposition of the Triassic, which lies over them discordantly. Naturally the whole mass was worked over again by the Alpine folding in the Tertiary. And under the influence of these multiple orogenic movements, the coal is everywhere transformed into anthracite (see p. 237).

The only basins which are actively exploited are La Mure, in the southern

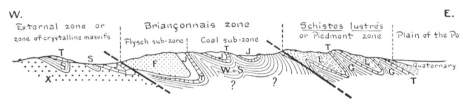

FIG. 50.   *Theoretical section showing the different types of the Carboniferous in the western Alps.*

F = Flysch: Tertiary
J = Jurassic (and Cretaceous)
L = *Schistes lustrés* (Secondary, Tertiary?)
T = Triassic

S = Stephanian and Westphalian D (external zone)
W + S = Westphalian C-D and Stephanian (Briançonnais)
G = Gneiss, in part Permo-Carboniferous (Piedmont)
X = Pre-Carboniferous schistose formations (external zone)

N. B.   This section has been made extremely simple; thus, between the Flysch of the border of the Briançonnais and the external zone, a sub-Briançonnais zone, in which the whole Carboniferous-Tertiary series is represented, should be intercalated.

part of the crystalline Massif of Belledonne, and Bourg-d'Oisans, where the extraction of coal comes to an end at 2,300 m. altitude in a narrow coal syncline of the Massif of Grandes-Rousses.

There Coal Measures are thick accumulations of shales, sandstones and conglomerates, sometimes (Grandes-Rousses) containing important andesitic lava flows. No trace of marine fossils has ever been found here.

The early studies of the floras,[157] made in particular by Zeiller (in Kilian and Révil) concluded that all these basins were of Stephanian age, as *Pecopteris lamurensis* is one of the most frequent plants. But, at least in some of the basins, the coal series begins, as in Gard, with Westphalian D (Houve bed) characterized by the association of *Mixoneura ovata* with *P. lamurensis*. This flora has been found by P. Bertrand [158] in the small basin of Servoz (Massif of Aiguilles-Rouges between St. Gervais and Chamonix).

Very recently, L. Moret [159] has collected *M. ovata* at the base of the shaly-sandy complex (*lauzes*) which so curiously caps the summit of the Grande-Lauziere (near Pics de Belledonne). In the La Mure basin, P. Pruvost [160] has noted *Estheria cebennensis,* a species of Westphalian D at Gard. But, according to P. Corsin, the flora indicates the base of the lower Stephanian, as at Vaulnaveys (near Uriage), while at Entraigues (east of La Mure) and at Grandes-Rousses, would be the top of the lower Stephanian. Finally, the famous deposit of Petit-Coeur, near Moutiers (Savoy) shows a transition from Westphalian D to Stephanian.

b) *Briançonnais Zone.*[161]   Continuing eastward, we find first, in the sub-Briançonnais zone, only narrow slices of the coal deposits (Stephanian?), appearing only in Tarentaise (region of Moutiers-Bourg-St. Maurice). But, in the axial part of the Briançonnais zone, the coal formations reappear extensively and with very different characteristics. This is the Briançonnais coal zone, so named because the Carboniferous crops out by itself here over a great width, shaped like a ribbon which begins a little south of Briançon, runs toward Maurienne (where it reaches its maximum breadth, 25 km., between Saint-Michel and Modane), next into Tarentaise, where the valley of the Isère broadens between Aime and Bourg-St-Maurice, and finally extends into Italy through the broad depression of the Petit-St-Bernard, circling around Mont-Blanc on the southeast.

The substratum of the Carboniferous is here unknown[162] but we can see a concordant transition to the Permian, that passes in its turn without discontinuity into the Triassic. There is an enormous thickness of shales and sandstones with beds of conglomerate exceeding 3,000 m. in thickness and forming whole massifs, in which, here and there, appear dikes or flows of eruptive rocks (especially microdiorites). As always no marine fossils are found, only numerous plant remains. On the basis of early collections made by C. Pussenot [163] and identified by R. Zeiller, it was thought that the species *Neuropteris schlehani* and *Sphenopteris höninghausi,* characteristic of Westphalian A, had been recognized in various parts of the Briançonnais and the presence of Westphalian A in the Alps was generally accepted through the classic work of Kilian and Révil. But according to P. Corsin, these conclusions resulted from errors of identification. In the vicinity of Briançon and Monetier, the floras indicate Westphalian C passing into Westphalian D. In fact, a specimen collected by C. Pussenot in Névache Pass between Briançon and Valmeinier, was determined by P. Pruvost (*in litt.*) as *Leaia tricarinata,* a species of Westphalian C. Farther north, at Valmeinier in Maurienne, the floras indicate Westphalian D. The Stephanian would then perhaps be sterile.

Because of the tectonic complications, any detailed stratigraphy is impossible in these Briançonnais Coal Measures. But although all the anthracite beds are crushed, laminated and discontinuous, small centers of mining have been kept working near Briançon, in Maurienne (St-Michel) and especially in Tarentaise (region of Moutier, Aime).

c) *Zone of the Internal Crystalline Massifs.* Between the Arc and the upper Isère, the western part of the Vanoise Massif, studied by P. Termier,[164]

still belongs to the Briançonnais zone and in it the normal, that is non-metamorphic, Coal Measures of this zone are found. But in the eastern part of
the area it seems (?) that these Coal Measures, and the Permian which overlies them, become rapidly more metamorphic and pass into crystalline schists
(without true gneiss or granite). This is the crystalline Massif of Vanoise,
the only region where, in the Briançonnais zone, late metamorphism, post-
coal, Alpine and not Hercynian, begins to affect the Alpine sedimentary
series.

Still farther east, in the zone of the *schistes lustrés* or of Piedmont, this
metamorphism affects even the Jurassic and Cretaceous, which have there
become the *schistes lustrés*. They overlie a Triassic very easily recognized
but very irregular (ranging from a few meters to several hundred meters
thick), and underneath these strata nothing more than crystalline or schistose
rocks is visible. In our judgment, and contrary to the opinion of E. Argand,
these thick schistose complexes do not certainly include the basal quartzites
of the Triassic. Some geologists (Cornelius, G. B. dal Piaz) even acknowl-
edge that these Franco-Italian internal crystalline massifs (Grand-Paradis,
Ambin, Doire-Maira, see map Fig. 62) were separated from the Secondary
covering by the Hercynian discordance, apparently effaced by laminage. It
remains possible that the Permian and Carboniferous may be locally present,
though unrecognizable in these metamorphic series. Thus in Italy, in the
Doire-Maira Massif, we find veins of graphite exploited (Pignerol graphitic
zone) which may represent the metamorphic equivalent of our Briançonnais
anthracite. But in some very crystalline gneisses (in Maurienne, Bonneval
gneiss, dependent of the Gd-Paradis Massif) and in certain gneissic granites
(in Switzerland, Arolla granites, in the Massif of Dt-Blanche), can be seen
the deep granites of anatexis, probably pre-Coal. Thus these crystalline internal massifs still contain many obscurities.

But, if we look at the whole assemblage of the French Alps, we see that
these Coal Measures, reduced to small isolated basins in the external zone,
become much thicker and more highly developed in the Briançonnais zone.
They finally become metamorphic in the Piedmont zone, and, to the east, take
on more and more geosynclinal characteristics. This term also calls to mind
the subsidences, which have permitted the gradual accumulation of sediments
as they were formed, and their later settling into the depths where they could
be affected by Alpine metamorphism.[165] From this point of view, here is
then the zone of *schistes lustrés* which seems to us the Alpine geosyncline
par excellence.

B. Swiss Alps.[166]   We should find in the Swiss Alps the extension of the
zone which we have just described in the French Alps. Here again, there is
a very clear contrast between an external (Helvetian) zone and an internal
(Pennine) zone, the two being separated by the surface of a great frontal
Pennine overthrust (see Fig. 62). In this Pennine zone the external border
should show Coal Measures with anthracite, a thin continuation of the Briançonnais coal band; this is the Pennine coal zone of the Swiss geologists,
which extends along the south flank of Valais. And toward the south these

Pennine Coal Measures quickly become metamorphic and pass into crystalline and schistose complexes called the Casanna schists. Here again we find our internal crystalline massifs, surrounded by *schistes lustrés*.

C. Provence. In Provence, the Hercynian Massif of Maures-Esterel appears like a Massif Central in miniature.[167] The principal Hercynian folds, accompanied by granitization, were produced here before the deposition of the Coal Measures, which, themselves folded before the Permian, are preserved in narrow N-S synclines.

We note, in the Maures, the Collobrières Coal Measures with a Stephanian flora, studied by P. Bertrand.[168] But the most interesting basin is that of the Reyran (a small coastal river) which extends into the Esterel north of Fréjus. At the base, in beds with a Stephanian flora (Rive-de-Gier horizon) are intercalated bituminous (boghead) coals with algae (*Pila*), which are treated by distillation (Boson mines). This is a facies that we find elsewhere in France only in the Permian. Above, 1,000 m. of sandstones and shales with the St. Etienne flora contain small beds that are not now mined.[169]

III. The Typical Series of the Marine Carboniferous in Russia [170]

The Carboniferous outcrops in Russia may be grouped in the following way:

1. The domain of the Russian Platform proper, where the Primary has remained horizontal: the different stages of the Carboniferous crop out there principally in concentric belts concave toward the east, centered about a point a little northeast of Moscow, and following Devonian and Silurian belts bordering the southeast edge of the Baltic Shield. The arrangement of these Paleozoic belts recalls exactly that of the Jurassic and Cretaceous belts of the southeast part of the Paris Basin.

2. The folded (Hercynian) chains of the Ural and of Timan.

3. The Hercynian coal basin of Donetz, north of the Sea of Azov, a region which we shall study separately.

Using the marine faunas, the Russian geologists distinguish three great divisions in their Carboniferous:

1st. A Lower Carboniferous (C1) or *Productus* stage. There are not yet either fusulines or schwagerines.

2nd. A Middle Carboniferous (C2) essentially characterized by *Spirifer mosquensis*. In the region of Moscow, the fusulines appear at the base but in the Donetz Basin they are not yet found at this horizon.

3rd. An Upper Carboniferous (C3) in which *S. mosquensis* has disappeared and is replaced by *S. supramosquensis,* which characterizes especially the lower part or Gjel stage[171] (it is at this horizon that the fusulines appear in the Donetz). The upper part or Uralian proper, is particularly characterized by the appearance of schwagerines.

4th. A Permo-Carboniferous (PC) which we shall leave in the lower Permian.

The C1 and C2 periods are especially well developed in the Moscow Basin and the C3 period in the Urals. In these regions, which we shall study together, the Carboniferous is comparatively thin (some hundreds of meters). Limestones predominate in it. In the Moscow Basin the facies are shallow and varied. Here was the edge of a continental, submarine shelf, and the detailed stratigraphy of the Carboniferous belt will be disclosed as similar to that of the Tertiary Paris Basin, with alternating transgressions and regressions. In the Urals, there was in general a deeper sea, especially in the Upper Carboniferous.

On the other hand, in the Donetz, the whole Carboniferous is well represented as complete and very thick (more than 5,000 m.). It has a kind of Flysch facies. We shall study it separately.

1. *Moscow Basin and the Urals*

A. Lower Carboniferous.   This has been studied especially in the Moscow Basin where, except in the western region (where a lacuna occurs at the base, corresponding to the whole Tournaisian), it is complete and passes in continuity into the Devonian. This continuity is even manifested by the existence of transition beds similar to those of the horizon of Etroeungt in the Ardennes Massif, and in which a mixed fauna is found. This is, south of Moscow, the Malievko-Mouraïevninsk stage,[172] which still contains many Devonian forms, and, in the central part of the basin, the limestone of the Upa river[173] in which there is a special *Spirifer* (*S. medius*), which we find at the same horizon in the Donetz.

This Lower Carboniferous is almost entirely calcareous. In the Moscow Basin we can distinguish a Tournaisian (30-40 m.) represented by the Tchernychino limestones with a *Spirifer* of the *tournacensis* group, corals (*Zaphrentis*) and a goniatite (*Pericyclus*), characteristic of the Tournaisian of western Europe. Then, after an intercalation of beds with plants (Dinantian flora) and bauxite beds (Tichvin and Touravlinsk strata) there are again limestones (40 m.) that can be assigned to the Visean, since *Productus giganteus* and *Dibunophyllum* are found in it. At the time of this Visean transgression the Russian seas must have communicated extensively with those of western Europe. But the top of these limestones (Serpuchov stage), although always containing large *Productus,* obviously should be classified as Namurian, as we shall see in the case of the Donetz Basin.

In the Urals, the detailed stratigraphy has been less studied. In the north, the series begins with limestones with *Productus mesolobus;* next come sandstones with plants (*Stigmaria, Nöggerathia*) and finally limestones with *Productus giganteus,* containing *Glyphioceras* at their base, which thus can be likened to the Visean. In the south, there are limestones with *P. giganteus,* but *S. tornacensis* has recently been discovered in the lower part (Lébédeff) so that the Tournaisian and Visean are both represented.

B. Middle Carboniferous.   This stage has been well defined in the Mos-

cow Basin for it is enclosed at the base and the top by red clayey beds, probably continental. There are still limestones (180 m.) characterized by the
appearance of fusulines and *Spirifer mosquensis*.

In the Urals, there are also limestones with fusulines, numerous *Productus*
(*P. semireticulatus, P. longispinus*), but *S. mosquensis* is much more rare.

C. Upper Carboniferous. This begins in the Moscow Basin with dolomites which the Russian geologists have called their Gjel or Gshelian stage.
In fact the fauna still greatly resembles that of the Middle Carboniferous,
but there are no longer schwagerines, and *S. mosquensis* has disappeared,
replaced by *S. supramosquensis*. Above comes the Uralian proper, represented by dolomitic limestones, sometimes made up of *Schwagerina princeps*
and already containing pelecypods with Permian affinities (*Macrodon*).

But the finest faunas of this stage come from the Urals, where the Upper
Carboniferous begins with 15 m. of limestones with *Omphalotrochus* (gastropod), *Spirifer marcoui* (characteristic form of this horizon), and *P. cora,*
overlain by 100 m. of other limestones with a very rich fauna (*P. cora, P.
boliviensis,* fusulines). And it is only above this that the stage with schwagerines begins, 50 m. thick, abounding here in cephalopods (*Gastrioceras,
Agathiceras, Pronorites, Medlicottia*). These Ural limestones are very fine
grained rocks, pelagic muds, very different from the organic limestones of
the Moscovian. Also, is it not surprising to find here schwagerines in abundance, with thin tests and light shells, which must be pelagic.

2. *Donetz Basin*

The Primary is here transgressive over ancient rocks, forming the crystalline
plateau of Azov-Podolia. It includes a little Devonian and especially an extremely thick (from 5,000 to 10,000 m.) and folded Carboniferous. This
Carboniferous begins with relatively thin limestones containing brachiopods
of the classic Dinantian and continues with a thick series of sandstones and
shales, the detrital material of which was furnished by the crystalline Massif
of Azov which must have extended over the present position of the Black
Sea.[174] In this Flysch facies, calcareous beds are intercalated, in which
brachiopods of the Russian stage are found, and also coal beds and plant-
bearing strata with the floras of the Coal Measures of western Europe. The
Donetz Basin will thus permit us to correlate the marine stages of the Russian Carboniferous and the stages based on plants worked out in the Coal
Measures of western Europe.

All this coaly Flysch of the Donetz was accumulated in a geosyncline or
at least in a trough of subsidence located on the borders of the Mesogean
seas. So the marine faunas are here richer and more normal than those of
the paralic basins of western Europe where only interior seas with impoverished faunas penetrated.

A. Lower Carboniferous. The continuity with the Devonian is marked
by transition beds (zone called Karakuba, 20 m.) containing *Spirifer medius,*
which we mentioned at this horizon in the Moscow Basin.

Above, limestones with *S. tornacensis* and *Zaphrentis* (100 m.) obviously correspond to the Tournaisian. The Visean begins with 200 m. of marly limestone, then 60 m. of coral limestone with *Productus giganteus* and *Dibunophyllum*. The series continues with a considerable thickness (1,800 m.) of sandstones and shales, the beginning of the Flysch facies. These beds contain intercalations of coal and plant beds, and also calcareous or shaly beds with a marine fauna. In these latter the great *Productus* of the *giganteus* group persists almost to the top (stage C_1^4, see table p. 213) though in France it does not survive the Visean, so that all this series was until recently attributed to the Visean. But as von Bubnoff and Schmidt have recently pointed out, Lébédeff notes, in Stage C_1^3, *Eumorphoceras* (*Reticuloceras*) *reticulatum,* a goniatite which in western Europe is characteristic of the top of the Namurian. Moreover, at the top of stage C_1^5 *Gastrioceras subcrenatum* and *G. listeri* are found, indicating the extreme base of the upper Westphalian. Finally stages C_1^2 and C_1^3 have yielded to Zalessky a *Pecopteris aspera* flora with Namurian affinities.

We are thus led to recognize that in the Donetz and, more generally, in all the open Russian seas, productids of the *giganteus* group could have persisted into the Namurian, although they no longer penetrated the lagoons and interior seas of western Europe. Thus all the top of the Russian Lower Carboniferous (C_1) would be equivalent to our Namurian.

B. Middle Carboniferous. It is as always characterized by the appearance of *Spirifer mosquensis* and fusulines. These fossils are contained in calcareous beds intercalated in a very thick series of shales and sandstones with numerous coal beds. The floras have recently been studied by Zalessky, who has found the succession of classical horizons of the Westphalian of western Europe. *Anthracoceras aegiranum* (of the marine horizon of Aegir in Westphalia, see p. 186) has also been noted in it. In France, this form marks the boundary between the Anzin and Bruay stages.

C. Upper Carboniferous. The same facies continue here. From the point of view of marine fossils, we can, as in the Moscow Basin and the Urals, distinguish two great subdivisions:

a) a lower division, in which *S. mosquensis* has disappeared and been replaced by *S. supramosquensis,* but in which there are as yet no schwagerines. The lower portion must still belong to the Westphalian for it contains the flora with *Mixoneura ovata* that in western Europe characterizes the La Houve stage and seems to have appeared earlier in the Donetz.

b) an upper division, characterized by schwagerines and in which are developed clearly Stephanian floras.

Still higher, in the Permo-Carboniferous stage (PC) of Russian geologists, there is already a flora transitional to the Permian. And finally the *Walchia* flora of the typical Permian is also known in the Donetz.

To summarize, this Donetz Basin is interesting to us because it shows a Carboniferous sedimentation entirely different from that of the Moscow Basin and the Urals. Between these two groups of regions, there are, for the Carboniferous, exactly the same differences that we find in the Nummulitic between the Paris Basin and the Alpine Flysch.

RUSSIAN NOMENCLATURE			FRENCH NOMENCLATURE	
Upper Carboniferous (C_3)	Schwagerine stage .... C_3^3	*Mizoneura ovata, Callipteridium pteridium, Sphenophyllum oblongifolum* ..	St. Etienne	Stephanian = Uralian
	Gjel stage; *Spirifer supramosquensis* . C_3^2		Rive-de-Gier	
	C_3^1	*Neuropteris scheuchzeri, N. rarinervis, Sphen. emarginatum*		
Middle Carboniferous (C_2)	*Spirifer mosquensis* .... C_2^{5-6}	*Mizoneura ovata, Mariopteris latifolia*	La Houve. D	Upper Westphalian = Moscovian
	C_2^4	*Neuropteris heterophylla, Sphenopteris obtusiloba*	Bruay. C	
	Spirifer mosquensis .... C_2^{1-3}	*Neuropteris schlehani, Sphenopteris höninghausi*	Anzin. B	
		Gastrioceras	Vicoigne. A	
Lower Carboniferous (C_1)	*Spirifer mosquensis*, very rare .... C_1^5			Lower Westphalian = Namurian
	Productus of *giganteus* group .... C_1^4	*Reticuloceras* ... *Pecopteris aspera*		
	C_1^3			
	C_1^2			
	Productus of *giganteus* group .... C_1^{1c-d}		Visean	Dinantian
	Spirifer tornacensis .... C_1^{1b}		Tournaisian	
	Karakuba horizon, *S. medius* .... C_1^{1a}		Etroeungt horizon	

Table of the Stratigraphy of the Carboniferous of the Donetz Basin.

The Russian nomenclature is based on brachiopod and fusuline faunas. In the Moscow Basin and the Urals, fusulines appear from the beginning of the Middle Carboniferous; in the Donetz, they seem to be unknown until the Upper Carboniferous. The correlations with the stages used in France have been established for the Dinantian and Namurian by brachiopods and goniatites, for the upper Westphalian and Stephanian, by using the correlations proposed by Zalessky and Waterlot, using the continental floras and faunas and based on recent work of Tchernychev (Trans. of the Geol. and Prospect. Serv. of U.S.S.R., 1931, fasc. 72).

We can now try to state precisely the synchronism between the marine Carboniferous of Russia and the stages defined in western Europe.

Considering only the larger divisions, we see that the Lower Carboniferous (C_1) of the Russians, or the *Productus* stage, would include not only the Dinantian but also our Namurian. Their Middle Carboniferous (C_2) or *Spirifer mosquensis* stage (Moscovian) would correspond approximately to our upper Westphalian (= Westphalian s. str.). Finally the schwagerine stage or Uralian would be roughly equivalent to our Stephanian.

IV. The Subcontinental Permian of Western Europe

1. *Germany*

The Permian outcrops are most widespread there. Usually there are only red sandstones (Rothliegende) overlain by the Zechstein, from which relationship came the ancient name Dyas (two formations) formerly given to the Permian, as opposed to the Triassic. We already know that only the Zechstein (= Thuringian) shows marine influences, so its boundary with the lower Permian is very clear. By contrast, the stratigraphy of the Rothliegende remains very inexact. After much discussion, the German geologists now distinguish in it only two large subdivisions, about equivalent to the Autunian and Saxonian stages of French geologists.

A. Autunian (= Unterrothliegende). Where the Stephanian exists (for example in the Saar) the Autunian follows it in continuity, with characteristics about intermediate between those of the Coal Measures and the Permian proper. There are generally shales, often dark colored, not always red, with some volcanic flows and still some coal beds. The continental flora (*Walchia piniformis, Callipteris conferta,* etc.) and fauna (*Palaeohatteria, Archegosaurus*) are quite rich and attest a still somewhat humid climate.

This Autunian has, however, a much smaller geographic extent than the Saxonian. It is known particularly in the neighborhood of the coal basins, for example, in the Saar, Saxony and Thuringia. The Hercynian movements had not yet ended and were shown especially by subsidences, which allowed the accumulation of Autunian sediments of enormous thickness (up to 3,000 m. in the Saar-Nahe basin).

B. Saxonian (= Oberrothliegende). It is in fact from the boundary between the Autunian and Saxonian that the last great Hercynian movements date. There was at that time a rejuvenation of relief, followed by erosion. So the Saxonian, ordinarily discordant on the Autunian, is especially represented by sandstones and conglomerates which extend so widely beyond the Autunian basins that the geographic distribution of the Permian no longer has any relation to that of the Coal Measures. A typical example of this was given recently by the discovery,[175] on the ancient platform of the Baltic Shield near Oslo, of *Walchia piniformis* in red sandstones formerly attributed to the Devonian and accompanied by volcanic flows. This is a striking proof of the resemblance of these continental, desertic facies (Old and New Red Sandstones) at all epochs.

At this time the great Saar-Nahe Basin[176] took shape, extending in a SW-NE direction between the Saar and the Lower Harz. It is filled with desert sediments, following a process that we shall describe at greater length *à propos* of the Triassic (see p. 278). But the total thickness of this Saxonian remains slight (500 or 600 m. at the maximum). The great subsidences which accompanied the last Hercynian movements were now succeeded by a period of stability. As has often been remarked, the tectonic and paleogeographic boundary between the Primary and the Secondary should be placed between the Autunian and the Saxonian.

Finally, it is in the depressed regions of these Permian deserts that the Zechstein lagoons began to advance.

C. Thuringian (= Zechstein). Its extent over all northern Germany, under the Tertiary and Quaternary covering, is considerable (Fig. 35). In Thuringia, the following subdivisions, now classic, are identified:

1. *Basal conglomerate,* not thick and rarely fossiliferous. However, we note in it the presence of *Productus cancrini,* a species here peculiar to this horizon, but which we shall find widespread throughout the Russian upper Permian.

2. *Kupferschiefer,* or bituminous shales with chalcopyrite,[177] a very thin bed (60 cms.), famous for its wealth of fish (*Palaeoniscus*). *Walchia* seems to have disappeared and to be replaced by *Voltzia,* a forerunner of the Triassic.

3. *Zechstein proper,*[178] a bed of dolomitic limestone from 5 to 10 m. thick. It contains a fauna rich in individuals but relatively poor in species and genera. It is the type called an impoverished fauna that is always found in interior seas, whether supersaline or fresh (present day Caspian and Baltic). Most of the forms have been eliminated by the necessity of adaptation to very special conditions of environment. Those (pre-adapted, Cuénot) that persist, thus deprived of their usual competitors, multiply enormously. The cephalopods are here reduced to very rare nautilids, and corals and echinoderms are practically absent. On the other hand, brachiopods (*Productus horridus, Strophalosia goldfussi, Terebratula* [*Dielasma*] *elongata,* etc.), pelecypods (*Schizodus obscurus,* etc.) and gastropods swarm. In the shore zone, the usual Zechstein type is replaced by a reefy facies, in which are developed rare echinoderms (*Eocidaris, Cyathocrinus*), certain brachiopods, and especially bryozoans (*Fenestella,* etc.) and enigmatic crusted organisms (*Stromaria*), so that this facies resembles a little the calcareous molasse that we shall describe in the peri-Alpine Miocene.

4. *The Salt-bearing formation.*[179] This marks the drying up in place, in some way, of the Zechstein sea. The saline concentration of the water became such that all life ceased and salt deposits began. There are then red clays with beds of dolomitic limestone and thick salt beds, anhydrite, rock salt, potash or magnesium salts.

All the German deposits of potash salts[180] belong to the Zechstein, but these salts form only rather thin beds (40 m. maximum) in the midst of rock salt and anhydrite many hundreds of meters thick. The total thickness of the salt formation is, however, considerably less in the south (Werra type) than in the north (Stassfurt type), where, in the middle of the upper Thuringian above the potash layer, are still found rare marine fossils (*Schizodus, Gervilleia, Terebratula*) in the sandy clays.

Let us note finally that, in the plains of northern Germany, wells sometimes traverse quite abnormal thicknesses of salts (1,200 m. in the wells of Sperenberg, near Berlin, 1,500 m. at Wietze-Steinförde), but this thickness has been increased by tectonic phenomena, which gathered the salts into salt domes (*eczemas*, Lachmann), like a kind of vertical column that rises, pierc-

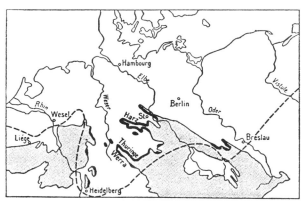

FIG. 51. *Map of the Zechstein sea in southern Germany (after Everding).*

Gray: Ancient massifs, pre-Permian formations
White: Post-Permian formations
Black: Outcrops of the Zechstein
- - - -   Probable southern limit of the Zechstein sea
St =   Stassfurt

ing its sedimentary covering (*diapirism*). This tectonic salt [181] has been particularly well studied in northern Germany, not only because of the pits and mine galleries of the potassium salt beds, but also because, in the aureoles of these salt domes of Hanover, oil pools[182] are found, the objectives of numerous wells. Thus it can be proved that the rising of these salt domes went on during the course of geologic ages, sometimes up to the present epoch.[183]

These salt deposits, which must have been produced in some kind of salt lake (*chott*),[184] do not everywhere accompany the red formations of the Upper Permian. Thus, there are no longer salts at this horizon in the Saar nor in the Vosges and it is evident that in these regions the distinction between the Saxonian and the Thuringian becomes impossible.

As for the Thuringian sea (see Fig. 35) which preceded the period of chotts, its extent can be defined exactly, thanks to the excellent stratigraphic landmark of the Zechstein fossiliferous limestone. In southern Germany,[185] its contours can be followed against the Hercynian Massifs, certain parts of which (see Fig. 51) had been invaded by the sea. Toward the southwest, in the direction of France, the last trace of the marine Zechstein is seen at Albersweiler (Palatinate, north of Wissemburg). At that point a dolomitic bed of some decimeters thickness contains *Schizodus obscurus*. But this Permian sea did not penetrate into France.

Toward the east [186] and northeast, it reached Courland where, at Prekuln, Zechstein limestone crops out. Moreover, the Purmallen well, near Memel, has yielded *Productus horridus* of the German Permian. But as we shall see

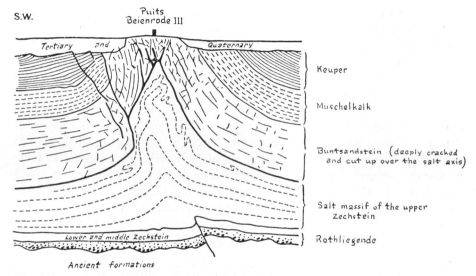

FIG. 52. *Section of a salt massif in the Permian of northern Germany (after E. Seidl, simplified)*.

Salt line of Dorm, east of Brunswick, in the region developed by the Puits Beienrode III.

The succession of beds in the salt massif are not given in detail; only the attitude of the beds is indicated.

Scale: 1/35,000.

later, it is probable that this German sea did not communicate with the Permian sea of Russia, where the fauna is a little different (not *P. horridus*).

Toward the north, it certainly covered all the German plains, reaching as far as the mouth of the Elbe. There, in fact, at Lieth (near Elmshorn) and at Stade, northwest of Hamburg, a Zechstein type was recently described, with brachiopods and fish (*Palaeoniscus*) of the Kupferschiefer.[187] Farther north, in Denmark, as far as Copenhagen, salt springs indicate, according to Stille, the probable presence of the Thuringian salt, at great depth.

Finally, toward the southwest, the Zechstein sea extended through the lower valley of the Rhine (wells of Wesel and Holland) as far as England where we shall find it again.

2. *Britain*

The Stephanian is missing in Britain as is also the Autunian. Therefore it is
easy to define the boundary between the Permian and the Coal Measures, of
which it is often entirely independent. It is very difficult, however, to define
exactly its upper limit so that the extent attributed on geologic maps to Permian sediments in relation to Triassic sediments, varies greatly according to
the authors. It is the whole assemblage of red formations of the Permian and
the Triassic which early British geologists designated as New Red Sandstone.

Aside from the constant absence of the Autunian, this British Permian has
the greatest similarity, even in detail, to the Permian of Germany.

A. Saxonian. This is a more or less thick complex of red sandstones and
conglomerates, thus inaugurating a regime completely different from that of
the Coal Measures. The lower beds are frequently conglomerate of torrential
origin and certain beds of sandstone are undoubtedly of eolian origin. The
desert regime thus begins to assert itself.

In the Eden valley, northeast of the Lake massif (Fig. 36), the lower conglomerates (here called, however, lower Brockram) are formed solely of
debris of the subjacent Carboniferous. Next, in the upper conglomerates
(upper Brockram) intercalated in the top of the Penrith sandstones (see table
following), appear pieces of Ordovician rocks. Similar relations can be found
near Ingleton. This shows that the faults of the Pennine Chain must have
started during the Permian, thus rejuvenating the relief in proportion as the
play of desert erosion tended to level it. The upper beds (Carboniferous) of
the pre-Permian platform were the first attacked by erosion, and only later
the Ordovician beds.[188]

B. Thuringian. Above the sandstones come formations that can be
grouped under the name of Thuringian, and which comprise, as in Germany,
three divisions, from bottom to top:

1. *Shales with fish* or plants (marl slates) similar to the German Kupferschiefer. These are the deposits of desert lagoons.

2. *Magnesian limestone,* frequently cellular (*cargneules*), with an abundant fauna identical to that of the type Zechstein of Thuringia, which indicates the arrival of an interior sea from Germany. In the east, the upper beds
already contain saline intercalations and the fauna is still more impoverished
than at the base.

3. *Gypsiferous marls,* sometimes even salty. This division is, however, in
general much less highly developed than in Germany. It becomes moderately
thick only in the region of the Tees estuary (Fig. 36), where these marls are
often assigned to the Triassic.

C. Regional Variations. As always, in the case of continental or lagoonal
formations, this series admits of numerous variations. In particular, two types
can be distinguished.

To the east, the dolomitic limestone facies is much more developed. The
magnesian limestone, quarried for construction use, reaches 180 m. thickness.
This type is well represented in a band of outcrops which, from the mouth of

the Tyne to Nottingham, ranges along the east border of the Newcastle coal basin, the Pennine Chain and the Sheffield coal basin (Fig. 36).

In the west, on the other hand, we have the New Red Sandstone facies which includes almost all the Permian. Here the magnesian limestone becomes too thin to figure on small scale maps. The most classic series of this western type is seen in the Eden valley.

The table below shows clearly the difference between these two regional types of the British Permian. The parallelism of detail between the two types can obviously only be hypothetical in the absence of fossils.

WESTERN TYPE: EDEN VALLEY	EASTERN TYPE: DURHAM
Gypsiferous marl (90 m.)	Marl and sandstone (15 m.)
Magnesian limestone (0-6 m.)	Magnesian limestone (180 m.)
Hilton beds with plants (45 m.)	Shale with fish (3 m.)
Penrith sandstone (300 m.)	Red sandstone (30 m.)
Lower conglomerates (Lower Brockram)	

Thus, as in Germany, the deposits of the Zechstein interior sea thin out little by little toward the west. On the other hand, they extend far toward the north. The fauna with *Productus horridus* and *Schizodus,* long known in Ireland, also exists at Spitzbergen and in Nova Zembla,[189] there with *Productus cancriniformis,* a Russian species.

But, in particular, the eastern coast of Greenland shows a very interesting Permian, with very rich faunas.[190] We see there coral and brachiopod facies, with faunas of the German Zechstein and the Russian Kungurian-Kazanian, made complex with beds of cephalopods containing especially *Cyclolobus,* unknown in the Russian faunas, but widespread in the Himalayan and Indo-Pacific faunas of the Upper Permian.

Thus Stille (note 187, this chap.) seems to be right in recognizing that the principal domain of the Upper Permian sea must be found north of the Scandinavian Shield, in the polar regions. From there two arms of the sea started, one passing by Spitzbergen and Greenland on to Britain and Germany, the other by Nova Zembla and the Petchora Basin spreading out over the Russian plains (see Fig. 53).

3. *The Continental Permian in France*

Since the Permian seas of Germany and Britain did not penetrate into France, there is no possibility of finding here the equivalent of the Thuringian. But the continental desert formations of the New Red Sandstone type are deposited almost everywhere. It is agreed to relate them to a Saxonian (s. l.), difficult to distinguish from the Triassic. Finally, in the vicinity of the Stephanian coal basins, we often find an Autunian incorporating the transition to the red sandstones.

On the eastern border of the **Armorican Massif,** in the Cotentin, red sandstones and shales crop out over large surfaces in the depressions of Valognes and especially of Carentan, where they follow the Stephanian of the small basins of Littry and Plessis. The upper strata, especially sandy, belong without doubt to the Saxonian. The lower strata, with numerous calcareous beds (lagoonal muds), reach a total thickness of 34 m.; since they contain *Estheria tenella* and *Anthracomya carbonaria,* species of the lower Permian of the Saar, they should be credited to the Autunian.[191]

In the **Massif Central** the Permian is developed only along the northern and southern borders.

In the north, it has been studied especially in the Autun Basin. There the Autun shales have served as type for the Autunian stage. They are transition beds to the Stephanian. Plant life was quite intense there, for coals with algae (*Pila bibractensis*) (bogheads) are found. There are also bituminous shales from which oils are extracted by distillation. But we already see the appearance of red coloring characteristic of the Permian and the flora especially is clearly Permian, including *Walchia piniformis* and *Callipteris conferta.* As in Germany, there are beds rich in fish (*Palaeoniscus*), in stegocephalians (*Protriton, Actinodon*), and in *Estheria.*[192]

This Autunian series is overlain by transgressive Saxonian sandstone, so the Permian history of the Autun Basin is entirely analogous to that of the Saar Basin.

In the Blanzy Basin, the Permian follows the Stephanian in continuity, a Permian in which there are three successive lithologic facies: shales with *Walchia,* white arkoses, and red sandstones. This series, still affected by folding, is covered discordantly by the Triassic.[193] Farther west, the Permian is found again at Bert and even extends west of Moulins.

In the south and southwest, the Permian appears over broad surfaces. In the neighborhood of the coal basins of Decazeville, Graissessac, Neffiès, etc., the Autunian is well distinguished by its flora, its fauna of fish and its bituminous shales, especially developed in the vicinity of Lodève, east of the Montagne-Noire. And the Saxonian sandstones are as usual transgressive. In this Mediterranean climate, the red Permian rocks make bare outcrops and vividly color the landscape, earning, in the local language, the name of *ruffes.*

In the **Vosges,** the Permian is found both on the north and the south of the Hercynian Massif. In the north, the Autunian, with characteristic flora,[194] follows the coal basin of Villé, overlain by red Saxonian sandstones. At the top, beds of dolomite and *cargneules,* unfortunately without fossils, correspond to a lagoonal phase in which we can see the last trace of the German Zechstein seas. We note, in the extreme north of the massif, near Donon, a fine development of acid volcanic rocks. These are the famous Nideck porphyries (Fig. 58), lava flows intercalated in the red sandstones. On the Lorraine slope,[195] in the vicinity of St-Dié, the locality of Val-d'Ajol is famous for the fine silicified tree stumps contained in the red Autunian shales. Finally, in the south, the Autunian and Saxonian crop out widely at the southeast of the small Ronchamp coal basin (Fig. 30).

In the **French Alps,** we have already referred to the Permian in discussing **the** Carboniferous. First let us say that no Permian fossil has ever been found there.[196] In the external zone or crystalline massifs, the Permian is only regularly developed, with its facies of conglomerates and red sandstones and shales, in the extreme south, on the edge of Mercantour. Farther north, there is no decisive evidence for attributing to the Permian the thick series of red sandstone and shale known only in two very limited areas: Allevard sandstone on the west edge of Belledonne and Rouchoux sandstone on the south border of Pelvoux, in the mountains of La Salette, above Corps. These beds, clearly discordant in relation to the Carboniferous, are on the contrary concordantly overlain by the Triassic, of which they may represent the base, but if so in a facies unknown elsewhere.[197]

On the other hand, in the Briançonnais coal zone, the Permian is usually recognizable in a continuous series between the Coal Measures and the Triassic. It is made up of sandstones, shales, or conglomerates, always vividly colored, red or violet. These quartzitic, variegated conglomerates are called *Verrucano*[198] by French or Swiss geologists. Sometimes there are volcanic rocks (andesites of Guillestre, south of Briançon). Finally in the internal, crystalline massifs, we already know that the Permian is perhaps represented in the upper part of the metamorphic series.

The great Permian outcrops of the Dome of Barrot, isolated in the Alpine folds, in which red shales are gashed, for several hundred meters, by the famous gorges of the Cians and the Var, provide a landmark between the Alpine Permian and that of Provence.

On the northern border of **Provence** the Hercynian Massif of Maures-Esterel is in fact girdled by a Permian zone. Soft red sandstones and shales produce the large depression followed by the railway between Toulon and Fréjus. But, farther east, there are associated hard conglomerates, forming in particular the beautiful mountain of Roquebrune[199] west of Fréjus. It is one of the French landscapes in which appears most sharply the characteristic relief of sandstones and conglomerates. In the Esterel, the acid volcanic rocks are greatly developed. These are the famous red porphyries which, surprisingly, extend to the north of Fréjus in great lava flows with the slight slope (P. Bordet) that is usually seen only in basic lavas. Along the coast they are cut in picturesque coves and their dikes rise in vertical walls on the slopes of Cap Roux. On the contrary the blue porphyry (esterellite, quartziferous microdiorite) quarried at Dramont, east of St-Raphael, which is used to pave Marseilles, occurs as a laccolith, sometimes believed to be of Tertiary age (for no pebble of it has been found in the Permian conglomerates, composed of red porphyry). But recently P. Bordet has been able to demonstrate by tectonic considerations that it was in place before the Triassic.

Permian floras in the Esterel (*Walchia, Callipteris*) resemble those of the Alps most closely. Toward the north, none are known until the edge of the Vosges is reached.

In the **Pyrenees,** the Permian is represented only by red sandstones and conglomerates mixed with puddingstones of very different age (for example, Cretaceous, see p. 427), impossible to distinguish from the Lower Triassic. So, geologists of the Pyrenees have adopted a Permo-Triassic stage. There, the famous pyramid of the Pic du/Midi of Ossau, composed of andesites, repeats on a much grander scale the red rocks of the Esterel.

Finally, at Mauléon-Barousse (Haute-Garonne) and at Gerri (Spain, south of Maladetta) M. Dalloni[200] has recently discovered floras with species determined by P. Bertrand and P. Corsin (*Psygmophyllum mongolicum, Neurogangamopteris, Odontopteris rossica*), identical or analogous to those of the Angara flora of northern Russia. We shall discuss later (p. 239) the significance of this unexpected discovery.

V. The Marine Permian in Russia[201]

The Permian system has the most widespread outcrops in Russia. It underlies the vast Russian plains between the arc of the Moscow Basin and the Urals. It is, however, commonly covered by the Quaternary; but in the hills and plateaus which form the western border, the foothills of the Urals, it crops out in the open. It is there, in the region of Perm, that the types of the system and of the stages into which it can be subdivided have been taken.[202]

These subdivisions are based especially on lithologic facies, naturally involving differences in the faunas. Actually important paleogeographic events occurred at this epoch in Russia. The Ural geosyncline was folded and transformed into a mountain chain; a first phase of folding took place at the beginning of the lower Permian and another at the beginning of the middle Permian. And the arm of the Russian sea which separated the North Atlantic continent from the North Asiatic continent dried up little by little. The Permian of the western border of the Urals could be compared to the Miocene molasse of the external border of the Alps, whose history we shall describe. Finally, at the end of the Permian, all of Russia emerged and the two continental masses were united in a great Eurasian continent.

A. Lower Permian or Artinskian. This is developed typically in the vicinity of the forges of Artinsk, a little southeast of Perm.[203]

The first folding of the Urals was felt up to that point so there is a slight discordance between the Uralian and Artinskian. The Permian begins, in the country of Artinsk, with the sandstones and clays of Artinsk, containing a very rich, long known fauna, which has been used to define the Artinskian paleontologically. To numerous brachiopods (*Productus artiensis, Chonetes*) are added cephalopods (*Pronorites, Parapronorites, Propinacoceras, Gastrioceras, Schistoceras, Agathiceras, Popanoceras,* etc.) which have not yet been revised by specialists. As these beds are transgressive, this Artinskian of Artinsk is probably incomplete at the base.

On the other hand, in Central Russia, and especially in the country of Nizhniy-Novgorod there is a continuous transition between the Uralian limestone and other limestones with fusulinids, corals, brachiopods and pelecypods, but unfortunately without cephalopods. These are the beds of Chustovo-Denjatin (village in the region of the Oka River, which joins the Volga at

Nizhniy-Novgorod); they are thin (15 to 180 m.) and yet they represent here all the lower Permian.

In the same way, far to the north of Perm, in the tundras west of the Urals, beds are known to contain many brachiopods (*Productus, Spirifer,* etc.) with Carboniferous affinities, with *Medlicottia.* These beds probably belong to a lower horizon than that of the Artinsk sandstones (Frédéricks made his sub-stage Keujimian of it, named for the Keujim-Teurovei River in the Pechora Basin).

B. Middle Permian or Kungurian. Its type was taken at Kungur, a town 80 km. southeast of Perm. It is composed of dolomites and limestones which pass in continuity through their base to the upper Artinskian. But this Kungurian contains no cephalopods, only a fauna rich in pelecypods (*Schizodus obscurus*) and gastropods. And the top of the stage is composed of dolomites, sandstones and marls, with gypsum, anhydrite, rock salt and potassium salts. At this horizon there are only traces of plants (*Callipteris conferta*). In the polar Urals, especially on the banks of the Usa River, a right-bank tributary of the Pechora, in the upper Kungurian, marine beds (*Productus cora, Pseudomonotis*) are found together with plant beds (*Pecopteris anthriscifolia, Noeggerathiopsis,* etc.). In the same region, along the Adzwa River, a right bank tributary of the Usa, and on the Oranet River, Zalessky has identified these same plants associated with *Gangamopteris.* There we have the characteristic elements of the Gondwana flora coming from the south, which we shall discuss later.

Finally, in central Russia, the Kungurian seems to be missing or at least to be represented only by red continental formations impossible to distinguish f.om the Upper Permian in this region.

C. Upper Permian or Kazanian. This is presented under two very different facies whose synchronism was established by Frédéricks and Zalessky in the region of Viatka (town north of Kazan and west of Perm), where these two facies are seen passing laterally one to the other.

To the east, there are red or variegated continental formations containing cupriferous sandstones which resemble the Kupferschiefer of the German Thuringian.[204] There are only lacustrine pelecypods and vertebrates in it. This is the Ufa stage (100 m. thick) in which species of the Gondwana flora are found.

To the west, however, are gray shaly-sandy rocks, with marine fossils. Two horizons can be distinguished, at the base a brachiopod horizon (*Spirifer, Productus cancrini, Strophalosia, Fenestella,* etc.) or Spiriferian stage, at the top the pelecypod horizon where only a few brachiopods (*Productus cancrini, Strophalosia horrescens, Athyris pectinifera, Terebratula* [*Dielasma*] *elongata*) continue to exist, but they are accompanied by numerous pelecypods (*Schizodus obscurus,* etc.). Above, the stage ends with purely continental beds with anthracosiids, passing into the Triassic (Tatarian stage).

These marine beds are especially developed around Kazan, from which comes the name Kazanian stage (= Kamian of Zalessky).[205] As we see, this fauna is the only one which has clear analogies with the Permian of western Europe, where the only horizon with a marine fauna is the Zechstein. So the first geologists who studied Russia reserved the name Permian for these marine beds of Kazan. All the lower beds were called by them Permo-Carboniferous. And as for the upper beds, they were called Permo-Triassic. These were in fact only lagoonal deposits that today are called the Tatarian stage, poorly defined, however, for as there is no marine Triassic in these regions, it is the floras alone that identify the lower limit of the Triassic.

The fauna of the Russian Kazanian is moreover quite different from that of the German and British Zechstein. So we have acknowledged (p. 219 and Fig. 53) with Stille and the Russian geologists (and contrary to the paleogeographic reconstructions of von Bubnoff) that the seas corresponding to these two faunas communicated only indirectly, around the north end of the Scandinavian Massif.

And study of the Russian Permian has shown us, in a very instructive way, how these Zechstein faunas developed through progressive impoverishment. We have first seen the cephalopods, so abundant in the Artinskian, disappear at the beginning of the Kungurian; then the lower Kazanian still contains a fauna rich in brachiopods and pelecypods. Finally, in the upper Kazanian, there are only special forms of pelecypods and very rare brachiopods, close relatives of the German Zechstein species.

VI. The Carboniferous and the Permian of the Mesogean Seas

Beginning with the Carboniferous a huge sea is clearly outlined, stretching out parallel to the equator and occupying all the mountainous area of Southern Asia (Himalaya) and the Mediterranean chains (Alps). This sea, whose history we shall follow up to Tertiary times, is today reduced to a western remnant which has become the Mediterranean. Therefore it is called the Great Mediterranean or the Mesogean sea.

It was bounded on the north by the North-Asiatic (or Angaride) and North European (or North Atlantic) continents, temporarily and imperfectly separated, up to the middle Permian, by the arm of the Russian sea. And to the south extended another continental mass, the Continent of Gondwana, including especially Australia, peninsular India, Arabia and central Africa. We shall discuss Gondwana later.

For the moment, we shall rapidly run over this Mesogean zone, noting in passing the regions where the Carboniferous and marine Permian have given rise to classic works or to recent research.

1. *Asia*

In the extreme east, our Mesogean sea spreads widely in a Pacific domain, which extends from the north of Australia (Timor) as far as southern Siberia

(Korea and Japan), covering Indo-China and China. These are the classic countries for the study of the marine Permo-Carboniferous.

The Island of Timor may be cited first for here Permian marine faunas, particularly rich in cephalopods and echinoderms, have been studied thoroughly under the direction of Wanner.[206]

In French Indo-China an important marine series represents the whole Carboniferous and Permian. It has been studied in the numerous publications of the geologic service of this country [France].[207] The Dinantian and the base

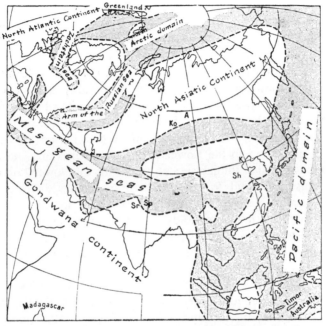

FIG. 53. *The great paleogeographic units at the end of the Permian.*

After a map worked up by Dainelli (inspired by de Lapparent, Koken, and Arldt for Europe, by Huang for southern China) and modified according to Stille for northern Europe.

Sp = Spiti; Sr = Salt Range; D = Djoulfa; A = Angara; Ko = Kousnetzk; K = Kaiping; Sh = Shansi; P = Petchora.

of the Moscovian are represented especially by sandy-shaly series, with calcareous beds, where cephalopods developed especially at the top (lower Moscovian). In transgressive relation to this first assemblage comes the thick series of *Productus* limestones, occasionally beginning at the end of the Moscovian and persisting until the Upper Permian. Cephalopods are rare in it and the stratigraphy (still being discussed)[208] has been based particularly on the succession of genera and species of fusulinids. In general, the Carboniferous faunas have European affinities (passing through China), while those of the Permian are related rather to the faunas of Japan and the Salt Range.

In China, we reach the edge of the great Northern-Asia continent, so that here are found, as in Europe, Permo-Carboniferous series where beds with a marine fauna are intercalated with continental beds containing coal.[209] An example of just this type is furnished by the coal basin of Kaiping,[210] east of Peking, where floras are found of the European type of the upper Westphalian, Stephanian, and Permian, and marine faunas of the Moscovian. The marine faunas of the Chinese Carboniferous have been studied [211] especially in the region of Tai-Yuan, Capital of Shan-Si, southwest of Peking, while Permian marine faunas developed in Mongolia were recently described by Grabau.[212]

In the Himalaya,[213] our stratigraphic knowledge of the great chain itself is still somewhat confused. But, at the southern edge of the high mountains, in the little massif of the Salt Range (Punjab) in the Indus valley, a marine series, long since classic, is developed which has been the subject of many papers.[214] We are now on the southern border of the Mesogean domain (Fig. 53). In fact, the Cambrian is overlain directly by continental formations, subordinate to the Gondwana series (which we shall study later) and attributed to the Upper Carboniferous. These are morainal deposits (Talchir formation). Above, and in discordance, comes the marine series which, according to the recent research of Reed,[215] is subdivided thus: a first division (about 200 m.), which can be compared to the Lower Permian (Artinskian), includes sandstones at the base (called Punjab series) and at the top, lower *Productus* limestones, with fusulinids and *Richthofenia*. After another discordance, comes the Middle Permian (about 200 m.), composed of upper *Productus* limestones with a very rich fauna (crinoids, brachiopods, numerous cephalopods). The Upper Permian is missing, below a transgressive Triassic whose base is characterized by ceratites. Obviously, we are on the border of a continental area.

These fossiliferous horizons have long been recognized but their stratigraphic interpretation remained very debatable. Especially the Punjabian stage, originated for the Punjab series and formerly adopted to designate the Middle Permian, with marine facies, has not been retained.

A little farther northeast, in Cashmir, the marine Carboniferous appears, represented by *Syringothyris* limestones and sandstones and muds with *Fenestella,* probably equivalent to the Dinantian and Moscovian. Above, after a short period of emergence marked by volcanic flows and plant beds (*Gangamopteris*), indicating the base of the Permian, comes a marine series resembling that of the Salt Range. A similar succession is also seen east of the Salt Range, in the vicinity of Spiti, where the marine Permian, represented by *Productus* shales, passes in continuity into a very famous marine Triassic of which we shall speak again.

Finally, further north, in the Karakoram, Tibet and Pamir, it seems that all of the Permo-Carboniferous may be marine. At Chitichum (Tibet) very rich faunas of brachiopods and cephalopods have been studied by Diener. We enter there the true Mesogean domain but the stratigraphy is still very doubtful.[216]

Through Afghanistan[217] where limestones with *Productus* and fusulinids are recognized, Turkey and Iran,[218] the Mesogean zone extends as far as

Armenia. There, in the classic region of Djulfa,[219] in the gorge of the Araxes, north of Lake Urmia, we can see the finest type of the Mesogean Permo-Carboniferous. A continuous marine series persists without interruption from the Devonian to the Triassic, with the Carboniferous represented by limestones with *Productus* and fusulinids and the Permian by marly limestones in which numerous cephalopods appear. There is no trace of Hercynian folding.

This Trans-Caucasian Permo-Carboniferous is connected by the Crimea (where Mlle. Malycheff has described a marine Permian with fusulinids) to that of the Russian arm of the sea. And it continues to the west, into Asia Minor, through the region of Amasia, where fusulines are found, as far as central Anatolia. There, near Ankara (Angora), E. Chaput [220] has recognized Visean sandstones and *Productus* limestones, Uralian limestones with fusulines and *Schwagerina princeps,* and Permian limestones with *Neoschwagerina* and *Sumatrina.* But the Triassic covers this series discordantly, so that again we approach the continental border. In fact, a little farther north, on the shore of the Black Sea, the small coal basins of Amasra and Zonguldak (also known as the Heraclea Basin) show us a Permo-Carboniferous of the usual western European type. A Culm facies of Visean age, with *Productus, Beyrichoceras* and *Glyphioceras,* here is overlain by a very thick exploited coal series, with a succession of Namurian, Westphalian and Stephanian floras. Above come red sandstones of Saxonian type.[221]

2. *Eastern Mediterranean*

Farther west, south of the Sea of Marmora, the marine facies of fusuline limestones continues as far as the Mediterranean. It certainly represents the Upper Carboniferous (schwagerines) and probably also the Permian (Dyrenfurth). The only rich faunas (brachiopods, cephalopods, etc.) are those of Balia-Maden.[222]

The Mediterranean of the Middle and Upper Carboniferous extended to the north of the present sea over Greece, Euboea and Dalmatia, where fusuline limestones have been known for a long time. And recently faunas certainly Permian, neoschwagerines and sumatrines, have been noted in the islands of the Aegean Sea.[223] In Jugoslavia[224] *Bellerophon* limestones contain, in their upper beds, Upper Permian faunas with Asiatic affinities.

Finally, we shall describe the northern extremity of this Permo-Carboniferous marine domain in the Carnic Alps, the classic region for the study of this system.

3. *Carnic Alps*

The Mesogean marine type is found in the southern part of the eastern Alps (or *Dinarides,* see p. 294) and especially in the Carnic Alps[225] which extend along the south side of the Gail valley (see Fig. 64) and are prolonged to the east by the Karawanken Mountains. Rich marine faunas have been studied there by Diener, Schellwien, Frech and more recently by Gortani, Vinassa de Regny, de Angelis d'Ossat, Caneva and Merla. Finally just lately Heritsch[226] has worked out an extremely careful stratigraphy of this region, seeking to establish for it a parallelism of detail with zones distinguished in Russia and even in America. We shall be satisfied to indicate the main features of it.

The Lower Carboniferous (Dinantian) is reduced to very restricted outcrops in the Gail valley (Nötsch deposit), which lie on the granite and are separated from the Middle and Upper Carboniferous by a discordance. There are shales, sandstones and conglomerates of Culm facies which, in the absence of fossils, are very difficult to distinguish from Silurian shales. At the base, a *Pericyclus* and a *Caninia* (zone C_1) characterize the upper Tournaisian. The zones C_2 (lower Visean) and S (middle Visean) are not paleontologically characterized, but there is probably no lacuna and zones D_1 and D_2 of the top of the Visean are found. It is then undoubtedly during the Westphalian, which is missing, that the great Hercynian folding took place.

A new series, discordant on the preceding, begins with the transgressive Uralian.

1. At the base are the beds of Auernig, near Pontebba (= Pontafel) west-northwest of Raibl (see map, Fig. 64). They are 800 m. thick (according to Heritsch) and composed of shales, sandstones and conglomerates with a few calcareous bands. They contain fusulines, numerous brachiopods (*Spirifer supramosquensis, Productus cora, P. cancriniformis*), *Conocardium*, corals, and also beds with Stephanian plants. They are almost equivalent to the Russian stage of Gjel, perhaps of the base of the Uralian.

2. Above come about 170 m. of complex strata, especially limestones, which Heritsch first identified under the name of Rattendorf beds. They may also be called schwagerine limestones. In the middle they contain an intercalation (*Grenzlandbänke*) in which the shaly-sandy facies of the Auernig reappear, so that formerly this complex was attributed sometimes to the Auernig stage and sometimes to the Trogkofel limestones, which we shall discuss. Through their brachiopod and coral fauna, these schwagerine limestones correspond to the Uralian proper of Russia.

3. The marine series terminates with the Trogkofel limestones (= Creta di Aip, northwest of Pontebba) and of Col Mezzodi near Forni Avoltri. The fauna includes corals, fusulines and especially cephalopods. *Medlicottia artiensis* appears at the base. At the top, in the Teufelschlucht near Neumarktl (Karawanken), there have long been recognized *Agathiceras, Popanoceras, Thalassoceras,* etc. Thus, this upper member represents the Artinskian. After this marine series there was an emergence; for, slightly discordant and especially in transgression, comes the continental formation known as the sandstone of Val Gardena (or Gröden), a region located on the northern slope of the Dolomites, northeast of Bolzano (= Bozen) and west-northwest of St. Cassian (see Fig. 64). It is very extensive in the whole eastern part of the Alps and greatly resembles the continental Permian of the western Alps. It begins with a conglomerate identical with the Verrucano (p. 221) and also contains thick volcanic flows of red porphyry (for example near Bolzano). These are red sandstones and shales, of Saxonian facies, with characteristic plants (*Walchia piniformis*, etc.).

But in the Carnic Alps and in the Karawanken, the marine facies return, with the formation improperly called the *Bellerophon* limestone.[227] It is actually a rather lagoonal complex, with shales, sandstones, bituminous limestone and gypsum, but also beds of marine limestone containing a fauna of brachiopods, pelecypods, gastropods and rare cephalopods having affinities both with the German Zechstein and the Upper Permian of the Salt Range and Djulfa. In the plant beds, the genus *Voltzia* appears. This is the Thuringian.

This melange of continental and marine formations indicates that we are here on the border of the Mesogean seas. In fact, north of Gail, at Stangalpe (north of Villach), the Permo-Carboniferous is represented by black shales with a Stephanian flora, lying directly on crystalline rocks. Thus we have here again found the type of the internal basins of the Hercynian Chain.

4. *Italy, Corsica, Sicily*

After having advanced as far north as the Carnic Alps, the Mesogean shores of the Middle and Upper Carboniferous and the Permian should come down again, through the site of the Adriatic, as far as Sicily where we find again a marine Permian. In peninsular Italy and the Tyrrhenian islands, however, the Permo-Carboniferous is of the western European type, where the Dinantian alone is marine, with Culm facies. But, because of the Alpine folding, detailed stratigraphy is impossible.

There is first, north of Pisa, the Permo-Carboniferous of the Pisan Mountains where a little spur named Monte della Verruca, has given its name to the Verrucano facies,[228] a name adopted long ago by Alpine geologists to designate the quartzitic conglomerate, red and violet, so frequent in their Permian. Deceived by complicated tectonics, Fucini claimed in 1915 that the rather badly preserved fossils (impressions of ferns and pelecypods) coming from this type locality, were of infra-Cretaceous age (Wealdian). His theory has had little acceptance except by two Austrian geologists, F. X. Schaffer and von Arthaber. But according to recent studies[229] it is possible that this red series of Monte della Verruca, beginning with the top of the Permian, belongs largely to the Triassic.

Farther south, in the metalliferous chain of Tuscany,[230] the Paleozoic platform of the ancient Tyrrhenides (see p. 524) reappears. These are shales and sandstones in which Carboniferous and Permian floras (*Callipteris conferta*) have been found, and even, at Iano, north of Volterra, poor marine Dinantian fossils (*Productus, Aviculopecten*). Similar formations are found in the Island of Elba,[231] with plants and *Productus, Bellerophon* and *Fenestella*. In Sardinia[232] only Permian floras are known. Finally, in Corsica, there are traces of both marine Dinantian faunas and Carboniferous and Permian continental sediments.

The only outcrop of Permo-Carboniferous found in Sicily is that known under the name of the Sosio deposit (name of a little coastal river) or of Palazzo Adriano, 100 km. south of Palermo. It consists of 5 small calcareous crags which appear in consequence of abnormal tectonic conditions in the midst of a Triassic region. But they have furnished one of the richest marine Permian faunas, known since the early studies of Gemmellaro. Recently

Fabiani, Parona, Silvestri, and Ruiz[233] have taken up the study of these fossils. They are probably from reef or sub-reef facies[234] but nevertheless include numerous ammonoids (*Parapronorites, Medlicottia, Propinacoceras, Gastrioceras, Agathiceras, Popanoceras, Thalassoceras*); out of 74 species, half are found in the Artinskian of the Urals. The brachiopods (*Productus, Spirifer, Lyttonia, Richthofenia,* etc.) have Asiatic or Carnic affinities. Pelecypods and gastropods are also abundant. Finally the fusulinid fauna is notable for the association of the genera *Fusulina, Neoschwagerina* and *Sumatrina*. On the whole, an Artinskian or at most a lower Kungurian age may be assigned to this deposit.

5. *Spain*

In the western Mediterranean, the Balearic Islands provide a valuable landmark for the northern extension of the Mesogean seas. At Minorca, the Carboniferous appears in the form of sandstone and shale of Culm facies, with plant and marine fossil beds. In particular, above a Visean with *Posidonomya* and *Glyphioceras,* two goniatite faunules have recently been noted,[235] one of the lower Namurian, the other (*Agathiceras, Paragastrioceras*) of the Uralian-Artinskian boundary. The marine facies have thus persisted in the Balearics much longer than in the typical regions of western Europe.

And that leads us to the Carboniferous of the Asturias.[236] There indeed the research of Barrois long ago made classic a marine series which is prolonged from the Dinantian into the base of the upper Westphalian. It includes:

1. A transgressive Visean, represented by griotte marble, a cephalopod facies similar to that we described in the Devonian (p. 137) but with ammonoids of the upper Visean (*Glyphioceras*).

2. The canyon limestones, 700 m. thick and playing a large role in the morphology of the Peaks of Europe. Brachiopods, discovered by Delépine, and fusulinellas appear at the top, indicating the lower Moscovian, while the base, formed of black, dolomitic limestones without fossils, could represent the Namurian.

3. The beds of Leña, from the village of Pola de Leña, south of Oviedo, show, at the base, beds with calcareous bands with a rich marine fauna with Moscovian affinities (*Spirifer mosquensis,* fusulines, etc.). Next come plant-bearing shales with beds of coal and some marine horizons. One of them in particular contains goniatites (*Anthracoceras,* etc.) characteristic of the Rimbert horizon, between Westphalian B and C. And in fact, above, is found the *Anthracomya phillipsi* of the Bruay bed (Westphalian C).

4. The Sama bed, containing the principal beds of exploited coal, again shows marine intercalations with fusulines and *Anthracoceras* of the upper Moscovian.

Finally, on this Westphalian or sometimes directly on the Devonian, in discordance, comes an entirely continental Stephanian.

So we find here a region where the marine facies not only are prolonged, as in northern France, well above the Dinantian but in which faunas with Mesogean (or rather Russian) affinities still appear.

Outside of the Asturias, the Carboniferous of the whole Iberian meseta[237] has a banal type. On a marine Dinantian of Culm facies come continental Coal Measures, mined in many small basins and containing Westphalian or Stephanian floras. It is the same in the coastal chain of Catalonia, which results from Alpine folding. Above cherty shales, assigned without decisive evidence to the Tournaisian, at Papiol near Barcelona,[238] a Visean with numerous trilobites (*Phillipsia*), *Posidonomya becheri, Spirifer, Productus* and *Glyphioceras striatum* is recognized. Possible Carboniferous sediments are included in the non-fossiliferous, sometimes metamorphic series of the Tertiary Betic [Andalusian] Chain or of the area south of the meseta.

Southern Portugal (Alentejo and Algarve) furnishes the Dinantian, Namurian and marine Westphalian containing some goniatites. In northern Portugal small, purely continental coal basins contain floras indicating Westphalian D, Stephanian, and Autunian.[239]

6. North Africa

The old massifs of the Algerian littoral (see map, Fig. 107) shows at different points, sandstones and black shales which may represent the Coal Measures and a Dinantian of Culm facies, and red formations referable to the continental Permian but perhaps confused with equally red Oligocene sandstones and conglomerates. In particular, at the southern edge of the crystalline massif of the Grand Kabylie, the Coal Measures have supplied some badly preserved fossils, plants[240] or marine mollusks (*Bellerophon ?*).[241]

But there are in reality in North Africa only two regions where precise paleontologic and stratigraphic studies have been made. One such study dealt with the marine Permian of Tunisia, the other with the Carboniferous and continental Permian of Morocco (with its Oran border).

A. Tunisia.   In Tunisia, where the Primary was unknown up to 1933, a very interesting fossiliferous marine Permian outcrop was discovered at Djebel Tebaga[242] about 70 km. south of Gabès.[243] We have there, in a section 1,700 m. thick, a very regular series of motley formations, sandstones, conglomerates, marls, calcareous beds, whose substratum is unknown. The fauna, extremely rich, is composed of fusulinids (*Fusulina, Neoschwagerina*), corals, *Cyathocrinus, Fenestella,* many brachiopods (*Productus opuntia,* an Asiatic form very close to the Russian *P. cancriniformis, Richthofenia, Spirifer* cf. *marcoui,* etc.), gastropods (*Bellerophon, Euomphalus*) and some cephalopods (*Medlicottia, Orthoceras, Glyphioceras*).

So this series, beginning at the base of the Middle Permian, includes, according to Solignac, all the Upper Permian. Very recently, R. Ciry and G. Mathieu,[244] using the syntheses of C. O. Dunbar (cited note 12 and note 306, this chap.) consider that there is a stratigraphic lacuna at the extreme top of the Permian. There would be nothing surprising in such facies, for above and in concordance come red sandstones associated with a continental Triassic.

B. Morocco.   In all the Primary Moroccan Massifs (see Fig. 12),[245] except in the Djebilet and the Anti-Atlas, the Carboniferous plays a very important role. The most extensive outcrops are of the Dinantian. The Westphalian and Stephanian appear only in small basins. Finally the Permian (continental) is again found only in the Moroccan meseta. If we add that marine influences do not extend higher than the upper Westphalian, that the whole series has a Culm facies, and lastly that we find here no trace of the fusulinid faunas which characterize our Mesogean sea, we can see that Morocco shows us a type of Carboniferous closely related to that of the paralic basins of northwestern Europe (Westphalia especially) or of Spain. We are already on the margin of the true Mesogean zone.

But the interest of this Moroccan Carboniferous is more than local. Especially, the goniatite faunas are much richer than in northern Europe and may be followed continuously into the upper Westphalian of local basins. Also Delépine's[246] fine studies have allowed detailed comparisons with Russia and North America.

In the Moroccan meseta (G. Lecointre, H. Termier), there was continuity of sedimentation with the Devonian only in the northwest (vicinity of Rabat).[247] The Etroeungt zone is found here, with *Spirifer strunianus,* represented by ferruginous graywackes (L. Neltner) with oolitic iron minerals[248] and followed by a Tournaisian in which plant beds are associated with marine beds containing *Spirifer tornacensis.* Everywhere else, in the rest of the meseta, the Carboniferous begins with the transgressive Visean, sometimes reaching 1,500 m. thickness. The lower Visean is composed of graywackes with *Davisiella comoides* and *Chonetes papilionacea,* palechinid limestones and shales with *Spirifer striatus.* The upper Visean is made up of limestones with *Productus giganteus* with which are associated sandstones containing plants.[249] The Namurian must be represented by a thick, shaly series (*Glyphioceras subcircularis* at the base) with some beds of crinoidal limestone. Above comes a continental Westphalian, recently dated at Sidi Kacem by plants (H. Termier, *in litt.*). And the Stephanian and Permian are no longer represented except by red plant beds, limited to very small basins, whose age can be determined only by floras, Stephanian at Sidi Kacem, Autunian at Khenifra and north of Oulmès (*Walchia piniformis* and numerous ferns).

In the High Atlas (L. Moret, L. Neltner), the series begins with the lower Visean, sandstones with *Chonetes papilionacea, Syringothyris cuspidata,* etc. The upper Visean is shaly-calcareous and sandy, with beautiful brachiopod faunas of the *Productus giganteus* zone. The Namurian, however, is more shaly, with cephalopods (*Prolecanites, Glyphioceras, Dimorphoceras*) and some coaly beds. There the marine series ends and the principal Hercynian folding must have occurred in the Westphalian. For lying discordantly on this first assemblage comes a series of red continental formations passing into the Triassic and localized in small basins south of Marrakech (Moret, Neltner, Clariond), in the Sous region and Ida or Zal (Roch, Clariond). At its base are found Stephanian florules (*Walchia lineariformis, Mixoneura neuropteroides,* etc.), lacustrine pelecypods (*Anthracomya prolifera*)[250] and some small coal beds.[251]

In the Skoura country, which extends east of the Primary Atlas of Marrakech, only the Visean is known, transgressive and discordant on ancient formations, but containing (E. Roch) fine faunas of *Productus giganteus, Prolecanites serpentinus, Glyphioceras,* etc.

In the northwestern Sahara (Menchikoff), the Carboniferous shows us two regional types, which, beginning with the Namurian, are quite different from each other.

a) In the west (regions of Tindouf, Tafilelt, Erfoud), there is sometimes (Tindouf syncline) continuity of sedimentation with the Devonian, and the Etroeungt zone can be recognized. The Tournaisian at Tindouf is represented by *Spirifer tornacensis* sandstones while in the green shales of Erfoud cephalopods (*Aganides rotatorius, Munsteroceras oweni*) of the upper Tournaisian appear. The Visean of Tindouf and Tafilelt is composed of shales or limestones with *Productus giganteus, P. cora, Spirifer bisulcatus, Dibunophyllum.* Finally, in the region of Tindouf, sandstones with plants correspond to the Namurian and Westphalian.

b) In the east, that is, in the basins of Oueds Guir, Zousfana, Saoura (Menchikoff, Daguin) there is a good continuous transition from the Devonian to the Carboniferous, but the Etroeungt fauna is unknown. The first fossils are Tournaisian, in the shales, brachiopod sandstones and cephalopod (*Aganides*) limestones of Saoura, and the sandstones and shales of Zousfana. The Visean is represented by the thick calcareo-dolomitic series (2,000 m.) of Saoura, containing limestones with *Productus giganteus.* The complexes of sandstones and shales, with plants, and goniatite limestones of Oued Guir correspond to the Namurian.

Next comes the coaly series mined in the little Kenadza basin, near Colomb-Béchar (South Oran).[252]

The Westphalian A and B are represented by 2,000 m. of sandstones and shales with plants and also thirty marine horizons. Above, 250 m. of sandstones and shales contain 5 or 6 more goniatite horizons, the highest of which has provided *Anthracoceras aegyranum,* characteristic of the Rimbert horizon at the boundary between Westphalian B and C. It is therefore to this last stage that a sandy complex of 1,000 m. belongs, with an exploited coal bed 40 cm. thick. There are still some marine horizons but the transition to red shales appears here. Some 400 m. of non-fossiliferous strata may be assigned to Westphalian D. And the series ends with shales and sandstones containing *Pecopteris, Estheria limbata, Anthracomya prolifera.* This is then the lower Stephanian with many red intercalations like the Stephanian of the High Atlas.

But, a little north of Colomb-Béchar, in the Djebel Grouz (Clariond, Leca, H. Termier), there is once more a lacuna representing the Tournaisian and even the lower Visean. The upper Visean, represented by limestones with *Sagittoceras* and brachiopods, lies directly on the Devonian. It is overlain by *Homoceras* limestones and sandstones with plants of the Namurian.

Finally, still farther north, south of Oudjda, the little Primary Massif of Djerada[253] appears in a gash in the midst of Secondary formations. Here the Carboniferous begins with the Visean transgressive and discordant on an ancient platform. A very thick complex of the Culm facies, with volcanic rocks, brachiopod-goniatite shales, and plant beds, corresponds to the Visean-

Namurian. Above comes a lacustrine Westphalian (*Anthracomya,* ostracodes, plants) in which are included recently discovered and exploited coal beds and marine beds comparable to those of the Franco-Belgian Basin (Clariond). B. Owodenko[254] lately published a very detailed local stratigraphy and in it noted [255] *Mixoneura,* showing that the series rises as far as Westphalian D.

Thus, if, in the whole assemblage, we find in Morocco a type of Carboniferous that recalls that of the Northern European paralic basins, nevertheless it is proper to insist with H. Termier on the differentiation of a marine trough which, at the boundary of Morocco and the great South Oran Erg, extends from south to north in Saoura and Zousfana. There the cephalopod facies, clearly marine, without plant beds, has persisted as far as the base of the upper Westphalian. Toward the west, a branch is detached from the trench and extends into the High Atlas and western meseta, where the marine facies persists as far as the Namurian. But we do not know how this Westphalian sea with cephalopods was connected with the Mesogean sea. In any case it came across either east or west of Djerada, where the Westphalian is almost entirely continental.

Besides, it is interesting to remark with L. Moret that the red desert facies, which will continue, in the meseta as well as in the High Atlas, until the Triassic,[256] begins here with the Stephanian, which is sooner than it usually does in western Europe. Should we see there the effect of a more southern latitude or simply of local climatic conditions? For example, the approach of the huge African continental block, a part of the still more enormous Continent of Gondwana, which we shall discuss later.

VII. The Permo-Carboniferous of North America

1. *The Carboniferous*

By the extent of the outcrops, the richness of the faunas and the distinctness of the stratigraphy, the Carboniferous of the United States is certainly the best representative of this system in the whole world.[257]

The great structural unities which have guided us in the study of the Cambrian and Devonian of America (Fig. 5) will again serve as a framework for description of the Carboniferous (Fig. 54). There is, as E. Haug has discerningly remarked, a striking parallel between the different regional types of the American Carboniferous and those of the European Carboniferous. First, the Carboniferous of the Central States, southern dependent of the Canadian Shield, corresponds to the largely marine Carboniferous of the Russian platform, rather thin, organic, not folded or little folded, beneath which the Baltic Shield extends, at depth, to the south. Second, the Carboniferous of the Atlantic border corresponds to the Carboniferous of the Hercynian and Caledonian Chains of Europe (Britain, massifs of middle Europe), very thick and often folded, with marine Dinantian overlain by the productive Coal Measures. We distinguish two provinces in it; the one composed of Nova Scotia and Newfoundland, identical with the Scottish type, the other extending over the Appalachians, where the faunas are different. Third and finally, the Carboniferous of western America, that is the Rocky Mountains and Pacific chains, very folded and marine, destitute of coal, would be equivalent to that of the Urals.

As an aid to the memory, it may be noted that the natural American re-

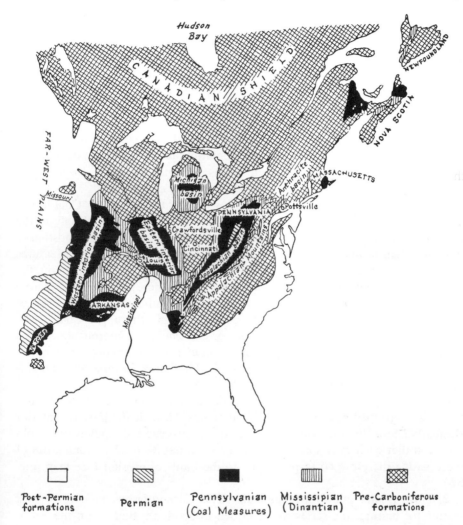

FIG. 54. *Map of Permo-Carboniferous outcrops in the central and eastern parts of the United States.*

gions are roughly symmetrical with analogous European regions in relation to a north-south axis through the middle of the North Atlantic.

1. The Central States. The Carboniferous here is of the continental type, not folded, in general shallow-water, divided by lacunas, with transgressions, regressions and multiple variations of facies. The faunas are very rich and the stratigraphy extremely clear and precise.

We distinguish in it, very naturally, a lower stage or Mississippian (Dinantian-Namurian), especially developed in the south, marine and without coal, and an upper stage or productive Coal Measures, called Pennsylvanian (upper Westphalian-Stephanian).

a) The Mississippian[258] shows alternating limestones and shales with very varied marine faunas, but generally littoral and not thick (maximum 500 m.). At the base are found ammonoids (especially *Aganides rotatorius*) characteristic of the Tournaisian of Europe. Next come limestones with *Productus punctatus* and marls which at Crawfordsville (Indiana) have furnished marvelously preserved crinoid cups.

The Visean begins with very transgressive limestones with *Goniatites striatus,* like the European form. The innumerable palechinids (*Melonites*), represented in every collection, come from this Visean (at St. Louis). While the end of the stage, represented by sandstones and found only in the Southern States, corresponds to a regression, the goniatite faunas of the top of the Mississippian (Chester series) contain forms (*Eumorphoceras, Homoceras*) which make possible correlation with the Namurian of Europe.

b) The Pennsylvanian is divided into lower, middle, and upper Coal Measures. The first, equivalent to the upper Namurian (?) correspond only to the beginning of the transgression for they are known (shales and sandstones) only in Arkansas and Texas, that is, in the south. The middle Coal Measures are, on the contrary, very transgressive toward the north and contain the principal coal beds, with a Westphalian flora. But there are frequent marine intercalations there, where *Gastrioceras listeri* especially is found, a species of the base of the upper Westphalian of Europe. Finally the upper Coal Measures are really everywhere marine, shales or extremely fossiliferous limestones with fusulines, *Productus cora, P. semireticulatus,* and many ammonoids. This is the Missourian stage, equivalent to the Uralian of Europe, and containing the finest known faunas of this epoch.

On the basis of their present distribution, the coal sediments of the Central States are grouped into four great coal basins (Michigan, Eastern Interior Basin, Western Interior Basin, and Texas), separated by outcrops of old rocks, so that each thus appears as a huge synclinal basin. The boundaries of these basins therefore correspond only to the limits of erosion (see map, Fig. 54).

2. Nova Scotia and Newfoundland. The Carboniferous here resembles, feature for feature, the series we described in Scotland, that is, on the European border of the North Atlantic continent (see Fig. 39). It is reasonable to conclude that these regions are found on the American border of the same continent and that the exchange of marine, lagoonal, and continental faunas was made freely along the shores and on the surface of this continent, whose existence is thus once more demonstrated.

The Dinantian begins with conglomerates, sandstones, and lagoonal marls, with fish and plants which are exactly like the Scottish Calciferous sandstone; even gypsum is found as at Glasgow. Then come the limestones with *Productus giganteus,* equivalent to the Scottish Calcareous division.

The Westphalian is composed of sterile beds, comparable to the Millstone

Grit, and productive Coal Measures, with a Westphalian flora identical with that of Europe.

Finally the Stephanian is not productive, but represented by red sandstones which foretell the Permian.

3. The Appalachians. The principal differences between the Carboniferous of the Appalachians and that of the Central States comes from the composition of the Dinantian (= Mississippian). This stage is represented, actually, in the Appalachians by detrital sediments, shales or sandstones, in which calcareous formations have only a secondary role. The whole stage is much folded and very thick (1,500 m.), although these deposits may be shallow sea or lagoonal. It is very clearly a geosynclinal type, which differs from that of Nova Scotia somewhat as the Culm facies of Devon differs from the Carboniferous limestone of the rest of England.[259] The series begins with sandstone, called the Pocono sandstone,[260] then continues with shales with sandy intercalations, representing the Namurian.

Above, in discordance, come the productive Coal Measures, beginning with the Pottsville conglomerate. This is the type Pennsylvanian,[261] represented by shales and sandstones, with an upper Westphalian flora at the base (Pottsvillian, including the Pottsville, Allegheny, and lower Conemaugh stages) and Stephanian[262] at the top (Missourian, including the upper Conemaugh, Monongahela, and Washington stages). There are intercalations of marine beds with Moscovian and Uralian faunas, and especially numerous coal beds, which constitute the famous Appalachian Basin. The coal there is poorer in hydrocarbons (less fat) as we progress toward the east, that is, as we penetrate the more intensely folded zones. So, the most easterly, small basins are generally set aside under the name of Anthracite Basins.[263] We see then that here, as in the Franco-Belgian Basin, the composition of a coal depends not on its age, but on the state of the deposit (or of its formation).

The sandy intercalations of this coal-bearing series constitute in part the rock reservoirs of the famous oil and gas of the Appalachian Basin. As for coals, we see here proof that the composition of these hydrocarbons is in proportion to the intensity of the folding. The lightest oils and those richest in gas are found in the easternmost zones, the most folded ones.

In this Appalachian province, the flora is always almost identical to the European flora which shows there must have been a connection with the North-Atlantic continent. But, on the other hand, the marine faunas are different enough from those of Europe so that we must conclude that the gulfs or lagoons of the Appalachians did not communicate with the sea which came from Europe to Nova Scotia, but rather must have been closed toward the northeast and opened into the seas of central United States.

4. Western United States. In the Rocky Mountains, the high plateaus, and Pacific chains, folded in the Tertiary, the stratigraphy and the distribution of Carboniferous outcrops are too complex for us to be able to synthesize them here.

We shall merely note that here no exploitable coal beds occur. The Carboniferous consists of marine beds with fusulines and schwagerines as in the

Urals. The faunas are sometimes very rich and present closer affinities to those of the Urals than to those of the Central States. It is therefore logical to conclude that there must have been a marine communication with northeastern Europe by northern Siberia and Alaska where marine Carboniferous is known, or perhaps through the Mesogean seas.

2. *The Permian*

The parallelism that we have just shown between the regional types of the Carboniferous in America and Europe persists in the Permian. The Permian of the Atlantic border recalls feature for feature the Permian of Western Europe and Britain. The outcrops which are preserved in the center of the Appalachian Basin and in Nova Scotia show us red sandstones of the New Red Sandstone facies and beds with European plants (*Walchia piniformis, Callipteris conferta*). We even find, in Nova Scotia, *Schizodus* magnesian limestones which are the exact equivalent of the Zechstein.

On the other hand, the great Permian outcrops that, in the western plains,[264] extend along the eastern border of the Western Interior Basin and Texas Basin belong to a completely different type.

We do find, especially at the base and at the top, intercalations of red and saliferous formations,[265] and in that desert climate the prominence of the outcrops has made possible the discovery of very fine occurrences of stegocephalians and theromorphs.[266] But clearly marine beds also appear, with ammonoids, containing the Artinskian fauna of the Urals.

Finally, along the Rocky Mountains, in the high plateaus of the West, and in the Pacific chains, a marine Permian is also known, sometimes difficult to distinguish from the Carboniferous and the Triassic, which are likewise marine. In particular, the thick Permian series that crops out in extreme western Texas, between the Pecos River and the Mexican frontier, has furnished an extraordinarily rich marine fauna, described by Girty under the name of Guadalupian fauna (from the Guadalupe Sierra).[267]

VIII. The Continent of Gondwana[268]

In four regions which today have nothing in common, to wit Brazil, equatorial and southern Africa (with Madagascar), peninsular India, and Australia, we find, beginning with the top of the Carboniferous and up to the Jurassic, very thick series of similar continental sediments, containing identical floras and in which very special groups of great theromorph reptiles are exuberantly developed, especially in South Africa.[269] These four regions then must have had the same history during this period and it is reasonable to think that they belonged at that time to one huge continental mass, to which has been given the name Continent of Gondwana.[270]

Indeed, in these four countries, we see, lying in discordance on ancient folded rocks, first glacial formations and then a thick series of continental sediments, of facies analogous to the Permo-Carboniferous of western Europe.

There are also beds of coal at the base. But the flora, though rather poor, contains ferns entirely unknown in the classic floras of the Carboniferous and Permian of the northern hemisphere. Such are the *Glossopteris,* so named because of their large uncut leaves, in the shape of tongues, and the *Gangamopteris* (fern of the Ganges). To this floral assemblage, the name of *Glossopteris* flora or Gondwana flora was given long ago.

Its age has been much debated. As it is found in the southern hemisphere at the base of a series with coal facies and as it is associated in the upper beds with Triassic forms, it was long believed to be Permo-Carboniferous and contemporary, at least at the base, with the Carboniferous flora of the northern hemisphere.

But later, an almost identical flora, which with Zalessky we shall call the Angara flora, was discovered at different points of Siberia and even in European Russia.[271] It is found especially in continental coal formations long known in the valley of the Angara, a river which carries the waters of Lake Baikal into the Lena. This continental series, rising, moreover, up to the Jurassic, has already enabled E. Suess to define his Continent of Angara or Angarides (see p. 375).

This flora has been especially well studied in the Coal Basin of Kusnetzk[272] in Siberia (see Fig. 53), where, lying on a Tournaisian and Visean comparable to those of Britain, the continental coal series reaches 8,000 m. in thickness and seems, according to recent studies, to extend into the Triassic. Lastly, it had previously been noted in the Pechora Basin, where we have already mentioned it (p. 223) associated with theromorph reptiles of the Gondwana type and with marine beds of the Middle and Upper Permian. And it is found farther south in the Permian border of the west flank of the Urals, in the Volga and Kama Basins, as far as Orenburg.

This flora of Angara is not exactly identical to that of Gondwana. The genus *Glossopteris* (which was noted there by Amalitzky) is replaced by the related genus *Pursongia* Zalessky. But *Gangamopteris* is found there, accompanied by several other characteristic forms, which are associated here with *Callipteris* of the Permian of Europe. The paleobotanists have agreed then to consider them as very close to and contemporaneous with the Gondwana flora, whose Permian age is thus established. It follows that communication must have existed, across the Mesogean seas of Central Asia and in a location still unknown, between the continents of Gondwana and Angara.

In addition, this Angara flora must have spread, at least locally, as far as Western Europe, for Dalloni (see p. 222) has recently found it in the Permian of the Pyrenees where the necessary climatic conditions probably were realized.

In fact, we may suppose that it is the more arid climate which ruled in the middle and upper Permian in western Europe which prevented the formation at the same time of coal beds and the development of the Angara flora, doubtless more humid than our normal Permian flora with *Walchia* and *Callipteris.* The heavy theromorphs (*Pareiasaurus, Inostranzevia, Permocynodon*) which in the Pechora accompanied the *Gangamopteris* flora, were doubtless better adapted to swamps than to dry deserts. So once more the climatic contrast of sedimentary landscapes corresponding on the one hand to black, coaly formations and on the other to red formations with evaporites is explained.

Finally, J. Piveteau[273] has recently drawn attention to the discoveries made almost everywhere in Eurasia, of reptiles related to the theromorph faunas of South Africa. He even deduces therefrom the northern origin of these groups, formerly believed peculiar to South Africa.

Thus, as happens for many old classic beliefs, the individuality of the Continent of Gondwana, from the double consideration of the flora and continental faunas, now tends to be effaced.

Lastly, let us add that Carboniferous floras of the European type are known in the eastern part of Asia. We have already mentioned them in Sumatra, Malaya, and in the Kaiping Coal Basin in China (Mathieu, see note 210, this chap.). They have also been carefully studied by Halle[274] in the Shansi Basin where Westphalian and Stephanian floras are overlain by a zone with *Gigantopteris nicotianaefolia* and *Callipteris* which corresponds undoubtedly to the Lower Permian. And then, in the Middle Permian, the *Gangamopteris* flora, coming from the Continent of Gondwana, appeared, but in different basins.

After this long but useful interlude, designed to define the Permian age of this *Glossopteris* flora, we return now to the southern hemisphere to describe there the different types of the Gondwana series, contemporaneous with that of Angara.

A. India.   All of peninsular India, south of the Ganges, is composed of an immense ancient massif, similar to the shields of the northern hemisphere and on which are preserved, in sunken troughs, very thick beds known as the Gondwana formation. They are completely continental and their base, which alone interests us at the moment, contains the *Glossopteris* flora. They begin with the conglomerate, called the Talchir bed,[275] which unquestionably represents ancient moraines.

The age of these beds in relation to the Carboniferous and Permian of Europe can be determined along the shores of the ancient Continent of Gondwana, where we begin to find Mesogean marine sediments. We already know (see p. 226) that this is true in the Salt Range. There, in fact, are found the old moraines of the Talchir stage lying directly on the Cambrian. They are associated with green sandstones, doubtless of fluvio-glacial origin, but containing some marine intercalations, with a very poor and very special fauna, including *Conularia* and especially a very curious type of thick shelled pelecypod, the genus *Eurydesma,* related either to aviculids or ostreids. This *Eurydesma* fauna, that we shall find elsewhere, would be a fauna of cold seas, characteristic of the old shores of the Continent of Gondwana, when the glaciers approached it. Then the sea definitely arrived in the Salt Range and deposited the lower *Productus* limestones which we have attributed to the Lower Permian. Thus, after much discussion, the geologists who have recently studied the question[276] assign the Talchir stage to the extreme top of the Carboniferous. And the Gondwana formation which covers it, with its *Glossopteris* flora, would represent the Permian. Let us add, also, that the extreme top of this formation contains Triassic floras and extends, always with continental facies, into the Jurassic.

B. Africa.[277]   North of the coastal mountains of the Cape, a Hercynian Chain folded E-W and composed of marine Devonian and Lower and Middle continental Carboniferous with very poor and uncharacteristic floras, extends a huge platform of ancient rocks, more or less metamorphic and non-fossiliferous, which makes up all Central Africa as far as the Sahara. On this platform and almost always discordantly, are found series of continental formations, sometimes very thick, distributed in a certain number of basins (see Fig. 55). The most southern and most important of these basins adjoins the Cape mountains immediately, to their north and northeast, in the Karroo plateaus and the mountains of Basutoland, both semi-desert regions.

The continental series of this basin, reaching 8,000 m. thickness, is classic under the name of the Karroo formation. It is completely analogous to the Gondwana formation. According to the lithologic characteristics and especially the continental floras and faunas (reptiles), there are from bottom to top, the stages of Dwyka, Ecca, Beaufort, and Stormberg.

1. *The Dwyka Stage*[278] (800 m.) is especially remarkable for the intercalation of a very thick conglomerate or tillite,[279] with striated pebbles, whose morainal origin is indisputable. At some places (in the north) it lies directly on old crystalline rocks, polished, striated and marked by roches moutonnées, and in the south, it is separated from them by lower shales which already contain traces of the *Glossopteris* flora. Finally in Southwest Africa, between Keetmanshoop and Gibeon, the stage contains marine intercalations, with *Eurydesma, Conularia* and even *Archaeocidaris*. The fish (*Palaeoniscus capensis*) are shown to be near relatives of European forms of the Upper Carboniferous. Lastly, this lower stage is characterized by the genus *Mesosaurus,* a reptile peculiar to the Continent of Gondwana and adapted to aquatic life. So it is generally agreed to synchronize the Dwyka stage with the Upper Carboniferous.

2. The *Ecca Stage*[280] sometimes contains beds of coal,[281] with the *Glossopteris* and *Gangamopteris* flora, but it is very poor in reptiles.

3. The *Beaufort Stage,*[282] on the other hand, poor in plants (*Gangamopteris* has disappeared), has supplied very rich reptilian faunas, successively pareiasaurians, dicynodonts and theriodonts. They may be used to define six paleontologic zones. We shall list them here as a unique example of a paleontologic stratigraphy based on reptiles. And we shall mention, following Piveteau (see note 273, this chap.), the regions of the northern hemisphere in which representatives of these faunas have been described.

Zone

Triassic
- 6—*Cynognathus* (*Capitosaurus* in Greenland, Spitzbergen and Germany).
- 5—*Procolophon* (Scotland?, Germany?).
- 4—*Lystrosaurus* (China).

Permian
- 3—*Cisticephalus* (Indo-China, China, Russia, Scotland).
- 2—*Endothiodon* (Russia)
- 1—*Tapinocephalus*

Thus in the upper part of this Beaufort stage are found genera (*Capito-saurus, Trematosaurus*) characteristic of the lower Triassic of Europe. We may conclude then that all the Ecca stage and the lower part of the Beau-fort stage represent the Permian.

FIG. 55. *Map indicating (in dotted areas) the extent of the outcrops of the Karroo formation (Upper Carboniferous to Jurassic) in South Africa and analogous continental formations in Equatorial Africa (in part after a map by F. Dixey, 1930).*

4. As for the *Stormberg Stage,*[283] it is equivalent to the Triassic and the Rhetian, always with an exclusively continental facies. It ends with formi-dable basaltic lava flows from which are carved the magnificent mountains of Basutoland.

North of the great Karroo Basin are found similar smaller basins in the area of the Zambezi,[284] in Rhodesia, then on the borders of Tanganyika and near the coast of the Indian Ocean, towards Mombasa. Finally, the northernmost point where the *Glossopteris* flora has been found is at Entebbe, on the north shore of Lake Victoria, that is, almost under the equator.

On the other hand, farther west, another huge basin of continental sedimentation is that of the Belgian Congo,[285] which is prolonged into the French Congo and Angola. But fossils are extremely rare there and of little significance, so that in spite of very extensive study, the parallelism of this Congo system with that of the Karroo is still very questionable. Fourmarier[286] adopts the following nomenclature:

1. At the base the system of the Lukuga.[287] Above a conglomerate of glacial origin, he includes coal beds with traces of *Glossopteris;* if we compare the basal conglomerate to that of the Dwyka[288] we should have there, some hundreds of meters thick, a reduced equivalent of the stages of Dwyka, Ecca, and perhaps Beaufort.

2. In fact, the system of the Lualaba,[289] more clayey, is represented near Stanleyville[290] by bituminous shales which have yielded a fish faunule of Upper Triassic or Rhetian age, according to Leriche.[291] This may be an equivalent of the Stormberg.

3. Lastly, the Sankuru system is made up of highly developed sandstones in the western Belgian Congo. It seems to correspond to the Jurassic.

Let us add that in Italian Somaliland and Abyssinia is found a continental series (sandstones of Adigrat in Abyssinia, Lugh beds in Somaliland). And there, in the region of Lugh,[292] we see it pass laterally into the marine Jurassic of the domain of the Indian Ocean.

Later, in the Cretaceous and Tertiary, it is in the Kalahari that continental sediments accumulate (Kalahari system).[293] And today, the immense and widely separated areas of the Kalahari and the Sahara, without outlets to the sea and with eolian accumulations, show us what the Karroo must have been in the Permo-Triassic. It is very suggestive to see this regime of successive accumulations in closed basins from the end of the Carboniferous up to the present time, changing position as a result of earth movements or a change in the regime of the winds.

C. Madagascar.[294] In Madagascar a continental series of the Karroo type has long been known, with the *Glossopteris* flora and a reptilian fauna, similar to that of the Cape, and also lying directly on the crystalline platform. But here—a more recent discovery—intercalations with marine faunas are sometimes found.

1. At the base, the Sakoa group (river near Betioky) includes 150 m. of black shales, with two horizons of conglomerate, perhaps morainal, which is the equivalent of the Dwyka stage. Next come coal beds (100 m.) with the *Glossopteris* and *Gangamopteris* flora. There are several coal beds whose total thickness reaches 10 m. and which extend for hundreds of km. Above is the lower red series, at the top of which calcareous lentils with *Productus*

and *Spirifer* with Permian affinities are intercalated, at Vohitolia on the Sakoa river. This whole complex may be called the Ecca stage.

2. The Sakamena group (river near Betioky) overlies the preceding stage discordantly through the medium of a basal conglomerate. It includes several hundred meters of sandstones and shales with a *Glossopteris* flora, without *Gangamopteris,* but especially a fine reptile fauna studied by Piveteau,[296] who has distinguished two zones of theromorphs correlated by him with the middle part of the Beaufort stage, that is the Upper Permian. Finally the group ends with shales of the upper red series. In the northern part of the island, at Ankitokaso, it is represented by marine beds lying directly on the crystalline platform. At the base there are sandstones with brachiopods (*Productus, Spirifer, Anthyris,* etc.) and pelecypods (*Schizodus, Goniomya,* etc.) containing also a cephalopod (*Xenaspis carbonarius*) of the *Productus* limestone of the Salt Range. Next come clays with Upper Permian cephalopods (*Cyclolobus, Medlicottia, Xenaspis, Hungarites*).[298] This marine series ends with the Anaborano clays with fish and ammonoid nodules of Triassic age.

3. Lastly the Isalo group (mountainous massif) is made up of very thick sandstones furnishing scarcely anything but silicified wood and very rare marine shells (*Myophoria*). It corresponds to the Upper Triassic. The base of these Isalo sandstones is very intensely impregnated with bitumen, which presents the possibility of the discovery of petroliferous strata.

Thus this Karroo formation of Madagascar is revealed as completely analogous to that of the Cape, and its age, Permian at the base, Triassic at the top is well defined by intercalations of marine faunas. Above, the marine upper Lias is only locally represented in the northwest of the island by beds with *Spiriferina rostrata* of the Ankera plateau. It is only in the middle Jurassic that a marine transgression comes to break more or less completely the continental connections between Madagascar and Africa.

D. Australia. Australia formed the extreme eastern point of the Continent of Gondwana, between the marine domain of the Pacific, which covered New Zealand, and the Mesogean sea, which we have seen advance as far as Timor, flooding western Australia,[299] where an entirely marine basin reaches 2,000 to 3,000 m. thickness in the Northwest Basin.

Indeed, while north of Timor, in Sumatra[300] and Malaya,[301] European Carboniferous floras[302] are found, in Australia, however, it is the *Glossopteris* flora, which appearing at the top of the Carboniferous, continues during the whole Permian, and is replaced at the beginning of the Triassic, as in South Africa, by a *Thinnfeldia* flora. The series is most complete in eastern Australia, in New South Wales, and especially in the Hunter River Basin (north of Sydney).[303] There, on the crystalline rocks, lies first a sandy-shaly complex, 750 m. thick, with fluvio-glacial conglomerates containing striated boulders. Only the flora called *Rhacopteris* has been found in it and it is assigned to the Middle or Upper Carboniferous. Next comes the lower marine series, 1,350 m. thick, in which the *Glossopteris-Gangamopteris* flora[304] appears. At the base, it contains the marine *Eurydesma* fauna and at the top

Permian ammonoids (*Agathiceras*) are found. This series may be paralleled with the Dwyka stage and the base of the Ecca. The Greta coal beds or Lower Coal Measures separate the lower series from an upper marine series, 1,800 m. thick, also containing blocks of glacial origin and beds with bryozoa (*Fenestella*) and crinoids. Then there are only continental formations, 1,300 m. thick, and including again two systems of coal beds (Middle and Upper Coal Measures). In these upper (or Newcastle) beds the *Glossopteris* flora still persists, so it all still belongs to the Permian (base of Beaufort stage). Above, the *Thinnfeldia* flora suddenly appears, marking the beginning of the Triassic (upper Beaufort and lower Stormberg).

Note that analogous series are found in Tasmania, in the state of Victoria, and opposite Timor, on the northwest coast of Australia, where they again start with glacial formations.

E. South America.[305] In the Tertiary chains which extend along the Pacific coast, there is marine Permo-Carboniferous which we shall not study here.[306]

But all the eastern part of the continent is composed of an immense platform of ancient rocks on which are spread continental formations of the Karroo type. They have been especially carefully studied in southern Brazil,[307] in the states of Santa Catharina and especially Parana.

In this Parana Basin[308] they begin with morainal conglomerates, indicating an immense inland glaciation, coming from the east. V. Leinz[309] has even tried to distinguish several glacial periods, for in the tillite there are intercalations of clays with varves, sometimes with beds of coal and plant remains (*Gangamopteris* and *Glossopteris* floras) indicating inter-glacial periods. These glaciations would date, then, as everywhere on the Continent of Gondwana, from the boundary between the Carboniferous and the Permian. Then, after the retreat of the glaciers, the *Gangamopteris* flora of the Lower Permian is definitely established and *Mesosaurus* appears. After a lacuna, the beds of Nova Estrada follow, still of Lower Permian age. A new and important lacuna precedes the deposit of the Rio do Rasto beds with very specialized rynchosaurids (*Cephalonia* and *Scaphonyx*) similar to those of the Middle Triassic (*Lettenkohle*) of England and Scotland.

These continental formations of the Gondwana type extend as far as northeastern Uruguay[310] and the *Glossopteris* flora, always with old moraines, is also known in the Falkland Islands.

Conclusions. In all the countries of the southern hemisphere which we have just studied, the same history may be reconstructed.

The Carboniferous ends with a great glacial development, not confined to mountain valleys but extending over immense spaces and thus comparable to the Quaternary ice caps of the northern hemisphere. Immediately after the disappearance of the glaciers and throughout the Permian, these regions were colonized by the *Glossopteris* flora and nourished an abundant population of reptiles, as diversely adapted as present day mammals. The climate at first remained humid enough for the formation of coal beds. Then, sooner or later according to the region, either in the Middle or Upper Permian or in the Triassic, the climate became arid and often there are only red series, azoic, difficult to date.

This common history requires a common explanation. There must have been continental connections between Brazil, South Africa, Madagascar, peninsular India, and Australia; which explains, as we have said, the idea of the Continent of Gondwana. It is not necessary to conclude that the Indian Ocean and the South Atlantic were entirely occupied by emerged lands. But the development of great ice caps simultaneously in all the lands of the southern hemisphere poses a much more difficult problem. Since the coral fauna with tropical characteristics continued to prosper uninterruptedly in the European seas, we cannot conceive of a general global chilling, but only of a chilling limited to the neighborhood of the south pole. Before the glaciation of Brazil was discovered, it was thought the south pole might have been displaced and located in the middle of the Indian Ocean, the center of the regions (South Africa, peninsular India, Australia) then known to have been glaciated. But the extension of this glaciation as far as Brazil became absolutely inexplicable with a simple displacement of poles in relation to supposedly fixed continents.

There is then no other solution than the relative displacement of some continental masses. This theory of drifting continents, developed by Wegener, is supported, moreover, by theoretic considerations which we cannot develop here. Without necessarily accepting it in the form offered by Wegener and many successors, we can retain only the concept which E. Argand has so happily qualified as mobility. For, independent of any hypothesis, this theory merely states that, across the breadth of a folded chain, there was of necessity contraction, and hence a relative drawing together (*rapprochement*) of the two borders of the chain.

Gerth has very judiciously emphasized that the close proximity of the coral faunas of the Permian of Timor and of the moraines of the Australian coast facing this island, can only be explained if Australia has more closely approached Timor since the Permian. We shall also be struck by the fact that the fragment of glaciated continental block which has traveled farthest to the north is peninsular India. And it is exactly at that spot that the tightening of the Mesogean zone must have been most important, since peninsular India and the Asiatic continent are now united by the broad folded Himalayan Chain.

The principle of mobility being accepted, nothing prevents the supposition that Brazil, South Africa, peninsular India, and Australia were at the end of the Carboniferous near the south pole of that period and that they later drifted more or less toward the north.

From another point of view, this history of the continent of Gondwana seems very different from that which we discern in the classic regions of western Europe. Let us say that a traveler, leaving the last chains of the Saharan Atlas, travels endlessly to the south and reaches the Mountains of the Cape, finding as post-Carboniferous formations only flat-lying continental [311] sediments in all this prodigious space. How far removed is such a grandiose permanence from the multiple geologic vicissitudes which have, since the Carboniferous, affected the countries of the Mediterranean and western Europe! And if we then see how little space on a terrestrial globe is occupied by the classic countries between Russia and Spain which we study, we shall agree that theirs is an exceptional geology. We learn to recognize in it only thin bands of geosynclinal formations, the edges of continental platforms, minute fragments of continental blocks with shifting shores. The life of geological phenomena, like that of civilizations, has evolved there in accordance with rapid and capricious rhythms which contrast with the calm and somnolence of immense Africa. But, to look only at the domain of the material, our feverish Mediterranean is abnormal and it is in Africa that the normal history of great continents is inscribed. So it has seemed to us indispensable to treat it briefly here.

REFERENCE NOTES

1. For Russian geologists sometimes use the term Permo-Carboniferous to designate their lower Permian (Artinskian).

2. Often called *Tethys* abroad and *Mésogée* in France, but this latter word etymologically means middle of the earth. We shall use the phrase *Mer mésogéenne* [Mesogean sea], which is the Greek form of the Latin *Mer mediterranée*.

3. The facies of the Dinantian in western Europe have been synthesized in a very clear way by G. Delépine, *Les faunes du Dinantien de l'Europe occidentale*, 1st Congress of Heerlen (1927), work cited below, note 5.

4. H. Paul, *Grundsätzliches zur Paläogeographie des europäischen Unterkarbons und über die Begriffs Kohlenkalk und Kulm*, Geol. Rundschau, 30 (1939), p. 641, with a diagrammatic map; this article develops ideas similar to those set forth here.

5. As comprehensive works on the coal basins, consult: *The Coal Resources of the World*, volume published by the Internat. Geol. Congress in Canada in 1913, Morgan and Co., Toronto (1913). *Geologie der Steinkohlenlager*, by Dannenberg, Berlin, Bornträger (1915–37). For Spain, which we shall not study here, a bibliography will be found in E. Lopez Agos, *Sintesis paleontologica del Carbonifero español*, Bol. R. Soc. esp. Hist. nat. XXII, Madrid (1921). Excellent résumés, by specialists, of the geology of the French Colonial basins (with maps) are found in *Les ressources minérales de la France d'Outre-Mer. I. Le charbon*, Sté. d'Editions géogr. maritimes et coloniales, Paris (1933). Finally, the fundamental works for the codification of international agreements, defining the limits of the Carboniferous stages, are the volumes of the C. R. of the two *Congresses for the Advancement of the Study of Carboniferous Stratigraphy* in Heerlen, in 1927 and in 1935, Imprimerie Vaillant-Carmanne, Liége (1928), and Maestricht (1937).

6. E. S. Moore, *Coal, Its Properties, Analysis, Classification, Geology, Extraction, Uses and Distribution*, 2nd edit., Wiley and Sons, New York (1940), 473 p., 151 fig. A. Lombard, *Le Charbon; composition, géologie, gisements*, 278 p., 65 fig., Librairie de l'Univ., Lausanne (1946). On the structure of the coaly sedimentation, P. Pruvost, *Sédimentation et subsidence*, Jubilee book of the Centenary of the Soc. géol. de France (1930). P. LeCompte, *Etude sur le mécanisme de la formation des dépôts houillers du N. de la France*, Ann. Soc. géol. du Nord, 51 (1927). X. Stainier, *Des rapports entre la composition des charbons et leur conditions de gisement*, Ann. Soc. géol. Belgique, 67, mém. fasc. I (1943). On the nature of plant remains in the different varieties of coals, A. Duparque, *Structure microscopique des charbons du Bassin houillers du N. et du Pas-de-Calais*, Mém. Soc. géol. du Nord, 11 (1933). On the chemical transformations of plant materials, F. Fischer, *Neuere Forschungen zur Entstehung der Kohlen*, Zeitschr. deutschen geol. Ges. 77 (1925).

7. M. Schwartzbach, *Bionomie, Klima und Sedimentationsgeschwindigkeit in Ober-schlesischen Karbon*, Zeitschr. deutschen geol. Ges. 94 (1942), p. 511: bibliography.

8. The working methods of these geologist-specialists in coal naturally have nothing in common with explorers of mountains. They have been described in a very instructive and picturesque way by A. Renier, *Considérations théoriques et pratiques sur la technique du levé géologique des travaux miniers*, 1st Congress of Heerlen.

9. At any rate, the Namurian becomes the lower Westphalian, and for the upper Westphalian, so defined, J. Cornet, *Leçons de Géologie*, Brussels (1927), p. 411, has proposed the name of Hannonian (from Hannonia). But this name has little chance of being adopted, because the coal specialists consider the Namurian as a special stage. Their Westphalian then becomes the equivalent of our upper Westphalian.

10. A study of the German Permian climate will be found in A. Strigel, *Zur Paläogeographie des Schwarzwaldes. Die Abrasionsfläche als klimatisch-tektonisches Problem des oberen Perms*, Verhandl. Naturhist.-mediz. Ver. zu Heidelberg, Beilageheft zu n. F., Bd. 15 (1922).

11. The silicification of plant remains, roots and trunks, so frequent in the red formations of the Permian, and whose structure was recently studied by A. Lacroix, would also be due to special, sub-desert climatic conditions.

12. A comprehensive view of the Permian facies in Russia, Greenland, America, Timor, etc. in C. O. Dunbar, "Permian Faunas; a Study in Facies," Bull. Geol. Soc. America, 52 (1941).

13. For greater accuracy, see the chart on p. 213.

14. The name Punjabian, proposed for the middle Permian of marine type, leads to confusion (see p. 226). As to Thuringian, its type is the Zechstein, marine but with a special fauna; strictly, this name should not be applied to the clearly marine formations, with very different fauna, of the Upper Permian of the Meditteranean regions.

15. The term *Hercynian* is used here in its current acceptance. For a discussion of its origin and its exact meaning, see E. Hennig, *Herzynisch*, Centralbl. f. min. Jahrg. (1926), Abt. B, no. 1.

16. A break which does not, however, coincide exactly with the end of the Hercynian folding. See the brief and clear explanation made by L. Bertrand, *Les anciennes mers de France*, p. 135.

17. The differentiation and nomenclature of the different, successive phases of folding have been carried to extremes by H. Stille, *Grundfragen der vergleichenden Tektonik*, Berlin (1925). But the number of these phases increases unceasingly, as the study of details progresses. Obviously they are only steps in the continuity. So, to speak of a *Breton phase* in America or an *Andean phase* in Europe, for example, seems to me as useless as to wish to define the directions of folds to the nearest degree and to insist on finding these all over the world, as was done in the time of Elie de Beaumont. Considered in the light of global unity, geologic phenomena have obeyed neither the baton of an orchestra leader nor the rule of a geometer.

18. For the tectonics of these massifs, we refer only to the following recent works: For Brittany, articles of Kerforne and Ferronnière in the Bull. Soc. géol. et min. Bretagne (1922); for the French Massif Central, E. Raguin, article cited note 34, chap. 1; P. Termier, *Etat actuel de nos connaissances sur la tectonique du Plateau central français*, C. R. Congrès géol. internat. in Belgium (1922), Liége (1923); for the Vosges, the memoir of J. Jung cited note 35, chap. 1; for the Ardennes, the work of P. Fourmarier cited note 27, chap. 4, for central Europe, the article of F. Kossmat, cited chap. 4, note 77; E. Raguin, *La tectonique hercynienne dans l'Europe centrale et occidentale*, Révue général des Sc. (Mar. 31, 1927). A. Demay, article cited note 8, chap. 2; finally, the fine work with numerous maps by von Bubnoff, *Geologie von Furopa*, II, 1, Berlin (1930).

19. A rather inaccurate name, for the Breton folds have a fan-shaped appearance; only those of southern Brittany have the true Armorican direction.

20. An equally unfortunate name; for if the folds in the Harz are well oriented SW-NE, this massif itself, on the other hand, restricted by its faults, ranges NW-SE. So the German geologists prefer the term *Variscan*.

21. A very brief and clear explanation by P. Bertrand, *Conférences de Paléobotanique*,

Ecole nat. des Mines de St-Etienne, Imprimerie Centrale du Nord, Lille (1926). See also the work of L. Moret cited Intro. note 3.

22. This is the theory of the "autochthonous" formation of coal, as opposed to the "allochthonous" theory, or that of transported plant debris.

23. An explanation of the latest ideas on the structure of the sigillarias will be found in H. Deltenre, *Les Sigillaires des charbonnages de Marlemont*, Mém. Inst. géol. Univ. Louvain, 3 (1924–27).

24. Their leafy branches are called annularia.

25. R. Florin, *Die Koniferen des Oberkarbons und des unteren Perms*, Palaeontographica, 85, abt. B., Lief. 1 (1938).

26. P. Bertrand, *Valeur des flores pour la caractérisation des différentes assises du terrain houiller et pour les synchronismes de bassin à bassin*, C. R. 1 Congrès Heerlen (1927). See also C. R. 2 Congrès.

27. When this stage contains shale with plants, the paleobotanists often designate it as Culm, as we have seen above (p. 157).

28. F. M. Bergounioux, *Découverte d'une tortue fossile dans le Permien de St-Christophe (Aveyron)*, C. R. Acad. Sc. (Jan. 24, 1938). The oldest fossil turtles known date from the upper Triassic; this one is already very close to the Tertiary cryptodires.

29. S. Van der Heide, *La Faune ichtyologique du Carbonifère supérieur des Pays-Bas*, Meded. geo. Stichting, ser. C-IV-3, no. 2, Maastricht (1943); an attempt to distinguish marine or lacustrine forms.

30. It may seem surprising to see freshwater pelecypods shown here as "good fossils" since in the marine upper Tertiary, for example, it is obviously impossible to use marine pelecypods with like precision. This must be due to the fact that conditions of life are, when one thinks about it, much more homogeneous in lakes and rivers than in seas (except for pelagic animals). Thus we could easily give a list of three or four species of fluviatile pelecypods which, by their prevalence and wide geographic distribution, characterize our present fresh waters, while we should be quite embarrassed to characterize our present seas by as small a number of species, because of the variety of depths and bottoms. See, on this subject, T. C. Yen, "Distribution of Fossil Fresh-water Mollusks," Bull. geol. Soc. Amer. 58, 4 (1947).

31. See pp. 164 and 200. The questions of biology and of faunal provinces are attacked by S. Van der Heide, *Les Lamellibranches limniques du terrain houiller du Limbourg du Sud (Pays-Bas)*, Meded. geol. Stichting, ser. C-IV-3, no. 1, Maastricht (1943).

32. Recent study of this genus by M. L. Thompson, "Fusulinids from the Lower Pennsylvanian Atoka and Boggy Formations of Oklahoma," Jour. Pal., 9, no. 4 (1935).

33. Let us note, however, that fusulinids have never been found in the terminal beds of the marine Permian with cephalopods (Gerth, Gubler).

34. Of which we cite only the most recent: J. S. Lee and Y. T. Chao, *Classification and Correlation of Paleozoic Coal Bearing Formations in North China*, Bull. geol. Survey of China, 5, Peking (1926). J. Fromaget, *L'Anthracolithique en Indo-Chine après la régression muscovienne; ses transgressions et sa stratigraphie*, Bull. service géol. Indo-Chine, 19, Hanoi (1931); *Note de la classification du Permien à Fusulinidés*, Bull. Soc. géol. France, 5th ser., 4 (1934). J. Gubler, *A propos de la classification du Permien à Fusulinidés* (ibid.); *Les Fusulinidés du Permien d'Indo-Chine; leur structure et leur classification*, Mém. Soc. géol. France, mém. no. 26 (1935).

35. R. Furon, *L'Indou-Kouch et le Kaboulistan; contribution à l'étude géologique et géomorphogénique de l'Afghanistan*, Thèse Sc., Paris (1927).

36. See note 242, this chapter, for references concerning these regions.

37. Bibliography and geographic distribution in work by Heritsch, cited note 226, this chapter.

38. On the biologic role of these spines, see G. Delépine, *Les Brachiopodes du marbre noir de Dinant (Viséen inf.)*, Mém. Mus. r. Hist. nat. Belgique, no. 37 (1928).

39. An ancestral form of belemnitid, seeming to establish a transition between the probelemnitids and the eubelemnitids, has been noted by R. H. Flower, "A Belemnite from Mississippian Boulder of the Caney Shale," Journ. Pal., 19 (1945), p. 490.

40. W. S. Bisat, "The Carboniferous Goniatites of North of England and their Zones,"

Proc. Yorkshire geol. Soc., 20 (1924); "The Phylogeny of the North of England Goniatites," Proc. geologists' Assoc., 44 (1933), p. 255.

41. The fundamental work is that of H. Schmidt, *Die carbonischen Goniatiten Deutschlands,* Jahrb. preuss. geol. Landesanst., 45 (1925). The note by the same author at the Congress of Heerlen adds only modifications of details.

42. J. de Dorlodot and G. Delépine, *Faune maritime du terrain houiller de la Belgique,* Mém. Inst. géol. Univ. Louvain, 6, fasc. 1 (1930). G. Delépine, *Les zones à Goniatites du Carbonifère,* Livre jubilaire Centenaire Soc. géol. France (1930). Revision of zones proposed by Schmidt, *Les Goniatites du Dinantien de la Belgique,* Mém. Mus. r. Hist. nat. Belgique, mém. no. 91, Brussels (1940).

43. R. G. S. Hudson, "The Goniatite Zones of the Namurian," Geol. Magaz., London (1945).

44. O. G. Toumanskaja, *La stratigraphie du système permien d'après les Ammonées* (abstracts of papers, 17 Internat. géol. Congr., 93–94, 1937). A. K. Miller, "Comparison of Permian Ammonoid Zones of Soviet Russia with those of North America," Bull. Amer. Ass. Petroleum Geologists, 22, no. 8, p. 1014 (1938).

45. It will be noted that the letters by which British geologists designate the zones are the initials of the names of the characteristic genera. The only exception is for zone P, referring to *Posidonomya becheri,* a pelecypod frequent at this horizon in England. The English stage names given at the right and used only to refer to their cephalopod faunas are drawn from the localities of Stafford, Lancaster, Bowland, Cracoe, which will be discussed later.

46. They have been studied, in Europe as well as in America, by R. T. Jackson. See summary in Gignoux, *Les Oursins réguliers fossiles; évolution et classification,* Travaux Lab. géol. Faculté Sc. Grenoble, 17 (1933).

47. B. Nekhoroshev, *Die Bryozoen des deutschen Unterkarbons,* Abhandl. preuss. geol. Landesanst., n. F., Heft 141 (1932).

48. H. Korn, *Die cryptostomen Bryozoen des deutschen Perm,* Leopoldina, Band VI, Walther-Festschrift (1930).

49. F. Demanet, *Les Pectinidés du terrain houiller de la Belgique,* Mém. Inst. géol. Univ. Louvain, 10 (1936). D. N. Newell, *Late Paleozoic Pelecypods; Pectinacea,* State geol. Surv. Kansas, 10, Lawrence, Kansas (1937), 122 p., 41 fig., 20 pl.

50. J. Weir, "The British and Belgian Carboniferous Bellerophontidae," Trans. Royal Soc. Edinburgh, 56 (1931).

51. On the classification and evolution of the Permo-Carboniferous trilobites, see R. F. C. R. Gheyselinck, *Permian Trilobites from Timor and Sicily, with a Revision of their Nomenclature and Classification,* Amsterdam (1937).

52. This name means "sandstone for millstones." The term *grit* is applied to hard, rough rocks and is almost the equivalent of *gratte* used by French miners for coarse sandstones and conglomerates.

53. The names Morganian and Ammanian were recently proposed by A. E. Trueman, Presidential Address, Quart. Journ. geol. Soc. London, no. 406, p. XLIX (1946), to replace old, poorly defined floral stages. Thus, the Lanarkian included the Namurian and Westphalian A, the Yorkian corresponded approximately to the Westphalian B and C, the Staffordian to the transition beds, the Radstockian to Westphalian D (see note 72, this chap. and p. 180). I owe this information to the kindness of M. P. Pruvost.

54. See, for example, A. Vaughan, "Correlation of Dinantian and Devonian," Quart. Journ. geol. Soc., vol. 71 (1915), the Communication of S. H. Reynolds to the Internat. Geol. Congress of Belgium in 1922 and the article of D. A. Allan in the C. R. of the Congress of Heerlen.

55. We have already seen an example of the coral zones in the German Devonian (see p. 105).

56. According to H. Paul (article cited note 86, this chap.) there would be no lacuna, but progressive transition between the Pilton beds and the upper Visean with *Glyphioceras striatum.*

57. We see how obscure this Carboniferous stratigraphy still is.

58. Local details and map in S. H. Reynolds, "The Carboniferous Limestone (Avonian) Rocks of the Bristol Coalfield," Proc. Geologists' Ass., 48 (1937).

59. The coral species chosen by Vaughan to characterize his zone K was related by him to the genus *Kleistopora*. But since then, L. B. Smith has shown that it should be classified as the genus *Vaughania*.

60. Actually the coral genus *Caninia* goes slightly beyond the boundaries of zone C. This zone is, then, better designated as the zone of *Syringothyris*, from a genus of brachiopods.

61. This zone S was named after a brachiopod formerly classified as the genus *Seminula*, at present as the genus *Composita*. For the coral faunas, the beginning of the zone is marked by the appearance of the genus *Lithostrotion*.

62. In *The British Isles*, cited note 23, chap. 1, from which we have drawn much of the information given here.

63. See *Geology in the Field*, p. 648, work cited note 23, chap. 1.

64. The structure and stratigraphy of this classic region of Craven are very clearly described, with maps and profiles, in an article by several collaborators, "The Geology of the Yorkshire Dales," Proc. Geologists' Ass., 44 (1933). See also D. A. Wray, "The Pennines and Adjacent Areas," *British Regional Geology*, Geol. Surv., London (1936).

65. See the excellent and brief, well illustrated monograph by T. Eastwood, "Northern England, British Regional Geology," Geol. Surv. London, 2nd edit. (1946).

66. This is the bed known as the Great Scar Limestone. We see in it a very thin thread of coal which Kendall considers to be the southernmost trace of the coal series of Northumberland (see Fig. 39).

67. Interesting ideas on sedimentation in J. E. Richey, "Areas of Sedimentation of Lower Carboniferous Age in the Midland Valley of Scotland," Summary of Progress, Geol. Surv. Great Britain (1935), Part II.

68. See a monograph by several collaborators, *The Oil Shales of the Lothians*, 3rd edit., Mem. geol. Surv. Scotland (1927).

69. Many details on the Millstone Grit of Lancashire will be found in an article by several collaborators, *The Geology of the Rossendale Anticline*, Mem. geol. Surv. of England (1927).

70. J. de Lapparent, *La boehmite et le diaspore dans les fireclays de l'Ayrshire (Ecosse)*, C. R. Acad. Sc. (Dec. 26, 1934).

71. See W. D. Ware, "The Millstone Grit of Carmarthenshire," Proc. Geologists' Ass., 50 (1939).

72. This is the flora which has served to define the old Lanarkian stage (see note 53, this chap.). But according to Jongmans, it lasts into the Westphalian A.

73. For the history of this island of Brabant, see the Communication of MM. Lohest and Fourmarier to the Internat. geol. Congress of Brussels in 1922.

74. D. A. Wray and A. E. Trueman, "The Non-marine Lamellibranchs of the Upper Carboniferous of Yorkshire, and their Normal Sequence," Summary of Progress, Geol. Surv. Great Britain, 1930, part 3, London (1931). W. B. Wright, "The Anthrocomyas of the Lancashire Coal Measures and the Correlation of the Latter with the Coal Measures of Scotland," ibid., 1936, part 2, London (1937). J. Weir and D. Leitch, "The Zonal Distribution of the Non-marine Lamellibranchs in the Coal Measures of Scotland," Trans. Roy. Soc. Edinburgh (1936). A. E. Trueman and J. Weir, *A Monograph of British Carboniferous Non-marine Lamellibranchs*, Pal. Soc. (1946), 99 and following.

75. R. Crookall, "Correlation of the British and French Upper Coal Measures," Summary of Progress, Geol. Surv. Great Britain, 1930, part 3, London (1931).

76. W. J. Jongmans, *Die Kohlenfelder von Gross-Brittanien*, Geol. Bureau Mijngeb., Mededeel., 1938–1939, Maastricht (1940), pp. 15–222.

77. E. Humblet, *Le bassin houiller de Liége*, Rev. univ. des Mines, 8 sér., t. 17, no. 12, Liége (1941).

78. See G. Delépine, *Recherches sur le Calcaire carbonifère de la Belgique*, Mém. et Trav. publiés par les Professeurs des Facultés catholiques de Lille, fasc. VIII (1911).

A. Carpentier, *Contribution à l'étude du Carbonifère du N de la France,* Mém. Soc. géol. du Nord, t. VII (1913). G. Delépine, *La transgression de la Mer carbonifèrienne et les modifications de la faune au début du Viséen dans l'Europe occidentale,* C. R. Congrès. géol. Internat. de Belgique 1922, Liége (1923) and the work by the same author cited note 3, this chap.

79. For the nomenclature of the coral zones, see p. 172.

80. R. Dehée, *Description de la faune de l'Etroeungt,* Mém. Soc. géol. France, n. s., t. 5, fasc. 2, Mém. no. 11, 64 p., 8 pl. (1929).

81. G. Delépine, *Sur la présence de Cymaclymenia camerata Schindewolf dans la zone d'Etroeungt à Sémeries (N de la France),* Ann. Soc. géol. du Nord, 54 (1929), p. 99.

82. Excellently described by G. Delépine, *La répartition des faciès waulsortiens en Europe occidentale,* Ann. Soc. sc. de Bruxelles, 45 (1926).

83. F. Kaisin, *Age géologique et "milieu générateur" de la Grande Brèche,* Bull. Soc. belge géol., 51 (1942), p. 84. F. Bourguignon, *Sur l'âge viséen de la grande brèche des Fonds de Leffe à Dinant,* Soc. géol. Belgique, Ann. Bull, 69 (1946).

84. Thus it may be compared to the "cordillera breccias" which we shall describe in the Jurassic and Cretaceous of the French Alps, and in particular to the breccias of the Upper Cretaceous (La Madeleine Breccia) the cement of which, often reddened by contributions of earth of continental alteration, contains rosalines, marine pelagic foraminifers discovered by L. Moret. So, in the history of the Hercynian Chain in the Ardennes, folded at the end of the Carboniferous, the Dinantian is shown to be homologous to the Cretaceous of the Alpine Chain, folded in the Tertiary.

85. A much more detailed and precise map has been published by Delépine in the *C. R. du 13ᵉ Congrès géol. international en 1922,* Liége (1923).

86. H. Paul, *Die Transgression der Viséstufe in Nordwest-Europa,* Verhandl. Naturwiss. Vereins Rheinlande u. Westphalens, 95, A, géol. Abt., Bonn (1937).

87. C. Ancion, W. Van Leckwijck and G. Ubaghs, *Sur l'âge famennien des grès de Val-Dieu et l'existence d'une lacune stratigraphique entre Namurien et Famennien dans la vallée de la Berwinne,* Acad. r. Belgique, Cl. des Sc. (June, 1943).

88. Bull. Soc. géol. Belgique, 68 (1944–45), p. B. 264, (map) and B. 294, observations of P. Fourmarier and of R. Marlière.

89. F. Charles, *Observations dans le massif de Visé,* Bull. Soc. belge Géol., 55, no. 1 (1936).

90. L. Calembert, *Le contact Namurien-Dinantien dans le massif de Visé,* Bull. Soc. géol. Belgique, 69, (1945), p. B. 45.

91. Bull. Soc. géol. de France (1921), p. 189.

92. A petrographic study of them has been made by P. H. Derville, *Les marbres de Calcaire carbonifère en Bas-Boulonnais,* Thèse Sc., Strasbourg (1931).

93. F. Demanet, *Faune et stratigraphie de l'étage Namurien en Belgique,* Mém. Mus. r. Hist. nat. Belgique, mém. no. 97 (1941).

94. J. de Dorlodot and G. Delépine, work cited note 42, this chap. F. Demanet, *La faune des couches de passage du Dinantien au Namurien dans le synclinorium de Dinant,* Mém. Mus. r. Hist. nat. Belgique, Mém. no. 84 (1938).

95. See G. Waterlot's very important work, *Les Productus du terrain houiller du N de la France,* Ann. Soc. géol. du Nord, 57 (1932).

96. Strictly speaking, this name would only fit the Chokier bed, for the Andenne sandstones contain small beds of poor coal. In the same way, the term Namurian was originally used in a more or less broad sense. See A. Renier, *La définition de l'étage Namurien* (Bull. Soc. belge Géol., 37, 1927). Here, we conform to the decisions made at the Congress of Heerlen. After this congress, an excellent general summary was published by A. Renier, *Considérations sur la stratigraphie du terrain houiller de la Belgique,* Mém. Mus. r. Hist. nat. Belgique, mém. no. 44 (1930).

97. On the mechanism of the Carboniferous sedimentation, see the very suggestive article of P. Pruvost, cited note 6, this chap.

98. In addition to the C. R. of the Congress of Heerlen, see, for France, the very brief and clear exposition of P. Pruvost, *Aperçu stratigraphique sur le terrain houiller*

du Nord de la France, Bull. Soc. géol. France, 4 sér., t. 28 (1928). For Belgium see the magnificent chart presented by A. Renier in the work cited in note 96, this chap. A more recent edition of this chart was published in 1938 as an appendage to *Flore et faune houillère de la Belgique,* edited by the national royal Museum of History of Belgium. Finally, all the fossils of our French Carboniferous are illustrated in P. Corsin, *Guide paléontologique dans le terrain houiller du Nord de la France,* Publication of the Inst. de la Houille de l'Univ. de Lille (1932).

99. These zones, classic in the Franco-Belgian Basin, have recently been defined in the Aix-la-Chapelle Basin. C. Hahne, *Die Verbreitung der Süsswassermuscheln im Profil des Aachener Steinkohlengebirges,* Zeitschr. deutschen geol. Ges., 90 (1938), p. 508.

100. For more details, see F. Demanet, *Les horizons marins du Westphalien de la Belgique,* Mém. Mus. r. Hist. nat. Belgique, mém. 101 (1943).

101. These two marine horizons are more radio-active than the surrounding rocks. They can thus be outlined, in the obscurity of the galleries and behind the timbering, by the instrument cited below: J. Chalard, *Application du compteur de Geiger-Müller à la stratigraphie dans le bassin houiller du Nord de la France,* C. R. Acad. Sc. t. 222 (1946), p. 506.

102. G. Delépine, *Goniatites et Nautiloïdes du niveau de Petit-Buisson à Heerlen (Hollande),* Ann. Soc. géol. du Nord, 42 (1937).

103. P. Pruvost, *Quelques observations sur le phénomène de plissement faites dans les bassins houillers,* Bull. Soc. géol. France, 5 sér., t. 9 (1939).

104. Likewise, in the Alpine Chain, where great thrusts date from the Oligocene, we shall see that conglomerates in the Eocene Flysch prove that the cordilleras were already emergent in the Briançonnais zone.

105. See especially the Memoir cited note 27, chap. 4. This tectonic interpretation of the "Theux window" was recently questioned by G. Waterlot, who contends that the autochthonous formations of the window are directly related, to the south, to the displaced formations of the nappe.

106. P. Fourmarier, *Observations sur l'estimation de l'importance du transport suivant le "charriage du Condroz,"* Ann. Soc. géol. Belgique, t. 56, Bull. (1932–33).

107. As an example of detailed structure, see the section given by P. Bertrand and P. Pruvost, *Structure du bassin houiller du Pas-de-Calais dans sa région centrale,* Ann. Soc. géol. du Nord, 59 (1934).

108. A bibliography of recent works on the subsurface of the Low Countries has been given by A. Briquet, work cited, note 18, chap. 6. For general review, see J. Van Baren, *Le sol des Pays-Bas,* 2 vol., Leyden (1929).

109. L. Dorsman, *The Marine Fauna of the Carboniferous in the Netherlands,* Meded. geol. Stichting, ser. C-IV-3, no. 3, Maastricht, (1945). S. van der Heide, *Stratigraphie et paléontologie animale du terrain houiller du Peel,* ibid., no. 4 (1946).

110. X. Stainier, *Y a-t-il encore des bassins houillers inconnus dans le Nord-Ouest de l'Europe?,* Bull. Soc. belge Géol., 46 (1936).

111. On the extension of the Ruhr Basin eastward, see H. Stille, *Ueber die nordöstliche Fortzetzung der westphälischen Steinkohlenformation,* Nachr. d. Ges. d. Wiss. zu Göttingen, Math.-Phys., Kl. (1926).

112. The detailed paleontologic stratigraphy of the base and the top of this limestone series of northern Germany has been studied by H. Paul, *Die Etroeungt-Schichten des bergischen Landes,* Jahrb. preuss. Landesanst., 59 (1939); *Die Dibunophyllum-Zone des bergischen Unterkarbons,* Neues Jahrb. f. Min., Abt. B, Beilage-Band 79 (1938).

113. Also the boundary of the Devonian and the Carboniferous has been much debated. O. H. Schindewolf, *Zur Kenntniss der Devon-Karbon Grenze in Deutschland,* Zeitschr. deutschen geol. Ges., 78, Abh. (1926). See also Vol. II of Von Bubnoff's work, cited note 15, chap. 1.

114. A map of the distribution of the three principal types of the German Dinantian (limestone facies, sandy littoral Culm, shaly, pelagic Culm) will be found in H. Paul, *Das Unterkarbon in Deutschland,* Geol. Rundschau, 31 (1940). A diagram of the Dinantian facies on the right bank of the Rhine is found in F. Kühne and W. Paeckelmann, *Die stratigraphische und fazielle Entwicklung des Carbons im nordöstlichen*

Sauerlande und ein Vergleich mit Nachbargebieten, Jahrb. preuss. geol. Landesanst. für 1928, Berlin (1929).

115. The fundamental work is that of P. Kukuk, *Geologie des Niederrheinisch-westphalischen Steinkohlengebietes,* 706 p., 743 fig., 48 tabl., 19 colored pl., J. Springer, Berlin (1938).

116. See the C. R. of the Congress of Heerlen cited note 5, this chap.

117. M. Schwartzbach, *Einige Zusammenhänge zwischen den marinen Horizonten und Paläogeographie im oberschlesischen Steinkohlenbecken,* Geol. Rundschau, 31 (1940).

118. See the magnificent monograph in 5 vol., *Bassin houiller de la Sarre et de la Lorraine,* under the direction of Ch. Barrois and G. Friedel, Lille, Imprimerie Danel (1930–34); 1. *Flore fossile,* par P. Bertrand; 2. *Faune fossile,* par G. Waterlot; 3. *Description géologique,* par P. Pruvost. An excellent summary was made by P. Pruvost, *La structure du Bassin houiller de la Sarre,* Revue universelle des Mines, 7 sér., t. 17, no. 2, Liege (1928).

119. H. Bode, *Einige Bemerkungen zur Stratigraphie des Saarbrücker Karbons,* Zeitschr. deutsch. geol. Ges., 93 (1941).

120. See the recent note, with map, of A. Robaux and M. Bernatsky, *Sur la tectonique des terrains secondaires de la Lorraine,* C. R. Acad. Sc. (Dec. 6, 1937). Critical remarks by L. Guillaume, work cited, note 20, chap. 7.

121. Beside the old classic works of Ch. Barrois, D. P. Oehlert, E. and L. Bureau, see especially the important memoir of Y. Milon, cited note 42, chap. 2, and the articles by Delépine cited note 78, this chap.

122. P. Pruvost and G. Waterlot, *Observations sur les grès d'Erquy et du Cap Fréhel,* Ann. Soc. géol. du Nord, 61 (1936).

123. A. Bigot, *Le Carbonifère de Montmartin-sur-Mer,* Bull. Soc. linnéenne Normandie, 8 sér., 10 (1938).

124. Y. Mioton, *Niveau marin dans le Culm, au S de Laval,* Bull. Soc. géol. France (1923).

125. Rock formed of arkose and of very laminated volcanic tuff.

126. A. Carpentier, *Le Carbonifère inférieur du Bassin de la Basse-Loire et ses rapports avec le Westphalien du Nord de la France,* Heerlen Congress.

127. G. Delépine, *Observations sur l'âge des formations dites du Culm inf. en France,* C. R. Soc. géol. France (Dec. 19, 1932).

128. A. Bigot, *Le terrain houiller de Basse-Normandie,* Bull. Soc. linnéenne Normandie, 9 sér., t. 5 (1947), p. 94.

129. C. Piquenard, *Sur le Carboniférien du Sud du département du Finistère,* C. R. Congrès géol. international Bruxelles (1922).

130. Work cited note 48, chap. 2.

131. See J. Jung, work cited note 35, chap. 1.

132. P. Corsin and G. Dubois, *Description de la flore dinantienne de Champenay,* Bull. Serv. carte géol. d'Alsace et de Lorraine, 2 (1933). G. Dubois, *Répartition des gisements certainement et vraisemblablement dinantiens dans la région de la Bruche (Vosges moyennes),* C. R. Soc. géol. France (June 17, 1946).

133. This word, curiously Germanized as *Püttig,* then latinized by German paleontologists, has served to christen different species from this locality as *püttigensis.*

134. See note of Delépine cited note 127, this chap.

135. G. Renouard, *Observations sur la stratigraphie et la flore des couches stéphaniennes et permiennes du bassin du Villé,* Bull. Serv. carte géol. Alsace et Lorraine, 3 (1936).

136. G. Mathieu, *Analyse stratigraphique de la série carbonifère dans le bassin de Ronchamp (Haute-Saône),* C. R. Acad. Sc., t. 225 (1947), p. 1016; *Observations géologiques sur le Stéphanien de la concession de Saint-Germain (Haute-Saône),* ibid., p. 1339.

137. See A. Michel-Lévy, *Quelques observations sur les formations primaires du Nord du Morvan,* Livre jubilaire du Centenaire de la Soc. géol. de France (1930).

138. A bibliography will be found in the excellent monograph by J. Jung (1946) cited note 36, chap. 1.

139. A. Demay, *Sur la découverte de grès et poudingues viséens à l'Ouest de Boën, dans le Forez, et sur l'âge des formations crystallophylliens sous-jacentes,* C. R. Acad. Sc., t. 226 (1948), p. 97.

140. G. Delépine, *Le Carbonifère du Sud de la France (Pyrénées et Montagne-Noire) et du Nord-Ouest de l'Espagne (Asturies),* C. R. 2 Congrès Heerlen, 1935, Maastricht (1937).

141. Actually, this trough is, in the south, oriented almost parallel to the pre-Stephanian tectonic directions, while in the north, it cuts them obliquely. These latter are in fact directed NW-SE, which shows the alignments of the Dinantian south of Montluçon. See E. Raguin, *Etude tectonique dans les terrains cristallins situés au voisinage du grand sillon houiller du Plateau central français,* Bull. Soc. géol. France, 4 sér., 28 (1928). Subsequent to the classic works of Mouret and de Launay, we turn also to the recent studies of E. Raguin and P. Termier, cited note 18, this chap.

142. For the other basins, we only mention a few recent studies:
G. Mathieu, Ann. Soc. géol. du Nord, 55 (1930) and 56 (1931), has described the structure and the floras (Stephanian) of the two small basins of Langeac and Brassac (south of the Limagne).

M. Thoral and J. Louis, *Sur le bassin houiller de Sainte-Foy-l'Argentière (Rhône),* C. R. Acad. Sc., 225 (1947), p. 1342. This is a basin of Sainte-Etienne in miniature, separating the Mts. of Lyonnais and the Mts. of Beaujolais.

F. M. Bergounioux, J. Doubinger and M. Sandre, *Observations sur la flore houillère du bassin de Messeix (Puy-de-Dôme),* ibid., 223 (1946), p. 1016. This basin, situated in the big coal channel, contains floras indicating the top of the middle Stephanian and the upper Stephanian.

F. M. Bergounioux and J. Doubinger, *Flore des découvertes de Decazeville,* ibid. (Dec. 13, 1943); three floral horizons can be distinguished, one in the middle Stephanian, two in the upper Stephanian; *Sur l'âge des petits bassins houillers au Nord de Figeac (Lot),* ibid. (May 7, 1943); thanks to a momentary resumption of exploitation, a succession of three floral horizons can be recognized, all Stephanian. These basins represent so many small isolated ancient lakes, without communication with the basin of Decazeville.

J. Doubinger, *Observations sur le gisement carbonifère de Sansac (Aveyron),* C. R. Soc. géol. France (1947), p. 47; in this deposit, located west of Rodez, the flora indicates the middle Stephanian.

P. Routhier, *Les bassins houillers de Ségure et de Durban (Aude),* Diplôme d'Et. sup., Fac. Sc. Paris, no. 733 (1939). P. Corsin and C. Monomakhoff, *Sur le Houiller de la Machine, Bassin de Decize (Nièvre),* C. R. Acad., Sc., 227 (1948), p. 980. P. Corsin, *Sur l'âge des couches houillères du Bassin de Blanzy (Saône-et-Loire),* ibid., p. 858.

143. P. Bertrand, *Les grandes divisions paléontologiques du Stéphanien du Bassin de la Loire,* C. R. Acad. Sc., 167 (1918), p. 689.

144. P. Pruvost, *La série stéphanienne du Bassin houiller de la Loire,* C. R. Acad. Sc., 225 (1947), p. 1236.

145. See the studies by F. Blondel, Rev. Ind. min. (Nov. 15, 1925) and by J. de Maistre, ibid., 485 (1944), p. 163.

146. Excellent summary in F. Roman, *Géologie lyonnaise* (Presses univ., Paris, 1926).

147. See the Notes by P. Termier and G. Friedel, C. R. Acad. Sc. (Nov. 3, and Dec. 29, 1919), P. Bertrand, ibid. (Feb. 9, 1920), J. Louis, C. R. Soc. géol. France (1948), p. 223, C. R. de la Réunion de la Soc. géol. de France dans le Gard in 1923, and the monograph by A. Livet, *Sur le terrain houiller du Gard,* 298 p., 436 fig., published by the author, Grande-Combe Mines, Gard, for many interesting detailed descriptions of the dislocations affecting the coal beds. The tectonics of the small nearby coal basin of Prades has just been studied by P. Lapadu-Hargues, *Etude sur le bassin houiller de Prades,* Diplôme Et. sup. Fac. Sc. Paris, no. 723 (1939).

148. Old spelling: Alais.

149. P. Bertrand, *Le sondage de Sanquinet (Gard),* Livre jubilaire du Centenaire de la Soc. géol. de France (1930).

150. Work cited note 140, this chap. See also M. Gignoux, *Sur les analogies des faciès à Radiolaires (lydiennes, radiolarites), d'une part dans le Dinantien méditerranéen, d'autre part dans le Jurassique supérieur des zones alpines internes,* C. R. Soc. géol. France (1948), p. 354.

151. G. Delépine, *L'âge des schistes de Mondette (Ariège),* C. R. Soc. géol. France (June 15, 1931).

152. Most of the granitic massifs of the Pyrénées axial zone would thus be post-tectonic injection granites, set in place after the great Hercynian folding, before the Carboniferous. E. Raguin, *Sur l'âge des roches granitiques dans les Pyrénées,* C. R. Acad. Sc., (Nov. 21, 1938); *Contribution à l'étude des gneiss des Pyrénées,* Bull. Soc. géol. France, 5 sér., 8 (1938).

153. See especially, M. Dalloni, *Etude géologique des Pyrénées catalanes,* Annales Fac. Sc., Marseilles, 26 (1930).

154. Cf. Kilian and Révil, *Etudes géologiques dans les Alpes occidentales,* Mém. Carte géol. France. For everything concerning the French Alps, we recommend, once for all, the *Répertoire de la bibliographie géologique du SE de la France,* Trav. Lab. Géol. Univ. Grenoble, XII (1922), XIII (1923), XV (1931), and general stratigraphic descriptions in M. Gignoux and L. Moret, *Un itinéraire géologique à travers les Alpes françaises, de Voreppe à Grenoble et en Maurienne,* Trav. Lab. Géol. Univ. Grenoble 15 (1931); *Description géologique du bassin supérieur de la Durance; itinéraire de Sisteron (et de Grenoble) à Veynes, Gap, Briançon, au Lauteret et au Galibier,* ibid., 21 (1938); *Géologie dauphinoise ou initiation à la géologie par l'étude des environs de Grenoble,* Arthaud, Paris-Grenoble (1944). L. Moret, work cited note 165, chap. 9.

155. M. Gignoux and L. Moret, *Les grandes subdivisions géologiques des Alpes françaises,* Ann. de Géogr., no. 43 (1934). L. Moret, *Précis de Géologie,* map. Fig. 197, p. 385.

156. With the exception, however, of the minute outcrop of Carboniferous (middle Stephanian) of Barles, north of Digne, which appears in the midst of the sub-Alpine chains, in which erosion has not been deep enough to reach the pre-Carboniferous platform.

157. The collections of Carboniferous plants of the Geol. Lab. of Grenoble University have recently been revised by P. Corsin, who was kind enough to give me his conclusions.

158. P. Bertrand, *Les gisements à "Mixoneura ovata" de la région de St-Gervais-Chamonix,* Bull. Soc. géol. France, 4 sér., 26 (1927).

159. L. Moret, *Précision sur la nature et l'âge des "chapeaux" houillers formant quelques sommets du massif de Belledonne,* C. R. Soc. géol. France (Mar 5, 1945).

160. C. R. Congrès géol. internat. at Brussels, in 1922, Liége (1923).

161. See the works on the Briançonnais Coal Measures, published under the direction of W. Kilian in the Trav. Lab. Géol. Univ. Grenoble, t. 13 (1923).

162. Or rather, appear only in the tiny sheets of granite or crystalline schists, which are enumerated, with diagrammatic map, in M. Gignoux and E. Raguin, *Découverte d'écailles de roches granitiques au NW du Col du Lautaret (Hautes-Alpes),* Bull. Soc. geol. France, 5 sér. t., 2 (1932). It seems probable that this substratum still belongs to the Hercynian type, with the Carboniferous discordant on the ancient platform.

163. A list of species classified by localities was given by C. Pussenot, *La nappe du Briançonnais et le bord de la zone des schistes lustrés entre l'Arc et le Guil,* Grenoble, Imprimerie Allier (1930). We may refer also to two Notes by the same author in the C. R. Acad. des Sc. t. 155 (1912), p. 1564 and t. 156 (1913), p. 97.

164. M. Gignoux, *Les problèmes géologiques de la région Vanoise-Mont-Pourri (Savoie),* Trav. Lab. Géol. Univ. Grenoble, 15 (1929). A very profound study of these massifs has been undertaken by F. Ellenberger (article cited note 59, chap. 6).

165. See the classic synthesis of P. Termier, *Les schistes cristallins des Alpes occidentales,* C. R. 9 Congrès Internat., Vienna (1903).

166. L. Wehrli and P. Christ, *Das produktive Karbon der Schweizer Alpen,* Beitr. z. Geol. d Schweiz, Geotechnische Serie, 11 (1925). R. Winterhalter, *Die karbonischen Sedimente der Schweizer Alpen,* C. R. Congrès Heerlen.

167. Old bibliography in L. Lutaud, *Etude tectonique et morphologique de la Provence cristalline,* Revue de Géogr., 12 (1924).

168. In H. Parent, *Le terrain houiller à Collabrières et aux environs d'Hyères*, C. R. Soc. géol. France (June 6, 1932).

169. P. Bordet, *Le Carbonifère et le Permien dans la dépression du Reyran (Esterel)*, C. R. Acad. Sc. 218 (1944), p. 415.

170. As recent French publications, we cite, in addition to the C. R. Congrès Heerlen, N. Lebedeff, *Sur las corrélation du carbonifère russe avec celui des autres contrées*, Ann. Soc. géol. du Nord, 53 (1928) and G. Fredericks, *Le Paléozoïque supérieur de l'Oural*, ibid. An excellent summary of the Russian Carboniferous (in particular, lists of marine faunas of Donetz, according to Lébédeff) is found in the fundamental work by von Bubnoff, *Geologie von Europa*, I, Berlin (1926). See also two more recent notes, von Bubnoff, *Ueber die Gliederung des Donezkarbons auf Grund der Pflanzenfunde und über die Beziehung zu Oberschlesien und Westeuropa*, Zeitsch. Oberschlesischen Berg- u. Hüttenmännischen Ver., 3 (1929), and H. Schmidt, *Vergleich unserer Karbonschichtenfolge mit der Russlands*, Zeitsch. deutsch. geol. Ges., 81 (1929). Brief, regional descriptions in J. Goguel, *Les bassins houillers de l'U. R. S. S., d'après les travaux du 17 Congrès géol. internat.*, Houille, Minerais, Pétrole, no. 4 to 6, Paris (1947).

171. From the name of a tributary of the Moscow River.

172. Or of Malevka-Muraevna, see p. 161.

173. Tributary of the upper course of the Don, south of Moscow.

174. In fact, in the Mesozoic conglomerates of the north flank of the Crimean mountains, blocks of crystalline rocks are found. These provide a curious analogy with the conglomerates with crystalline blocks that we shall describe (p. 430) in the Turonian of La Ciotat, where these blocks are derived from an eastern extension, to-day hidden under the sea, of the ancient massif of Maures.

175. O. Holtedahl, *Jungpaläozoische Fossilien im Oslo-Gebiet*, Norsk. geol. Tiddskrift, 12 (1931).

176. Broken, however, by several areas which remained elevated, whose detail has been studied by von Freyberg.

177. W. Siegl, *Zur Genesis des Kupferschiefers*, Min.-petr. Mitt. 52, Leipzig (1941). The names Rothliegende and Zechstein come from the old language of the miners who worked these cupriferous shales. The *Rothliegende* was the foot wall (*Liegendes*), formed of red (*roth*) beds of the ore deposit. The *Zechstein* was the hard (*zäh*) rock (*stein*) in which they dug the bases of their pits.

178. A very suggestive explanation of the assemblage, with bibliography, paleogeographic maps and complete list of the fauna is given by B. von Freyberg, *Paläogeographie der Zechsteinriffe Thüringens*, Mitt. geol. Inst. Univ. Tübingen (1932), no. 3. See also, by the same author, *Zur Paläogeographie des Jungpaläozoikums in Deutschland*, Zeitschr. deutsch. geol. Ges., 87 (1935). Lastly we cite the volume, 409 p., 100 fig., edited by the Preussische geol. Landesanst.: *Handbuch der vergleichenden Stratigraphie Deutschlands: Zechstein*, Berlin, Bornträger (1935).

179. For a detailed stratigraphy, see E. Fulda, *Die Stratigraphie des thüringischen Zechsteins nach Tiefbohrungen*, Jahrb. preuss. geol. Landesanst. f. 1926, 47.

180. With the exception, of course, of the extension of the Alsatian Tertiary potash in the Pays de Bade.

181. Brief summary, with bibliography, in M. Gignoux, *La tectonique des terrains salifères; son rôle dans les Alpes françaises*, Livre jubilaire Centenaire Soc. géol. France (1930).

182. Excellent explanation, with maps and sections, in A. Roux and M. Solignac, *Etude comparative des dômes pétrolifères du Hanovre et des structures tunisiennes*, Ann. Office nat. Combustibles liquids, 12th yr., no. 3 (1937). Recently, petroleum and combustible gases have even been discovered in the Zechstein dolomites at Volkenroda in Thuringia: K. Fiege, *Uebersicht über das Vorkommen der Erdöle, Erdgase und Asphalte in Deutschland*, Kali, Verwandte Salze und Erdöl (1934). L. Barrabé, *Les recherches de pétrole dans l'Allemagne NW au cours de la guerre*, Houille, Minerais, Pétrole, no. 5–6, p. 139–154, 17 fig., Paris (1946).

183. See figure, p. 41, in L. Riedel, *Ueber Transgressionserscheinungen im hohen Schon Hannover's und das Aufsteigen der Salzstöcke von Hänigsen-Wathlingen und Wienhausen-Sandlingen*, Zeitschr. deutsch. geol. Ges., 89 (1937).

184. On the technique of the formation of the salt deposits, see F. Lotze, *Steinsalz und Kalisalze Geologie*, 830 p., 353 fig., Berlin, Bornträger (1938).

185. Everding, *Zur geologie der deutschen Zechsteinsalze*, in "Deutschlands Kalibergbau," Berlin (1907). For more paleogeographic details, see the article by von Freyberg, cited note 178, this chap.

186. In this direction a recent discovery was made in Poland, to the south and southwest of the great bend of the Vistula below Warsaw, of the two salt domes of Inowroklaw and Wapno, absolutely similar to those of Hanover. J. Poborski, *Recent Contributions to the Geology of the Salt Beds in Western Poland*, Serv. geol. Pologne, Bull. 36 (1947).

187. See H. Stille, *Neueres über die nördliche Fortsetzung und nördliche Umradung der deutschen Dyas*, Review "Kali" (1932), Heft 16–17.

188. This shows how the study of the nature of the pebbles in a series of conglomerates may allow the dating of these conglomerates by comparison with others. We shall find a quite similar example in the Alsatian Oligocene. The Brockram was compared by B. Smith (Geol. Magaz., XLI, 1924) to the cones of breccias which form at the foot of mountains bordering desert basins (See Fig. 1).

189. H. Frebold, *Der geologische Bau Nowaja Semljas*, Geol. Rundschau, 31 (1940).

190. W. Maync, *Stratigraphie und Faziesverhältnisse der oberpermischen Ablagerungen Ostgrönlands*, Meddedelse om Grönland, 115, no. 2, Copenhagen (1942). For a description of the whole, see Lauge Koch, *Ueber den Bau Grönlands*, Geol. Rundschau, 27 (1936). A recent bibliography in *Grönland 1939, Tagung der Naturforsch. Ges. Schaffhausen*, Mitt. Naturforsch. Ges. Schaffhausen, Schweiz (1940).

191. A. Bigot and P. Pruvost, *Contribution à l'étude du Houiller et du Permien du Cotentin*, Bull. Soc. linnéenne de Normandie, 7 sér., 8 (1925).

192. Depéret and Mazeran, *Les Estheria du Permien d'Autun*, Mém. Soc. d'Hist. nat. d'Autun, 25 (1912).

193. After J. Louis, *Nouvelles observations sur le Permien du Bassin de Blanzy*, C. R. Acad. Sc., 223 (1946), p. 426.

194. See article cited note 135, this chap.

195. G. Choubert and G. Gardet, *Le Permien des Vosges*, Revue Géogr. phys. et Géol. dynam., 8 (1935).

196. *Walchia piniformis*, formerly noted by Heer near the Chamonix Coal Measures, already appears in the Stephanian.

197. M. Gignoux and L. Moret, *Le Permien des zones externes des Alpes françaises*, C. R. Acad. Sc., 226 (1948), p. 853.

198. For the origin of this name, see p. 229.

199. P. Bordet, *Observations sur le Permien des environs de Roquebrune-sur-Argens (Var)*, C. R. Soc. géol. France (Mar. 15, 1943).

200. M. Dalloni, *Sur des dépôts permiens des Pyrénées à flore d'Angaride*, Ç. R. Acad. Sc., 206 (1938), p. 115.

201. See the work of von Bubnoff cited note 15, chap. 1. As articles in French, in addition to the study of G. Frédéricks cited note 170, this chap., see the publications of D. Zalessky cited note 271, this chap.

202. We shall not discuss the Permian of the Donetz Basin, whose synchronism with that of other Russian regions is not exact enough. For the very interesting Kousnetzk Basin in Siberia, we refer to Zalessky, Ann. Soc. géol. du Nord, 53 (1928), pp. 117 and following.

203. For the geographic names, see map, Fig. 35.

204. Beds of industrially exploitable potassium salts are even found north of Perm, on the banks of the Kama.

205. From the river Kama which passes Perm and joins the Volga south of Kazan.

206. J. Wanner, *Die marine Permfauna von Timor*, Geol. Rundschau, Sonderband, 17 (1926).

207. Brief résumé in *Les principaux traits de la structure géologique de l'Indo-Chine*

française (*d'après les explorations antérieures à 1931*), Bull. Serv. géol. de l'Indo-Chine, 19, fasc. 1 (1931).

208. See the studies of Fromaget and Gubler, cited note 34, this chap.

209. Excellent comprehensive summary by A. Carpentier, *Les flores primaires de la Chine*, Revue générale des Sciences (Oct. 31, 1928).

210. F. F. Mathieu, G. Delépine and P. Pruvost, *Observations sur le terrain houiller de Kaïping* (*Chine*), Ann. Soc. géol. du Nord, 52 (1923). F. F. Mathieu, *La stratigraphie du Bassin houiller de Kaïping* (*Chine*), Public. Mus. r. Hist. nat. Belgique, 48 p., 14 fig., Brussells (1939).

211. W. H. Wong and W. Grabau, "Carboniferous formations of China," C. R. Congrès géol. internat. in Belgium in 1922, Liége (1923).

212. A. W. Grabau, *The Permian of Mongolia* (*Central Asia Expedition*); *Natural History of Central Asia*, vol. IV, Amer. Museum of Nat. Hist., New York (1931). In this very important work the author has taken up the study of the principal known faunas of the marine Permian. See also T. K. Huang, *The Permian Formations of Southern China*, Geol. Mem., Peiping (1932). This work contains paleogeographic maps.

213. See the magnificent series of works entitled *Relazioni scientifiche della spedizione italiana de Filippi, nell'Himalaya, Caracorum e Turchestan Cinese*, Bologna (1934), and in particular, G. Danielli, *La serie dei terreni*. A very complete bibliography of the Asiatic Permo-Carboniferous will be found here.

214. The saline formations which have christened this massif have been attributed to the Tertiary, the Cambrian, or the Precambrian. It is actually a matter of the saline Eocene on which the fossiliferous Cambrian is superposed, by tectonic thrusting. R. van Vleck Anderson, "Symposium on Age of the Saline Formation of the Salt Range, India," Amer. Journ. of Sc. (Feb. 1946), 244, p. 140. "Evidence for Eocene Age of Saline Formation beneath Salt Range Thrust," Proc. Nat. Acad. Sc. of India, 16, p. 169 (1946).

215. F. R. C. Reed, "New Fossils from the Productus Limestone of the Salt Range," Mem. geol. Surv. of India, Palaeontologia indica, n. s., 17 (1931).

216. G. Merla, *Osservazioni preliminari sul Permiano della valle Shaksgam* (*Caracorum*), Boll. Soc. geol. ital., 54 (1935).

217. Bibliography in R. Furon, *L'Hindou-Kouch et le Kaboulistan* (Thèse Sc., Paris, 1927); *Sur la géologie de l'Hindou-Kouch et du Pamir* (Bull. Soc. géol. France, 5 sér., 4, 1934). M. L. Thompson, "Permian Fusulinids from Afghanistan," Journ. Pal. (Mar. 1946), 20, p. 140, including a comparison with the American marine Permian (Guadalupian stage).

218. A. Rivière, *Contribution à l'étude géologique de l'Elbourz* (*Perse*), Rév. Géogr. phys. et Géol. dynam., 7 (1934). R. Furon, *Géologie du plateau iranien* (*Perse, Afghanistan, Béloutchistan*), Mém., Mus. nat. Hist. Nat., n. s., 7, fasc. 2, p. 177–414, carte géol. couleurs, Paris (1941).

219. P. Bonnet, *Note préliminaire sur la constitution géologique de la gorge de Djoulfa et de ses environs*, Bull. Soc. géol. France, 4 sér., 12 (1912), with magnificent photographs; *Description géologique de la Transcaucasie méridionale*, Mém. Soc. géol. France, mem. no. 53 (1947). A. Stoyanow, "Revision of the Permo-Triassic Sequence at Djulfa, Armenia," Bull. geol. Soc. Amer. (1942), 53, p. 1823.

220. E. Chaput, *L'Anthracolithique dans l'Anatolie Centrale*, C. R. Acad. Sc. (Nov. 13, 1933). For all of Turkey, see the comprehensive restatement by C. Jacob, *Quelques traits géologiques de la Turquie, d'après Ernest Chaput*, Bull. Soc. géol. France, 15 (1945).

221. J. L. Wilser, *Die Steinkohlen in der Schwarzmeer-Umrandung, insbesondere bei Heraklea-Zonguldag* (*Nord-Anatolien*), Geol. Rundschau, 18 (1927). F. Charles, *Note sur le Houiller d'Amasra* (*Asie mineure*), Ann. Soc. géol. Belgique, 54, Bull. no. 4 (1931). M. Lucius, *Paléogéographie et Géologie de la formation carbonifère en Anatolie*, Bull. Soc. des naturalistes luxembourgeois (1931), nos. 9 and 10, with diagrammatic map. G. Ralli, *Le bassin houiller d'Héraclée et la flore du Culm et du Houiller moyen*, 184 p., 45 fig., 48 pl., Zelitch, Péra, Istamboul (1933).

222. References in A. Philippson, *Kleinasien*, Handbuch der regionalen Geologie (1918).

223. Y. Ozawa and A. Tobler, "Permian Fusulinidae Found in Greece," Eclogae geol. Helvetiae, 22 (1929).

224. Simič, *Das Oberperm von Westserbien,* Mém. Service géol. Royaume de Yougoslavie, 1, Belgrade (1933). F. Heritsch, *Die oberpermische Fauna von Zažar und Vrzdenec in den Savefalten,* Bull. Serv. géol. Royaume de Yougoslavie, 3 (1934).

225. See the article by Gortani, cited note 67, chap. 2.

226. F. Heritsch, *Die Stratigraphie von Oberkarbon und Perm in den Karnischen Alpen,* Mitt. geol. Ges. in Vienna, 6 (1933), Vienna (1934); *Karbon und Perm in den Südalpen und in Südosteuropa,* Geol. Rundschau, 30 (1939), p. 529. The second article contains a bibliography relating to all the eastern Mediterranean as far as Asia Minor and the Caucasus.

227. G. Merla, *La fauna del calcqre a Bellerophon della regione dolomitica,* Mem. Ist. geol. R. Univ. Padova, 9 (1930).

228. For the origin of this name, see R. Masini, Boll. Soc. geol. italiana, 42 (1924).

229. R. Redini, *Contribuzione allo studio geologico del Monte Pisano,* Boll. R. Uff. geol. Italia, 60 (1935); *Sulla natura e sul significato cronologico di pseudofossili e fossili del Verrucano tipico del Monte Pisano,* Riv. ital. di Pal., Suppl. all'anno 40 (1938). F. von Hühne, *Das Alter des Verrucanos auf Grund Reptilfährten,* Eclogae geol. Helvetiae, 33, no. 2 (1940).

230. R. Teichmüller and G. Selzer, *Das Paläozoicum von Toscana und Korsika,* Beitr. z. Geol. d. westl. Mediterrangebiete, no. 7, Berlin, (1931).

231. C. de Stefani, *Fossili carboniferi dell'Isola d'Elba,* Palaeontographia italica (1917).

232. V. Novarese, *L'Autuniano in Sardegna,* Boll. Soc. geol. italiana, (1918).

233. A summary of these works, with bibliography, was given by Solignac (work cited note 242, this chap.). Later, the important works of B. Greco appeared, *La fauna permiana del Sosio,* Palaeontographia italica, 35 (1935), 37 (1937), 38 (1938).

234. R. Fabiani and L. Trevisan, *Di alcune novita geologiche nel territorio del foglio Termini Imerese (Palermo),* Boll. Soc. Sc. nat. econom. Palermo, 19 (1937). These authors note new outcrops of Permian under a facies (shales and breccias with fusulines) unknown up to the present time in Sicily. They even briefly mention limestones with large *Productus* cf. *cora,* perhaps Carboniferous.

235. J. S. Hollister, *Die Stellung der Balearen im variscischen und alpinen Orogen,* Abhandl. Ges. d. Wissenschaften zu Göttingen, Math.-Phys. Kl., III Folge, Heft 10 (1934).

236. G. Delépine, *Sur les faunes marines du Carbonifère des Asturies (Espagne),* C. R. Acad. Sc. (Sept. 3, 1928); *Sur l'extension des mers paléozoiques en Asturies (Espagne),* ibid. (Dec. 27, 1932). See also an article by the same author cited note 140, this chap. and *Les faunes marines des Asturies (Espagne),* Mém. Acad. Sc. Inst. de France, 66, p. 1–122, 6 pl. (1943).

237. See the article by M. Faura y Sans in the C. R. of the Congress of Heerlen. E. Lopez Agos, *Sintesis paleontologica del Carbonifero español,* Boll. R. Soc. española Hist. nat., 22, Madrid (1921). H. Schmidt, *Das Paläozoicum der spanischen Pyrenäen,* Abh. Ges. Wiss. Göttingen, Math.-Phys. Kl., III F., H. 5 (1931).

238. P. Pruvost, *L'âge des schistes pourprés de Papiol, près Barcelone,* Ann. Soc. géol. du Nord, 41 (1912).

239. C. Teixera, *O Antracolitico continental português,* Bull. Soc. geol. Portugal, 5, Porto (1945), 139 p., 64 fig.

240. F. Ehrmann, *Découverte de Lepidodendron et Calamites dans le Houiller de Chellata (Djurdjura oriental),* C. R. Soc. géol. France, Mar. 1 (1937).

241. G. Bétier, *Sur le faciès du Carbonifère du Djurdjura (Département d'Alger),* ibid. (Jan. 17, 1938).

242. *Le Permien marin de l'Extrême-Sud tunisien:* 1. *Considérations générales, le Djebel Tebaga,* by M. Solignac and E. Berkaloff; 2. *Les Fusulinidés de la Tunisie,* by H. Douvillé; 3. *Les Crinoïdes permiens du S de la Tunisie,* by R. P. Dom Aurélien Valette, Mém. Serv. Carte géol. Tunisie, n. s. no. 1 (1934). This work contains a valuable bibliography relating to the European and Asiatic marine Permian.

243. This small massif is found in the northern part (or region of Matmata) of the Ksours Mountains shown in the general Atlas. Do not confuse this region with the Djebel Tebaga shown in the same Atlas, between Gabès and Chott Djeridj.

244. *Sur la faune des calcaires dits à Bellérophons du Permien supérieur de l'extrême Sud Tunisien,* C. R. Soc. géol. France (1947), p. 189.

245. See the works referred to in note 70, chap. 2, and note 112, chap. 4. In addition, for everything concerning the coal of Morocco, consult the summary made by L. Clariond in *Les ressources minérales de la France d'Outre-Mer: 1. Le Charbon,* Publi. du Bureau d'études géol. et minières coloniales, Paris (1934).

246. G. Delépine, *Les niveaux à Goniatites du Carbonifère de Kenadza (confins algéro-marocains),* C. R. Soc. géol. France (Jan. 16, 1939); *Extension et caractère des faunes marines des bassins houillers de Djerada (Maroc) et de Kenadza (Sud-Oranais),* C. R. Acad. Sc. (Mar. 27, 1939); *Les Goniatites du Carbonifère du Maroc et des confins algéro-marocains du Sud (Dinantien-Westphalien),* Serv. Mines et Carte géol. Maroc. Mém. no. 56, p. 1–105, 27 fig., 8 pl. (1941).

247. G. Lecointre and G. Delépine, *Etudes géologiques dans la région paléozoïque comprise entre Rabat et Tiflet,* Notes et Mém. Serv. Mines et Carte géol. Maroc (1933).

248. This zone is also found near Ben Ahmed and Mrirt. H. and G. Termier, *Caractères paléontologiques du Strunien marocain,* C. R. Soc. géol. France (1948), p. 102.

249. A. Carpentier, *Flore viséenne de la région de Kasba ben Ahmed,* Notes et Mém. Serv. Mines et Carte géol. Maroc (1930).

250. For the name of this species, see the chart p. 164.

251. L. Clariond and F. Leca, *Etudes sur le Stéphanien du versant N de l'Atlas de Marrakech,* Bull. Soc. géol. France, 5 sér., 3 (1933).

252. P. Deleau, *Le bassin de Colomb-Béchar-Kenadza et le bassin du Guir,* Bull. Soc. géol. France, 15 (1945), p. 625, and 16 (1946), p. 3.

253. A. L. Brichant, *Observations sur les terrains paléozoïques du Maroc oriental,* C. R. Soc. géol. France (Mar. 7, 1932).

254. B. Owodenko, Ann. Soc. géol. Belgique, 70 (1947).

255. C. R. Acad. Sc., 225 (1947), p. 884.

256. And even, in the heart of the African Continent, up to the present time.

257. Fine map of the coal basins in *The Coal-Fields of the United States. General Introduction,* by M. R. Campbell, U. S. Geol. Surv., Prof. Paper no. 100 (1929). A comprehensive study: M. G. Cheney, "Classification of Mississippian and Pennsylvanian Rocks of North America," Bull. Amer. Ass. Petro. Geol. (Feb. 1945), 29, p. 125–169. Marine faunas, Schuchert, "Review of the Late Paleozoic Formations and Faunas," Bull. Geol. Soc. Amer., 39 (1928). Beede and Knicker, *Species of the Genus Schwagerina and their Stratigraphic Significance,* Univ. of Texas, Bull. no. 2433 (1924). On the parallelism with European faunas, articles by Heritch cited note 226, this chap.; G. Delépine, *Corrélations entre les divisions du Carbonifère aux Etats-Unis et dans le NW de l'Europe,* C. R. 71 Congrès Soc. sav., Lille (1928); A. E. Trueman, "Stratigraphical Problems in the Coal Measures of Europe and North America," Quart. Journ. geol. Soc., London, 102 (1946); floras: P. Bertrand, *Les flores houillères d'Amérique,* Ann. Soc. géol. du Nord, 58 (1933); W. C. Darrah, "American Carboniferous Floras," C. R. 2 Congrès Stratigraphie carbonifère, Heerlen (1935), p. 109.

258. S. Weller, "Faunal Zones in the Standard Mississippian Section," Journ. of Geol., 34 (1925). I have not yet been able to make use of the recent article, the work of numerous collaborators, "Correlation of the Mississippian Formations of North America," Bull. Geol. Soc. Amer., 59 (1948), no. 2.

259. The transition from the Central type to the Appalachian type is effected in the band of the Mississippian which extends along the east flank of the great anticlinal dome of Cincinnati. There are alternations of detrital and calcareous facies at that point.

260. From the name of a mountainous ridge on the east edge of the Anthracite Basin.

261. R. C. Moore, "Correlation of Pennsylvanian Formations of North America," Bull. Geol. Soc. Amer. (June 1944), 55, p. 657–706. C. B. Read, "Pennsylvanian Floral Zones and Provinces," ibid., 57 (1946).

262. W. C. Darrah, *Sur la présence d'équivalents des terrains stéphaniens dans l'Amérique du Nord,* Ann. Soc. géol. du Nord, 61 (1936).

263. These metamorphic influences reach their maximum in the outcrops in Massachusetts, where we see 4,000 m. of sandstones and shales, sometimes phyllitic, with thin veins of graphitic coals (and granite intrusions?). This is the true geosynclinal type.

264. C. N. Gould, "Our Present Knowledge of the Permian of the Great Plains," Journ. of Geol., 34 (1926).

265. There are even beds of potassium salts, as in Germany. See W. B. Lang, *Potash Investigations in 1924,* U. S. Geol. Survey, Bull. 785-B (1926), and *Mineralogy of Drill Cores from the potash Field of New Mexico and Texas,* Id. Bull. 833 (1932). Note moreover that, as in Germany, it is doubtless this saliferous Permian formation which constitutes the famous salt domes of the plain of the Gulf of Mexico, along which exploitations of petroleum and sulphur have been developed. See bibliography in article by M. Gignoux cited note 181, this chap. L. S. Brown, "Age of Gulf Border Salt Deposits," Bull. Amer. Ass. Petro. Geol., 18 (1934), has suggested considering this saliferous formation as Cretaceous (Danian?).

266. E. C. Case, "The Permo-Carboniferous Red-beds of North America and their Vertebrate Fauna," Carnegie Inst. Public., 207 (1915); "The Environment of Vertebrate Life in the Late Paleozoic in North America: a Paleogeographic Study," ibid., Public. 293 (1919).

267. N. H. Darton and J. B. Reeside, "Guadalupe Group," Bull. Geol. Soc. of Amer., 37 (1926).

268. A very suggestive map from the principal documents relative to the Continent of Gondwana was made by H. Gerth, *Die Korallenfauna des Perm von Timor und die permische Vereisung,* Leidsche geol. Meded., 12 (1926).

269. F. von Hühne, *Die Saurier der Karoo-, Gondwana- und verwandten Ablagerungen in faunistischer, biologischer und phylogenetischer Hinsicht,* Neues Jahrb. f. Min., Abt. B, 83 (1940), p. 246–347.

270. Name of a province occupying the middle of the northern part of the Dekkan plateaus, India.

271. Summaries of these works will be found in D. Zalessky, *Flore permienne des limites ouraliennes de l'Angaride,* analysis by P. Bertrand, Ann. Soc. géol. du Nord, 53 (1928). D. Zalessky, *Sur l'extension du continent de l'Angaride et premières données sur la flore de ses limites oussouriennes* (ibid.). D. Zalessky, *Observation sur l'extension d'une flore fossile voisine de celle du Gondwana dans la partie septentrionale de l'Eurasie,* Bull. Soc. géol. France, 5 sér., 2 (1932).

272. M. D. Zalessky and Th. Tschirkowa, *Phytostratigraphische Untersuchungen im Bereich der kohlenführenden Schichten der permischen Becken von Kusnezk und von Minussinsk in Sibirien,* Palaeontigraphica, Bd. 82, Abt. B, Lief. 5–6 (1937). B. Yavosky, *Le bassin houiller de Kouznetsk,* Excursion sibérienne, 17ᵉ Congrès géol. intern. USSR, Leningrad-Moscow (1937), p. 33–65. A. Rotay, *Stratigraphy of the Lower Carboniferous of the Kuznetsk Basin,* Trans. central geol. and prospecting Inst., fasc. 102, Moscow (1938).

273. J. Piveteau, *Un reptile dicynodonte d'Indo-Chine; les Reptiles Théromorphes et la notion de continent de Gondwana,* Ann. Soc. géol. du Nord, 62 (1937). See also a brief note by the same author in the C. R. Soc. Biogéogr. no. 142 (Feb. 16, 1940).

274. T. G. Halle, *Paleozoic Plants from Central Shansi,* Paleontologia sinica, sér. A, vol. II, Peiping (1927). See the very interesting analysis of P. Bertrand, Ann. Soc. géol. du Nord, 53 (1928).

275. Or Talcher, town situated about 400 km. south-west of Calcutta.

276. H. Holland, "The Geological Age of the Glacial Horizon at the Base of the Gondwana System," Quart. Journ. geol. Soc. of London, 89 (1933).

277. See the work by A. L. du Toit, *The Geology of South Africa,* 2nd edit., Edinburgh (1939), and the C. R. of the 15th Internat. Geol. Congress in South Africa in 1929, Pretoria (1930). For Africa in general, E. Krenkel, *Geologie Afrikas,* I (1925); II (1928); III, 1 (1933), Bornträger, Berlin.

278. Name of the upper course of a little coastal river rising in the southwest part of Karroo.

279. The English word *till* is equivalent to the French expression *agile à blocaux.* A *tillite* is then an *argilolite* or indurated clay.

280. From the pass of Ecca, northeast of Grahamstown, a town located northeast of Port Elizabeth.

281. Which, in 1940, produced 18,934,000 tons of coal.

282. From the town of Beaufort-West, in the Great Karroo.

283. Mountains located on the left bank of the upper Orange River, in southern Basutoland.

284. Zeiller formerly described, as originating in Zambezi, a Carboniferous flora comprising only European types. But, according to oral information from P. Bertrand, this origin was certainly erroneous and due to an error in labeling.

285. M. Leriche, *L'état actuel de nos connaissance sur la Paléontologie du Congo,* Ann. Soc. r. zool. Belgique, 49 (1938). Excellent summary with interesting illustrations in M. Robert, *Le Congo physique,* 3rd edit. Vaillant-Carmanne, Liége (1946).

286. P. Fourmarier, *Le système de Karroo au Congo belge,* C. R. 15th Internat. geol. Congr., Pretoria (1930). L. Cahen, A. Jamotte, J. Lepersonne and G. Mortelmans, *Etat actuel des connaissance relatives à la stratigraphie des systèmes du Kalahari et du Karroo au Congo belge,* Bull. Serv. géol. Congo belge, no. 2 (1946), fasc. 2.

287. Name of a river through which the waters of Lake Tanganyika flow to the west into the Lualaba, name given to the upper course of the Congo River.

288. We are reminded of the existence of other glacial conglomerates in the Belgian Congo, in the very oldest beds (see p. 41), formerly wrongly included with the Dwyka conglomerate.

289. Corresponding to the stage called Lubilache, of Cornet. The region of the River Sankuru-Lubilache is found about 800 km. east of Leopoldville.

290. Town on the Congo, at the equator.

291. M. Leriche, *Sur les premiers fossiles découverts, au Nord de l'Angola, dans le prolongement des couches du Lubilash et des couches du Lualaba,* C. R. Acad. Sc., 195 (1932), p. 398.

292. G. Stefanini, *Successione e età della "serie di Lugh" nella Somalia italiana,* C. R. 15th Inter. Geol. Congr., Pretoria (1930); *Saggio di una Carta geologica dell'Eritrea, della Somalia e dell'Etiopia (A.O.I.),* 2nd edit. Florence (1936).

293. A. Jamotte, *Nouvelles observations sur l'extension des formations du type des "formations du Kalahari" au Katanga,* Bull. Soc. géol. Belgique, 60, no. 3 (1936).

294. As for all the overseas French Territories, a general description will be found, with geologic map and bibliography, in *La Géologie et les Mines de la France d'Outre-Mer,* Publ. du Bur. d'études géol. et min. coloniales, Paris (1932).

295. H. Besairie, *Recherches géologiques à Madagascar,* Thèse Sc., Paris (1930). Id., *1re suite: la géologie du Nord-Ouest,* Mém. Acad. malgache, fasc. 21 (1936); *2e suite: l'extrème Sud et le Sud-Sud-Est,* Bur. géol., Tananarive (1948); *La Géologie de Madagascar en 1946,* Ann. géol. Serv. Mines, Tananarive (1946).

296. J. Piveteau, *Paléontologie de Madagascar; Amphibiens et Reptiles,* Ann. de Paléon., 15 (1926).

297. G. Astre, *La faune permienne des grès à Productus d'Ankitokaso, dans le N du Madagascar,* Ann. géol. du Serv. des Mines de Madagascar, fasc. 4, Tananarive (1934).

298. Mme. I. Vaillant-Couturier, *Sur le Permien marin de Madagascar,* C. R. Acad. Sc. (May 3, 1926).

299. C. Teichert, "Stratigraphy of Western Australia," Bull. Amer. Ass. Petrol. Geol., 31 (1947).

300. W. Jongmans and W. Gothan, *Beiträge Zur Kenntniss der Flora des Oberkarbons von Sumatra,* Verh. geol. mijnb. Nederland en Kolonien, geol. Serv., The Hague (1925).

301. W. N. Edwards, "Carboniferous Plants from the Malay States," Journ. Mal. Brahm. Roy. Asiatic Soc., 4 (1926).

302. See the very important article by B. Sahni, "The Southern Fossil Floras: a Study in the Plant Geography of the Past," Proc. of the 13th Ind. Sci. Congr. (1926).

303. C. A. Süssmilch and T. W. E. David, "Sequence, Glaciation and Correlation of

the Carboniferous Rocks of the Hunter River District," Journ. and Proc. Roy. Soc. New South Wales, 53, Sydney (1919). A. K. Miller, "A new Permian Ammonoid Fauna from Western Australia," Journ. Pal. (1936).

304. C. Teichert, "*Gangamopteris* in the Marine Permian of Western Australia," Geol. Magaz., London (Dec. 1942), 79: restoration of the leaf; the first appearances of this genus in the marine beds of the Punjab, Cashmir, and western Australia are almost contemporaneous.

305. J. C. Branner, "Outlines of the Geology of Brazil," Bull. Geol. Soc. Amer., 30 (1919). H. Gerth, *Geologie Sud-Amerikas,* I. Teil, Berlin (1932).

306. E. Fossa-Mancini, *Las transgressiones marines del Antracolitico en la America del Sur,* Rev. Mus. la Plata, Geol., 2 (1944). C. O. Dunbar and N. D. Newell, "Marine Early Permian of the Central Andes and its Fusuline Fauna," Amer. Journ. of Sc., 244 (1946).

307. Bibliographic list in J. M. Campos, *Notas bibliograficas sobre os terranos gondwanicos do Brasil,* Minist. Agric. Brasil, div. geol. min. Bol., no. 108 (1940). E. de Oliveira, *Estado actual da Paleobotanica brasileira,* Mineração e Metallurgia, no. 7 (May–June, 1937).

308. F. von Hühne, *Das unterpermische Alter aller Mesosaurier führenden Schichten,* Zentralb. f. Min., B (1940).

309. Neues Jahrb. f. Min. (1938), Beil Bd. 79, B.

310. J. D. Falconer, *La formacion de Gondwana en el Nordeste del Uruguay,* Inst. Geol. y perforaciones, Bol. no. 23, b. Montevideo (1936). R. Lambert, *Estado actual de nuestros conocimientos sobre la Geologia de la Republica oriental del Uruguay,* Inst. geol. Uruguay, Bol. no. 29, 1940, Montevideo (1941); fine photograph of block with glacial striations.

311. Nevertheless, at the time of the brief transgression of the Upper Cretaceous, shallow arms of the sea advanced to the heart of the Sahara (see p. 449).

Chapter Six

The Triassic

I. Generalities

1. *Facies and Subdivisions*

In Lorraine and central Germany the name Triassic has long denoted a series of three formations, very easy to distinguish from each other by their lithologic characteristics. They are, from bottom to top:

1st. Variegated sandstone or *Buntsandstein* (*grès bigarré*);
2nd. Shelly limestone or *Muschelkalk;*
3rd. Varicolored marl or *Keuper.*[1]

Of these three units only the middle is plainly marine and contains an abundance of littoral marine fossils. The other two are continental or lagoonal.

This type of Triassic makes up the Germanic or Vosgian facies. Its distribution corresponds roughly to the regions where the continental type of New Red Sandstones already prevailed in the Permian. All of Europe, with the exception of the Mediterranean countries (Alpine Chains) were thus occupied by an immense continental area, over which, in the Middle Triassic, the epicontinental sea of the Muschelkalk advanced.

In the Mediterranean regions—eastern Alps, Apennines, Balkans, Greece—we find, however, a geosynclinal sea in the Triassic. There the Triassic is represented by a thick series of marine deposits, often abyssal, clayey, calcareous or dolomitic with many ammonoids. This is called the Alpine facies.

Stages of the Alpine Type	Stages of the Germanic Type
Norian......................	} *Keuper*[2]
Carnian.....................	
Ladinian....................	} Muschelkalk
Virglorian or *Anisian*...........	
Werfenian or *Scythian*............	Buntsandstein

265

This Alpine facies was not studied in detail till long after the Germanic facies. Only recently has it been possible to specify its subdivisions and to synchronize them with the stages of the Germanic Triassic, for the faunas of the two facies are very different.

2. Fauna and Flora.[3]

Continental Flora.   Traces of these are found in certain zones of the Buntsandstein. Besides various genera of ferns, we see new forms develop: *Voltzia* (conifer) already present in the top of the Permian but becoming very plentiful here, and *Pleuromeia,* a curious desert plant, biologically similar to the Cacti of present deserts. In the Keuper, *Equisetaces* are sufficiently numerous in certain beds to have merited the name of sandstone with reeds. This is also the period of prosperity of the Gingkos (gymnosperms) and *Pterophyllum* (cycad).

Marine Flora.   In the Alpine Triassic, there are huge massifs of dolomitic limestones largely constructed of the remains of calcareous algae, related to *Acetabularia* (present day Mediterranean siphonates) which are commonly designated as gyroporelles or diplopores. They have small hollowed stems perforated with pores, decorated with transverse rings or a kind of hexagonal mosaic, and according to these different characteristics they are distributed in the genera *Gyroporella, Physoporella, Diplopora.*[4]

Some species of these diploporids penetrate into the area of the German Triassic and can thus be used to establish a synchronism with the Alpine Triassic.[5] So the form long known in the Muschelkalk of Lorraine as *Diplopora lotharingica* is actually a variety of *Physoporella pauciforata*, plentiful in the Alpine Virglorian. The *Diploporella annulata,* a species of the Alpine Ladinian, is very abundant in the Muschelkalk of Upper Silesia and the vicinity of Cracow. That place then must be one of the regions through which the Muschelkalk sea communicated with the Alpine sea. Finally *Gyroporella* swarms in the *Hauptdolomit* of the Alpine and Mediterranean regions (Norian).[6]

Sponges and Coelenterates.   The coral limestones are highly developed only in the Alpine Triassic, forming the famous reefs of the Dolomites of the Tyrol. From this time on there are hexacorals, very different from the Primary forms. Tetracorals have already almost entirely disappeared but the stromatoporids persist until the Cretaceous. A large number of calcareous sponges (Pharetrones) are added, a group always characteristic of the littoral facies.

Echinoderms.   Crinoids are among the most abundant fossils in the Muschelkalk. *Encrinus liliiformis* is a form characteristic of this formation. Certain horizons of crinoidal limestones furnish good stratigraphic guides, as we shall see.

In the Triassic true *Cidaris* appears, in which the origin of all the Secondary and Tertiary echinoids can be seen. Like Jurassic *Cidaris,* Triassic *Cidaris* lived especially in the neighborhood of reefs, in the Alpine region.

Brachiopods.   Beside the divers forms with Primary affinities (koninckinids, *Spiriferina, Spirigera, Athyris*) some of which (*Spiriferina*) still persist in the Lias but others (*Spirigera*) do not survive beyond the Rhaetian (extreme base of the Lias), the predominant note is the great development of rynchonellids and terebratulids, both in the Alpine facies and in the Germanic. *Terebratula* (*Coenothyris*) *vulgaris* is one of the most widespread fossils in the Muschelkalk, where *Terebratula* beds are distinguished.

Pelecypods. This fauna is very rich and varied in all the facies.

In the Germanic type, the abundance of pelecypods (*Muscheln*) has given it the name Muschelkalk. *Myophoria* (several species of which are characteristic of definite horizons), *Gervilleia, Avicula, Mytilus, Modiola, Ostrea, Lima,* and *Pecten* are the most wide-spread genera, all littoral.

In the fine grained limestones or shales of the Alpine facies, we see the development of thin-shelled forms: *Pseudomonotis, Daonella, Halobia.*

Lastly, *Megalodus* and *Dicerocardium* with thick shells and strong hinges are characteristic of the Mediterranean regions, Eastern Alps and Apennines.

Gastropods.[7] Rare in the Muschelkalk, gastropods are, however, found in abundance in certain marly facies of the Eastern Alps (beds of St. Cassian), rich in forms and remarkably beautifully preserved. They are for the most part small shelled, belonging to Secondary or Tertiary genera.

Descendants of Carboniferous families, pleurotomariids (*Worthenia*) and *Bellerophon* are found in limestones of the Alpine Triassic. *Worthenia solitaria* is a fossil characteristic of the Hauptdolomit of the Norian.

Ammonoids. The Triassic faunas which seem to have been first studied are those of the Muschelkalk. But the ammonoids of this Muschelkalk are, with rare exceptions, ceratites, characterized by their sutures whose lobes only are pinked out. So for a long time, it was believed that this ceratite type represented a genuine stage of evolution, realized in the Triassic, intermediate between the Primary goniatites and the true ammonites of the Jurassic.

But when the Alpine Triassic could be closely studied, it was seen that the Muschelkalk fauna represented an extremely trifling and very special part of the Triassic fauna. In the Alpine facies indeed, ammonoids are very abundant and varied. Very few of them have the ceratite sutures. It must then be concluded that the ceratites of the Muschelkalk represent only a lateral, aberrant regressive branch in the normal evolution of ammonites. In fact, they are extraordinarily plentiful as individuals but with little variety in species, true characteristics of aberrant branches, near extinction and confined to special environments. In fact, paleogeography will show us that the Muschelkalk sea must have remained relatively isolated from the Alpine sea. This is another example of the help that stratigraphy may give to the study of biological evolution.

Although not numerous, the ceratite species of the Muschelkalk play an important stratigraphic part in distinguishing paleontologic zones. We see the succession from bottom to top of *Ceratites antecedens, nodosus* and *semi-partitus.*

Very few ceratites are found in the Alpine Triassic. We note *C. binodosus* and *C. trinodosus,* the latter of much interest, for it characterizes a special zone at the top of the Virglorian. Some specimens have been found in the Germanic Muschelkalk which permit the establishment of a synchronism between the two types of Triassic.

Outside of ceratites, the only genus of ammonoids represented in the Germanic Triassic (except Upper Silesia, see p. 271) is *Beneckeia,* of which one species (*B. tenuis*) characterizes the top of the Buntsandstein and the other (*B. buchi*) the base of the Muschelkalk.

The ammonoids of the Alpine Triassic are extremely numerous and varied and they serve to characterize the successive stages.[8] We shall mention only the *Trachyceras* of the Upper Triassic, the *Arcestes* appearing in the Middle Triassic and the *Pinacoceras* beginning in the Middle Triassic but especially plentiful in the Norian, where it is represented by very large forms with very complicated sutures, truly the end of the series. All these branches are extinct however at the end of the Triassic. The only exception is the group of *Monophyllites,* considered to be the source of the Jurassic ammonoids.

These ammonoids of the Alpine facies are most frequently found in fine grained, muddy limestones of gray, white, or red color. This is the normal facies of cephalopod limestones.

Crustaceans. In the lagoonal facies of the Germanic Triassic (Buntsandstein and Keuper) there is an extraordinary abundance of *Estheria,* minute shells of phyllopod crustaceans, playing the part in lagoons and salt lakes of that epoch which is now played by *Artemia salina* in the salt lakes of the Russian and Asiatic steppes.

Vertebrates. Among the fish, we must mention especially the genus *Ceratodus* (a dipnoid) whose teeth, very frequently found in the lagoons of the Lettenkohle (upper Muschelkalk), are almost identical to those of present species living in similar biological environments (see p. 113).

The batrachians (stegocephalians) and reptiles (dinosaurs, theromorphs) are relatively frequent in the continental facies. We already know that in certain regions these great vertebrates were sufficiently abundant and characteristic to have been used to define paleontologic zones (ex., South Africa, p. 241, China, p. 305). The impressions of their footprints, named *Cheirotherium,* are frequent everywhere in the Buntsandstein and have sometimes been used in stratigraphy (see note 229, Chap. 5).

II. The Germanic Triassic Facies

1. *Type of This Facies: Central Germany*

In all the huge zone that stretches from the Rhenish Schiefergebirge to the Black Forest on the west and the Bohemian Massif on the east, the sunken Hercynian Chain disappears under a covering of Secondary formations in which the Triassic occupies a large place. Hanover and Thuringia are to the north, Franconia and Swabia to the south. There is found the type of the Germanic Triassic (see map, Fig. 28).

Naturally the boundaries of the Triassic outcrops are simply the boundaries of erosion and do not correspond to the limits of sedimentation. At certain periods nevertheless, in the Middle and especially the Upper Triassic, sediments covered almost the whole of the Hercynian massifs which encircle the central German Basin.[9]

A. Lower Triassic: Buntsandstein. This consists, in general, of continental or lagoonal sediments: conglomerates, sandstones or shales, generally red or violet. Very rare fossil beds contain faunas which we shall discuss later.

1. The lower part of the Buntsandstein is quite varied, but in general made up of rather soft, fine grained rocks with banks of clay or clay pebbles. In southern Germany they are called *Tigersandstein* (spotted sandstones) for they show dark spots on a light background. This lower Buntsandstein is, however, limited in extent. It is deposited in the bottom of a continental basin which, while broad between the Rhenish and Bohemian Massifs, comes to a point toward the southwest, on the north side of the Black Forest, before reaching the Vosges.

2. Next comes the *Hauptbuntsandstein* or principal variegated sandstone, 200 to 300 m. thick but sometimes reaching 600 m. It is characterized by its coarser grain, more compact texture and the appearance of conglomerate beds.

3. Finally, at the top, marine influences are felt and fossils appear in great numbers: *Myophoria* (*M. tenuis*), *Hörnesia, Lingula,* and even *Beneckeia tenuis.* This presages the Muschelkalk sea but at certain places there are still lagoons where gypsum and dolomite are deposited. These lagoonal-marine beds of the upper Buntsandstein are called Röth (20 to 150 m. thick).

B. Middle Triassic: Muschelkalk. This may be 200 to 400 m. thick. Four principal subdivisions are distinguished in it, which are, from bottom to top:

1. The *Wellenkalk* or corrugated limestone (70 to 80 m. thick), so named because the altenating calcareous and marly beds are separated by wavy surfaces.[10] The clearly marine, although not deep-water, regime is proven by the fauna, which already contains the characteristic elements of the Muschelkalk: brachiopods (*Spiriferina, Terebratula vulgaris*), pelecypods (*Myophoria, Lima, Hörnesia socialis*) and crinoids (*Encrinus*). As for ammonites, there are scarcely any except *Beneckeia buchi.*

The Wellenkalk facies are varied, however, as the map (Fig. 56) shows. In particular, the approach of old shores is shown by the appearance of a sandy facies (Muschelsandstein) which we shall find again in describing the Triassic of Alsace and Lorraine.

2. The *Anhydritgruppe,* or the anhydrite group (30 to 100 m.). These beds are principally marly or dolomitic with gypsum, anhydrite or rock salt, indicating a temporary return to the lagoonal regime. Fossils become very rare and do not differ from those of the Wellenkalk.

3. The *Hauptmuschelkalk* or Muschelkalk proper (40 to 120 m.).[11] There the marine facies are most obvious and fossils most abundant. The base is made up especially of accumulations of crinoidal remains; *Encrinus liliiformis*

must have constituted veritable submarine prairies. These crinoidal lime-stones (Trochitenkalk) are extensively quarried as ashlar or building stones. At the top, on the other hand, are sandier and deeper facies: ceratite lime-stones in which relatively thin limestone beds alternate with marly beds. At the surface of the limestone banks pelecypods are found by the thousands, the "Muscheln" from which the stage is named: *Myophoria vulgaris, Hörnesia socialis, Pecten discites,* etc. Ceratites are very plentiful and are used to distinguish a lower zone with *C. nodusus,* and an upper zone with *C. semi-partitus.*[12] At the base or in the middle of this latter zone kneaded layers of large *Terebratula (Coenothyris) vulgaris,* known as Terebratelbänke, often develop.

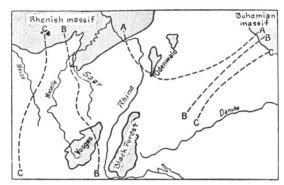

FIG. 56. *Diagrammatic map of the facies of the Wellenkalk (lower Muschel-kalk) in the southern part of the Germanic Basin (after Brinkmann, simpli-fied).*

Stippled: Hercynian massifs.
AA =   Southern limit of the typical Wellenkalk facies (relatively deep-water limestones).
Between AA and BB, more coastal dolomitic facies.
Between BB and CC, littoral sandy facies (*Muschelsandstein*).
CC =   Shores of the Wellenkalk sea (hypothetical).

4. The *Lettenkohle* (literally, coal of clays) (10 to 50 m.).[13] This is the end of the Muschelkalk sea and we see an alternation of marine beds con-taining Muschelkalk fossils and lagoonal or subcontinental beds containing plant remains and even beds of coal, unexploitable, however. At the top, dolomitic layers (Grenzdolomit: boundary dolomite) contain a characteristic species, *Myophoria goldfussi.*

C. Upper Triassic: Keuper.[14]   This term is used here in the limited sense given it by French geologists; so it corresponds only to the middle Keuper (or Gypskeuper) of the German geologists, for whom the Lettenkohle con-stitutes the lower Keuper and the Rhaetian becomes their upper Keuper.

In the French meaning the Keuper is essentially a lagoonal, saliferous for-mation. In a thickness totalling 450 m., there are many-colored marls, green or red, often very hard (Steinmergel), *carneugles* or porous dolomitic lime-

stones (Zellendolomite),[15] beds of gypsum and anhydrite, and finally sandstone banks sometimes rich in plant impressions (Schilfsandstein: reed
sandstones, for the equisetales, which play a biologic role similar to that of
present day reeds, are very abundant in it). Thürach has shown that these
sandstones were deposited by streams of water which excavated their beds
in the gypsiferous marls. These plants indicate oases or rather forest-strips
bordering these rivers. Other coarser, white sandstones known as Stu-
bensandstein[16] have yielded especially reptilian remains.

Near the base, a marine intercalation contains, at certain points, *Myo-
phoria kefersteini,* which is found in the Raible beds (lower Carnian) of the
Eastern Alps, important evidence for the synchronism of the two types,
Alpine and Germanic.

2. *Variations of the Germanic Type Toward the East: Upper Silesia and Poland*

On the other, eastern side of the Bohemian Massif, that is in Upper Silesia
and Poland (see Fig. 59), we find the Germanic Triassic with interesting
modifications.

First the Muschelkalk offers there a mixture of Alpine forms and Germanic forms. In the Wellenkalk appear brachiopods, diploplores, ammonites
(*Ceratites trinodosus, C. antecedens, Ptychites*) characteristic of the Virglorian of the Eastern Alps. This fact is very important, first because it shows
that this Wellenkalk, here highly developed, is equivalent to the Virglorian,[17]
and next because it proves that in Upper Silesia the Muschelkalk sea in all
probability communicated with the Alpine sea.

Finally the Keuper here has lost in part its lagoonal character. There are,
instead, fresh-water limestones with paludines and unios. Thus, from the
Keuper, the communications with the Alpine sea were partially broken. In
place of gradually discharging into the Alpine sea, the Germanic Muschelkalk sea then in some way dried up in place, which explains the importance
of the saline deposits in the typical Germanic Keuper.

3. *Western Europe: the Northern and Western Shores of the Muschelkalk Sea*

For the Triassic stratigraphy of the European continental area, the extent
of the Muschelkalk sea is of fundamental importance, for it is this sea that
helps us make divisions in the Triassic. Where the Triassic has only continental or lagoonal facies, it becomes very difficult to make any stratigraphic subdivision having general value.

Neither the Russian Platform nor the Baltic Shield was covered by this
sea. We find its last traces extending, by way of the Berlin subsurface, toward
the north of the island of Helgoland.

Toward the northwest, deep wells at Bentheim and in the western part
of the Low Countries have shown an already modified Muschelkalk, whose
limestone facies are partially replaced by sandstone, dolomites, and red gypsif-

erous marls. The thickness, still 142 m. at Bentheim, is very rapidly reduced toward the west. The shore then should be found a little west of the frontier of the Netherlands.[18]

A. Britain. The Triassic in Britain occupies very broad surfaces, especially in the central part. In the Liverpool-Bristol-Nottingham triangle, it fills the gap existing between the Primary massif of Wales and the southern extremity of the Pennine Chain (see map, Fig. 76).

But there are no marine fossils and no trace of the Muschelkalk sea, so a rigorous stratigraphy is impossible.[19] The lower part, in general more or less conglomeratic, is assigned to the Buntsandstein (Bunter of British authors). Joined to the Permian, it formed the New Red Sandstone of early geologists. The upper part, where red marls predominate, corresponds to the

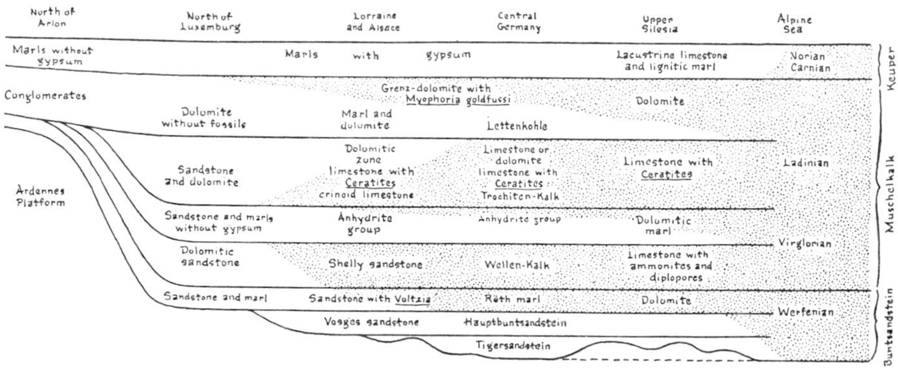

North of Arlon	North of Luxemburg	Lorraine and Alsace	Central Germany	Upper Silesia	Alpine Sea	
Marls without gypsum	Marls	with	gypsum	Lacustrine limestone and lignitic marl	Norian Carnian	Keuper
Conglomerates	Dolomite without fossils	Grenz-dolomite with Myophoria goldfussi		Dolomite		
		Marl and dolomite	Lettenkohle			
	Sandstone and dolomite	Dolomitic zone limestone with Ceratites crinoid limestone	Limestone or dolomite limestone with Ceratites Trochiten-Kalk	Limestone with Ceratites	Ladinian	Muschelkalk
Ardennes Platform	Sandstone and marls without gypsum	Anhydrite group	Anhydrite group	Dolomitic marl		
					Virglorian	
	Dolomitic sandstone	Shelly sandstone	Wellen-Kalk	Limestone with ammonites and diplopores		
	Sandstone and marl	Sandstone with Voltzia	Röth marl	Dolomite		Buntsandstein
					Werfenian	
		Vosges sandstone	Hauptbuntsandstein			
			Tigersandstein			

FIG. 57. *Facies of the Germanic Triassic between the gateway of Upper Silesia and the ancient shores of the Ardennes, showing the advance of the Muschelkalk sea and the progressive reduction toward the west of the marine facies (in gray).*

N. B.   No account is taken of the thickness of the beds, only of their correlations.

Keuper. In addition to the usual salts of this stage, exploited deposits of strontium sulphate in the region of Bristol may be noted.

British geologists seem to agree in seeing desert formations in their Triassic. The sandstones are often composed of aeolian sands and, north of Leicester (Mount Sorel), the classic works point out that a little granite ridge on which lie Triassic sandstones has been grooved by wind-blown sands.[20] The Keuper lagoons are compared by Richardson to the Great Salt Lake of Utah.

B. The Ancient Shores of the Ardennes. Like Britain, the Armorican Massif remained distant from the touch of the Muschelkalk sea. Only insignificant remnants of red sandstones and marls are known there, in the Cotentin, difficult to separate from the Permian.

In fact, the shores of the Muschelkalk sea are found in the eastern region of the Ardennes Massif, especially on the northwest border of the Triassic Gulf of Luxemburg. Van Werveke[21] has meticulously studied the way in which the Muschelkalk ends. First the Wellenkalk, in the region of the Saar, is transformed into dolomitic sandstones (Muschelsandstein). Then, north of Luxemburg, this facies of dolomitic sandstone also invades the upper Muschelkalk just when the Lettenkohle ceases to contain marine fossils. Finally, farther west, north of Arlon, we see, lying on the ancient rocks of the Eifel, only thin deposits of red sandstones, conglomerates, and marls. Every trace of marine influence has ceased (see Fig. 57).

Blanckenhorn has studied similar conditions toward the northern outlet of the Gulf of Luxemburg, on the northern border of the Eifel.

Thus, excepting the Ardennes, it seems that the whole Rhenish Massif may have been invaded by the sea. The expression, Triassic Gulf of Luxemburg, applies then only to the present distribution of outcrops. The western border alone of this gulf marks approximately the ancient shores of the Muschelkalk sea.

We shall see that the Black Forest and the Vosges likewise were covered by the Triassic sea.

C. Vosges and Lorraine. There the Trias forms a broad girdle around the Hercynian Massif of the Vosges. In northern Alsace it reaches a thickness of 650 m. These are the most extensive Triassic outcrops in all of France and deserve a special description.[22]

1. The Buntsandstein, completely siliceous and very permeable, produces here a region of wooded plateaus (pines and firs), unfit for cultivation, where beds of harder conglomerates stand out in steep ridges or isolated rocks. These are the sandy Vosges.

a. The lower part of the stage, or Vosgian sandstone of the French geologists (so named because in general it is the only portion in the high parts of the Vosges, on the Hercynian core, spared by erosion) is rather coarse and conglomeratic. It is customary to end this lower part with an especially thick and compact layer of conglomerate, called principal conglomerate (Hauptconglomerat). Most of the precipitous rocks (example, Ste. Odile), at the top of which rise the old Vosges chateaus, are composed of this conglomerate. But, in the absence of any fossil, there is nothing to prove that these subdivisions have a real chronological value.

Thus defined, this Vosgian sandstone diminishes in thickness progressively from north to south between Niederbronn and the region of Hohneck. A similar reduction is observed in the zone where the Triassic of Lorraine is covered by the Jurassic. The Vosgian sandstone, still 300 m. thick in the wells of Nancy, is no more than 15 m. thick east of Neufchâteau (Corroy). And in fact its materials seem to derive from a massif, hidden today, which must have risen in the midst of Triassic deserts northwest of the Vosges containing outcrops of Taunusian quartzites and Gothlandian radiolarites, rocks which are found in pebbles in the conglomerates of the Vosgian sandstone.[23]

b. The upper part of the Buntsandstein, or Buntsandstein proper, is also called the *Voltzia* sandstone because of the abundance of plant remains which have been collected in old quarries. Here, in fact, the grain is finer and more regular, and some thin, clayey beds delimit banks easy to break up, so this rock was formerly much used for building. Many monuments of Alsace are built of it, in particular the Strasbourg Cathedral.

The facies are no longer clearly marine as in the Röth of central Germany, for we are farther from the sphere of influence of the Germanic seas of the Middle Triassic.

However, our knowledge of the faunas and floras of the Buntsandstein of Alsace has been enriched by the magnificent discoveries of L. Grauvogel, which have so far only been the subject of brief preliminary notes.[24] Many plants have been found with their fruits, stamens, and seeds. Except coelenterates, sponges, echinoderms and cephalopods, which could not live in this lagoonal medium, all the groups of animals are represented by thousands of specimens: worms, brachiopods (*Lingula*), pelecypods (*Anoplophora, Myophoria, Pecten*), limulids, arachnids, scorpions, crustaceans, and especially insects, among them a libellulid insect of 30 cm. spread, dipneust fish and ganoids, and an almost complete skeleton of a sauropterygian.

This whole series of *Voltzia* sandstones is in fact lagoonal-lacustrine. The fossiliferous beds were deposited in small streams of water which must have wandered through the swampy plains, fed thenceforth by continental fresh water at the time of rare rains and, during long periods of dryness, by the contributions of brackish lagoons, a country comparable to that of the present coastal plains of Tunis. Finally the lakes or lagoons spread everywhere depositing the boundary clays (Grenzletten) with which the Lower Triassic ends.

2. The first truly marine fossils, in fact, appear only in the dolomitic beds with which the lower Muschelkalk or Wellenkalk begins. Here this sub-stage is represented by dolomitic or often sandy (Muschelsandstein) facies, especially in Lorraine (Ruaux sandstone, 15 m.), showing the proximity of shores. But, formerly connected with the Buntsandstein because of their lithologic facies, these sandstones already contain the classic fauna of the Muschelkalk.

The anhydrite group resembles the one in central Germany; in Lorraine, it is the horizon called Pexonne clays, about 40 m. thick. It even contains rock salt at Sarralbe and near Baccarat (a well mentioned by Corroy).

Finally, the Muschelkalk proper also shows the same succession of beds as in Germany.[25] Nevertheless we note that the top is represented by dolomites without fossils in which the boundary of the Keuper is indefinite; this is the dolomitic region. In Lorraine, a Lettenkohle called Emberménil horizon begins with lignite beds, and then continues with dolomitic limestone with a clearly marine fauna, with *Bactryllium*[26] and even, at the top, *Ceratites semipartitus*[27] accompanied by *Myophoria goldfussi*.

In the field, this Middle Triassic is clearly distinguished from the Buntsandstein. Extensive farming has succeeded the forests and we have an undulating country with broad horizons in which great white gashes appear in the distance caused by quarries for cement, lime rock, or ashlar.

3. The *Keuper*[28] is also of the true Germanic type. It contains rock salt exploited in Lorraine (Dieuze, Château-Salins, vicinity of Varangéville) in

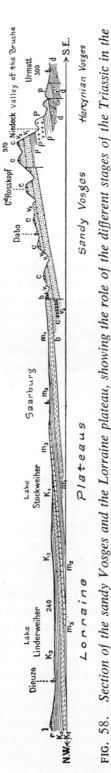

FIG. 58. *Section of the sandy Vosges and the Lorraine plateau, showing the role of the different stages of the Triassic in the topography.*

1 = lower Lias; r = Rhaetian; k_2 = Marls of the upper Keuper; k_1 = Marls of the lower Keuper; m_3 = upper Muschelkalk; m_2 = middle Muschelkalk: marls with anhydrite; m_1 = lower Muschelkalk: shelly sandstone; b = Buntsandstein; c = principal conglomerate; v_2 = upper Vosgian sandstone; v_1 = lower Vosgian sandstone; p = Permian (with porphyry P); d = Devonian.

Vertical scale: 1/74,000   Horizontal scale: 1/370,000 the middle Keuper, crowned by beds with *Equisetites arenaceus* (with carbonaceous beds) which are equivalent to the Schilfsandstein and are also found in Alsace. Finally, the upper Keuper is composed of compact dolomite still containing, in Lorraine, *Bactryllium* and *Myophoria goldfussi*.

On the whole, this Keuper, in which impermeable marls predominate, crops out over huge surfaces in Lorraine and presents a flat countryside dotted with ponds.

D. The Jura and Massif Central. The small Hercynian Massif of La Serre, near Dôle, an isolated ridge between the Vosges and the Massif Central, shows us another belt of marine Muschelkalk. It is the Vosgian type.

But the Triassic is very reduced on all the eastern border of the Massif Central. Some dolomitic beds with *Myophoria goldfussi* (Lettenkohle species) represent here only traces of the Germanic Sea. Fossils are no longer found except in Morvan, the Lyonnaise Mont-d'Or and at Crussol, near Valence.[29] On the other hand, in the French Jura, only the Keuper crops out in the axis of some anticlines (rock salt of Salins and Lons-le-Saunier). We may ask then if the Muschelkalk sea has not terminated there in a point.

But recent wells have shown that the marine Muschelkalk existed at depth under the southern Jura. It was first noted, in the form of crinoidal limestones, in the well at Torcieu (southeast of Ambérieu-en-Bugey).[30] Then wells at Grozon (7 km. north of Poligny) at Baume-les-Messieurs and at Revigny (6 km. southeast of Lons-le-Saunier) have passed through 100 m. of it.[31] Farther south we do not find true marine Muschelkalk either in the border of the Massif Central or around the crystalline massif of Belledonne (vicinity of Grenoble) but, near the plains of the Rhône, at Propiac (Fig. 59) north of Ventoux, are outcrops of limestone with marine fossils having exactly the type of the Provencal Muschelkalk (C. R. Soc. géol. France, 1923, p. 171). So an arm of the Muschelkalk sea must certainly have passed under the Jura and probably under the plains of the Rhône to spread out over Languedoc and Provence.

E. Provence, Languedoc, Pyrenees. In fact, in Languedoc, on the southeast edge of the Massif Central (vicinity of Lodève and Alès), in Lower Provence and the eastern Pyrenees, we find a Triassic completely similar to that of Germany, with its three subdivisions.

In Provence, the sandstones of the Lower Triassic are comparatively poorly developed. They are overlain by an horizon of gypsum and *carneugles,* recognized by E. Haug in the Toulon region, equivalent to the anhydrite group. The Muschelkalk proper is very thick, with its Germanic fauna of brachiopods and ceratites, having come through the arm of the sea of the Jura. But it is the saliferous Keuper which plays the great part in outcrops, for following the caprices of the salt tectonics, it is introduced into the zones of dislocation, at the contact of the most diverse formations.

In the western Pyrenees and Cantabrian Mountains, the Muschelkalk is greatly reduced and appears only sporadically. P. Lamare[32] recently called attention to a *Pseudomonotis* in it, an Alpine Virglorian form. This is the last evidence toward the northwest of the Alpine influences that we shall see farther south, in Spain. But very often this Triassic of the western Pyrenees is reduced to red sandstones and conglomerates, impossible to distinguish from the Permian (Permo-Trias of Pyrenean geologists), and to gypsiferous marls.[33] Thus this Triassic of the western Pyrenees greatly resembles that of Britain. We have in fact reached the region of the North Atlantic Continent which escaped marine influences.

F. Spain. In all of Spain, the Triassic retains the Germanic facies, with a frequently fossiliferous Muschelkalk. The Iberian Meseta (see Fig. 104) thus was part of the great European continental area.

But into this basin southwest of the Muschelkalk sea, some representatives of the Alpine faunas were able to penetrate. There are pelecypods (*Daonella* and *Megalodus*) in the Balearic Islands and in southern Spain, and even ammonites in Sardinia, Majorca, Minorca and the Catalonian Chains (Mora de Ebro). A region of communication between the two domains[34] must have existed there.

These Alpine influences are especially marked in the Tertiary chains which encircle the Iberian Meseta on the east and south, particularly in the sub-Betic domain (see Fig. 104), where the Triassic crops out very widely. There, a very thick saliferous complex, with multi-colored marls, *carneugles* and gypsum, formerly attributed to the Keuper, was in reality intercalated between the red sandstone of the Lower Triassic and a thick Muschelkalk, beginning here as in many other western Mediterranean regions (P. Fallot), with the very characteristic horizon of vermicular limestone, first described in the Briançonnais (p. 285). The lagoonal Keuper, however, shows only a very reduced development, as in the Briançonnais.

It is interesting to note that this rather special type of the Triassic, which we may call the Briançonnais type, is found here, as in the internal zones of the French Alps, in a domain intermediate between that of the Germanic Triassic and that of the true Alpine Triassic of the eastern Mesogean seas.

G. North Africa. The Triassic is here again the Germanic type, but the marine Muschelkalk shows very few fossiliferous localities. That of Djebel Chettaba, near Constantine (*Myophoria vulgaris, Hörnesia socialis*) allowed Marcel Bertrand to prove for the first time the presence of the Triassic in North Africa. Another, near Souk-Arras (department of Constantine) recently provided J. Flandrin[35] with numerous *Myophoria vulgaris*. A. Lambert has noted a Muschelkalk with pelecypods in Kabylie des Babors. Finally, J. Marçais[36] collected in the eastern Rif, northwest of Taza (Morocco), a little faunule (*Myophoriopsis keuperina, Macrodon* sp., gastropods) indicating perhaps a brackish Keuper.

The stratigraphy however is greatly obscured by the anomalies due to the salt tectonics. Thus, in the neighborhood of the ancient massifs of the littoral zone (Great and Little Kabylie, see Fig. 106), that is to say, where we should expect to see a complete Triassic, the most mobile formations, essentially the saliferous Keuper, have often been forced out by flow which could support the theory of a stratigraphic lacuna of the Keuper. But we find these saliferous complexes in the state of huge, chaotic accumulations injected into the Secondary and Tertiary covering south of these massifs, in the Tell zone.[37] And at the edge of the Sahara even mountains of salt[38] rise, showing in plain view structures similar to those which in the salt domes of Hanover and Texas are hidden beneath the plains.

4. *Summary and Conclusions: The Desert Facies; the Individuality of the Muschelkalk Sea*

In summary, all the domain of the Germanic facies, that is to say all the European continental area, shows a Triassic with a relatively uniform type of sediments. If we except the episode constituted by the Muschelkalk sea, to which we shall return, we may say that the variegated sandstones and the multicolored marls, over the vast space encompassed between Spain, Britain and Bohemia, remain everywhere recognizable at a glance. This similarity is evidently due to identical geographical conditions. This was a natural region whose dimensions are not abnormal if compared with those of certain present natural regions, for example, the great desert belt (already suggested apropos of the Permian) which extends from the coast of western Africa to the plains of Mesopotamia.

And this comparison expresses exactly the idea which most geologists now have of Triassic Europe.[39]

For the varicolored marls, with their dry lakes, this is evident: in the Keuper near Stuttgart a whole tribe of small crocodiles (*Aetosaurus*) has been found which must have been buried alive by a sand storm. For the Buntsandstein, it is, at first, less evident: the great bulk of these sandstones, the rare intercalations of marine shell beds, lead to the hypothesis of a marine transgression. But the aeolian influences are manifest: in Thuringia the Buntsandstein contains faceted pebbles, sculptured by the wind; it also contains pellicles of dried, cracked clay, rolled into coils, then enveloped unchanged in the sand, proving that this sand was carried dry, that is to say, by the wind. The marine shells are explained by lagoons, similar to the African chotts or to the salt lakes with *Artemia salina* of the Russian or Asiatic steppes (see p. 268). The flora also shows examples of desert adaptation (see p. 266). Finally the enormous development of coarse, detrital formations, sandstone and conglomerate, is exactly a characteristic of desert regions where the size of inundations compensates for their rare occurrence, and where alluvium accumulates indefinitely in spreading grounds, lacking rivers to carry it to the sea. Finally the predominant red colors of the Triassic are today considered by many geologists as often related to desert facies or sub-tropical climates with alternating long periods of great droughts and great rains.[40]

So Europe, in the Triassic as in the Permian, was a vast desert strewn with lakes. The coarse sediments (Vosgian sandstone) of the beginning of the period give evidence of a still vigorous relief, but the cycle of desert erosion leveled the relief little by little while filling the depressions with a cloak of torrential and aeolian formations. And at the end of the period, the finer deposits of multi-colored marls suggest a flat country where temporary lagoons extended as far as the eye could reach.

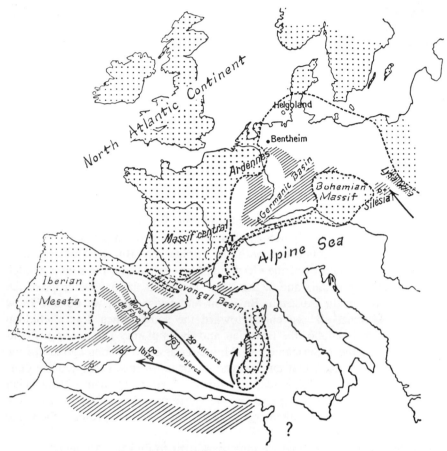

FIG. 59. *Map of the Muschelkalk sea in western Europe (after maps of E. Tornquist and P. Fallot, greatly modified).*

Stippled: the great regions where the Triassic is entirely continental.
Ruled: the principal regions of outcrops of the Germanic Triassic, with marine Muschelkalk.
P = Propiac and T = Torcieu, last beds of Muschelkalk marking the transition from the Germanic Basin to the Provençal Basin.
+ = Cephalopods and o = pelecypods migratory from the Alpine sea into the Muschelkalk sea; arrows indicate the direction of the migrations.

N. B.   The Alpine sea probably communicated with the Provençal Basin over the location of the Maritime Alps, for the Triassic of this region is not the reduced or continental type. The Muschelkalk extends into the Basque Pyrenees.

Into the middle of this desert the Muschelkalk sea advanced. Its animal population had very special characteristics. It was a fauna rich in individuals but poor in species and with little variety: echinoids, corals, sponges almost entirely lacking, and cephalopods and brachiopods reduced to a very few species. In brief, we may qualify it as an impoverished and selected alpine fauna, as, for example, the Caspian and Baltic faunas are today in comparison to the sea faunas of the Mediterranean and North Seas. That can be explained, of course, only by special living conditions and especially by a relative isolation (see Fig. 59).

In fact, we have seen that the Muschelkalk sea was closed toward the north and east by the Russian platform and the mass of the old Baltic and Scandinavian continent. Toward the west, the southern border of the Ardennes shows unquestionable shore facies. Then, through the Vosges, the sea advanced into Lorraine as far as the Paris Basin and there we do not know its western shores, but we do know that it did not reach Brittany or England or even to the northwest of Paris, the Pays de Bray, where a deep well [41] traversed only 22 m. of Permo-Triassic red marls without marine Muschelkalk. Farther south, it died out on the eastern border of the Massif Central which it followed, to spread out in Provence, Languedoc, the western Pyrenees and the Spanish region.

Toward the south, we have less information. We know that the Muschelkalk sea did not invade Bohemia, that it circled around by the north[42] to make, in Silesia, its connection with the Alpine sea. But west of Bohemia, between the last outcrops of the Germanic Muschelkalk on the southern edge of Swabia and Franconia and in the Basel Jura, and the first outcrops of the Alpine Triassic in the Austrian, Bavarian and Swiss Alps, we do not know where the Muschelkalk sea ended toward the south, since it is all hidden under recent sediments of the Bavarian and Swiss plains. The enormous contrasts shown by these Germanic and Alpine Triassic types long ago led to the conclusion, by Gümbel, that an emerged chain must have separated the Germanic sea from the Alpine sea, to which he gave the name Vindelician Chain.[43] And we find direct proof, in the western Alps (see p. 281), of the existence of this hypothetical emerged barrier for which we preserve the name originated by Gümbel.

It is this emerged zone that we must pass over to find the Alpine sea.

III. The Alpine Triassic

1. *The French Alps*[44]

The Triassic plays a very important role here, for even in regions where the stratigraphy is difficult, it is always easy to recognize and so provides a valuable point of reference to the Alpine geologists.

We have already seen (p. 205) that a certain number of tectonic zones can be distinguished in our [French] Alps, ranging parallel to the axis of the chain. This concept has an equally great stratigraphic importance, for each of these zones is more or less characterized by special facies of the formations of which it is composed. They began to be individualized well before the great Alpine folding of the Tertiary. We shall see evidence of them in the paleogeography of the Jurassic and the Cretaceous, in a succession of troughs and cordilleras corresponding to as many zones of facies.

Nevertheless, in the Triassic, these precursory folds had not yet begun; the region which will later become the French Alps is still only the edge of the

European continental area. In the west (external Alpine zones), the Triassic still shows the Germanic type. Moving eastward we enter into the domain of the Mesogean seas so that the Briançonnais and Piedmont types of the Triassic show thick massifs of diplopore limestone, marine but still littoral. The true Alpine Triassic with its deep-water ammonite facies, appears only in the eastern Alps (Tyrol and Trentino).

It must be noted that here as everywhere the stratigraphy of the Triassic was often distorted by anomalies due to the salt tectonics. The salt complexes, plastic and mobile masses, were usually expelled from their original stratigraphic positions and injected into their Jurassic or even Cretaceous cover.

A. External Alpine Zones. We shall distinguish from north to south, two sections.

a. *From Mont Blanc to Pelvoux.* The Triassic naturally appears everywhere in the borders of the old massifs (Mont Blanc, Aiguilles-Rouges, Belledonne, Grand Châtelard, Grandes-Rousses, Pelvoux). It is usually rather thin (some tens of meters or even just a few meters), so it is often said that it is a reduced Germanic type. At the base, sandstone, from zero to a few meters thick, represents the Lower Triassic; siliceous or dolomitic limestone, light gray in a fresh break but with a more or less deep yellow patina (*capucin* dolomites, light yellow dolomites) can be compared to the Muschelkalk and finally a few meters of *cargneules* and multi-colored shales, usually without gypsum, correspond to the Keuper.[45]

But turning away a bit from the crystalline massifs, we find, in the overlying Lias, chaotic masses of gypsum and anhydrite several hundred meters thick, or else, very long, thin streaks of *cargneules,* the only evidence of the dissipation of these sulphate rocks. It may be supposed then that a thick saliferous Keuper originally existed everywhere, but that it was expelled from the "tegument" (P. Lory) adhering to the crystalline massifs, to be injected at a distance into the Liassic cover, for it would be absurd to imagine any relation whatever between the present limits (due to erosion) of these massifs and the distribution of the saliferous sediments in the Triassic paleogeography.[46]

So, the Triassic of the external Alpine zones is indeed reduced here, in the sense that the Buntsandstein and the Muschelkalk are rudimentary. We recognize there the Vindelician threshold that must have separated the Alpine sea from the arm of the sea uniting the Jura to Provence. But this reduction does not apply to the Keuper, which, expelled from the "tegument" of the old massifs, is found in great thickness in their Jurassic cover. The only fossils found in this domain are impressions of stems of *Equisetites* discovered in the midst of the gypsum of Mont-Charvin (south of Saint-Jean-de-Maurienne)[47] in sandstone recalling the reedy sandstone of the Germanic Keuper.

b. *South of Pelvoux.* The Triassic is again the normal Germanic type which we have already seen developed in Provence. Along the south edge of Pelvoux the capucin dolomites become thicker and assume a clearly marine facies. They contain, at Champoléon, in the high valley of the Drac,[48] myophores and especially diplopores,[49] and, at Dourmillouse,[50] some carditids. South of Remollon, the Muschelkalk limestones are already very thick and typical and around the little coaly ridge of Barles, the Buntsandstein develops to an extent unknown elsewhere in the Alps and even in Provence, so there we have a Triassic country curiously reminiscent of the Vosges.

Finally the Triassic of the Maritime Alps is the direct continuation of that which we have described in Provence. There we see, as around Toulon, a gypseous horizon (equivalent to the anhydrite group) at the base of the Muschelkalk,[51] a horizon that we shall find again, more highly developed, in the Briançonnais. At the boundary between the Alps and Provence, in the vicinity of Grasse, the Keuper contains, as I myself had demonstrated and as J. Gogel, then L. Guillaume and J. Ricour (C. R. Soc. géol. France, 1947, p. 35) have pointed out, thick beds of compact dolomite, which, confused with the classic Hettangian dolomite of Provence, have been the basis for erroneous tectonic conceptions (the lower Provençal duplications indicated on the sheet Nice 1/80,000, 2nd edit.).

On the other hand, the phenomena of diapirism due to the salt tectonics often cause the appearance of enormous masses of gypsum, *cargneules* and variegated marls[52] as far as the very heart of the Cenomanian (region of Puget-Theniers) which led to the belief in a Cenomanian with gypseous facies (1st edit. of the Nice sheet), while in the valleys of the Rhône and Durance (Gigondas Massif north of Ventoux and region of Laragne north of Sisteron), ridges of gypsum in the *terres-noires* of the Oxfordian were interpreted as debris from a thrust nappe (Suzette nappe).

Thus, in these southern Alps, the Vindelician zone is no longer found, with its rudimentary Muschelkalk. The Provençal Muschelkalk sea there must have communicated broadly with the Alpine sea.

B. Internal Zones. These are separated from the external zone, over which they are thrust, by a great line of tectonic discontinuity which we shall call, with E. Argand, Pennine frontal overthrust, which, starting from around Sion in Switzerland, passes near Courmayer, near Moutiers and Saint-Jean-de-Maurienne, and at the front of the nappes of Embrunais-Ubaye (notched by the window of Barcelonnette) to twist at last behind the Mercantour (see maps, Fig. 60 and Fig. 62). We can distinguish there—

a. *A sub-Briançonnais zone,* forming the western edge of the Briançonnais. South and east of Pelvoux[53] it is reduced to scales, piled up locally to great thicknesses in the fine massifs of Morgon and Chabrières, which dominate the two banks of the Durance between Gap and Embrun. These scales here lie on the autochthonous Jurassic *terres-noires* of the eastern border (or ultra-Dauphinois zone) of the external zone, and they are overlain by the Flysch nappe of Embrunais-Ubaye, which can be conceived as the original Tertiary cover of the Briançonnais zone, a cover which has moved toward the west, rolling out beneath it the sub-Briançonnais scales.

North of Pelvoux[54] the sub-Briançonnais zone crops out much more widely. It is the sub-Briançonnais which determines the broad depression of the Galibier Pass, where it is bordered on the west by the band of Flysch of the

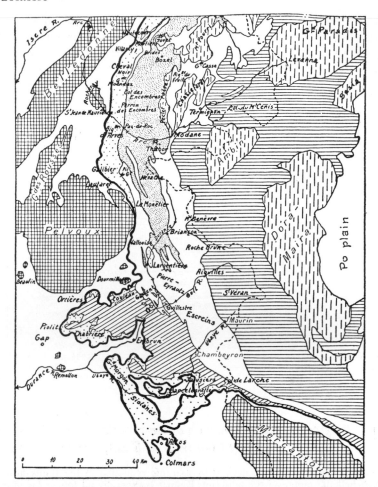

FIG. 60. *Structural map of the internal zone of the French Alps south of the Arc, by M. Gignoux and L. Moret (compare section, Fig. 84).*

Cross-ruled	External crystalline (Hercynian) massif ⎫ External
White	Their autochthonous sedimentary covering ⎭ Zone
Heavy line	Pennine overthrust front.
Sparsely stippled	Sub-Briançonnais zone.
Oblique-ruled	Flysch of Embrunais-Ubaye ⎫
White	Mesozoic Briançonnais ⎬ Briançonnais Zone
Densely stippled	Carboniferous Briançonnais ⎭
Vertical dashes	Internal crystalline massifs ⎫ Piedmont
Horizontally ruled	Their Mesozoic envelope (*schistes lustrés*) ⎭ Zone
Broken line	Old Franco-Italian frontier

N. B.   The fragments of crystalline schists (*schistes lustrés?*) appearing in the Briançonnais zone are not shown on this map; for that, see the map, Fig. 82.

Aiguilles d'Arves, which is attached to the ultra-Dauphinois zone. Crossing the Arc River at the Pas du Roc, it stretches out interminably between Maurienne and Tarentaise, in the great massif of Perron des Encombres, always bordered on the west by the ultra-Dauphinois Flysch of the Cheval-Noir. Finally, north of Moutiers, it includes especially the zone of Tarentaise breccias, the tops of which dominate the right bank of the Isère between Moutiers and the Little Saint Bernard.

The sub-Briançonnais Triassic is already thicker and more marine in char-

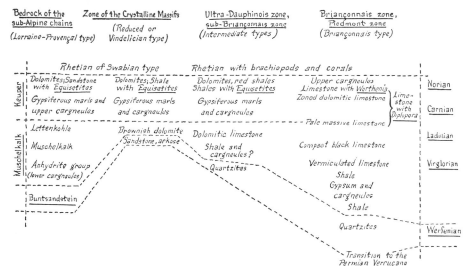

FIG. 61. *Diagrammatic representation of the variations of the Triassic facies in the tectonic zones, proceding from West to East in the French Alps.*

The Vindelician zone is characterized by extreme reduction of the Buntsandstein and the Muschelkalk; moreover the saliferous Keuper is generally no longer found in place, but injected into the Liassic cover, which again emphasizes the reduction of the Triassic overlying the crystalline massifs. However this Vindelician type does not extend south of Pelvoux; around the Mercantour, the Muschelkalk remains well developed and enclosed between two zones of gypsum and cargneules.

In the Briançonnais zone (?) and especially in the Piedmont zone, calcareous facies, clearly marine, seem to invade the Keuper, while in the lower Muschelkalk a strong saliferous complex develops, usually injected above the limestone.

acter than that of the external zone. And we see the characteristic facies of the Briançonnais zone appear and develop progressively as we travel from the west (lower or external scales or digitations) toward the east (upper or internal scales).

This Triassic thus begins with white quartzites, already very thick in the internal scales. Then comes a salt complex (equivalent to the anhydrite group), with chaotic masses of gypsum, *cargneules* and variegated marls, sometimes very thick, sometimes completely streaked out. The Muschelkalk proper is represented by dolomitic limestone massifs (perhaps including the Keuper) exceeding 100 m. thickness in the internal scales (Chabrières). After a return of the salt facies at the top of the Keuper, the Triassic often ends, in the external scales, with very characteristic red shales[55] (summit of Morgon), a facies already apparent in the ultra-Dauphinois zone (vicinity of Saint-Jean-de-Maurienne).

b. The wide *Briançonnais zone* (s. str.) is composed, however, of great recumbent folds or primary nappes (nappes of the Guil of W. Kilian; scales of the "mountains between Briançon and Vallouise" of P. Termier) in which the stratigraphy is clearer. It includes, at the center, a Coal Measures core (Briançonnais coal zone, see p. 207) surrounded by Mesozoic, which is buried toward the west under the thick cover of the Flysch of Embrunais.

The Triassic, having become very thick, there constitutes entire mountains. It includes from bottom to top the following divisions:[56]

1st. Very pure, fine-grained quartzites, which at their base pass imperceptibly into the Permian Verrucano. Reaching 200 m. thickness, these very hard rocks produce sharp peaks surrounded by dead white debris, while on their altered surfaces they are bronzy green in color, because of the development of a calcifuge lichen (*Lecidea geographica*).

2nd. Variegated shales with *cargneules,* gypsum, anhydrite, and sometimes marine salts at depth (old excavations of Salins, near Moutiers). Because of migration due to salt tectonics, the development of this horizon is very irregular. It is often almost entirely streaked out. Locally, however, it gives rise to thick, chaotic accumulations of gypsum and *cargneules,* rising sometimes into rounded mountains (Petit Mont Blanc of Pralognan, southeast of Moutiers) or more often being represented by depressed zones, strewn with collapse funnels due to the subterranean solution of the gypsum (Passes of Galibier, Izoard, etc.).[57]

3rd. Limestones, several hundred meters thick, greatly broken up by orogenic movements, constitute the larger part of the notched summits of the Briançonnais (Briançonnais limestones). The lower part shows stratified banks, with shaly beds and irregular, enigmatic impressions on the surface of the beds (vermicular limestones).[58] But the upper part is composed of great massive dolomitic beds, with a light colored gray or white patina, in which fossil remains are occasionally found; carditids, small gastropods, and especially diploporids.[59] The base of these limestone massifs probably corresponds to the upper Muschelkalk, but the Keuper may be represented (?) in the upper part, for at certain places they lie directly below the fossiliferous Rhaetian (lower Lias).[60] In any case they represent, in the French Alps, the equivalent of the gyroporelle limestones which we shall see developed typically in the Dolomites of the Tyrol.

c. In the *schistes lustrés* or *Piedmont zone,* sometimes separated from the Briançonnais zone by a line of abnormal contact (nappe of *schistes lustrés* of P. Termier and W. Kilian, whose base is marked, in Maurienne and Tarentaise, by a thick gypsum zone exuded from the Briançonnais substratum), all the formations become metamorphic. The Primary makes up the internal crystalline massifs (see p. 208) and the *schistes lustrés* undoubtedly begin with the Lias.

Between the two, a very thick Triassic is often found, identical to that of the Briançonnais and scarcely marked by metamorphism: basal quartzites, with phyllitic minerals developed, enormous accumulations of gypsum and especially typical Triassic limestones, several hundred meters thick and transformed into crystalline marbles. In Italy, S. Franchi has pointed out some eastern Alpine fossils in it, in particular, *Worthenia solitaria,* characteristic species of the Hauptdolomit of the Tyrol. As in the Briançonnais, they include diplopores.[61]

But sometimes, suddenly, between the crystalline massifs and their envelope of *schistes lustrés,* we find no more than a Triassic reduced by streaking to a few meters of quartzites, dolomitic limestones, and *cargneules* (example, The Pass of Evettes, in Maurienne above Bonneval). E. Argand recognized that the Triassic quartzites there were inclosed in the old crystalline schist series, while the rest of the Triassic was represented by the base of the *schistes lustrés.* It is thus possible that there may have been a progressive transition from the Primary to the Secondary, in a comprehensive series, geosynclinal, without discontinuity or lacuna of sedimentation. I believe, however, that this local disappearance of the Triassic is due to intense streaking out; and certain Alpine geologists (Dal Piaz, Cornelius) even concede that, in the zone of the *schistes lustrés,* the Hercynian discordance of the external Alpine zone would be found, with a lacuna representing the Coal Measures and Permian.

2. *The Triassic in the Alps as a Whole*

A. Introduction: General Structure of the Alps.[62]   As the French Alps have already foretold, the facies of the different formations in the Alpine Chain are arranged according to the tectonic elements. And the particular interest of the study of the Alps lies precisely in the search for the relationship between structure and facies. We begin then by setting the tectonic units in order and then using this framework to study the facies of all the formations.

We shall describe successively the Western Alps and the Eastern Alps, whose boundary is approximately at the longitude of Lake Constance (see maps, Figs. 62 and 64).

a. WESTERN ALPS.   The Pennine frontal overthrust that we have followed from the French Alps as far as Sion (see p. 282), continues toward the northeast passing immediately behind the Gothard crystalline massif, to follow the right bank of the Rhine in the Rhätikon. As in France, this line separates two very different regions:

1st. *The Helvetides.*   On the exterior (at the northwest) is the domain of the Helvetides, corresponding to the external zone of the French Alps, where the Dauphiné facies prevail in France (as opposed to the Briançonnais facies), the Helvetian in Switzerland (as opposed to the Pennine). The great Hercynian crystalline massifs of Aar and Gothard play the same role as the external crystalline massifs of the French Alps.[63] The French sub-Alpine chains, which, in front of the latter, correspond to their folded cover, extend into Switzerland as the Helvetian nappes. In fact, while the French chains were affected only by long faulted folds, evidence of slight thrusting, traveling eastward, we see these thrusts increase in size and evidenced by recumbent folds. The lowest, the Morcles-Aravis Nappe, is shown by a frontal thrust which we see originate southeast of Annecy. This first nappe thus includes all the internal part (Aravis chain) of the Bornes Massif (between Annecy and Arve) and of the Sixt Massif, northeast of the Aiguilles-Rouges whose highly streaked out, autochthonous cover it has just coated. The superposition of this nappe and the autochthon is easily seen in the Arve valley and especially in the deep cut of the Rhône valley, in the Dent de Morcles Massif. Its roots correspond approximately to the Chamonix syncline, between Aiguilles-Rouges and Mt. Blanc. Northeast of the Dent de Morcles, this nappe is over-run by another, that of the Diablerets, with more internal roots. The second nappe is in its turn covered by a third, the Wildhorn nappe. These three Helvetian nappes, Morcles, Diablerets, and Wildhorn, thus compose the whole structure of the Swiss calcareous Alps, in front of the Aar Massif [64] and as far as the Rhine, beyond which they extend to the edge of the eastern Alps. They have their roots either on the Aar Massif itself or immediately behind it.

2nd. *The Pennides.* Southeast of the Pennine frontal overthrust extends the domain of the Pennides, the prolongation of the internal zone of the French Alps. It includes Paleozoic massifs, corresponding naturally to anticlines or cores of nappes, separated from each other by a common cover of Mesozoic formations.

In France, the most external of these great Paleozoic cores was made up of the Briançonnais coal-bearing zone. But north of the Arc, we have already seen (p. 208) that the eastern part of these Coal Measures became metamorphic and made up the internal crystalline massifs of the Vanoise—Chasseforêt (northeast of Modane) and Mont Pourri. And we also know that this same structure is prolonged into Switzerland. The external part remains non-metamorphic, containing anthracites. This is the Pennine coal-bearing zone[65] forming a thin strip on the left bank of the Upper Rhône opposite Sion; while the broader, internal part no longer shows anything but Primary metamorphic gneisses and micaschists of the Great Saint Bernard. The upper part, the least metamorphic and very similar to the crystalline schists of the Vanoise, is often designated by the old name of Casanna schists, a little vague but nevertheless convenient.

The whole of this first Paleozoic core is called, by Swiss geologists, the Saint Bernard nappe. In fact, in the region of the Simplon, beneath the St. Bernard gneiss, there is a Mesozoic sheet under which three new Paleozoic cores come to light. These are the nappes of Simplon and Tessin, tectonically lower than the St. Bernard nappe. Toward the east, these nappes are buried again under the crystalline mass of the Adula from which they are separated by a Mesozoic cushion. This Adula nappe thus represents the extension of the St. Bernard nappe, removed by erosion from the dome of the Simplon-Tessin nappes. The connection between the two is no longer evident except through a thin root zone which passes behind the Simplon nappes.

On the other hand, between Zermatt and the Great St. Bernard, the St. Bernard gneisses are buried at the southeast under their Mesozoic cover

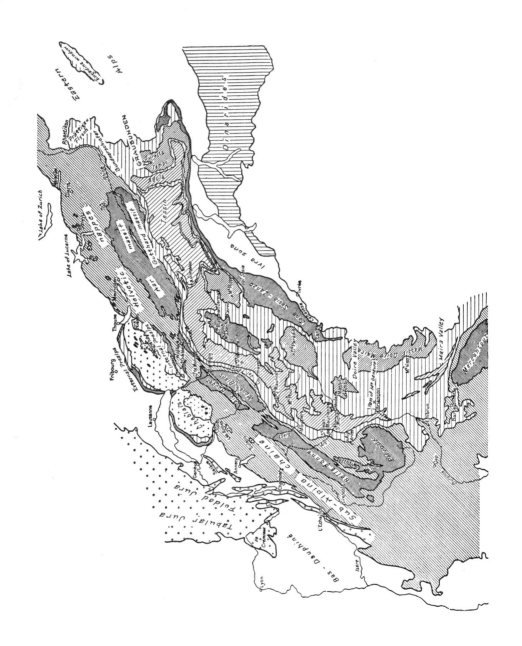

288

Dinarides

Austrides

Pennides

Helvetides

Venetian and Lombard Alps

Eastern Alps (Austro-Alpine nappes, Grisonides and Tyrolides)

Niesen Flysch nappe (internal-external Prealps)

Breccia nappe (Chablais and Hornfluh)

Median Prealpine (or Klippe) nappe

Prealpine nappes

Non-metamorphic Secondary and Tertiary formations of the external border of the Pennine nappes (Sion-Val Ferret zone, sub-Briançonnais and Briançonnais zones) and schistes lustrés separating the Primary cores of the Pennine nappes

Dent-Blanche nappe (roots—Sesia-Lanzo zone)

Monte Rosa (and Tambo-Suretto) nappe

St. Bernard (and Adula) nappe; in France the Briançonnais Coal Measures zone

Simplon (and Tessin) nappes

Primary cores of the Pennine nappes (internal crystalline massifs)

Ultra-Helvetic nappe (internal-external Prealps)

Helvetic nappes (in France, sub-Alpine chains) and autochthonous cover of the crystalline massifs

External crystalline massifs (Hercynian)

Jura

FIG. 62. *Structural map of the western Alps (after E. Argand).*

289

(Triassic and *schistes lustrés* of Zermatt). And, southeast of Zermatt, under the *schistes lustrés,* a great crystalline dome appears, the Monte Rosa nappe. It has been pushed under the south edge of the St. Bernard nappe (see section, Fig. 63), but, according to E. Argand, it really belongs above the latter and its prolongation in the canton of Graubünden is represented by two digitations, the Tambo and Suretta nappes.

Finally, between the St. Bernard and Zermatt, in the midst of the *schistes lustrés* cover of the St. Bernard nappe, a third crystalline mass appears, the Dent-Blanche nappe. E. Argand suggests that this immense sheet of the Dent-Blanche in effect floats entirely on a substratum of *schistes lustrés.* Its roots would be found in the crystalline Sesia-Lanzo Massif.

In summary, the structure of the Pennides, as it results from the syntheses of M. Lugeon and E. Argand in the Simplon-Monte Rosa-Dent Blanche-Sion region, may be explained by the following section (Fig. 63) which shows this succession of these Swiss Pennine nappes:[66]

> Higher nappes with internal roots:
> Dent-Blanche Nappe (VI) . . . . roots—Sesia-Lanzo Massif.
> Monte Rosa Nappe (V) . . . . Tambo and Suretta
> Saint Bernard Nappe (IV) . . . . Adula
> Simplon Nappes (I, II, III) . . . . Tessin
> Lower nappes with external roots.

The question now is to determine how we can interpret, in relation to this scheme, the other internal crystalline massifs of the Franco-Italian Alps, those of Grand Paradis, Ambin, and Doire-Maira. In outcrops, these massifs appear as vast cupolas of crystalline schists rising from the midst of the *schistes lustrés.*

Many Swiss geologists believe, with E. Argand, that all the tectonic elements known on the right of the Sion-Zermatt region should be prolonged toward the southwest, in the direction of the chain, with thrust sheets of almost constant amplitude. They liken each of these elements to a regular cylinder whose generatrices are parallel to the general direction of the chain. The reconstruction of the deep (and aerial) tectonics then follows immediately from the section of these different elements through the topographic surface.[67] They are thus led, by a series of constructions, to conclude that the three forementioned massifs represent the reappearance of the Paleozoic core of the Monte Rosa nappe. The St. Bernard nappe (here the Briançonnais coal-bearing zone) would be prolonged beneath them and the Simplon nappes would still be present at depth although not seen in outcrops.

We must now say a few words about the Mesozoic series that envelops these Primary cores. In the southern part of the French Alps and as far as Moutiers in Tarentaise, we have found evidence (p. 282) of the sub-Briançonnais zone in front of the Briançonnais Mesozoic proper. There, these formations are not metamorphic and they lend themselves to a detailed stratigraphy that we shall follow up to the Tertiary.

But, north of Moutiers, many problems still exist. We already know that,

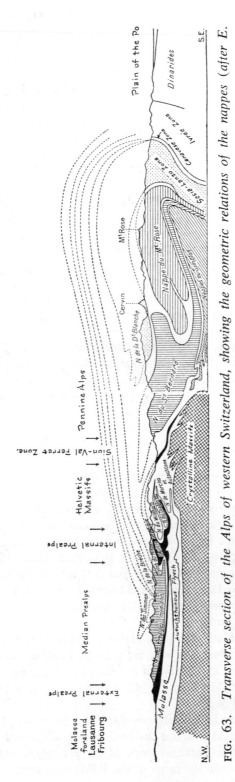

FIG. 63. *Transverse section of the Alps of western Switzerland, showing the geometric relations of the nappes (after E. Argand; compare map, Fig. 62). N. = nappe.*

Note that the hypothesis indicated here for the location of the roots of the Prealpine nappes is that adopted in the classic syntheses of the Swiss geologists. In this work, however, we conclude that these nappes are rooted directly behind the ultra-Helvetic root, in front of the St. Bernard nappe.

outside the Briançonnais zone, the sub-Briançonnais stretches out broadly in the mountains on the right bank of the Isère, comprising different sub-zones, the most important of which is that of the Tarentaise breccias (Jurassic and Tertiary),[68] but the stratigraphy there is still very uncertain. This nonmetamorphic Pennine extends back of Mont Blanc into Italy and Switzerland, always contained between the schists of the St. Bernard nappe and the Pennine front; it is the Sion-Val Ferret zone. The prolongation of the non-metamorphic Briançonnais Carboniferous is found again, as we know, in the Pennine coal-bearing zone (p. 287), at the exterior of which must pass the probably very thin extension of our sub-Briançonnais zone. But, on the south slope of Valais, covered with vegetation and moraines, the stratigraphy of this Sion-Val Ferret zone is still very poorly known. It is there, however, that the problem of the connection of the French Alps with the Swiss Alps and that of the origin of the Swiss Prealpine nappes could be solved.

On the other hand, back of the Pennine coal-bearing zone there is, in all this immense Pennine area, nothing more than metamorphic Mesozoic in the state of *schistes lustrés,* with, at the base, a Triassic, very sporadically streaked out or swelled, similar to that of the zone of *schistes lustrés* of the Franco-Italian Alps.

3rd. *The Prealpine Massifs.* The two principal massifs, separated by the canyon of the Rhône, are the Chablais Prealps, south of Lake Geneva, and the Romande Prealps, between Lake Geneva and Lake Thun. To them must be added, on the southwest, the two klippes of the Annes and of Sulens in Haute-Savoie, and on the northeast, a whole series of diminutive massifs known as Swiss Prealpine klippes. Each of these exotic massifs, without roots, set on the Helvetides, is itself made up of a series of superposed nappes, certain of which may in addition be locally streaked out. They are as follows, beginning with the lower nappes (with external roots):

a) *Ultra-Helvetic Nappe.*[69] Forming the base of the prealpine structures, this nappe crops out at their edge like a piping, although often streaked out. This piping is especially developed on the two edges of the Romande Prealps, in the zones called Prealpine *bordières* (internal on one side, external on the other). The Helvetic nappe of the Diablerets is pushed under, in this ultra-Helvetic nappe of the internal Prealps, so that a thin ultra-Helvetic scale is found pinched between the Diablerets and Morcles nappes. This is the Neo-comian scale with cephalopods (see Fig. 103) which will play an interesting part in our stratigraphic syntheses.

Around the Chablais Massif, the ultra-Helvetic nappe is found, especially along the external border (Faucigny hills, on the right bank of the Arve). It is almost entirely streaked out at the base of the klippe of the Annes, but forms a fairly large aureole (not shown in Fig. 62, to avoid overloading the drawing) all around the klippe of Sulens.

In this nappe, the facies have many similarities with those of the upper Helvetic nappes. Moreover M. Lugeon has been able to determine exactly the position of the roots, on the southeast slope of the Wildhorn, opposite Sion. They are placed there between the roots of the Wildhorn nappe and the Pennine frontal thrust. Thus, this nappe, not coming from the Pennine domain, could fairly be called ultra-Helvetic. It may be considered as a strip of the Helvetic country pushed ahead by the advance of the upper Prealpine nappes.[70]

b) *Niesen Flysch Nappe.* This was formerly believed to be composed principally of Tertiary (Paleogene) with some scales of Secondary formations. But it has recently been shown that most of this Niesen Flysch is of Upper Cretaceous age. In the Romande Prealps this nappe is well developed on the borders, where it contributes, with the ultra-Helvetic nappe, to the construction of the external Prealps and particularly the internal Prealps (where the Niesen Mountain is found). And it is found in the Sulens klippe. The facies greatly resemble those of the most external part of the French sub-Briançonnais zone.[71] It roots immediately back of the Pennine frontal thrust (external edge of the Sion-Val Ferret zone) and so is of Pennine origin.

c) *Nappe of the Middle Prealps.* This is so named because it makes up the greater part (the middle) of the Romande and Chablais Prealps. It is found at the top of Sulens and the Annes and finally it makes up the Swiss klippes, from which comes its other name, Klippe nappe. The Mesozoic there has facies which sometimes recall those of the sub-Briançonnais zone, sometimes those of the external part of the Briançonnais zone. Thus it is always rooted in this complex Sion-Val Ferret zone in the vicinity of the Pennine coal-bearing zone.

d) *Breccia Nappe.* This is characterized by the great development of the breccia facies in the Jurassic. It is especially developed in the southern part of the Chablais (massif called that of the Chablais Breccia) and bits of it are found in the Romande Prealps (Hornfluh). The stratigraphy and even the position of the nappe in relation to that of the median Prealps has been a matter of much discussion. At present, it is agreed that it lies on the middle Prealps. Its root would always be found in the Sion-Val Ferret zone.

e) *Simme Nappe.*[72] Its superposition on the Breccia nappe has recently been questioned.[73] It consists of some patches, scattered over the Romande Median Prealps, where Jurassic radiolarites are found, more or less associated with greenstones. In the Chablais, blocks of granitic rocks, scattered (*Plateau des Gets*) on or in the Flysch of the Breccia nappe, are sometimes referred to it. Nothing disproves the theory that it also is rooted in the Sion-Val Ferret zone.[74]

b. EASTERN ALPS. They are separated from the western Alps by a line which, starting from Canavese (Fig. 62), extends first toward the ENE as far as the high valley of the Adige, then turns north to end in the Rhaetikon. Along this last sector, the whole structure of the western Alps is buried under the eastern Alps. But, crossing the latter, it reappears, cropping out in two windows, that of the Engadine and that of the Hohe Tauern. The Engadine window is in a region of subdued topography for there only the soft *schistes lustrés* of the Pennides are seen. In the Hohe Tauern window, however, two great massifs of gneiss rise in the middle of an immense girdle (*Schieferhülle*) of metamorphic schists, similar to the *schistes lustrés*. As the formations of the eastern Alps which border these two windows are composed of the Primary, we see that if we concede the reality of these two windows and the Mesozoic age of the schists of the Engadine and of the *Schieferhülle* of the Hohe Tauern, it follows that the entire structure of the eastern Alps, can be conceived as a gigantic piling up of nappes, rooted to the south of these windows and thrust over a base formed by the prolongation of the western Alps (Fig. 65). This is the essence of the nappe theory (Deckentheorie) of the eastern Alps, first formulated by P. Termier, then accepted by the Austrian geologists (Uhlig, Kober) and the Swiss (R. Staub) but at present again much disputed, especially in Austria. An echo of these controversies will be found in volumes 92 (1940) and 93 (1941) of the *Zeitschr. der deutschen geologischen Gesellschaft,* where, in a series of articles and discussions, the ultra-nappists and the autochthonists present their opposing arguments. Some of the autochthonists even go so far as to deny the reality of the window of the Hohe Tauern. For them, the *Schieferhülle* is not buried under the crystalline of the eastern Alps and there is continuity between this crystalline (of the Oetztal) and that of the Hohe Tauern.

We shall now describe the great regional units of the eastern Alps themselves, or the Austrides. We shall distinguish there primarily:

1st. A central (or axial Paleozoic) zone, which is composed mostly of Primary formations, generally crystalline. Nevertheless, east of Innsbruck, its northern edge is composed of a zone of graywackes (Silurian-Devonian).

2nd. The northern calcareous Alps, north of the preceding zone, composed of Mesozoic formations and bordered on the north by a narrow piping of Flysch (Cretaceous and Tertiary) prolonging the front of the western Alps.

3rd. The southern calcareous Alps, however, deserve to be set apart from the rest of the Alps. Their tectonics are very different. Here we no longer have the successions of scales or the piles of nappes characteristic of Alpine structure. Here the beds often retain, over great distances, a tabular appearance, scarcely folded. The folds or faulted folds are inclined toward the south and not toward the north as everywhere else in the Alps. Finally, the facies are, as we shall see, very different. Consequently for a long time, this zone was separated from the true Alps under the name of Dinarides. However, the partisans of the nappe theory recognize that the calcareous chains of the Gail and Karawanken, bordering the axial Primary zone at the south, do not belong to the Dinarides, but to the Alps. For these chains then, the name southern calcareous Alps should be reserved. And there are located the roots of the northern calcareous Alps, roots which at the west are rolled out between the axial zone and the Dinarides.

In these Dinarides, we shall only enumerate some natural regions whose names we have already met or shall meet in the course of our stratigraphic explanations. The Bergamasque Alps (Mesozoic) extend between Lake Como and Lake Garda and are bordered on the north by a crystalline and Permian zone. The Trentino Alps are a prolongation of the Bergamasque Alps north of Lake Garda. On the northeast, around Bolzano (Bozen) a wide crystalline and especially Permian zone (noted p. 228) separates these Trentino cal-

FIG. 64. *Structural map of the eastern Alps (after R. Staub, very much simplified; compare Fig. 65).*

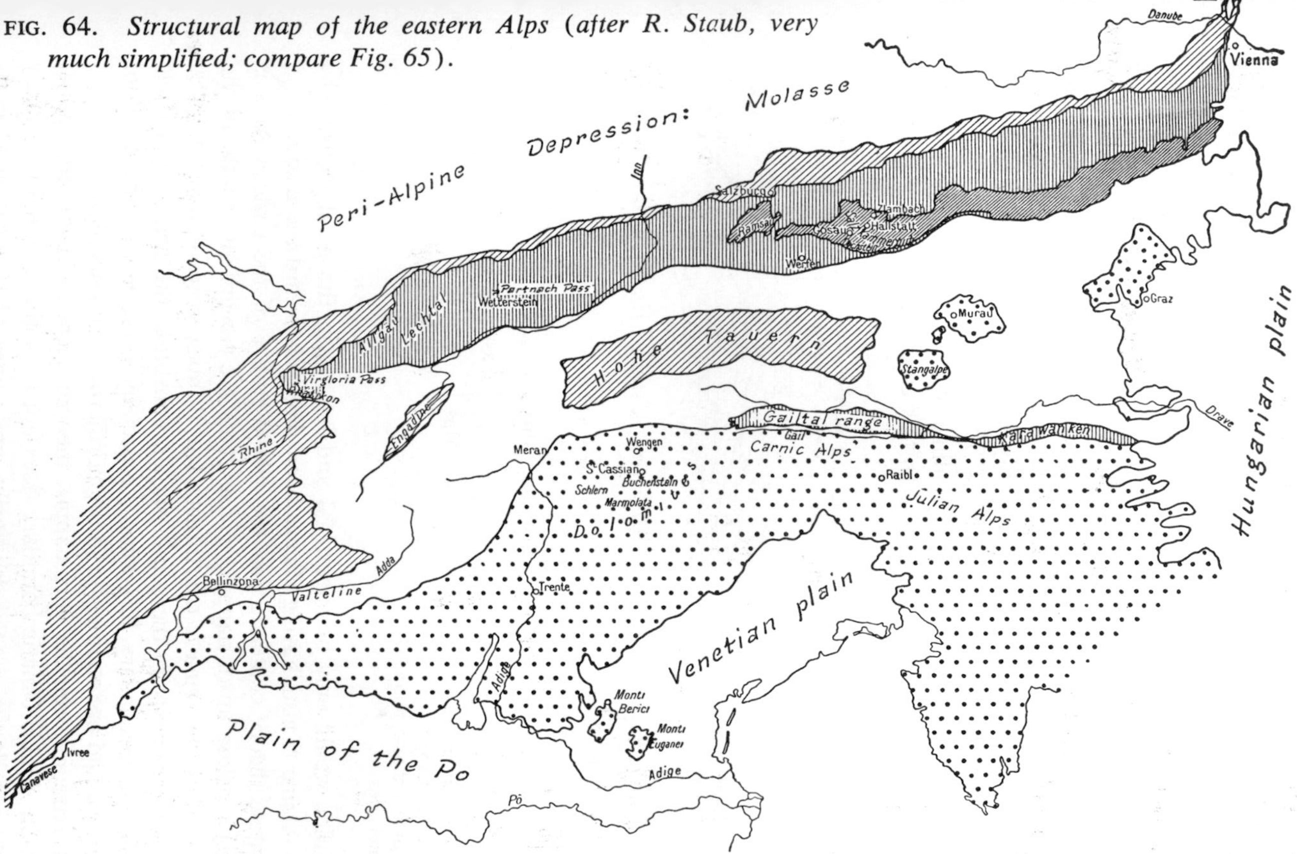

1   Dinarides and Dinaric klippes thrust over the eastern Alps (Graz, Murau, Stangalpe) } Dinarides
     Super-Alpine nappe (Hallstatt, Dachstein)
2   Secondary formations of the upper Austro-Alpine nappes (Bavarian nappe)
3   Secondary formations of the roots of the upper Austro-Alpine nappes (Gailtal, Karawanken)
4   Formations, especially Primary or crystalline, of the Austro-Alpine nappes and of their roots
5   Helvetic nappes, Flysch, Pennine nappes (windows of the Engadine and Hohe Tauern) } Western Alps

1.   Northern Calcareous Alps } Eastern
   Southern Calcareous Alps } Alps
   Central Zone

careous Alps from the great Dolomite Massif, where the Triassic limestones play a very important part. Finally, farther north, the Primary border of the Dinarides constitutes the small range of the Carnic Alps, in which we have described (pp. 137 and 227) a classic section of the Devonian and Permo-Carboniferous.

The boundary between the Dinarides and the Alps proper has been the subject of much discussion. This Alpine-Dinaric boundary was formerly conceived as a formidable dislocation, a cicatrix placing two completely different domains in mutual contact. P. Termier even accepted the theory that the Dinarides had been thrust over all the eastern Alps, thus playing the part of a *traîneau-écraseur* [crushing sledge] entirely removed, however, by erosion. R. Staub interprets the Paleozoic islets of Stangalpe, Murau and Graz (Fig. 64) as remnants of a cover over the crystalline of the central Alpine zone and as originating from the Dinaric domain. In this case, the southern dip of the

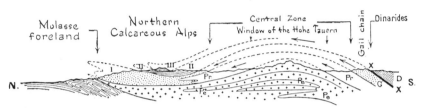

FIG. 65.   *Diagrammatic section across the eastern Alps (ultra-nappist interpretation, V. Uhlig).*

III = Dachstein nappe ⎫
II = Hallstatt nappe   ⎬ Northern Calcareous Alps ⎤
I = Bavarian nappe   ⎭   ⎥
Pr = Primary formations: central zone   ⎬ Eastern Alps
G = Gail chain (roots)—Southern Calcareous Alps ⎦
Pe = Pennine nappes   Western Alps
X = Alpine-Dinaric boundary
D = Dinarides

Dinaric folds would only be superficial and later than the great thrusts, the principal Alpine thrusts having always been directed toward the north.

The nappe theory contends that the whole edifice of the eastern Alps is formed by a piling up of nappes, whose roots are toward the south, in the neighborhood of the Dinaric overthrust. The Primary cores of these nappes, cropping out especially to the south, should constitute the central Paleozoic zone, while the Secondary formations, especially preserved at the front of the nappes, should be found again in the northern calcareous Alps.

In this extreme form, the ultra-nappist theories seem decidedly unacceptable. First the Alpine-Dinaric boundary does not have the continuity formerly attributed to it. It was traced arbitrarily, and zones of dislocation of completely different significance were connected. It is even difficult to believe that the nappes of the northern calcareous Alps have their roots only south of the Primary axial zone.

We shall nevertheless continue to use the classic language of the nappists, while stating that these nappes may correspond only to regional units, rooted in place or almost in place, not resulting from long distance thrusting.

Thus objectively described, the nappes of the eastern Alps or the Austro-Alpine nappes are as follows:

1st. The *Grisonides* (lower Austro-Alpine nappes = *Unter- und Mittelostalpine Decken*), appear naturally at the base of the structure, at the contact of the substratum formed by the western Alps. Their Primary core, here composed of amphibolites, is thus placed immediately southeast of the Pennine Massif of Sesia-Lanzo. There it is called the Ivrea zone of amphibolites. At its southwest extremity, in the Canavese, it is enriched by some Mesozoic scales making up particularly the Canavese zone. The stratigraphy is too uncertain and too incomplete to be described here. Nevertheless, it is there that many Swiss geologists locate the roots of the Prealpine nappes, which would therefore belong to the Grisonides and not, as we have earlier suggested, to the Pennides. Cropping out quite widely south of the Engadine window, in Graubünden [Grisons], and south of the Hohe Tauern window, the Grisonides would thus form thin zones of Mesozoic scales on the north border of these windows, and on the western border of the eastern Alps, as far as the Rhaetikon.

2nd. Above come the lower Tyrolides (upper Austro-Alpine nappes = *Oberostalpine Decken*), which, by themselves, constitute the greatest part of the eastern Alps. Their Paleozoic cores extend into the central Primary zone and their Mesozoic front makes up the northern calcareous Alps. There, we sometimes distinguish three superposed digitations which are, from bottom to top, the nappes of Allgaü, Lechtal, and Inntal-Wetterstein. We are not interested in differentiating them and so group them under the name, Bavarian nappe. South of the Primary cores, the Mesozoic covering of the lower Tyrolides reappears in the Gail chain (also called Drave chain or Drauzug) and in the Karawanken, calcareous spurs located just on the edge of the Dinarides. The Triassic facies there are similar to those of the Bavarian nappe, the root zones of which would be represented by these chains, if we accept the nappe theory.

3rd. Finally, under the name of upper Tyrolides (super-Alpine nappes = *Hochostalpine Decken*), a zone of northern calcareous Alps is sometimes identified, where some believe they see evidences of two nappes (of Hallstadt and Dachstein) characterized by special Triassic facies and placed without roots on the Bavarian nappe. The roots of these nappes would then be placed between the Gail chain and the Alpine-Dinaric boundary.

In conclusion, in the whole assemblage, what we call the Alpine arc is formed by a great movement of sediments, directed from the southeast to the northwest, having begun during the Jurassic and perhaps still going on at the present time. It has been arranged in three great arcs (*Deckenbogen*), which, following each other obliquely, successively form the external border of the chain (Fig. 87). They are: 1st. a sub-Alpine arc between the Mediterranean and Savoy, which dies out in successive waves, in the broad gap between Maures-Esterel and the Massif Central; 2nd. a Pennine (or Prealpine) arc, between Savoy and the Rhine, where the front of the nappes of the Pennides, more or less cut up in the Prealpine massifs, reaches as far as the edge of the Alps;[75] 3rd. an Austro-Alpine arc, east of the Rhine, where the nappes of the Austrides emerge in their turn.

B. The Triassic in the Western Swiss and Savoy Alps.

a. *Helvetides* (*Autochthon and Helvetic Nappes*). The Triassic is here identical to that which we have described farther south in the corresponding zone, that is, in the zone of crystalline massifs and their sedimentary border. The most conspicuous members are the Rötidolomit (from Röti near Tödi, southeast of the Lake Lucerne), which corresponds to the capuchin-dolomites of the French Alps, and the Quartenschiefer (from Quarten, village on the shores of the Walensee), equivalent of the French *schistes bariolés* (variegated shale). This, then, is also a reduced facies.

It is interesting to note that Paulcke (Geolog. Rundschau, 1915) called attention to the occurrence in the Rötidolomit of the autochthonous sedimentary covering of the Aar Massif, at Innertkirchen, near Meiringen, of fossils characteristic of the Germanic Muschelkalk (*Myophoria, Gervillia*). This is exactly in the most external zone of the Helvetides and it is natural to see there the most southern traces of the Germanic Muschelkalk sea.[76]

b. *Pennine Nappes.* Along the external edge of the St. Bernard nappe, that is, at the contact of the Sion-Val Ferret zone, the Triassic, still non-metamorphic, is shown completely analogous to that of the Briançonnais. We find there a great development of quartzite, gypsum and *cargneules*,[77] and finally, limestones that are certainly marine, called Pontis limestones (from the gorges of Pontis, in the Val d'Anniviers [Valais]), identical to the Briançonnais limestones, but nonfossiliferous.

Then, south of the Pennine coal-bearing zone, the Triassic becomes more or less metamorphic, and similiar to that of our *schistes lustrés* zone, but among the dark rocks which enclose it (gneisses and Paleozoic mica schists, Jurassic *schistes lustrés*) its quartzites and dolomitic limestones, becoming slaty (more rarely gypsum and *cargneules*), stand out as light bands which provide the valuable guiding threads for reading in the mountain panoramas, the complicated tectonics of the Pennine nappes (for example, Zermatt region).

c. *Prealpine Nappes.* The Triassic of the lower Prealpine nappes (ultra-Helvetic and Niesen Flysch) is very similar to that of our sub-Briançonnais zone. We find especially a great development of *cargneules* and gypsum, which form, in the internal Prealps, a line of depressions known as the zone of Cols or zone of Bex. The rock salt is here exploited in the salt mines of Bex (right bank of the Rhône, between Martigny and Lake Geneva). And, in particular, thick deposits of red shales are noted, quite similar to those mentioned earlier in the sub-Briançonnais zone.

The Triassic of the most external part of the Median Prealps still preserves about the same characteristics. But that of the internal part becomes completely identical to the Briançonnais Triassic. The quartzites, left behind at the time of the thrusts, are very slightly developed. There are great masses of gypsum and *cargneules,* often tectonically displaced. We see especially the appearance of thick calcareous masses[78] (for example, the St. Triphon limestones, near Bex), several hundred meters thick and identical to the Briançonnais limestones. The base, better stratified, is equivalent to the French vermicular limestones. At the top, dolomitic beds, with *Gyroporella,* provided Rabowski, in the Simmen valley, a rich fauna, in which pelecypods of the Germanic Muschelkalk are associated with characteristic species of the Middle Triassic of the Eastern Alps (*Worthenia, Spirigera,* etc.). It is, on the whole, the Briançonnais type, but more fossiliferous, a statement that we shall have occasion to repeat for all the other stages.[79]

Finally, the Triassic of the Breccia nappe,[80] although not well known, seems to show, curiously, affinities less Briançonnais, less internal, than that of the Median Prealps.[81]

The diagram (Fig. 66) recapitulates these observations. It shows the succession of Triassic facies in the different zones of the French Alps, and the succession that we find crossing the Swiss Alps from Fribourg to Ivrea.

C. The Triassic in the Eastern Alps. It is the eastern Alps which show us the true home of the Triassic of the Alpine type, which deserves to be studied in detail. E. Haug has presented, in his *Traité,* a magnificent synthesis of it, which we shall briefly summarize.

As we shall see, the Alpine Triassic is largely calcareous. Also it constitutes the framework of the calcareous chains of the eastern Alps. We shall study the following:

1. *The northern calcareous Alps,* made up chiefly of the tectonic units which we have agreed to combine under the name of Bavarian nappe. But in one part of these northern Alps, corresponding to the Hallstatt and Dachstein nappes, the Triassic has special facies.

2. The *Gail chain* (or Drauzug), an appendage of the southern calcareous Alps, but one in which the Triassic facies are very similar to those of the Bavarian nappe. Thus E. Haug, followed by partisans of the nappe theory, saw there the roots of this nappe.

3. Lastly, the *Dinarides,* which make up almost the whole of the southern calcareous Alps. We shall describe only the Triassic in the classic region of the Dolomites.[82]

So, Bavarian nappe, Hallstatt nappe, Dachstein nappe, and Dolomites, these are the four Triassic types that we shall study. The individuality of these nappes considered as zones of facies, is of course recognized even by the contemporary Austrian geologists who reject the nappe theory.[83] Thus they differentiate, in their Triassic, a Prealpine type (Bavarian nappe), a Hallstatt type, and a high Alpine type (Dachstein nappe).

The faunas there have long established the definition of the different stages of the Alpine Triassic. But the abnormal superpositions, which are the rule in the country of nappes, have long led to great confusion as to the true order of succession of these stages.

a. *Triassic of the Bavarian Nappe.* This type is also called normal, for the Bavarian nappe is extensive (Fig. 64).

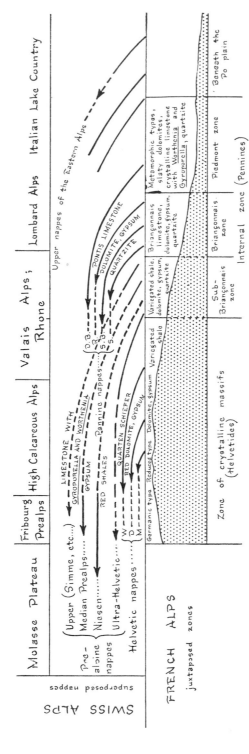

FIG. 66. *Attempt to show the connection between the Triassic facies in the French Alps and in the nappes of eastern Switzerland (and of Savoy).*

The different Helvetian and Pennine nappes are distinguished by their initials.

The heavy lines ending in arrows correspond to the regions in which the nappes have been preserved; the broken lines, to those where they have been removed by erosion.

It will be seen especially that, in the Prealps, the superposition, on the same vertical line, of the Triassic with gyroporelles (Pennine facies) above Triassic of the reduced Germanic type is understandable only by appealing to a tectonic synthesis based on the nappe theory.

300

The Werfenian[84] is formed of sandstones, conglomerates, or shales, which are, however, fossiliferous only in the eastern part of the nappe, in the Austrian Alps. There, they contain *Myophoria costata.*

The Virglorian,[85] above sandy marls with *Myophoria,* includes especially its typical member, the limestones of Virgloria (pass in the Vorarlberg). These are dark limestones, sometimes of deep-water facies, for, beside brachiopod beds, there are beds with cephalopods (*Ptychites, Monophyllites, Ceratites trinodosus*). Many species are also found in the Wellenkalk of Upper Silesia (p. 271) which proves the Virglorian age of this Wellenkalk.

The Ladinian is represented by two successive facies. At the base are the Partnach shales, still deep water with *Megaphyllites, Daonella* and brachiopods. At the top is the Wetterstein limestone, up to 1,000 m. thick. These are reef limestones with diplopores and corals. Sometimes one of these facies makes up the whole stage.

The Carnian marks a return to detrital sedimentation, rather shallow-water. There are especially marls or *Cardita* sandstones, without cephalopods. In the eastern part, in Austria, at this horizon, sandstones with brackish facies are found, with the same plants and the same *Estheria minuta* as in the Germanic Keuper.

The Norian is represented by the principal dolomite (*Hauptdolomit*), very thick, with a reef fauna, including *Gyroporella, Worthenia solitaria* and *Megalodus.*

b. *Triassic of the Hallstatt Nappe.*[86] In its Triassic facies this nappe is very different from the Bavarian and Dachstein nappes, which inclose it. The classic localities are found in the mountains which surround Salzburg and in the Salzkammergut.

The Werfenian there has its typical development: the variegated shales and sandstones of Werfen (near Salzburg) with *Myophoria* and exploited salt beds, from which the name Salzburg and salt nappe.

The Virglorian and the Ladinian are represented either by dolomites without fossils or cephalopod limestones, in which *Ceratites trinodosus* is found with the species which usually accompany it. The facies have then become deep-water.

The Carnian and the Norian also usually show a deep-water facies. They are composed especially of the Hallstatt limestones in which can be differentiated as many as seven zones of ammonites, associated with *Daonella* and *Halobia.* These limestones, relatively thin, fine grained, often nodular and variegated red or green, greatly resemble the Guillestre marbles of the Briançonnais Upper Jurassic, or the Griotte marbles of the Devonian. This is the most typical representative of the deep-water Alpine Triassic.

c. *Triassic of the Dachstein Nappe.* This is the Triassic which makes up, in the Austrian Alps, near Salzburg for example, very high, rugged mountains of the Hallstatt nappe which rise above the lower regions. Only the upper members of the Triassic are known here.

The Ladinian is dolomitic and reefy (Ramsau dolomites).

The Carnian is represented, as in the Bavarian nappe, by beds with *Cardita.*

The Norian is made up of Dachstein limestones, with reef facies, with gyroporelles, corals and megalodonts.

Very similar facies are found in the domain of the Dinarides and especially in the Julian Alps, situated south of the Primary Massif of the Carnic Alps. It is there that E. Haug would seek the roots of the Dachstein nappe. The Carnic is represented there by beds rich in pelecypods, the Raibl beds, a name currently used as a synonym of Carnian.

d. *Triassic of the Dolomites.* It is in this celebrated massif that the true home of the Dinaric Triassic is found. So the succession of beds, all classic, deserves a detailed description.

The Werfenian[87] here is detrital: shales, sandstones, marls, with *Myophoria* and other pelecypods, and rare ammonites (*Tirolites cassianus*).

The Virglorian is represented by sandy cephalopod limestones, overlain by dolomites with diplopores.

The Ladinian is very complex, because of frequent variations of facies.

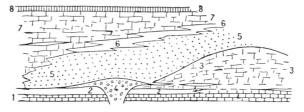

8 = Raibl beds
7 = Schlern dolomite
6 = Wengen and St. Cassian beds
5 = Volcanic tuff, sandstone, conglomerate

4 = Volcanic agglomerate
3 = Marmolata limestone
2 = Buchenstein beds
1 = Upper Virglorian dolomite

FIG. 67. *Diagram of the facies of the Middle Triassic (Ladinian) in the region of the Marmolata (Dolomites) (after H. P. Cornelius and Marta Furlani-Cornelius).*

In fact either cephalopod marls, in which three horizons are distinguished (Buchenstein, Wengen and St. Cassian beds), or reefy dolomites or limestones (Marmolata limestone, Schlern dolomite) with corals and diplopores can be found. The transitions from one facies to the other are very frequent and very abrupt.[88] There must have been numerous isolated reefs between which marls were deposited. Relieved of their marly girdle by erosion, these reefs now appear like so many isolated mountain fortresses. If we add that beds of volcanic tuff are frequently intercalated in the marls, it will be evident how complex the detail of this Ladinian stratigraphy may become (Fig. 67). From the paleontologic point of view, the St. Cassian marls are celebrated for their extraordinarily rich fauna, in which all animal groups are represented by very small shells. This pygmy fauna has been compared to that found in the beds of algae at certain places in the Mediterranean, or again to that of certain Liassic marls, giving evidence of similar biologic conditions.

The Carnian presents the same complexity. It is represented by the Raibl beds, with littoral facies, often red, sometimes dolomitic, sometimes marly and rich in pelecypods (*Myophoria kefersteini*). These soft and impermeable beds, lying between calcareous masses, produce passes or verdant valleys.

The Norian facies is the Hauptdolomit with *Worthenia solitaria,* reaching 1,000 m. thickness. This beautiful rock constitutes part of the celebrated summits of the southern part of the massif.

e. *Summary.* If we except the Werfenian, represented everywhere by littoral or even lagoonal, detrital facies, we see that the different tectonic zones (or facies) which we have just described in the eastern Alps, follow each other from north to south as follows:

1) *Bavarian nappe:* shallow-water facies; cephalopods are found but rarely and only in the Virglorian limestones.

2) *Hallstatt nappe:* it corresponds to the maximum depth of the Alpine

	Bavarian Nappe	Hallstatt Nappe	Dachstein Nappe	Dolomites (Dinarides)
Norian Carnian	Principal dolomite Beds with <u>Cardita</u> (littoral)	Hallstatt limestone (deep-water facies)	Dachstein coral limestones or dolomites Raibl beds with <u>Cardita</u>	Principal dolomite Raibl beds
Ladinian Virglorian	Coral limestones of the Wetterstein Partnach shales Virgloria limestones Sandy marls with <u>Myophoria</u>	Dolomites or limestones with cephalopods	Ramsau dolomites	*Marly facies* *Coral* (with tuffs) *facies* St-Cassian Lime- Schlern Wengen stone of dolo- Buchenstein Marmolata mite Dolomites with diploporids Sandy limestones with cephalopods
Werfenian	Sandstone Conglomerate (Verrucano facies)	Werfen sandstone and shale (Salzkammergut salt)		Sandstones and shales (salts)

FIG. 68. *Table summarizing the stratigraphy of the Triassic in the eastern Alps.*

sea; the cephalopod facies are not at all rare in the Middle Triassic, and the Hallstatt limestone represents, no doubt, the deepest-water type of the Upper Triassic in all the eastern Alps.

3) *Dachstein nappe* and the *Dinarides* in general (Dolomites in particular): this facies becomes again less deep-water; reefy dolomites and limestones predominate.

D. General Conclusions. If we attempt now to show the position of the Triassic zones of sedimentation, we obtain the following picture:

1st. A northern zone, that of the *Helvetides,* with a very reduced Lower and Middle Triassic, in which, toward the north, are found the last thin deposits of the Germanic Muschelkalk sea (Innertkirchen fauna, p. 298) but which in general shows only thin lagoonal or continental sediments. There, a Vindelician chain must have existed, which remained more or less emerged in the Muschelkalk and which separated the Alpine sea from the arm of the Germanic sea advancing into the Jura. South of Pelvoux, however, and around Mercantour, the Provençal Muschelkalk Basin communicated widely with the Alpine sea as we shall find in the following zones.

2nd. In fact, in the *Pennides* (including the Prealpine nappes) we see the Triassic become progressively thicker and thicker, and more and more marine. The basal quartzites doubtless represent old beaches or coastal dunes (ripple-marks are found in them) which bordered the Buntsandstein continent. And the Middle Triassic seas deposited thick beds of diplopore limestones there. These seas seem to have sometimes persisted even during the Upper Triassic.

3rd. The domain of the *Austrides* (northern part of the eastern Alps) corresponds to the deepest part of the Alpine sea, with the trough of the Hallstatt limestone, bordered on the north by the more littoral zone of the Bavarian nappe.

4th. Finally the *Dinarides* again show shallower seas, extending south of the Hallstatt trough, with an enormous development of coral reefs.

IV. The Triassic in Other Regions of the Globe[89]

A. *Mesogean Domain*

In Italy, the Triassic retains its Alpine type. The most remarkable units are the limestones, such as the famous Carrara marble, which makes up whole mountains in the Apuane Alps, a small massif located between Pisa and La Spezia, largely composed of Triassic. Southeast, the soft and monotonous ridges of the northern Apennines are formed of clayey or sandy Tertiary (or Cretaceous) formations. But the Triassic limestones reappear in the central Apennines of Abruzzi, where they constitute especially the massif of the Gran Sasso d'Italia, the highest point of the Italian peninsula. Finally, at the other end of the Apennines a very important final massif of Triassic limestone is found. This is the chain of Monte-Pollino, in which the Apennine limestone ends in the south, to be replaced by the crystalline massifs of Calabria.

In Sicily, there are likewise very fossiliferous Triassic limestones with a clearly Alpine fauna. There the true Mesogean domain advances farthest to the west into the present Mediterranean. For, farther west, in North Africa, Spain and Sardinia, it is the Germanic type Triassic which prevails. We recollect, nevertheless, that we have called attention in the two latter countries to species derived from the Alpine sea.

Leaving the eastern Alps, the Alpine Triassic extends into the Carpathians,[90] into the Bakony Forest (situated in the interior of Hungary, within the Carpathian arc, a subsidiary of the Dinarides, into the chains which border the Adriatic,[91] and finally into the whole Balkan region.[92] It extends also into the Crimea, the Caucasus, Asia Minor,[93] and to Djulfa (p. 227).

In the Himalayas the finest development of ammonite facies of the Triassic is found, either in the region of Spiti of the central Himalayas or in the Salt Range, a small range south of the western Himalayas (p. 225). These two localities are famous for their wealth of cephalopods.

B. *Pacific Domain*

By way of the eastern Himalayan chains and the Malay Archipelago (very fossiliferous Triassic on Timor),[94] this Mesogean zone of the Triassic is connected to a Pacific zone.

Indeed, the marine Triassic is known all around the Pacific: in Indochina and Southern China,[95] Japan, the Pacific chains of North America (and the Rocky Mountains),[96] Mexico, Peru,[97] the Argentine Republic,[98] New Zealand,[99] and New Caledonia.

C. *Continent of Gondwana*

Brazil, southern Africa, Madagascar, the Indian Peninsula and Australia show a Triassic of continental formations continuing those of the Permian, which can be summarized by saying that the Continent of Gondwana (see p. 238) has retained the same character during the Triassic as in the Permian. These are the beds of the middle Gondwana series in the Deccan, and the middle Karroo (top of the Beaufort stage and base of the Stormberg, pp. 241–242) in southern Africa.

These continental deposits of the southern hemisphere have facies a little like the Buntsandstein and Keuper of the northern hemisphere. However, in Australia and especially in India, thick beds of coal, constituting true Coal Measures, are often intercalated. *Glossopteris* still persists in it, accompanied by other species of ferns unknown in the Permian (*Thinnfeldia*, p. 244).[100]

The Triassic of Madagascar deserves special mention. First a thick formation of sandstone is known there (Isalo group, p. 244), probably semi-continental or lagoonal, impregnated with bitumen, whose Triassic age is based on its position beneath Liassic sediments, to which we shall refer again. And especially, in the northeast of the island, the series of Anaborana clays ends, as we have seen, with Lower Triassic ammonite beds. These ammonites have affinities with Himalayan forms.[101] It can be assumed then that an arm of the sea, leaving the Mesogean zone in the region of the Himalayas, advanced over the Continent of Gondwana as far as northeastern Madagascar. This is the beginning of the cutting up of this continent, a fragmentation which we shall see accentuated in the Jurassic.

D. *The North Atlantic Continent in America*

As in the Devonian, Carboniferous, and Permian, the North Atlantic continent, which could have been called at that period the continent of New Red Sandstone (and variegated marl), extended into the northern part of the United States. A continental Triassic, composed of red sandstone and marl, identical to the Germanic facies, is found all along the Atlantic Coast, from Nova Scotia as far as the southern end of the Appalachians. It even penetrates to the interior of the chain in a long depression, ranging SW-NE, called the Appalachian valley.

But, in this Triassic series of the Germanic type, no marine episode is intercalated comparable to the Muschelkalk sea. To find Triassic marine fossils in the United States, it is necessary to go as far west as the Rocky Mountains (Pacific domain).

E. *The Arctic Seas*

Marine Triassic is known in Bear Island, Spitzbergen,[102] in eastern Greenland,[103] boreal America, and northern Siberia. These northern Triassic seas could not have been directly connected with the Mesogean sea. They were in fact separated by the North Atlantic continent and the Sino-Siberian continent (or Continent of Angara), joined to each other since the arm of the Russian Sea (p. 222) was closed at the beginning of the Triassic.[104] On the other hand, the Arctic seas must have been connected to the Pacific domain, passing between the Sino-Siberian and the North Atlantic continents, by way of British Columbia and the Bering Straits.

And in fact, the Arctic and Pacific faunas show close affinities. They are characterized in the Upper Triassic by the same pelecypod species, *Pseudomonotis ochotica*. Thus a definite Arctic-Pacific province is found in this epoch, as contrasted to a Mesogean province.[105]

REFERENCE NOTES

1. Corruption of a German dialect term which means variegated.

2. This stage name is used here in its French acceptance (see p. 270).

3. Figures of all the German Triassic fossils will be found in Martin Schmidt, *Die Lebewelt unserer Trias,* Nachtrag 1938, Hohenlohesche Buchh., Oehringen (1938), 144 p., 265 fig.

4. J. von Pia, *Uebersicht über die fossilen Kalkalgen und die geologischen Ergebnisse ihrer Untersuchung,* Mitt. geol. Ges., Vienna, 33 (1940); contains a table of distribution by stages and regions of the Triassic algal faunas.

5. J. von Pia, *Die Diploporen der deutschen Trias und die Frage der Gleichsetzung der deutschen und alpinen Triasstufen,* Zeitschr. deutsch. geol. Ges., Monatsb., 78 (1926); *Grundsatzliches zum Vergleiche germanischer und alpiner Trias,* Mitt. geol. Ges., Vienna, 23 (1930).

6. Some undetermined diploporids have also been noted in various other places outside of the Alpine domain: in Thuringia, near Apolda, J. von Pia, loc. cit.; on the eastern edge of the Black Forest, V. Hohenstein, *Beiträge zur Kenntniss des mittleren Muschelkalkes und des unteren Trochitenkalkes am östlichen Schwarzwaldrand,* Geol. und pal. Abh., 16, 2, Jena (1913); in Provence, W. Kilian, C. R. Soc. géol. France (1922), no. 4; on Majorca and in the province of Tarragona, see later.

7. A. Kutassy, *Triadische Faunen aus dem Bihar-Gebirge. I. Teil: Gastropoden,* Geologia hungarica, ser. pal., 13, Budapest (1937).

8. On the phylogeny of Triassic ammonites and the numerous zones over the whole globe which they serve to characterize, see especially the works of J. P. Smith cited note 96, this chap.

9. Interesting paleogeographic maps in R. Brinkmann, *Tektonik und Sedimentation im deutschen Triasbecken,* Zeitschr. deutsch. geol. Ges., 78 (1926), Abh.; A. Strigel, *Das Süddeutsche Buntsandsteinbecken,* Verh. Naturhist.-Medizin. Vereins Heidelberg, N. F.,

16 (1929); H. Steinlein, *Das Buntsandsteingebiet zwischen Kulmbach und Bayreuth*, Abhl. preuss. geol. Landesanst., Berlin, N. F., H. 180 (1938); M. Frank, *Ergebnisse neuer Untersuchungen über Fazies und Bildung von Trias und Jura in Südwest-Deutschland*, Geol. Rundschau, 28 (1937).

10. On the lithologic peculiarities, see L. Rüger, *Der Wellenkalk*, Beitr. z. Geol. Thüringen, 4, H. 4, Thüring. geol. Ver. (1936).

11. H. Kleinsorge, *Paläogeographische Untersuchungen über den Oberen Muschelkalk in Nord und Mitteldeutschland*, Mitt. geol. Staatsinst., Hamburg, 15 (1935). A. Vollrath, *Zur Stratigraphie und Bildung des Oberen Hauptmuschelkalks in Mittel- und Westwürttemberg*, Jahresber. u. Mitt. Oberrhein, geol. Ver. 27 (1938). E. Jorg, *Die Tonmergellagen des Hauptmuschelkalkes im Breisgau und im Gebiet der Dinkelberg, ihre Fauna und ihre stratigraphische Bedeutung*, ibid., 30 (1941).

12. See Riedel, Jahb. d. K. preuss. geol. Landesanst. (1916). Other zones are there differentiated.

13. G. Richter, *Der Sedimentationsraum des Unteren Keupers zwischen Harz und Thüringer Wald*, Festschr. z. H. Stille, Stuttgart, F. Enke (1936).

14. B. Von Freiberg, *Die Randfazies des Mittleren Keupers in Mittelfranken*, Sitzungsber. Phys.-Mediz. Soziétat z. Erlangen, 67 (1935-36). A complete list of the species of the Germanic middle Keuper, classified by horizons in R. Markthaler, *Die Feuerlettenkonglomerate und das Transgressions-probleme im Mittleren Keuper Frankens*, Abh. Naturwiss. Ges. Nürnberg, 26, H. 3 (1937).

15. These *cargneules*, very characteristic rocks of the Triassic all over Europe, seem to always be associated with gypsiferous formations. W. Brückner, *Ueber die Entstehung der Rauhwacken und Zellendolomite*, Eclog. geol. Helvetiae, 34, no. 1 (1941), believes that they were originally dolomitic, gypseous rocks, in which gypsum has been replaced by calcite and in which the dolomite has been partially dissolved, leaving vacuoles. This interpretation has recently been accepted by C. E. Burckhardt.

16. H. Stoll, *Versuch einer stratigraphischen Gliederung des Stubenstandsteins im westlichen Württemberg*, Jahrb. und Mitt. d. overrheinischen geol. Vereins, N. F., 18 (1929).

17. In the Muschelkalk of Lower Silesia, H. Rassmus, Jahr. K. preuss. geol. Landesanstalt (1914) has mentioned ammonites (*Balatonites*) of the Alpine Ladinian. See also A. Lunievski, *Les éléments alpins dans la faune du Muschelkalk du versant N des Montagnes de Swiety Kryzyz (Lysa Gora)*, Bull. Serv. geol., Poland, II (1923).

18. References in the excellent summary of A. Briquet *Le sous-sol des Pays-Bas d'après les recherches récentes*, Ann. de Géogr., 30 (1921). New information in A. Benz, *Ueber das Mesozoicum und den Gebirgsbau im preussisch-hollandischen Grenzgebiet*, Zeitschr. deutsch. geol. Ges., 78 (1926).

19. This is the conclusion of the work by R. L. Sherlock, "A Correlation of the British Permo-Triassic Rocks," Proc. Geologists' Ass., 37 (1926) and 39 (1928).

20. Nevertheless, some British geologists have recently remarked that there was, in the neighborhood, some Quaternary glacial polish.

21. Cf. L. Van Werveke, *Die Küstenausbildung der Trias am Südrande der Ardennen*, Mitt. geol. Landesanst. Elsass-Lothringen, X, 2 (1916). E. Kraus, *Von der Westküste des Muschelsandsteinmeers*, Centr. f. Min. (1921), no. 14. M. Lucius, *Die Geologie Luxemburgs in ihren Beziehungen zu den benachbarten Gebieten*, Veröff. Luxemb. Geol. Landesaufnahme-Dienstens, 1 (1937); *Beiträge zur Geologie von Luxemburg* ibid., 2, 1940 and 3 (1941).

22. Note, as recent works, G. Corroy, *Les Vertébrés du Trias de Lorraine et le Trias lorrain*, Ann. de Pal., 17 (1928); *Etude stratigraphique et tectonique des régions Nord du seuil de Bourgogne*, etc., Ann. Fac. Sc. Marseille, 7 (1934). G. Minoux, *Le Trias et le Lias des environs de Mirecourt (Vosges)*, Bull. Soc. géol. France, 5 sér., 4 (1934).

23. F. Forche, *Stratigraphie und Paläogeographie des Buntsandsteins im Umkreis der Vogesen*, Mitt. geol. Staats-Inst. Hamburg, 15 (1935), p. 36.

24. L. Grauvogel, C. R. Soc. géol. France (1947), pp. 35, 64, 90; C. R. Acad. Sc., 225 (1947), p. 1165.

25. Details on the stratigraphy of the Muschelkalk in L. Guillaume, *Observations sur*

la stratigraphie du Trias lorrain; forage de St. Clément (Meurthe-et-Moselle), Bull. Soc. Sc. Nancy, n. s., 2 (1939).

26. Small enigmatic impressions, in the shape of little rods, a few mm. long, sometimes considered related to diatoms. In France, they are found in the Trias of the Rhone Valley, at Propiac (see p. 276).

27. P. Maubeuge, *Sur les Cératites du Muschelkalk lorrain*, C. R. Soc. geol. France (1947), p. 162.

28. H. Tobien, *Ueber mittleren Keuper am Südrand der Vogesen*, Jahresber, u. Mitt. oberrhein. geol. Ver., 30 (1941). A. Robaux and M. Bernatzky, *Du rejeu de failles primaires pendant le dépôt des terrains secondaires en Lorraine*, C. R. Acad. Sc. (Dec. 13, 1937); these authors try to explain the variations of facies of the Keuper by contemporary tectonic movements.

29. See pp. 368 and 369.

30. See the work of F. Roman, referred to in note 146, chap. 5.

31. E. Friedel, *Sur quelques sondages profonds du Jura et de la Bresse*, C. R. Soc. géol. France (1944), p. 123.

32. P. Lamare, *Le problème du Trias dans les Pyrénées basques*, Mém. Soc. géol. France, 4 sér., 28 (1928); *Recherches géologiques dans les Pyrénées basques*, Mém. Soc. géol. France, t. 12 (1936), no. 27; Thèse Sc.

33. In one of the Triassic ridges which crop out in the plains north of the western Pyrenees, a well in the vicinity of Dax (Landes) encountered beds of potassium salts in the Keuper. See M. Dalloni, *Note préliminaire sur la structure géologique et la recherche des gisements de sels de potasse dans la région des Landes*, C. R. Congrès internat. des Mines, etc., Liége (1930). G. Kimpflin, *La potasse des Landes*, La Nature (Sept. 1, 1947). The small oil deposit of Gabian, south of the Montagne-Noire, which has been exploited for several years, is also in Triassic dolomites.

34. See P. Fallot, *Etude géologique de la Sierra de Majorque*, Thèse, Paris, Béranger (1922). More recent studies, particularly those of M. Schmidt, are summed up in P. Fallot, *Essais de la répartition des terrains secondaires et tertiares dans la domaine des Alpides espagnoles; 1ᵉʳ livr., Introduction et Bibliographie sommaire; 2ᵉ livr., Le Trias*, Géol. de la Médit. occid., vol. IV, no. 1, Barcelona (1931).

35. J. Flandrin, *Nouvelles observations sur le Trias de Souk-Arras (Algérie)*, Bull. Soc. géol. France, 5 sér., 2 (1932).

36. J. Marçais, *A propos d'un gisement de Trias fossilifère dans le Rif oriental*, C. R. Acad. Sc. (Feb. 18, 1935).

37. P. Fallot, *Observations sur le Trias d'Algérie* (Bull. Soc. géol. France, 12, 1942). M. Gignoux, *Remarques sur la répartition des faciès du Trias en Algérie*, C. R. Soc. géol. France (1946), p. 20. A. Lambert, *Le Muschelkalk à faciès de calcaires vermiculés du secteur sud-oriental de la Kabylie des Babors (Algérie)*, ibid. (1948), p. 221. We shall describe later similar phenomena around the Hercynian crystalline massifs of the Alps.

38. See the plate in the article by M. Gignoux cited note 56, this chap.

39. Principally following J. Walther. Somewhat different ideas will be found developed by W. Deecke in, *Der paläogeographischer Charakter der germanischen Muschelkalk-Binnenmeeres*, Verh. Naturf. Ges. Basel (1922) and in A. Tornquist, *Die Binnenmeerfacies der Trias*, Geolog. Rundschau, vol. III (1912). On the other side, the desert origin of the Buntsandstein is still vigorously upheld by K. Frenzen, *Die Bildungsgeschichte des oberen Buntsandsteins Südwestdeutschlands im Lichte der Paläontologie*, Zeitschr. deutsch. geol. Ges., 83 (1931).

40. P. Raymond, "The Significance of Red Colors in Sediments," Amer. Journ. Sc., 5 sér., 13, no. 75 (1927).

41. P. Pruvost, *Le sondage de Ferrières-en-Bray*, Ann. de l'Off. nat. des Comb. liquides, 3 année, 3ᵉ livr. (1928).

42. There, the variations of Muschelkalk facies in the vicinity of the ancient Bohemian shore have been studied in detail by T. W. Gevers, *Der Muschelkalk am Nordwestrande der böhmischen Masse*, Neues Jahrb. f. Min., Beilage-Band, 56, Abt. B (1927).

43. Unfortunately Gümbel (imitated by others) tried to follow the history of this chain into the Tertiary and there his views can not be accepted today.

44. With the exception of their northern part in Haute-Savoie, north of a line drawn from Annecy to Albertville, a region which will be studied later, at the same time as the Swiss Alps.

45. It is generally nearly at the boundary between the Triassic and the Lias that flows and tuffs of basic volcanic rocks, generally qualified as spilites, appear in the edge of the southern part of Belledonne and around Pelvoux. Their petrographic study has recently been undertaken by M. Bellair, *Caractères magmatiques des roches d'épanchement de la couverture des massifs centraux dauphinois*, C. R. Acad. Sc., 222 (1946), p. 1303; and by M. Vuagnat, *Sur le caractère spilitique des mélaphyres de la région du Pelvoux*, C. R. Soc. Phys. Hist. nat. Genève, 64, no. 2 (1948), p. 63.

46. See M. Gignoux and L. Moret, *Géologie dauphinoise*, Arthaud, Paris-Grenoble (1944), p. 73, Fig. 10.

47. M. Gignoux, C. R. Acad. Sc. (Jan. 3, 1938): deposit examined by J. Ricour.

48. P. Jodot, *Sur la présence d'une faune à Myophoria goldfussi dans le Trias de la bordure S du Pelvoux (Hautes-Alpes)*, Bull. Soc. géol. France, 4 sér. 26 (1926).

49. Unpublished discovery, owed to E. Roche.

50. M. Gignoux and L. Moret, *Sur la Géologie de la région de Dourmillouse (Hautes-Alpes)*, C. R. Soc. géol. France (Dec. 7, 1931).

51. P. Bordet, *Les plis du Trias dans la couverture du N du Dôme de Barrot*, Bull. Serv. Carte géol. France, no. 216, 45 (1945), p. 237.

52. Containing, at Notre Dame du Laus, southeast of Gap, blocks of sandstone with *Equisetites;* see Gap sheet, scale 1/80,000, 2nd edit.

53. For this region, see M. Gignoux and L. Moret, *Description géologique du bassin supérieur de la Durance*, Trav. Lab. Géol. Univ. Grenoble, 21 (1938).

54. R. Barbier, *Les zones ultradauphinoise et subbriançonnaise entre l'Arc et l'Isère*, Mém. Serv. Carte géol. France (1948); Thèse Sc., Grenoble.

55. A fact already emphasized by E. Haug, in the fundamental article to which we refer once for all: E. Haug, *Contribution à une synthèse stratigraphique des Alpes occidentales*, Bull. Soc. géol. France, 4 sér., 25 (1925).

56. W. Kilian and C. Pussenot, *La série sédimentaire du Briançonnais oriental*, Bull. Soc. géol. France, 4 sér., 13 (1913). M. Gignoux and E. Raguin, *Sur la stratigraphie du Trias de la zone du Briançonnais*, C. R. Acad. Sc. (Jan. 12, 1931).

57. In Maurienne, the Briançonnais Coal Measures are separated from the sub-Briançonnais Rhaetian only by the thick gypsum zone of the Pas du Roc. And the Triassic, Jurassic, and Cretaceous cover of these Coal Measures, normally more than 500 m. thick, is represented only by klippe blocks scattered in the midst of this gypsum. This is one of the most striking tectonic phenomena of the whole Alpine Chain. See M. Gignoux and L. Moret, *Itinéraire géologique à travers les Alpes françaises, de Voreppe à Grenoble et en Maurienne*, Trav. Lab. Géol. Univ. Grenoble, 15 (1931), and R. Barbier, work cited note 54, this chap.

58. See plate 5 of the work of F. Blanchet, *Etude géologique des Montagnes d'Escreins*, Trav. Lab. géol. Univ. Grenoble, 19 (1935).

59. D. Schnéegans, *Sur la découverte de nouveaux gisements de Diplopores dans le Trias de la zone du Briançonnais*, Trav. Lab. géol. Univ. Grenoble, 17 (1933). These are *Diplopora annulata*, a form of the Alpine Ladinian. Diplopores have recently been noted also in Vanoise by F. Ellenberger, *Sur la série stratigraphique de la Vanoise*, C. R. Soc. géol. France (1948), p. 325.

60. Very rarely (near Col de Larche, Basses-Alpes), according to D. Schneegans, thin beds of "upper *cargneules*" at the top of the Triassic; but almost all of the masses of gypsum and *cargneules* indicated on geologic maps as belonging to the Upper Triassic in reality come from the horizon below the limestones and have been tectonically displaced.

61. Amalia Baretti, *Contribuzione allo studio delle Sifonee verticillate del calcare di Villanova-Mondovi*, Atti. Soc. ital. Sc. Nat., 58 (1919).

62. We refer once for all to the magnificent work of A. Heim, *Geologie der Schweiz*, Leipzig (1921) and to the *Guide géologique de la Suisse*, published by the Swiss Geological Society on the occasion of its 50th anniversary (1934). For the eastern Alps, see

also L. Kober, *Bau und Entstehung der Alpen,* Berlin (1923). Finally, we draw special attention to the very clear and well illustrated little work of L. W. Collet, *The Structure of the Alps,* London (1927).

63. The Aar Massif would be an extension of the Mount Blanc Massif, so that the tectonic zone to which the Gotthard belongs and which still contains small crystalline massifs near Courmayeur (back of Mt. Blanc) does not, in France, present any important outcrops of crystalline rocks.

64. There, in eastern Switzerland, they are designated by local names, which we shall not use here.

65. We may also suppose that these Pennine Coal Measures prolong the narrow band of Carboniferous which appears in the sub-Briançonnais zone between Moutiers and Aime and passes into Italy through the Petit-Saint-Bernard Pass, remaining in front of the true Briançonnais Carboniferous.

66. Recently P. Bearth, *Ueber die Zusammenhang von Monte-Rosa- und Bernhard-Decke,* Eclogae geol. Helvetiae, 32 (1939), has shown that the Monte-Rosa nappe was not actually distinct from that of St. Bernard. This opinion has been accepted by the eminent tectonic geologist of Zurich, R. Staub, who proposes to combine these two in a single nappe called the *Mischabel.* See the important works in which this author tries to find in Graubünden all the zones (ultra-Dauphiné, sub-Briançonnais, Briançonnais) identified in the French Alps: R. Staub, *Einige Ergebnisse vergleichender Studien zwischen Wallis und Bünden,* Eclogae geol. Helvetiae, 31 (1938); *Gedanken zum Bau der Westalpen,* Vierteljahrschr. Naturforsch. Ges. Zurich, 82 (1937), 87 (1942).

In the last named (1942) of these works, R. Staub, depending on homologies with the Eastern Alps, tries to demonstrate that a good part of our sub-Briançonnais scales (in particular the mountains which rise above the window of Barcelonnette on the south) represent remains of nappes (Austro-Alpine) originating beyond the zone of *schistes lustrés,* thus from the plain of the Po near Turin. This interpretation seeming quite inacceptable, we may ask if there would not be reason to revise the presently accepted ideas on the tectonics of eastern Switzerland, which would tend to raise the problem of the relation between the western and eastern Alps.

We believe we should continue to explain here the great classic Alpine syntheses, precisely because they are classic and easy to diagram and because, under this heading, they provide an indispensable base, a convenient point of departure for future syntheses.

67. These are entirely gratuitous geometrizations. But it seems to us extremely dangerous to insist on always finding the same nappes from one end of the Alpine Chain to the other, from Vienna to Nice (and even beyond, in Corsica). The nappes seem rather like local festoons, advancing in turn and replacing each other at the front of the chain.

68. J. Schoeller, *La nappe de l'Embrunais au Nord de l'Isère,* Bull. Serv. Carte géol., France, no. 175 (1929). R. Barbier, work cited note 54, this chap.

69. It has been recently divided by M. Lugeon and E. Gagnebin into several elementary nappes, which they have endeavored to identify from Sion to Sulens.

70. In the French Alps between Pelvoux and Mercantour, just under the Pennine frontal thrust, are found some scales having the same facies characteristics but not terminating in true nappes. We have called them ultra-Dauphiné scales, see Fig. 84. R. Barbier has shown that, north of Pelvoux, the band of Flysch of the Aiguilles d'Arves and Cheval Noir should also be attached to this ultra-dauphinois zone, since formerly the nappe of the Aiguilles d'Arves was included with the Flysch nappe of the Embrunais and attributed to the Pennine domain.

71. In fact, the mountain of Piolit, external part of the sub-Briançonnais Massif of Chabrières, east of Gap, has had the same history as the Niesen. It was long considered to be made up wholly of Tertiary (Gap sheet, 1st edition), and we now see a stacking of scales, particularly Jurassic and Cretaceous (Gap sheet, 2nd edition).

72. La Simme Noir and La Simme Blanche are rivers of the Romande Prealps. This nappe was formerly called the Rhaetic nappe, because it was likened to one of the nappes of the Eastern Alps in the Rhätikon.

73. B. Campana, *Observations sur les nappes de la Simme et de la Brèche dans la région des Saanenmöser et leur position réciproque,* Eclogae geol. Helvetiae, 35 (1942).

The author concludes that the Breccia nappe, above the Simme nappe, is thus the highest of the Prealpine nappes.

74. The question of the roots of the Prealpine nappes is highly controversial, except for those of the ultra-Helvetic nappe, on which everyone agrees. In particular, most Swiss geologists suppose, for these nappes, a much more distant origin; they have them come from the zone of Ivrea and Canavese which, back of the Pennine domain, prolongs the eastern Alps (p. 397). Also they call the Prealpine nappes, Austro-Alpine. Indeed, we shall see that the Prealpine Mesozoic corresponds to some well dated fossiliferous horizons, with facies quite different from those of the Helvetides. But, when we cross the Alps to the right of the classic region of St. Bernard-Sion-Simplon, after having left the Helvetian domain, we find the Sion-Val Ferret zone, with obscure stratigraphy, where non-fossiliferous Lias and Triassic are known. Next we reach the domain of the metamorphic Pennines and before we again find the fossiliferous Mesozoic, having certain analogies with that of the Prealps, we must go as far as the Canavese zone and the region of the Italian Lakes. In France, however, the sub-Briançonnais and Briançonnais Mesozoic shows a fossiliferous non-metamorphic Pennine, entirely identical, even in its details, to that of the Prealpine series. So we have accepted the opinion of E. Haug and consider the Prealpine nappes to be of external, Pennine origin. Their roots, unrecognized up to the present and perhaps unrecognizable, should be found in the Sion-Val Ferret zone or in the neighborhood of the Pennine coal-bearing zone. See the articles by E. Haug (cited note 55, this chap.), of M. Gignoux and L. Moret (cited note 155, chap. 5), and of M. Gignoux and E. Raguin (cited note 162, chap. 5).

75. Beyond the great trough of the Swiss Tertiary, the arc of the Jura, more external, marks the extreme limit of advance between the Massif Central and the Vosges-Black Forest.

76. On the north slope of the Aar Massif, crinoidal or gastropod limestones of the Muschelkalk type have been studied, especially by K. Rohr, *Stratigraphie und tektonische Untersuchung der Zwischenbildungen am Nordrande des Aarmassivs*, Matériaux Carte géol. Suisse, n. s., 57 livr., and by W. Bruderer, *Les sédiments du bord septentrional du Massif de l'Aar, du Trias à l'Argovien*, Bull. Lab. Géol. Univ. Lausanne, no. 37 (1924).

77. The Swiss geologists say *cornieules*. This word, borrowed from the dialect of Savoy and French Switzerland, is pronounced a little differently in different regions. The German equivalent is *Rauhwacke;* the Italian, *"dolomia cariata."*

78. These are the *Médianes rigides* of the recent syntheses of M. Lugeon and E. Gagnebin, *Observations et vues nouvelles sur la Géologie des Prealpes romandes*, Bull. Lab. Géol. Univ. Lausanne, 72 (1941).

79. A very general statement, however; the fossils are always better preserved in the drifted masses, transported in the block, than in the root zones, with their isoclinal structure, where everything has been deformed by flow.

80. H. H. Renz, *Pflanzenführender Keuper in der Breccien-Decke des Simmentals,* Eclogae geol. Helvetiae, 29 (1936).

81. A similar statement may be made for the Jurassic. We recall that formerly M. Lugeon considered the Breccia nappe of Chablais as tectonically lower than that of the Middle Prealp nappe which it would only apparently overlap, as the result of an envelopment. But this idea is now abandoned by the Swiss geologists.

82. Probably unique example of a natural region whose name is derived from that of a French savant, the Dauphinois mineralogist Déodat de Dolomieu.

83. See, for example, F. Heritsch, *Die österreichischen und deutschen Alpen (Ostalpen)*, Handbuch der regionalen Geologie, Heft 18 (1915).

84. Also called Scythian.

85. Also called Anisian, from the Latin name (Anisus) of the Enns river, passing south of the Dachstein, in the Austrian Tyrol.

86. The tectonic elements of which E. Haug made an independent nappe, called *salt nappe,* must be joined to it.

87. P. Leonardi, *Il Trias inferiore delle Venezie*, Mem. Istit. Geol. Univ. Padova, 11 (1935–37). This important work contains a rapid survey of the lower marine Triassic of the whole world (see map, p. 107).

88. It is possible that this abruptness may often be emphasized by suppression of strata due to tectonic stretching or by disturbances caused in the development of the reef organisms by volcanic eruptions (Cornelius). As recent works on this classic region, we note Mrs. Ogilvie-Gordon, *Das Grödener-, Fassa- und Enneberg-gebiet in den Südtyroler Dolomiten,* Abh. geol. Bundesant., 24, Vienna (1927); *Geologie des Gebietes von Pieve (Buchenstein), St. Cassian und Cortina d'Ampezzo,* Jahrb. geol. Bundesanst., 79, Vienna (1929); *Geologie von Cortina d'Ampezzo und Cadore,* ibid., 84, Vienna (1935) with geologic map. H. P. Cornelius and M. Furlani-Cornelius, *Ueber die Tektonik der Marmolatagruppe (Südtyrol),* Neues Jahrb. f. Min., Beilage-Band 56, Abt. B (1927). G. Mutschlechner, *Geologie des Gebietes zwischen St. Cassian und Buchenstein,* Jahrb. geol. Bundesanst., 83, Vienna (1934).

89. For a general study, more recent than the *Traité de Géologie* of E. Haug, see especially, C. Diener, *Die Marinen Reich der Triasperiode,* Denksch. d. k. Akad. d. Wiss., Vienna (1915). For the Alps, the author does not accept the nappe theory.

90. D. Andrusov, *Stratigraphie du Trias des Carpathes slovaques,* Bull. Serv. géol. Republique tchécoslovaque, 11 (1935).

91. J. von Pia, *Die Diploporen der Trias von Süd-Dalmatien,* Sitzungsber. Akad. Wiss. in Wien, Math-Naturw. Kl., Abt. 1, Band 133 (1924).

92. I Simionescu, *Les couches à Daonelles de Dobrogea,* Public. Fondation Adamachi, Acad. Romana, 9, no. 43, Bucharest (1925).

93. G. von Arthaber, *Die Trias von Bithynien (Anatolien),* Beitr. z. Pal. u. Geol. Oesterreich-Ungarns u. des Orients, XXVII (1915). E. Chaput, *Observations géologiques en Asie mineure: le Trias de la région d'Angora,* C. R. Acad. Sc. (May 17, 1932).

94. J. Wanner, *Die Malaiische Geosynklinale im Mesozoïcum,* Gedenkboek Verbeek, Verh. van het geol.-mijnbouwkundig Genootschap voor Nederland en Kolonien, Geolog. Ser., 8 (1925).

95. At the approach of the old Asiatic Continent of Angara (p. 239) the Triassic naturally becomes continental. Mei Nien Bien, "The Red Beds of Yunnan," Bull. Soc. geol. China, 21 (1941). And we find in China the same succession of reptilian genera as in the Beaufort and Stormberg series of South Africa. Chung Chien Young, *The Triassic Vertebrate Remains of China,* Amer. Mus. Novitates, no. 1324 (1946).

96. The marine faunas of this Pacific Triassic, and especially the ammonites, have recently been studied by J. P. Smith, who extended his comparison to the Mesogean and Arctic Triassic, and showed that many ammonite zones had a worldwide extent. We refer only to the last of his works, in which will be found a complete bibliography: J. P. Smith, *Lower Triassic Ammonoids of North America,* U. S. Geol. Surv., Prof. Paper 167 (1932).

97. K. Körner, *Marine (Cassianer-Raibler) Trias am Nevado da Arrotambo (Nord-Peru),* Palaeontografica, 86, Abt. A (1937).

98. P. Groeber, *Descubrimiento del Triasico marino en la Republica Argentina,* Communic. d. Mus. Nac. Hist. nat. Buenos-Aires, II, 9 (1924).

99. C. T. Trechmann, "The Trias of New Zealand," Quart. Journ. geol. Soc. London, 73 (1917).

100. Bibliography in A. Carpentier, *Etudes paléobotaniques sur le groupe de la Sakoa et le groupe de la Sakamena (Madagascar),* Ann. géol. Serv. Mines Madagascar, 5 (1935).

101. Cf. H. Douvillé, Bull. Soc. Géol. France, 1910. P. Lemoine, *Madagascar,* Handbuch der regionalen geologie (1911). J. Cottreau, C. R. Soc. géol. France (Feb. 18, 1924).

102. L. F. Spath, "On Ammonites from Spitsbergen," Geol. Mag., 58 (1921). H. Frebold, *Das Festungsprofil auf Spitzbergen. V. Stratigraphie und Invertebratenfauna der älterer Eotrias, nebst Beschreibung anderer Vorkommen in Spitzbergen,* Skriften om Svalbard og Ishavel, n. 77, Oslo (1939).

103. L. F. Spath, "Eotriassic Ammonites from East Greenland," Geol. Mag., 64 (1927). H. Stauber, *Die Trias-Ablagerungen von Ostgrönland,* Medd. om Grönland (1942), 132, no. 1, p. 1–125.

104. The Mediterranean Werfenian is transgressive in the southern part of Asiatic

Russia. Perhaps through the eastern part of the Urals there was, at that time, communication with the Arctic seas. But beginning with the Middle Triassic this communication must have been interrupted. Cf. Diener, work cited note 89, this chap., p. 447.

105. The presence of a related form, *P. caucasica,* in the Crimea and in the Caucasus, poses a curious problem: this species of the Pacific must have reached the Mesogean province by way of the Himalayas, yet none are known in the Himalayan faunas.

Chapter Seven

The Jurassic

I. Generalities

1. *Stratigraphic Subdivisions*

The Jurassic formations derive their name from the Jura Chain, of which they constitute the framework. Their description has a special interest for us, for it was in connection with their study that the principles of stratigraphy were first formulated.

In describing the Swabian Jura, Quenstedt and Leopold von Buch distinguished three successive groups of rocks, to which they gave the names Black Jura, Brown Jura, and White Jura, in accordance with their appearance in outcrops. These three groups correspond approximately to what we now call the Lower Jurassic or Lias, the Middle Jurassic or Dogger and the Upper Jurassic or Malm.[1]

Then, in further detail and using both the lithologic characteristics of the beds and the faunas that they contained, Quenstedt divided each of these three groups into six stages which he designated by Greek letters alpha, beta, zeta (from bottom to top). This nomenclature (Lias α, Dogger γ, etc.) is still used in Germany.

Oppel carried this study of faunas further. He distinguished in the Swabian Jurassic a whole series (33) of horizons or paleontologic zones, each named for a characteristic fossil, usually an ammonite. He could find most of these zones in neighboring regions, but he recorded that often the nature of the rock had changed. Thus the concepts both of the paleontologic zone and of facies and their reciprocal independence were defined.

Ever since, we have continued to use Oppel's methods. The number of paleontologic zones could be increased and it has been recognized that only ammonite species have a chronologic value independent of the facies. The assemblage of these ammonite zones constitutes a stratigraphic standard that we try to find in all countries and across all the facies. This has been fairly successful for Europe.[2]

The number of these zones being very great, in general descriptions it becomes necessary to group them in more comprehensive stages. These groupings have varied greatly with different authors, for the stages were first defined by lithologic groups depending on local facies and having only a regional value. It is necessary then to indicate always the relation between the stages adopted and the ammonite zones, which we shall do later on (see pp. 323, 326 and 328).[3]

To give immediately a concrete foundation to this long list of stages, we indicate in the following table the localities and type facies of each of them. These facies are found moreover in a good number of the regions which we shall study.

Upper Jurassic	*Portlandian*	*Purbeckian*—Lacustrine and brackish deposits of Purbeck (Dorsetshire). *Bononian*—Marine limestones and sandstones of Portland (Dorsetshire) and the Boulonnais.
	Kimmeridgian	—Black marls of Kimmeridge (Dorsetshire).[4]
	Lusitanian (Portugal)	*Sequanian* = *Astartian*—*Astarte* limestones of Franche-Comté (= Sequania). *Rauracian*—Coral limestones of the Rauraces country (ancient tribe of the Jura). *Argovian*—Gray marls with siliceous sponges of the Aargau Jura (Switzerland).
	Oxfordian	—Black marls of Oxford.
	Callovian	—Sandy limestones of Kellaways (Wiltshire).
Middle Jurassic	*Bathonian*	—White oolitic limestones of Bath (Somersetshire).
	Bajocian	—Ferruginous oolitic limestones of Bayeux (Calvados).
Lower Jurassic or Lias	*Aalenian*	—Ferruginous beds and black marls with *Trigonia navis* of Aalen (Wurttemberg).
	Toarcian	—Black marls of Thouars (Deux-Sèvres).
	Charmouthian	—Black marls of Charmouth (Dorsetshire).
	Sinemurian	—Black limestones with *Gryphaea arcuata* of Semur (Côte-d'Or).
	Hettangian	—Sandstones with *Cardinia hybrida* of Hettange (Moselle).
	Rhaetian	—Ammonite shales and brachiopod limestones of the Rhaetic Alps: special facies in Alpine and Mediterranean regions. Moreover, very littoral beds with *Avicula contorta* and bone beds.

2. Faunas and Facies

The facies of the Jurassic are infinitely varied. But, in most of the regions which interest us, certain facies occur at almost the same epochs, over a large area, from Swabia to England, passing through the Jura and Lorraine. Also, to a first approximation, there is a normal type of the Jurassic in which the facies are distributed as follows:

The lower Lias includes black, marly limestones. The middle and upper Lias are almost always plainly marly and likewise black (Black Jura). The

Middle Jurassic is on the whole formed of hard limestones, among which limestones with crinoids, corals or oolites predominate, with more or less ferruginous beds (Brown Jura). The Callovian and especially the Oxfordian are almost always represented by black clays. The Lusitanian is quite varied, with marly limestones, sometimes with sponges, or coral facies. Finally, the Kimmeridgian and especially the Portlandian point to a return to the limestone sedimentation (White Jura).

If we add that this normal type of the Jurassic is plainly marine but that it is very often enclosed at the base and the top by lagoonal or continental beds, we can understand how in practice we can see easily both the individuality of the Jurassic as a whole and that of its subdivisions, which are easy to recognize on the ground. The repeated alternations of limestones and marls provide the key to the morphology of all Jurassic countries.

There remains to be noted the part taken by the principal groups of animals in these different facies.

Protozoans. We mention first the Radiolaria, whose siliceous skeletons accumulate in the cherts (fine-grained siliceous rocks) called radiolarites, a facies characteristic of the Upper Jurassic of the internal zones of the Alps (Rhaetic and Italian Alps, see p. 361). Although they cannot always be compared definitely to the radiolarian oozes of the present abysses, as some have wished to do, these radiolarites none the less represent a sometimes deep-water or, in any event, a pelagic facies.[5]

Sponges. The siliceous sponges (hexactinellid and lithistid) prospered on the muddy bottoms at certain periods of the Jurassic, especially toward the base of the Lusitanian. They form the marly limestones of the sponge facies, containing magnificent specimens in the French and Swiss Jura. Even when the sponges have not been preserved, the accumulation of the siliceous spicules has caused the formation of rocks (the Oxfordian earths of the Ardennes, for example) that L. Cayeux termed spongoliths. The mobility of this silica often leads to the formation of black flints called *chailles* or to the silicification of various other fossils.[6]

The calcareous sponges, all related to the extinct group of pharetrons, are, on the other hand, found only in the littoral organic facies. They are, moreover, relatively rare. We only see them flourish in the Middle Jurassic limestones in England and Normandy.

Coelenterates. The corals all belong to the present group of hexacorals, but their determination, always very difficult, has scarcely any stratigraphic interest. Fleeing the muddy depths, they developed only at certain epochs, producing compact white limestones, very important for local stratigraphy.

In the Lias, they are hardly found except in certain parts of the Alps (eastern Alps, for example) and, very locally, in England (region of the Mendip Hills, see p. 340). In the Middle Jurassic, they are distributed everywhere at horizons varied according to the region. Finally in the Lusitanian and especially the Rauracian, the coral limestones become so preponderant that early geologists gave the name Corallian to that stage, and in the course of the Lusitanian we shall see them recede little by little toward the south, so that in the Kimmeridgian and Portlandian, they remain confined to Alpine and Mediterranean regions. It seems difficult not to see in this geographic localization proof of the existence of differentiated climatic zones.

Along with the corals proper, the hydrozoans should be noted and especially *Ellipsactinia,* with skeletons formed of concentric layers. In certain Mediterranean regions they have built, in the Upper Jurassic,[7] *Ellipsactinia* limestones forming huge white cliffs (Capri, south of Naples) and they extend, moreover, into the Lower Cretaceous.

To the group of alcyonarians, marine hydrozoa, must be related, according to Lucas,[8] the easily recognizable impressions in the "brush marks," previously attributed to algae, under the name of *Cancellophycus* (= *Spirophyton*) *scoparius.* Often abundant in the limey shales of the Middle Jurassic, they there characterize the relatively deep-water facies called *Cancellophycus* Dogger (p. 362).

Echinoderms. The crinoids played a big role in the Jurassic whether found isolated in limestones or marls, or constructing crinoidal limestones. *Pentacrinus* is particularly abundant in the Lias, *Apiocrinus* in the Middle Jurassic and *Millericrinus* in certain facies of the Upper Jurassic (*chailles* formations). The maximum development of crinoidal limestones very commonly took place in the Middle Jurassic, especially in the Bajocian.

Echinoids are extremely abundant and varied, so that they are often used as characteristic fossils. Certain ones, with thin shells, little decoration and with sharp corners, are found even in the muddy facies, such as *Dysaster* (*D. ellipticus,* Callovian) and *Stomechinus* (*S. bigranularis,* Bajocian), ancestors of our present edible echinoids. But the greater part are characteristic of the organic calcareous facies and have a thick shell, very ornate, or well developed petals: *Clypeus ploti* in oolitic limestones of the Middle Jurassic, *Glypticus hieroglyphicus* (of the Lusitanian) which has given its name to the Glyptician stage (Rauracian with coral facies) of the early geologists, and finally innumerable *Cidaris* (*C. florigemma* of the reefy Rauracian, *C. glandifera* of the Portlandian with coral facies in the Mediterranean regions).

Pelecypods. Few of these are strictly localized in a particular facies. *Posidonomya* should be mentioned particularly, known especially in the facies of slightly bituminous, black shales—*P. (Steinmannia) bronni* of the upper Lias of Germany and Lorraine and *P. alpina* of the Bathonian-Callovian of southeast France.[9]

On the other hand, the thick shelled *Diceras,* distant ancestor of the Cretaceous rudistids, is always associated with the coral facies of the Lusitanian. These are warm water animals, which never even reached England. Likewise the last megalodontids, coming from the Triassic, still persist in the Rhaetian and Alpine Lias and are there localized in the reef facies of the eastern and Lombard Alps.

Aucellas, however, seem to characterize a northern province in the Upper Jurassic of Europe. They are particularly abundant in the Russian seas, but they have recently been found in India, the Indian Archipelago, New Zealand, Mexico, and the South American Cordillera. Their distribution, like that of many marine animals, seems to depend much more on currents than on climate.

The other pelecypods are found more or less everywhere, provided the facies be somewhat littoral. The *Mya*-like forms (pholadomyas) predominate in the muds, certain smooth and concave oysters (*Gryphaea*)[10] in the marly limestones, *Astarte* in fine-grained limestones (former Astartian stage = Sequanian), while in the sandstones or detrital limestones, cardinians, pectens, limas,[11] aviculids, mytilids, ornate oysters, etc. abound.

Gastropods. They are very rare and of little interest. *Pleurotomaria*,[12] an archaic group, is well represented. In the coral facies are found thick-shelled nerineas; numerous species occur in the Lusitanian.[13] In the marls of the middle Lias, a pigmy fauna is frequently found in which gastropods abound (*Trochus subduplicatus*, etc.), which suggests the same comparison as the biologically similar fauna of the Triassic marls of St. Cassian (see p. 302). Finally the muddy marl-limestones of the Kimmeridgian sometimes contain in abundance a large, winged gastropod, *Harpagodes* (formerly called *Pteroceras*) *oceani,* which earned the old name Pterocerian for the lower part of this stage.

Ammonites.[14] They are distributed, in the Jurassic, in every region and in all the marine facies (except the coral reefs) and it is on them that the stratigraphy of the system is based.

Most of the species have, indeed, a rather limited longevity so that they characterize zones.[15] Naturally the vertical extension of zones thus defined varies with the species which characterize them; one species will persist unchanged while a whole series of others beside it appear and disappear. So, in the choice of characteristic species, those should be used which have the briefest possible duration and which, at the same time, are found in a sufficient number of different regions in relative abundance. These conditions are often difficult to reconcile, which explains the fact that the ammonite zones accepted by different authors may not always be the same, and why the zone names remain unceasingly subject to revision. The list of zones generally accepted in France will be found later (pp. 323, 326 and 328) following E. Haug.

As we shall see, it is very rare that several successive zones correspond to transformations in place, to stages of evolution of a single branch. More often, the characteristic species which follow each other belong to different genera; that is to say, the sudden arrival and departure of each of them should be attributed to migration. For reasons we do not understand, certain forms have had sudden prosperity at a given epoch; like a wave of settlers, they have suddenly overrun immense areas, to disappear some time later, leaving the place to other waves. There is nothing incredible in this, for the plant or animal world at the present time offers examples of species thus rapidly invading huge areas.

The stratigraphic usefulness of ammonites is further augmented by the fact that they penetrate into relatively varied facies. Nevertheless certain species, small in number, with smooth unornamented shells, are shown to be confined exclusively to the deepest-water facies: such are species of *Phylloceras* and *Lytoceras*. We shall see, moreover, that certain genera (*Cardioceras, Virgatites, Craspedites*) are, in the Upper Jurassic, localized in northern regions while others (*Reineckeia, Oppelia*) are limited to Mediterranean regions; but here we are doubtless dealing with differences of provinces, not of facies. In the same way *Gravesia* (= *Pachyceras*) characterizes, in the lower Portlandian (Bononian), a western province (E. Haug) that includes southern Britain, the Paris Basin, and the Aquitanian Basin and extends as far as the Jura and Hanover by way of the Morvan-Vosgian Straits and Poitou.

From the stratigraphic standpoint, if we consider only the best known genera, we can make the following statements. In the Rhaetian, no ammonites are found in Europe outside the eastern Alps; the lower Lias is the domain of arietitids; the middle Lias, of amalthids; the upper Lias, of *Harpoceras;* the Middle Jurassic, of *Sonninia, Oppelia* and *Parkinsonia;* the Callovian-Oxfordian, of *Macrocephalites, Reineckeia* and *Cardioceras;* and the Upper Jurassic, of *Pachyceras* (*Gravesia*) and *Perisphinctes*.

Belemnites. Equally distributed in all facies, they are much more difficult to determine and do not give as precise stratigraphic information.

Only forms without a ventral groove (*B. excentricus, B. paxillosus*) exist in the lower and middle Lias. Forms with a ventral groove, starting from the point of the guard, appear in the upper Lias (*B. irregularis, B. giganteus*). Then, beginning with the Middle Jurassic, there are forms in which the ventral groove only starts above the point (s.g. *Belemnopsis, B. hastatus*). At the top of the Jurassic, *Belemnopsis* is replaced in northern Europe by *Cylindroteuthis* (*B. excentricus, B. absolutus*), a group with northern affinities, while in the Mediterranean regions the special group of *Duvalia* or the flat belemnites appears.

Brachiopods. They are extremely abundant in slightly littoral facies. They are mostly terebratulids or rhynchonellids, highly polymorphous, and having only empirical local value for determining horizons.[16] Nevertheless certain archaic forms (example, *Spirigera*), descending from Primary and Triassic groups, characterize the Carpathian facies of the Rhaetian (see p. 357). Among them spiriferinids persist everywhere as far as the end of the Lias.[17]

In the deep-water facies of the Alpine region there is found a special group of thin-shelled terebratulids, *Pygopes*—*P. aspasia* of the Lias of Lombardy and Spain, *P. janitor* of the Portlandian of the French sub-Alpine chains, *P. diphya* of the Portlandian of the Lombard Alps.

Vertebrates. With the Jurassic, the era of great reptiles dawned in Europe. The most frequent here are the ichthyosaurians, the plesiosaurians, and the pterosaurians. But these curious animals, so well preserved in certain Liassic shales of Britain (Lyme Regis) or of Germany (Boll, Wurttemberg) have scarcely any stratigraphic interest. It is the same with fish, of which the lithographic limestones of Solnhofen (Franconia) and of Cerin near Belley (Ain) have yielded magnificent specimens.

3. *Paleogeography and Regional Distribution in Europe*

At the end of the Triassic, Europe presented the following picture: to the south, a deep sea, the Mesogean or Alpine geosyncline sea, spreading over Alpine and Mediterranean regions, and to the north, a vast continent, remnant of the ancient Hercynian Chain, almost completely leveled off and transformed into a huge desert, previously dotted with the lagoons of the Keuper.

The same contrast prevails during the course of the Jurassic. The Mesogean sea persists and grows larger. But to the north, the continental domain is invaded by a marine transgression which, beginning with the Rhaetian, ends only with the Portlandian. Thus the northern Jurassic presents a great sedimentation cycle, enclosed by two periods of regression. However, this transgression is not accomplished at a single stroke. We shall follow its progressive advance as well as its vicissitudes. Thus, Middle Jurassic time seems here to correspond to a retreat or at least to a diminution in depth of the sea (lacunas of sedimentation, iron minerals, organic limestones, etc.).

In this sea which thus advances over a country of plateaus with little variation, very little coarse detrital sediment was deposited, but mostly marly muds or organic formations. So the Jurassic is, in these regions, the period par excellence of limestones and marls. And the seas which invaded the old desert continent of the Triassic generally remained rather shallow. They are epicontinental seas. The Secondary here is not thick and is neither folded nor metamorphic, which contrasts these epicontinental regions to the domain of the Alpine geosyncline.

This conquest of the ancient Hercynian Chain by the sea was not entirely complete. From the beginning of the Triassic, we see a differentiation between certain parts of this chain.

A. Some parts rise higher or, if you prefer, were not reduced. They play, in the course of the following periods, the role of islands or more or less extensive platforms. Either because they were not deposited, or because they remained thinner and were removed by erosion, the Jurassic beds no longer cover these areas, where the older formations are exposed. These isolated fragments of an originally continuous Hercynian Chain constitute what we have called the Hercynian Massifs.

B. Between these ancient massifs stretch regions which, on the contrary, have had a tendency to be depressed. These are the submerged areas, or more simply, basins, connected to each other by straits and bounded by ancient Jurassic shores.

These structural characteristics are seen at the first glance at a geologic map of Europe. They serve as a framework to describe the stratigraphy of the whole Secondary. They are:

1. *The Anglo-Parisian Basin.* Cut in two by the present Channel, it is bounded on the west by the old massifs of western Britain and by the Armorican Massif, on the south by the French Massif Central, on the east by the Rhenish Massif (Ardennes) and the Vosges. It is prolonged on the north by the present North Sea, passing west of the Scandinavian Massif.

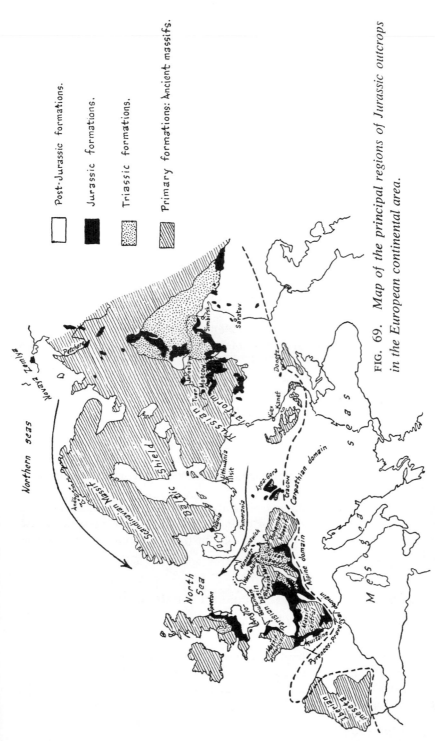

FIG. 69. *Map of the principal regions of Jurassic outcrops in the European continental area.*

The dashed line marks the approximate boundary between the European continental area to the north and the Mesogean seas to the south. The arrows indicate the avenues of communication between the Russian seas and the North Sea in the Upper Jurassic. N. B. The Jurassic formations are much folded in the Mesogean zone and their outcrops have a very complicated pattern and are not shown here.

321

2. *The Aquitanian Basin.* It communicates with the preceding by way of the Strait of Poitou, between Brittany and the Massif Central. It joins the important Jurassic region of the Strait of the Causses, between the Massif Central and its dependent, the Montagne-Noire, a strait through which we enter the Rhône Basin. On the south, its terminus hidden under the Tertiary plain,[18] the Aquitanian Basin is bounded by the Pyrenees zone, a fragment of the Alpine Chain, a zone itself bounded on the south by the immense Hercynian Massif of the Iberian Meseta (see Figs. 104 and 105).

3. *The Rhodanian Basin.* This is, as a matter of fact, in its southern part only a dependent of the great Alpine Chain, for the Pyrenees folds join the Alps by way of Languedoc and Provence, west of the ancient Maures-Esterel Massif. But in the northern part, it is distinguished by an independent element, the Jura Chain, which, from the point of view of Jurassic facies, clearly remains outside of the Alpine domain, and is joined rather to the Paris Basin, with which the Rhodanian Basin communicates through the Strait of the Côte-d'Or.

4. *The Swabian Basin* between the Black Forest, the Rhenish Massif and Bohemia. This is a remnant of extensive Jurassic outcrops representing a much larger arm of sea, called by E. Haug, the Germanic cuvette [basin], which is prolonged to the east by way of Hanover, as far as the Scandinavian Massif in Scania.

All these basins (except the Swabian Basin) have, however, also been invaded by Cretaceous and Tertiary seas, so that, in their centers, the Jurassic remains covered and crops out only around the borders. On the other hand, the external limits of these Jurassic aureoles are erosion boundaries and indicate only the minimum extent of the Jurassic seas. So, the Vosges-Black Forest area remained under water from the Rhaetian to the Callovian, at least. Likewise, a good part of the Massif Central must have been invaded in the Middle and Upper Jurassic.

The stratigraphy of the Jurassic, like that of the Cretaceous, is then the history of these basins, the study of their ancient shores, their coastal facies, the invasion of the straits, in a word, of the transgressions and regressions on their borders.

II. A Type Series of the Jurassic: Eastern Border of the Paris Basin (Burgundy and Lorraine)

From Morvan to the southern Ardennes, across Burgundy, Lorraine and Luxemburg, a wide band of Jurassic borders the Paris Basin. This is the most extensive outcrop in France and even in Europe and it is there that we take our type.[19]

1. *The Lias*[20]

The exact definition of the stages that we have adopted in the Lias results from their agreement with the most commonly accepted ammonite zones, following E. Haug.[21]

Aalenian.........	19. *Harpoceras concavum.* 18. *Harpoceras murchisonae.* 17. *Harpoceras opalinum.* 16. *Dumortieria pseudoradiosa, D. levesquei, Harpoceras (Pleydiella) aalense.*		

Toarcian.........	15. *Lytoceras jurense.* 14. *Harpoceras (Hildoceras) bifrons.* 13. *Harpoceras falciferum, H. serpentinum.*

Charmouthian.....	12. *Amaltheus (Paltopleuroceras) spinatus.........* 11. *Amaltheus margaritatus....................*	} Domerian
	10. *Deroceras (Prodactylioceras) davoei, Aegoceras capricornu............................* 9. *Polymorphites (Uptonia) jamesoni, Phylloceras ibex.................................* 8. *Deroceras armatum.......................*	} Pliensbachian

Sinemurian	upper	7. *Arietites (Echioceras) raricostatus, Oxynoticeras oxynotum.............................* 6. *Arietites (Asteroceras) obtusus, Aegoceras planicosta.................................* 5. *Arietites (Asteroceras) turneri, Deroceras birchi..*	} Lotharingian
	lower	4. *Arietites (Arnioceras) semicostatus...........* 3. *Arietites bucklandi.......................*	} Sinemurian (s. str.)

Hettangian.......	2. *Schlotheimia angulata* 1. *Psiloceras planorbis*

Rhaetian.........	No ammonites outside the Eastern Alps.

Rhaetian and Hettangian. This is the Infralias of early authors. The sedimentation still remains quite variable from one point to another. And it is only toward the end of the Hettangian that the Liassic transgression, at last victorious, leads to a greater uniformity of facies.[22]

The Rhaetian (10 to 30 m. approximately) does not have its type facies of the Rhaetic Alps here, but a facies called Swabian. Its base is clearly defined by the appearance of marine shells, forming true shell-marbles, characterized by *Avicula contorta* and many other littoral pelecypods. But above these marine beds are sometimes found recurrences of the red, clayey facies of the Keuper, indicating a momentary return to the lagoonal regime: such are, at the top of the Rhaetian, the Levallois marls (named for a local geologist), 7 to 8 m. thick and of a characteristic brownish red. This is why the German geologists place the Rhaetian in the Triassic. The changes in salinity of the Triassic lagoons must have been in some cases very rapid, to some degree catastrophic, as the Rhaetian contains bone-beds, filled with remains of fish (teeth, scales, spines), without doubt killed *en masse* by the sudden change of environment.

This Swabian facies of the Rhaetian is found everywhere in Europe out-side of the Alpine domain. It is characterized by the absence of cephalopods, corals, and brachiopods. This first Jurassic sea constituted then a special biologic environment, like the Muschelkalk sea, the normal sea being still, as in the Triassic, confined to the Alpine and Mediterranean regions.

The Hettangian, generally thin (up to 10 m.) has a quite varied develop-ment. There are sometimes marls or marly limestones with *Psiloceras planorbis,* overlain by limestones with *Schlotheimia angulata* passing into Sinemurian limestones, sometimes more or less sandy sediments, called In-fraliassic sandstones (sandy limestones with cardinias, sandstones with *Pecten valoniensis,* etc.).

Sinemurian.   Here, on the other hand, are very uniform facies of lime-stones with arcuate gryphaeas and arietites (lower Lias of early authors), blue-black, more or less marly, sometimes exploited for hydraulic lime. They often terminate with harder beds, called *Pentacrinus* banks, forming bars above the basin sediments of the marls of the Keuper and Infralias. Their thickness is of the order of 10 to 30 m.

The upper Sinemurian or Lotharingian is again more marly, but it also ends with calcareous or ferruginous beds, sometimes with phosphatic nodules. These are the ochreous limestones, very fossiliferous near Nancy[23] and for that reason chosen by E. Haug as the type of his Lotharingian stage (zones 5, 6, 7). But actually it is very difficult to mark the limits of this stage, for this ochreous limestone facies sometimes is prolonged into the Charmouthian (zones 8 and 9).

In Burgundy, the Hettangian and Sinemurian are both transgressive and end by lying directly on the old formations of the Morvan. It is there, at Semur, that the type of the Sinemurian was taken.

Charmouthian and *Toarcian.*[24]   These stages are principally marly and represent a new depressed zone.

In Lorraine, the lower Charmouthian or Pliensbachian begins with thin, ferruginous beds corresponding to zone 8. Near Nancy, we have seen that the ochreous limestone facies was even prolonged into zone 9. Then come marls (10 m. thick) where *Terebratula (Zeilleria) numismalis* abounds. Zone 10 is often a little more calcareous (marl-limestones with *Deroceras davoei*), but zone 11 (or lower Domerian) is composed of very loose and very thick (70 m.) marls, often micaceous, called *Amaltheus* marls or ovoid marls, for they contain characteristic ellipsoidal nodules. Zone 12, on the contrary, is made up of thin beds of more or less sandy and ferruginous limestones, the *Amaltheus spinatus* sandstones of the Lorraine geologists, sometimes making a little bar in the midst of the marls.

Finally, the Toarcian, sometimes reaching 100 m. in thickness, represents another great development of marly facies, in this case shallow-water. There is even a bed of lignite in the lower Toarcian. Bituminous shales[25] or paper shales or *Posidonomya* shales are included, then very fossiliferous marls with *Lytoceras jurense* and numerous small gastropods (*Trochus sub-diplicatus*). But actually this *Posidonomya* facies does not correspond to a definite stratigraphic horizon and can be found in different zones of the Toarcian (Corroy).

In Burgundy[26] the marl-limestone complex of zones 8–10 is exploited for cement at Venarey. Zone 11 is in very thick (60 m.) micaceous marls. Zone

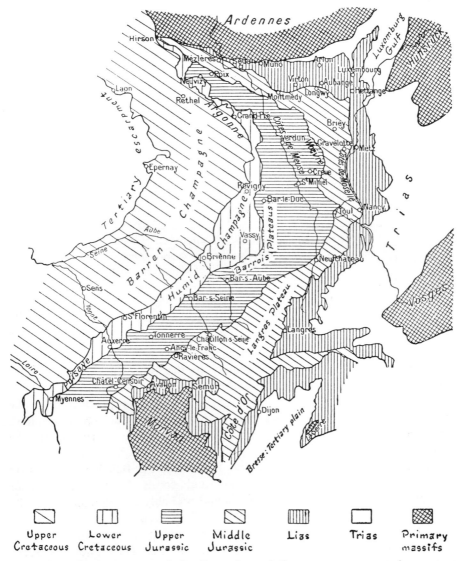

FIG. 70. *Geologic map of the Jurassic and Cretaceous arcs on the eastern border of the Paris Basin.*

12 is composed of marly limestone with giant gryphaeas (*G. regularis, G. latior*).[27] Finally, the marl-limestones of the base of the Toarcian supply great cement factories at Avallon and Isle-sur-Serein.

Aalenian. This corresponds to a decrease in depth, prelude to the organic facies of the Middle Jurassic. Here are, in fact, marls with marly or sandy limestones, more or less oolitic and ferruginous (there are even conglomerates), in which are developed the 8 or 10 beds of the famous Lorraine iron ore (*minette*) which are spaced across the four zones of the stage.[28] The zone of mining this mineral, determined by the iron content, is restricted in France to two fairly limited basins, that of Briey-Longwy and Nancy. The facies of ferruginous oolite tends to disappear toward the south. Thus, in Burgundy, the marly facies extends into the lower Aalenian, while the upper Aalenian is found to be represented by compact crinoidal and coral limestones, thus forming the base of the Middle Jurassic escarpments. These organic facies mark the approach of the ancient shores of the Massif Central.

2. *The Middle Jurassic*

The distribution of ammonites is as follows:

Bathonian	7. *Oppelia* (*Clydoniceras*) *discus.* 6. *Oppelia aspidoides.* 5. *Oppelia fusca.*
Bajocian	4. *Cosmoceras* (*Garantia*) *garanti, Parkinsonia parkinsoni* 3. *Coeloceras* (*Stepheoceras*) *blagdeni, Witchellia romani* ⎤ *Oppelia subradiata* 2. *Sphaeroceras* (*Emileia*) *sauzei, S.* (*Stepheoceras*) *humphriesianum* 1. *Sonninia sowerbyi, Witchellia laeviuscula*

In its entirety, the Middle Jurassic corresponds to an interruption of the marly regime and to its complete or partial replacement by organic limestones. At the base, there are especially crinoidal or coral limestones which were formerly attributed indiscriminately to the Bajocian. At the top are oolitic limestones making up the Bathonian. Recent research, more exact, has shown that these subdivisions, very convenient in practice from the cartographic standpoint, do not tally with the ammonite zones. We have just seen that in Burgundy the crinoidal limestone facies descends into the Aalenian.

In any case, in all of Lorraine and Burgundy, the Bajocian begins with organic limestones containing crinoids and corals forming escarpments (Côtes de Moselle) above Liassic marls and probably corresponding to zones 1 and 2. Above, the facies are diversified. There seem to have been lacunas of sedimentation almost everywhere, corresponding not to true emersions, but rather to a regime of violent submarine currents, which swept the rocky bottoms and could even gully them. In these facies of littoral platforms, ammonites are very rare, so that the correlations proposed between different regions seem very weak. We shall not stop to explain them in detail.[29]

In the central part of Lorraine, in Woëvre and as far as Toul, above the coral and crinoidal limestones of the Bajocian and perhaps after a lacuna of sedimentation corresponding to a good part of the Bathonian, the top of this

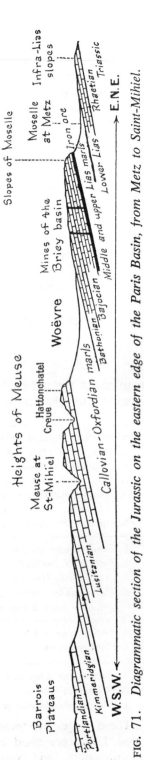

FIG. 71. *Diagrammatic section of the Jurassic on the eastern edge of the Paris Basin, from Metz to Saint-Mihiel.*

The marls make humid depressions, the limestones form slopes and dry plateaus.
Horizontal scale: 1/575,000. Vertical scale greatly exaggerated.

327

stage is hardly represented except by marly sediments which with the Callovian-Oxfordian marls produce the swampy plains of Woëvre.

South and north of this central region, however, are found more littoral facies, especially well studied in the region of Metz-Montmédy. There, between the Longwy marls and the Gravelotte marls (near Metz), a thick mass of yellow, oolitic limestone is intercalated, exploited as ashlar (Jaumont oolite, near Metz) which, according to Thiéry,[30] still belongs to the Bajocian, contrary to earlier belief. The Bajocian ends with white oolites (Doncourt oolites) and the upper Bathonian is represented by rough marl-limestones with *Rhynchonella alemanica* (up to the present time, wrongly called *R. varians*).[31]

Likewise, in the south, in the Côte-d'Or, it is probably to the Bathonian that, acording to Mlle. S. Gillet and M. Rouyer, the beds of white oolite now exploited along the Burgundy Canal (stone of Ravières) should be assigned. Above, the Bathonian ends with organic, calcareous massifs, containing coral debris, which form large calcareous plateaus, stony or thinly forested, separating the Basin of the Saône from that of the Seine (Plateaus of Langres and Côte-d'Or).

3. *The Upper Jurassic*

There is a good deal of argument about the nomenclature of the stages in this division, so that it is indispensable to relate them to ammonite zones:[32]

Portlandian	Purbeckian. . . .	In the Paris Basin, brackish or continental facies.[33]
	Bononian.	12. *Perisphinctes bononiensis.*
		11. *Pachyceras (Gravesia) portlandicum*
Kimmeridgian. .	Virgulian.	10. *Aulacostephanus pseudomutabilis, Aspidoceras caletanun, A. orthocera.*
	Pterocerian. . . .	9. *Oppelia (Streblites) tenuilobata, Rasenia cymodoce*
Lusitanian	Sequanian.	8. *Perisphinctes achilles* (= Astartian).
	Rauracian.	7. *Peltoceras bicristatum* (= *P. bimammatum*) = beds with *Hemicidaris crenularis.*
	Argovian.	6. *Peltoceras transversarium, Ochetoceras canaliculatum* = beds of Effingen and of Birmensdorf.
Oxfordian.		5. *Cardioceras cordatum.*
		4. *Cardioceras mariae.*
Callovian		3. *Cardioceras lamberti, Peltoceras athleta.*
		2. *Reineckeia anceps.*
		1. *Macrocephalites macrocephalus.*

Callovian and Oxfordian.[34]   These stages everywhere mark a return to clayey sedimentation. Always zone 1 is represented in the north by marly limestones still containing ferruginous oolites, and in the south by limestones with remains of pelecypods and crinoids, which give brilliant cleavage surfaces. This is the facies of the same nacreous flagstone of Burgundy[35] that we shall find again in the Jura, and which thus establishes a transition from the oolite flagstones of the upper Bathonian. But marls predominate in zone 2. This is the beginning of the thick series of Woëvre clays. The ferruginous oolite facies are no longer found except in Burgundy, thus marking the approach of the ancient shores of Morvan (see Fig. 73). The clayey facies develop in zones 3 and 4, represented by pyritic ammonite marls or marls with *Creniceras renggeri,* which we shall see progress toward the south across the whole Jura Range. The ferruginous oolite facies of the Morvan margin have again receded toward the southeast. Finally zone 5 has the very uniform type of the flint-bearing formation, with nodules of silica (flints) and siliceous sponges, a type equally common in the Jura and which foretells the more littoral facies of the Lusitanian.

Lusitanian. A new paleogeographic fact governs the history of the Lusitanian in Lorraine and Burgundy. This is the probable emersion of the Vosges-Black Forest Massif, an emersion which must have happened in the course of this period.[36]

In fact, while up to this time only the Ardennes and the Massif Central were emerged, so that we have been able to see facies of the high seas very near the Vosges, from the Lusitanian, however, littoral influenecs are inaugurated in Lorraine, producing coral reefs. We may suppose that these reefs were supported on shallow appendages of the Vosges Massif, emerged or in course of emergence. And it is in Burgundy that the muddy facies persist, thus showing the existence of a Morvan-Vosgian strait. There will be, however, no more marls, but marly limestones, preparing for the shallower-water facies of the Kimmeridgian and the Portlandian.

Thus it is that in the Côte-d'Or, a good part of the Lusitanian is represented by marly limestones with cephalopods, of which certain horizons are exploited for cement along the Burgundy Canal (Ancy-le-Franc, Frangey). This rather monotonous series is interesting, nevertheless, for ammonite zones can be found in it and from them the reef facies of Lorraine can be dated.

In Lorraine, the facies are however quite varied in details.[37] There may be coral or *Diceras* reefs, certain of which must have been emergent; because plant remains are found in them, or coral breccias resulting from the destruction in place of cliffs of these reefs, or oolitic limestones originating from the precipitation of calcium carbonate in the vicinity of the reefs, or lastly, compact, fine-grained limestones formed by the calcareous muds which were deposited more in the open sea. These thick masses of varied limestones produce a scarp above the Callovian-Oxfordian marls, the *côte* of the heights of the Meuse, rising west of the swampy plains of Woëvre.

The organic facies are not, however, absolutely general and sometimes sandy limestones are found at this horizon. Such is the case with the celebrated Creue limestones in which ammonite faunas mark the Argovian (*Peltoceras transversarium*), Rauracian and Sequanian (*Perisphinctes achilles, P. lothari*).[38] Aside from these exceptions, the Lusitanian generally has the Corallian facies. The base, usually remaining more marly, contains especially remains of echinoids, *Cidaris* and *Glypticus* (old Glyptician stage);

then come the true or coral reefs proper, overlain by limestones with nerineids and *Diceras* (Diceratian). In the Sequanian, there are oolitic or organic limestones of varied types. Certain fine-grained banks are covered with impressions of a small pelecypod, *Astarte supracorallina* (old Astartian stage).

Kimmeridgian and Portlandian.[39] These stages mark the end of the Corallian regime and the return to a sandy sedimentation, more or less calcareous, which killed the reefs. The ammonites reappear momentarily, but at the end of the Portlandian the brackish facies is established everywhere. The whole Paris Basin is emergent. This is the great regression at the end of the Jurassic.

The Kimmeridgian is rather clayey. At the base are especially marly, pebbly limestones with *Harpagodes* (old Pterocerian stage, see p. 318) and at the top are marls with *Ostrea virgula:* this is the old Virgulian stage, in reality a simple facies which can be found locally at other horizons even as high as the Portlandian.

The Portlandian is rather calcareous. Here are the Barrois limestones, with *Pachyceras* (*Gravesia*). They form great plateaus in the region of Bar-le-Duc, Bar-sur-Aube, Bar-sur-Seine, Tonnerre. At the top there are sometimes sandy beds with *Trigonia gibbosa,* corbulids, and cyrenids, brackish shells indicating the end of the marine regime. The whole corresponds, however, only to the lower Portlandian or Bononian. The Purbeckian exists neither in Lorraine nor in Burgundy. It is represented no doubt by a period of erosion (Fig. 78).

III. The Ancient Jurassic Shores Northeast of the Paris Basin (Luxemburg, the Ardennes, Boulonnais, Bray)

During the whole of the Jurassic the northwest part of the Rhenish Massif must have remained emergent and have served as shore for the seas which filled the Paris Basin. This is what the study of the facies and the lacunas of the Jurassic from Luxemburg into the Boulonnais will show us.[40]

The Rhaetian is known only in Luxemburg and the eastern part of the Ardennes, where it is naturally represented by the littoral sandstones of the Swabian facies.

The different stages of the Lias are in fact transgressive. By degrees as we move towards the northwest we see them all disappear successively from the oldest to the most recent so that at Hirson the Charmouthian lies directly on the Primary. At the same time the calcareous or marly facies of the normal type are partially replaced by sandy or gritty facies corresponding to former beaches. And naturally, these littoral facies are placed correspondingly higher in the series as we travel toward the northwest, as the diagram (Fig. 72) indicates. The most famous of these sandy beds is the Luxemburg sandstone, relatively hard, which produces a wooded slope along the Ardennes; its lower part, more particularly called the Hettangian sandstone,

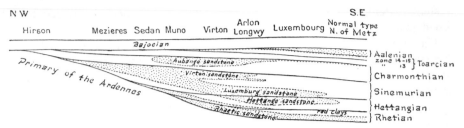

FIG. 72. *Diagram of the Lias facies in the Ardennes and Luxemburg; showing the transgression of the Liassic seas (except the Aalenian regression) over the Ardennes Massif, and the distribution of the littoral facies (stippled), sandy, gravelly or ferruginous in the neighborhood of the massif (after P. Lemoine, M. Leriche and L. van Werweke; compare to map, Fig. 70).*

containing *Cardinia hybrida,* is fossiliferous enough to have served as the type for the Hettangian stage.

The Middle Jurassic is represented by its usual littoral facies, oolitic limestones, with crinoids and corals. Leaving Hirson, it disappears under the Cretaceous, but wells show that it continues at depth south of a line connecting Hirson and Montreuil, which marks the ancient shore. It is found again in the Boulonnais where oolitic limestones of the Bathonian lie practically on the Primary, just above a sandy and clayey transgression facies.[41]

The Callovian and Oxfordian, which were almost completely marly in Lorraine, here show interesting variations. The base remains marly but the zone with *C. mariae* assumes the siliceous organic facies. It is a clayey sandstone entirely silicified by an opal cement which embodies spicules of sponges, very abundant at this horizon. This relatively hard rock stands out in relief above the clays of Woëvre. The littoral influences are affirmed in the zone with *C. cordatum.* We have there oolitic, ferruginous limestones, formerly exploited, containing silicified fossils. The famous bed of iron ores of Neuvizy (the Ardennes) serves as a guide in the local stratigraphy (former Neuvizyan stage).

In the Boulonnais, the Callovian and Oxfordian have become clayey, suggesting the approach to the English Oxford clay. It is probable that this

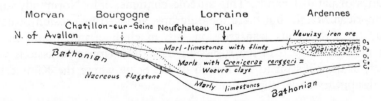

FIG. 73. *Diagram of the Callovian-Oxfordian facies on the eastern edge of the Paris Basin, showing the appearance of facies of ferruginous ooliths (stippled) and lacuras, in the vicinity of the ancient shores (Morvan and the Ardennes) (compare map, Fig. 70).*

western extremity of the Ardennes Massif was at this period covered by a broad sea.

The same observation applies to the Lusitanian, for, while in the Ardennes this stage is entirely overrun by coral facies (except the Astartian which is composed of the Astarte limestones), in the Boulonnais we observe alternating coral-bearing beds and cephalopod clays.

The Kimmeridgian presents nothing special in the Ardennes. The Portlandian is unknown, but both stages crop out in the Boulonnais and in the isolated anticline of the Pays de Bray north of Beauvais.

The Kimmeridgian of the Boulonnais (90 m. thick) is formed of clays containing oysters but it begins to be intercalated with sandy horizons. The Portlandian (60 m.) is classic.[42] Here we have an alternation of ammonite beds and estuary deposits with *Trigonia gibbosa,* cyrenids, corbulids, physids, planorbids, drift wood, and littoral pebbles. Together with the *Perisphinctes* and *Gravesia* already noted in the eastern part of the Paris Basin, the marine beds contain a fauna with northern affinities (*Pseudovirgatites, Cylindroteuthis, Aucella*).[43] These immigrants from the North do not seem to have penetrated as far as the Pays de Bray, where the facies are analogous to those of the Boulonnais.

But in the Boulonnais as well as in Bray these beds with marine intercalations correspond only to the lower part of the Portlandian (sub-stage Bononian).[44] They are crowned by a thin bed of lacustrine limestone which represents a reduced equivalent of the Purbeckian stage (upper Portlandian with continental facies). And, in the Boulonnais, the whole is gullied by sands likewise continental (Wealdian) which correspond to the base of the Cretaceous, while in Bray there seems to be a continuous transition from the Jurassic to the Cretaceous through continental, sandy-clayey facies.[45]

IV. The Jurassic on the Western Border of the Anglo-Parisian Basin (Normandy, England)

Supported against the Primary massifs of western England, the English Jurassic forms a great aureole, in which all the stages succeed each other regularly in a series of parallel bands. This aureole continues into Normandy, against the Armorican Massif, but there the outcrops, attacked by erosion or covered over by the Cretaceous transgression, are much interrupted and only the Lower and Middle parts of the Jurassic persist. The Upper Jurassic is visible, however, in the cliffs up to the mouth of the Seine where the Kimmeridgian finally disappears under the Cretaceous.

1. Normandy[46]

The Lias. Here we are near the ancient shores of the Armorican Massif, and we shall find again the same phenomena of transgression and the same littoral facies as in the Ardennes.

The transgression seems, however, to have come from the northeast, from the location of the English Channel. It extends at first only into the depression of Carentan. The Jurassic series begins there with clays and sandstones with plant remains, where, in a well at Valognes (see map, Fig. 11), *Avicula contorta* of the Rhaetian has been incorrectly identified. In reality, the first marine faunas date from the Hettangian, which has its typical facies of sandy limestone with *Cardinia*. In the Sinemurian, the sea reaches the region of Bayeux and deposits marls and marly limestones with gryphaeids and arietitids. There the Sinemurian is overlain by the Charmouthian, represented by marly limestones and marls containing belemnites and pyritic ammonites. The Charmouthian is transgressive to the south of Caen (May) and lies directly on the

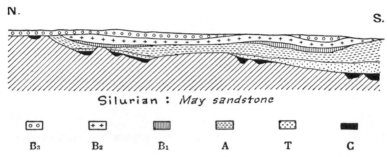

N.

S.

Silurian : *May sandstone*

B₃ B₂ B₁ A T C

FIG. 74. *Section of the Jurassic in quarries in the vicinity of May, near Caen, showing the lacunas and the irregularity of the sedimentation (after A. Bigot, simplified).*

Length of the section: about 200 m.

B₃ = White oolite
B₂ = Ferruginous oolite } Bajocian
B₁ = Phosphated limestones
A = Sandy limestones .... Aalenian
T = Limestones with crinoids or ferruginous oolites Toarcian
C = Conglomerates .... Charmouthian

Primary, in a very littoral facies of conglomerates, sandstones and brachiopod limestones.

But, while the Toarcian and Aalenian are still locally transgressive on the Primary and littoral in the region of Caen, where ancient reefs were still emergent in the Jurassic seas (E. Deslomchamps, 1864, and A. Bigot), it is with the upper Charmouthian that the Strait of Poitou opened, becoming still larger in the Toarcian. At Thouars, south of Saumur, on the edge of the Vendée Massif, the very type of the stage is constituted by marls very rich in ammonites,[47] separated from the Primary by a basal conglomerate.

In fact, in Normandy and more or less everywhere else, it is in the Toarcian that the Liassic seas seem to have reached their maximum depth. For in the Aalenian the facies becomes more littoral and is characterized by discontinuities. The two upper zones (*H. murchisonae* and *H. concavum*) of this stage are represented, around Caen, by 5 to 10 m. of sandy and phos-

phatic limestones (*mâlières*) containing rich ammonite faunas described by
S. S. Buckman.

The Middle Jurassic. The same regime of lacunas, local transgressions
and regressions, continues in the Middle Jurassic, where there is a succession
of quite varied littoral sediments, not very thick (total of 100 m.), in the
midst of which islets or reefs of the Hercynian platform sometimes spring up.[48]

Thus, near Caen, we find the two lower zones of the Bajocian in the state
of very fossiliferous, phosphatic limestones, while near Bayeux, the two upper
zones are represented in the celebrated ferruginous oolite, less than a meter
thick, but which supplied admirable fossils to all collections and for that reason was chosen as the stage type. Finally, the Bajocian ends with white
"oolite," which is in reality a whitish marly limestone, non-oolitic, poor in
fossils, up to 10 m. thick.

The Bathonian[49] can be subdivided into three members.

FIG. 75.   *Profile of the Norman cliffs in the region of Trouville, seen from
the sea (after A. Bigot, simplified).*
Horizontal scale 1:180,000; heights greatly exaggerated.

C = Cenomanian: opaline earth, glauconitic and calcareous sands.
A = Albian: ferruginous sands.
K = Lower Kimmeridgian: marly limestones with *Pteroceras.*
s = Sequanian: sandy clays and marls.
r = Rauracian: Hennequeville sandstone with *Trigonia bronni.*
a = Argovian: oolitic and coral limestones.
o = Oxfordian: black clays (oolitic limestone at the top).

1st. The Lower Bathonian (zone 5) is represented in the environs of
Caen and Falaise, by fine-grained, white limestone, exploited in subterranean
quarries for building stone or statuary material. This is the Caen stone, cele-
brated for its remains of great marine reptiles (*Teleosaurus, Stenosaurus,
Megalosaurus*). Toward the west these limestones pass progressively into the
black marls of Port-en-Bessin, easily seen there in the cliffs where they lie
on thin beds with *Cancellophycus,* containing a fauna transitional between the
Bajocian and Bathonian. This lower Bathonian, which is equivalent to the
English Fuller's Earth, is often wrongly correlated with the Vesulian of
Vesoul (see note 61, this chap.).

2nd. The middle Bathonian (zone 6), equivalent to the Bradfordian of
England, corresponds to the complex quite improperly called miliary oolite,
including oolitic limestones, reefs of sponges (pharetrons) and marly banks
(*Rhynchonella boueti* horizon) with numerous "hard-grounds" described by
A. Bigot (work cited, note 34, Intro.).

3rd. Finally, the upper Bathonian (zone 7), compared to the Cornbrash of British geologists, but very localized (Luc-sur-Mer) marks the beginning of clayey facies which will extend into the Callovian.

Farther south, as far as the Loire, the Middle Jurassic crops out locally all along the edge of the Armorican Massif, represented again by more littoral facies—sandstones, arkoses and even lignitic beds. This massif, then, remained at least partially emergent in the Jurassic. We shall find analogous facies in Yorkshire, at the extreme northern edge of this Anglo-Parisian Basin.

The Upper Jurassic. The transgression is maintained and the stages, thicker here, assume more constant characteristics.

The Callovian is in the state of clays and marly limestones. It ends with beds of very fossiliferous, ferruginous limestones, especially visible in the Department of Orne and having exactly the facies of Kellaways Rock, the type horizon of the English Callovian.

But the Oxfordian is especially interesting here. These are the black marls (marls of Dives and of Villers, 50 m.), easily visible in the famous cliffs of Vaches-Noires, near Trouville, in which the abundance of ammonites has enabled R. Douvillé to make detailed studies of stratigraphic paleontology. But with the *Cardioceras cordatum* zone the more littoral facies (oolitic limestone) begins.

Following the cliffs toward the Seine, we shall find more and more recent stages.

Thus, the Argovian is represented at Trouville by limestone with oolites or corals (reef of Bénerville). We may attribute to the Rauracian the silicified limestones (called "Hennequeville sandstone") with *Trigonia bronni*.

Finally, the Sequanian is, on the coast, composed of the Villerville clay in which already a variety of *Ostrea virgula* appears, while in the south, very fossiliferous, sandy intercalations develop more and more, reaching 30 m. thickness. These are the Glos sands, near Lisieux, with the famous Cordebugle locality, rich in finely preserved shells.[50]

Still farther east, the Kimmeridgian forms the cliffs of the Cape of La Hève, near Havre. It approximately conforms to the type described above, marly limestones at the base, clays with *Ostrea virgula* at the top. The Portlandian, eroded away by the Cretaceous transgression, no longer exists in this region.

2. *Britain*

The Jurassic of Britain has long been studied and has provided many stage types. In addition, because of recent meticulous research by several paleontologists (example, S. S. Buckman) the succession of ammonite zones has been established with incomparable precision and detail.[51] This has verified once again the generalization that the formations distinguished by the first stratigraphers did not correspond to rigorous chronological division or, in other words, that the limits of facies did not exactly coincide with the limits of stages or zones.

For these varied reasons, the British Jurassic deserves a short description, in which we shall follow the excellent summary by A. M. Davies,[52] and treat the Portlandian by itself.

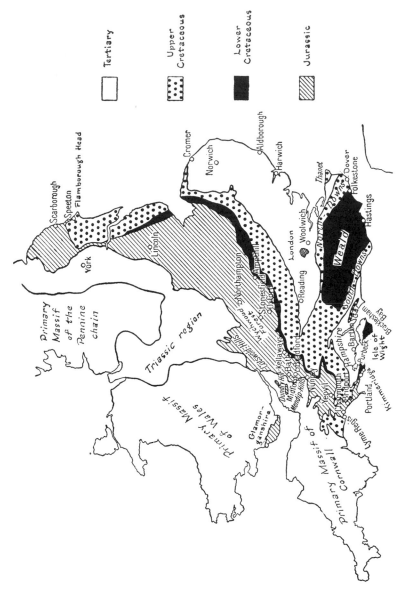

FIG. 76. Geologic map of the Jurassic and Cretaceous arcs and the Tertiary basins in southeastern Britain (very diagrammatic: no account is taken of the Quaternary formations which almost completely hide the underlying formations in the northeast, York, Lincoln, and Norwich).

The Jurassic crops out principally in a wide band, which crosses England like a sash, SW-NE in direction, between the coasts of Dorset (region of Charmouth) and Yorkshire. At the southeast it disappears under the transgressive Cretaceous[53] and toward the northwest it lies against the Primary massifs or the Triassic, but on this side the limit of Jurassic outcrops is a simple erosion boundary and does not correspond at all to ancient shores. We again find remains of the Lias in Glamorganshire (southern Wales), in Ireland, Scotland, and the Hebrides. Thus, in the Lias at least, the Anglo-Parisian sea widely attacked the North Atlantic continent.[54] Nevertheless the Jurassic of Scotland (which we shall not study here) gives evidence, by its littoral facies, of the nearness of ancient shores.

Finally, a zone of outcrops connected to the southern extremity of this band extends along the coast between Charmouth and the Isle of Wight, bordering the Tertiary basin of Hampshire on the south. Here we see only the northern slope, greatly trimmed, of a WNW-ESE anticline whose axis and southern flank are under the channel. This fold, approximately parallel to that of the Weald (see p. 411), possibly represents a distant prolongation of the Pays de Bray. Only the Upper Jurassic is visible there, in the type localities of Kimmeridge, Portland, and Purbeck.

A. Normal Series of the British Jurassic (except the Portlandian). A glance at Figure 77 shows at once, if we except details, the resemblance between the British Jurassic and the type-series of Lorraine.

Lias. The Rhaetian includes marls, sandstones, and bone beds and often ends with light colored calcareous banks, forming the white Lias.[55]

Above, the Hettangian and lower Sinemurian are composed of regular alternations of calcareous and marly banks, easily visible in the cliffs of Lyme Regis where they have yielded magnificent skeletons of marine reptiles. The calcareous banks are often exploited for cement stone (as in Burgundy) and sometimes contain more littoral ferruginous beds (similar to the ochreous limestone of Lorraine, but a little older) mined as iron ore in Lincolnshire.

Next, the upper Sinemurian and lower Charmouthian[56] (Pliensbachian) are represented by thick ammonite marls, as in Lorraine. Toward the north, the facies seem to become a little less deep-water; iron ores in it are mined in Lincolnshire, and in Yorkshire there are sandy-ferruginous concretions called "doggers."

The upper Charmouthian or Domerian (middle Lias of the British) has very constant characteristics. It corresponds to a diminution of depth. The base is formed by micaceous sandy clays and the top by ferruginous calcareous sandstones (improperly called marlstones) similar to the *Amaltheus spinatus* beds of Lorraine. Thus this middle Lias often forms a line of prominent outcrops between the marls of the lower Lias and those of the upper Lias.

The Toarcian is also very consistently marly. In Yorkshire it likewise seems to assume a more littoral facies. There, at the base, are found fragments of hard, black lignite (jet) formerly exploited for jewelry.

Middle Jurassic. On the other hand, beginning with the upper Toarcian and including the Callovian, we find a series of littoral beds, generally calcareous, which on the whole correspond to the calcareous episode of the Middle Jurassic of our [French] type series. Thus, as in France, the Middle Jurassic determines a zone of cuestas (example, the Cotswold Hills, Fig. 76, similar to the *côtes* of Moselle)[57] along the British aureole, topped by stony plateaus, the sites of intensive farming, contrasted to the damp, lowland areas reserved for pasturage, formed on the clays of the upper Lias and Oxfordian.

There are first, at the base, sands (of Midford, Yeoville, the Cotswolds) of various ages (see Fig. 77), older as we go north. Between Oxfordshire and Lincolnshire, there is even a lacuna at this horizon, evidence of emergence.

Above come limestones corresponding to the Aalenian, Bajocian, and lower Bathonian. These are very littoral deposits, ferruginous,[58] sandy, often oolitic (lower Oolite of early geologists), with numerous discontinuities of sedimentation. These still marine facies are reduced in proportion toward the north. Thus, in Northamptonshire and Lincolnshire, the Lower Estuarine Beds, continental or lagoonal sands, appear at the base, overlying the marine sands of Northampton[59] and covered by the oolitic limestones of Lincolnshire. Above these limestones, a second subcontinental sandy horizon forms the very thick Upper Estuarine Beds. Lastly, in Yorkshire,[60] we see the oolitic limestones almost entirely replaced by a new estuary formation, the Middle Estuarine Beds, separated from the Upper and Lower Estuarine Beds by thin strata of marine limestones.

These thick estuarine deposits (which are found again in Scotland), with brackish pelecypods (*Cyrena*) or lacustrine pelecypods (Unios, *Anodonta*) and a rich flora, may reach a total of 200 m. thickness. They forcefully indicate, in these northern regions, the approach of great emerged lands, dependents of the North Atlantic continent.

The Great Oolite complex corresponds approximately to the Bathonian stage. In the region of Bath, a series of beds are distinguished by classic terms, from bottom to top, as follows: 1st. Fullers Earth, a sort of non-plastic clay, of varying age according to the region. 2nd, the Great Oolite proper, oolitic limestone; at its base some banks of fine grained, well stratified, sandy limestone (Stonesfield slates), which have yielded remains of marsupials.[61] 3rd, the Bradford Clay, a clayey bank 3 m. thick with which the substage Bradfordian begins, including all the upper Bathonian. 4th, the Forest Marble, a compact, blue limestone, quarried as marble in the Wychwood Forest near Oxford. 5th, the Cornbrash[62] (literally, soil with corn),[63] marly limestone, never oolitic, whose alteration produces soil very suitable for the cultivation of cereals, unlike the Oxfordian clay which overlies it.

But all these beds are not everywhere recognizable. Thus the Great Oolite no longer exists on the Dorset coast, where it is replaced by the Fuller's Earth facies. Bradford Clay scarcely exists except in the vicinity of Bradford. Finally, in Yorkshire, all these beds are missing or are perhaps represented by the top of the Upper Estuarine Beds.

Upper Jurassic. The name Callovian comes from a bed, quite thin, known as Kellaways rock, which is very fossiliferous. The Callovian is a more or

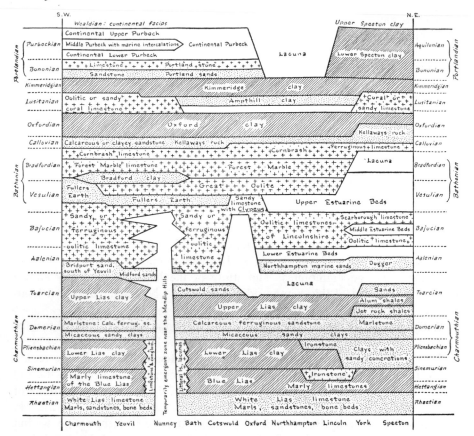

FIG. 77. *Diagrammatic representation of the succession of Jurassic facies in Britain, along the zone of outcrops (see map, Fig. 76) between the coast of Dorset (Charmouth) and Yorkshire (Speeton) (after information from A. M. Davies, simplified).*

Ruled: Relatively deep-water marine facies, clayey or marly-calcareous.
Stippled: Various littoral facies (sandstones, sands, sandy clays).
Crosses: Limestone facies.
White: Lacunas (emergence or submarine erosion); continental or lagoonal facies.

N. B. The Vesulian substage, as understood by British geologists, corresponds approximately to the French zones 4 (top of the Bajocian) and 5 (base of the Bathonian); so a separate stage is often made for it between the Bajocian and the Bathonian (for the definition of the type Vesulian, see p. 349).
According to new theories of Spath (see p. 342), the whole series of Speeton clays should be assigned to the Lower Cretaceous; thus there would be a lacuna between the Kimmeridgian and Valanginian at Speeton.

less calcareous or clayey sandstone, a facies that in the north includes younger zones.

The type of the Oxfordian is composed of Oxford clay,[64] a thick series of clays which is found all over Britain with very consistent characteristics and which has yielded many remains of great marine or continental reptiles, notably at Peterborough.

The Lusitanian corresponds approximately to the complex of relatively coherent rocks which separates the Oxford clays from the Kimmeridgian clays, and which the British long ago named the Corallian stage.[65] Highly variable littoral facies are found there, more or less sandy or calcareous, sometimes oolitic (Corallian oolite), sometimes rich in corals (Coral rag). But there are no true reefs, nor *Diceras*. The influence of the northern climate already begins to be felt there. All these organic facies stop suddenly toward the north in Oxfordshire; for in Northamptonshire and Lincolnshire they are replaced by gray or black clay called Ampthill clay, containing especially oysters.[66] Finally, in Yorkshire, the coral or sandy-calcareous facies reappears.

The Kimmeridgian has as its type the thick clayey series of Kimmeridge clay, very consistent from the Channel coast as far as Yorkshire and making an excellent cartographic guide mark. It contains marine reptiles, abundant *Ostrea virgula* and ammonites. The study of the latter has recently shown that the upper part of this Kimmeridge clay should be classified as Portlandian, as we shall see.

With this great Kimmeridgian sea, this unit of the stratigraphic history of Britain ends; so we shall examine the Portlandian by itself (see p. 342).

B. Variation of Facies in the Vicinity of the Mendip Hills. In the region where the Jurassic aureole which we have just described approaches the old massif of the Mendip Hills (see p. 336 and Fig. 76), sudden variations of facies and lacunas are recorded, indicating that the oscillations of the old core have here given rise to a locally emerged zone,[67] comparable to but larger than the little reefs described by A. Bigot on the edge of the Armorican Massif.

In fact, the normal series is profoundly modified. The different stages of the Lias[68] sometimes thin out to a few meters or decimeters. The marls or marly limestones are replaced by conglomeratic limestones formed at the expense of Carboniferous rocks. There are multiple lacunas with small, local transgressions or regressions. We note for example that at Nunney the base of the Bathonian lies directly on the Primary.

It seems, however, that the Bathonian marks approximately the end of these local episodes of emergence. Indeed, we can see that from one part to another of this emerged zone the faunas, particularly brachiopods, fastened to the sea floor, were different. From their differences we can distinguish two provinces in the Aalenian and Bajocian, a southern or Dorset province, and a northern or Cotswold province, separated by the emerged region. This zone of emergence does not, however, coincide strictly with the axis of the massif of the Mendip Hills, for the Jurassic of Dundry Hill, situated on the northern slope of the Mendips, still belongs to the southern province. Then, after the Bathonian, a general submersion unites the two provinces and the fauna becomes uniform again.

But we see how these traces of emergence are different from the thick

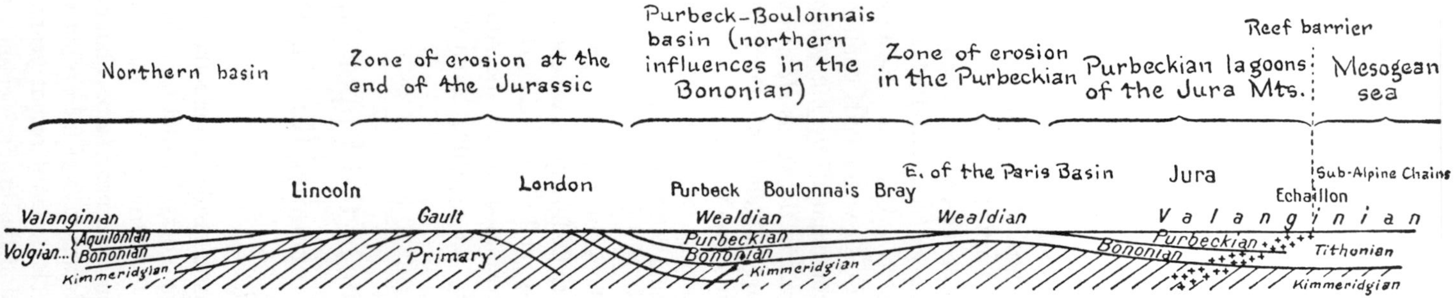

FIG. 78. *Diagrammatic section from Britain to the Alps at the end of the Jurassic, showing the distribution of facies of the Portlandian.*

estuarian formations that we find as we approach the North Atlantic continent. Here, clearly, there were only small peninsulas unable to nourish a great detrital sedimentation, perhaps even simple shoals swept by currents.

C. The Portlandian of Southern and Central Britain.   The type of the Portlandian stage is on the south coast, the name coming from the Portland peninsula.[69] The following succession can be distinguished:

1. *Portlandian* (s. str.) (Bononian).   In the French (and even Continental) nomenclature, the top of the clayey series of the Kimmeridge Clay is attributed to the lower Portlandian, though British geologists leave it in their Kimmeridgian and sometimes call it Bolonian, a name originated by Blake in 1880. These clays contain, in fact, Portlandian ammonites and particularly *Virgatites*.[70] This is, thus, the beginning of the northern influence that we saw appear at the same time in the Boulonnais. Then come very different lithologic formations with which British geologists begin their Portlandian stage.

These are, at the base, the Portland sand, glauconitic sand or sandstone, reaching 40 m. thickness, and at the top, the Portland stone (about 30 m.), littoral limestone with *Trigonia gibbosa* and *Perisphinctes*.[71]

2. *Purbeckian*.   This name is taken from the Purbeck Hills, forming a peninsula[72] east of Portland. Fresh water beds containing physids and unios alternate with marine beds containing *Trigonia gibbosa* and brackish beds containing gypsum. The presence of the genus *Hemicidaris* in the marine beds in the middle of the stage clearly attaches this Purbeckian to the Jurassic. At the top, it passes gradually into the Wealdian, the continental facies of the Lower Cretaceous. Conventionally, the Cretaceous begins at the horizon where there is no longer anything but sand, without marly or calcareous intercalations.

Toward the north, the Purbeckian is greatly reduced and loses its marine intercalations. Then, in northern Oxfordshire, we come to a region where there is a lacuna between the Jurassic and the Cretaceous. This emergent zone, the result of a single period of erosion, separates the Anglo-Parisian Basin, thus dried up in place (as shown by the gypsum), from the northern basin which we shall now discuss.

V. The Northern Basin in the Upper Jurassic (Northern Britain, Northern Germany, Russia, Poland)

1. *Northern England*

In the region where the Jurassic girdle around the English Primary Massif meets the North Sea, that is, in Yorkshire and Lincolnshire, the Upper Jurassic, often concealed by the Quaternary, can be studied especially in the natural sections of the Speeton cliffs near Cape Flamborough.

There, above the Kimmeridgian clays of the ordinary type, comes the thick series of the famous Speeton clays. Until recent years, it was believed there was a continuous succession and the lower Speeton clays were attributed to the Portlandian and the upper ones to the Lower Cretaceous. But in 1924,

Spath,[73] basing his conclusions on the ammonite faunas of these clays, believed he could attach the whole assemblage to the Lower Cretaceous. Thus there would have been there an emergence corresponding approximately to the Portlandian. Nevertheless, at the base of this Cretaceous series, immediately above the Kimmeridgian, some thin beds with phospatic nodules contain some altered ammonites and belemnites, close to the Russian Portlandian forms. These would be, according to these new conceptions, the only evidences, in northern Britain, of the proximity of a northern basin at the end of the Jurassic, a basin whose deposits would have been destroyed by the infra-Cretaceous transgression.[74] This basin must then have extended over the present location of the North Sea, and we shall find it again in Russia and northern Germany.

2. *Russia and Poland* (see Fig. 69)

The Liassic seas did not cover the Russian platform. In fact, it is only very far to the south that we find traces of the approach of the oldest Jurassic seas, which at this epoch belong to the Mesogean domain.

Thus, in the Donetz Basin, the marine series begins with the Toarcian. But there we are outside of the domain of the Russian platform proper. Farther west, near Cracow, we see, above the estuarian clays with plants, a sandy-clayey marine Aalenian, supporting a Bajocian, likewise marine. Then in the vicinity of Kiev and in southeastern Russia (region of Saratov) we find the marine Bathonian. This Bathonian sea perhaps already communicated with a gulf coming from the Germanic basin and covering Pomerania, Posen, and eastern Prussia (south of Tilsit, see Fig. 69).[75] For we know the sandy-clayey, transgressive Bathonian, in Pomerania and in the well at Hohensalza (between Posen and the elbow of the Vistula). All these sediments of the Russian upper Liassic and the German and Polish Dogger are shallow-water: sandy and glauconitic clays, with fossils as well preserved as present-day shells, or ferruginous, oolitic limestones, like the famous Balin oolite (near Cracow), also very fossiliferous (Bathonian-Callovian-Oxfordian).

With the Callovian, the clayey facies with pyritic or phosphatic ammonites generally begins, a facies often remarkably well preserved which will continue to the end of the Jurassic. And at the same time a great transgression took place, which opened broad communications with the Germanic domain. Towards the north, the sea advanced as far as Lithuania (famous Popilany locality, north of Tilsit)[76] and even as far as Latvia (Niegranden), on the border of the old Baltic Shield. Even the center of the Russian platform was invaded as far as the region of Moscow, Tver, Jaroslav and Pechora. Thus, in the Callovian there was reconstituted an arm of the Russian sea that, as in the Permo-Carboniferous, united the Arctic seas to the Mesogean sea.

In the central part of this arm of the sea, in the region of Simbirsk, the sedimentation remained continuous to the end of the Jurassic. But on the edges there were a few lacunas, due either to momentary emergences or perhaps to simple absences of sedimentation, with weak submarine erosion. The history of these local vicissitudes should not distract us too long.[77]

However, the section of the Upper Jurassic in this Russian arm of the sea[78] shows a marine lower Portlandian or Bononian, with *Pachyceras* (*Gravesia*), related to *P. portlandicum,* and especially *Virgatites* and *Aucella.* In the upper Portlandian or Aquilonian, there are associated with the aucellas and *Cylindroteuthis* species of *Craspedites* and *Garnieria* which have allowed the definition of three successive zones. Above, in continuity, comes the marine Cretaceous.

This Portlandian of the northern basin, so different from that of the Anglo-Parisian and Mediterranean regions, was first described by Russian geologists as a Volgian stage (from the Volga), whose exact position near the boundary between the Jurassic and Cretaceous they could not precisely determine. It is largely due to E. Haug and W. Kilian that this Volgian was shown to be the exact equivalent of the Portlandian and thereby of the Tithonian of the Mediterranean regions (see p. 354).

3. Intermediate Regions

The northern influences which were felt at the extreme end of the Jurassic, in the Boulonnais and Britain, render *a priori* very probable the existence of marine communication, in the Portlandian, between the North Sea and the Russian seas, either south or north of the Scandinavian-Baltic continent which remained emerged. Let us examine successively, with E. Haug, these two avenues of communication:

A. On the northern route, a landmark is provided by a fragment of Jurassic formations consisting of 10 square km. of surface preserved on the Isle of Andö, one of the Lofoten islands (see Fig. 69). There, overlying carbonaceous beds with a Jurassic flora, are sandstones with *Gryphaea dilatata* of Oxfordian age, then sandstones with aucellas of the Russian upper Volgian. Evidently this thick series (510 m.), a minute remnant of which has been preserved by a happy chance in a small depressed trough, must correspond to a very extensive sea. According to Vogt, a good part of Norway must have been invaded at this epoch.[79] And, in any case, this northern Jurassic sea must have extended very far towards the north, since a marine Jurassic with Russian affinities is known in Nova Zembla, Spitzbergen, Franz-Josef Land and Greenland.[80]

B. The southern route would necessarily pass through Poland and northern Germany. Exactly there, in Pomerania, a Portlandian with aucellas and *Virgatites,* thus equivalent to the lower Volgian, is known, almost completely hidden under the Quaternary.

Thus, it is through northern Germany that the Russian and Polish *Virgatites* would have reached the basin of the North Sea, as far as the Boulonnais, in the lower Portlandian.[81] In the upper Portlandian, however, as we shall see in a moment, northern Germany (Hanover) was occupied by Purbeckian lagoons, so that it is very natural to assume, for this epoch, a communication by the northern route.

VI. The Jurassic of the Germanic Cuvette
(Franconia, Swabia, Hanover)

Broad Jurassic outcrops exist between the southern Black Forest and Bohemia. This is the Swabian Jura at the west and the Franconia Jura at the east.
The calcareous cliffs of this plateau country (Swabian Alb) dominate the
plains of the Danube, and their borders, eaten away by this river, have receded
little by little toward the north. North of this wide band, in the space inclosed
between Thuringia and the Rhenish Massif, there is now only Triassic. But
the Jurassic must formerly have extended through this strait, for fragments of
it are found in Hanover, with the same history as in Swabia, at least up to
the Middle Jurassic (see maps, Figs. 28 and 69).

It is to this N-S arm of the sea, which thus extends from the Bavarian plains
of the Danube as far as the Baltic countries,[82] Denmark,[83] and Scania,[84] that
we, with E. Haug, shall give the name of Germanic Basin. For the Lias and
Middle Jurassic are represented by very deep-water, muddy facies or at least
very pelagic facies, as in the Anglo-Parisian Basin. During these periods, it is
probable that the Bohemian Massif and its branches formed the shore on the
eastern edge of this basin. On the west, the western part of the Rhenish Massif
must also have remained untouched.[85] But the Vosges-Black Forest Massif
was certainly not emergent before the Upper Jurassic. So, up to that epoch, a
broad communication existed with the Anglo-Parisian Basin and the Jura,
through Alsace, where fragments of the Jurassic crop out in the small fracture
blocks at the foot of the Vosges. This is the Franco-German Strait of R.
Abrard (p. 329).

Lias. The Rhaetian transgression[86] covered at once the whole extent of the
Germanic Basin, sparing Bohemia. It is in the environs of Stuttgart that the
type of the Swabian facies of this stage was chosen, a type facies that we have
already described. The extreme northern limit of this transgression is found
on the southern edge of the Scandinavian Massif, in Scania. There, wells have
shown, above the Silurian basement, a thick (500 m.) continental series
(Kägeröd formation) without fossils (Permian?), overlain by 10–30 m. of
carbonaceous Rhaetian with a *Lepidopteris* flora, already containing a bed with
marine fossils. The Vosges-Black Forest Massif must again have formed an
island at this epoch, for the sandstones and marine bone-beds of the lower
Rhaetian are missing between Strasbourg and Belfort (A. de Lapparent),
while the lagoonal clays of the upper Rhaetian are found everywhere in
Alsace.

The Hettangian[87] (about 10 to 40 m. thick) still retains a somewhat littoral
character, for it frequently contains intercalations of sandstone with *Cardinia*
which, on the north shore, in Scania, are found in the Helsingborg series, containing at its base a *Thaumatopteris* flora and overlain by beds with arietites

(Döshult formation). The submergence of the Vosges-Black Forest Massif does not seem to have been complete until the zone with *Schlotheimia angulata.*

The German Sinemurian (20–50 m.) is calcareous only toward its base (gryphaeid limestones). Near the top a marly facies begins and subsequently predominates.

In fact, all the rest of the Lias is represented by marls in which only the faunas make subdivision possible. In the Charmouthian or middle Lias (15–20 m.) there is a *numismalis* marl, or marl with *Terebratula* (*Waldheimia*) *numismalis,* followed by marls with amalthids.[88] In the Toarcian or upper Lias[89] (about 10 m.) are shales with posidonids, whose bituminous content has caused, as in France, efforts at distillation. It is these shales which at Boll (Wurttemburg) have yielded a multitude of marine or flying reptiles, in the zones of *H. falciferum* and *H. bifrons.* Above comes the *jurensis* marl or marl with *Ammonites* (*Lytoceras*) *jurensis.*

The Aalenian is included by German geologists in the Middle Jurassic or Dogger.[90] It contains marls with *Trigonia navis* or marls with *H. opalinum,* 100 m. thick, above which a few more calcareous and slightly ferruginous (ferruginous oolites of Aalen = zone with *H. murchisonae*) banks form cuestas above the marls, representing the last trace of the littoral facies with iron minerals which we described in Lorraine.

Through its facies, the Lias of Alsace seems to be closer to that of the Germanic Basin than to that of Lorraine, thus showing clearly that no trace of ancient shores exists on the present location of the Vosges and the Black Forest.[91]

Thus it is that in Alsace marly facies prevail almost exclusively from the Sinemurian on. The rare sandy-calcareous or ferruginous more littoral banks that persist, are less marked than those observed in Lorraine at the same horizons. In zone 7 is found a limestone with *A. raricostatus* and in zone 10, a limestone with *D. davoei.* The Toarcian remains marly but the absence of ammonite zones and the presence of ferruginous or phosphated horizons give evidence of a regime of currents. Finally a few thin beds of ferruginous sandstone represent the only equivalent of the iron ores of Lorraine, and also occur on the right bank of the Rhine in the Baden area.[92]

Middle Jurassic. It is in the Middle Jurassic that the contrasts of facies between the Anglo-Parisian Basin and the Germanic Cuvette are greatest. For in the deep part of the latter and especially in Hanover, Brunswick, and Westphalia, we find no trace of the littoral facies, the oolitic, coral, or crinoidal limestones which give to the Anglo-Parisian Bajocian-Bathonian so accentuated a morphologic individuality. Here are only marls and inorganic marly limestones.

To find somewhat more littoral facies again, we must approach the ancient shores.[93] Thus, towards the south, in Swabia, banks of ferruginous oolites begin to appear, especially in the Bajocian. This is, in conjunction with the Aalenian, the Brown Jura of early authors.

Finally, in Alsace,[94] the Middle Jurassic, decidedly more littoral again, greatly resembles that of Lorraine. The lower Bajocian especially is a little more marly but with ferruginous, oolitic beds. Above comes thick oolitic limestone (Great Oolite) which, as in Lorraine, was formerly attributed to the Bathonian. This last stage, however, is represented by some twenty meters of marly limestone or marl with *Rhynchonella alemanica* (*R. varians* of early authors).

Upper Jurassic.[95] The Callovian and Oxfordian continue the series of clayey facies. Rare remnants of Callovian and Oxfordian shales which have persisted in Alsace point to the conclusion that the Vosges and Black Forest were again emergent. Although containing horizons with ferruginous oolites,

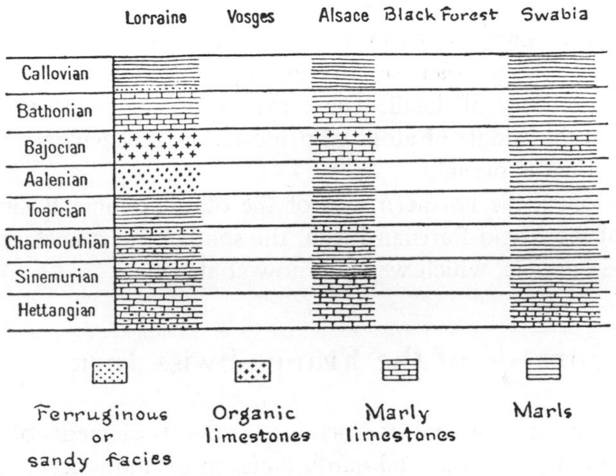

FIG. 79. *Diagram of the facies of the Lias and the Middle Jurassic in Lorraine (vicinity of Metz), in Alsace and in the Germanic Cuvette (Swabia), showing the progressive disappearance of the littoral facies (sandy or organic) of the Anglo-Paris Basin in the Middle Jurassic approaching the Germanic Cuvette.*

this Alsatian Callovian is complete, at least as far as the latitude of Strasbourg.[96]

But after the Lusitanian a great change took place, and the individuality of the Germanic Basin finally disappears.

To the north, in Hanover, the facies in fact become identical with those which we described in the Anglo-Parisian Basin: the Lusitanian in a Corallian state,[97] the Kimmeridgian with marly limestones containing *Pteroceras oceani* and *Ostrea virgula*. Above, the lower Portlandian again contains ammonites, *Gravesia* (*Olcostephanus, Pachyceras*) *gigas, G. gravesi*. Then come beds with pelecypods, marine, brackish and even continental, among them the Münder marl, 300 m. thick. The last marine influences are marked by the serpulite limestones containing serpulas (tubes of marine annelids) and reaching 50 m. in thickness. Finally the Jurassic ends with a purely continental

Purbeckian, difficult to distinguish from the Wealdian, which marks the continuation of the same facies in the Lower Cretaceous.

But this Portlandian of northern Germany is deposited in an arm of the sea bounded on the north by the Finnish-Scandinavian continent and on the south by the emerged Rhenish Schiefergebirge, along which are found marginal facies, marked by conglomerates, reduced thicknesses, and lacunas.[98]

In the south, on the other hand, in Franconia and Swabia, the Lusitanian shows alternating cephalopod marls and compact limestones with sponges, while the lower Portlandian is invaded by quite varied reefy facies. Massifs of coral limestones correspond to the position of ancient reefs and are in juxtaposition with well stratified, fine grained limestones, exploited as lithographic stone. The famous quarries of Solnhofen (Franconia) have provided rare but precious impressions of swimming or flying animals (fish, crustaceans, flying reptiles), fallen on the muddy bottom and fossilized with an extraordinary delicacy of detail. There existed at that point, no doubt, tranquil lagoons in the middle of atolls or protected by reef barriers.[99] Finally, the upper Portlandian is missing.

In conclusion, if the northern part of the old Germanic Basin thus shares the history of the Anglo-Parisian Basin, the southern part is clearly connected with the type Jurassic, which we shall now study.

VII. The Jurassic of the Franco-Swiss Jura

The relief of the Jura, as that of Lorraine, draws its elements of variety from the alternation of calcareous and marly facies in the Jurassic.

The compact limestones of the Bajocian and Bathonian constitute the whole array of plateaus which border the chain from the Isle of Crémieu,[100] south of the Rhône, to Belfort. The Liassic marls scarcely show except to form the talus slopes of these plateaus. The whole framework of the folded Jura is supported by the limestones of the Lusitanian-Kimmeridgian-Portlandian stages, whose abrupt exposures form the ridges and dominate the escarpments, while the Oxfordian marls determine the little grassy valleys.

Lias.   The Lias of the Jura is identical to that of Lorraine. We find there the Rhaetian with Swabian facies, the limestones with gryphaeids, and the black marls of the middle and upper Liassic overlain by ferruginous oolitic horizons of the Toarcian, or Aalenian, distant prolongations of the *minette* [ferruginous oolite of the *Harpoceras opalinum* zone of the Toarcian] of Lorraine. The old excavations of La Verpillière, in the Isle de Crémieu, have provided specimens of fine Toarcian fossils for all collections. The top of the Aalenian is represented by marly limestones with *Cancellophycus* which correspond to the *murchisonae* zone. Then begin the facies of crinoidal limestones, which extend into the Bajocian.[101]

Middle Jurassic.   The lower Bajocian is very uniformly represented by a thick calcareous mass (100 to 300 m.), of rather crinoidal limestone in the

The Jurassic

lower part (the base being still Aalenian as we have seen) and rather coral limestone at the top.

The upper Bajocian begins with marly beds (10–20 m.) with *Ostrea acuminata,* formerly wrongly compared to the British Fullers Earth, and overlain by thick oolitic limestones (50 m.) equally wrongly correlated with the Great Oolite. For this assemblage, whose lower part especially is very fossiliferous around Vesoul, the sub-stage Vesulian was formerly devised and believed to be equivalent to the lower Bathonian. But, following the ammonite faunas, which are very rare, and making comparison with other regions (Lorraine, Mâcon),[102] this Vesulian has been found to correspond to the upper Bajocian, as we have defined it here. The term Vesulian is therefore rejected, to avoid ambiguity.

Above, the Bathonian corresponds to beds with varied facies, sometimes limestone,[103] sometimes marl, containing brachiopods especially.

But, at the eastern extremity of the chain, in the Argovian Jura, south of

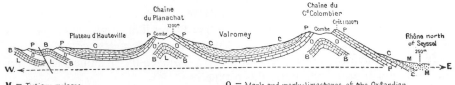

M = Tertiary molasse
C = Limestones with littoral facies of the Lower Cretaceous
P = Compact limestones of the Upper Jurassic
O = Marls and marly-limestones of the Oxfordian
B = Oolitic or organic limestones of the Bajocian-Bathonian
L = Marls and marly limestones of the Lias
Scale: Vertical, 1/112,500; Horizontal, 1/225,000

FIG. 80. *Semi-theoretical section across the Southern Jura, showing the orographic role of the different Jurassic and Cretaceous formations.*

Oxfordian combes (little valleys), limestone ridges (*crêts*) of the Upper Jurassic, valleys filled with Cretaceous. At the left, beginning of the so-called "Tabular Jura": limestone plateaus of the Middle Jurassic.

the Black Forest, the Middle Jurassic assumes little by little the type of the Germanic Basin. There the Bajocian again contains intercalations of ferruginous oolite, while the Bathonian becomes entirely marly.

Callovian-Oxfordian. The Callovian, unimportant morphologically, is reduced to thin veneers (2–15 m.) coating the calcareous massifs of the Middle Jurassic. It is generally represented by ferruginous oolites, but at its base appear small plaques of limestone the surfaces of which are plated with numerous oyster shells and crinoid plates, from which comes the expressive name, nacreous flagstone. These Callovian oolites are very interesting for their richness in fossils (deposits at Chanaz, near Culoz, Mont-du-Chat, and Chézery, near Bellegarde) (Fig. 82).[104] In the Argovian Jura, they are again replaced by marls.

The Oxfordian is, as in Lorraine, uniformly marly and plays a very important role (100 m.). Its top sometimes assumes, as in the Anglo-Parisian Basin, the calcareous nodular facies, with silicified fossils (Ferrette deposit, Haut-Rhin).[105]

Lusitanian-Portlandian.   Above the Oxfordian marls comes a thick group of especially calcareous beds, that end only with the end of the Jurassic, forming great escarpments, more or less cut up by cornices. The facies are highly varied. We see a succession from one region or one stage to another, of relatively deep-water limestones with cephalopods, rough marly limestones with siliceous sponges, and coral limestones in all their varieties.

The finest examples of the sponge facies, with large sponges with well preserved external forms, are seen in the Argovian. The localities of Birmensdorf and Effingen in the Argovian Jura have served as type for this sub-stage. A fine deposit is found, similar to that at the other end of the chain, at Trept (Isle of Crémieu).

The distribution of coral facies was the subject of interesting syntheses by Abbé Bourgeat. In general, the reefs of a single epoch are arranged in bands parallel to the axis of the chain; and these bands are also more internal (closer to the Swiss plain) in proportion as the epoch considered is more recent.

Thus, on the northwest border (vicinity of Besançon), there is the same succession as in the Meuse. Above the upper Oxfordian, represented by beds with flints (*terrains à chailles*), lies a Lusitanian more or less completely invaded by coral formations, reefy or oolitic. Above, the Kimmeridgian and the Portlandian are of the Paris Basin type.

To the southeast, at the base reefs give place to the sponge facies. Thus, in the central Jura (Saint-Claude), this facies includes both the upper Oxfordian and the Argovian. The reef limestones begin only in the Kimmeridgian, covering the Sequanian cephalopod limestones, and they are overlain by coral oolites with *Ostrea virgula* (Virgulian). A good example is the fine reef of Valfin, near St. Claude, famous for its wealth of *Diceras.*

Farther southeast, finally, in the most internal folds, directly overlooking the Swiss plain (Faucille pass, for example), the reefs are in the Virgulian and Portlandian. Fine-grained limestones represent the ancient lagoonal centers of atolls. The famous Cerin (Ain) deposit is thus comparable through its facies and its fauna to that of Solnhofen in Franconia, previously mentioned. At Echaillon, near Grenoble, where the last chains of the Jura join the subAlpine chains, the coral facies extend without interruption even into the Cretaceous.[106]

Everywhere else in the Jura, the Jurassic ends as in the Paris Basin. The lower Portlandian is represented by limestones with very rare ammonites (*Gravesia*) or by dolomites with *Trigonia gibbosa.* The upper Portlandian has Purbeckian facies—gypsiferous marls, breccias with black pebbles, lacustrine limestones with cyrenas, lymnids, *Unio,* algae (*Chara*), etc. Toward the south, the final evidence of this Purbeckian Jurassic was recently discovered at La Buisse, near Voreppe, some kilometers north of Echaillon.[107]

Thus, at the end of the Jurassic, the Jura must be represented as a flat area, bounded on the southeast by a fringe of reefs which, leaving a Paris Basin transformed into an inland sea, have receded progressively toward the south, thus remaining on the border of the great Alpine sea. And behind these reefs

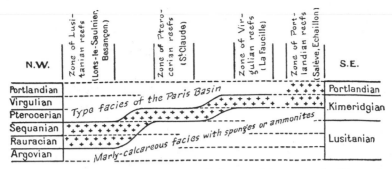

FIG. 81. *Diagram of the distribution of the coral facies in the Upper Jurassic in the French Jura, on a transverse section from Lons-le-Saulnier to Faucille and Salève.*

extended enormous Purbeckian lagoons, sometimes super-salty, sometimes fresh. North of these lagoons, the Paris Basin proper was already entirely continental and emerged and we must go as far as Britain to find again brackish facies in the Purbeckian, prelude to the northern basin (Fig. 69).

Now let us cross this reefy barrier and penetrate the Alpine sea.

VIII. The Jurassic in the Alps

In all the regions we have just described, the Jurassic deposits were formed in epicontinental seas; only in the Alps do we enter into a truly geosynclinal domain. From the Jurassic on, we shall see on the one hand deep troughs, where the Jurassic sediments, continuous and without lacunas, may be very thick on the bordering slopes but may become very thin in the bottoms of furrows; and on the other hand, "cordilleras," that is zones of relief, islands or shoals, bordered by littoral neritic or brecciated sediments and marked by lacunas and transgressions, which clearly show the carrying into the sea of the red sideroliths formed on the emerged cordilleras.

As we have already seen, the fauna has special characteristics. Through the whole duration of the period, we see *Phylloceras* and *Lytoceras* prosper, probably because of the depth of the sea. But at the top of the Jurassic the presence of numerous special species (*Oppelia, Belemnopsis,* corals, *Diceras*) as well as the absence of characteristic species of the northern basin, can be explained only by a difference in province, doubtless due to the climate. Thus the Alps became part of a Mesogean tropical zone, of which we shall describe the northern border in the Jura and which we shall see extending into the Cretaceous.

However, many regional peculiarities diversify the Alpine Jurassic. Guided by W. Kilian and E. Haug, we shall begin our study with the French Alps.[108]

1. *The French Alps*[109]

We have already seen (pp. 205 and 280) that successive facies belts can be distinguished in the Alps, elongated in the direction of the chain and coincid-

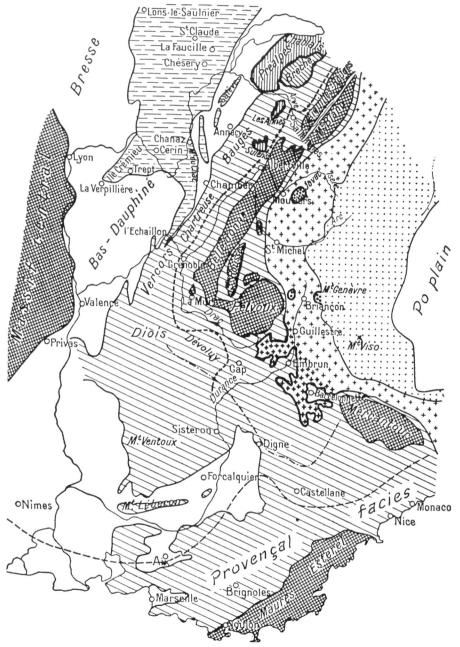

FIG. 82.   *Structural sketch of the French Alps, showing the distribution of facies in the Jurassic (suggested by W. Kilian, P. Termier, E. Haug).*

ing more or less exactly with the tectonic zones. The interest of the Alpine stratigraphy lies precisely in the establishment of this coincidence. The zones already defined can be used here.

A. Jurassic of the Dauphinois Type (Sub-Alpine Chains and Zone of the Crystalline Massifs). The westernmost part of the external zone of the French Alps (see Fig. 82), in which the Primary or crystalline formations no longer appear, is known as the sub-Alpine chains. Relatively narrow in the north (Massifs of Bauges, between Annecy and Lake Bourget, then of Grande-Chartreuse between this lake and the Isère), they broaden out in the south in Vercors (south of the Isère), Diois and the mountains of Drôme, Basses-Alpes and Alpes-Maritimes. The Jurassic crops out only in the anticlinal axes, separated by the Cretaceous.

But at the east, crystalline massifs appear beneath the Jurassic of the sub-Alpine zones. In this new zone the Jurassic plays a very important part as the sedimentary cover of these massifs. Thus, a wide Jurassic depression can be followed through Sallanches, Albertville, Grenoble and Gap, along the whole internal margin of the sub-Alpine chains and west of the crystalline massifs. This is the sub-Alpine furrow.

In all these regions, the Jurassic has a very uniform aspect. There is a continuous succession of deep-water deposits in which the extremely impoverished fauna includes scarcely more than ammonites and belemnites.

Above a very thin Rhaetian with Swabian facies, the Lias is represented by black, relatively soft sediments. The base, a little more calcareous, has been called the calcareous Lias and corresponds approximately to the Hettangian, Sinemurian, and lower Charmouthian. Above comes the shaly Lias. In the

Tertiary basins.

Hercynian massifs.

In the north, sub-Alpine chains (Bauges, Chartreuse, Vercors, Diois and the Basses-Alps): Dauphine facies. In the south, the Mountains of Provence: Provençal facies.

Jura: Jurassian facies.

Sub-Alpine border.

Southern limit of the deep-water (Dauphinois) facies in the Lias.

Southern limit of the deep-water facies in the Middle and Upper Jurassic.

Internal zone: Briançonnais zone with the sub-Briançonnais zone on the external edge; Briançonnais and sub-Briançonnais facies.

Nappes of the Ubaye-Embrunais, coming from the internal zone, with sub-Briançonnais scales in their bases: sub-Briançonnais facies.

Piedmont zone: schistes lustrés facies.

Thrust slices coming from the Piedmont zone (after P. Termier?).

Nappes of the Prealps (Chablais, Les Annes, Sulens): Prealpine facies, similar to the sub-Briançonnais and Briançonnais facies.

The Breccia Nappe of the Chablais: breccia facies.

aggregate, this Dauphinois Lias reaches thicknesses of the order of a thousand meters.[110]

The Bajocian is again composed of black limestone, a little more resistant than the shales which enclose it, so that it forms a ridge with a smooth profile. The Bathonian, Callovian and Oxfordian form a thick shaly ensemble, in which ammonites are extremely rare, though beds of posidonomyas are present. These are the impermeable black earths of Basses-Alpes, celebrated for their erosion and their devastating torrents.

With the Lusitanian, the rocks become lighter colored and more solid, for the proportion of limestone, which forms only nodules or "round loafs" in the Oxfordian, increases progressively. They are first, in the lower Lusitanian (Argovian-Sequanian) gray, marly limestones, exploited for cement (particularly at the Vicat Works, at Vif, south of Grenoble) and generally attributed to the Rauracian; but except for certain special deposits,[111] the stage boundaries cannot be defined. Then banks of light colored limestones, thin at first, appear little by little in the marls. These represent the lower Kimmeridgian. Finally in the upper Kimmeridgian and the Portlandian, there are true compact limestones, light gray, in thick, well stratified banks. But the deep-water facies always persist, as is evidenced by the faunas, reduced to ammonites and very rare *Pygope janitor* (so named after the deposit of the Porte-de-France, at Grenoble). There is no trace of emergence at the boundary of the Cretaceous.[112] To this deep, special type of the Alpine (and more generally, Mediterranean) Portlandian, the name Tithonian[113] is often given, for its ammonite fauna is entirely different from those of the Portlandian and Volgian of northern Europe.

According to the excellent research of W. Kilian and his collaborators, three successive zones of ammonites can be identified in this Tithonian.

	Upper............	Zone containing *Perisphinctes senex, Hoplites progenitor, H. chaperi.*
Tithonian	Middle...........	Zone containing *Perisphinctes contigus* and the first *Hoplites (Berriasella)*
	Lower...........	Zone containing *Oppelia lithographica*

These three zones[114] taken together are equivalent to the Portlandian and consequently to the Volgian. But parallelism in detail with the type Portlandian and Volgian is impossible.

The morphology of the sub-Alpine furrow and its borders is easily explained. Around the high crystalline massifs, carved into spires, wooded or grassy hills correspond to the calcareous and shaly Lias, often little differentiated and much folded. These black rocks are seldom exposed except in gorges caused by recent erosion. The very bottom of the furrow, followed successively by the Arly, Isère, and Drac rivers, is in general excavated in the soft shales of the upper Lias or the Bathonian Oxfordian.

And on the western border of the furrow, a formidable rampart rises, about 1,500 m. high, the sub-Alpine border. The talus of the base is derived from the Callovian-Oxfordian. Then the slope is increased and calcareous banks appear through the vegetation. This is the Lusitanian. Finally a regular escarpment corresponds to the light colored limestones of the Kimmeridgian-Portlandian. This is the Tithonian cornice (see Fig. 93). Above comes the Cretaceous which we shall study later.

B. Western and Southern Boundaries of the Dauphinois Type; the Ancient Shores of the Maures-Esterel Massif. The boundary of the deep-water Dauphinois or sub-Alpine facies of the Jurassic is very easy to trace in the west and north, with respect to the Jurassic facies studied above. For they exactly coincide, especially in the Upper Jurassic, with the tectonic boundaries of the Alps and the Jura. The Swiss Tertiary Basin separates these two chains and the little isolated spurs which appear between Geneva and Annecy (Salève, etc.) should be attached to the Jura, for the Jurassic there shows reefy formations overlain by the Purbeckian. Thus our boundary passes through Annecy and Chambéry, leaving Lake Bourget in the Jura. Starting there, the Swiss Tertiary Basin extends in the form of a narrow molasse syncline, which, by way of St. Laurent-du-Pont, cuts the Isère valley at Voreppe, passing just east of Echaillon, the locality whose Jura facies we have already described. Farther south, the last folds of the Jura join the Cretaceous plateaus of Vercors, and we see no more of the Jurassic.

Still farther south, while the Dauphinois type is prolonged through Gap, we see it bounded, in the region of Sisteron, Digne and Castellane, by a somewhat different facies. There littoral types of limestones with gryphaeas and crinoids appear in the lower Lias. In addition, sandy limestones are developed at the top of the Charmouthian, forming high russet cliffs, at the foot of which Digne is sheltered. Finally, a limestone scarp develops in the middle Aalenian. In this Gap-Digne region, made classic by the thesis of E. Haug, the northeastern deep-water facies begins to change to the southwestern littoral facies, and the Lias reaches its maximum thickness, following a general law (see Fig. 1) that we shall find again in the Lower Cretaceous. This Lias with mixed facies appears, in the gorge of the Durance south of Gap, to reach a thickness of 2,000 m. But, on the other hand, in the Middle and especially in the Upper Jurassic, these Provençal littoral influences do not reach as far north and we shall find the Tithonian type as far north as the borders of the Massif Central, in the region which will later become the Vocontian trough of the Lower Cretaceous.

Still farther beyond, an important element of differentiation is added by the Maures-Esterel Massif. On its banks the Provençal type of the Jurassic develops.[115] Above a very typical Rhaetian with Swabian facies, come nonfossiliferous dolomites corresponding, no doubt, to the Hettangian, above which the Sinemurian is rarely distinguished.[116] The rest of the Lias and the Middle Jurassic are represented by quite varied facies, more and more littoral as we approach the ancient massif: ferruginous or siliceous limestones, sandstones, dolomites, uneven marls with pelecypods, brachiopods, echinoids; certain horizons still have ammonites but there are no more examples of *Phylloceras* or *Lytoceras*. On the other hand, we note the meagerness of the detrital contributions (no true sandstone) which shows that the old massif, emerged farther south, only supported a purely organic sedimentation.[117] Especially in the Aalenian, Bajocian and lower Bathonian, these oolitic, sometimes dolomitic limestones with corals and crinoids were amassed in great thickness, reaching 300 or 400 m. in the great russet cliffs (Baous) bordering the Alps between the lower Var and Grasse. It is the Bathonian to upper Oxfordian sequence that retains, farthest south, the marly-calcareous, muddy facies with ammonites.[118]

In fact, south of a line connecting Castellane and Puget-Theniers, in the Upper Jurassic, truly corallian, often dolomitic facies with corals, *Diceras* and nerineas appear. These are white limestones, which, in the landscapes of Haut-Provence and the Alpes-Maritimes, play a role similar to that of the Urgonian (missing between Nice and Castellane) in the northern sub-Alpine chains, forming the canyons of the Verdon enclosed between vertical walls more than 400 m. high. They are spread out in great karst plateaus between Castellane and Grasse. Finally, their high white cliffs dominate the Côte d'Azur between Nice and Mentone where, on the other hand, the Lias seems to be missing and the Dogger very reduced. Curiously, at the top of these white limestones of Nice, indications of Purbeckian facies are found (remains of *Chara,* fresh-water algae, beds of green marls, breccias with black pebbles) identical to those of the Jura, from which, however, they were separated by the broad expanse of the deep Alpine sea.[119]

C. Jurassic of the Internal Zone.   The stratigraphy of this zone cannot be stated precisely nor supported by fossiliferous deposits, except in the regions located south of Moutiers and Vanoise, whose structure we have already described (p. 282).

1. *Sub-Briançonnais Zone.*   Our knowledge has progressed from south to north, as the Jurassic was studied first in the Mesozoic scales intercalated between the autochthonous black-earths and the Flysch nappe of Embrunais-Ubaye, that is to say, in the massifs of Ancelle and Chabrières (between the Drac and the Durance), of Morgon (between the Durance and the Ubaye) and of Ubaye (periphery of the Barcelonette window). In the whole assemblage, there are characteristics intermediate between those of the Dauphinois Jurassic and the Briançonnais Jurassic. The lower or external scales (Ancelle, Morgon) have a more Dauphinois facies, the upper or internal scales (Chabrières, Ubaye) characteristics more Briançonnais.[120]

Farther north, the sub-Briançonnais zone, very much narrowed east of Pelvoux, broadens out considerably leaving Galibier Pass and at the crossing of the Maurienne. There, between the Arc and Isère, it is the Jurassic which constitutes almost entirely the imposing massif of Perron des Encombres, prolonged on the north as far as Moutiers, through Niélard. R. Barbier distinguished there a whole succession of tectonic units (which have, at the same time, zones of facies corresponding to as many troughs or cordilleras) succeeding each other in festoons, sometimes sheared into scales, sometimes spreading out freely in digitations or elementary nappes, where fine exposures often permit the stratigraphy to be easily deciphered.

On the whole, the finest sections of this sub-Briançonnais ensemble are, from south to north; a) the south slope of Morgon between Barcelonnette and the Ubaye-Durance confluence; b) the south slope of the Piolit-Chabrières Massif, east of Gap (Fig. 84); c) the classic section of the Pas-du-Roc, on the south slope of the Encombres Massif, between St. Jean and St. Michel-de-Maurienne.

The Rhaetian, especially characterized by shell marbles with *Avicula contorta,* in Maurienne has provided a very typical fauna of the famous Pas-du-Roc locality (defile of the Arc, down stream from St. Michel-de-Maurienne). There, in the shell marbles and bone beds of the Swabian facies, calcareous banks are associated with numerous brachiopods (*Terebratula gregaria, Spiriferina münsteri*)[121] and corals. This is the type of the Rhaetian called Carpathian because it is developed particularly in the true domain of the Alpine Triassic (eastern Alps and Carpathians). In fact, its fauna, more normal and more marine than that of the Swabian type, is distinguishable from the latter about as the fauna of the Alpine Middle Triassic differs from that of the Germanic Muschelkalk.

The Lias is much more littoral and more reduced than the Dauphinois type; it is only a few tens of meters thick. We can distinguish in it, in general, a calcareous lower Lias (limestones with gryphaeas or crinoids in the Morgon, crinoidal or siliceous limestones with rare silicified arietitids in the Pas-du-Roc) and a shaly upper Lias, with fairly rich ammonite faunas of the Toarcian and Aalenian in the Morgon and in the Encombres Massif.

The Dogger, still thick and muddy, marly-calcareous, in the external digitation of the Encombres Massif (Grand Moëndaz) is reduced (50–100 m.) and becomes more Briançonnais-like in the more internal units: oolitic limestones and "Dogger with *Mytilus*" of the Morgon, organic coral limestones of the bar of the Pas-du-Roc (rich lime rock). It ends with calcareous shales (Dogger with *Cancellophycus*) containing an ammonite faunule of the upper Bathonian, at Lake Allos (Ubaye, Madame Gubler-Wahl).

The base of the Malm is still represented in the more external units (Piolit, cement stone quarries of the Pas-du-Roc) by deep, Dauphinois facies, the black earths (Bathonian-Oxfordian), which are rapidly reduced in more eastern units. There, the famous Telegraph Breccia (from Telegraph Fort, situated near the highway of Galibier and dominating, on the south, Pas-du-Roc)[122] doubtless must be attributed to the Oxfordian, as well as the magnificent red radiolarites found by D. Schneegans in the plunging fold of the Caire (east of the Morgon Massif).

The upper Malm (Lusitanian-Tithonian) is still, in the more external units (Piolit) in the state of muddy calcareous shales with belemnites and *Aptychus* and thin beds of green radiolarites, which pass imperceptibly into the Cretaceous. But, in the more internal units, it presents varied limestone facies: limestones with calpionellas,[123] thick masses of white coral limestones (cordilleras) in the Morgon and the high summits of the Ubaye south of Barcellonnette, and, particularly, the very characteristic facies of the Guillestre marble, which we shall find again in the Briançonnais but which appeared earlier in the more internal sub-Briançonnais units (Chabrières).

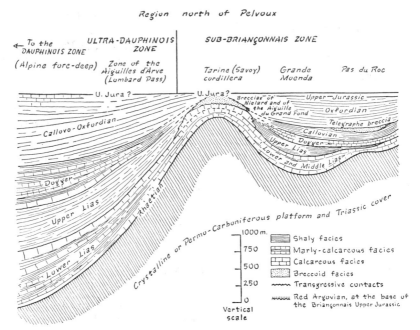

FIG. 83. *Diagram of the Jurassic facies in the internal zones of the French Alps (by R. Barbier).*

This diagram shows first the reduction of the thickness of the Dauphinois muddy facies approaching the bottom of the Alpine fore-deep (ultra-Dauphinois zone). In the sub-Briançonnais zone, this fore-deep is broken by small local cordilleras. In fact, in this zone, the different tectonic units (and facies units) do not extend from north to south along the range, but are arranged in successive arcs. Thus, north of Pelvoux (R. Barbier) the sub-zones of the Tarine cordillera, of Grande Moenda and the Pas du Roc disappear successively toward the south and are separated from the Briançonnais Carboniferous platform only by the gypsum zone of the Pas du Roc, where the remnants of the more internal zones are found, streaked out in block-klippes. South of Pelvoux (D. Schneegans), the front of the chain is composed of more internal units (Piolit, Séolanes, Dramonasq) unknown north of Pelvoux. At Tête du Grand-Pré (north of Briançon), the external Briançonnais unit, the last examples of the Lias and of the Callovian-Oxfordian *terres-noires,* very streaked out, are still seen.

For more details, see works by D. Schneegans, R. Barbier, H. Schoeller and by M. Gignoux and L. Moret, cited note 120, chap. 7, notes 54 and 68, chap. 6 and note 154, chap. 5.

The Embrunais-Ubaye nappes thus furnish a particularly striking first example of the superposition on the same vertical line of several different facies of the same stages (Fig. 84).

The top of these nappes is composed of the Flysch which envelops the Briançonnais zone. Below it, the Mesozoic scales (Permian to Tertiary) of the sub-Briançonnais zone appear like anticlinal crests sheared off and dragged by the thrust. Still lower in the bottoms of the valleys of the Durance (half-window of Embrun) and the Ubaye (window of Barcelonnette) are shown the autochthonous black earths (upper Lias to Oxfordian) of the external zone. So, mounting the heights of Chabrières, for example, one traverses three

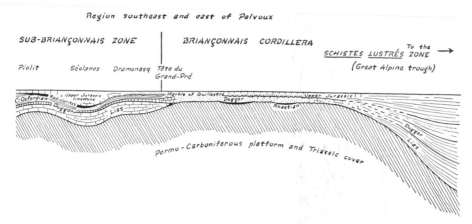

Region southeast and east of Pelvoux

SUB-BRIANÇONNAIS ZONE | BRIANÇONNAIS CORDILLERA

Piolit   Séolanes   Dramonasq Tête du
                                  Grand-Pré

To the
SCHISTES LUSTRÉS ZONE →
(Great Alpine trough)

times the same series of formations but with facies progressively modified: a) the autochthon with its uniformly deep-water facies without lacunas; b) the lower sub-Briançonnais scales with their Triassic red shales, their littoral Lias, their organic limestones of the Dogger, their Oxfordian black shales followed in continuity by the Malm and Lower Cretaceous; c) the upper scales already having the Briançonnais facies: thick Triassic limestones with diplopores, no Lias, organic Dogger, no Oxfordian shales, transgressive Argovian in the form of Guillestre marble, no Lower Cretaceous.

2. *Briançonnais Zone.* Aside from the Rhaetian, represented in some places (Pierre-Eyrautz Massif, south of Briançon, where, as discovered by M. Lugeon, it follows the Triassic in continuity), the Lias seems to be missing almost everywhere. The Jurassic begins with breccias, attributed to the transgressive Dogger, which are overlain by oolitic limestones and fossiliferous calcareous shales, containing a neritic fauna of rhynchonellids, nerineas, corals, stromatoporids and especially numerous pelecypods (*Mytilus*). At some places there are coal beds which were formerly mined. This is the very littoral facies called *Mytilus* Dogger which we shall find again in the Prealpine nappes.

The shaly facies of the Callovian-Oxfordian has completely disappeared. A new transgression begins with the Argovian, which lies either on the Dogger or directly on the Triassic limestones. At the bottom of the seas red, muddy sediments were then deposited, coming from the working over of the terra rossa (siderolithic), which was formed on the emerged calcareous (Triassic and Dogger) prominences.[124] This is the equivalent of the red Argovian of the Prealpine nappes. Very often these muds were consolidated in nodular limestones, variegated red and green, exploited as Guillestre marbles[125] and displaying very rare Argovian ammonites. Above come light colored limestones, more massive, representing the Rauracian-Tithonian, with some intercalations, toward the base, of red radiolarites (D. Schneegans). The top contains calpionellas and has provided, in the Lauzon Pass (northeast of Guillestre), a rich ammonite fauna, with Carpathian affinities, studied by F. Blanchet.

On the whole, this series of the Briançonnais Jurassic hardly exceeds 150 to 200 m. It is a great contrast to the Dauphinois facies.

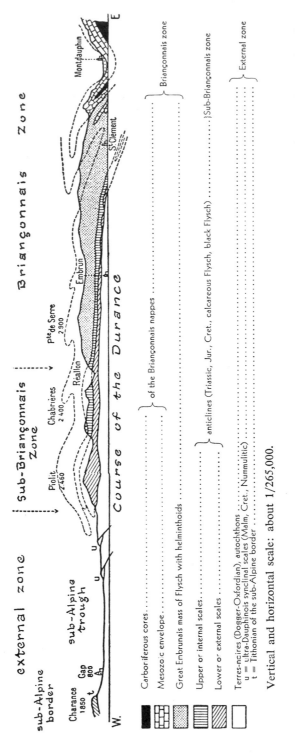

FIG. 84. *Diagrammatic profile of the mountains on the right bank of the Durance, between Gap, Embrun and Montdauphin, showing the nappes of the Embrunais (after M. Gignoux, L. Moret, D. Schneegans).*

3. *The Jurassic of the Piedmont Zone: Schistes lustrés.*[126]   Between the internal crystalline massifs with their Triassic cover, we find, in all the Franco-Italian mountains of the Piedmont zone, only rocks called *schistes lustrés.* This name applies to a thick series (probably more than 1,000 m.) of sediments very monotonous in the mass, but fairly varied. They are usually more or less metamorphic calcareous shales, with phyllitic minerals which give them a brilliant luster. The shales may become either more clayey or more calcareous, more massive and more crystalline. On the average, they can be defined as phyllitic calc-schists (*calcescisti lucenti* of the Italian geologists), which are distinguished from the metamorphic rocks of the Primary by their calcium content.

Because of their metamorphism, these crystalline schists were formerly attributed to the Archean. But they seem to overlie the Triassic limestone in continuity. S. Franchi discovered, near the base, rare Liassic fossils (belemnites and arietites).[127] In Italy, east of Mont Genèvre, they contain beds of radiolarites similar to those of the Briançonnais Malm. Finally, at the boundary of the Briançonnais and Piedmont zones, a continuous passage is sometimes seen (W. Kilian, C. Pussenot, F. Blanchet) from this schistose assemblage to different parts of the Jurassic, the Upper Cretaceous and even the Briançonnais Tertiary.[128] So today, it is agreed to attribute these *schistes lustrés* to the Jurassic and Cretaceous, perhaps even to the lowest Tertiary. Moreover, very often at or near the contact of the Briançonnais and Piedmont zones, and separating them from each other, an important tectonic discontinuity exists, that, according to W. Kilian and P. Termier, marks the base of a nappe of *schistes lustrés.*[129]

A characteristic feature of these *schistes lustrés* is the presence of intercalations or massifs of greenstones (*pietre verdi*) almost everywhere. These are basic crystalline rocks (gabbros, diorites, peridotites), generally much changed (into prasinites or serpentines) by dynamic metamorphism, which represent laccolithic injections or perhaps submarine eruptions dating from the Jurassic or Cretaceous.[130]

Finally, in this preeminently geosynclinal series of *schistes lustrés,* there sometimes are intercalations of breccias, indicating the momentary uprising of cordilleras.

2. *The Swiss and Savoy Alps*

We have already defined their tectonic units, which will serve as a framework for the description of the Jurassic facies.

A. The Helvetides. There, in the autochthonous covering of the external crystalline massifs and in the Helvetic nappes, the Jurassic retains, on the whole, the Dauphinois type of the external zone of the French Alps. Still, whereas the latter, farther south, were uniformly deep-water (Alpine foredeep), with only a few Vindelician islets (dome of La Mure, Ch. and P. Lory) still emergent at the beginning of the Lias,[131] in Haute-Savoie and Switzerland these emergent zones assume greater importance. They thus constitute a new paleogeographic element, the Helvetic Dome.

Its influence is shown in the autochthonous sedimentary covering of the massifs of the Aiguilles Rouges and the Aar. The Lias, very incomplete and reduced, generally begins with the Aalenian in the form of crinoidal limestones (*Echinodermenbreccie*) overlain by Aalenian shales with *H. opalinum,* often quite thick, and by sandstones. In the Dogger crinoidal limestones are found, and in the Callovian ferruginous oolites (*Eisenoolit*). These stages are sometimes transgressive; thus in the northern part of the Aiguilles-Rouges, near the Franco-Swiss frontier, the fossiliferous Bajocian[132] directly overlies the crystalline rocks (Paréjas). Then the depth increases; the Argovian, here called Schiltkalk and Schiltschiefer,[133] has its typical facies of the Aargau Jura. The Lusitanian and Kimmeridgian are represented by the Quintner-kalk,[134] reaching 600 m. thickness. The Portlandian is sometimes composed of coral limestones with the fauna of Echaillon (*Troskalk*). All these limestones of the Malm are often designated by the old name Hochgebirgskalk (limestones of the high mountains), for they form the great calcareous escarpments of the high chains which border the crystalline massifs on the north.[135]

In the Helvetic nappes, the Jurassic consists only of the basal beds and becomes a deeper and still deeper facies as we penetrate the higher tectonic units, which is equivalent to saying that as we turn south from the emerged zone, we enter a deep sea, the Valais geosyncline of E. Haug, the prolongation of the eastern part of our Dauphinois fore-deep.[136]

B. The Prealpine Nappes. The study of the Jurassic facies (as, also, that of all the other series) is of great interest because of the inferences about the location of the roots of these nappes.

1. The Jurassic of the ultra-Helvetic nappe still greatly resembles that of the upper Helvetic nappes. A very thick Lias is found there, more calcareous at the base, more shaly at the top (as in the Dauphinois type). The Dogger includes a few crinoidal banks but it has on the whole the marly limestone facies with *Cancellophycus* (often called *Zoophycos* in Switzerland). The Malm, beginning with thick Callovian-Oxfordian shales, is wholly identical to that of the Dauphinois type.

2. In the Niesen nappe, the Jurassic is exposed only in small laminated scales. They seem analogous to the Jurassic of the external scales of the sub-Briançonnais zone.

3. The Jurassic of the Median Prealps is, however, very well known. We find there, even in details, all the characteristic facies of the Briançonnais and sub-Briançonnais zones.[137] The Rhaetian shows the same association of the Swabian and Carpathian types as in the Pas-du-Roc. The Lias is much varied, sometimes well developed, sometimes very littoral and sometimes completely missing. Then the Dogger is often transgressive; in the northwest (external) part, it has the relatively deep-water type of the Dogger with *Cancellophycus* of the external, sub-Briançonnais scales; in the southeastern (internal) part, it is a Dogger with *Mytilus,* identical to that of the internal sub-Briançonnais scales and the Briançonnais. Finally, above more or less well developed Callovian-Oxfordian shales, comes a red Argovian, sometimes

trangressive and locally producing marbles (marbles of Vernaz, south of Thonon) identical to the Guillestre marbles. And the Malm always ends with light colored limestones, sometimes with corals as in the Ubaye.

4. The stratigraphy of the Breccia nappe is more hypothetical because of the almost complete lack of fossils. Only the Rhaetian, identical with that of the Median Prealps, is well characterized. The thick series of lower Ardois shales is assigned to the Lias, and the series of lower breccias, sometimes transgressive on the Triassic, is assigned to the Dogger. Beds of variegated shales, with plant remains, are assigned to the Callovian-Oxfordian (?). And the Malm is almost surely represented by the upper breccia, with calcareous banks containing calpionellas (L. Moret).

From this quick survey, we get two impressions: 1st. In this series of nappes, Helvetic, ultra-Helvetic, Niesen, Median, the facies vary progressively. In a general way, the depth increases up to the ultra-Helvetic zone, which would correspond approximately to the maximum depth of the Alpine fore-deep. Then the littoral facies appears. This is the edge of a geanticline,[138] which we can call the Briançonnais geanticline.[139] 2nd. Actually we have described, in the Embrunais-Ubaye nappes, the same succession of facies. The ultra-Dauphinois scales also indicate the maximum depth of the Dauphinois fore-deep. The most external facies of the sub-Briançonnais scales are analogous to those of the Niesen nappe. And the Medians would correspond to the internal sub-Briançonnais scales and to the extreme edge of the Briançonnais.

And, in fact, the fine researches of M. Lugeon have definitely established that the ultra-Helvetic nappe was rooted immediately behind the Helvetic roots and in front of the frontal Pennine overthrust, which here bounds, on the north, the Sion-Val Ferret zone. It is exactly here that our sub-Briançonnais zone would end and it is there that we are led to seek the roots of other Prealpine nappes as we come from France.

C. The Pennides. The Prealpine nappes may be thought to show elements of Pennine origin, but without the Pennine metamorphism. South of the Pennine coaly zone begins the domain of the metamorphic Pennines. This is extension of the French zone of *schistes lustrés*. Thus we pass there the summit of the Briançonnais cordillera and enter the domain of the great Alpine trough, where we are still ignorant of the Jurassic stratigraphy.[140] We shall merely note that, locally, the *schistes lustrés* pass into thick accumulations of breccias, for example at Mont Dolin, in the cover of the south flank (normal flank) of the great anticlinal Primary core of the Dent Blanche. As E. Argand has suggested, these breccias correspond to ancient cordilleras which complicated the bottom of the great Alpine trough.

3. *Summary: Paleogeography of the Western Alps in the Jurassic*

If we "unroll" the nappes, placing, in imagination, each of the tectonic units in its original zone of sedimentation, we see that the different facies follow each other in a coherent order. It is such harmonious concordance between

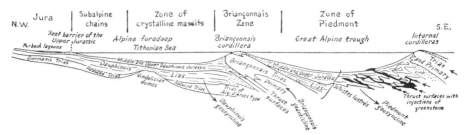

FIG. 85. *Diagrammatic section indicating the probable appearance of the French Alps toward the end of the Jurassic (suggested by W. Kilian and E. Argand).*

Dots indicate the littoral facies of the Jurassic: organic limestone, reefs, breccias.
Black indicates greenstones which possibly began to be injected in the Jurassic.
Vertical scale greatly exaggerated.

tectonic and stratigraphic syntheses that earn the name of science for geology.

From the exterior to the interior of the Alps we find thus, in the Jurassic, the following paleogeographic units (Figs. 85 and 86):

First, an Alpine foreland in which the influence of the Hercynian basement is still evident. On its external border, the epicontinental facies, with changing shores, are shown in the Jura type (reaching almost to Grenoble), the Rhodanian type (which we shall study on the edge of the Massif Central) and the Provençal type (edge of the Maures-Esterel) of the Jurassic. Then we enter the Alpine foredeep, with its muddy and very thick Jurassic, of the Dauphinois type in France, Helvetic in Switzerland. But in this Helvetic domain, convexities of the substratum introduce, especially in the Lower and Middle Jurassic, littoral facies and lacunas. This is the Vindelician zone, represented by the dome of La Mure in the Dauphiné, by the Helvetic dome in Haute-Savoie and Switzerland. Farther in the interior, the sediments of the deep part of the Dauphinois trough (in Switzerland, the Valais geosyncline of E. Haug) have been stripped and moved ahead under the Pennine thrusts, producing, in France, the ultra-Dauphinois scales, in Haute-Savoie and Switzerland, the ultra-Helvetic nappe.

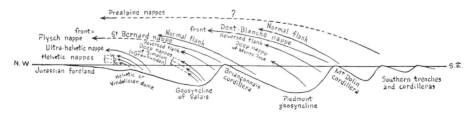

FIG. 86. *Diagram explaining the ideas of the Swiss geologists on the relationship between the nappes of western Switzerland and the paleogeographic units of the end of the Jurassic.*

W, D, M = nappes of the Wildhorn, Diablerets and Morcles; for the Prealpine nappes see note 74, chap. 6.

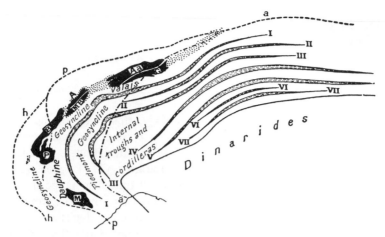

FIG. 87. *Diagrammatic map of the paleogeographic units of the Western Alps in the Jurassic (after R. Staub, slightly modified).*

Dots = Helvetic dome (Vindelician chain) — Helvetides.

I = Briançonnais cordillera ⎫
II = Tambo-Suretta cordillera (ending in the west in the deep nappe of Monte Rosa) ⎬ Pennides.
III = Cordillera of Mont-Dolin (or of the Dent-Blanche) ⎭

IV–VIII = Southern (or internal) cordilleras — Grisonides.

Black = Hercynian massifs:
        M—Mercantour; P—Pelvoux; B—Belledonne; MB—Mont Blanc; A—Aiguilles Rouges; G—Gotthard; Aa—Aar.

h = Present external boundary of the Helvetides: sub-Alpine arc.

p = Present external boundary of the Pennides (including the Prealpine nappes): Prealpine arc.

a = Present external boundary of the Austrides: Austro-Alpine arc.

Note. For *Geosyncline Dauphine,* read *Dauphinois geosyncline;* for *Geosyncline valais,* read *Valais geosyncline.*

Then we reach the Pennine or intra-Alpine zone. Littoral facies and lacunas appear in the Jurassic, announcing the approach of the Briançonnais cordillera (St. Bernard nappe), the overthrust front of which, toward the north, has advanced far over the external zone, taking shape as an enormous Prealpine festoon (see p. 297). First there is the sub-Briançonnais zone which in the south has broken out in the Embrunais-Ubaye nappes and in the north in the Savoy and Swiss Prealpine nappes. We see the succession of a series of cordilleras, with their Jurassic, Cretaceous, and Tertiary breccias (zone of the Tarentaise breccias, Breccia nappe), in front of the great Briançonnais cordillera. All this constitutes the non-metamorphic, external Pennine domain.[141]

But on the internal slope of the great Briançonnais cordillera (normal flank of the St. Bernard nappe), we reach the great Alpine trough, where the whole Jurassic (added to the Cretaceous) is metamorphic. This is the Piedmont or *schistes lustrés* zone, enveloping the Paleozoic cores of the internal crystalline massifs (Monte Rosa, Dent Blanche, Grand Paradis, etc.).

Nevertheless, still more interior narrow cordilleras rise, shown locally by breccias. In the western Alps, there is first the Dent-Blanche Cordillera, marked by the breccias of Mont Dolin (E. Argand). Then come the cordilleras of the eastern Alps or Austrides (R. Staub) which we shall not study here.

Finally, leaving the great Alpine trough, we should again find epicontinental, non-metamorphic facies, in the Dinarides.

From the point of view of general geology, this study of the Jurassic of the Alps leads us to envision a very special type of sedimentation, that of cordilleran facies, already foreseen by E. Haug, but definitely elucidated, with an expressive terminology, by the Swiss geologists (M. Lugeon, E. Argand, R. Staub). A cordillera appears to us as the front of a nappe in motion,[142] pushed slowly, by successive strokes, but irresistibly, over the trough in front of it and accompanied by thick collapsing breccias, doubtless largely submarine, which have mixed violently with the muds (sometimes transformed into metamorphosed shales) in the bottoms of the troughs. While the epicontinental neritic or bathyal sedimentation, which is stable, or rather continuous, is easy to understand through observation of the bottoms of present seas, the sedimentation of the cordilleran facies, because of its catastrophic character, its tectonic movement, its shock tectonics, is ouside of our ordinary experience.[143]

IX. The Ancient Jurassic Shores Around the Massif Central; The Causses

It is certain that the Jurassic seas covered, at certain epochs, extensive regions of the Massif Central. This is shown by the study of the girdle of Jurassic deposits which encircles it. It is, however, only in the southern part that this border becomes wide enough to form an important natural region: the Causses.

From Lyons to the northern end of Morvan, the Jurassic is not very different from that of the southern Jura or Burgundy. But it is reduced to narrow fragments, cut up and tilted by faults, where the slopes of upper Lias marls are capped with scarp-forming limestones of the Middle Jurassic. The most characteristic and the best known of these small tabular fragments, hugged against the Hercynian Massif, is the southernmost of them, the Lyonnais Mont d'Or, immediately north of Lyon. Above gryphaea limestones, the Liassic marls are surmounted by iron ore of the *H. bifrons* zone, topped immediately by limestones with *Cancellophycus,* then with crinoidal Aalenian. The lower Bajocian is reduced to isolated veneers, leveled off by the transgression of the upper Bajocian, which is represented by a limestone containing silicified fossils, known as *ciret*.[144] Thus the succession of facies resembles that of Lorraine and of the Jura, though its different elements do not occupy the same place on the stratigraphic scale. Above, the Bathonian is represented only by poor outcrops of oolitic limestones. The Upper Jurassic has been removed by erosion.

Farther north, in the Beaujolais, the Mâconnais[145] and the Côte-d'Or of Burgundy, there are still escarpments of Middle Jurassic limestone which extend the length of the border of the crystalline massif and support the celebrated vineyards of this region.

North of the Morvan, in the Yonne, the series ends with the addition of the Upper Jurassic. The Argovian has its typical facies with sponges and calcareous nodules. The Rauracian sees a great development of coral facies, as in the Meuse; the famous reef of Châtel-Censoir is 160 m. thick. Coral intercalations are still found in the Sequanian.

From there to the Strait of Poitou, the Jurassic border shrinks and contains the usual littoral facies of the Paris Basin. The Bathonian even assumes a facies of lacustrine, lignitic beds with paludinas (St. Gauthier, Indre).

The Strait of Poitou was, as we have seen, opened only in the Charmouthian and it is perhaps for that reason that in the Aquitaine Basin, studied by P. Glangeaud, the base of the Jurassic border is no longer of the usual type of the Paris Basin. The Hettangian is often lagoonal and the characteristic faunas of the typical Sinemurian are unknown (as in Provence). But in the middle and upper Lias, the customary marls are found and, as in the north, the Bathonian sometimes shows brackish or lacustrine facies with lignite beds. In the Portlandian, the facies with nerineas, which is found in Aquitaine, the Causses and the southern Jura, but not in the Paris Basin, shows that the warm Mesogean fauna must have spread along the southern edge of the Massif Central, but not along the northern edge.[146]

A. The Causses. At the southern extremity of the massif, Jurassic formations acquire a very special importance, for there they form the calcareous plateaus called the Causses. The Jurassic seas there covered part of the Massif Central, forming a true strait which separated it from the Montagne-Noire. Erosion has carried away the Jurassic sediments which occupied the central part of this strait, so that today the Montagne-Noire seems joined to the Massif Central by an isthmus of crystalline formations, an isthmus separating two Jurassic gulfs:[147] the one on the west, scarcely evident, is the Causses of Quercy and Rouergue; while the other, to the east, very deep and sinuous, is the Grands-Causses (of Sauveterre, Méjean, Noir and Larzac).[148]

The lower Lias is represented there by marly limestones which surmount more solid banks, with corals and gryphaeas (Sinemurian), forming plateaus. The middle and upper Lias have their usual facies of thick black marls, whose fine pyritic ammonite faunas have inspired numerous monographs.[149] *Lytoceras* and *Phylloceras* are as numerous as in the Dauphinois facies. Thus we have an enormous area of submergence and deepening, the like of which is hardly found outside the Alps, except in the Germanic Cuvette. These marls form great slopes, at the foot of the walls of gorges cut in the plateaus (example, the famous Tarn gorges). For, with the Aalenian, the calcareous and dolomitic facies[150] begin, which prevail through all the rest of the Jurassic,

with local variations that we shall not describe. These are the limestones and
the dolomites that constitute the plateaus of the Causses, a karst region, with
the characteristic gulfs, subterranean rivers, stony soil and poor vegetation.

These littoral facies of the Upper Jurassic persist in Languedoc, Gard and
the edge of the Cevennes. In the Callovian and Oxfordian, "hard-grounds"
and lacunas sometimes encompass the whole Oxfordian,[151] evidence of more
shallow seas, swept by currents. And the Portlandian is represented by coral
limestones with fine *Diceras* faunas, which were earlier the subject of the
thesis of F. Roman.[152]

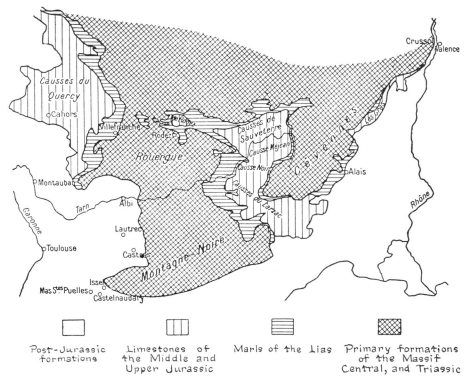

FIG. 88.   *Diagrammatic geologic map of the regions of the Causses.*

Farther north, in the Ardèche, we reach, on the other hand, a region where
the Upper Jurassic assumes deep facies. The type section is that of the mountain of Crussol.

B. The Crussol Section.   Crussol Mountain, opposite Valence, rises like a
rampart against the ancient massif, dominating the plains of the Rhône. This
section is classic.[153]

Overlying the Triassic (see p. 276) there are first sandstones of doubtful
age (upper Charmouthian?). Then the Toarcian is transgressive, followed by
the Aalenian, made up of crinoidal limestones, sandy or ferruginous, in blocks
a few decimeters thick. The same very littoral facies continue in the Bajocian,
represented by ferruginous, crinoidal limestones, rich in brachiopods, scarcely

more than 1 m. thick and cut across by lacunas of sedimentation.[154] Like-wise, a few meters of marly limestone with *Cancellophycus,* with kidney-like blocks of black silica (*chailles*), correspond to the Bathonian. In spite of their thinness and their littoral [155] character, these Middle Jurassic beds of the border of the Massif Central must have extended very far to the west, because residues of them, in the form of isolated *chailles* are found as far as Haute-Loire. In this epoch, the sea must have advanced toward the southwest and thus joined the Strait of the Causses.

But in the upper Bathonian, deeper-water facies begin. These are first, marls with *Posidonomya alpina* which continue into the lower Callovian. In the up-per Callovian is a last littoral episode with a bed of phosphatised debris. Then, starting with the Oxfordian, there are finally found the Dauphinois uniformly deep-water facies of the sub-Alpine chains; marls in the Oxfordian, marly limestones in the Lusitanian, compact limestones very rich in cephalopods in

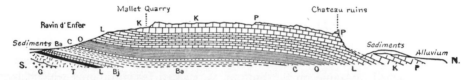

FIG. 89.   *Profile of the Mountain of Crussol (near Valence), seen from the east (from the Valley of the Rhône) (after A. Riche and F. Roman, modi-fied).*

P = Portlandian: Tithonian limestone of the Chateau. K = Kimmeridgian: cephalopod limestone of the Mallet quarry. L = Lusitanian: marly limestones. O = Oxfordian: marls with pyritic ammonites. C = Callovian: marls with *Posidonomya*. B_a = Bathonian: marls with *Posidonomya* and limestone with *Cancellophycus*. B_j = Bajocian: crinoidal limestone. L = Lias: sandstone and ferruginous limestone. T = Trias: sandstone and fossiliferous dolomite. G = Granite of the Massif Central. Vertical and horizontal scales: about 1/57,000.

the Kimmeridgian and also in the lower and middle Portlandian, which thus are of the Tithonian type. This is the famous Crussol fauna, figured by Fon-tannes in a monograph used by stratigraphers all over the world.

But, at Crussol itself, the series stops there. To study the upper horizons of the Tithonian, we must go farther south into the region of Privas, Chomérac, Berrias (Ardèche). There, rich calcareous ammonite faunas of the top of the Tithonian and the base of the Cretaceous (Berriasian stage), studied ear-lier by Toucas, have allowed W. Kilian to define the boundary between the two systems. More recently, a pyritized fauna was discovered there.[156]

West of Crussol, an isolated fragment of Upper Jurassic with the same deep-water facies is known (W. Kilian). So it is very certain that the seas of the Upper Jurassic must have spread out widely over the eastern part of the Massif Central, then included in the deep sea of the sub-Alpine chains. This example shows once more that we must beware of assuming that the present limits of outcrops of a formation indicate the ancient shores of the correspond-ing epoch.

South of Crussol,[157] in a relatively broad band of Jurassic, the Lusitanian and Tithonian limestones determine a small natural region, a sort of miniature Causse traversed by the gorges of the Ardèche. These are the Plateaus of the Gras (see Fig. 88), whose name (from the Latin *gradus*) calls to mind small regular ledges developed by outcrops of calcareous beds along the edges of the plateaus.

X. Conclusion (The Face of the Earth in the Jurassic)

Let us now examine all western Europe in a broader view and try to render an account of the role played in the Jurassic by all the regions we have just described in relation to the rest of the globe.

The great paleogeographic units defined for the Triassic (see p. 304) will continue to guide us here.[158]

1. *Mesogean Domain*

The study of the Jurassic of the French and Swiss Alps has shown that, leaving the European continental area and going south, a zone of generally deep seas is reached, unstable on the bottom, variegated by cordilleras which already delineate the future Tertiary folds. This picture covers an immense Mesogean domain, even more extensive than in the Triassic. Beyond the present Mediterranean, it includes all the recently folded chains of Europe, North Africa, and Asia.

A. Italian Alps, Carpathians, Apennines. We shall be satisfied to name here the most interesting facies and the classic localities.

In the Lombard and Venetian Alps, good types of Mediterranean facies of the different stages of the Jurassic are found.

The Rhaetian is represented by widely varied facies, the Swabian facies with pelecypods (on the shores of Lake Como) and especially the Carpathian facies with brachiopods (see p. 357). In the Lias, we note especially the famous locality of Monte Domaro, in the Val Trompia north of Brescia.[159] This is the type of the Domerian stage, represented by siliceous limestones (locally called *medolo*) with beds of black shales with pyritic ammonites, which through the abundance of *Phylloceras* and *Lytoceras* recall the Lias of the Causses. The Toarcian is there usually called *Calcare ammonitico rosso inferiore*. This is a rose or greenish limestone, a little like the Griotte marbles (see p. 137), a pelagic, muddy deposit with cephalopods. Among the latter (studied by Parona), Mediterranean *Phylloceras* and *Lytoceras* still prevail. The very rich fauna described by Benecke at Cape San Virgilio (Lake Garda) corresponds to the Aalenian. Farther west, on the contrary, in Vicentin, the Lias assumes a more littoral type, gray limestone with *Megalodus*.

The Middle and Upper Jurassic are generally pelagic and deep-water. They are shales with *Posidonomya alpina* or limestones with *Aptychus,* sometimes red like the Lias sandstones and then called *Ammonitico rosso superiore*.[160] The Kimmeridgian is especially fossiliferous on the shores of Lake Garda, where Benecke has made it classic under the name of "beds with *Aspidoceras acanthicum.*" In the Portlandian, the deep-water facies continue. This is the home of the Tithonian: limestones with *Pygope diphya,* compact white limestones (majolica), shales with *Aptychus* and cherts with radiolaria (radiolarites),[161] developed, for example, in the Canavese zone, near Ivrea, situated behind the Sesia-Lanzo crystalline Massif (see map, Fig. 62), where many Swiss geologists would locate the roots of the Prealpine nappes.

In the Carpathians, we mention only the Stramberg beds (Stramberk) in Moravia, studied by Zittel, and famous for their rich fauna: upper Tithonian ammonites are associated with littoral forms, brachiopods, echinoids and corals. So this deposit is referred to in all paleontologic studies dealing with the Upper Jurassic.

These deep-water facies of the Jurassic are found again in the central part of the Apennines. On the other hand, in southern Italy, from Monte Gargano and Capri as far as Sicily, a transgressive Tithonian is found, with littoral faunas and limestones with *Ellipsactinia* which extend into the Cretaceous.[162] They are associated, as at Stramberg, with ammonites and *Pygope janitor.*

B. The Pyrenees. The structure and paleogeographic history of the Pyrenees is very different from that of the Alps.[163] The Secondary exists only in two marginal zones, French and Spanish, separated by a Primary axial zone. For some people, this zone must have remained emergent at least during all of the Jurassic, and this is the hypothesis followed on the map (Fig. 90). For others (G. Dubar),[164] however, the Jurassic seas, at least at certain periods, covered this axial zone, excepting the two extremities of the emerged zone shown on the map, the eastern extremity being represented by the Primary Massif of Barcelona; and there were periods of erosion prior to the great transgression of the Upper Cretaceous which destroyed the Jurassic deposits of the axial zone. In fact the facies give no indication of the approach of ancient shores along this axial zone.

On the other hand, all agree in recognizing the existence of an emerged region corresponding to the small Primary Massif of Monthoumet, as well as the Corbières and Montagne-Noire, and perhaps even extending toward the northwest under the Aquitaine Basin (sub-Pyrenean Massif of L. Bertrand).[165]

A first group is formed by the *Infra-lias* (Rhaetian and lower Hettangian). The Rhaetian sea with *Avicula contorta,* coming from the Alps, only reached the eastern part of the northern slope of the Pyrenees and the rest of the Infralias is composed of lagoonal sediments (*cargneules,* dolomites, marls, sandstones).

The lower Lias (upper Hettangian-Sinemurian) earns the name of calcareous Lias. It includes, at its base, dolomites which resemble the Hettangian dolomites of Provence and at the top (Lotharingian), streaked limestones with brachiopods and pectens, but not gryphaeas.

The middle and upper Lias are rather shaly and contain rich faunas of ammonites, especially in the western part of the chain where sedimentation becomes more uniform and deeper-water (Basque facies of G. Dubar).

The Middle Jurassic is represented by thick black or gray dolomites which play the principal role in the orography of the Pyrenean Jurassic. They are however not fossiliferous. They are overlain directly by the transgressive Aptian and it is recognized that the Upper Jurassic is missing. Especially in the western part of the chain, in the Basque Country, the dolomites are replaced by fossiliferous limestones, forming a series that extends up into the Lusitanian.

C. Iberian Peninsula. The skeletal structure of this peninsula is determined by an old Hercynian massif similar to our Massif Central, called the Iberian Meseta (see map, Fig. 105).

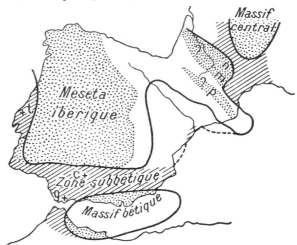

Dotted area ~ Regions emergent in the Lias
Continuous heavy line ~ Limits of the seas in the Lusitanean
Ruled ~ Tithonian seas
n = Primary massif of the Montagne Noir
m = Primary massif of Monthoumet
p = Primary axis of the Pyrenees
t = Torres-Vedras
c = Cabra
g = Gibralter

FIG. 90. *Diagrammatic map of the Jurassic seas in the Iberian Peninsula and in the Pyrenees (after maps of L. Bertrand and P. Fallot).*

It seems quite possible that this massif remained emergent in the Jurassic, doubtless forming a southern dependency of the North Atlantic continent. But the Mesogean seas encroached upon its boarders.

1. A gulf must have invaded the coastal region of Portugal.[166] We note especially the cephalopod beds of Torres-Vedras, north of Lisbon, type (rather mediocre) of the Lusitanian stage.

2. Along the southern edge of the Meseta, on the present location of the sub-Betic Chain (see p. 443), there extended a deep arm of the sea (geosyncline), bordered on the south by the ancient Betico-Riffian Massif, whose individuality is nevertheless hypothetical. There, the Jurassic[167] is represented by a continuous series of marine beds, with facies similar to those described

in the Italian Alps. The Lias[168] is composed of shaly or calcareous sediments with ammonites and *Pygopa* (*Glossothyris*) *aspasia,* sometimes red and similar to the *ammonitico rosso*. But in the border of the Meseta, it passes to more littoral facies with rhynchonellids and terebratulids (called *espagnol* facies). The Dogger, especially calcareous, is much less fossiliferous and less well known. Finally, in the Malm,[169] we see the reappearance of red, nodular limestones, made classic by the studies of W. Kilian at Cabra (Andalusia). But this red facies, called Andalusian, formerly believed Tithonian, is from the Lusitanian (red Argovian, as in the Briançonnais), reappearing in the Tithonian, which has led to a mixture of faunas in early descriptions. This Tithonian with ammonites and *Pygope diphya* seems analogous to the Diphyakalk of the Dinaric chains.

3. Finally, in the province of Alicante, the Jurassic Mediterranean turns to the northeast around the Meseta. In the Lias and again in the Middle Jurassic, there must have been a wide arm of the sea, covering the Cantabrian Mountains and extending as far as the Primary axis of the Pyrenees (see reservations made above). Then, after the Oxfordian, the Cantabrian Mountains and the two slopes of the Pyrenees emerged, transforming this arm of the sea into the Aragon Gulf,[170] closed toward the northwest in the region of Burgos. In particular, G. Dubar[171] has recently discovered in the Asturias a transgressive marine Kimmeridgian, thus indicating an Asturian gulf, coming from the Atlantic (not indicated on the map, Fig. 90). At the end of the Jurassic a great regression occurred, as in the Anglo-Norman Basin, and the whole Aragon Gulf became emergent. It is only in the vicinity of the mouth of the Ebro that dolomites without fossils can be tentatively related to the marine Tithonian.

D. North Africa.[172]   South of the Mesogean seas, we find the border of the great Saharan Continent, northern extremity of the immense Continent of Gondwana. In fact, as Savornin has said, "One can quite exactly define the Sahara: the part of North Africa destitute of Jurassic sediments." [173]

On this edge, emerged or covered with lagoons in the Upper Triassic, the Jurassic seas advanced unevenly toward the south. But their extreme limit in this direction is marked by a line that, leaving the Atlantic coast a little south of Agadir, passes through the region of Colomb-Béchar, then follows the southern edge of the Saharan Atlas as far as the great chotts of southern Tunisia, and there turns back toward the south, outlining a south Tunisian Gulf; where, in the Mountains of Ksour, a lagoonal-marine series with gypsum beds contains fossiliferous strata, with littoral facies, the oldest of which is Bathonian and the most recent Kimmeridgian.[174] Finally this line rejoins the coast near the frontier of Tripoli, because farther east and as far as Egypt the marine Jurassic is not found. The Jurassic there is included in the thick continental series of Nubian sandstones[175] which represent, in the northern part of the Continent of Gondwana, the Karroo formations of the southern part. It is only on reaching the Suez Gulf that the marine Jurassic reappears.[176]

Moreover the Jurassic outcrops are not extensive in eastern Algeria. It is only in the department of Oran and especially in Morocco that they constitute great natural regions: the karst areas of southern Oran prolonged by the plateaus of the Middle Atlas, high mountains of the eastern Morocco Great Atlas.[177] It is especially in Morocco that the Jurassic stratigraphy can be described by using the same ammonite zones as in Europe.

The Saharan continent sends out toward the north several promontories (or "dorsals" [Savornin]), where the Jurassic is incomplete or littoral. Note first the Moroccan dorsal which, leaving the central Great Atlas, extends through the Moroccan Meseta as far as the Atlantic, between Safi and Rabat. On its two borders, the Jurassic is represented by continental or lagoonal red beds (of the Keuper type), which extend into the Cretaceous. On the west, a Mogador-Agadir Gulf is indicated by the marine Upper Jurassic which, in the east, ends in red beds (E. Roch). On the eastern edge of the dorsal, calcareous Lias with brachiopods appears in these red formations (L. Moret). Then this series ends and in the Ayachi trough (of Djebel Ayachi in the eastern Great Atlas) are found thick calcareous or shaly series, several thousand meters thick, very fossiliferous, including the Lias and the Dogger, and extending with its more or less neritic facies throughout the Middle Atlas (H. Termier, G. Dubar).

Farther east, a second promontory, the Zousfana dorsal, extends as far north as the Algerian-Moroccan frontier (shoals of Oudjda). Thus in the southern Oran plateaus, south of Tlemcen, above a reduced, calcareous Lias and Oxfordian shales with *Posidonomya,* comes a thick series of plant-bearing sandstones and variegated shales, topped by cliff-forming dolomites and coral limestones of the Upper Jurassic.[178] East of this promontory comes another trough corresponding to the Mountains of Ksour, a section of the Saharan Atlas located northeast of Aïn-Sefra. Finally, a third promontory corresponds to the shoals of the Mountains of Mzab (Saharan Atlas) south of Hodna.

The Lias and Dogger are generally calcareous, outside of the forementioned troughs, and especially represented by facies with brachiopods of the type called Mediterranean (see note 16, this chap.) or, more rarely, by red marly limestones with ammonites (*ammonitico rosso inferiore*). In the Callovian-Oxfordian, shaly facies with *Posidonomya* are often found. Finally, the Upper Jurassic, where it is not corallian, shows, as in Andalusia, facies of red ammonite limestones (*ammonitico rosso superiore*) or limestones of the Tithonian type, especially developed in northeastern Algeria.

There, in the calcareous chain of Djurdjura,[179] on the southern edge of the old massif of Grande Kabylie, the Jurassic series, recently worked out, shows curious analogies with that of the Briançonnais. It begins with a fossiliferous Rhaetian, while thick organic, sometimes dolomitic limestones correspond to the Lias and Dogger. A red Argovian is transgressive and contains jasper and conglomerate with crystalline pebbles. The series ends with calcareous shales containing *Aptychus.*

In northern Tunisia,[180] cephalopod facies are known in the Tunisian dorsal. Southwest of Kairouan[181] they seem to pass into the littoral and lagoonal facies of southern Tunisia (dome of Jefara).

E. Asiatic Chains. Through the Crimea, Caucasus and Sinai (where the

Jurassic was discovered by J. Barthoux and H. Douvillé), the Mesogean seas extended as far as the Himalayan chains. There we must mention two classic localities.

1. The peninsula of Katch (or Cutch) at the mouth of the Indus, where Waagen found, long ago, a whole succession of European ammonite zones: zones with *Macrocephalites macrocephalus,* with *Reineckeia anceps,* with *Peltoceras athleta,* etc. We can hardly find a more impressive example of the usefulness of cephalopods to establish correlations at a long distance.[182]

2. A thick shaly series in the central Himalaya (see p. 226 and Fig. 53), comprising the Lusitanian, Kimmeridgian and Portlandian, passing into the Lower Cretaceous, is known as the Spiti beds. Its very rich ammonite faunas are rather specialized, although a few genera (*Spiticeras*) are also found in the Mediterranean Tithonian.

2. North Atlantic Continent

We have shown that, in the Jurassic, all of Europe north of the zone of Hercynian massifs should be considered as a vast continental area, over which epicontinental seas advanced only moderately.[183] At the west, in the Iberian Meseta, Brittany, and the British Primary massifs, it seems evident that we see parts of this continental area which remained continuously beyond marine influences (see Fig. 69).

It is natural to continue to assume, as in preceding epochs, that this continental area continued across the site of the Atlantic to North America. In fact, neither in the United States nor in Canada do we recognize the slightest evidence of the Jurassic; to find it, it is necessary to go as far as the Rockies or Mexico, that is, into the Pacific domain, to be studied later.

3. Sino-Siberian Continent

Starting from the Callovian epoch, it is certain that an arm of the sea extended across Russia, separating the Scandinavian-Baltic part of the North Atlantic continent from an immense emergent domain composing all of Asia north of the Himalayan chains. This is the Sino-Siberian continent [184] or continent of Angara, so named by Suess after the Angara River, which, coming from Lake Baikal, passes by Irkutsk and flows into the Yenisei.

For this river crosses Jurassic formations, continental sandstones and conglomerates containing coal beds with a rich flora. These deposits, called the Angara series,[185] cover very extensive areas in this part of Asia. Their final prolongations to the south are found in certain coal basins in China[186] and especially Tonkin. These coals of Tonkin, actively exploited, seem to be of Rhaetian age, though according to recent research, some of them would date from the Upper Triassic.[187]

4. The Fragmentation of the Continent of Gondwana

The Mesogean seas were bordered on the south, as in the Triassic, by the great continental mass formed by Brazil, central and southern Africa, Madagascar, the Indian Peninsula, and Australia, which we have previously called the Continent of Gondwana (see p. 238). This continent must have extended as far north as the ancient Mediterranean shores, in the region of the Saharan and Libyan deserts.

At various points continental formations with Jurassic plants, fish, and reptiles are known, such as the upper Karroo beds in southern Africa, the upper Gondwana beds in India, continuations of analogous formations of Permo-Triassic age (see p. 305).

But from the beginning of the Jurassic, the attack on this continent by the sea, an attack already begun in the Triassic (see p. 305), becomes still more definite.

The Middle Jurassic is transgressive on the southwest coast of Australia. But even as early as the Lias the sea had begun to advance on the present position of the Mozambique Channel, which, as today, separated Madagascar from Africa. In fact, on the west coast of Madagascar we see a marine Jurassic series beginning with the Lias, while on the African coast facing the great island, we find the marine Bathonian. These Malagasy Jurassic faunas show some affinities with the Himalayan regions, so it is possible that this arm of the sea of the Mozambique Channel may have come from the north-east, from the Mesogean regions, the marine Jurassic of Somaliland forming an intermediary landmark.[188]

So the Continent of Gondwana seems partially divided into two great masses, an Australo-Indo-Malagasy continent and an Africano-Brazilian continent. For no marine Jurassic has been found either on the western shores of Africa or on the eastern shores of Brazil.

But the unity of this land of Gondwana is again marked by the uniformity of its Jurassic flora. A single species of fern (*Thinnfeldia odontopteroides*) is abundant at the same time at the Cape, in India, in Australia, and in south America. Gothan took it as the type of a new genus *Dicroidium,* which would be peculiar to the Continent of Gondwana[189] where it appeared, as we have seen, as early as the Triassic.

5. *The Pacific Domain*

We do not know what happened over the enormous surface of the Pacific, but in the folded chains which border it, the marine Jurassic is known almost everywhere, in New Zealand, New Caledonia, the Sunda Isles, Japan, and the whole length of the American Pacific chains.[190] Let us note especially the Jurassic outcrops of Mexico,[191] the Argentine Republic, and Chile.[192] In the Lias and Middle Jurassic a number of European ammonite zones are found. These analogies are explained if we remember that the Mesogean sea must have been connected with the Pacific domain in Central America.[193] Then, in the Upper Jurassic, Mediterranean Tithonian forms are seen mixed with the Volgian forms, the latter coming doubtless from Arctic seas through Bering Strait, for they are found in the Jurassic of the Rocky Mountains.

6. *The Arctic Seas*

Actually, the Arctic seas, whose influence has been recognized in northern Europe, must have been very extensive at certain periods of the Jurassic. North of the North Atlantic and Sino-Siberian continents, their deposits are found in Arctic America, the Spitzbergen archipelago (with continental beds with gingkos and marine Middle Jurassic), in Nova Zembla and on the Siberian coast (mouth of the Lena).

There, during the Upper Jurassic, was the homeland of aucellas and cardioceratids, that is to say, the Volgian fauna.

7. *Provinces and Climates in Europe*

Among the differences already pointed out between the Jurassic faunas of the Mediterranean regions and those of northern Europe, certain ones are explained by questions of facies, particularly of depths. It is thus that the *Phylloceras, Lytoceras* and *Pygope,* so frequent in the Mediterranean Jurassic, seem especially connected with deep-water facies (with those which, in certain epochs, penetrated the Causses and the Germanic Cuvette). And it is the same for the contrast, so marked in the Upper Jurassic, between the Jura Mountains and sub-Alpine types, despite their juxtaposition.

But, from the beginning of the Upper Jurassic, these differences seem largely climatic,[194] especially since at this epoch the Russian seas established broad communications between the northern basin and the Mesogean sea, so that geographic isolation cannot be invoked. From this moment, then, two faunal provinces can be identified in Europe: the one, boreal, characterized by the abundance of *Cardioceras, Cylindroteuthis,* and in the Portlandian *Craspedites, Virgatites, Garnieria* and *Aucella* of the Volgian; the other, tropical, defined by the absence of the preceding genera and the presence of *Reineckeia, Oppelia, Creniceras, Belemnopsis, Duvalia,* a few *Diceras* and reef corals.[195]

Russia and the basin of the North Sea form the characteristic domain of the boreal province, and the Mediterranean regions, south of the Massif Central, the Vosges-Black Forest and Bohemia, that of the tropical province. The regions between these two domains are, according to the ease of marine communications and the regime of currents, submitted to the influences of the north or of the south. Thus, in the Callovian-Oxfordian, the northern elements predominate in the fauna of the Anglo-Parisian Basin and the Germanic Cuvette; while in the Lusitanian the reverse is true, as we have seen reefs extend, at that time, as far as Hanover and southern Britain. Then the reefs retreated slowly toward the south, so that in the Portlandian the Mediterranean forms penetrated no farther than the Paris Basin, but the northern forms descended then as far as the Boulonnais, a region which thus allows the establishment of a correlation between the Volgian type with *Virgatites* and the Portlandian proper, characterized by *Pachyceras* (*Gravesia*), a genus very abundant in the Anglo-Parisian Basin.

Thus, in the Upper Jurassic, we have quite clear proof of differentiated climates. It is highly probable that such a differentiation also existed earlier, in the Primary.

REFERENCE NOTES

1. Lias, Dogger, and Malm are terms of English origin, taken over by Oppel (see notes 55 and 59, this chap.).

2. W. J. Arkell, "Standard of the European Jurassic," Bull. Geol. Soc. Amer., 57 (Jan. 1946), p. 1–34, 7 tabl.

3. The subdivisions used here, Lias, Middle Jurassic, and Upper Jurassic, correspond to those adopted in the *Carte géologique de France* 1/1,000,000. However, the Bajocian of this map includes our upper Aalenian while our lower Aalenian remains in the Lias. On the other hand E. Haug, followed by certain French geologists, proposed in his *Traité* an entirely different classification. He subdivided the Jurassic into Lias and Oolithic, the latter made up of three parts, lower, middle and upper. But the *stages* which we adopt here are the same as those of E. Haug.

4. It was formerly written *Kimeridgian*. I have adopted here the spelling used since 1898 by British geologists. See p. 68, note 1, of the work of W. J. Arkell cited note 69, this chap.

5. See M. Gignoux, article cited note 150, chap. 5.

6. It is, however, probable, that for the most part, the silica of the sediments is not derived directly from the skeletons of the organisms, but results from the precipitation of colloidal silica dissolved in the water either of seas or of lakes.

7. In Tunisia, at Djebel Zaghouan, *Ellipsactinia* is found in the limestones of the Lias with *Terebratula aspasia*, according to M. Solignac, *Etude géologique de la Tunisie septentrionale*, Thèse Sc., Paris (1927).

8. G. Lucas, *Les Cancellophycus du Jurassique sont des Alcyonaires*, C. R. Acad. Sc. (June 20, 1938). Judging by related living genera, this author believes that these *Cancellophycus* should live at depths of 200 to 1,000 m., which seems exaggerated. R. LeGrand, *Observations à propos des Spirophyton du Tournaisis*, Bull. Soc. belge Geol., 44 (1948), fasc. 2, describes and figures impressions in the Dinantian similar to the Jurassic *Cancellophycus* and questions the interpretation of G. Lucas.

9. L. Guillaume, *Révision des Posidomyes jurassiques,* Bull. Soc. Géol. France, 4 sér., 27 (1927).

10. W. J. Arkell, "The Oysters of the Fullers Earth and on the Evolution of the Upper Jurassic Catinulas and Gryphaeas," Proc. Cotteswold Naturalists Field Club, 25, Gloucester (1934).

11. C. Déchazeaux, *Limidés jurassiques de l'Est du Bassin de Paris,* Mem. Mus. r. Hist. nat. Belgique, 2 sér., fasc. 8 (1936); *Pectinidés jurassiques de l'Est du Bassin de Paris,* Thèse Sc., Paris (1936). Ann. Pal., 25 (1936).

12. G. Delpey, *Etude critique du genre Pleurotomaria Defrance,* Bull. Soc. géol. France, 6 (1936).

13. Mlle. M. Levasseur, *Contribution à l'étude des Nerineidae du Rauracien de Lorraine,* Bull. Soc. géol. France, 5 sér., 4 (1934).

14. F. Roman, *Les Ammonites jurassiques et cretacées: essai de genera,* 534 p., 53 pl., Paris, Masson (1938).

15. On the significance of the ammonite zones, see the work of Roché, cited note 145, this chap.

16. A brief summary of the succession of brachiopod faunas in the Mediterranean Lias is found in J. Dareste de la Chavanne, *Sur la répartition géographique du Lias du type alpin et sicilien à faciès à Brachiopodes dans l'Afrique du Nord et dans les régions voisines circum-méditerranéennes,* C. R. Congrès de l'Ass. française pour l'Avancement des Sc. à Constantine, en 1927. G. Dubar, *Etudes paléontologiques sur le Lias du Maroc;*

Brachiopodes, Térébratules et Zeilléries multiplissées, Serv. géol. Maroc, Mém. no. 57 (1942).

17. G. Corroy, *Les Spiriféridés du Lias européen et Principalement du Lias de Lorraine et d'Alsace,* Ann. de Pal., 16 (1927). G. Astre, *Persistance de Spiriférines dans les mers aaléniennes,* Bull. Soc. Hist. nat. Toulouse, 72 (1938).

18. L. Bertrand acknowledges that there must have been an emerged Primary massif there, a prolongation of the Montagne-Noire now hidden under the Tertiary. (see Fig. 90).

19. See especially the fundamental work of P. Lemoine, *Géologie du Bassin de Paris,* Paris, Hermann (1911), and the summary given by G. Corroy, *Synchronisme des horizons jurassiques de L'Est du Bassin de Paris,* Bull. Soc. géol. France, 27 (1927).

20. L. Guillaume, *Contribution à la stratigraphie et à la tectonique du Lias dans la région de Thionville,* Bull. Soc. géol. France, 11 (1941); a very conscientious study of the thickness of the different stages of the Lorraine Lias and recognizable horizon-guides in wells. Note that in the Thionville trough, this Lias becomes about 500 m. thick.

21. The specialists now use more detailed subdivisions, with a whole nomenclature of sub-stages: L. F. Spath, "The Ammonite Zones of the Lias," Geol. Magaz., London (Sept.–Oct., 1942).

22. G. Corroy, *Le Rhétien et l'Hettangien dans l'Est du Bassin de Paris,* C. R. Acad. Sc. (July 11, 1932). C. Gérard and G. Gardet, *L'Hettangien et le Sinémurien inférieur-moyen de Meurthe-et-Moselle,* Bull. Soc. géol. France, 8 (1938).

23. C. Gérard, *Note sur la formation dite "calcaire ocreux" de Meurthe-et-Moselle,* Bull. Soc. géol. France, 1 (1931).

24. G. Corroy and C. Gérard, *Le Toarcien de Lorraine et de Bassigny,* Bull. Soc. géol. France, 3 (1933). See also articles by G. Corroy and by G. Minoux cited note 22, chap. 6, and articles by Schirardin cited note 92, this chap.

25. M. Burseaux, *Les schistes bitumineux de la base du Toarcien dans l'Est de la France,* Ann. Office nat. Combustibles liquides, 13th yr., no. 1 (1938), a summary of all the analyses and prospect holes. He concluded that no prospected zone is at present economically exploitable.

26. R. Mouterde, *Une coupe du Lias moyen au Nord d'Avallon,* C. R. Soc. géol. France (1946), p. 325, uses the ammonite zones of Spath and Buckman.

27. The classic ideas on the nomenclature and geographic distribution of the different species of gryphaeas have recently been revised and modified by Mlle. C. Déchazeaux, *Principals espèces de Gryphées liasques,* Bull. Soc. géol. France, 4 (1934). See also the correction of nomenclature made by G. Dubar, *Observations au sujet de Gryphaea cymbium Lmk. et Gryphaea cymbula Lmk.,* C. R. Soc. géol. France (Dec. 3, 1934).

28. J. Bichelonne and P. Angot, *Le Bassin ferrifère de Lorraine,* Berger-Levrault, Nancy-Strasburg (1939), a magnificent monograph with atlas. C. Gérard and J. Bichelonne, *Les Ammonites aaléniennes du Minerai de fer de Lorraine* Mém. Soc. géol. France, n. s. 19 (1940). M. Lucius, *Die Luxemburger Minetteformation,* Beitr. z. Geol. Luxemburg, 4 (1945).

29. G. Corroy, *Le Bajocien sup. et le Bathonien de Lorraine; correlations avec les régions voisines, en particulier avec le Jura franc-comtois,* Bull. Soc. géol. France, 29 (1929). G. Gardet, *Tableau de coordination du Bajocien supérieur de la Lorraine centrale: Toulois,* Bull. Soc. Sc. Nancy, no. 4, (July, 1945), uses Buckman's paleontological zones (*hemerae*); *Le Bathonien de la Lorraine,* Bull Serv. Carte géol. France, no. 217, t. 45, 1945, Paris (1947). G. Gardet and N. Théobald have described in detail the Bajocian of the environs of Pont-à-Mousson in the Bull. Soc. Sc. Nancy (April, 1936), no. 4.

30. C. R. Acad. Sc., May 8 (July 3, 1922).

31. The type of *R. varians* is in fact a Cretaceous fossil (Rollier).

32. For further details, see Salfeld (works cited note 95, this chap.) and Léwinski, *Monographie géol. et pal. du Bononien de la Pologne,* Mém. Soc. géol. France, no. 56 (1923). I did not believe I should adopt the new classifications proposed on p. 864 of the important work of F. L. Spath, *Revision of the Jurassic Cephalopod Fauna of Katch (Cutch),* Pal. indica, n. s., 9, mem. 2, part 6, Calcutta (1933).

33. See on p. 354, the ammonite zones of the Mediterranean regions.

34. G. Corroy, *Le Callovien de la bordure orientale du Bassin de Paris,* Mém. Carte géol., France (1932). Mlle. C. Déchazeaux, *L'Oxfordien sup. de la bordure Est du Bassin de Paris,* Bull. Soc. géol. France, 5 sér., 1 (1931).

35. H. Poinsot, *Contribution à l'étude du Callovien et de l'Oxfordien des environs de Dijon,* Bull. sc. de Bourgogne, 8 (1938).

36. R. Abrard, *Sur la formation du détroit morvanovosgien,* C. R. Acad. Sc., 222 (1946), p. 967; *Le détroit franco-germain,* ibid., 225 (1947), p. 1,014. This author believes that the Vosges must have already been emergent during the upper Bathonian and the lower Callovian. But the reductions of thickness and the neritic or ferruginous facies, at the approach of this massif, give evidence of a regime of currents, perhaps with submarine erosion and lacunas, but not necessarily of true emergence. In any case, the Callovian and lower and middle Oxfordian are known in Alsace (see p. 347). There erosion must have removed the more recent beds. But on the opposite or Baden bank, the Lusitanian with its littoral facies of the Alsatian Jura traces back toward the north as far as the latitude of Strasbourg, thus showing that the southern part of the Black Forest (and hence probably the Vosges) must not have emerged until after the Lusitanian. These uncertainties show once again how difficult it is to draw precise and detailed paleogeographic maps.

37. G. Corroy, *Les variations des faciès et de puissance de l'Argovien dans la bordure Est du Bassin de Paris,* C. R. Acad. Sc. (Nov. 30, 1931).

38. J. H. Hoffet, *Les calcaires de Creue,* Bull. Soc. géol. France, 5 sér. 3 (1933).

39. A. Durand, *L'étage Kimmeridgien dans les départements de la Meuse et de la Haute-Marne,* Bull. Soc. géol. France, 5 sér., 2 (1932).

40. A. Bonte, *Contribution à l'étude du Jurassique de la bordure septentrionale du Bassin de Paris,* Bull. Serv. Carte géol. France, t. 42, no. 205 (1941), 440 p., 12 pl.

41. Nevertheless, in western Boulonnais, that is, in the extension of the zone of ancient shores, the Lias has been found in deep wells. See P. Pruvost, *Note sur l'existence du Lias en profondeur dans le Bas-Boulonnais,* Ann. Soc. géol. du Nord, 47 (1922).

42. P. Pruvost, *Les subdivisions du Portlandien d'après les Ammonites,* Ann. Soc. géol. du Nord, 49 (1924).

43. A. P. Dutertre, *Les Aucelles des terrains jurassiques supérieurs du Boulonnais,* Bull. Soc. géol. France, 4 sér., 26 (1926).

44. Following E. Haug, we shall use the word *Bononian* in a broad sense, including therein all the beds below the Purbeckian.

45. The Jurassic beneath this northeast part of the Paris Basin has been traversed by two deep wells. That of Ferrières-en-Bray (see articles of P. Pruvost, cited note 6, chap. 5, and note 41, chap. 6) reached mica schists at 1,150 m. depth. The Jurassic, whose total thickness in this region is 1,200 m., has facies analogous to those of the east edge of the Paris Basin. Lacunas of sedimentation still correspond to the Sinemurian and the upper Aalenian. But the Lias is again 325 m. thick. On the other hand, a well at Amiens has shown the Gedinnian overlain directly by the Bathonian, as in the Boulonnais. See E. LeRoux and P. Pruvost, *Résultats géologiques d'un sondage profond à Amiens,* Ann. Soc. géol. du Nord, 60 (1935); sections and maps show the Jurassic transgression between Bray, Lorraine, and the Boulonnais. These facts have been summarized and developed in the work of A. Bonte, cited note 40 this chap.

46. Local details and bibliography in the regional monograph of A. Bigot, cited note 32, chap. 2.

47. P. A. Gillard, *Observations stratigraphiques sur le Toarcien supérieur du détroit de Poitiers,* Bull. Soc. géol. France, 9 (1939).

48. A. Bigot, *Les récifs bathoniens de Normandie,* Bull. Soc. géol. France, 4 (1934).

49. The recent works of A. Bigot and L. Guillaume are shown and summarized in J. Mercier, *Etudes sur les Echinides du Bathonien de la bordure occidentale du Bassin de Paris,* Mém. Soc. linnénne de Normandie, n. s., Géol., vol. 2 (1932).

50. A. Chavan, *Les Lamellibranches hétérodontes des sables astartiens de Cordebugle (Calvados),* Journ. de Conchyliologie, 76 (1945).

51. The ammonite zones generally used are even subdivided by Buckman into shorter

periods called "hemerae," but the species or varieties on which these "hemerae" are based can hardly be correctly determined except by specialists.

52. In *The British Isles,* cited note 23, chap. 1. Later there has appeared the fundamental work of W. J. Arkell, *The Jurassic System in Great Britain,* 682 p., 41 pl., 97 fig., Oxford (1932).

53. Numerous wells have given some idea of the Jurassic in this southeast part of England. See G. W. Lamplugh, F. L. Kitchin, J. Pringle, *The Concealed Mesozoic Rocks in Kent,* Memoir, geol. Survey, London (1923). On p. 190 will be found information regarding the most recent work on the stratigraphy of the English Jurassic. The work of Dudley Stamp, cited note 23, chap. 1, gives an excellent summary of the structure of the subsurface of this region, on which we cannot dwell. See also works cited note 65, chap. 9.

54. The Rhaetian was discovered in Scotland by G. W. Lee and E. B. Bailey, *The Pre-Tertiary Geology of Mull, Loch Aline, and Oban,* Mem. geol. Surv. Scotland (1925). And toward the north, the northernmost Lias known is that of the east coast of Greenland; see E. Haug, *Fossiles du Lias moyen recueillis par la mission Charcot au Cap Stewart (Terre de Jameson, Groenland oriental),* C. R. Acad. Sc., 182, p. 329 (1926), and the work of Lauge Koch cited note 66, chap. 8.

55. Lias is an old term used by English quarrymen, derived, according to Buckman, from the Gaelic word *Leai* (flat stone) and designating regular beds of hard limestone. This would be the equivalent of the French *liais* in *pierre de liais* [freestone or Portland stone].

56. On the type locality of Charmouth, the most recent work is that of W. D. Lang, "The Lower Lias of Charmouth and the Vale of Marshwood," Proc. Geologists' Ass., 43 (1932).

57. Information on this region is found in the recent work by several collaborators, "The Geology of the Gloucester District," Proc. Geologists' Ass., 45 (1934).

58. Aalenian iron ores, contemporaneous with those of Lorraine, are mined in various regions of Britain.

59. Because of the sandy concretions or "doggers" which they contain, these sands have often been called the *Dogger,* a name since used by German geologists to designate the whole Middle Jurassic.

60. R. H. Rastall and J. E. Hemingway, "The Yorkshire Dogger," Geol. Magaz., 77 (1940) and 78 (1941).

61. Fullers Earth, Stonesfield slates and Great Oolite are comparable respectively to the black marls of Port-en-Bessin, the stone of Caen and the miliary oolite which we described in Normandy at the same horizons. To all this lower Bathonian, the name of Vesulian substage (see p. 349) is often given, wrongly as we see it. W. N. Edwards and H. H. Thomas, *Guide to the Fossil Plants in the Department of Geology and Paleontology of the British Museum,* London (1925), have described at Stonesfield an impression of a dicotyledon (?) leaf, which would represent the oldest known angiosperm.

62. J. A. Douglas and W. J. Arkell, "The Stratigraphical Distribution of the Cornbrash," Quart. Journ. geol. Soc., 84 (1928).

63. The English *brash* is about equivalent to the French *groix* or *groise,* earth and rubble formed from the accumulation of stony debris produced by the alteration of underlying limestones.

64. W. J. Arkell, *The Geology of Oxford,* 87 p., 49 fig., 6 pl., Oxford, Clarendon Press (1947); "The Upper Oxford Clay at Purton, Wiltsh., and the Zones of the Lower Oxfordian," Geol. Magaz., 78 (1941). L. F. Spath, *The Ammonites Zones of the Upper Oxford Clay of Warboys, Huntingdonshire,* Bull. geol. Survey Great Britain (1939), no. 1.

65. W. J. Arkell, "The Corallian Rocks of Oxfordshire, Berkshire and North Yorkshire," Phil. Trans. roy. Soc., London, ser. B, vol. 216 (1927).

66. W. J. Arkell, *Report on Ammonites Collected at Long Stanton, Cambsh., and on the Age of the Ampthill Clay,* Summ. of Progress, Geol. Survey Great Britain (1935), part 2.

67. Similar variations are also found in other parts of the aureole. The Mendip Hills are described here only as an example.

68. J. W. Tutcher and A. E. Trueman, "The Liassic Rocks of the Radstock District," Quart. Journ. geol. Soc., 81 (1925).

69. For this classic region, Kimmeridge, Portland, Purbeck, we refer once for all to the magnificent monograph by W. J. Arkell, *The Geology of the Country around Weymouth, Swanage, Corfe and Lulworth*, Mem. geol. Survey Great Britain (1947). All the recent bibliography will be found therein.

70. See the publications of H. Salfeld cited note 95, this chap., and the work of Lamplugh, Kitchin and Pringle, cited note 53, this chap. (particularly p. 222 and pl. II). A new detailed study of these ammonite zones has been undertaken by E. Neaverson, Geol. Magaz., 61 (1924).

71. Very famous as building stone. See F. H. Edmunds and B. A. Schaffers, "Portland Stone; Its Geology and Properties as a Building Stone," Proc. Geologists' Ass., 43 (1932).

72. Often called Isle of Purbeck.

73. L. F. Spath, work cited note 69, chap. 8.

74. We should mention, however, that in Lincolnshire, beds with phosphatic nodules, called Spilsby sandstone and attributed to the upper Portlandian, have supplied *Aucella*.

75. Interesting paleogeographic maps in the work of von Bubnoff cited note 15, chap. 1 and in R. Brinkmann, *Der Dogger und Oxford des Südbaltikums*, Jahrb. preuss. geol. Landesanst. f. 1923, 44, Berlin (1924).

76. R. Brinkmann, *Der ostpreussisch-litauische Dogger und Unteroxford*, Mitt. geol. Inst. Univ. Königsberg, n. F., 70 (1927).

77. We find here, on a very small scale, paleogeographic phenomena similar to those described in the Devonian on the great Primary platform of the Central United States of North America (see p. 143).

78. See the work by Lewinski cited note 32, this chap. A comparison of the Upper Jurassic in Russia and northern and southern Britain will be found in W. J. Arkell, "The Zones of the Upper Jurassic of Yorkshire," Proc. Yorksh. geol. Soc. 35 (1945).

79. Another example of the danger in reconstructing the contours of ancient seas according to the extent of present outcrops.

80. M. Parat and P. Drach, *Le Portlandian du Cap Leslie dans le Scoresby Sund (Groenland)*, C. R. Acad. Sc. (June 19, 1933). H. Frebold, *Untersuchungen über die Verbreitung, Lagerungsverhältnisse und Faunen des oberen Jura von Ostgrönland*, Medd. om Grönland, 94, Copenhagen (1933). For everything concerning this country, see the work of Lauge Koch, cited note 66, chap. 8.

81. Precisely these *Virgatites* are lacking in Pechora.

82. Wells between Memel and Tilsit have encountered the Callovian and Oxfordian, cf. Tornquist, Zeitsch. d. deutsch. geol. Ges. (1910). We have already spoken of the communications which were established, through these regions, between the Germanic and Russian Seas.

83. A. Noroang, "Marine Lias in Jutland (a preliminary notice)," Medd. Dansk. geol. Forening, 11, 1, Copenhagen (1946).

84. G. T. Troedsson, "On the Sequence of Strata in the Rhaetic-Liasic Beds of NW Scania," Geol. Foren. Förhandl., 60, 3, no. 414, Stockholm (1938).

85. The shore facies of this region were studied in the work of Benz, cited note 18, chap. 6.

86. Recent bibliography in M. Pfannenstiel, *Das Südliche Rheintal an der Zeitwende von Rhät und Lias*, Geol. Rundschau, 23 (1932). Paleogeographic maps in O. Prattje, *Die Jura-Transgression im Bereiche von Schwarzwald und Vogesen*, Frankfurt, a. M. (1924). I. Rüger, *Versuch einer Paläogeographie der süddeutschen Länder an der Trias-Lias Wende*, Verh. naturhist.-mediz. Ver zu Heidelberg, n. F., 15 (1924).

87. W. Lange, *Zur Paläogeographie und Ammonitenfauna des Lias α, nebst einer Revision der Nürtinger Psilonotenfauna*, Zeitschr. deutsch. geol. Ges., Abh., 77 (1925). W. Lange, *Die Ammonitenfauna der Psiloceras-Stufe Norddeutschlands*, Palaeontografica, A (1941), 93, 192 p., 138 fig., 20 pl.

88. L. Krumbeck, *Stratigraphie und Faunenkunde des Lias γ in Nordbayern*, Zeitschr. deutsch. geol. Ges., 88 (1936).

89. On the German upper Lias, see the very important stratigraphic and paleontologic work of W. Ernst, Paläontographica, 65–66 (1923–1924).

90. E. Schmidtill, *Zur Stratigraphie und Palaeogeographie der Eisenerze im Dogger-sandstein der Frankenalb*, Zeitschr. deutsch. geol. Ges., 87 (1936). Paleogeographic map of the *murchisonae* zone between Basel, Metz and Bohemia in P. Dorn, *Die Beziehungen zwischen Dogger Beta und der untercretacischen "Amberger Erzformation*," Zentralbl. f. Min. (1937), Abt. B, no. 12.

91. H. Jüngst, *Der Pfälzer Lias und seine palaeogeographische Bedeutung*, Mitt. der Pollichia, N. F., 7 (1938); paleogeographic map of the relation between the Germanic Sea and the Paris Basin.

92. N. Théobald, *Développement des minerais de fer dans les étages de l'Aalénien et du Bajocien de la vallée du Rhin moyen (Alsace, Bade)*, Mém. Serv. Carte géol. Alsace et Lorraine, mém. no. 8 (1948). For the comparative study of the Lias in northern and southern Alsace and Lorraine, see J. Schirardin, *Note sur le Lias inf. du Bas-Rhin*, Bull. Service Carte géol. Alsace et Lorraine, 1 (1923); *Sur une coupe du Lias moyen près de Metz*, ibid.; *Nouvelles observations sur le Toarcien de l'Alsace*, Bull. Ass. philomathique Alsace et Lorraine 8, 6 (1938). The famous locality of Gundershoffen was re-examined by N. Schneider, *Etude stratigraphique et paléontologique de l'Aalénien de Gundershoffen (Bas-Rhin)*, Mém. Serv. Carte géol. Alsace et Lorraine, 3 (1927).

93. W. Schott, *Paläogeographische Untersuchungen über den Oberen Braunen und Unteren Weissen Jura Nordwestdeutschlands*, Abh. preuss. geol. Landesanst., N. F., Heft 133 (1931). E. Schmidtill and L. Krumbeck, *Die Coronaten-Schickten von Auerbach (Oberpfalz, Nordbayern)*, Zeitschr. deutsch. geol. Ges., 90 (1938), littoral facies of the Bajocian of northern Bavaria and comparison with the ammonite zones of Buckman.

94. S. Gillet, *Sur le Bathonien et le Bajocien de Basse-Alsace*, Bull. Soc. géol. France, 27 (1927); *Les Ammonites du Bajocien d'Alsace et de Lorraine*, Mém. Serv. Carte géol. Alsace et Lorraine, no. 5 (1927).

95. See works by H. Salfeld, Neues Jahrb. f. Min., Beilage-Band, 37 (1914), and Centralblatt f. Min. (1922). But the numerous ammonite zones distinguished by this author are based on too localized species. The zones of the Oxford-Kimmeridgian were re-examined by B. Dohm, *Ueber den Oberen Jura von Zarnglaff i.P. und seine Ammonitenfauna*, Abh. geol. Inst. Univ. Greifswald (1925). See also A. Roll, *Stratigraphischer Vergleich zwischen nordwest europäischem und süd-deutschem oberen Malm*, Neues Jahrb. f. Min., Beilage-Band 68, Abt. B (1932). W. Schott, *Stratigraphische und Paläogeographische Untersuchungen über der unteren weissen Jura in der weiteren Umgebung von Braunschweig*, Jahrb. preuss. geol. Landesanst., 1937, 58, Berlin (1938). E. Hennig, *Der schwäbische Obere Weissjura, eine Zusammenschau*, Neues Jahrb. f. Min. (1943), Abt. B, Heft 4.

96. J. Schirardin, *Sur le Callovien de la bordure sousvosgienne en Basse-Alsace*, C. R. Acad. Sc., 226 (1948), p. 415; *Sur l'existence de l'Oxfordien dans la zone des collines sousvosgiennes de la Basse-Alsace*, ibid., 227 (1948), p. 211.

97. C. Speyer, *Die Korallen des nordwestdeutschen oberen Jura*, Verh. naturhist.-mediz. Vereins zu Heidelberg, N. F. 15 (1926).

98. W. Kauenhowen, *Die Faziesverhältnisse und ihre Beziehungen zur Erdölbildung an der Wende Jura-Kreide in Nordwestdeutschland*, Neues Jahrb. f. Min., 58, Beilage-Band, Abt. B (1927). H. Raecke, *Paläogeographische Untersuchungen über den obersten Jura und den Wealden Nordwestdeutschlands*, Jahrb. preuss. geol. Landesanst., 53 (1932).

99. On the conditions of sedimentation of the Solnhofen limestone, see M. Wilfarth, *Die Gezeiten im Meere des Malm Zeta bei Solnhofen*, Zeitschr. deutsch. geol. Ges., 88 (1936).

100. The extreme southern tabular Jura is so called; it is separated from the rest of the chain by the course of the Rhône (see Fig. 82).

101. See A. de Riaz, A. Riche and F. Roman, *Les minerais de fer, l'Aalénien et le Bajocien de la région lyonnaise*, Bull. Soc. géol. France, 4 sér., 13 (1913). Summary in the work of F. Roman, cited note 146, chap. 5. R. Mouterde and J. Rosset, *Le Lias de Saint-Quentin-Fallavier (Isère)*, C. R. Soc. géol. France (1948), p. 172.

102. M. Lissajous, *Etude sur la faune du Bathonien des environs de Mâcon. Appen-*

dice: Bajocien et Bathonien dans le Mâconnais et le Jura méridional, by A. Riche, Trav. Lab. Géol. Univ. Lyon, fasc. 5, mém. 3 (1923). See also the article by G. Corroy, cited note 29, this chap.

103. Such is the "choin de Villebois," taken from great quarries southeast of Ambérieu-en-Bugey on the banks of the Rhone, and much used as freestone. It is recognized by its brown vermiculations and numerous stylolitic seams, which do not affect its strength.

104. F. Roman and F. Blondet, *Le Callovien et l'Oxfordien de l'île de Crémieu (Isère)*, Bull. Soc. géol. France, 4 sér., 25 (1925).

105. Mlle. S. Gillet and D. Schnéegans, *Stratigraphie des terrains jurassiques dans la région de Ferrette (Jura Alsacien)*, Bull. Serv. Carte géol. Alsace et Lorraine, t. 2, fasc. 1 (1933).

106. Mlle. Faure-Marguerit, *Monographie paléontologique des assises coralligènes de l'Echaillon (Isère)*, Trav. Lab. Géol. Univ. Grenoble, t. 12, fasc. 1 (1919).

107. L. Moret, *Sur la Géologie de l'extrémité septentrionale du Semnoz, près Annecy, et sur les limites méridionales des lagunes purbeckiennes*, Trav. Lab. Géol. Univ. Grenoble, t. 17, fasc. 1 (1933). A. Carozzi, *Etude stratigraphique et micrographique du Purbeckien du Jura suisse*, Thèse, Arch. Sc., Geneva (1948).

108. Explanations of the whole subject and bibliography in the works of M. Gignoux and L. Moret, cited note 154, chap. 5.

109. Except the Alps of Haute-Savoie, which will be studied with the Swiss Alps. For there, north of the Annecy-Albertville line, appear Prealpine nappes which extend into Switzerland and necessitate special study. It is the Prealpine festoon (see pp. 297 and 365) as opposed to the sub-Alpine festoon, subject of this first paragraph.

110. Certain very limited regions of the zone of crystalline massifs resisted the Liassic transgression at first. Such, for example, is the Dôme de la Mure (carefully studied by P. Lory) south of Grenoble, which was not completely covered until the Toarcian and around which calcareous Lias makes a girdle of littoral facies, with crinoid fragments or brachiopods. We can see there the last vestiges of the Vindelician Chain (see p. 281), which already separated the Muschelkalk sea from that of the Alpine Triassic, the supreme resistance of the Hercynian massifs to their embodiment in the Alpine domain. We shall find analogous examples in the Swiss Alps, on a larger scale (see Fig. 86).

111. For example, at Savournon, between Laragne and Veynes (Htes-Alpes) where a very rich ammonite fauna (lower Oxfordian, zone of *C. lamberti,* 200 species) is being studied at the moment by M. Breistroffer.

112. In the vicinity of this boundary, pseudo-breccias often appear, about which there has been much discussion. For they sometimes resemble clotted limestones, sometimes true breccias or conglomerates. However, even conceding this last hypothesis, there is no question of an emergence, but of phenomena of alteration in place due to shoals or currents ("hard-grounds").

113. Tithonus was the husband of Eos, Aurora [dawn]. This name evokes the infra-Cretaceous affinities of certain ammonites of the top of the Mediterranean Jurassic which thus seems like the dawn of the Cretaceous.

114. The upper Tithonian was up to the present qualified as the zone with *Hoplites privasensis.* In reality, this species (like *H. calisto*) is a rather mediocre stratigraphic fossil. It appears first in the middle Tithonian and is particularly abundant in the Berriasian (base of the Cretaceous). See G. Mazenot, *Les Palaehoplitidés tithoniques et berriasiens du Sud-Est de la France,* Mém. Soc. géol. France, n. s. 18, mém. no. 41 (1939).

115. A Lanquine, *Le Lias et le Jurassique des Chaînes provençales.* 1: *Le Lias et le Jurassique inf.,* Bull. Serv. Carte géol. France, no. 173 (1929). II: *Le Jurassique moyen et sup.,* id., no. 191 (1935). G. Corroy and G. Denizot, *La Provence occidentale,* Géol. régionale de la France, Hermann, Paris (1943).

116. C. Gouvernet and R. P. Charles, *Présence du Sinémurien supérieur fossilifère près de Broussan au NNW de Toulon,* C. R. Soc. géol. France (1948), p. 278; on the infra-Liassic dolomites, they note limestones with *Gryphaea arcuata* var. *obliqua* and *Echioceras,* overlain by a Pliensbachian with *G. cymbium.*

117. This is a striking contrast to the thick sandy and estuarine formations shown

by the Jurassic of northwest Britain at the approach of the ancient shores of the great North Atlantic continent.

118. H. Parent, *Sur un important gisement d'Ammonites bathoniennes au Nord du département du Var,* C. R. Acad. Sc., August 8 (1938).

119. M. Gignoux and L. Moret, C. R. Soc. géol. France (1937), p. 116.

120. Y. Gubler-Wahl, *La nappe de l'Ubaye au Sud de la vallée de Barcelonnette; essai géologique,* Thèse Sc., Paris (1928). D. Schnéegans, *La Géologie des nappes de l'Ubaye-Embrunais entre la Durance et l'Ubaye,* Mém. Serv. Carte géol. France (1938). R. Barbier, Mém. cited note 54, chap. 6.

121. G. Dubar, *Sur les genres de Térébratulidés rhétiens,* Ann. Soc. géol. du Nord, 59 (1934).

122. This beautiful rock, made classic by W. Kilian who attributed it to the lower Lias, is given this age in all the Alpine syntheses. Next, I assigned it to the Dogger, and then R. Barbier showed that it was more recent than the Dogger of the Pas-du-Roc.

123. Small single-chambered infusorians, which in all Mediterranean regions are characteristic of the Tithonian and the Berriasian. Recent bibliography in N. Vassoevitch, *Les Roches à Calpionella Lorenz du Caucase et de la Crimée,* C. R. Soc. géol. France (May 18, 1936). R. Laffitte, *Sur les Calpionelles en Algérie,* Ibid. (May 24, 1937).

124. Other examples in L. Trevisan, *Sul significato geologico del colore rosso nelle rocce sedimentarie marine,* Atti Soc. toscana Sc. nat., 49, no. 1, Pisa (1940).

125. Formerly attributed to the Tithonian by W. Kilian. But Charles Lory earlier recognized in it *Peltoceras transversarium.*

126. See E. Raguin, *Haute-Tarentaise et Haute-Maurienne (Alpes de Savoie),* Mém. Serv. Carte géol. France (1930).

127. In Switzerland, some remains of belemnites and pentacrines have been found in the *schistes lustrés* in the vicinity of Zermatt (Wegmann, Arbenz); moreover, belemnites have long been known in the *schistes lustrés* of the Grisons *(Bündnerschiefer),* also metamorphic but perhaps not representing a true extension of the Franco-Italian *schistes lustrés.*

128. There, in fact, the Briançonnais Jurassic series becomes again more geosynclinal and ends with the lower units. Thus, in the thick shaly series of Grands-Becs, on the Italian frontier north of Mt. Genèvre, C. Pussenot has pointed out Hettangian fossils *(Schlotheimia angulata)* and even Sinemurian *(Arietites,* F. Blanchet). This series really seems to be prolonged toward the north in eastern Vanoise (Grande-Casse, Grand-Motte), by thick calcareous shales which P. Termier attributes to his middle Muschelkalk and which reach even into the Upper Cretaceous. It is what I formerly called the Vanoise-Chaberton zone, thus corresponding to the eastern slope of the Briançonnais cordillera, on the edge of the great Alpine trough.

129. The true *schistes lustrés,* with *roches vertes,* are often separated from the transition zone to the Briançonnais by an important tectonic discontinuity, marked by a zone of extravasated Triassic gypsum. W. Kilian and P. Termier saw there particularly the base of a great nappe of *schistes lustrés* which, thrust toward the west, left on the Briançonnais country "advance fragments" (P. Termier), a few of which are indicated on the map (Fig. 82). The most famous is the "fourth scale" of the "Mountains between Briançon and Vallouise," shown west of Briançon on this map, and made up of basic crystalline rocks and gneiss. I have proposed, however, that this is a ridge of the Primary substratum. And I wonder whether this same interpretation could not be suggested for the other similar, diminutive fragments of the vicinity of Briançon (see 2nd edition of the Briançon sheet at 1/80,000), for, as C. Pussenot has remarked, these so-called *schistes lustrés* are curiously associated with quartzite of the Triassic and the Permian Verrucano.

130. P. Routhier, *Essal sur la chronologie des "roches vertes" mésozoïques des Alpes occidentales,* Bull. Soc. géol. France, 14 (1944).

131. It is probable that subsequent studies will reveal other similar domes (unpublished observations of R. Barbier in the neighborhood of Grand-Châtelard near St. Jean-de-Maurienne).

132. W. Bircher, *Studien im obern Bajocien der Ostschweiz,* Dissert. Zürich (1935); paleontologic monograph.

133. The Schilt is a summit overlooking Glarus.

134. Quinten is a village on the edge of the Walensee.

135. E. Rod, *Stratigraphie des Malm der Graustock-Hutstock-Gruppe,* Bern (1937), a revision of the stratigraphy of the Helvetic Malm.

136. See diagram, Fig. 87.

137. H. Renz, *Zur Stratigraphie und Paläontologie der Mytilus-Schichten der Préalpes romandes,* Eclogae geol. Helvetiae, 28 (1935). The author visited, in my company, our Briançonnais and sub-Briançonnais Dogger.

138. For this term, used by E. Haug and W. Kilian, that of cordillera is now preferred.

139. This Briançonnais cordillera was, however, preceded by other cordilleras, similar but more localized in time and place, which modified the Alpine fore-deep. Peterhans thus recognized in Chablais, in the Lias of the Medians, a whole series of geanticlines similar to those described by D. Schnéegans and R. Barbier in the sub-Briançonnais of the Ubaye and the Maurienne.

140. The stratigraphy of the *schistes lustrés* between the Grisons and Valais is at present the subject of very interesting studies by R. Staub and his students, who are trying to find there the different stages of the Jurassic. In the radiolarites, attributed to the Malm, H. Grunau, *Geologie von Arosa (Graubünden) mit besonderer Berücksichtigung des Radiolarit-Problems,* Diss. Bern (1947) has described the wood of silificied conifers with very well-preserved structure. This discovery, rather unexpected in rocks often considered abyssal, is related to the frequent silicified plants in the lydianstone of the Dinantian of the Montagne-Noire and the Pyrenees, see G. Delépine, and M. Gignoux, works cited note 140, and note 150, chap. 5.

141. The *schistes lustrés* and *roches vertes* of Mont-Jovet and Miravidi (Schoeller's zone of the Petit-St-Bernard), with the gneissic ridge of Tête-Rousse in Italy, and the *schistes lustrés* of Sion ("*brisés du Valais*") elements located in front of the (Briançonnais and Pennine) non-metamorphic coal zone, pose a disturbing question. Perhaps they are prolonged toward the east by the *schistes lustrés* of the Grisons or by the cores of the Simplon nappes. There the sediments from the bottom of the Valais geosyncline have been affected by metamorphism. As always we run into the problem of metamorphism, which remains the greatest enigma in all the orogenic syntheses.

142. The great recumbent folds that, more slowly, originated in the bottoms of the great troughs, without ever being expressed on the surface by cordilleras, could be described as deep nappes (for example: nappe of Monte Rosa) and thus contrasted to the "frontal nappes" (for example, nappe of St. Bernard-Briançonnais cordillera).

Finally, let us remember, if we adopt the modern tectonic theories of "gravity flow" this orogenic history can be told in quite another language, using a vocabulary entirely different from that of E. Argand. The earth's crust, in the scale of its dimensions and geologic time, could be considered as fluid, and the concepts of "pushing" and "lateral compression" could then be replaced by those of "suction," "swelling," "boiling" and ascending or descending "magmatic and crustal currents." And the progression of nappes is described as a superficial flow of this crust under the action of gravity. See the articles by M. King Hubbert, "Strength of the Earth," Bull. Amer. Ass. Petrol. Geol., 29, no. 11 (1945), and M. Gignoux, *Méditations sur la tectonique d'écoulement par gravité,* Trav. Lab. Géol. Univ. Grenoble, 27 (1948).

143. Let us recall especially the strange facts told by the savants of Japan following the 1921 earthquake. Differences in level of over 500 m. suddenly occurred along the submarine cliffs; and the north slope of this submarine cordillera was involved in a slide 10 km long, filling the bottom of the furrow with debris more than 230 m. thick. See N. Yamasaki, "Physiographical Studies of the Great Earthquake of the Kwanto District," Journ. Faculty Sc. Imp. Univ. Tokyo, 2 (1926), p. 99. However, as M. Ruellan pointed out and as the Japanese geographers themselves were well aware, the submarine topography before the earthquake was not well enough known to substantiate the accuracy of the numerical data.

144. See the work of F. Roman, cited note 146, chap. 5, and F. Roman and C.

Pétouraud, *Etude sur la faune du Bajocien sup. du Mont-d'Or lyonnais* (*ciret*), Trav. Lab. Géol. Univ. Lyon, fasc. 11, mém. 9 (1927).

145. See work of Lissajous cited note 102, this chap., and P. Roché, *Aalénien et Bajocien du Mâconnais et de quelques régions voisines,* Thèse Sc. Lyon (1939).

146. R. Abrard, *Les relations entre le bassin d'Aquitaine et le Jura au Portlandien inférieur,* Bull. Mus. nat. Hist. nat., 2 sér., 16, no. 5 (1944).

147. The boundaries of these Jurassic outcrops are due to erosion, and do not at all correspond to the ancient shores.

148. H. Agalède, *Les Causses majeurs; essai de Géologie stratigraphique,* Sc. nat., t. 1, no. 3 (March, 1939). The traveling geologist will profit by using this little article, in which the most interesting fossiliferous localities are indicated.

149. J. Monestier, *Le Toarcien sup. dans la région Sud-Est de l'Aveyron,* Bull. Soc. géol. France, 4 sér., 20 (1920); *Ammonites du Domerien de la region Sud-Est de l'Aveyron, etc.,* Mém. Soc. géol. France, n. s., mém. no. 23 (1935). C. Roquefort and F. Daguin, *Le Lias moyen et sup. du versant S du Causse du Larzac,* Bull. Soc. géol. France, 4 sér., 29 (1929). P. de Brun et P. Marcelin, *Etude stratigraphique des Petits-Causses des environs de Florac* (*Lozère*), Bull. Soc. d'Hist. nat. de Toulouse, 66 (1934). C. Roquefort, *Contribution à l'étude de l'Infra-Lias et du Lias inférieur des Causses cévenols,* Bull. Soc. géol. France, 4 (1934). M. Brousse, *Le Lias inférieur des Cévennes aux environs d'Alès* (*Gard*), ibid., 17 (1947).

150. H. Agalède, *Mode de formation des calcaires dolomitiques du Jurassique moyen et supérieur dans la région des Causses majeurs,* Bull Soc. Hist. Toulouse, 79 (1944).

151. H. Tintant, M. Mainguy et M. Gottis, *Lacunes dans le Callovien et l'Oxfordien au Sud des Cévennes,* C. R. Acad. Sc., 223 (1946), p. 814. H. Tintant, *Observations sur le Jurassique supérieur de Naves* (*Ardèche*), C. R. Soc. géol. France (1946), p. 337. P. de Brun, *Etude géologique et paléontologique des environs de St. Ambroix* (*Gard*), Bull. Soc. Etudes Sc. nat. Nîmes (1919–1932), Bull. Soc. sc. et litt. d'Alès (1935).

152. Tsan-Hsun Yin, *Etude de la faune du Tithonique coralligène du Gard et de l'Hérault,* Trav. Lab. Géol. Univ. Lyon, fasc. 17, mém. 14 (1931); this work contains a map of the coral facies of the Portlandian in Europe.

153. A. Riche and F. Roman, *La Montagne de Crussol,* Trav. Lab. Géol. Univ. Lyon, 1 (1921).

154. South of Crussol, these littoral facies and these lacunas were described by F. Roman and J. Goguel, *Les failles des environs de Privas,* C. R. Soc. géol. France (Jan. 20, 1936).

155. Similarity will be noticed between the base of the Jurassic series of Crussol and that of May (Fig. 74). In the two cases, the invasion of the Armorican Massif and of the Massif Central is shown by the same stratigraphic phenomena.

156. F. Roman and G. Mazenot, *Découverte d'une faune pyriteuse d'âge tithonique supérieur aux environs de Chomérac* (*Ardèche*), Bull. Soc. géol. France, 7 (1937).

157. G. Sayn and F. Roman, *Monographic stratigraphique et paléontologique du Jurassique moyen de La Voulte-sur-Rhône,* Trav. Lab. Géol. Univ. Lyon, fasc. 4, mém. 11 (1930). A diagram will be found there of the variations of facies of the Aalenian-Rauracian series on the border of the Massif Central, between Montpelier and the Lyonnais.

158. As a study of the whole unit which has appeared since the *Traité de Géologie* by E. Haug, the following must be mentioned: V. Uhlig, *Die marinen Reiche des Jura und der Unterkreide,* Mitth. d. geolog. Ges. in Wien, Bd. 3 (1911).

159. History of the type locality in O. Vecchia, *Sulla presenza del Lotaringiano nel "Medolo" del Monticola* (*Sebino, Lombardia*), Pubb. Ist. geol. pal. Univ. Milano, ser. G, no. 38 (1948).

160. On the coasts of Albania and Greece, in the upper Lias and Dogger, these same two facies—the Mediterranean type of *ammonitico rosso* and the European type of shales with *Posidonomya*—are found in juxtaposition. See the paleogeographic map in C. Renz, *Die Verbreitung und Entwicklung des Oberlias und Doggers im adriatisch-ionischen Faziesgebiet von Hellas und Albaniens,* Verh. Natur. Ges. in Basel, 38.

161. This association of radiolarites and of shales and limestones with *Aptychus* is usually considered evidence of deep seas (see p. 316). We suppose that the calcite *Aptychus* resisted solution in the course of descending to the bottom, while the ammonite shells, of more soluble aragonite, were destroyed. In the Alps, this type of sedimentation is found, for example, in the Malm-Lower Cretaceous complex of lower sub-Briançonnais scales (Piolit Massif, each of Gap). It corresponds there to the bottom of the Alpine fore-deep.

162. C. F. Parona, Rendic. R. Acad., Lincei, ser. 5, vol. 28, Rome (1919).

163. C. Jacob, *Zone axiale, versant Sud et versant Nord des Pyrénées,* Livre jubilaire du Centenaire de la Soc. géol. de France (1930). See also the work of Dalloni, cited note 153, chap. 5, and M. Casteras, *Recherches sur la structure du versant N des Pyrénées centrales et orientales,* Bull. Serv. Carte géol. France, no. 189 (1933).

164. G. Dubar, *Etudes sur le Lias des Pyrénées françaises,* Mém. Soc. géol. du Nord (1925); this work contains good maps of facies. G. Dubar, *Les mouvements des mers dans les Pyrénées et dans le NW de l'Espagne aux temps jurassiques* C. R. du 14 Congrès géol. internat., Madrid (1927).

165. Paleogeographic maps in L. Bertrand, Bull. Soc. géol. France (1911), p. 122.

166. R. Mouterde, *Le Lias moyen de San Pedro de Mael (Portugal),* C. R. Soc. géol. France (1947), p. 137.

167. Recent works, specially that of Jimenez de Cisneros and of Bataller, are indicated and synthesized by P. Fallot, note 34, chap. 6: *3 livr.* (1932), *Le Lias; 4 livr.* (1933) *Le Dogger; 5 livr.* (1934) *Le Jurassique sup.*

168. D. Jimenez de Cisneros, *El Lias alpino medio del SE de España,* C. R. du 14 Congrès géol. internat., Madrid (1927).

169. P. Fallot, *Contribution à l'étude du Jurassique sup. subbétique,* Bol. R. Soc. española Hist. nat., 31 (1931).

170. See thesis by P. Fallot cited note 34, chap. 6, and work of Dalloni cited note 153, chap. 5. J. R. Bataller, *Sur le Jurassique de la partie méridionale de la Catalogne,* Bull. Soc. géol. France, 4 sér., 26 (1926); *El Jurasico de la Provincia de Tarragona,* Trab. Museo nac. Ciencias nat., no. 29, Madrid (1922). F. Broili, *Der obere Jura von Monsech (Provinz Lerida) im Vergleich mit den oberen Juravorkommen von Cerin (Dept. Ain) und von Franken,* Géol. de la Médit. occid., 2, no. 16 (1932); this describes a Kimmeridgian with the same fauna and same facies as that of Cerin and Solnhofen.

171. G. Dubar, *Note sur les formations du Lias et du Jurassique sup. dans les Asturies,* C. R. Acad. Sc., Jan. 19 (1925).

172. The recent works are cited and briefly correlated by J. Savornin, *La géologie algérienne et Nord-africaine depuis 1830,* Masson, Paris (1931) and by L. Moret, cited note 70, chap. 2. For Algeria, L. Glangeaud, *Etude géologique de la région littorale de la province d'Alger,* Bull. Serv. Carte géol. Algérie, 2 ser., no. 8 (1932). For the Moroccan Lias and Dogger, see work by H. Termier cited note 70, chap. 2.

173. For the relations of the Atlas and Sahara to the Primary, Secondary, and Tertiary, very interesting diagrams in N. Menchikoff, *Etudes géologiques sur les confins algéromarocains du Sud,* Bull. Soc. géol. France, 6 (1936).

174. In a recent note by G. Mathieu this has again been precisely stated, *Discordances et faciès dans l'Extrême-Sud tunisien,* C. R. Acad. Sc., 211 (1940), p. 69.

175. This name is applied to a comprehensive series, mostly continental, but with marine intercalations, which begins in the Visean, J. Cuvillier, *Présence du Carbonifère marin dans l'ouadi Abou Darag, Désert arabique,* C. R. Acad. Sc. (June 14, 1937) and which we shall see prolonged into the Cretaceous. On the Nubian sandstones in general, see P. Lamare, *Structure géologique de l'Arabie,* Paris, Béranger (1936), and L. Picard, "Outline on the Tectonic of the Earth, with Special Emphasis upon Africa," Bull. geol. Dep. Hebrew Univ., 2, Jerusalem (1939), p. 50.

176. H. Sadek, *The Distribution of the Jurassic Formation in Egypt and Sinaï,* C. R. 13 Congrès géol. Internat. en Belgique en 1922, Liége (1925). W. Hume, *Recent Researches on the Tertiary and Mesozoic Formations in Egypt and Sinai,* ibid.

177. G. Choubert, *Sur le Dogger du Haut-Atlas oriental,* C. R. Acad. Sc. (Jan. 17, 1938). *Le Dogger des Hauts-Plateaux et de la moyenne Moulouya,* ibid. (Jan. 24, 1938).

178. G. Lucas, *Description géologique et pétrographique des Monts du Ghar Rouban et du Sidi el Abed (frontière algéro-marocaine)*, Bull. Serv. Carte géol. Algérie, 2 sér., no. 16 (1942).

179. F. Roman, *Le Tithonique du massif du Djurdjura*, Matériaux Carte géol. Algérie, 1 sér., Pal. no. 7 (1936). A. Lambert, *Découverte du Rhétien à Avicula contorta Portl. dans la chaîne du Djurdjura*, C. R. Acad. Sc. (Nov. 15, 1937); *Sur le Tithonique de la "chaîne calcaire" (zone Ic de L. Glangeaud)*, C. R. Soc. géol. France (1945), p. 86.

180. M. Solignac, *Etude géologique de la Tunisie septentrionale*, Serv. des Mines, Tunis (1927).

181. H. Schoeller, *Présence de Jurassique au SW de Kairouan (Tunisie)*, C. R. Soc. géol. France (June 7, 1937).

182. Which is confirmed by the more recent work of L. F. Spath, *On the Blake Collection of Ammonites from Katch, India*, Mem. geol. Surv. of India, IX (1924). See especially the work by the same author cited note 32, this chap.

183. Their maximum depth, in the regions we have studied, corresponds to the Lias of the Germanic Cuvette and the Lias of the Causses.

184. W. A. Obrutschev, *Geologie von Sibirien*, Fortschritte der Geol. und Pal., Berlin (1926).

185. We have already seen (p. 239) that this series began with the Permian.

186. See the work by F. Stockmans and F. F. Mathieu recently published by the Royal Museum of Natural History of Belgium, devoted to the stratigraphy, tectonics and flora of the Jurassic in the coal beds of northern China.

187. See the chapter relating to French Indo-China, edited by Ch. Jacob, in *La Géologie et les mines de la France d'Outre-Mer*, Publ. du Bur. d'Etudes géol. et min. coloniales, Paris (1932).

188. The relation of Ethiopian faunas to the Madagascar and Himalayan faunas was discussed by E. Daqué, *Neue Beiträge zur Kenntniss des Jura in Abessynien*, Beitr. z. Pal. u. Geol. Oestr.-Ung., XXVII (1915). See also the article by Stefanini, cited note 292, chap. 5. J. Cottreau, *Invertébrés jurassiques de la région de Harar (Abyssinie)*, Bull. Soc. géol. France, 4 sér., 24 (1924). W. A. MacFayden, *Geology and Paleontology of British Somaliland*, Govt. of Somal. Protect. (1933), describes very fossilferous marine series in the Jurassic and Eocene.

189. This species is, however, close to Rhaetian forms of Europe. See the critical bibliography in the very useful work of A. Carpentier, *Revue des travaux de Paléontologie végétale publiés dans le cours des années 1910–1919*, Revue gén. de Bot., 35 (1923), p. 70. See also the article by the same author cited note 100, chap. 6. General information in the work by A. C. Seward, *Plant Life through the Ages*, Cambridge Univ. Press (1931).

190. A. A. Baker, C. H. Dane and J. B. Reeside, *Correlation of the Jurassic Formations of Parts of Utah, Arizona, New Mexico and Colorado*, U. S. Geol. Surv. Prof. Paper no. 183 (1936).

191. R. L. Imlay, "Upper Jurassic Ammonites from Mexico," Bull. Geol. Soc. Amer., 50 (1939).

192. See E. Jaworski, *Beitrage zur Kenntniss des Jura in Süd-Amerika*, Neues Jahrb. f. Min., Beilage-Band 37 (1914); *Die Trias-, Lias-, und Doggerfauna der Andinen Geosynklinale, und ihre verwandschaftlichen Beziehungen*, Geol. Rundschau (1926). E. Jaworski, F, Krantz and H. Gerth, *Beiträge zur Paläontologie und Stratigraphie des Lias, Doggers, Tithons, und der Unterkreide in der Kordilleren im Süd der Provinz Mendoza (Argentinien)*, Geol. Rundschau, 17a, Steinmann-Festschrift (1926), and especially the very important work by C. E. Weaver, *Paleontology of the Jurassic and Cretaceous of West Central Argentina*, Mem. Univ. of Wash., 1 (1931). A. F. Leanza, "Upper Limit of the Jurassic System," Bull. Geol. Soc. Amer., 58 (1947), no. 9, a comparative study of the ammonite faunas of Argentina and of the Mediterranean Tithonian.

193. Certain groups appear earlier than in Europe. Thus the echinoid genus *Stomechinus*, which exists in Europe only after the Bajocian, appears in the Andean Lias. Trigonias are abundant from the lower Lias, while in Europe they are abundant only in the upper Lias. Among others, the group of scabras appears in Europe in the Cretaceous, here in the Middle Jurassic.

194. For H. Salfeld (work cited note 95, this chap.) it is to the clayey facies which generally rule in the northern domain that the particular characteristics of its fauna should be attributed.

195. W. Maync, *Stratigraphie der Jurabildungen Ostgrönlands,* Medded. om Grönland, 132, no. 2, Copenhagen (1947), an interesting study of the relationship between the boreal and southern provinces.

Chapter Eight

The Cretaceous

I. Introduction (Stage Divisions)

The name Cretaceous comes from Chalk (*Craie, Kreide*), a white and soft calcareous rock, known by all, which is exposed over vast areas in France, England, and Germany.

Chalk is only a facies, so that we are first obliged to place in the Cretaceous rocks contemporary with the chalk but different from it (for example, sandstones in Bohemia). Moreover, it has been demonstrated that, in the chalk countries, beneath this rock lie other beds which gradually merge into it. The lower boundary of the Cretaceous will naturally be defined by the emergence which took place in most of Europe at the end of the Jurassic. To be specific, we shall choose a region where this period of emergence was particularly brief, the Jura Mountains. There, above the continental or lagoonal formations of the Purbeckian, which crown the Jurassic, we find marine beds which mark the extreme base of the Cretaceous. Following these beds step by step, we learn that they pass under the chalk. So, a first general division is reached, a Lower Cretaceous, in which no chalk is found, and an Upper Cretaceous usually composed of chalk.

The upper boundary, in the greater part of the three countries, corresponds to a retreat of the sea and a lacuna of sedimentation; at this break we end the Cretaceous and the Secondary era. The Cretaceous, enclosed by two regressions, thus appears on the whole as a sedimentary cycle.

This first rough division has been followed by subdivision of the Cretaceous into stages, based this time on paleontologic evidence, which we shall indicate as we go along.[1] If we heed the history of the faunas and especially that of the ammonites, we are led to introduce a Middle Cretaceous (Albian-Turonian); but for greater convenience in regional descriptions, we preserve the classic grouping of stages into a Lower and Upper Cretaceous, a grouping adopted in particular in the geologic map of France, 1/1,000,000.

Here is the list of these stages, with the type localities and an indication of the facies found in those localities or generally in western Europe.

Upper Cretaceous	Danian—Bryozoan limestone of Denmark.		
	Senonian: white chalk of Sens [west of Paris]	Aturian (Adour)	Maestrichtian—siliceous chalk of Maastricht, Holland, with *Belemnitella mucronata*. Campanian—white chalk of Champagne[2] (east of Paris), with *Belmn. quadrata*.
		Emscherian (Emscher)	Santonian—Saintonge chalk, with *Micraster coranguinum*. Coniacian—chalk of Cognac [western France], with *Micraster cortestudinarium*.
	Turonian—siliceous chalk of Touraine, southwest of Paris (generally, marly chalk).		
	Cenomanian—sands of Maine, west of Paris (generally, glauconitic chalk).		

Lower Cretaceous	Albian—greensands and blue clays with ammonites of the Aube, southeast of Paris (= Gault, English name for these clays)..	
	Aptian—limestones and marls with ammonites of Apt (Vaucluse) [in southeastern France].	
	Barremian—marly limestones with ammonites of Barrème (Basses-Alpes) [in southeastern France].	
	Hauterivian—marly limestones of Hauterive, near Neuchâtel [Switzerland].	Neocomian
	Valanginian—marly limestones of Valangin, near Neuchâtel.	(Neuchâtel).

The same essential features that guided us in Jurassic paleogeography continue to do so in the Cretaceous. There is even the contrast between a Mediterranean or Alpine region, where deep troughs existed in which the marine Cretaceous follows the Jurassic without interruption, and a northern continental area where, between Hercynian massifs playing the role of islands, the epicontinental seas advance in transgression over the North Atlantic continent. In these epicontinental deposits are found most of the type facies that we shall enumerate.

Finally, as in the Jurassic, the faunas allow us to recognize two provinces in Europe: a Mediterranean or tropical province and a northern, cooler province whose influence, competing with that of the warmer province, is felt more or less far to the south, in the European epicontinental seas.

With these concepts we can begin the study of the Cretaceous fauna.

II. The Cretaceous Fauna

Foraminifers

The *microscopic foraminifers,* benthonic or pelagic, are amassed by thousands in the chalk: globigerinids, miliolids, lagenids, rosalines, etc. This richness in globigerinids, especially, so struck the first observers that they compared the chalk to the globigerinid muds of present seas, and consequently considered it a deposit of very deep seas (several thousand meters). Since then, it has been recognized that this comparison is false. The chalk is a simple calcareous mud, formed of the remains of all genera. Fragments of coastal organisms are numerous in it, and we shall see later (*a propos* of sponges) that the depths at which these organisms must have lived was not too great, some hundreds of meters at most. Thus, chalk is a formation of a calm sea, without clayey or sandy contributions, depositing only fine muds off low calcareous coasts. Just these conditions were realized in the epicontinental sea of the European Cretaceous,[3] and if foraminifers are numerous in it, globigerinids among others, it is simply because this calcareous milieu agreed with them and especially because, through lack of detrital contributions, their number per unit of volume of sediment was greatly increased.

All these miscroscopic forms are, however, especially interesting in that they allow the definition of lithologic facies: globigerinid, lagenid, rosaline, or miliolid chalk, etc. In addition, certain groups, the cuneolines (*Cuneolina, Discocyclina*)[4] and especially the rosalines (of the genus *Globotruncana*),[5] are characteristic of the Upper Cretaceous. They are often the only fossils found in the marly series of many oil-bearing regions, where beds traversed by wells are characterized by them. So studies of them, based especially on the works of Cushman, have been financed by industry and are in current use.[6] But many specialists seem a little too hasty in attributing a general value to the scale of microforaminifers, which are indeed very useful for local correlations between neighboring wells. In addition, these minute shells are frequently redeposited so that they are found, in a perfect state of preservation, in much more recent sediments than their original horizon, causing many errors.[7]

Among the *large foraminifers,* two groups have real stratigraphic importance, the orbitolines and the orbitoids.

The orbitolines, represented here and there in the Jurassic by very rare ancestral forms,[8] are very characteristic of more or less reefy, coastal facies of the tropical province during the Lower Cretaceous and through the Cenomanian, to such a point that H. Douvillé[9] was able to establish a scale of species which succeed each other through a whole series of stages. Most of these forms are, however, difficult to determine and we shall be satisfied to group them as follows:

a) The Lower Cretaceous is the domain of small orbitolines (less than a centimeter in diameter). They are found in abundance especially in the limestones called Urgonian (see p. 406), coral facies distributed at different horizons of the Barremian and Aptian of the Mediterranean region (southern France). They are, in general, impossible to isolate and are visible only in thin sections. But in intercalated marly banks they are easily isolated and then appear, scattered over the outcrops, in such great numbers that they have won for these banks the name of orbitoline beds. Such are the *O. conoidea-dis-*

coidea beds, so widespread in the Barremian of the sub-Alpine chains, and the *O. lenticularis* beds of the upper Aptian of Perte du Rhône, near Bellegarde.

b) In the Cenomanian, however, large orbitolines (from 1 to 5 centimeters in diameter) are found. They are distributed either in limestones with rudistids or corals, or in sandstones. *O. concava* is very common in all southern France. After reaching this maximum size the orbitolines suddenly disappeared.

The orbitoids, on the other hand, begin at the base of the Aturian and belong to the group of orbitoids destined to flourish in the Tertiary. But the genus *Orbitoides* (s. str.) remains characteristic of the Upper Cretaceous.[10] These also are southern forms, but in the Maestrichtian, warm currents took them, together with a few rudistids, as far north as the Maastricht chalk (*O. media*).

Sponges

These are especially facies fossils, whose difficult identification makes them of little practical use for stratigraphy.

1. The calcareous sponges (pharetrons) are localized in littoral deposits. We shall see them abundantly represented in the Aptian sands of Farringdon (England), on the shores of the sea which then bathed the English Primary Massif. Other classic deposits of the same epoch are found in the littoral limestones of the Jura Mountains (La Presta, near Neuchâtel). The genus *Barroisia,* which is easy to recognize, seems, up to the present, to be localized at this horizon (Aptian).

2. Siliceous sponges,[11] on the other hand, flourish in the muddy sediments of deeper or calmer seas. Chalk is one of their favorite environments. However, the sponge is usually very poorly preserved; it is reinforced with added silica and transformed into a true flint. If the chalk is then dissolved and carried away by water, these silicified sponges remain as evidence and are abundant in the clay with flints, a residue of the dissolution of the chalk. They thus help us to follow the extent of the Cretaceous seas beyond the limits of present outcrops of the chalk (ex.: Massif Central, Burgundy, Jura Mountains, etc.).

Among the siliceous sponges, the monactinellids and lithistids predominate in the somewhat sandy or glauconitic littoral facies, while the hexactinellids are more abundant in the white chalk proper. In Hanover, where there are localities with very well preserved sponges we can even attempt an estimate of the depth of the Chalk seas (see Fig. 91),[12] using as standards the depths at which some of these same genera are living today.

Coelenterates

As in the Upper Jurassic, the coral reefs are confined exclusively to the Mediterranean regions. As they can scarcely be used easily in stratigraphy, we shall see later (*à propos* of the rudistids) in what stages the principal coral limestones are distributed. We note especially the genus *Cyclolites,* a very simple, characteristic coral, limited to the Upper Cretaceous (Provence, Aquitaine, eastern Alps).

Encrusting hydrozoa of the group of stromatoporids have contributed to

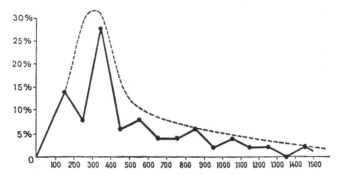

FIG. 91. *Estimate of the depth of the Cretaceous seas according to the sponge faunas of Hanover (from data gathered by Schrammen).*

Frequency curve of the depths at which were dredged living genera of hexactinellids represented in the Oblrg Chalk of Hanover.

Abscissas, depths in meters; ordinates, percentages of samples collected at the different depths. Dashed line represents the probable appearance of the frequency curve if the statistics were based on a larger number of samples.

the formation of the Urgonian limestones of southeastern France and the Cenomanian limestones of l'Île Madame (Charente). But they are sometimes very difficult to distinguish from the bryozoans which accompany them in the same facies.

Echinoderms

Crinoids do not play as important a part in the Cretaceous as in the Jurassic. Nevertheless, there are still crinoidal limestones or spathic limestones (Jura, sub-Alpine chains) in the Lower Cretaceous. In the chalk, cups of unattached crinoids, *Marsupites* and *Uintacrinus,* peculiar to the Upper Cretaceous, are sometimes found.

Echinoids, however, furnish a great number of characteristic fossils. Among the littoral forms, scattered in the organic limestone facies, *Pygurus* is abundant in the Valanginian, *Cidaris* species continue as in the Jurassic, and *Discoidea* is peculiar to the Middle Cretaceous in the glauconitic sands.

But the dominant feature of the echinoderm fauna is provided by the great development of irregular echinoids without teeth, limivores (mud eaters), peculiar to the marly, muddy or chalky bottoms, whose most typical representatives are the spatangids. These facies are so well characterized in the Lower Cretaceous that they have been called spatangid marls. The species of *Toxaster* provide a true chronologic scale for the stratigraphy of these spatangid marls, defined by the work of Lambert:[13]

Aptian	*Toxaster collegnoi.*
Barremian	*T. ricordeaui, T. amplus.*
Hauterivian	*T. retusus.*
Valanginian	*T. granosus.*

Heteraster, a related genus, is particularly abundant in the Barremian. Finally in the Upper Cretaceous comes the long list of chalk echinoids: *Micraster, Ananchytes, Holaster, Hemipneustes,* etc. Their internal moulds are often silicified and thus recognizable in the clay with flints. The most useful for stratigraphy is *Micraster,* which in the Emscherian (*Micraster* chalk) has furnished the species for the establishment of paleontologic zones.

Brachiopods

In spite of the abundance of individuals, the small number of genera in the Cretaceous already indicates the gradual decline of the group. As in the Jurassic, *Pygopes* still persists in the Mediterranean deep-water facies of the Lower Cretaceous, while in the chalk there are terebratulids and rhynchonellids.[14] On the other hand, in the detrital chalks, small, littoral brachiopods swarm, for example, *Crania* and *Thecidea* in the siliceous chalk of Maastricht.

Pelecypods[15]

Very few are interesting from a stratigraphic viewpoint.

In the really deep-water, marly facies of the Mediterranean regions scarcely any are found except nuculids. It is only in somewhat neritic sediments that pelecypods become frequent.

Inoceramus is abundantly represented in the Albian by small forms, some ornamented with radial ribs (*I. sulcatus*), others with concentric flanges (*I. concentricus*). Only this latter type of ornamentation persists in the *Inoceramus* species of the chalk, where the size increases until the group becomes extinct at the end of the Cretaceous. In certain chalk countries where ammonites are rare, *Inoceramus* species are used to establish numerous paleontologic zones (Germany).[16]

The species of Pholadomya persist in coastal muds, along with the spatangids of the Lower Cretaceous (*P. elongata*) of the Hauterivian; they are associated with *Panope. Plicatula,* frequent in the Neocomian and especially in the Aptian (*P. placunea*), is a somewhat deeper dwelling genus.

Oysters are extremely abundant. Some of them are (like the living *O. cochlear*) relatively deep-water forms and are found in marly facies or chalk. Thus, in the Lower Cretaceous, *O. couloni* is very common in the spatangid marls of the Hauterivian. They are followed in the Aptian marls by a very large mutation, *O. aquila.* These smooth oysters with a very concave shell are likewise very abundant in the true chalk (*O. vesicularis,* etc.). Other groups, however, with thicker, more ornate shells, often frilled (*Alectryonia*), are peculiar to littoral facies, organic limestone or sandstone. Thus *A. rectangularis,* in the Jura and sub-Alpine chains, characterizes the organic facies of the Valanginian. In the Upper Cretaceous, when the sediments are sandy, oysters become abundant enough to define the ostracean facies (Maine,

Perche) along the shores of the chalk seas, bordering ancient massifs. On the southern shore of the Mediterranean, these ostracean facies are widely developed (N. Africa, Calabria, Egypt, Syria). A few special species (*O. owervegi, O. syphax*) are found there, indicating an African province, perhaps separated from the European faunas by the Mediterranean depths, a barrier for the littoral oysters.

The aucellas, which lived especially in northern seas during the Upper Jurassic, still persist in the same seas during the Neocomian and contribute to the characterization of a relatively cold climatic province.[17]

Finally the group of pachyodonts (rudistids, s.l.), pelecypods peculiar to the coral facies of the Mediterranean province, deserves detailed treatment here,[18] for in these facies, where ammonites are missing, they can be used to establish paleontologic zones and, for that purpose, are currently used by the stratigraphers of southern Europe. Four great successive rudistid faunas (H. Douvillé) are seen:

1st. A Neocomian fauna, characterized by the persistence of *Monopleura* and the presence of the characteristic genus *Valletia*. Occurrences of these are very rare (sub-Alpine chains of Savoy).

2nd. A fauna called Urgonian, characterizing the coral facies from the Barremian to the lower Aptian. To *Monopleura* is here added *Requienia* (*R. ammonia*) and *Toucasia* (*T. carinata*). Praecaprinids (*Praecaprina, Offneria*) appear here and are extremely widespread in southern France (Languedoc, Provence, sub-Alpine chains, Jura Mountains) and all around the Mediterranean.

3rd. In the upper Aptian a similar fauna is called Urgo-Aptian, as it occurs in limestone identical with the Urgonian limestones. It is characterized by *Toucasia santanderensis, Polyconites verneuili,* and *Horiopleura lamberti.* They are known in the Pyrenees, the Corbières, Spain,[19] North Africa and the Forest of Bakony in Hungary.[20]

4th. Finally, beginning in the Cenomanian and persisting until the Danian, come the rudistid faunas proper: *Hippurites, Radiolites,* caprinids, etc. The sub-genera and species of hippurites and radiolites, which succeed each other very rapidly, allow the distinction of a large number of paleontologic zones, which we cannot describe in detail.[21] These zones are used for the stratigraphic classification of the Upper Cretaceous of Aquitaine,[22] Provence,[23] southern Italy, the Balkans,[24] etc.

Gastropods

The forms used by stratigraphers are very rare. Let us note the acteonellids, large shells characteristic of the acteonellid limestone, a facies associated with rudistid limestone in the Upper Cretaceous of the Mediterranean region. In the Urgonian limestones, we again find nerineas descended from the forms of the Jurassic reefs, but here becoming much larger, before dying out at the end of the Upper Cretaceous. In the organic limestones of the Valanginian, large specimens of *Natica leviathan* (Jura) are abundant. Finally, at the end of the Cretaceous, the continental facies become frequent and contain rich terrestrial or lacustrine gastropod faunas. The genus *Lychnus,* very abundant in Provence, is characteristic of the Danian.[25]

Ammonites

Ammonites persist up to and including the Maestrichtian and may be used to distinguish paleontologic zones; but the use of these zones is common only up to the Cenomanian. In the Upper Cretaceous, ammonites become rare in many regions and then echinoids, belemnites, *Inoceramus* or rudistids are used.

So, without giving the complete list of ammonite zones which can be identified,[26] we shall limit ourselves to naming the most characteristic forms of each stage, mentioning separately the genera peculiar to the northern province, whose fauna, however, assumes a cosmopolitan character beginning with the Aptian.

Danian . . . .   No ammonites, *Nautilus danicus.*

Maestrichtian . . . . .   *Bostrychoceras polyplocum, Baculites anceps.*

Campanian . . . .   *Placenticeras bidorsatum.*

Santonian . . . .   *Mortoniceras texanum.*

Coniacian . . . .   *Tissotia, Barroisiceras.*

Turonian . . . .   *Mammites nodosoides, Vascoceras.*

Cenomanian . . . . . .   { *Acanthoceras rothomagense, Scaphites aequalis* / *Acanthoceras mantelli* } *Schloenbachia varians* / Vraconian.—*Mortoniceras rostratum*

Albian . . . .   { *Mortoniceras hugardianum, M. varicosum* / *Hoplites dentatus* . . . . / *Hoplites tardefurcatus* . . . . } *Douvilleiceras mamillatum*

Aptian . . . .   { Gargasian—*Oppelia nisus.* / Bedoulian—*Hoplites deshayesi, Ancyloceras matheroni.*

Barremian . . . .   { *Macroscaphites yvani* . . . . / *Pulchellia pulchella* . . . . / *Hoplites angulicostatus* . . . . / *Desmoceras difficile* . . . . } Northern province: *Simbirskites*

Hauterivian . . . . . .   { *Crioceras duvali* . . . . / *Hoplites radiatus* . . . . } Northern province: *Polyptychiles.*

Valanginian . . . .   { *Hoplites neocomiensis* . . . . / Berriasian—*H. boissieri,* /   *H. ponticus* . . . . } Northern province: *Garnieria, Craspedites, Polyptychiles.*

As in the Jurassic, it is these ammonite zones which permit a rigorous definition of the different stages. We recall also that the less ornate forms are peculiar to the Mediterranean regions (phylloceratids, lytoceratids, *Desmoceras*) while the very ornate forms pervade the coastal facies (*Hoplites, Douvilleiceras, Mortoniceras, Schloenbachia,* etc.).

Belemnites

These are very useful from the stratigraphic viewpoint.[27]

a) In the northern province, we have, in the Cretaceous as in the Jurassic, the genus *Cylindrotheutis,* characterized by a groove on the flattened ventral side. Above the Cenomanian, true belemnites disappear and are replaced by

Belemnitella, which, developing until the end of the Senonian, renders great service for the stratigraphy of the chalk in northern France, England, and Germany. Thus, in the Cenomanian-Emscherian, there is the sub-genus *Actinocamax* (ex. *Belemnitella plena*) with non-alveolate rostrum; the Campanian is characterized by *Goniotheutis* (ex. *B. quadrata*) with rostrum equipped with a square pseudo-alveola; the Maestrichtian contains *Belemnitella* (s. str.) (ex. *B. mucronata*) with a round alveola and a strong spine (mucron) at the end of the rostrum.

b) In the Mediterranean province, *Belemnitella* is unknown, so there are no more belemnitids above the Albian.[28] On the other hand, the Lower Cretaceous contains special groups. First there is the continuation of the Jurassic *Belemnopsis,* with a groove notching the edge of the alveola, not reaching the point. In the related sub-genus *Pseudobelus* (*B. minimus* of the Gault), the groove begins only at a distance from the point. And there are especially *Duvalia* or flat belemnites, forms of the deep Mediterranean facies, providing a true stratigraphic scale: *D. lata* (Tithonian-Valanginian), *D. eymerici* (upper Valanginian-Hauterivian) *D. dilatata* (Hauterivian).

III. The Lower Cretaceous in the Typical European Regions

1. *The Lower Cretaceous in Southeastern France*[29]

A. The Southern sub-Alpine Chains: The Vocontian Trough. The southern sub-Alpine chains which extend to the south of Vercors (see Fig. 82) and Gapençais, as far as the region of Digne-Castellane and the high valley of the Var, constitute the only region in France where the deep-water facies may have persisted without interruption, including the whole Jurassic and continuing through the Lower Cretaceous and even into the lower part of the Upper Cretaceous. During this time a deep sea, succeeding that of the Dauphinois facies of the Jurassic, undoubtedly extended over the location of the external crystalline massifs and as far as the boundary of the internal zone of the Alps. This deep sea, stretching out in the direction of the chain, pushed a gulf toward the west, its boundary marked on the north by Vercors, which belongs to the northern sub-Alpine chains, and on the south by Mt. Ventoux where the littoral facies, called Provençal, begin to appear, which we shall study later (see Fig. 92). It is in this great E-W gulf, which extends as far as the Massif Central, that the deposits of the Lower Cretaceous with deep-water facies have been best studied. V. Paquier called it the Vocontian trough, from the name of the tribes of Voconces, who inhabited the Vaison-la-Romaine region, south of Nyons.

In all this mountainous country, composed of Upper Jurassic and Cretaceous, the Lower Cretaceous has enormous outcrops. They are represented by very uniform continuously deep-water sediments, marls or marly limestones, up to 2,000 m. thick. There are neither hard limestones nor sandstones, so

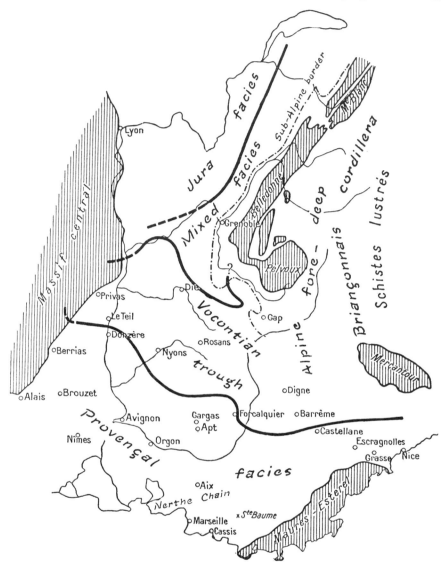

FIG. 92. *Diagrammatic map showing the distribution of the great zones of facies in the Lower Cretaceous in southeastern France (after data from W. Kilian and his collaborators).*

that, the southern climate helping, it produces a country of unproductive ridges, much gullied and monotonous. But the colors remain generally rather pale,[30] yellowish or whitish, in contrast to the black country of the Jurassic.

The fauna consists almost entirely of cephalopods, among which *Lytoceras, Phylloceras* and *Desmoceras* of the deep-water facies are abundant. Belemnites are those of the tropical province, *Duvalia* and *Belemnopsis*. In addition there are a few rare deep-water pelecypods (*Nucula*) and smooth brachiopods (*Pygope*).

In this monotonous lithologic assemblage, only the cephalopods make subdivisions possible.

Valanginian. Above the light gray limestones of the Tithonian, whose ridges supply an excellent stratigraphic landmark, first comes a transition zone composed of marly limestones. This is the zone with *Hoplites boissieri* and *H. ponticus,* which detailed study has shown to be contemporaneous with the first marine beds overlying the Purbeckian in the Jura Mountains. This then is Cretaceous and it is called the Berriasian sub-stage, from the locality of Berrias (Ardèche).

This Berriasian thus forms the transition between the Tithonian limestones and the thick marly beds which continue to the top of the stage. In these Valanginian marls a rich fauna of small pyritic ammonites is found. So the facies completely resembles that of the Oxfordian marls.

Hauterivian. The sedimentation continues muddy and deep-water, though very thin and very regular intercalations of marly limestones appear in the marls, which give a characteristic streaked aspect to the sides of the ravines. The fauna permits the recognition of the two zones listed above.

Barremian. The marly limestones form larger banks here; as they are colored gray-blue by pyrite which oxidizes and becomes yellow near alteration surfaces, they are often called bicolored limestones. Four ammonite zones are distinguished. The type of the stage was taken at Barrème, near Digne.

Aptian. The base of this stage is still formed by marly limestones in thick banks which, following those of the Barremian, delineate ridges with a smooth profile. This is the zone of *Ancyloceras matheroni* and *Hoplites deshayesi,* or Bedoulian sub-stage (from the locality of La Bédoule, near Cassis, east of Marseilles, where these limestones are worked for hydraulic lime).[31]

Above come the Aptian marls or Gargasian sub-stage (from Gargas, near Apt) which exactly reproduces the facies with pyritic ammonites of the Valanginian marls, but with black tints. This is the zone with *Oppelia nisus* and *Hoplites dufrenoyi.*

Albian. The facies of black marls continues, but it begins to be intercalated with banks or "kidneys" of sandstone, called "super-Aptian." The ammonites become rarer except in a few pyritic occurrences.

The domain of the deep-water facies has varied slightly in the course of the Lower Cretaceous. It is only in the center of the Vocontian trough (vicinity of Rosans) that they prevailed during this whole period. On the edges, they are mixed with the littoral facies which we shall now describe.

B. Southern Border of the Vocontian Trough: Provençal Facies.[32] South of the Vocontian trough, we approach the Maures-Esterel Massif, which we know remained emerged during the Lower Cretaceous, not because there is no Cretaceous on its surface at present, which would be insufficient evidence, but because, approaching it, we see the appearance of more and more coastal facies, more or less inshore according to the epoch. The coastal facies, called Provençal, are characterized by organic facies with remains of shells or corals, by glauconitic or phosphatic beds, sandstones, lacunas, and finally by faunas in which pelecypods and echinoids gradually replace cephalopods.

Very strikingly, the thicknesses are greatest in the boundary zone between the deep-water and the littoral facies. Thus the Valanginian-Barremian series, which were hardly 150–200 m. thick in the center of the Vocontian trough, reach 1,000 m. on the northern slope of Ventoux (J. Jung).[33] We shall find analogous facts on the northern border of the Vocontian trough and in the Swiss Helvetic nappes (Fig. 102).

Valanginian. The Valanginian of Provence proper seems to begin with the top of the white limestones which we noted in the Upper Jurassic. Then come marly beds, sometimes greenish, providing a good stratigraphic marker. And the stage ends with a second mass of organic white limestones, in which are found *Natica leviathan* characteristic of the Valanginian of the Jura Mountains. But in the north (vicinity of Moustiers-Ste-Marie), the transition from the deep-water facies is established by less organic and more marly sediments with *Toxaster granosus* and *Hoplites,* which is the first appearance of the spatangid facies which predominate in the following stages.

Hauterivian. At its base, the most important horizons of the Provençal Neocomian are developed. These are the spatangid beds with a fauna close to that of the Hauterivian of the Jura: *Toxaster amplus,*[34] *Ostrea couloni.* Then come a few calcareous beds—siliceous limestones in the Marseilles region, glauconitic or phosphatic limestones farther north. *Hoplites,* abundant in the north, becomes more and more rare as we approach the old massif.

Barremian and Aptian. Two regional types are recognized for these stages.

a) To the east, between Castellane and Nice, the Barremian becomes glauconitic and is progressively reduced to a few meters of glauconitic beds distinguished only by their fauna from the equally glauconitic Hauterivian and Albian. This fauna includes pulchellas, many pelecypods (plicatulas) and brachiopods. The Aptian is missing.

b) To the west, however, in the Provence limestones, the littoral influences are less abrupt and are shown only by the appearance, in one or the other of these two stages, of the Urgonian facies, which deserves detailed account.

The Urgonian facies. The type was taken at Orgon, east of Tarascon on the south bank of the Durance River. Here white, organic limestones, very hard and compact, were produced by an accumulation of remains of more or less crushed and altered organisms: foraminifers (miliolids and orbitolines), corals, hydrozoa, bryozoa, rudistids, nerineas, etc., The fauna is very different from that of the stage-types of the Vocontian trough. So early geologists made an independent stage of it, placed above the Neocomian and below the Albian. More exact study[35] has shown that this was only a facies, however, which occurred at different horizons. It sometimes begins in the lower Barremian (south of Marseille). Everywhere it makes up the upper Barremian and sometimes it extends into the lower Aptian. The stratigraphy of these two stages thus becomes rather complicated. At Apt, the marls of the upper Aptian (Gargasian) with pyritic ammonites directly overlie the Urgonian, while at La Bédoule, near Cassis, in Provence proper, we have seen the lower Aptian (Bedoulian) represented by marly limestone with large cephalopods, above the Urgonian.[36]

We shall be satisfied with emphasizing the important morphologic role played by the Urgonian limestones in Provence. The Provençal landscape owes its most characteristic features to their regular cornices, like pediments of ancient temples, and to their ridges, rocky and dazzling in the sunshine. With their whiteness, they dominate the blue sea of the coves of Marseilles and from the high Ste. Baume Massif command the whole countryside of Provence.[37]

These Urgonian landscapes on the south side of the Vocontian trough extend from Marseilles and Aix beyond the Rhône.[38] The Donzère pass or "Gate of Provence," excavated in the Urgonian limestones by the river, marks approximately the northern boundary of this Provençal Urgonian.[39]

Albian. A rather thin zone of glauconitic sandstone, sometimes phosphatic, extends from Nice (Eze locality) and Grasse (famous Escragnolles locality, between Grasse and Castellane) into the southern part of the Drôme. It marks the ancient Provençal shores of that epoch and is prolonged into Gard and Ardèche.[40] In the vicinity of Apt, these Albian-Cenomanian glauconitic sediments have completely oxidized and been transformed into ferruginous sands and clays, with exploited ochres (bright red facies), evidence of old continental alterations. This is the emerged region of the Durance isthmus which we shall take up later (p. 429). The deep-water Albian, in the form of black marls, is henceforth localized north of this isthmus, in the much narrowed central part of the Vocontian trough (region of Rosans). And the marine Albian, on the contrary, in the form of shales with *Douvilleiceras,* which is known in Nerthe Chain near Marseilles, no longer belongs to the Vocontian trough, but to a new entity, the "Gulf of Basse-Provence" (p. 428), situated south of the Durance isthmus. We shall study its history in connection with the Upper Cretaceous.

C. Western Edge of the Vocontian Trough, against the Massif Central. At the edge of the Massif Central the deep-water or at least marly facies must have advanced fairly far beyond the present boundary of the crystalline formations, just as was the case in the late Jurassic. Thus, south of Privas, pyritic ammonites of the Lower Cretaceous are found, similar to those of Diois. The type locality of Berrias is found there (see p. 401) and at Teil, opposite Montélimar, marly limestones of the Aptian are quarried for cements and hydraulic lime.[41] Farther south, however, more littoral facies are found. Crossing the Rhône at Donzère, the Provençal Urgonian limestones form enormous rocky wastelands (famous fossiliferous locality of Brouzet-lès-Alès) between the Jurassic Plateaus of Gras, Nîmes and Avignon (see p. 370).

D. Northern Edge of the Vocontian Trough: the Northern Sub-Alpine Chains: Lower Cretaceous of the Mixed Type. The marly landscape of the

Vocontian trough does not extend beyond Diois on the north. It stops there, at the foot of high Urgonian cliffs that form the southern extremity of the Vercors plateaus.[42] With this massif, we reach the northern sub-Alpine chains, defined above (Fig. 82).

In all these chains, Vercors, Chartreuse, Bauges, Bornes (between the Bauges and the Arve) and the Massif of Sixt (north of the Arve), the Lower Cretaceous, which assumes prime importance here, presents a mixed type, so called because of the repeated alternations of compact, organic limestones and deep-water marly facies. This mixed type is thus contrasted to the deep-water type of the Vocontian trough and to the Jurassian type where organic limestones become the rule. And it is precisely to these alternations that the landscapes of the northern sub-Alpine chains owe their richness and variety of form. These are neither the monotonous, marly ridges of the Vocontian countryside, nor the heavy and bulky calcareous masses of the Jura Mountains, but a harmonious succession of grassy or wooded little valleys dominated by regular calcareous cornices.

Along the sub-Alpine border, for which we now complete the description of the section (see p. 353), the following series is seen:

Valanginian. The lower part (30 to 40 m.) follows the Tithonian, still keeping the deep-water facies of the Vocontian trough. The marly limestones of the Berriasian there were the source of the natural cement industry ("Gate of France" at Grenoble) for certain banks contain the exact proportion of 24% of clay demanded by this industry. Above, thick Valanginian marls (300 to 400 m.) prolong the lower part of the Diois marls.

The upper Valanginian (60 to 100 m.) assumed, however, a littoral facies like that of the Jura Mountains, with flinty or ferruginous organic limestones, containing *Alectryonia rectangularis, Pygurus rostratus* and rare *Hoplites* (called limestones of Fontanil, a locality 9 km. NW of Grenoble). They form a steeper slope or russet yellow cornice above the marls.[44]

Hauterivian. Above these limestones, the Hauterivian begins with a glauconitic or phosphatic bed, only a few decimeters thick, but very fossiliferous,[45] which extends from Vercors into the Bornes.[46]

Above, deeper-water facies reappear, recalling the Vocontian type: marls and non-fossiliferous marly limestones (100 m.).

At the top there is again a slightly shallower facies. The marls become a little sandy and are called spatangid marls because of the abundance of *Toxaster amplus.* This species, incorrectly confused, up to the present time, with the Hauterivian *T. retusus* of the Paris Basin, and some very rare ammonite remains (*Hoplites angulicostatus*) would perhaps lead to the classification of these terminal beds as lower Barremian. But, from the cartographic point of view, it is more convenient to attach them still to the Hauterivian, for their boundary with the unmistakably Hauterivian lower marls is not evident in the morphology and is generally impossible to determine in the field.

Barremian and Aptian. Some banks of yellow limestone with panopes,

forming the lowest part of the huge mass of Urgonian limestones (300 m.),
are again attributed to the poorly defined lower Barremian.

Indeed, we find there a reefy facies identical to that of the Orgon limestones but reaching a greater thickness. These high Urgonian cliffs constitute
most of the summits (synclinal: inversion of relief) of the sub-Alpine chains,
standing as bastions between the Tertiary plains and the sub-Alpine trench.

Here and there, these limestones inclose marly intercalations called orbi-

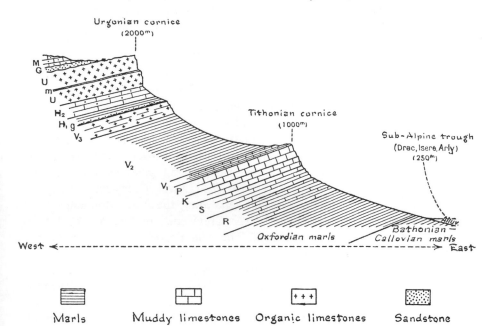

FIG. 93. *Section at the sub-Alpine border (between Grenoble and Chambéry) showing the facies and relative thicknesses of Jurassic and Cretaceous
formations (principally after data from C. Lory and W. Kilian).*

M = Maestrichtian: sandy, marly or organic limestones—lacuna— G = Albian:
glauconitic sandstone and echinoderm limestone of the Gault—lacuna— U = Urgonian: reef limestones (m = orbitoline beds). H₂ = Upper Hauterivian: sandy marls
with spatangids. H₁ = Lower Hauterivian: marls (g = glauconitic bed). V₃ = Upper
Valanginian: Fontanil limestone. V₂ = Middle Valanginian: Valangianian marls. V₁
= Lower Valanginian: marl-limestones with cement (Berriasian). P = Portlandian:
massive Tithonian limestone. K = Kimmeridgian: massive Tithonian limestone. S =
Sequanian: marly limestone. R = Rauracian: marl-limestone.

toline beds, producing very small grassy cornices, sometimes fossiliferous
enough to provide valuable stratigraphic guides (Vercors). Some such intercalations near the middle of the Urgonian have furnished a fauna representing the base of the Aptian (lower orbitoline beds) and others are sometimes
seen at the top of this Urgonian, with an upper Aptian fauna. Thus these
Urgonian limestones usually seem to correspond to the upper Barremian and
lower Aptian, a conclusion established by studying the lateral transition

of these limestones toward the south into the typical ammonite formations of the Vocontian trough.[47]

The upper Aptian is missing or reduced to these very localized remnants of orbitoline beds. These horizons have been studied in detail by Ch. Jacob.

Albian.[48] The transgressive Albian (2 to 40 m.), however, is everywhere represented by glauconitic, crystallized limestones (improperly called Gault shell-marbles) and by marls and sandstones, not usually thick but always fossiliferous (phosphatic horizons) and producing a cornice covered with vegetation at the top of the Urgonian cliffs, beneath Senonian limestones, to be studied later.

2. *The Stages of the Infra-Cretaceous Transgression Between Southeastern France and England*

We can adopt here, without inconvenience, the analytical method, that is, to describe first a succession of regional sections and then, connecting them step by step, deduce the movements of the seas and the paleogeography.

A. The Jura Mountains: Jurassian Type of the Lower Cretaceous. The tectonic definition of the Jura Range (see p. 355) gives us also the area of distribution of the Jurassian type of the Lower Cretaceous. If, going northwest, we pass over the syncline separating the Jura Mountains from the sub-Alpine chains we find a Lower Cretaceous represented by littoral facies throughout its whole thickness. The cephalopods are reduced to rare *Hoplites* and other ornate genera.

In this area the Lower Cretaceous is less prominent topographically; it fills the axial parts of all the great synclines (*vals* or dales, see Fig. 80) in the eastern part of the chain.

Valanginian. The first marine beds overlying the Purbeckian represent, by definition, the base of the Valanginian, whose type was taken precisely in the vicinity of Neuchâtel. They are first marls and rough limestones, thin and localized, with *Toxaster granosus*. Then come thick banks of fine-grained, organic limestones, white or pink, called bastard marble, which contain *Natica leviathan* and nerineas. The upper Valanginian is composed of ferruginous reddish limestones similar to the Fontanil limestone and containing the same fauna. Sometimes, at the top, a horizon of very fossiliferous, rough marls is found (bryozoan marls of Villers-le-Lac, near Pontarlier).

Hauterivian. As in the mixed type, the base has a facies relatively deeper-water than the top. Here belongs the marl of Hauterive, a spatangid facies, very fossiliferous in the vicinity of Neuchâtel, but with a more littoral fauna than in the sub-Alpine chains: *Toxaster retusus, Exogyra couloni, Alectryonia rectangularis, Pholadomya elongata, Hoplites radiatus.*

Above come the Neuchâtel limestones, much exploited for construction: they are oolitic or spathic organic limestones.

Barremian and Aptian. No more ammonites are found here, so that comparison with the stages of Barrème and Apt becomes very difficult. In any case, Urgonian limestones are very thick and they clearly correspond to the Barremian. The Aptian is represented only locally, as we shall see.

Albian. As in the sub-Alpine chains, the Albian is transgressive, with its customary facies of fossiliferous sands and glauconitic sandstones. But these thin sediments have usually been carried away by later erosion and are preserved in only a few localities, two of which deserve special mention, since the sections observed have provided starting points for the detailed stratigraphy of this stage.

1) *La Perte du Rhône.* At the gates of Bellegarde, near the Swiss frontier, the Rhône is sunk in a canyon or *perte,* excavated in the Urgonian but now lost in the backwater from the great Génissiat dam. Above the Urgonian cliffs there is the following section: a. marly limestones and sandstones with *Orbitolina lenticularis,* the lower Aptian (the old Rhodanian stage of some authors); b. glauconitic sandstones and sands with *Ostrea aquila* representing the upper Aptian; c. very fossiliferous greensands with *Hoplites tardefurcatus* and *Douvilleiceras mamillatum,* representing the lower zone of the Albian; d. fossiliferous sands[49] corresponding to the zone with *Hoplites dentatus;* e. then the principal fossiliferous horizon, that of the *Perte du Rhône,* characterized by *Mortoniceras varicosum* and *Inoceramus sulcatus;* f. finally A. Jayet found the Vraconian there, with *Mortoniceras rostratum.* Above come Eocene continental sands, gullying the previous formations and containing reworked fossils from the different zones of the Albian, which has led to confusion.

2. *Environs of Ste. Croix* (Swiss Jura). There, a Rhodanian marly limestone (very fossiliferous at La Presta, in the Val de Travers) and a few calcareous banks of the upper Aptian overlie the Urgonian. The Albian is represented by very fossiliferous sands and sandstones, with two zones of *Hoplites tardefurcatus* and *H. dentatus.* Above, at La Vraconne, come sands with *Mortoniceras perinflatum,* but without *Schloenbachia varians.* This fauna served as type for a Vraconian stage (characterized by *Mortoniceras rostratum* and *Turrilites bergeri*) which we place at the base of the Cenomanian but which many authors still attribute to the Albian (M. Breistroffer, work cited note 40, this chap.).

On the whole, the deepest-water facies in this series of the Jura Mountains type is realized by the spatangid marls of Hauterive. It is impressive to record that precisely at this epoch the Jura Mountains sea extensively invades the Paris Basin to the northwest. We shall follow its route, for the study of the northeast shore of the Jura Mountains sea holds nothing of interest. The Vosges and the Black Forest were certainly emerged, but erosion has caused the disappearance of the deposits which would show the exact position of the ancient shores.

B. The Lower Cretaceous of the Southeast Border of the Paris Basin.[50] Excepting only those in the southeast and in the Jura Mountains, the greatest exposures of Lower Cretaceous in France are found on the southeast rim of the Paris Basin. They form an arc (see Fig. 70) which, starting from Hirson (Ardennes) crosses the Argonne, passes through Revigny, Brienne, St. Florentin, Auxerre and in Nièvre and Cher curves north of the Massif Central. The sediments are partially marly, especially in the upper part, producing, between the calcareous plateaus of Barrois (see p. 330) and the chalk of Champagne, a humid country (*Champagne humide*) forming a low-land belt, in which there is no longer any stream but which was formerly followed by ancient routes of communication.

It is by the Morvano-Vosgian Strait that the Cretaceous sea thus came to invade the Paris Basin. Remnants of the Valanginian with Jurassian facies are still preserved immediately south of this strait, near Chalons and Tour-nus.[51] And on the other side of the Jurassic isthmus of the Langres plateau, we find, in Yonne, isolated remnants of white limestones, probably Valan-ginian.[52] But it is only in the Hauterivian that the transgression becomes general and that the southeastern part of the Paris Basin is invaded by the sea.

There, in the Lower Cretaceous, we have a narrow arm of the sea between the Massif Central on one side, the Vosges and Ardennes on the other, and it is only in the central part that we find an almost uninterrupted succession of marine sediments from the Hauterivian up. To the northeast (the Ar-dennes) and to the southwest (Nièvre, Cher) we shall see, however, the approach of shores manifested by sandy or continental formations or by lacunas. Therefore it becomes necessary to study the following three regional sections separately:

1. *Central part of the arm of the sea (Aube)*. The upper Valanginian seems to be represented there by organic white limestones, with cidarids and oysters, reduced to very localized remnants. That indicates a regime of cur-rents marking the beginning of the transgression.

In the *Hauterivian,* this transgression becomes general, for this stage cor-responds to the marly limestones with spatangids, whose extent is very great and whose fauna is identical with that of the Hauterivian of the Jura Moun-tains: *Toxaster retusus, Pygurus rostratus, Ostrea couloni, Hoplites radiatus.*

The *Barremian* is represented by ostrean clays, with *Ostrea leymeriei* and *Toxaster ricordeaui*. At the top, a few sandy-clayey beds with freshwater fossils (unios) generally appear. These are the last traces of the continental facies of variegated sands and clays that we saw highly developed on the borders of the arm of the sea. Above, a very thin but very fossiliferous, clayey bed, known as the red bed of Vassy, with *Heteraster oblungus* and numerous pelecypods, marks the return of the sea.

The *Aptian* has the facies of the plicatulid marls, containing *Plicatula pla-cunea, Ostrea aquila* and a small *Oppelia* of the *nisus* group. G. Corroy has shown that this *Oppelia* belongs not to the Gargasian species, *O. nisus* but to older forms such as *O. nisoides*. Thus these marls with plicatulas, which also contain *Hoplites deshayesi,* represent the Bedoulian and not the Gargasian, which corresponds to a decrease in depth (sands or discontinuities).

The *Albian* there has a completely typical development. Glauconitic or green sands (8 to 10 m.) are overlain by the Gault clays, up to 90 m. thick, with *Douvilleiceras mamillatum* at the base, *Hoplites dentatus* at the top. Classic sections of the stage are visible in the workings of the numerous tile factories near St. Florentin (Paris-Dijon line) where the clays show a sandy intercalation which disappears in Aube and Haute-Marne.[53]

2. *Region of the northeastern shores.* North of the preceding zone, in the environs of Vassy and as far as Revigny, there is still little change: the white limestones of the upper Valanginian are replaced by black, lacustrine sands and clays, with remains of turtles and, under the red bed of Vassy, which is marine, ferruginous sands and clays (Vassy iron ore) with fresh-water faunas (paludinas, unios, cyclas).

But north of Revigny, it is the transgressive Albian that lies directly on the Jurassic and its facies become more and more littoral as one approaches the Ardennes Massif.

In the vicinity of Revigny, the Albian is still similar to that of Yonne. Especially the greensands contain, there, phosphatic nodules (called *co-quins*), formerly exploited at Grand-Pré, while the Gault clays are much thinner (2 to 25 m.).

In the region of Rethel, the clayey facies have disappeared. Directly above the greensands with *Douvilleiceras mamillatum,* lies the *gaize,* a calcareous sandstone impregnated with opal and more or less decalcified, which makes it porous and light (suitable for the manufacture of dynamite, or refractory crucibles), though it remains compact enough to form the escarpment of the Argonne forests. This morphologic feature, essentially connected with this special facies of the Albian, gives the Argonne a well marked individuality in comparison to the humid Champagne, which it prolongs geologically. Especially rich in remains of sponges, this *gaize* contains ammonites showing that it corresponds to the upper Albian and lower Cenomanian (zone with *Mortoniceras rostratum*).

3. *Region of the southwest shores* (*Nièvre and Cher*). In Cher, the lower stages become progressively thinner toward the southwest. The spatangid limestone lies directly on the Jurassic. The entire Barremian assumes the facies of variegated clay, a continental formation that we shall find again, far away in the Pays de Bray north of Paris. Finally, it is the Albian that directly overlies the Jurassic southwest of Cher.

During this time, the Albian has taken on littoral facies. Beginning southwest of Auxerre, above the basal sands, only the lower part of the St. Florentin beds keeps the clayey facies; these are the clays of Myennes on the Loire. The upper part of these beds is replaced by thick, sandy beds, up to 150 m., the Puisaye sands, whose development gives rise to a naturally wooded region. Farther west this series is reduced. The basal sands disappear first, then the Myennes clays, finally the Puisaye sands.

The diagram (Fig. 94) summarizes these variations of facies.

C. The Lower Cretaceous in the Pays de Bray and the Center of the Paris Basin. In all the central part of the Paris Basin, the Cretaceous is concealed under more recent formations. It appears with the Jurassic (see p. 332) in the isolated anticline of the Pays de Bray. Marine influences were felt still later than in the southeast edge of the Basin (Fig. 96).

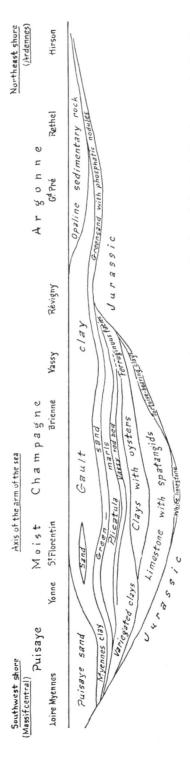

FIG. 94. *Diagram of the facies of the Lower Cretaceous along the southeastern border of the Paris Basin (principally after the data of P. Lemoine; compare with map, Fig. 70). Horizontal scale about 1:500,000.*

410

The marine *Valanginian* is completely missing. This stage and the Hauterivian as well are probably represented by largely continental formations which we find again under the name of Wealdian in the Boulonnais and in England: white sands exploited for glassware, refractory clays for pottery and earthenware; only a few sandy beds with *Panopaea neocomiensis* witnessing fleeting marine influences, the last traces toward the north of the sea of spatangid limestone.

The *Barremian,* here as in Cher, appears as streaked sands and variegated clays without fossils, decalcified formations, certainly continental.[54]

The *Aptian,* on the other hand, marks the arrival of the sea and has its usual facies of marls with plicatulas and *Ostrea aquila.*

The *Albian*[55] has the same composition as in Yonne. It is the open and deep-water marine regime. In fact, the transgression at this epoch covered the whole Paris Basin.

Very recently, a well drilled to a depth of 744 m. at Ivry-sur-Seine, in the

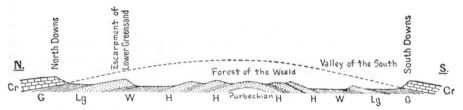

FIG. 95.   *Transverse section of the anticline of the Weald (after R. S. Herries, in* Geology in the Field, *note 23, chap. 1*).

Cr = Upper Cretaceous: The Chalk
G = Gault clay
Lg = Aptian sandstone: Lower Greensand
W = Weald clay
H = Hastings sand (with clayey beds) } Wealdian

Parisian outskirts, showed the composition of the Lower Cretaceous below Paris itself.[56] This well reached continental Wealdian (Valanginian-Hauterivian) containing impressions of ferns (*Lonchopteris*). Above is a completely continental complex of 45 m. of variegated clays and sands. The lower Aptian is marine, represented by 41 m. of marls with plicatulas, *Hoplites deshayesi,* and *Saynella rarefurcata.* Then comes the Albian, known long ago from the famous artesian wells of Grenelle, fed at 500 m. depth by a subterranean aquifer contained in the greensands at the base of the stage; the Gault clays keep this aquifer captive. The Aptian and Albian thus have here the same composition as in the eastern border of the Paris Basin and in the Pays de Bray.

Farther north, we again see Albian outcrops on the two banks of the Seine estuary, but there it is reduced to 5 m. of glauconitic, sandy clay, for here we approach the ancient Breton shore. The sediments corresponding to that ancient shore have, however, been destroyed or concealed by the Cenomanian transgression (Fig. 75). Nevertheless, very rare bits of the Albian are known east of Mans. So the sea extended from Brittany to the Ardennes and to the Massif Central.

D. The Lower Cretaceous in the Boulonnais and Southern England. Another anticline, cut in two by the present channel, shows Lower Cretaceous outcrops in the English Weald and in the Boulonnais in France. Not extensive in the Boulonnais, the outcrops of this formation are, on the contrary, very important in England.[57] They are principally soft clayey or sandy rocks, determining a natural lowland, the Weald, enclosed by two lines of chalk cliffs, the North Downs on the north, the South Downs on the south (Figs. 76 and 95).

The *Valanginian, Hauterivian* and *Barremian* stages are represented there by a thick series of continental beds, the Wealdian of British geologists, comprising at its base the Hastings sands (300 m.),[58] fluvial or deltaic lacustrine alluvium; at the top, the clays of the Weald (300 m.). The fauna is composed of paladinas, unios, cyclas, cyrenas, and large reptiles (remains of *Iguanodon* in the Hastings sandstones). This Wealdian is prolonged into the Boulonnais.[59] And under the chalk, the coal pits of the Franco-Belgian Basin have made possible its discovery there, directly overlying the Carboniferous limestone. And it is in a cavity of this limestone, filled with Wealdian sands and clays, that the famous iguanodons of Vernissart (between Mons and Tournai) were discovered, skeletons of which furnish a whole room in the Museum of Brussels.[60]

The *Aptian* marks the arrival of the sea. It begins in the Boulonnais with yellow sands containing trigonias, in England with the glauconitic sands and clays of Atherfield containing pelecypods (*Ostrea leymeriei, Panopaea neocomiensis*) with Barremian or Hauterivian affinities. But *Hoplites deshayesi* is found in its lower part, proving the Aptian age of these clays.[61] Then come sediments generally sandy and glauconitic, well characterized by their fauna: *Hoplites deshayesi, Plicatula placunea, Ostrea aquila.*[62]

The *Albian* is represented, in the Boulonnais and all of Britain, by thick blue clays (100 m.) known under the local name of Gault. They contain fine pyritic fossils in abundance, especially *Hoplites,* which can be collected loose on the beach of Wissant,[63] north of Boulogne. Opposite, the Folkestone cliffs show a famous natural section, where L. F. Spath (Proc. Geol. Ass., 37, 1926) has distinguished a whole series of ammonite zones, recently restudied by M. Breistroffer (work cited note 26, this chap.).

In northern France, the Albian is very widely transgressive and represented by very thin beds at the base of the *morts-terrains* which overlie the Franco-Belgian Coal Measures. Under its blue clay facies, it is found as far as the region of Douai, where P. Corsin and R. Dehée (Ann. Soc. géol. du Nord, 52, 1928, p. 300) have reported *Hoplites dentatus* from a mine pit. And to the Albian must be attributed the "Meule de Bracquegnies," a fauna rich in pelecypods and gastropods.[64]

On the edge of the English Primary Massif, the Albian crops out widely. Very transgressive, the lower stages are usually concealed, but at certain points it can be shown that the Aptian also is transgressive. At Farringdon

(Oxfordshire) ferruginous Aptian sands, lying directly on the Jurassic, contain a famous fauna of littoral, calcareous sponges (pharetrons).

Thus the British geologists usually distinguish three great divisions in their Lower Cretaceous: at the base, the *Wealdian* (Neocomian-Barremian), then the *Lower Greensand*[65] (Aptian) and finally the *Gault clay* (Albian).

The morphology of the Weald (see Fig. 95) is then easily explained. South of the chalky cliff of the North Downs, comes a depression filled with Gault clay; the Lower Greensand forms a second rampart which rises to 300 m. altitude, culminating point of the whole region; farther south a new depression corresponds to the clays of the Weald; the Hastings sand, with thin clayey intercalations, constitutes the wooded relief of the central part (Forest of the Weald). On the southern slope, the Lower Greensand escarpment has lost its importance, so that the two depressions which enclose it are combined in a wide, low plain, the Southern Valley.

As Fig. 96 shows, the marine influences were felt later and later as we go from the Vocontian trough up to the Boulonnais. The transgression then clearly comes from the south, from the Alpine sea. On the other hand, the northern forms that we pointed out (p. 332) in the Portlandian of the Boulonnais reveal the proximity of a northern sea. This is the Northern basin whose history in the Lower Cretaceous we shall now study.

3. *The Lower Cretaceous of the Northern Basin*

At the end of the Jurassic and the beginning of the Cretaceous, an epicontinental sea must have existed in northern Europe, covering all the northern part of the North Atlantic continent. Most of its deposits must be hidden now under the North Sea and the Arctic Ocean,[66] for we no longer find the Lower Cretaceous which was deposited in it, except in three regions:

1st. Northern England (Yorkshire and Lincolnshire). This area was occupied by a gulf coming from the north, between the Scandinavian Massif [67] and the English Primary Massifs and including the present location of the North Sea. In the Aptian, this gulf communicated with the Mediterranean seas through the Anglo-Parisian Basin.

2nd. Northern Germany. From this Cretaceous North Sea, a lateral gulf must have extended toward the east, between the Scandinavian Massif and the ancient massifs of central Europe (Rhenish Massif, Bohemia).

3rd. Russia. Lastly another great gulf, whose vicissitudes we shall study, covered Russia between the Urals and the Baltic countries.

The unity of this northern basin, present evidence of which is very discontinuous, as we have seen, is proven by the similarity of faunas and their contrast, already noted, to the Mediterranean faunas. The Neocomian is characterized by *Polyptychites, Craspedites, Garnieria,*[68] the Barremian by *Simbirskites.* In the Aptian the fauna loses its individuality. Finally, the absence of reefs and the presence of *Aucella* and *Cylindroteuthis,* to the exclusion of *Belemnopsis,* complete the characterization of this northern province.

A. Northern England (York and Lincoln): the Speeton Section. In York-

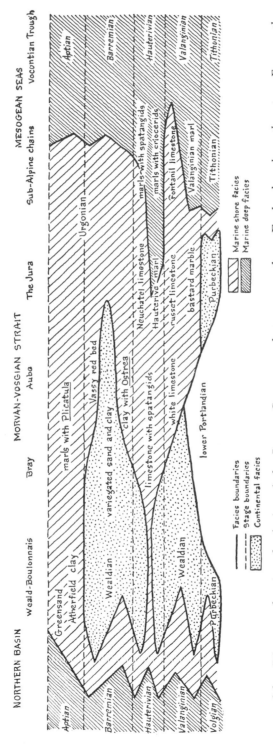

FIG. 96. *Diagram showing the facies of the Lower Cretaceous between northern England and southeastern France, the infra-Cretaceous transgression, and the establishment of communication between the Northern Basin and the Mesogean seas.*

N. B. Such communication has been incorrectly indicated in the Hauterivian; actually the Wealdian is entirely continental.

414

shire and Lincolnshire, the Lower Cretaceous is usually hidden; a single fine section may be seen in the cliffs of Speeton (see p. 342). The whole Lower Cretaceous is represented by the famous Speeton clays, in which the faunas alone distinguish the stages.[69]

The *Valanginian* and *Hauterivian* there have only a northern fauna, with *Polyptychites* and *Cylindroteuthis*. In fact no communication could have existed with the Mediterranean seas since the marine Neocomian is missing in the northern part of the Paris Basin.

The *Barremian* is well identified by its *Simbirskites,* a typical genus of the Russian faunas.

Finally, with the *Aptian,* the arm of the Parisian sea established communication with the seas of southern Europe for at Speeton we find *Hoplites deshayesi* and *Belemnopsis* associated with *Cylindroteuthis.*

And the Albian even more definitely has its customary facies, described in southern England.

Thus the paleogeographic conclusions reached by study of the faunas are in perfect accord with those deduced from the distribution of the facies of sediments. This is a remarkable example of stratigraphic synthesis (Fig. 96).

B. Northern Germany (Hils); Denmark, Poland. The most extensive and most interesting outcrops of the Lower Cretaceous in the German gulf are found in Hanover and especially in the hills of Hils (see map, Fig. 28). This is the location of the deepest part of this ancient gulf and the Lower Cretaceous is extremely thick.[70] Nevertheless, the marine facies does not start, as at Speeton, from the base of the Cretaceous. Over the Purbeckian, indeed, come sands with Wealdian facies and it is only above that the Hils clays (300 m.), comparable to the upper part of the Speeton clays, begin. There again, the faunas are very rich (Hildesheim localities) and make subdivision possible, more than thirty zones of ammonites or belemnites according to Stolley.[71]

The base of these Hils clays, marking the arrival of the sea,[72] corresponds to the upper Valanginian distinguished by its *Garnieria* and *Polyptychites.* Then come the Hauterivian with *Hoplites radiatus* and the Barremian with *Simbirskites.* The top of the clays, with *Oppelia nisus* and *Hoplites deshayesi,* thus contains the cosmopolitan fauna of the Aptian. The Albian[73] has its customary clayey facies, at least in the north, but toward the south in the region of Hildesheim-Braunschweig, the clays pass laterally to sands and sandstones, indicating the approach of ancient shores.

This German gulf extends far northward, for clays analogous to those of Hils are found on the Island of Helgoland, while northeast of this island, in Jutland (Denmark),[74] sandstones indicate the approach of old Scandinavian shores. The southern shore is indicated in the same way, on the edge of the Harz, by conglomerates and sandstones with *Toxaster retusus,* brachiopods and pelecypods.[75]

Toward the east, between the Harz and Schleswig-Holstein, an emerged zone must have existed in the Lower Cretaceous, over which the Albian was transgressive. This is Pompeckj's[76] threshold. In fact, the facies and faunas in the eastern part of northern Germany are not the same as in the west. Here we enter into a domain which, according to Lewinski, communicated with the Russian seas, perhaps beginning with the Valanginian. For this author has recently discovered at Tomaszow (100 km. SW of Warsaw) Valanginian faunas containing a mixture of northern and Mediterranean forms (*Garnieria, Hoplites neocomiensis, Saynoceras verrucosum*, etc.).[77]

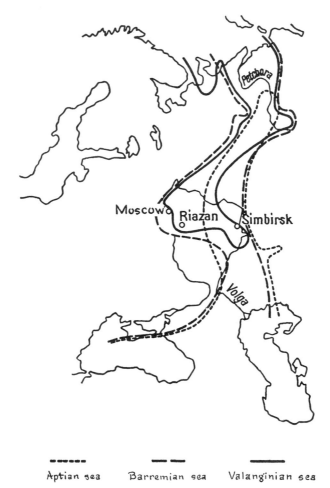

Aptian sea   Barremian sea   Valanginian sea

FIG. 97.   *Map of the Lower Cretaceous seas in central Russia (after Pavlov).*

He concludes that this must have been a region of junction between the Russian, German, and Mediterranean seas (through the Carpathians).[78]

C. The Lower Cretaceous in Russia.   The history of the Russian gulf is more varied. It may be subdivided for convenience into three principal groups of outcrops: the region of Pechora in the north, of Moscow-Riazan in the east and of Simbirsk at the southeast.

According to Pavlov the *Valanginian* is missing west of Moscow[79] and east of Simbirsk. On the other hand, in Pechora and at Riazan, it is represented by glauconitic sandstones with phosphatic nodules and with the characteristic northern fauna. Thus, the sea formed a gulf closed toward the south (?).

The *Hauterivian* seems to be missing everywhere (except, of course, in the Mesogean zones of Crimea and the Caucasus). The sea had left central Russia.

The Russian *Barremian* (Simbirskian) has its type at Simbirsk. The black clays abound with *Simbirskites*. At Moscow, nearer the ancient shore, there are ferruginous sandstones. This is the period of the greatest extent of the infra-Cretaceous sea. One arm of the sea, coming from the Arctic Ocean, in the vicinity of Pechora, covered all Russia between Moscow and Simbirsk and connected in the south, through Crimea and the Caucasus, with the Mediterranean seas.

The *Aptian,* in its turn, marks a great change. There are sands and clays with the usual cosmopolitan fauna (*Hoplites deshayesi,* etc.). The arm of the sea is transformed into a comparatively narrow gulf (at Moscow, there are already subcontinental facies), open to the south. This is the inverse of conditions in the Valanginian.

The *Albian,* often destroyed or hidden by the Cenomanian transgression, is in the form of glauconitic sandstones with phosphatized fossils. The sea, covering all of southern Russia, joined the German sea through Poland.

At this epoch, the ancient arm of the Russian sea, which since the Volgian had extended in a southern direction, was replaced by a trough in the equatorial direction.

But on the whole, this Lower Cretaceous does not exceed 50 to 60 m. in the center of the Russian platform and only reaches 300 to 350 m. on the lower Volga and in the vicinity of the Emba. It is a typical domain of a continental area, in contrast to the geosynclinal series of the Caucasus, 3,000 m. thick.

IV. The Upper Cretaceous in the Typical European Regions

1. *The Upper Cretaceous in the Paris Basin*

We shall see that, in the Upper Cretaceous, the Paris Basin must have communicated widely with the Alpine sea, through the Jura Mountains and the Morvano-Vosgian strait, though cold currents coming from the north prevailed there and brought belemnitellid faunas into the sub-Alpine chains.

Thus it is perforce by the west and southwest that communications were established with the warm seas that covered the Atlantic and had advanced as far as the northern part of the Aquitaine Basin, in the Charentes. In the lower Cenomanian, according to Abrard,[80] the sea had not yet inundated the Strait of Poitou and the orbitolines, which are found at this period in the southwestern part of the Paris Basin, had not reached there by way of

Aquitaine through this strait, but by circling the emerged Armorican Massif, through the English Channel. In fact, these southern forms are found in Cotentin and southern England. But, beginning with the upper Cenomanian, the Strait of Poitou broke through, and up to and including the Santonian, it was through this strait that these southern forms moved into the south-west Paris Basin. In the Campanian, on the other hand, the direction of these migrations was reversed, and echinoids from the Paris Basin (*Ananchytes, Micraster*), and even rare belemnitellids, appeared in the Charentes, from which rudistids were then retreating. Finally, in the Maestrichtian, these exchanges seem to have been made exclusively through the English Channel, allowing Mediterranean orbitoids to travel as far as Maastricht.

A. Cenomanian. The facies, quite varied, can be grouped as follows:[81]

1. *Sandy facies with orbitolines.* This transgression facies is found at the entrance of the Strait of Poitou and it is at Mans that the type of the stage is taken, because of its wealth of fossils. We see there, lying directly over the Jurassic, the following succession of beds, from bottom to top: a) glauconitic clays and sands with *Schlönbachia varians, Orbitolina concava,* etc.; b) Sands of Maine, with *Acanthoceras rothomagense,* echinoids and numerous mollusks. The upper part of these sands, coarser and brightly colored, is sometimes called the Perche sands; c) Sandy marls with oysters (*Ostrea columba, O. flabellata, O. biauricularis,* etc.) and rudistids (*Caprotina, Praeradiolites*).

This almost exclusively sandy facies continues as far as the Loire valley and through Brittany to the Cotentin, where bits of glauconitic sandstone containing *Orbitolina concava* and *Ostrea columba* lie directly on the Primary.

2. *Facies of glauconitic chalk.* When, toward the center of the Basin, we advance toward the northeast, glauconitic, calcareous facies are gradually substituted for the sands. So we reach the classic type realized at Rouen, where the section of the cliffs of Cap de la Hève has been used to define the stage of glauconitic chalk of the early authors. We have there, from bottom to top: a) *gaize* with *Mortoniceras inflatum,* containing a transition fauna from the Albian to the Cenomanian; b) more or less glauconitic, calcareous beds with *Acanthoceras mantelli;* c) true glauconitic chalk with *Acanthoceras rothomagense* or Rouen chalk (old Rothomagian stage), especially typical at the Côte Ste-Catherine near Rouen.

3. *Deep-water marly facies of the Aube and the Yonne.* The glauconite of the Cenomanian of Rouen still shows the distant influence of the Breton shores; because, as we push farther toward the southeast, we see this glauconite diminish little by little. Finally we pass into a deep-water marly-calcareous type well developed in the Aube and Yonne districts (for example, vicinity of St. Florentin). The base, called the marls of Brienne on the Aube, becomes transitional between the Gault clays and the chalk, and contains *Mortoniceras inflatum.* Above come marly chalks with *Acanthoceras mantelli* and *A. rothomagense.*

Similar facies are seen in the Pays de Bray and the Boulonnais, where the Cenomanian is worked for the manufacture of the so-called Boulogne cements. Thus, as in the Albian, the Yonne-Bray-Boulonnais line corresponds to the deepest channel of the Paris Basin at this epoch.

4. *Littoral facies of the northwest border.* Like the Breton shore, the shore of the Ardennes shows littoral transgressive facies. In the southern part of the Ardennes where the Cenomanian overlies the Albian, we already know that its base is composed of the top of the *gaize* with *Mortoniceras rostratum.* Above come glauconitic marly sands. In the north, and especially in the region of the Franco-Belgian coal pits, it is usually the Cenomanian which forms the base of the horizontal *morts-terrains* overlying the ancient Hercynian Massif. It is in the form of glauconitic conglomerates with *Acanthoceras mantelli* and *A. rothomagense.*[82] This is the *tourtia* of the miners, thus located at the base of the chalk and above the bits of transgressive Albian that are sometimes preserved there, as we have seen.[83]

B. Turonian. The contours of the sea hardly changed between the Cenomanian and the Turonian. So, in this slack sea, so to speak, the facies are quite uniform. We shall be satisfied to distinguish two types:

1. *Touraine type.* Touraine is used to name the stage and there, in fact, facing the Strait of Poitou, the Turonian is represented by facies more detrital than elsewhere, with richer faunas, indicating currents coming from the south.

The base is still sandy; then comes a marly zone with *Inoceramus labiatus,* overlain by the principal member, the tuffeau of Touraine. This is a micaceous, grainy chalk, somewhat organic and detrital, forming a sort of calcareous molasse, soft, easy to dress and hardening in the open air. Some troglodyte villages were developed in it, and it is this rock that has been used to build most of the chateaus of the Loire. At the top rudistids are found again, having migrated from Aquitaine.

These sandy and *tuffeau* facies are found all along the Breton Massif.

2. *Marly chalk type.* Everywhere else in the Paris Basin, the Turonian is composed of marly chalk, the type of which can be taken at Rouen (Côte Ste-Catherine). It begins with a bank filled with *Belemnitella plena* which serves to mark its contact with the Cenomanian when the latter (as in Yonne) also has a marly chalk facies. Then comes a lower zone with *Inoceramus labiatus* and an upper with *Holaster planus,* subdivisions having, of course, only empirical value.

In some places in Flanders where the Turonian is slightly transgressive,[84] the lower beds with *B. plena* become glauconitic.

C. Senonian. It is in the Senonian that the white chalk-with-flints facies, in all its purity, is realized. The broad sea which occupied the Paris Basin must have been bordered by continents with reduced relief, and must have been little agitated by currents, for pelagic sedimentation prevailed over detrital sedimentation.

This chalk occupies large areas in the Paris Basin. But, uncovered at different places since the beginning of the Tertiary, its surface has been altered by atmospheric agencies. The result of this alteration forms what we call clay with flints.[85] When this clayey covering has been preserved, it makes for the chalk country a rather impermeable, wet, sometimes very fertile soil, especially in the north and northwest regions of the Basin.[86] But, where this covering is missing, we then have a chalky, permeable soil, without surface streams, from which scanty brush disappears only to make way for a few pine groves and especially extensive and monotonous cultivation of grain. This is the typical aspect of the Barren Champagne, which encircles the whole basin on the southeast, between the humid Champagne of the Lower Cretaceous and the Tertiary Ile-de-France (Fig. 70).

The stratigraphy of this chalk could hardly be determined without the aid of fossils. *Micraster and Belemnitella* permit the recognition of the four substages indicated on p. 392, while ammonites are rare. The famous outcrop of Meudon chalk in the outskirts of Paris (see Fig. 112) where *Belemnitella mucronata* is found, belongs then to the Maestrichtian.[87]

The marine domain shrinks greatly from the end of the Emscherian. In the Aturian, it is reduced to an elongated gulf, extending as far as Rouen, Orléans and Sens and opening on the North Sea through the region of Lille.[88] The extreme top of the Maestrichtian, as well as the Danian, is always missing (see reservations made on p. 474).

The only modifications of facies at all notable are the following:

1. *Touraine.* As in the Turonian, the influence of ancient Breton shores is felt here. The chalk is more detrital and consequently richer in fossils, with oysters, ornate ammonites, echinoids and even rudistids coming through the strait of Poitou, while belemnites are missing. Such is the chalk of Villedieu (village located north of Tours and southeast of Vendôme). Farther west, there are even sandy facies.

2. *Cotentin.* There was a local transgression here which brought the Maestrichtian directly upon the Primary formations. It is represented by the famous chalk with baculites, quite thin (15–20 m.), but extremely fossiliferous. Farther west, a minute and isolated remnant of Senonian limestone, recently discovered at Roscoff (Finistère) by J. Bourcart (C. R. Soc. géol. France, Nov. 19, 1945) has proved that the Cretaceous Channel must have encroached fairly widely on the old Armorican Massif.

3. *Northeast edge; Belgium and Holland.* Even on the Somme indications of littoral facies appear. These are the horizons of phosphatized chalk whose residues, collected in pockets of decalcification, have been the origin of outstanding but short-lived exploitations of Picardy phosphates. The western part of the Ardennes was submerged, but the sea was not deep. There are glauconitic, neritic facies, intercalations of conglomerates, and lacunas.[89] In the northeast, in Limbourg, the Campanian lies directly on the Primary. There the famous Maastricht *tuffeau* is found, a detrital, very fossiliferous chalk, with many bryozoans and coastal brachiopods (*Thecidea radiata*) and orbitoids.[90] This is the type of the Maestrichtian stage and the source of the famous *Mosasaurus* skull studied by Cuvier.

The wells of Campine (see note 18, chap. 6) have given information on the extent of the Upper Cretaceous seas in Holland. The sea which covered, as we shall see, a part of eastern Britain, the North Sea and Holland, sent gulfs into the emerged regions of the Ardennes and the Rhenish Massif. One of these gulfs, that of Campine, was bounded on the south by the Massif of Brabant and on the north by a promontory occupying the northern part of Dutch Limbourg and the northeastern part of Belgian Limbourg.

2. *The Upper Cretaceous in Northern Europe*

A. Britain. The Upper Cretaceous here is quite analogous to that of the Paris Basin.[91]

Cenomanian. This is the Lower Chalk of the British, in which the following subdivisions are identified, from bottom to top:

1st. Upper Greensand, or glauconitic sandstone of Cambridge.[92]

2nd. Chloritic marl, or glauconitic chalk with *Acanthoceras mantelli, Schloenbachia varians.*

3rd. Chalk marl and gray chalk, or marly chalk with *Acanthoceras rothomagense* and *Holaster subglobosus.*

Turonian. This is the Middle Chalk, with the same paleontologic divisions as in the Paris Basin:

1st. Lower zone with *Belemnitella plena.* British geologists generally attribute this zone to the Cenomanian because *Holaster subglobosus* is still found in it.

2nd. Zone with *Inoceramus labiatus* and *Rhynchonella cuvieri.*

3rd. Zone with *Inoceramus brongniarti.*

4th. Upper zone with *Holaster planus* and *Ananchytes gibbus,* sometimes joined to the Senonian.

Senonian or Upper Chalk. It is characterized approximately as in the Paris Basin, by the appearance of flints. The same paleontologic zones are distinguishable in it as in France.[93] The Senonian sea had certainly advanced far to the west, covering part of the North Atlantic continent, for the Senonian is known in Scotland and northeastern Ireland where it directly overlies the Primary.

The *Danian* is unknown in any part of Britain.

B. Germany, Denmark, Scania. The southern shore of the German sea was formed by the Rhenish and Bohemian Massifs (see p. 415). These regions, emerged since the end of the Jurassic, were locally covered with continental deposits containing a subtropical flora (called the *Credneria* flora). But they had been at least partially invaded beginning with the Cenomanian.[94] Their influence is shown by detrital, littoral deposits, so that we must distinguish two types of facies:

1. *The Deep-Water or Northern Type.*

a. *Cenomanian-Turonian.* These stages are represented by the formation called *Pläner,* contracted from Plauener Schichten or Plauen beds, near Dresden (see map, Fig. 28). These are well-bedded grayish, marly limestones, containing cephalopods, echinoids of muddy bottoms (spatangids), and very rare rudistids.[95] The best type of this facies is found in Hanover and Westphalia in the Münster Basin, included between the Rhenish Massif on the south and the Osning sill. It extends from southeast to northwest from the Eggegebirge as far as the region of Osnabrück. Numerous paleontologic zones have been identified in it.

1st. The *Lower Pläner,* equivalent to the Cenomanian, often begins with glauconitic sandstones with *Schloenbachia varians,* which are transgressive on the Coal Measures of Westphalia and so represent the exact equivalent of the *tourtia* of the Franco-Belgian miners. So, the Rhenish Massif was attacked by the sea on the northern slope as well as on the western. Above come two zones, one with *Holaster nodulosus* and another with *H. subglobosus* and *Acanthoceras rothomagense.*

2nd. The *Upper Pläner* corresponds to the Turonian, for it begins, as in France, with a bed containing *Belemnitella plena.* German geologists then distinguish in it a mass of zones characterized by *Inoceramus:* a zone with *I. labiatus* (*mytiloides*) or "Mytiloides-Pläner," a zone with *I. lamarcki* (*brongniarti*) or "Brongniarti-Pläner," a zone with *Scaphites* or "Scaphiten-Pläner," a zone with *I. schloenbachi* (*cuvieri*) or "Cuvieri-Pläner."

b. *Senonian.* The true white chalk with flints is found only in Pomerania, Denmark and the Baltic islands. In the classic regions of Westphalia and Hanover, the facies are a little different.

The Coniacian is represented by the *Emscher-Mergel* or simply *Emscher,* deep-water gray marls with cephalopods, well developed (330 m.) in the valley of the Emscher, a tributary of the Rhine in Westphalia north of the Ruhr, in which two *Inoceramus* zones are distinguished. It is only above this that German geologists begin their Senonian, which has the shallower-water facies of sandy marls or sandstones and whose subdivision is very difficult. The Santonian corresponds to the chalk with *Marsupites* or Granulatenkreide (chalk with *Gonioteuthis granulata*). The Campanian is the Quadratenkreide with *Belemnitella quadrata;* there are many siliceous sponges (*Coeloptychium*) and ammonites, here on the point of disappearing and reaching their maximum size (*Parapachydiscus* 2.5 m. in diameter). The Mucronatenkreide, with *Belemnitella mucronata,* corresponds to the Maestrichtian.

In the vicinity of Brunswick, north of the Harz, that is in the Cretaceous sub-Hercynian syncline, G. Beck (see note 72, this chap.) presented evidence for a transgression which, beginning with the top of the Emscher, advances toward the east and reaches its maximum in the Maestrichtian, still marly at Brunswick, but already sandy farther east, along the valley of the Aller.

c. *Danian.* In Denmark and Scania, above the Maestrichtian chalk and separated from it by a small break in sedimentation, we see fossiliferous beds with a special fauna, which is made the type of the Danian stage. The best known example is the organic limestone (bryozoans, etc.) of Faxe, exploited in great quarries south of Copenhagen. Ammonites, belemnitids and *Inoceramus* are no longer found in it, but certain forms which are present have an appearance Cretaceous rather than Tertiary: *Holaster, Ananchytes, Ostrea vesicularis, Crania ignabergensis* (a Maastricht species). A characteristic species is *Nautilus danicus,* which is found elsewhere at the same horizon.

This Danian of Denmark[96] is, however, overlain in discontinuity by greensands and Tertiary marls (Montian). Here then, in this central part of the Cretaceous North Sea, there was only a brief break in sedimentation at the boundary between the Secondary and the Tertiary.

In Germany, on the contrary, even in northern Germany (Pomerania and wells in Berlin), the Danian is missing.

2. *Sandy or Southern Type.* This is represented by a sandstone called the Quadersandstein, because of its tendency to break up in parallelepiped masses. These are littoral sediments, with cross stratification, beach or dune sands. Their age has been established in limited regions where they pass intricately into the Pläner facies.

These sandstones are especially developed in Bohemia and Saxony,[97] where they constitute a natural region, the Saxon Switzerland (Fig. 28), with its picturesque landscapes, corrugated cliffs, plateaus gashed with steep gorges, the perfect type of sandstone relief. The materials of these sandstones were evidently produced by the destruction of the crystalline rocks of the Bohemian Massif.[98]

In Bohemia, these Quadersandsteine rise no higher than the Coniacian. To find more recent Senonian beds, sandy or lignitic, we must return to a more northern zone, in Silesia or the edge of the Harz.

C. Russia. An arm of the German sea passed south of the Finnish-Scandinavian Massif and extended into central Russia, where the same succession of formations is found, with a glauconitic facies at the base[99] and then a marly or chalky facies. The thickness of the Upper Cretaceous may reach 600 m.

But the Russian sea was closed toward the north, thus continuing the regime established in the Aptian. On the other hand, it opened at the south, through the Caucasus into the Mediterranean seas.

3. The Upper Cretaceous of the French Mediterranean Regions

In the Aquitaine Basin, the Pyrenees and Provence, the Upper Cretaceous shows a very different fauna from those we have studied in the northern countries. Belemnitellas become extremely rare,[100] but on the other hand, there are rudistids, orbitolines, corals and reef hydrozoans (stromatoporids, etc.), many echinoids and special pelecypods, the ammonites alone remaining about the same.

This shows that these faunal differences, leading to the contrast between a tropical Mediterranean zone and a northern zone can scarcely be due to geographic isolation. In fact, we already know that broad communications existed between the two provinces, beginning with the Aptian and Albian. It is more probable that climate is the principal cause of the differentiation, for the characteristic animals of the Mediterranean province are reef building organisms, precisely analogous to the present day species that are peculiar to warm seas.

A. Northern Border of Aquitaine. In the whole center of the Basin of Aquitaine, the Cretaceous is concealed under Tertiary deposits and it appears only on the northern border, against the Armorican Massif and the Massif

Central, and on the southern border, in the Pyrenees, a folded chain which we shall study by itself.

On the northern border, the Lower Cretaceous is unknown. The transgression began only with the Cenomanian; it opened the Strait of Poitou in the Turonian[101] and still continued in the Upper Cretaceous, so that the Cenomanian and Turonian, hidden under the Senonian, have only very restricted

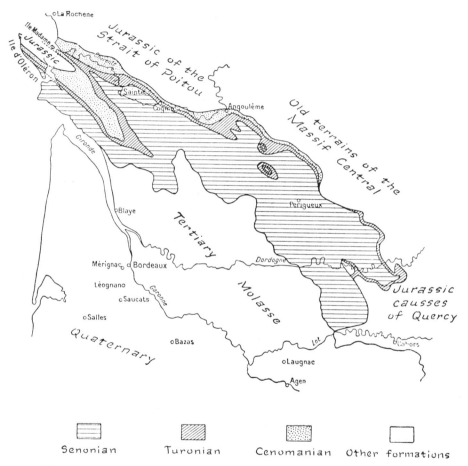

FIG. 98.   *Diagrammatic geologic map indicating the outcrops of the Upper Cretaceous in northern Aquitaine.*

outcrops. They form first a thin border along the valley of the Charente, between La Rochelle and Angoulême, then reappear a little farther south, brought up by a NW-SE anticline, which, starting from the Island of Oléron separates the Gironde from the Charente valley (see Fig. 98).

Cenomanian.   The base, marking the beginning of the transgression, is still very littoral; sands with lignitic clays and pieces of amber. *Acanthoceras rothomagense* and *Schloenbachia varians* well date the arrival of the sea. Above comes the first limestone with rudistids, containing *Ichthyosarcolithes,*

Praeradiolites and *Caprina.* Then there are sands identical to the Maine sands, with the same oyster fauna. A second rudistid horizon ends the stage.

The transgression came from the present location of the Atlantic, for by degrees as we proceed southeast, the facies become more littoral and lignites develop. Near the present coast, however, the facies are more marly and of deeper-water. There, the famous Cenomanian reef of zonatelles (bryozoans formerly considered stromatoporids) of the Ile Madame is found.

Turonian. The base (Ligerian sub-stage) represented by marly limestones with *Inoceramus labiatus,* corresponds to the maximum depth of the sea. Above, in fact, (Angoumian sub-stage) come rudistid limestones in which the first hippurites and radiolites appear. A slight lacuna even exists between the Turonian and Senonian.

Senonian. A new transgression brings the sea as far as the Lot valley, so the Senonian covers large areas in northern Aquitaine.

There is no chalk facies here, but more or less sandy or organic limestones with frequent intercalations of rudistid horizons, making true reefs. The fossils are very numerous and the Coniacian, Santonian, and Campanian stages are defined by them. The Maestrichtian was there called the Dordonian (from the Dordogne River).[102]

But the Danian is missing, as well as the base of the Tertiary.

B. The North Slope of the Pyrenees. North of the Primary axis of the Pyrenees lies a basin called the North Pyrenean, whose northern edge, hidden under the Tertiary, is unknown (see note 165, chap. 7).

L. Bertrand believed in the existence of an ancient crystalline threshold, prolonging to the west, beneath the Tertiary, the Primary massif of Monthoumet, isolated between the Pyrenees and the Massif Central. And in fact, oil wells recently completed north of St. Gaudens, in the Gensac and Aurignac anticlines (Petit-Pyrénées) have reached an Upper Cretaceous with deltaic facies, indicating the approach of a shore line.[103]

Indeed, in this North-Pyrenean Basin, the Upper Jurassic and the base of the Cretaceous are missing. The sea did not return until the Aptian. All along the first Pyrenean foothills, from the Basque country to the Corbières, limestones with coral facies, on a very reduced scale, play a role similar to that of the Urgonian limestones of the sub-Alpine chains. So they are called the Urgo-Aptian limestones. They contain special rudistids (*Polyconites verneuli, Toucasia santanderensis*) and their Aptian age can be demonstrated in the Corbières, while farther west they are completely recrystallized and generally no longer contain determinable fossils. Finally, in the western Pyrenees (Béarn, Bigorre) they pass into more sandy facies.[104]

The maximum depth corresponds to thick, black marls with very rare ammonites that are usually attributed to the Albian. Their outcrops are especially developed in the eastern Pyrenees (great syncline of the Agly valley), producing fertile soils and landscapes with smooth, monotonous relief.

During this time, the Pyrenean axial Primary zone remained more or less completely emergent. In the western Pyrenees, Dubar[105] saw Urgo-Aptian limestones, beginning with basal conglomerates directly overlying the Triassic or the Jurassic, while farther south appear conglomeratic series formerly attributed to the Permian. Such are the Mendibelza conglomerates[106] containing *Orbitolina subconcava,* in the Basque country. They seem to begin in the Aptian or Albian and extend into the Cenomanian. This Cenomanian transgression must have covered a large part of the Pyrenean axial zone. Likewise, farther west, in the mountains of Bagnères-de-Luchon, Dalloni[107] recognized the Cenomanian age of a thick series of sandstones and conglomerates formerly classified as Devonian, while in the same region but farther north and

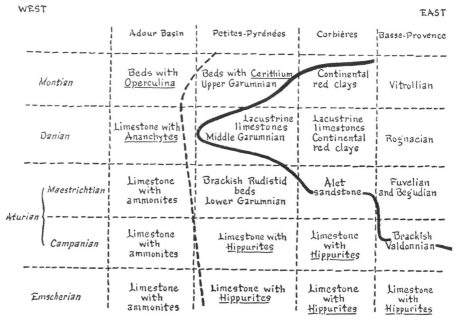

WEST   EAST

	Adour Basin	Petites-Pyrénées	Corbières	Basse-Provence
Montian	Beds with Operculina	Beds with Cerithium Upper Garumnian	Continental red clays	Vitrollian
Danian	Limestone with Ananchytes	Lacustrine limestones Middle Garumnian	Lacustrine limestones Continental red clays	Rognacian
Aturian { Maestrichtian	Limestone with ammonites	Brackish Rudistid beds Lower Garumnian	Alet sandstone	Fuvelian and Begudian
Aturian { Campanian	Limestone with ammonites	Limestone with Hippurites	Limestone with Hippurites	Brackish Valdonnian
Emscherian	Limestone with ammonites	Limestone with Hippurites	Limestone with Hippurites	Limestone with Hippurites

FIG. 99. *Diagram showing the facies of the Upper Cretaceous in the Provençal north-Pyrenean gulf and the regression at the Cretaceous-Tertiary boundary (compare with Fig. 124).*

The broken line indicates the limit of the deep-water marine facies of the Aturian gulf (at the left) and the marine shore facies (at the right).

The heavy line separates the marine shore facies (at the left) from the lacustrine or continental facies (at the right).

thus farther from the shore zone, shales formerly attributed to the Silurian are, in fact, Cenomanian.[108]

Still farther north, in the central region of the North Pyrenean Basin, the Albian black marls are followed by thick sandy-shaly or shaly-calcareous series with conglomerate banks. This is the Pyrenean Cretaceous Flysch, which, as L. Bertrand has pointed out, plays in the history of the Pyrenees, a pre-Oligocene chain, a role completely analogous to that of the Eocene Alpine Flysch in the history of the Alps, a post-Oligocene chain. Reaching a thickness of more than 1,500 m., this Cretaceous Flysch was accumulated in a basin in process of sinking,[109] but in the middle of which, narrow cordilleras[110] were rising, with crests more or less emerged, along which breccias comparable to the Alpine Wildflysch were deposited. Formerly confused with mylonites (tectonic breccias), they show fine outcrops in the cliffs of the Basque slope (Hendaye, Bidart).[111] And such Cenomanian breccias, reached by wells, contain combustible gas, exploited north of St. Gaudens.

South of Pau, this Flysch facies rises to the base of the Senonian.[112] But the whole of the Senonian of this region (departments of Basse-Pyrénées and Landes) has a more muddy and deeper-water facies, somewhat comparable to the calcareous Flysch of the Alps. These are marly limestones with fucoids and rare ammonites which served as the type of the Aturian stage (from Adour). These deep-water facies, at the same time, determine an important paleogeographic element, the Aturian gulf, broadly open to the Atlantic and whose distant extension we shall follow as far as Provence.

The sea did not withdraw from this gulf at the boundary between the Secondary and the Tertiary, which makes it interesting. Above the typical Aturian, we see, in fact, particularly in the Bidart cliff (south of Biarritz) and especially in the Tercis anticline (near Dax, see Fig. 123), marly or compact limestones, without ammonites, but containing *Ananchytes* and *Nautilus danicus*. This is the Danian. At Tercis, the upper banks even contain *Micraster tercensis,* a species sometimes considered characteristic of the Montian, base of the Tertiary. But in reality, according to J. Cuvillier,[113] a lacuna here separates the Cretaceous from a lower Eocene with nummulites, containing redeposited Cretaceous echinoids and pre-Danian rosalines.

To see a continuous series, we must go toward the southeast as far as the Petits-Pyrénées.

In this direction the closing of the Aturian gulf is especially interesting to study. In the Senonian, the arm of the north Pyrenean sea still extends as far as the Corbières (and perhaps, as we shall see, as far as Provence). It is indicated by very fossiliferous limestones with rudistids, where a stratigraphic scale of five successive zones with hippuritids was established. But the Maestrichtian, represented in Haute-Garonne by the top of the Flysch, Nankin limestone and Auzas marls, becomes sandy in the Corbières (Alet sandstone, south of Carcassonne). It still contains banks of crinoidal limestone at Villeveyrac,[114] north of Montpellier, while in Provence it is represented only by brackish facies.

But in the Danian the Aturian gulf is closed toward the east, and the sea must not have gone farther than the latitude of Toulouse. For south of that city, in the chain of the Petits-Pyrénées, at this horizon, transition beds to the Tertiary are found, for which early geologists, not knowing their exact horizon, made the Garumnian stage (from the Garonne). The lower Garumnian there includes beds with a brackish fauna but with intercalations of rudistid horizons. Because of these latter, it must belong to the upper Senonian. The middle Garumnian is represented by lacustrine limestones with indeterminable shells,[115] which can be considered Danian. In fact, the base of the upper Garumnian already contains a fauna with a Tertiary stamp (*Cerithium inopinatum,* etc.), identical to that of the typical Montian (see p. 489).

East of the Petits-Pyrénées, there is, above the Senonian, nothing but continental facies, connected with those we shall study in Provence.

C. The Basse-Provence Gulf.   The characteristic feature of the paleogeography of the Upper Cretaceous in the region of Provence is the existence of a Basse-Provence gulf, a concept which allows a rational grouping, according to E. Fallot, of all the complex stratigraphic facts studied in this area (see Fig. 100).[116]

This gulf, open to the west, was restricted to the south and east by the

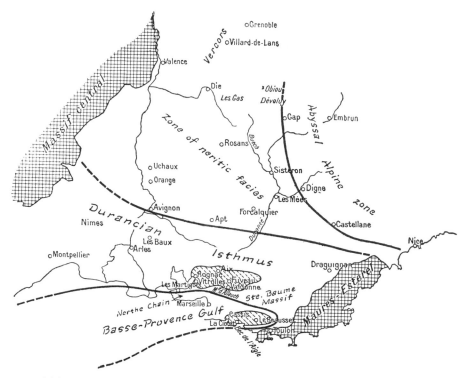

FIG. 100.   *Map of the paleogeographic units in the Upper Cretaceous in southeastern France (compare section, Fig. 101).*

The limits of the Durancian isthmus during the Cenomanian are indicated here; later, becoming larger, the isthmus was displaced toward the north.

ancient Maures Massif, and to the north by an emerged region which we shall call the isthmus of the lower Durance, separating our gulf from the Alpine sea. This Durancian isthmus was joined to the Maures by way of the Draguignan region, then extended over the lower Durance valley and the region of Aix-en-Provence. Through Nîmes and Languedoc it connected with the Massif Central.

The Maures Massif at that epoch must certainly have been prolonged toward the west, south of Toulon and Marseilles, and we may be tempted to assume that it joined the Pyrenees.[117] The Basse-Provence Gulf, however, would then be only the eastern extremity of the North Pyrenean Basin and in fact the history of the facies in these two regions leads to this conclusion.

The bauxites of the Durancian isthmus.[118]   This isthmus seems to have been most extensive after the Aptian. Everywhere in fact are Urgonian limestones deeply corroded and covered by bauxite (aluminum hydroxide) which certainly represents continental alteration products. This bauxite fills very irregular pockets in the subjacent limestones and its exploitation as aluminum ore is consequently often a risk venture.[119] The deposits are, in their turn, covered by marine or lacustrine sediments whose age is proportionately more recent (Cenomanian to Aturian) as we move nearer the axial region of the isthmus, that is, toward the north. There was, then, as we shall see, a transgression over the isthmus, a transgression coming from the south. Thus the bauxite, whose formation coincides with the phase of emergence, could not all be of exactly the same age.

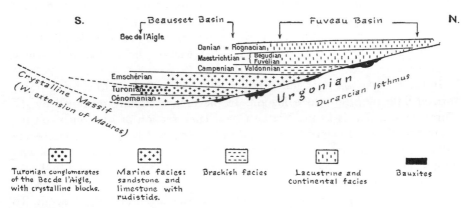

FIG. 101.   *Diagram of the facies of the Upper Cretaceous in Basse-Provence, showing the end of marine influences in the Basse Provence gulf and the transgression over the Durancian isthmus (after data from Collot; compare Fig. 100).*

These deposits make landmarks on the Durancian isthmus. The easternmost are found north of Toulon, from where they extend toward Allauch. The typical locality is the picturesque village of Baux, on the south slope of the Alpilles (east of Arles). And on the right bank of the Rhône they are found in the vicinity of Montpellier (Villeveyrac), on the Secondary border of the Massif Central.

The Transgression in the Gulf.   We have already seen (p. 403) that the gulf of Basse-Provence was outlined in the Albian, since the marine sediments of that epoch are localized in the Nerthe Chain, north of Marseilles, and consequently remain south of the already emerged Durancian isthmus.

The *Cenomanian*[120] begins there and is widely transgressive toward the north and east. To the east, the sea covers all the synclinal Beausset Basin, on the circumference of which the Cenomanian forms a continuous girdle from Cassis to north of Toulon. There, we have sandstones overlain by sandy limestones with orbitolines and rudistids (caprines, *Ichthyosarcolithes*)[121] with an intercalation of sands containing oysters, like those of Maine. But at the eastern end of this Beausset Basin, there are only sandy facies with oysters, overlying beds with a brackish fauna. Toward the north, the Cenomanian sea reaches the Allauch Massif, on the eastern extension of the Nerthe range, but it covers neither the Fuveau Basin nor the Ste. Baume Massif.

The *Turonian* covers approximately the same area. Its lower part, the Ligerian, is often composed of very thick, black marls (vicinity of Cassis). In the upper Turonian or Angoumian, sandstones or rudistid limestones predominate, in which, for the first time, as in Aquitaine, hippurites and radiolites appear. The beautiful cliffs of the Bec de l'Aigle, separating the bays of Cassis and La Ciotat, show a classic example of lateral variation of facies. In the northern part of this promontory the upper Turonian shows its normal facies with hippurites, while at the extreme southern point, the marine beds pass progressively, by intercalations, to torrential conglomerates with great blocks of crystalline rocks.[122] Thus we reach there the southern bank of our Basse-Provence gulf, bounded on the south by a crystalline massif, today largely sunk under the Mediterranean, the Maures being the sole visible evidence.

In the *Emscherian*, our gulf enlarges by transgression, before being transformed little by little into a lagoon. In the region already occupied by the Turonian sea, that is in the Nerthe Chain (fine section at Martigues, on the south bank of the Lake of Berre) and in the Beausset Basin, the Emscherian followed in continuity the Turonian rudistid limestones. The Coniacian and Santonian show very fine reefs of hippurites, sometimes surrounded by banks with remarkably well-preserved siliceous sponges,[123] and end with a bed of oysters (*Ostrea galloprovincialis*) which indicates a diminution of depth. To the north, expanding beyond the Cenomanian and Turonian, the Emscherian sea invaded the southern part of the Fuveau Basin. There, overlying the bauxite, are found Santonian limestones with hippurites.

The brackish facies of the end of the Cretaceous: Aturian and Danian.[124] Above the marine Santonian there is in fact nothing more than a thick series of brackish or lacustrine beds difficult to compare with normal marine stages and for which local names have been created.

There is first the *Valdonnian* (from Valdonne, south of Fuveau), lacustrine limestones or lignitic clays with brackish horizons with *Cyrena globosa* and *Melanopsis galloprovincialis*. This formation continues the northward movement of transgression. In fact, it invades the northern part of the Fuveau Basin where it directly overlies the bauxite. This Valdonnian corresponds approximately to the Campanian.

Next comes the *Fuvelian* (from Fuveau), then the Begudian (from La Bégude, 1 km. southwest of Fuveau), approximately equivalent to the Maestrichtian.[125] Both are developed especially in the Fuveau Basin, which they fill. The Fuvelian, reaching 500 m. thickness, is formed of marly limestones and lacustrine marls with lignites actively quarried. *Melanopsis galloprovincialis* persists but the cyrenes are replaced by *Unio galloprovincialis*. The rich vegetation which was the source of the lignites was that of tropical lakes, as is shown by the impressions of leaves of water lilies and palm trees.[126] Above, the Begudian is distinguished by a much more detrital continental facies, especially variegated gravelly sandstones with lively colors, containing intercalations of conglomerates or lacustrine limestones with *Lychnus* and *Physa galloprovincialis.*

The *Rognacian* (from Rognac) which overlies these beds at the west, is likewise composed of continental stream deposits, with lacustrine episodes. At the base are the red clays of Rognac, with remains of sauropod dinosaurs,[127] demonstrating that we are still in the Cretaceous. Then comes the bar of Rognac limestone, very compact, forming a cliff which dominates the Lake of Berre. This is the deposit with *Lychnus matheroni.* Thus the Rognacian approximately represents the Danian. In fact, in the bright red clays of Vitrolles (south of Rognac), above it, there are intercalated banks of lacustrine limestone with *Physa montensis,* a species of the Mons limestone, the type of the Montian, base of the Tertiary.

This Rognacian-Vitrollian series, with its red marl slopes and its cliffs of white, lacustrine limestone, constitutes a magnificent natural section that can be admired even from the railway in the vicinity of the Rognac station.

All this succession is progressively transgressive toward the north.

D. The Rhodanian Basin and the Sub-Alpine Chains. To the north, after having crossed the isthmus of the lower Durance, we enter into a different domain, which is tributary to the Alpine sea. As in the Lower Cretaceous, there must have been a deep sea, in the eastern part, bordered on the south and west, against the Maures-Esterel, the Durancian isthmus and the Massif Central, by a zone of coastal deposits, which, varied by numerous lacunas, extends from south of Castellane to the lower valley of the Rhône, then over the sub-Alpine chains to the Jura Mountains.

In the northern sub-Alpine chains, including Vercors and the Dévoluy, the Upper Cretaceous is a dependent of the northern province, for belemnitellas are found in it. But to the south, around the shoals of the Durancian isthmus, large orbitolines and rudistids characteristic of the tropical province begin to appear.

1. *Deep-water eastern zone.* Clear evidence of this is found only in the southern part of the Alps. There the deep-water facies begin near Nice and are prolonged through the region of Castellane as far as the vicinity of the upper Durance between Embrun and Sisteron. As for the Vocontian trough,[128] so marked in the Lower Cretaceous, it is progressively reduced. In the Turonian, it still outlines a small gulf, reaching Rosans in the west (Fig. 92); then it completely disappears.

Throughout this zone, there are uniformly deep-water and continuous sediments, but they are of little interest because of the rarity of fossils. Thus, in the Maritime Alps, the Cenomanian is represented by black marls, topped by the fairly compact limestone of the Turonian, producing a first small scarp. The Coniacian is a marly limestone with poorly preserved sponges. The Santonian is marked by a return of marly facies (blue marls). Finally the

Campanian is again limestone, sometimes a little marly (large quarries for cements and hydraulic limes in the vicinity of Nice), sometimes compact enough to rise in white cliffs. Above comes the transgressive Eocene.

Thus the Maestrichtian is missing, at least near Nice where the stratigraphy was determined by very rare echinoids and ammonites.[129]

2. *Southern and western coastal zone.*   Northeast of the deep-water zone of Nice we find, in Italian territory, in the autochthonous covering of the Mercantour, a littoral Upper Cretaceous, with hippurites. These are the famous deposits of the Argentera (or Larche) Pass, in the high valley of Stura di Cuneo.

As for the zone of littoral facies which borders the deep trough on the south, its sediments are found north of Maures and Esterel, from the region of Nice and Escragnolles (see Fig. 92) as far as south of Castellane. Cenomanian glauconitic sandstones there contain large orbitolines. Recently H. Parent [130] has studied at Cap Ferrat, east of Nice, the very rapid transition from these glauconitic neritic facies to the deep-water marly facies of the Alpine foredeep. And J. Goguel has pointed out, at Brenon south of Castellane, caprotines and radiolites together in Senomanian brackish beds.[131]

Still farther west, near Forcalquier-Apt, is a Cenomanian with large orbitolines and *Ichthyosarcolithes* (rudistids), studied by Ch. Jacob. In this valley of the Durance, the extreme northern limit of these southern orbitolines seems to be the station of Peyruis-les-Mées (south of Sisteron, personal observation).

Finally, in the lower valley of the Rhône, the Cenomanian-Emscherian stages are represented by particularly sandy deposits, sometimes several hundred meters thick, cut by frequent lacunas and brackish or lagoonal intercalations (lignites of Piolenc and Montdragon, north of Orange and Pont-Saint-Esprit, Gard),[132] but a few rudistid horizons are found. The Turonian sandstones of Uchaux, north of Orange,[133] are well known for their wealth of fine, silicified fossils. A very interesting occurrence of Turonian ammonites was recently described on the right bank of the Rhône, in Gard.[134] On the left bank, in Drôme, the stratigraphy of the Upper Cretaceous was recently revised by J. Sornay,[135] using as a guide-horizon, beds with quartz pebbles originating in the Massif Central and reaching as far as Drôme. He could thus identify, in the Dieulefit Basin, a Turonian hitherto misunderstood, represented by sandstones overlying thick white limestones containing flint and echinoids, formerly attributed to the Senonian.

Likewise, farther north, Turonian limestones girdle with an imposing scarp the famous perched syncline of the Forest of Saou, an isolated bastion on the left bank of the lower Drôme.

The Coniacian and the Santonian are represented only by very littoral facies with rudistids or lignite. Finally the Campanian and Maestrichtian are missing or are reduced to sands or refractory clays passing into the continental Eocene.

Thus ends the history of the Rhodanian Gulf, which, north of the Durancian isthmus, succeeded the Vocontian trough of the Lower Cretaceous.

Quite different is the picture presented by the northern sub-Alpine chains.

In the Dévoluy, a massif situated between Grenoble, Veynes and Gap, the Upper Cretaceous plays a most important role. The Senonian is transgressive there, upon a Jurassic or Lower Cretaceous folded sub-stratum ("pre-Senonian movements" of P. Lory) and it forms entire mountains; Obiou (2,793 m.) is the highest limestone summit of the French Alps. We have there several hundred meters of bryozoan limestone or sandy limestone in thin plaques, which, aided by drought and periodical use for pasturage, present an arid and desolate natural region, with great depressions ("Dévoluy"). The drainage appears only at the periphery, in the Vauclusian springs.

In Vercors,[136] Chartreuse and Bauges, the Upper Cretaceous forms only narrow, synclinal bands. The Cenomanian, coming from the Vocontian trough, continues as far as Fauge (near Villar-de-Lans, Vercors), where it is represented by white marly-sandy beds with *Schloenbachia varians*[137] overlying greensands containing *Discoides, Turrilites,* and *Mortoniceras inflatum* of Vraconian age. But elsewhere in Vercors and especially farther north, in Chartreuse and Bauges, the Gault is directly overlain by the Maestrichtian, which sea thus invaded the sub-Alpine chains just when it abandoned the lower valley of the Rhône.

These Senonian limestones, several hundred meters thick, rise in white cliffs above the verdant benches of the Albian. Their base, composed of well stratified banks (the *lauzes*), is quite variable, sometimes conglomeratic (gorges of Les Gas, east of Die, Fig. 100), sometimes sandy, with redeposited Albian fossils, sometimes marly and exploitable for hydraulic lime (Sassenage, near Grenoble); the higher limestones with flints are more massive. Fossils, always rare, are found especially in Chartreuse: belemnitelles, echinoids and ammonites, still incompletely studied. Without absolute proof, a general absence of the Turonian and even of the Campanian is assumed.

Still farther north, in the massifs of Bornes and Sixt, a Cenomanian represented by black, sandy marls is found under the Senonian.[138]

It is certain that these Upper Cretaceous seas must have covered the Jura Mountains. Minute strips of limestone with rosalines have been pointed out at Chésery, north of Bellegarde (Ain) and at Cuiseaux, 24 km. south-southwest of Lons-le-Saulnier.[139] Farther north, especially at Lake Narlay (28 km. east of Lons-le-Saulnier) and in the Rousses syncline, breccias or conglomerates, probably of Oligocene age, show pebbles or fragments of these rosaline limestones. Isolated blocks, containing orbitoids and a Cenomanian *Acanthoceras,* were discovered on the edges of Lake Bienne, in the Swiss Jura.[140] Finally flints from the chalk, scattered through clays of superficial alteration, have been found at different points in the southern Jura.[141] Even on the Morvan, silicified echinoids of the chalk (*Ananchytes*) are found.

These constitute so many proofs of an original covering of Upper Cretaceous which was an extension of the chalk of the Paris Basin through the Morvan-Vosgian strait.

V. The Cretaceous in the Western Alps

We have already described the Lower (p. 399) and Upper (p. 431) Cretaceous of the French sub-Alpine chains, classic regions which deserved detailed study, and which are joined, moreover, to Provence and the Jura Mountains. It now remains to follow northward this external zone of the Alps, where the Helvetic nappes and Prealpine massifs appear, that is, in Haute-Savoie and Switzerland. As to the internal (Pennine) zone, the Cretaceous is known particularly (but rather poorly) in the southern French Alps. Nevertheless, that is where we shall start for we shall there find interesting points of comparison with the Prealpine facies.

1. *The Cretaceous in the Internal Zone of the French Alps*

When we leave the sub-Alpine chains, where the Cretaceous plays so great a role, and enter the zone of the external, crystalline massifs, we naturally find no more Cretaceous outcrops. Nevertheless, between Pelvoux and Mercantour,[142] just under the brow of the Embrunais-Ubaye nappes, a few evidences of the Cretaceous are found in the ultra-Dauphinois scales of Ubaye and Gapençais (see p. 282 and Fig. 84), which constitute the eastern edge of the external zone. There the Lower Cretaceous remains deep-water but becomes relatively less thick and represented by a monotonous series of dark calcareous shales with belemnites and *Aptychus,* difficult to separate from the Malm and in which separate stages cannot be lithologically distinguished. This is the type of the "Neocomian with cephalopods" which we shall find in the ultra-Helvetic nappe in Switzerland. In this same ultra-Dauphinois zone, the Upper Cretaceous, formerly confused with Eocene Flysch, also remains deep-water, with thick series of calcareous shales and marly limestones with rosalines. Thus we approach the bottom of the Alpine fore-deep.

In the internal zone itself, the Lower Cretaceous long remained unknown.[143] In the most external (lower) scales of the sub-Briançonnais zone (see p. 355), it exists nevertheless (Durance valley, between Gap and Briançon) in the form of calcareous shales with beds of very rare shell-marbles with *Aptychus* and banks of micro-breccias, indicating a decrease in depth. And farther north, between the Arc and the Isère, in the massif of Perron des Encombres, R. Barbier[144] was recently able to identify a Lower Cretaceous represented by shales and micro-breccias with *Duvalia*[145] and *Aptychus* and by limestones with siliceous zones, beds formerly attributed to the Lias by W. Kilian. In the same way, the Upper Cretaceous is represented there by the type that we shall find in the Prealpine nappes under the name of "red beds." There are alternating calcareous shales, dark shales, sandstones with very rare *Inoceramus* and particularly red or green marly beds, rich in rosalines. All this indicates the approach of the Briançonnais cordillera (see p. 364).

In fact, in the most internal scales of the sub-Briançonnais zone and in the Briançonnais zone, the Lower Cretaceous is missing.[146] The cordillera must have been emerged at this epoch and the Upper Cretaceous, transgressive over the Trias or the Dogger, is represented by the formation long known as "plaquette marbles." These are in fact calcareous shales with a highly glazed and shiny surface, very thin banks of which have a marmoreal fracture and certain zones have bright red or green colors. The only characteristic fossils are rosalines. This soft formation presents gentle slopes or conical summits, gleaming pale and bright. It often begins with thick basal breccias, formerly attributed to the Lias.[147] Such are the breccias of La Madeleine, south of Guillestre, several tens of meters thick. They were attributed to the Jurassic by W. Kilian, but L. Moret discovered rosalines in their red cement.

Finally, approaching the Piedmont zone, these marbles in plaquettes become more and more metamorphic and are lost in the great mass of *schistes lustrés*. In the Vanoise Massif, E. Raguin discovered rosalines in the metamorphic calcareous schists themselves, formerly attributed to the Middle Triassic by P. Termier.[148]

2. The Cretaceous in the Swiss Alps (and Haute-Savoie)

North of Vanoise, absolutely nothing has been known, up to the present time, of the Cretaceous in the whole internal zone, east of the Pennine frontal overthrust, in Switzerland or in France. But recently[149] some Cretaceous foraminifera have been pointed out in Tarentaise at Villete north of Moutiers in the limestones of the sub-Briançonnais zone, which were formerly attributed to the Jurassic. And other similar discoveries may be hoped for.

But, on the other hand, the Cretaceous is very well known in the Prealpine and Helvetic nappes, where it is worthy of detailed study. In fact, by "unrolling" these nappes, that is to say replacing the zones of facies in the geographic order they occupied before the Alpine folding, it is demonstrated that the different facies of the Cretaceous followed each other in coherent order, which will present a magnificent example of a synthesis both stratigraphic and tectonic.

A. Autochthon and the Helvetic Nappes. All these stages assume proportionately deeper-water facies as we reach the higher nappes, or, what amounts to the same thing, the more southern zones. Thus we pass from an almost Jura Mountains type (realized in the autochthonous covering of the massif of Aiguilles-Rouges, in the vicinity of St. Maurice, Valais and that of the Aar Massif) to a mixed type similar to that of the French sub-Alpine chains, then to a deep, almost Vocontian or ultra-Dauphinois type.

Thus (Fig. 102) the *Valanginian* is reduced in the autochthon to organic limestones (limestones of Oehrli, top of the Säntis chain), recalling the bastard marble of the Jura Mountains, overlain by spathic limestones (Echinodermen-Breccia) equivalent to the Fontanil limestone. Toward the south, these limestones gradually disappear, to be replaced by two marly masses, the lower of which (Oehrli marl) can be compared to the Berriasian limestones, while the upper represents the Valanginian marls proper.

The *Hauterivian* which, in the lower nappes, is composed of limestones with flints, recalling, although more littoral, the spatangid marls of the French sub-

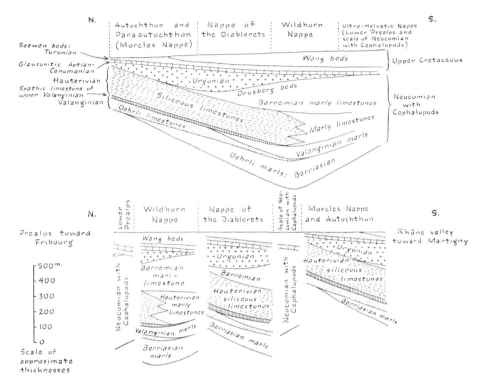

FIG. 102. *Cretaceous facies in the Helvetic nappes of western Switzerland (an example of stratigraphic and tectonic synthesis) (after data of Lugeon, Jeannet, Gagnebin, etc.; suggested by similar diagrams established by Arnold Heim for eastern Switzerland).*[150]

Deep-water facies are white: the different littoral facies are represented by patterns.

BELOW: Succession of the zones of facies as they are seen from north to south (compare Fig. 103): the facies follow from one zone to the next in a completely disordered way.

ABOVE: Succession of these facies when the different zones (nappes) are restored to the order they occupied before folding: the sediments are of deeper and deeper facies toward the southeast (Alpine fore-deep); the maximum thickness is not, however, found in the zone of deepest water, but rather as the northern littoral zone is approached.

Alpine chains, passes by repeated intercalations into a thick mass of deep, marly limestone in the Wildhorn nappe.

The *Urgonian*, very reduced in the autochthon, reaches its greatest thickness in the nappes of Morcles and Diablerets where it forms the bold limestone crown of the mountains dominating the Rhône valley toward St.

Maurice and the Lakes of Thun, Brienz and Lucerne. Then in the Wildhorn nappe, it is greatly reduced and replaced gradually by marl and marly-lime-stone facies whose upper part forms the beds of the Drusberg (mountain between Schwyz and Glarus).

The *Aptian, Albian,* and *Cenomanian* correspond to a period of emergence, marked by corrosion surfaces and glauconitic facies similar to those of the French sub-Alpine chains and like them, fossiliferous (Engelberger-Aa occurrence, south of Lake Lucerne).

The *Turonian* is represented by the gray or pink Seewen limestone (quar-ries near Schwytz). Above come the Seewen shales, then the Amden shales which are pelagic facies with *Globigerina* and rosalines, especially developed in the south.

Finally, the *Senonian,* transgressive as in the French sub-Alpine chains, is composed of deep, marly shales. Corresponding to the Maestrichtian are the Wang beds (Alpe near Iberg, between Schwyz and Glarus), shaly at the base, calcareous at the top, almost missing in the Morcles nappe, very thick in the Wildhorn nappe.[151]

B. Ultra-Helvetic Nappe (*Lower Prealps*). The development of deep-water facies, reaching its maximum in the southern part of the normal flank of the Wildhorn nappe, thus progressively leads to the type realized in the lower Prealps or the ultra-Helvetic nappe.

Its most characteristic portion is the Lower Cretaceous, represented by a monotonous series of marls and marly limestones in which almost the only fossils are ammonites. This is the "Neocomian with cephalopods," long known by Swiss geologists. It is overlain by foraminiferal limestones of the Turonian and lower Senonian, followed by the Wang beds.

Streaked out under the Medean Prealps, this ultra-Helvetic nappe is reduced to thin strips cropping out on the external edge of the latter (external Prealps) or their internal edge (internal Prealps). To the external Prealps belong the classic deposits of Châtel St. Denis, of the valley of the Veveyse (east of Lausanne) and of Montsalvens (near Bulle), whose recently restud-ied section[152] led to the discovery there of a final trace of Urgonian limestones, reduced to a few meters' thickness. To the internal Prealps belongs the famous plate called the scale of "Neocomian with cephalopods" which, in the wide depression of Anzeindaz, above Aigle, appears so curiously pinched out by folding between the Morcles and Diablerets nappes (see Fig. 103). The presence of this plate of deep-water Lower Cretaceous, crushed between two series containing a thick Urgonian facies, was long an enigma which has only been solved by tectonic studies. It is a fine example of the application of tectonic syntheses to the solution of a problem of coordination of facies.

C. Prealpine Nappes Proper.

1. *Flysch Nappe of Niesen.* The Lower Cretaceous has long been known here, represented by clay shales and calcareous shales with *Aptychus,* with occasional lentils of orbitoline limestone, the last traces of the Urgonian facies that we have already seen represented in a rudimentary way in the ultra-Hel-vetic nappe. Intercalations of marly limestones with rosalines, representing

the Upper Cretaceous, are also known. But almost the whole of this thick accumulation of Flysch was assigned to the Eocene.

Recent studies have, however, proved that almost all this Flysch is of Upper Cretaceous age. In the whole assemblage the facies seem analogous to those we have described in the ultra-Dauphinois zone or in the external scales of the sub-Briançonnais zone. In France, too, these beds were formerly attributed to the Eocene Flysch. So the interpretation of this famous mountain of Niesen has evolved in Switzerland exactly as the evolution in France of the interpretation of the sub-Briançonnais mountains which rise east of Gap (Piolit massif, Ancelles mountains).

2. Median Prealps. The Lower Cretaceous is represented in the north by shales or marly limestones with very rare fossils (belemnites or *Aptychus*), facies prolonging those of the ultra-Helvetic nappe. But, in the south, there are more littoral facies, with brachiopods, and there seems to be, at certain points, a lacuna representing the Lower Cretaceous (geanticline).

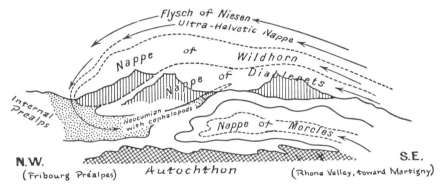

FIG. 103. *Diagrammatic section of the Helvetic nappes of western Switzerland, showing the position of the scale of Neocomian with cephalopods (after M. Lugeon; compare with Figs. 62 and 102).*

The Upper Cretaceous[153] is in the form of red beds, a very characteristic transgressive formation. These are varied sediments, shales, sandstones, or marly limestones, in which banks of bright red or green colors appear, easy to recognize even from a distance. Under the microscope multitudes of foraminifers, globigerines, rosalines and textulaires are seen. Also these sediments were sometimes wrongly compared to the globigerine muds of present great depths. The fossils are much less rare than in the Briançonnais and have allowed the recognition of the Cenomanian, Turonian and Senonian. There are even some rudistids. It may be supposed that, as on the edges of the Mercantour (see p. 377), these tropical faunas populated the southern shores of the Alpine fore-deep (that of the Wang beds), whose northern shores belonged to the northern province with belemnitelles.

3. Breccia Nappe. The Lower Cretaceous is unknown here. There seems to have been a lacuna, as in the southern part of the Median Prealps and, in fact, the transgressive red beds begin with a basal conglomerate.

4. *Simme Nappe.*[154]   In this nappe, still poorly defined, the stratigraphy of the Cretaceous remains very obscure. We note only the presence of an Upper Cretaceous with *Cyclolites* and large orbitolines (Cenomanian), southern forms which call for the same observations as above.

In summary, we find, in the Cretaceous of the Prealpine nappes, successions of facies similar to those we have just described in the internal zones of the Durance valley. The principal difference lies in the faunas of the Upper Cretaceous which thus far have not been found in the Briançonnais. Nothing is contrary to the idea then that these nappes are rooted, as we have assumed, in the Sion-Val-Ferret zone, which represents the extension in Switzerland of the French Briançonnais and sub-Briançonnais zones.[155]

VI. The Cretaceous in the Eastern Alps, Carpathians, and Apennines

Without attempting a paleogeographic synthesis, we shall merely cite the most classic formations and localities.

A. *The Eastern Alps*

On the northern slope, the most interesting Cretaceous formation is that of the famous Gosau beds (Salzkammergut),[156] joined to the Bavarian nappe (see p. 299). These are very littoral deposits, sometimes brackish and lignitic. Two fossiliferous horizons with hippurites and three with cephalopods allow the recognition of the series of Cretaceous stages from the Turonian to the Maestrichtian. The fauna is clearly Mediterranean, with corals (*Cyclolites*) and rudistids.

These beds are transgressive and lie discordantly on a previously folded substratum, on which lateritic and bauxitic deposits were formed in the course of the Middle Cretaceous-Turonian period.[157] These are the pre-Gosau movements of Austrian geologists, similar to the pre-Senonian folding which we have mentioned in Dévoluy (p. 431). But in every case, they have been overtaken by the Alpine displacements.

Recently,[158] in lower Austria, near Nieder-Fellabrunn, there have been found, at the top of the Cretaceous, bryozoan limestones containing echinoids (*Garumnaster*) with Garumnian affinities (see p. 427) and especially *Nautilus danicus*. This seems to be the only representative of the Danian stage known in central Europe.

On the southern slope (Dinarids) the Lower Cretaceous is represented in the Lombard Alps by the *majolica*. These are fine grained, white, compact limestones and pelagic, muddy facies with *Aptychus* and rare ammonites which indicate that the base of these limestones still belongs to the Tithonian and the top to the Neocomian and Barremian. Farther east, in the Venetian Alps, a similar facies of the same age, white limestones veined with red and green and containing light colored flints, is classic under the name of *bian-*

cone. Fossils are very rare[159] except in certain favored occurrences, such as the famous Barremian cephalopod fauna of the Alp Puez (between Marmolata and St. Cassian, see Fig. 64), studied by E. Haug. Finally, in eastern Venetia, organic facies with rudistids of the Urgonian type appear.

After a period of coarse and rather shallow-water[160] sedimentation, corresponding to the base of the Upper Cretaceous, this system ends, in Lombardy as well as in Venetia, with the *scaglia*. This is rather soft, marly limestone, with a scaly (or conchoidal) fracture, a pelagic facies with many foraminifers and radiolaria, a few echinoids, belemnites (*B. mucronata*) and ammonites. But toward the east, in Frioul, organic facies with rudistids are also found.

B. *Carpathians*

In the western Carpathians of Czechoslovakia, a very fossiliferous, infra-Cretaceous series has been made classic by the paleontologic studies of Uhlig. The Valanginian is represented by the Teschen beds (ammonite shales), the Hauterivian by the Grodischt beds (sandstones with pelecypods and ammonites), the Barremian by the Wernsdorf beds (marly limestones with ammonites).

Farther east, the Lower Cretaceous of the Tatra has recently been studied by Passendorfer.[161] In the Upper Cretaceous, a pelagic facies is found, similar to the scaglia and the red beds, and always dated by rosalines which swarm there.[162] This facies extends into the Romanian Carpathians. It is the very characteristic facies called Senonian red marls by the Romanian geologists.[163]

In the Bakony Mountains (or Hungarian Massif Central) a very interesting Lower Cretaceous series has recently been described.[164] Above a marine Valanginian-Hauterivian, it presents Barremian bauxites[165] (a little younger than the bauxites of Provence), overlain by an Aptian with intercalations of limestone containing *Requienia* and a marine Albian, then by Gosau beds (Turonian-Senonian) with hippurites. Sometimes a second bauxitic horizon overlies these beds and is covered by the Eocene with nummulites.

C. *Apennines*

In the northern Apennines, the Cretaceous, with relatively few fossils, is represented especially by shaly or sandy sediments. To the Neocomian are attributed limestones with light colored flints and containing *Aptychus*. But the most important member is the *pietraforte* of Tuscany. This is a compact sandstone with a few occurrences of ammonites and inocerames. Elsewhere the stratigraphy is very obscure because of tectonic complications and differences in interpretation caused by the famous formation of *scagliose* clay. This thick series of clayey shales, much dislocated and very treacherous, is sometimes attributed to the Tertiary (see p. 523) but usually it is viewed as a sort of comprehensive series, including the Jurassic and Cretaceous. In the central Apennines, the scaglia facies, dated by echinoids (*Stenonia*), is found in the Upper Cretaceous.

In the southern Apennines, however, and in the Apulo-Garganian domain

(p. 524), the whole Cretaceous is represented by thick series of coral limestones. There, beginning with the top of the Jurassic (see p. 371) there is
a whole series of rudistid faunas, with *Heterodiceras* in the Neocomian,
Requienia and *Toucasia* in the Urgonian, *Himeraelites* in the Cenomanian,
and *Hippurites* and *Radiolites* in the Turonian and Senonian. We shall see
that these organic facies extend without interruption in these regions
(Apulia, in particular) even into the Pliocene.[166]

Thus the southern Apennines, with their high and rugged white-faced limestone mountains, have a much more vigorous and picturesque relief than the
northern Apennines, where the monotonous shaly or sandy ridges present
only smooth, characterless outlines.

In Sicily and Calabria, a famous Cenomanian with African facies (see p.
450) has long been known.[167]

VII. The Cretaceous in the Iberian Peninsula[168]

The facies are arranged around the ancient Hercynian Massif of the Iberian
Meseta, which was an emerged island, like the French Massif Central. On
its perimeter the Cretaceous thus has an epicontinental aspect, with littoral
facies, lacunas, and transgressions.

A second region, probably emergent in the Cretaceous, is the Primary axis
of the Pyrenees, which thus separated the Iberian domain from that of the
French North-Pyrenees, which we have already studied (see p. 425). The
ancient Catalonian Massif, between Barcelona and Gerona, must also have
remained emergent. As for the Betic crystalline Massif, it has none of the
significance of the Meseta, for it does not belong to the Hercynian Chain.
On the contrary, it appears in the midst of a Betic Chain, folded in the
Tertiary, whose tectonics are very complicated and still a matter of dispute.[169]

On the other hand, the only region where the Cretaceous may be represented by an uninterrupted succession of marine deposits, generally deep-
water (at least up to the Cenomanian), is the sub-Betic Chain, which extends,
between the Betic Massif and the Meseta as far as the Balearics. This is
the sub-Betic geosyncline.

Thus, from the point of view of Cretaceous facies, we are led to identify,
with R. Douvillé, a number of natural regions, which we shall study successively.

A. *Western Border of the Meseta: Portugal*[170]

This is an epicontinental type. Along the present coast, all the Lower Cretaceous is represented by sediments of the Jura Mountains facies. Thus, in
the vicinity of Lisbon (Cintra) are found Valanginian limestones with *Natica
leviathan* and *Ostrea rectangularis,* Hauterivian spatangid marls, Barremian
limestones with *Toucasia carinata,* and finally Aptian sandstones. But farther
north, approaching the Primary formations, we see, in the region of Torres-
Vedras, the whole Lower Cretaceous pass into continental formations of the

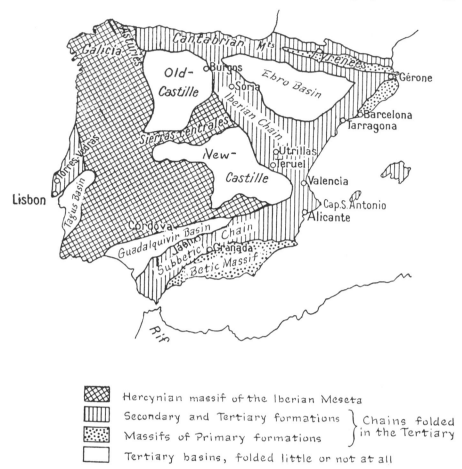

Hercynian massif of the Iberian Meseta
Secondary and Tertiary formations ⎫ Chains folded
Massifs of Primary formations   ⎬ in the Tertiary
Tertiary basins, folded little or not at all

FIG. 104.   *Very diagrammatic structural map of Spain.*

Wealdian type, fluviatile sandstones with plant beds. There the celebrated Cercal deposit, near Torres-Vedras, is found, in which the first European dicotyledons appear.[171]

The Cenomanian marks, as everywhere, a very appreciable transgression, which covers the Wealdian with marly limestones containing ornate ammonites, orbitolines, echinoids, oysters and rudistids, corresponding to different stages of the Upper Cretaceous. But the Senonian is sometimes marine, sometimes fluviatile, marking the general regression at the end of the Secondary.

B. *Sub-Betic Geosynclinal Zone*

Its type may be taken in the region of Granada, Cordova, and Jaen. There the Cretaceous is similar to that of the Vocontian trough (see p. 399). In the Lower Cretaceous, there is a monotonous series of marls and marly limestones with pyritic ammonites, concordant at its base with the bathyal

Jurassic. As for the Upper Cretaceous, it is represented either by the pelagic facies of the red beds, with rosalines, or by marly limestones with echinoids, with the stages still poorly defined. And it seems there may have been an emergence at the end of the Secondary.

In the Balearics, we have the same bathyal Lower Cretaceous, where the facies with pyritic ammonites persist into the Albian (see p. 450), but here the emergence began at the beginning of the Upper Cretaceous, the sea withdrawing toward the south (P. Fallot).

C. Sub-Betic Littoral Zone or Southeast Edge of the Meseta

This is developed north of the preceding zone and its best type is found at the boundary of the Provinces of Valencia and Alicante.

There, the marls of the preceding region alternate with littoral formations in such a way that the Lower Cretaceous has a mixed type similar to that described in the sub-Alpine chains (see p. 404). Thus, limestones with *Natica leviathan* are found in the Valanginian. The Barremian or Aptian show intercalations of beds containing small orbitolines, or Urgo-Aptian limestones (see p. 397). Quite varied facies correspond to the Albian and Upper Cretaceous—beds with large orbitolines, reef limestones with rudistids, sandy limestones with echinoids and ornate ammonites. These are the organic limestones of the Upper Cretaceous which constitute the greatest part of the high mountains dominating the coast in the region of Cape San Antonio.

D. Eastern Edge of the Meseta: Teruel Province

Here we finally turn away from the axis of the sub-Betic geosyncline, which must extend toward the Balearics, and so the epicontinental character is accentuated. There was emergence at the boundary of the Jurassic and Cretaceous, and it is the corresponding lacuna which defines this fourth domain. This lacuna becomes more and more important toward the northwest, for we have seen (p. 373) that the entire Ebro Basin (or Aragon Basin) was emergent at the end of the Jurassic. It was invaded in the Cretaceous both by way of its Mediterranean embouchure and its northwest extremity in the Atlantic (Cantabrian) region, as will be indicated later. Thus, continuing our comparisons, if our third region corresponded to the sub-Alpine chains and the Jura Mountains, we can say that the Aragon Basin was equivalent to the Anglo-Parisian Basin, the double invasion of which, by the Mediterranean and the North Sea, we have already described.

The Lower Cretaceous there comprises an Urgonian with orbitolines and *Toucasia,* with intercalations of continental red formations which are moreover of variable age. Thus, in the classic locality of Utrillas,[172] the Urgonian with *Toucasia* is overlain by beds with trigonias, with exploited lignite layers, probably corresponding to the Aptian-Albian boundary. The Albian is then represented by nonfossiliferous limestones, and the Cenomanian by limestones and marls with oysters of the facies called African (see p. 450). The

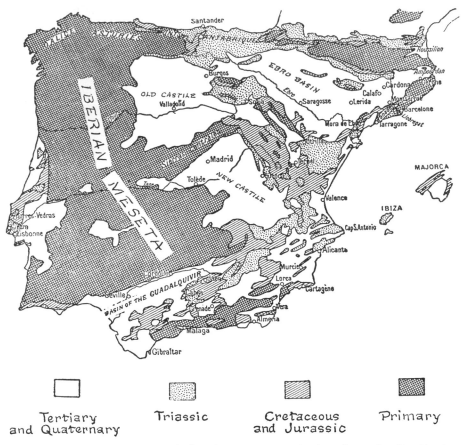

FIG. 105. *Geologic map of the Iberian Peninsula* (*to show the distribution of Cretaceous outcrops*) (*after the map published by Faura y Sans in the* Enciclopedia universal, *very diagrammatic*).

Cenomanian is, however, widely transgressive, even extending over the Primary formations of the Meseta. The balance of the Cretaceous, still poorly known in this region, ends with Danian beds with *Lychnus*.

E. *North Edge of the Meseta: Soria-Burgos Region*

The distinctive feature of this zone consists in the development of a thick series of Lower Cretaceous with Wealdian facies,[173] thus recalling, in the Aragon Basin, similar facies of the Anglo-Parisian Basin. There are conglomerates, sandstones, marls with gypsum, lacustrine limestones containing a fauna of paludines, unios and cyrenes. The whole series exceeds 1,000 meters in thickness.

Above, the transgression begins only with the Cenomanian, which has its African facies of marls with oysters (*O. africana*). The rest of the Upper Cretaceous is represented by sandy limestones containing echinoids, with

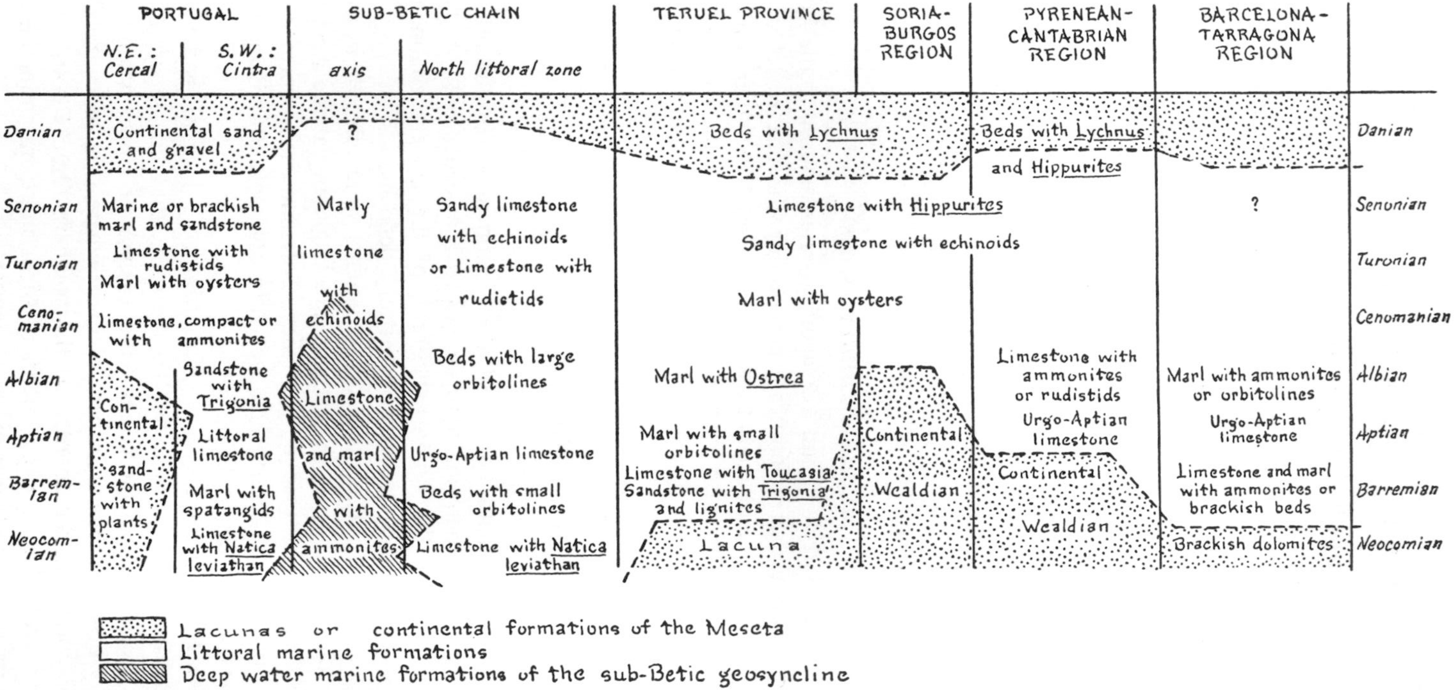

FIG. 106. *Diagram of the Cretaceous facies around the Iberian Meseta.*

Transgression, more or less delayed, occurred everywhere along the border of the Meseta except in the sub-Betic gosyncline, where the marine Jurassic and Cretaceous were continuous. At the end of the Cretaceous there was general regression.

Lacunas or continental formations of the Meseta
Littoral marine formations
Deep water marine formations of the sub-Betic geosyncline

445

banks of hippuritids. Near Soria there are even rich ammonite faunas. The series ends with a continental Danian with *Lychnus.*

F. *Pyrenean-Cantabrian Region*

In the Cantabrian Chain, which prolongs the Pyrenees on the south side of the Gulf of Gascony, we find, in the Lower Cretaceous, a Wealdian absolutely identical to that we have just described farther south; but here its age is more exactly fixed, for the marine transgression begins with Urgo-Aptian limestones similar to those which marked the return of the sea in the North-Pyrenean zone (p. 372). Above, the Albian is represented by limestones with rudistids or sometimes ammonites. The balance of the Cretaceous is quite varied. There are sandy limestones with ammonites, inocerames, and echinoids. Beds with hippuritids are developed there, particularly well studied on the south slope of the Pyrenees,[174] where Toucas and H. Douvillé found a whole series of paleontologic zones defined by these fossils. Finally, the Danian, here called the Garumnian, as on the north slope, includes the last beds with hippurites, overlain by *Lychnus* beds.

G. *Edge of the Catalan Primary Massif*

Here we see, between Barcelona and Tarragon, a series reduced to the Lower Cretaceous. Above brackish dolomites, representing the last traces of the Wealdian facies[175] in the southeast, there is a marine Neocomian with pelecypods, still containing brackish intercalations, overlain by the Urgo-Aptian, while the top of the Aptian and the Albian consists of marls containing ammonites or orbitolines.

VIII. The Cretaceous of North Africa[176]

Here we are on the northern border of the Continent of Gondwana and from south to north, the following natural regions are recognized:

1. *The Sahara,* where the Primary bedrock of the ancient continent is hidden only by horizontal Cretaceous or Tertiary deposits.

2. *The Saharan Atlas.* The Mesozoic sediments were affected by regular East-West folds of the Jura Mountains type. Beginning at the west with the Moroccan Great Atlas (see p. 63) these Saharan chains form everywhere the edge of the great desert, then they turn obliquely toward the north and expand over all Tunisia south of Tunis.

3. *The High Plateaus or Steppes.* The Mesozoic formations become, once more, horizontal over vast areas. To the west, the zone separates the Moroccan Middle Atlas from the Great Atlas (region of Upper Moulouya). It becomes very broad in the department of Oran where it includes the Oran Causses to the north and the country of the southern Oran Chotts, to the south. Already narrowed in the departments of Alger and Constantine (Hodna Basin, Lake country), it no longer exists in Tunisia.

4. *The Tellian or Littoral Atlas.* This zone has a tormented relief at

the edge of the Mediterranean. The folds here are much more complicated, of Alpine style, with scales and a structure often isoclinal.

5. *Kabylie Primary Massifs.* Lastly, in the northern part of the Tellian Atlas, the massifs of the Great Kabylie and the Little Kabylie appear in the midst of Tertiary folds. They are comparable to the crystalline massifs included in the French Alpine Chain. And, as the Tellian Atlas was prolonged into Morroco by the Rif Chains, so this border of Primary massifs is found in the Rif Primary Massif, facing the Betic crystalline Massif. Thus, we often speak of a Betic-Rifian Massif, the middle part of which is buried under the waters of the Mediterranean.

On the whole, the Cretaceous of this southern edge of the great Mesogean sea shows a succession of facies comparable to that described on its northern

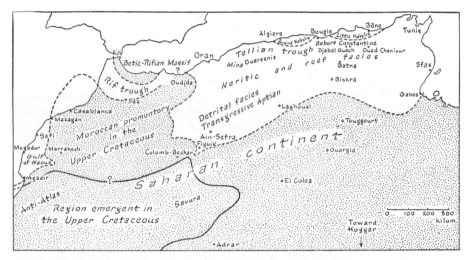

FIG. 107. *Paleogeographic diagram of North Africa in the Lower Cretaceous and the limits (heavy line) of the Cenomanian transgression on the African continent (after maps of J. Savornin and E. Roch).*

shore. A deep-water Cretaceous, equivalent to that of the Alpine fore-deep, is found in the Tellian Atlas. The zone of the high plateaus and the Saharan Atlas have a Cretaceous with littoral facies of the Jura Mountains type. Finally, the Sahara, comparable to the Hercynian girdle of the Massif Central-Vosges, generally formed the shore and was not invaded by the sea until the Cenomanian.

A. *Lower Cretaceous*

The deep-water sediments which occupy the Tellian Atlas zone are, in general, marls with pyritic ammonites, similar to those described in the Vocontian trough and in which the smooth-shelled forms also predominate (phylloceratids, lytoceratids, desmoceratids). In the department of Constantine, the occurrences of Djebel Ouach (Barremian) and Oued Cheniour (Aptian) are celebrated (J. Blayac); those of Mina (Oran) have been studied by Dalloni. In Morocco, rich pyritic faunas have recently been reviewed by Lacoste; they are not found, however, in the deepest-water zone of the Riffian threshold, where the sediments are often lifeless, but rather, approaching its southern border, in the pre-Riffian zone, already varied by shoals. Likewise, in Algeria, fossils become more rare in the northern part of the Tellian Atlas. The Primary Kabylie Massifs must have constituted small emerged crests, comparable to the Alpine cordilleras.[177] In different regions, L. Glangeaud was able to find evidence of littoral facies with orbitolines and Ehrman pointed out, in the Kabylie of Babors, a Lower Cretaceous with very rare, pyritic ammonites and micro-breccia banks which recall somewhat the types of sedimentation of the borders of the Alpine cordilleras.[178] And on the shoreline west of Oran, the Lower Cretaceous has even assumed almost azoic facies of shales and quartzites which long caused it to be confused with the Primary. Thus here we run into a confused stratigraphy, similar to that of the internal zones of the French Alps.

In the high plateau region, on the contrary, the Lower Cretaceous becomes more and more coastal as one goes farther south. There are sandy marls, sandstones or organic limestones, rich in echinoids, brachiopods, and pelecypods. Sometimes a typical Urgonian is found, with its *Requienia ammonia* and *Toucasia carinata* fauna. Moreover, at the boundary of the high plateaus and the Tell, in the transition region from one facies to the other, we see, in the vicinity of Guelma, organic limestones with Urgonian facies, but with a different rudistid fauna (*Polyconites verneuli, Toucasia santanderensis, Horiopleura lamberti*). An Urgo-Aptian similar to that of the Pyrenean region is also found, whose age is here well defined. For farther south, in the high plains at Djebel Sidi Rghis, J. Blayac saw reefy beds intercalated between lower marls with *Ostrea aquila* and upper marls with *Oppelia nisoides*.

Finally, toward the Saharan Atlas, the coral facies cease and in the water, shallow and charged with terrigenous debris, which bordered the desert platform, subcontinental sometimes variegated marls and sandstone are deposited, to a thickness of 2,000 m. near Batna. In southern Algeria, the marine transgression often occurs in the Aptian and a marine Albian, 200 m. thick, is known as far as Aurès.[179]

On the other hand, south of the Riffian trough, which we have just discussed, most of Morocco remained emergent. The shallow seas of the Causses and great Chotts of Oran ended in the west, between Oudjda and Figuig, against a great advance promontory of the Saharan continent. To find the marine Lower Cretaceous in Morocco, we must cross this promontory and go almost to the Atlantic seaboard, between Agadir and Mazagan. There, as in the Jurassic, a gulf was encroaching on the continent and a Lower Cretaceous of the Jura Mountains type, containing ammonites along the present coast, passes, on the east, into facies with brachiopods and echinoids, then into continental red formations, which in the western Great Atlas mark the end of this Gulf of Haouz de Marrakech (E. Roch).

During this time, the location of the Sahara remained emergent. It was the northern extremity of the Continent of Gondwana, whose southern extremity we have described, with its Permian, Triassic, and Jurassic continental formations. In the French Sahara, it is often recognized that continental sedimentation only began in the Albian. It is indeed to the Albian that many Algerian geologists attach the continental sandstones of alluvial origin, known as "dragée sandstones," for in this alluvium, many times shifted over the desert plateau, most of the pebbles ended by disappearing (impoverished or emaciated alluvium) except the unchangeable quartz pebbles which stand out like white sugared almonds (*dragées*) over the deep red or yellow of the sandstone. Scattered over the desert floor, silicified trunks of gymnosperms, rare teeth of lagoonal fish (*Ceratodus*) and reptile bones (*Megalosaurus saharicus*) are frequently found. In the north, near Aïn-Sefra (northwest of Figuig) these sandstones overlie the marine Aptian which advances that far. And they are, all over the Sahara, covered in turn by marine deposits of the Cenomanian transgression, which we shall take up later. This relationship justifies their assignment to the Albian. But elsewhere they may very well include older beds. In fact, farther east, in the Libyan desert, these sandstones are replaced by Nubian sandstone, which we have already discussed and whose base is undoubtedly Jurassic or even Carboniferous. We can then recognize a reduced and younger equivalent of the Karroo formations of South Africa. They are, in any case, pre-Cenomanian.

B. *The Cenomanian Transgression; The Upper Cretaceous*

Important paleogeographic changes indeed took place in the middle of the Cretaceous. This is the great transgression called Cenomanian, which in reality often (except in the Sahara) began in the upper Albian.

It was then that the sea invaded central Morocco, attacking the great promontory, which, south of the Riffian threshold, had limited the Lower Cretaceous seas to slight advances west of the Figuig-Oudjda line. This sea advanced toward the west and joined the Atlantic. Passing between the Middle Atlas and the High Atlas, which remained emerged, the Albian-Cenomanian seas formed a Strait of Upper Moulouya, which debouched on the site of the submerged Moroccan Meseta. Only a few small islands, corresponding in particular to the Primary outcrops of Djebilet and Rehamna, marked by shore facies, survived the invasion. Farther south, the infra-Cretaceous Gulf of Haoutz de Marrakech, advanced to the southeast. Above the submerged western High Atlas, a Strait of Glaoua was formed, through which the sea spread out at the foot of the eastern Great Atlas. From there, through the Strait of Colomb-Béchar, it rejoined the great Saharan sea.

In fact, in the Cenomanian, the sea invaded the Sahara[180] for the first and last time. The continental promontory, which in the Cenomanian advanced as far as the Oudjda region south of the Riffian trough, goes no farther north than the vicinity of Colomb-Béchar. A large arm of the sea passes between it and the Hoggar. Certain valleys of this latter crystalline massif were even invaded and were transformed into a kind of rias (C. Kilian). By way of the Tademaït and Tanezrouft Plateaus (where Menchikoff [181] has recently confirmed the presence of marine Upper Cretaceous), this Saharan sea passed north of Gao, to Zinder and, through the Strait of Bénoué, rejoined the Atlantic.

Over these vast areas, the transgressive Cenomanian is represented by marls and marly limestones with oysters of the African type, where special species (*O. africana, O. syphax*), numerous echinoids and some ammonites (*Neolobites*) are added to the oysters of the Maine fauna (*O. columba, O. flabellata*). The Turonian, more generally calcareous, is also dated by *Vascoceras* and rudistids. The Senonian likewise shows limestones with rare cephalopods (*Lybicoceras*) and African pelecypods (*Roudeireia auressensis*), as well as frequent gypsiferous intercalations. It ends with beds of *Cardita beaumonti* which are usually attributed to the Danian and which are found in the Sudan, with numerous nautiloids.[182]

The outcrops of these different calcareous horizons of the Upper Cretaceous are represented, all over the Sahara, by vast rocky plateaus or *hamadas,* whose surface is sometimes covered with a desert crust, glazed and black (from oxidation of iron salts). This is the black hamada of a peculiarly sinister aspect.

During this period, sedimentation continued in the regions already occupied by the sea in the Lower Cretaceous. In the Saharan Atlas and the high plateaus, the seas remained shallow, with lagoonal episodes. The Cenomanian, rather marly, always contained rich faunas of oysters and echinoids (famous deposits of the Batna region), which makes one of the easiest horizons to identify in all North Africa. In the Turonian, thick limestones with rudistids often developed. The Senonian shows limestones with inocerames (rocks of El Kantara, or desert gates, north of Biskra) or gypsiferous formations. But, although shallow-water, this Upper Creatceous of the Saharan Atlas is nevertheless very thick. In Aurès, the Albian-Senonian series, entirely marine, exceeds 3,000 m.[183]

Farther north, in the Tellian Atlas, the facies become more clearly marine and deeper water.

Thus it is that in the deepest parts of the Tellian trough, the Upper Cretaceous begins with shales with banks of fine sandstone sometimes compared to the Alpine Flysch (Albo-Aptian Flysch of L. Glangeaud) and like it deficient in fossils. But on the borders, in Algeria and still more in Tunisia, the Albian and Cenomanian marls contain fine pyritic ammonites, with swarms of very interesting lytoceratids and phylloceratids, but the relatively shallow-water European faunas of these stages are missing (they are found in the Balearics). The Turonian is usually more calcareous and its littoral facies with rudistids reach quite far to the north at this period (Rock of Constantine, cut by the gorges of the Rummel).

The Senonian, however, marks an increase of depth. There are either thick, black marls or pink or white marly limestones, somewhat similar to the scaglia of the Italian Alps. Ammonites, rare in Europe, are found there, particularly peculiar phylloceratids and lytoceratids. In the Riffian trough, the supra-Cretaceous marls contain almost nothing but rosalines, but in shallower-water zones inocerames and echinoids appear, accompanied by the "ceratites of the Chalk."

Finally, on the south side of the Moroccan High Atlas, in Aurès,[184] in the southern part of the Algerian Tell, and in Tunisia, there is a transition to the Tertiary through marine beds equivalent to the Danian, of which we shall speak again (p. 528). In the zone of the Kabylies and in northern Tunisia, there was long believed to be a lacuna representing the whole Upper Cretaceous. Actually, a Senonian Flysch with rosalines and inocerames is shown to be transgressive as far as the Mediterranean shores (vicinity of Dellys), lying on the Albo-Aptian Flysch and even on schists,[185] but there does seem to be an absence of the Danian.

C. *Conclusions*

Thus a Saharan or North African continent bordered the great Mediterranean geosynclinal region on the south, as the North Atlantic continent bordered it on the north. And on both sides of the geosynclinal formations, often deep-water and always folded, we find on the two shores, in Europe and in Africa, coastal facies and littoral faunas (Urgonian, Urgo-Aptian, marls with spatangids, sandstones with oysters), similar but not completely identical, for the deep sea perhaps presented an obstacle to the migration of certain littoral species.[186]

However, we note, with R. Lafitte, that the formations of deepest facies, the marls with pyritic ammonites of the southern Tellian trough, are relatively thin. The thickness of individual stages can be measured in tens of meters. Farther south, however, in the high plateaus and Saharan Atlas, the abundant terrigenous materials supplied by the great Saharan continent, accumulating indefinitely in place, thanks to a continuous subsidence, give to these same stages thicknesses figured in hundreds and even thousands of meters.

In the French and Swiss Alps, we established the same contrast between the thin pelagic sediments of the bottom of the Alpine fore-deep (Neocomian with cephalopods of the ultra-Helvetic nappe and the ultra-Dauphinois zone) and the thick accumulations of the external edge of this same fore-deep (Helvetic nappes, perimeter of the Vocontian trough in Ventoux and southern Vercors).

This double example thus illustrates the general law which was formulated in the Introduction to this work (see p. 10 and Fig. 1).

IX. The Cretaceous in North America

1. *The Lower Cretaceous*

Three different types can be distinguished.

A. Atlantic Type or Potomac Formation. On the whole Atlantic shore

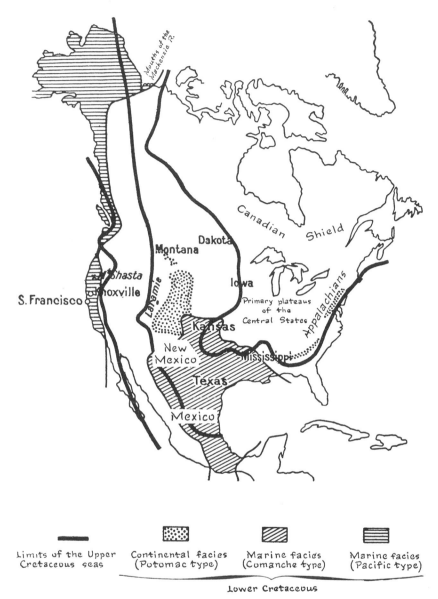

| Limits of the Upper Cretaceous seas | Continental facies (Potomac type) | Marine facies (Comanche type) | Marine facies (Pacific type) |

Lower Cretaceous

FIG. 108. *Diagrammatic map of the principal domains of facies in the Cretaceous in North America. For more exact paleogeographic maps, see Schuchert (cited Note 4, Chapter 1).*

of North America, as far as the middle of the Gulf of Mexico, the Lower Cretaceous is represented only by continental deposits similar to the Wealdian of Europe. There are sands, sandstones, clays and lignites, with a flora of dicotyledons similar to that found, at the same period, in identical facies, in Portugal. This Potomac formation (200 m. thick), so named after the river which flows by Washington, forms a coastal band all along the south-eastern slope of the Appalachians and is prolonged into the state of Mississippi and even into Montana, where it is called the Kootenai beds and contains coal.

So, the Canadian Shield, enlarged by the Hercynian Appalachians and Primary plateaus of the central states, continues to form, as in the Jurassic, a vast North American Continent, respected by the infra-Cretaceous transgression.

B. Central American Type or Comanchean. This type is developed in Mexico and farther north in Texas[187] (where the Comanche Indians lived), Arkansas, New Mexico, etc. There is a very thick series there, reaching 1,500 m. of marine sediments transgressive over the Primary formations. The domain of the Comanchean thus corresponds to a part of the North American Continent which was invaded by the Cretaceous sea. This sea, however, remained epicontinental and there are frequent intercalations of coastal or organic deposits. The fauna (orbitolines, *Toucasia,* echinoids) has clearly Mediterranean affinities.[188]

Thus, as the Potomac flora leads us to believe in a continental connection with the flora of Portugal, in the same way the coastal fauna of the Comanchean leads us to suspect a coastal connection between the Mediterranean regions and North America. So we may suppose that the North American Continent and the European Continent must have been more or less united in a huge North Atlantic continent.[189]

C. Pacific Type or the Knoxville Beds (Shasta series). All along the Pacific Coast, from Alaska[190] into California, a thick series of deep-water deposits (Knoxville beds and Shasta series),[191] with rich ammonite faunas, was formerly attributed to the Lower Cretaceous. In reality, the Knoxville beds belong to the Upper Jurassic. Lying discordantly upon older beds, they reach 4,000 m. thickness and contain six faunal horizons. *Simbirskites, Polyptychites, Aucella* are found, indicating communication with the northern domain of Europe. Above, the Lower Cretaceous is represented by the Shasta series, also generally beginning with a discordance and reaching 4,000 to 6,000 m. The ammonite faunas in it show species unknown in Europe and very different from those of the Comanchean.

So, this huge geosynclinal domain of circum-Pacific Tertiary chains must have communicated with the northern domain and joined there, perhaps north of Siberia, with the seas of Northern Europe.

And in order to clarify and coordinate this general idea of the distribution of faunas and facies in America, it must be recognized that an emerged land separated the Pacific geosyncline from the Comanchean sea of Texas. Its location would correspond to the Rocky Mountains and western Mexico.

2. *The Upper Cretaceous*

The distinction between the three regional types, which we have just studied in the Lower Cretaceous, becomes much less clear in the Upper Cretaceous. In fact, a great transgression took place at this epoch, which, as in Europe, tended to unify the fauna by establishing easier communications.

The geosynclinal conditions persist on the Pacific Coast in California. Over the Shasta series lie several thousand meters of shales containing faunas with Asiatic affinities, which make it possible to recognize the different stages of the Chalk.

Elsewhere on the North American Continent the transgression took place in the two following regions.

A. The Atlantic Slope of the Appalachians. Here, the transgression did not advance very far, so that the Upper Cretaceous forms only a narrow band at the foot of the mountains, on the edge of the coastal plain. Its marine sediments overlie the Potomac continental formation.

B. Central States.[192] Here the transgressive Lower Cretaceous sea had already deposited the Comanchean marine formations as far as Kansas. But the transgression assumed much larger proportions in the Upper Cretaceous and its deposits lie either on the Comanchean or on the continental Potomac or, in the north, on the Jurassic and the Primary. First, there is the Dakota formation, of Cenomanian age, still containing intercalations of continental sandstones. Then come the Colorado and Montana marine formations, which extend through the Maestrichtian.[193] So, at this epoch, there was an immense arm of the sea[194] which, passing between the Canadian Shield and the Rocky Mountains, extended from the Gulf of Mexico to the mouth of the Mackenzie. In Texas, Kansas and Iowa, true chalks are deposited in a shallow sea, bordered by flat coasts with lakes and lagoons. There flourished the gigantic dinosaurians which now populate the museums of America. From there also come birds provided with teeth, *Hesperornis* and *Ichthyornis.*

Finally the Cretaceous ends with the thick (4,000 m.) lacustrine beds of Laramie (or of Lance). The arm of the sea was transformed into an immense lake, a true area of subsidence which sank by degrees as the sedimentation tended to fill it. The base of this Laramie series, rich in varied dinosaurians and containing a flora similar to that of the Potomac, is clearly Cretaceous. At the top, it ends with the *Triceratops* beds of Wyoming, containing hardly more than the last surviving dinosaurians, accompanied by small multituberculate mammals. There is no sign of the rich fauna of placental mammals which will appear at the base of the Tertiary. So this is probably an equivalent of the Danian. Moreover, in North Dakota, the Lance series still contains, at the top, a last marine intercalation, the Cannonball beds, with Cretaceous mollusks. And in the Wasatch Mountains (Fig. 132) a recent discovery of dinosaurians[195] confirms that the Cretaceous-Tertiary boundary must be raised to the top of the Lance series, just below the Fort Union beds, with which the Tertiary begins.

Farther south, in Texas, the Midway group has long been attributed to the Danian,[196] as forms are found which are practically identical to *Nautilus danicus* and *Venericardia beaumonti,* which characterize the Danian of the Old World. But, at the present time, most American authors assign this Midway formation to the Tertiary and indeed, M. Leriche (1940, note 231, chap. 9) finds that its fish fauna, composed of new species, has clearly Tertiary affinities.

As we see, the boundary between the Cretaceous and the Tertiary poses the same problems as in Europe.[107]

X. Conclusions (Generality of the Upper Cretaceous Transgression; Eustatic Movements)

At the close of this study, it is impossible not to be struck by the fact that the three great continental masses that we have learned to recognize, the Continent of Northern Europe, the North American Continent, and the African or Saharan Continent,[198] are all widely attacked by the transgression of the Upper Cretaceous.

In Europe, the Strait of Poitou opens in the Cenomanian, the sea advancing toward northern Aquitaine, between Brittany and the Massif Central; the Ardennes, at the same period, is at least partially invaded; in Britain, the North Sea advances into Ireland and Scotland, while toward the east, its beaches cover Bohemia, from whence its tides extend into Scania, breaking against the ancient rocks of the Scandinavian Massif.

In America, its waves begin to strike against the first Atlantic hills of the Appalachians and the whole central part of the United States is covered like a scarf by the long arm of the sea which later will die away in place, producing the Laramie lakes.

For the first time since the Primary era, and for the last as well, the Mediterranean overflows to the heart of Africa, burying beneath its sandy beaches the whole northern part of the old Saharan continent.

And all these regions are exactly the ones whose geologic history reveals them as the most stable part of the globe since the Primary. Comparing this stability with the irresistible power of the marine movement which submerged them, we are tempted, with Suess, to seek in the sea itself, in the limitless sea, the causes of a movement which extended over such vast spaces. When we see the huge Saharan platform, between the Gulf of Gabès and the Gulf of Guinea, invaded by a sea whose depth must never have exceeded 50 or 100 m., it is evidently easier to attribute such a uniformity to a rise of the marine level than to the necessarily more capricious deformation of the continental platform. Thus, it would not be the continents which would be lowered, all together at this period, obliterating themselves beneath the tides of a passive flood. Instead, it would be the sea itself, the boundless sea, which in the same assault embracing Europe, Africa, and America, would everywhere have submerged motionless lands.

To these characteristic oscillations of the oceanic surface, Suess has given the name *eustatic movements*. To one such movement, a positive oscillation, the transgression of the Upper Cretaceous would be due.

But, upon closer examination, this grandiose image loses its sharpness. We have seen how long prepared, how interrupted by vicissitudes (example,

Aquitaine) was the transgression. Its timid and local attempts do not always accord with the conception of a great, universal flood. Not one of its different phases is everywhere contemporaneous. And in any case, the local deformations of the continental platforms must often have interfered with the oscillation of the sea level. The discussion of this eustatic theory would go beyond our framework and it is sufficient to have shown by this example how stratigraphic studies have led to its conception.[199]

REFERENCE NOTES

1. A general table of the stages and zones of ammonites, belemnites, echinoids, small foraminifers, in S. W. Muller and H. G. Schenk, *Standard of Cretaceous System,* Bull. Amer. Ass. Petrol. Geol. 27, no. 3 (1943).

2. This name is derived, not from the Champagne of the Paris Basin, celebrated for its wines, but from a small chain of hills located near Cognac, also named *Champagne,* where the liqueur called *fine Champagne* brandy is produced.

3. In addition to the classic works of L. Cayeux, see the recent study of E. B. Bailey, "The Desert Shores of the Chalk Seas," Geol. Magaz., 61 (1924). This author notes grains of quartz, in the chalk, brought by the wind. For him, the shallow chalk seas, which terrigenous sediments never reached, were bordered by deserts, a conclusion which is undoubtedly too extreme.

4. J. Pfender, *Sur la valeur stratigraphique de Cuneolina D'Orb.,* C. R. Soc. géol. France (June 19, 1939).

5. Related genera: *Globorotalia,* beginning in the Upper Cretaceous, but especially Tertiary and Recent; *Hantkenina,* characteristic of the Eocene and lower Oligocene.

6. See for example, Ab Ten Dam, *Les microfaunes de l'Albien des Pays-Bas comparées avec les faunes contemporaines du Nord-Ouest de l'Europe,* C. R. Soc. géol. France (1944), p. 105. E. Williams, "The Zonal Value of Foraminifera in the Chalk of England," Proc. Geol. Ass., 59, 2 (1948).

7. A typical example is given by Y. Gubler, *Remaniement d'une microfaune du Crétacé supérieur dans le Lutetian de Tréziers (Aude),* C. R. Soc. géol. France (May 3, 1943). There, the detrital beds with nummulites alternate with fine muds with rosalines. See also J. Cuvillier and J. Dupouy-Camet, *Remaniements des Rosalines dans l'Eocène de l'Aquitaine occidentale,* ibid. (1947), p. 141.

8. Revision of these forms and a bibliography by J. Pfender, *Sur un Foraminifère nouveau du Bathonien des Montagnes d'Escreins (Hautes-Alpes):* Kilianina blancheti, *nov. gen., nov. sp.,* Trav. Lab. Géol. Univ. Grenoble, 18 (1935).

9. Bull. Soc. géol. France (1904), p. 653 and C. R. Acad. Sc. (Sept. 23, 1912).

10. However, according to different Italian paleontologists (G. Checchia-Rispoli), true orbitoids continue into the Eocene (see pp. 470 and 525). An excellent summary and bibliography in R. Abrard, *Répartition géographique et migrations des Orbitoïdes,* Mém. Soc. Biogéogr., 7, Paris (1940), p. 55–73.

11. L. Moret, *Contribution à l'étude des Spongiaires siliceux du Crétacé sup. français,* Mém. Soc. géol. France, n. s., mém. no. 5 (1926); some French occurrences as fine as those of Hanover, investigated by this author and M. Regnard, are reported here for the first time.

12. This estimate, made by A. Schrammen, Palaontographica, suppl. V. (1910–1912), using the method of means, led him to the figure of 600 m. In reality this very high figure comes from isolated discoveries of Cretaceous genera at great present depths. Using the much preferable method of frequency curves, as has been done here (Fig. 91), we reach a figure of about 300 m. This Oberg chalk is, however, much deeper than the mean for the chalk.

13. See note 34, this chap.

14. G. Fage, *Les Rhynchonelles du Crétacé inférieur des Charentes*, Bull. Soc. géol. France, 4 (1934).

15. See the thesis of Mlle. S. Gillet, *Etudes sur les Lamellibranches néocomiens*, Mém. soc. géol. France, n. s., no. 3 (1925).

16. The inocerames of the Upper Cretaceous of the whole world have recently been studied in numerous works by R. Heinz. See the list, in the last of these, in Zeitschr. deutsch. geol. Ges., 85 (1933).

17. See, however, M. Breistroffer, *Sur la présence d'Aucellines dans l'Albien inférieur de la Nerthe (B.d.R.)*, C. R. Soc. géol. France (Nov. 3, 1941).

18. Complete bibliography in C. F. Parona, *Saggio bibliografico sulle Rudiste*, Boll. R. Comitato geol. italiano, XLVI, pp. 1–78 (1916).

19. P. Fallot, *Sur la répartition des Pachyodontes urgoniens dans le Sud de l'Espagne*, C. R. Soc. Biogéogr. (1914); a map of the facies of the Urgo-Aptian in the western Mediterranean.

20. See H. Douvillé, C. R. Soc. géol. France (May 15, 1933).

21. We note only that the true *Hippurites* and *Radiolites* appear in the Turonian.

22. P. Sénesse, *Variations et classification chez les Hippurites pyrénéens*, Bull. Soc. Hist. nat., Toulouse, 81 (1946).

23. A. Antonini, *Sur l'évolution et la classification des Hippurites de la Provence*, Bull. Soc. géol. France, 8 (1938).

24. B. Milovanovič, *Les Rudistes de la Yougoslavie*, Ann. géol. de la Péninsule balkanique, 12 (1934). The zones of *Hippurites* established by Toucas in the Senonian are discussed here.

25. This genus has just been discovered in the Oligocene (Sannoisian) of the Balearics, by M. Vidal.

26. Principally following W. Kilian and his collaborators for the Lower Cretaceous, Ch. Jacob for the Albian and de Grossouvre for the Upper Cretaceous. Specialists will consult, for the Lower and Middle Cretaceous, the works of Spath, cited note 69, this chap., and for the Albian, M. Breistroffer, *Sur les zones d'ammonites dans l'Albien de France et d'Angleterre*, Trav. Lab. Géol. Univ. Grenoble, 26 (1947), 88 p.

27. E. Stolley, *Die leitenden Belemniten des norddeutschen Neokoms*, 17. Jahresber. Niedersächsischen geol. Vereins, Hannover (1925). J. A. Jeletsky, *Zur Kenntniss der oberkretazischen Belemniten*, Geol. Fören. Förhandl. (1946), 68, p. 87–105.

28. In reality this opinion, popularized by E. Haug's *Traité de Géologie*, is too inflexible, for very rare belemnitellas are found in the Upper Cretaceous of the Aquitaine Basin (see note 100, this chap.).

29. See the numerous works by W. Kilian (in particular in the *Mémoires du Service de la Carte géologique de France*, and in *Lethaea geognostica*).

30. Except for the black marls of the upper Aptian-Cenomanian.

31. E. Roche, *Etude stratigraphique et paléontologique de l'Aptien inf. de La Bédoule, près Cassis (Bouches-du-Rhône)*, Mém. Soc. géol. France, n. s., mém. no. 8 (1927).

32. J. Goguel, *Contribution à l'étude paléogéographique du Crétacé inférieur dans le Sud-Est de la France*, Bull. Serv. Cart. géol. France, no. 215 (1944, 1945).

33. J. Jung and H. Erhart, *Structure géologique des Baronnies au N du Mont-Ventoux*, Trav. Lab. Géol. Univ. Grenoble, 17 (1933).

34. *Toxaster retusus* and *T. amplus* are generally confused by authors. In truth, they are two distinct species, as J. Lambert has shown, and they are successive in time, according to Denizot (Mém. cited note 36, this chap.). But it is the first which is found in the Hauterivian of the Jura Mountains and Paris Basin, and the second which is frequent in the Provençal and sub-Alpine Hauterivian and perhaps continues into the lower Barremian.

35. Since the classic works of W. Kilian, a very meticulous stratigraphic study of these transitions has been made by J. Goguel, *Sur l'extension des faciès urgoniens dans les Monts de Vaucluse*, Bull. Soc. géol. France, 5 sér., 2 (1932).

36. The question of the age of the Provençal Urgonian is clearly explained by

G. Denizot, *Description des Massifs de Marseilleveyre et de Puget,* Ann. Musée Hist. nat. Marseille, t. 26, mém. 5 (1934).

37. G. Corroy, *Le massif de la Sainte-Baume,* Bull. Serv. Carte géol. France, no. 201, t. 41 (1939). J. Goguel, *Essai d'une synthèse tectonique de la Provence,* Bull. Soc. géol. France, 13 (1943).

38. J. Goguel, *Extensions des faciès urgoniens dans l'Ardèche,* C. R. Soc. géol. France (May 18, 1936).

39. But we shall soon describe, north of the Vocontian trough, a sub-alpine Urgonian.

40. M. Breistroffer, *Révision des Ammonites du Vraconien de Salazac (Gard) et considérations générales sur ce sous-étage albien,* Trav. Lab. Géol. Univ. Grenoble, 22 (1940). J. Sornay, *Sur le Crétacé moyen de Viviers-sur-Rhône,* C. R. Soc. géol. France (1943), p. 168; *Remarques sur la transgression du Crétacé moyen en Ardèche,* C. R. Soc. géol. France (1944), p. 183.

41. W. Kilian and P. Reboul, *Contribution à l'étude des faunes paléocrétacées du Sud-Est de la France; I, La faune de l'Aptien inférieur des environs de Montélimar (Drôme) (Carrière de l'Homme d'Armes),* Mém. Serv. Carte géol. France (1915). This work is very important for the stratigraphic study of the Lower Cretaceous and the Urgonian in particular.

42. It is in this transition zone of the marly facies to the calcareous facies that the maximum thicknesses are observed. Thus the Barremian stage, by itself, may reach 1,000 m. and the same is true for the Hauterivian.

43. Bibliography and local details in M. Gignoux and L. Moret, *Géologie dauphinoise, ou Initiation à la Géologie par l'étude des environs de Grenoble,* Arthaud, Paris-Grenoble (1944). See especially for the Albian.

44. Mlle. M. Morand, *Etudes de la faunes des Calcaires valanginiens du Fontanil (Isère),* Trav. Lab. Géol. Univ. Grenoble, 10 (1914).

45. Revision of this fauna, by M. Breistroffer, in the Trav. Lab. Géol. Univ. Grenoble, t. 18 (1936).

46. L. Moret, work cited note 165, chap. 9.

47. J. Goguel, *Observations sur l'Urgonien du Vercors,* Bull. Serv. Carte Géol. France, no. 221, t. 46 (1946 [1947]).

48. For work following the classic studies of Ch. Jacob, see M. Breistroffer, *Etude de l'étage Albien dans le Massif de la Chartreuse (Isère et Savoie),* Trav. Lab. Géol. Univ. Grenoble, 18 (1935).

49. A. Jayet, *Etude stratigraphique de la Perte du Rhône, près de Bellegarde (Ain, France),* Eclogae geol. Helvetiae, 20 (1926).

50. See P. Lemoine, work cited note 19, chap. 7, and G. Corroy, *Le Néocomien de la bordure orientale du Bassin de Paris,* Thèse, Nancy (1925).

51. In this same region of Tournus, a fossiliferous remnant of the Albian, establishing a landmark between the Albian of the Jura Mountains and that of the Paris Basin, has just been discovered by G. Mazenot, C. R. Soc. géol. France (Feb. 6, 1933).

52. On this question, see the works of Lambert, Mém. Soc. Acad. de l'Aube (1916) and Corroy, C. R. Acad. Sc. (Dec. 26, 1922).

53. G. Houard, *Notes sur l'etage albien aux environs de St.-Florentin (Yonne),* Bull. Soc. Sc. Yonne (1932, Auxerre, 1934); *L'étage albien et sa faune aux environs de St.-Dizier (Haute-Marne),* Bull. Soc. géol. France, 9 (1939). C. Larcher *Contribution à l'étude de l'Albien du Département de l'Aube,* Bull. Sc. de Bourgogne, 6 (1936).

54. R. Abrard, *Sur l'extension des sables barrémiens et hauteriviens dans le Pays de Bray,* Bull. Mus. Nat. Hist. nat. 2 sér., t. 9, no. 3 (1937).

55. R. Abrard, *Les variations d'épaisseur du Gault dans le Pays de Bray,* C. R. Soc. géol. France (Mar. 1, 1937). J. P. and P. Destombes, *Remarques sur l'Albien du Pays de Bray,* C. R. Acad. Sc. (Oct. 24, 1938).

56. P. Lemoine, R. Humery and R. Soyer, *La découverte du Wealdian sous la région parisienne,* C. R. Acad. Sc. (Dec. 26, 1934); *Les forages profonds du bassin de Paris; la nappe artésienne des sables verts,* Mém. Mus. Nat. Hist. nat., n. s., t. 11, Paris (1939). In this important article, in addition to a hydrologic study of the aquifer, many details on the stratigraphy of the Lower Cretaceous will be found.

57. J. F. Kirkaldy, *The History of the lower Cretaceous period in England,* Proc. Geol. Ass., 50, 3 (1939).

58. H. J. Osborne White, *The Geology of the Country near Hastings and Dungeness,* Mem. Geol. Surv. England (1928). F. H. Edmunds, *The Wealden District,* 2. edit. (1948), British reg. Geol., Geol. Surv. and Mus.

59. A. P. Dutertre, *Sur le Crétacé inférieur du Boulonnais,* Ann. Soc. géol. du Nord, 62 (1937). A. Carpentier, *Sur l'extension du Wealdien dans le Nord de la France,* C. R. Acad. Sc., Oct. 18 (1926); *Comparison entre les faciès à végétaux d'âge éocrétacique du Bray et du Nord de la France,* Congrès intern. Mines, etc., 7 sess., Paris, 1935, sect. Géol. appliquée, p. 301, Paris (1936). For the Wealdian in the Ardennes, see M. Leriche, work cited note 38, chap. 9.

60. R. Marlière, *Deltas wealdiens du Hainaut,* Bull. Soc. belge Géol., 55 (1946), p. 69–101.

61. See p. 232, of the work of Lamplugh, Kitchin and Pringle, cited note 53, chap. 7.

62. For more details, see A. P. Dutertre, *Remarques sur le Crétacé inf. du Bas-Boulonnais et du SE de l'Angleterre,* Ann. Soc. géol. du Nord, 49 (1924). P. Pruvost, *Observations stratigraphiques et tectoniques dans le Boulonnais,* Bull. Serv. Carte géol. France, no. 151 (1924).

63. J. P. and P. Destombes, *Sur l'Albien supérieur de Wissant,* C. R. Soc. géol. France (Dec. 20, 1943).

64. R. Marliere, *Contributions à l'étude des formations crétacées et tertiaires du bassins de Mons* (2ᵉ fasc.), Bull. Soc. géol. Belgique, 63 (1939–40), no. 2 and 3; very expressive diagram on p. 74.

65. In contrast to the *Upper Greensand* of the Cenomanian (see p. 421).

66. Except for the remnants discovered in King Charles Land, at the mouth of the Lena, and on the east coast of Greenland. On this country, see Lauge Koch, *Stratigraphy of Greenland,* Medd. om Grönland, 73, Copenhagen (1929).

67. The Scandinavian shore of this gulf has been located by the very important discovery of a block of fossiliferous Neocomian conglomerate in the Lofoten region. See the article by J. Ravn and T. Vogt in *Norsk geol. Tidsskrift,* vol. III, 3, no. 4 (1915), with German summary.

68. A few rare *Polyptychites* and *Garnieria* have been noted in southeastern France by W. Kilian and his collaborators.

69. L. F. Spath, "On the Ammonites of the Speeton Clay and the Subdivisions of the Neocomian," Geol. Magaz. LXI (1924). As we have seen (p. 342), the lower part of these clays was formerly attributed to the Portlandian.

70. In northern Hanover, E. Harbort, Zeitsch. deutsch. geol. Ges. (1919), p. 333, estimates its thickness, Albian not included, at 1,000 m.

71. Cf. E. Stolley, *Die Systematik der Belemniten,* XI Jahrb. niedersächsischen geolog. Vereins, Hannover (1919). See also the work cited note 27, this chap.

72. A map giving the extent of Wealdian deposits and infra-Cretaceous seas is found in G. Beck, *Tektonische und paläogeographische Untersuchungen im Gebiet zwischen Hildesheim und Braunschweig,* Abh. preuss. geol. Lands., N. F. Heft 85 (1920). A. Kumm, *Die Schichtenfolge im Kanaleinschnitt bei Wenden,* Jahrb. preus. geol. Lands. (1936), 37; this work describes the Neocomian-Albian series with thicknesses and modern paleontologic zones.

73. E. Stolley, *Die Stratigraphie des norddeutschen Obergaults, Minimus-Ton und Flammenmergels, im Vergleich mit dem englischen Lower und Upper Gault,* Neues Jahrb. F. Min., Beilage-Band 78, Abt. B (1937).

74. V. Nordmann, V. Madsen, etc. *Aperçu de la géologie du Danemark,* (published in 4 languages), Danmarks geol. Undersôgelse, ser. 5, no. 4, Copenhagen (1928).

75. W. Kauenhoven, *Das Basisconglomerat der unteren Kreide im nördlichen Harzvorlande und seine Eisenerzführung,* Neues Jahr. f. Min., Abh., Abt. B, 55, Beilage-Band (1926).

76. L. Riedel, *Der Westrand der Pompeckj'schen Schwelle zur Kreidezeit in Hannover,* Zeitschr. deutsch. geol. Ges., 90 (1938); the map, plate I, indicates the western shores of this threshold at different infra-Cretaceous stages, according to the information pro-

vided by wells around the salt domes; *Zur Paläogeographie de Kreide in Nordwest-deutschland,* Jahrb. Reichstelle f. Bodenforschung, 61 (1941). W. Haack, *Der Untergrund der Lüneberger Heide,* Abh. Natur. Ver. Bremen, 31, H. 2 (1939).

77. The genus *Blandfordiceras,* a lower Valanginian ammonite known only in India, has just been recognized in Germany by L. Riedel, *Zur Stratigraphie der tieferen Unterkreide in Nordwestdeutschland, besonders in den Erdölgebieten,* Jahrb. Reichstelle f. Bodenforschung (1939), 60.

78. *J. Lewinski, Sur le Néocomien en Pologne,* C. R. Soc. géol. France (Jan. 19, 1931). *Das Neokom im Polen und seine paläogeographische Bedeutung,* Geol. Rund., 23 (1932). For the Albian of these regions, see J. Samsonovicz, *Esquisse géologique des environs de Rachowa, sur la Vistule, et les transgressions de l'Albien et du Cénomanien dans le sillon Nord-Européen,* Sprawozdania Polskiego Inst. geol., 3, Warsaw (1925).

79. Remember especially the Valanginian which we mentioned in Poland, following Lewinsky.

80. R. Abrard, *Sur la pénétration des formes tempérées dans le Nord du bassin aquitanien pendant le Crétacé supérieur,* C. R. Acad. Sc., 218 (1945), p. 844.

81. According to P. Lemoine.

82. Very rare rudistids are found, beginning in the Cenomanian and continuing into the Senonian. See R. Dehée, *Observations sur les Rudistes des terrains crétacés du Nord de la France,* Ann. Soc. géol. du Nord, 52 (1927).

83. R. Marlière, *La transgression albienne et cénomanienne dans le Hainaut,* Thèse Sc. Lille, 1939; Mém. Mus. roy. Hist. nat. Belgique, no. 89 (1939); *Ce qu'est le "Vraconien" en Belgique,* Bull. Soc. belge Géol. (1942), 51; *Les mers albiennes et cénomaniennes en bordure méridionale du continent ardennais,* Bull. Soc. r. belge Géogr., 69 année (1945); with a map of these seas between Scotland and the Ardennes.

84. J. Cornet, *La disposition transgressive du Turonian dans le Bassin du Mons,* Ann. Soc. géol. Belgique, t. 51, Bull. no. 3, 1927, Liege (1928).

85. B. Brajnikov, *Recherches sur la formation appelée "argile à silex" dans le Bassin de Paris,* Revue Géogr. phys. et Géol. dynam., 10, fasc. 1 and 2 (1937). See also the work by L. Moret cited note 11, this chap.

86. From this point of view, it is very instructive to compare the last two editions of the geologic map of France, scale 1/1,000,000. In the first, the covering of clay with flints was represented, in the Tertiary, in all the northern part of the Paris Basin; in the second (1934), it was with reason omitted, which resulted in greater unity for these immense stretches of the Chalk.

87. Recently, M. Leriche, relying on the fish faunas and some invertebrate groups, has proposed raising the lower limit generally allowed for the Maestrichtian. He would thus be led to attribute the Meudon chalk to the Campanian. The true Maestrichtian would be represented only in Belgium and Holland and would no longer be recognized in the Paris Basin. See M. Leriche, *Les Poissons du Crétacé marin de la Belgique et du Limbourg hollandais; les résultats stratigraphiques de leur étude,* Bull. Soc. belge Géol., 37 (1927).

88. Such is, at least, the classic opinion, expressed by the paleogeographic maps of A. de Lapparent. But it is based especially on the present extent of outcrops and not on the appearance of littoral facies. It is thus to be used with caution.

89. M. Leriche, *Sur le Crétacé supérieur du Hainaut et du Brabant,* Ann. Soc. geol. Belgique, 48 (1934). This Belgian Maestrichtian gives evidence of a regime of violent currents, with submarine erosion, phosphatized beds and hard-grounds of tough chalk perforated by borers (well illustrated).

90. According to Abrard (see note 80, this chap.), these Mediterranean orbitoids could have arrived only through the Channel, for he considers, as does Leriche, that the Paris Basin was already emergent at this epoch.

91. The English Turonian and Senonian have been divided into numerous ammonite zones by L. F. Spath, "On New Ammonites from the English Chalk," Geol. Magaz., 63 (1926). For the Cenomanian, see also L. F. Spath, Proc. Geol. Ass., 37 (1926). Finally, very recently, microforaminifers have been used for the stratigraphy of the chalk in wells; E. Williams-Mitchell, "The Zonal Value of Foraminifera in the Chalk of England," Proc. Geol. Ass., 59 (1948).

92. M. Breistroffer, *Sur l'âge exact des grès verts de Cambridge (Angleterre)*, C. R. Soc. géol. France (1946), p. 309.

93. Numerous echinoid zones are distinguished in the Senonian by C. T. A. Gaster, "The Stratigraphy of the Chalk of Sussex," Proc. Geol. Ass., 48 (1937).

94. This Cenomanian transgression was described for the Rhenish Massif by R. Bärtling, *Transgressionen, Regressionen und Fazies-Verteilung in der mittleren und obern Kreide des Beckens von Münster*, Zeitschr. deutsch. geol. Ges., 72 (1920) and for the Bohemian Massif by H. Schauder, *Die cenomane Transgression im mittleren Elbtalgebiet*, ibid., 75 (1923).

95. T. Wegner, *Die Rudisten des norddeutschen Turons*, Zeitschr. deutsch. geol. Ges., 76 (1924). In the Turonian there are only *Durania* and *Sauvagesia; Durania*, known from the upper Albian in Dauphiné (L. Moret), becomes relatively common in the north during the Cenomanian and Turonian; *Sauvagesia* is not very rare in Germany in the Senonian, while radiolitids and hippuritids are completely missing.

96. Sometimes assigned to the Tertiary. A discussion, with bibliography, will be found in Poul Harder, *Sur la limite entre le sable vert de Lellinge et le calcaire de Saltholm, avec quelques remarques sur la division du Tertiare inf. du Danemark*, Danmarks geologiske Undersogelse, II R., no. 38, Copenhagen (1932). See also J. P. J. Ravn, *Sur le placement géologique du Danien*, ibid., no. 43 (1925). H. Odum, *Studies of the Danian in Jutland and Funen*, ibid. (1926). J. P. J. Ravn, *Etudes sur les Pélécypodes et les Gastropodes daniens du calcaire de Faxe*, Mém. Acad. roy. Sc. et Lettres, Danemark, Sect. Sc., 9 sér., 5, no. 2 (1933); this fauna is different both from that of the Cretaceous and that of the Montian. A. Chavan, *L'évolution des faunes marines de Mollusques dans le Nord-Ouest de l'Europe de la fin du Crétacé à celle de l'Eocène*, Bull. Soc. géol. France, 16 (1946); a meticulous study of the distinctive characteristics of the Danian and Montian faunas.

97. C. Zahalka, *Die böhmische Kreideformation in der sächsischen Bucht* (in Czech, with a German summary), Bull. Serv. géol. Repub. Czechoslovak, sup. to vol. 3, 1923, Prague (1924). W. Pozaryski, *Senonstratigraphie im Durchbruch der Weichsel zwischen Rachow und Pulawy in Mittelpolen*, Bull. Serv. geol. Pologne, no. 6 (1938).

98. H. Sculpin, *Zur Paläogeographie des sudetischen Kreidesmeeres*, Zeitschr. deutsch. geol. Ges., 88 (1936).

99. A. Luniewskie, *Les Mésocrétacé sur le versant NE de Lysogory et son substratum*, C. R. Soc. Sc. et Lettres, Warsaw, no. 28 (1936).

100. Isolated specimens of *Belemnitella quadrata* and *mucronata* have been found in the Corbières and Charentes; R. Balland, *Sur une nouvelle trouvaille de Bélemnitelle (Gonioteuthis quadrata, Blainville) dans le Crétacé supérieur de Saintonge*, C. R. Soc. géol. France (1948), p. 17.

101. According to Abrard, whose opinion is confirmed by G. Delpey, *Paléogéographie du Sud-Ouest de la France au Crétacé supérieur*, Bull. Soc. Hist. nat. Toulouse, 73 (1939), p. 250; maps of facies for each stage.

102. R. Abrard, *Contribution à l'étude des étages Campanien et Maestrichtien aux environs de Royan*, Bull. Soc. géol. France, 4 sér., 24 (1924).

103. D. Schneegans, *Evolution des faciès du Flysch néocrétacé sous les Petite-Pyrénées de la Haute Garonne*, C. R. Soc. géol. France (Mar. 6, 1944).

104. S. Douvillé, *Le Crétacé inférieur dans le Béarn et la Bigorre*, Bull. Soc. géol. France, 4 sér., 30 (1930).

105. G. Dubar, *Sur la transgression éocrétacée dans les Pyrénées occidentales*, Bull. Soc. géol. France, 4 sér., 29 (1929).

106. P. Lamare, *Les formations détritiques crétacées du massif de Mendibelza*, Bull. Soc. géol. France, 5 sér., 16 (1946), p. 265. Y. Gubler, M. Casteras, R. Ciry and P. Lamare, *Sur l'âge des poudingues dits de Mendibelza, dans le bassin de Laurhibar, au SE de Mendive (Basses-Pyrénées)*, C. R. Soc. géol. France (1947), p. 329.

107. M. Dalloni, *Transgression du Cénomanien sur la zone primaire axiale des Pyrénées ariégeoises*, C. R. Acad. Sc., 206 (1938), p. 195.

108. M. Castéras et E. Raguin, *Seconde Note sur les schistes de la bordure Nord du Massif de Castillon (Ariège)*, C. R. Soc. géol. France (Mar. 15, 1943).

109. However, this basin was very narrow, for at Tercis, southwest of Dax, a littoral Cenomanian is found on its northern shore, with rudistids and alveolines and even lignites, which, at St-Lon south-southwest of Dax, contain *Glauconia*, a brackish mollusk that is found again in the Cenomanian lignites of Montdragon, on the north shore of the Durancian isthmus. See F. Daguin and G. Delpey, *Sur l'âge des couches à lignites de St-Lon (Landes)*, C. R. Acad. Sc. (Dec. 29, 1941).

110. D. Schneegans and P. Michel, *Le front Nord-pyrénéen entre le Salat et l'Adour*, Bull. Soc. géol. France, 5 sér., 13 (1943).

111. J. de Lapparent, *Etude lithologique des terrains crétacés de la région d'Hendaye*, Mém. Serv. Carte géol. France (1918).

112. Y. Gubler, *La stratigraphie du Flysch au Sud de Pau (B.-P.)*, Bull. Soc. géol. France, 5 sér., 16 (1946), p. 265.

113. J. Cuvillier, *Relations du Crétacé et de l'Eocène inf. en Aquitaine méridionale*, C. R. Soc. géol. France (Dec. 3, 1945).

114. M. Dreyfuss and M. Gottis, *A propos des couches marines du bassin de Villeveyrac (Hérault)*, C. R. Soc. géol. France (1947), p. 143.

115. Note especially in these lithographic limestones *Bauxia baylei*, a gastropod of the melanid family, which is found in the Rognacian of Baux in Provence, at the same stratigraphic horizon.

116. Convenient stratigraphic summaries in G. Corroy and G. Denizot, *Guide géologique de la Provence occidentale*, Lab. Géol. Univ. Marseille (1935), and work cited note 115, chap. 7.

117. Some authors even recognize the existence of an emerged Pyrenean-Corsican-Sardinian Massif. The important work by G. Richter, *Das Grenzgebiet Alpen-Pyrenäen, Tektonische Einheiten des süd-ost-französischen Raumes*, Abh. Ges. Wiss. Göttingen, Math., Phys. Kl., III Folge, Heft 19, Berlin (1938) brings no new facts but, for all the Secondary and Tertiary, many very interesting paleogeographic maps, diagrams of thicknesses, etc. The Durancian isthmus is called "Vaucluse-Estérel Schwelle."

118. J. de Lapparent, *Les bauxites de la France méridionale*, Mém. Serv. Carte géol. France (1930).

119. All the more as this exploitation is covered by legislation for quarries and not by that for mining concessions. The result is that work in galleries, even at great depths, cannot be undertaken except after preliminary agreement with all the property owners of the surface land.

120. S. Fabre, *Le Crétacé supérieur de la Basse-Provence occidentale*, Ann. Fac. Sc. Marseille, sér. 2, t. 14 (1940).

121. J. Pfender, C. R. Soc. géol. France (June 13, 1938) has recently pointed out the genus *Chrondrodonta*, a large pelecypod, very characteristic of the rudistid facies of the eastern Mediterranean, but unknown up to the present time in Provence.

122. H. Parent, *Poudingues de la Ciotat fossilifères, Ile Verte (Baie de la Ciotat)*, C. R. Soc. géol. France (1938), p. 91. We see that, in the great Pyrenean-Provençal gulf, these conglomerates play exactly the same role, in relation to the ancient Maures Massif, as the conglomerates of Mendibelza (Basque Pyrenees) in relation to the Pyrenean Primary axial zone.

123. Fine deposit of St. Cyr-sur-Mer, southeast of La Ciotat, studied by L. Moret (see note 11, this chap.).

124. Local details in G. Denizot, *Bassins de Fuveau et de l'Arc*, Bull. Serv. Carte géol. France (1941–1943), 43, p. 417.

125. J. Repelin, C. R. Soc. géol. France (Apr. 27, 1936) has recently proposed placing the Fuvelian in the upper Campanian by reason (?) of its still brackish *Corbicula*-bearing intercalations. Then only the completely continental Begudian would be equivalent to the Maestrichtian.

126. P. H. Fritel, *La flore aturienne de Fuveau* (Bull. Mus. nat. d'Hist. nat., 1927, no. 5).

127. A. F. de Lapparent, *Les Dinosauriens du Crétacé sup. du Midi de la France*, Mém. Soc. géol. France, n. s., t. 26, fasc. 4, no. 56, p. 1–54, pl. 9–14.

128. M. Breistroffer, *Note sur le Cénomanien inf. de la fosse vocontienne (Htes-Alpes et Drôme)*, C. R. Acad. Sc., 208 (1939), p. 1,514.

129. E. Maury, *Note stratigraphique et tectonique sur le Crétacé sup. de la vallée du Paillon (Alpes-Maritimes)*, Bull. Soc. géol. France, 4 sér., 7 (1907).

130. H. Parent, C. R. Soc. géol. France (Mar. 15, 1943 and May 28, 1945).

131. J. Goguel, C. R. Soc. géol. France (Nov. 20, 1933).

132. P. Pruvost, *Un bassin houiller paralique d'âge cénomanien: les lignites de Pont St.-Esprit*, Bull. Soc. géol. France, 5 sér., 12 (1942).

133. For the detailed succession of the beds of the Cenomanian-Santonian, see P. de Brun and C. Chatelet, *Le massif crétacé d'Uchaux (Vaucluse) et son auréole miocène*, Bull. Soc. Etudes Sc. Nat. Vaucluse (1935), no. 2, and (1937), no. 3.

134. M. Faraud, *Le Ligérien de la colline de Bernon, près de Tresques (Gard)*, Bull. Soc. d'Etudes Sc. Nat. de Vaucluse (1934), no. 1.

135. J. Sornay, *Le Crétacé sup. dans l'Ouest de la Drôme*, Trav. Lab. Géol. Univ. Grenoble, 26 (1946), 27 p., 4 pl.

136. M. Breistroffer, *Note sur le Cénomanien du Vercors (Isère)*, C. R. Soc. géol. France (May 1, 1939).

137. Naturally there are no more orbitolines here. L. Moret has noted in the greensand the presence of the genus *Durania*, a curious rudistid that we have seen (note 95, this chap.) appear in the North Sea.

138. See work of L. Moret cited note 165, chap. 9.

139. L. W. Collet and E. Paréjas, *Sur la présence du Crétacé sup. à la Rivière, près de Chésery (Ain)*, C. R. Soc. Phys. Hist. nat. Genève, 42, no. 3 (1925). H. Vincienne, *Le Crétacé sup. de Cuiseaux (S.-et-L.)* C. R. Soc. géol. France (Mar. 30, 1936).

140. O. Renz, *Ueber ein Maestrichtien-Cenomanien Vorkommen bei Alfermée am Bielersee*, Eclogae Geol. Hevetiae, 29 (1936), and ibid., Exkursionsbericht, 34. no. 2 (1941), p. 205 and pl. XI.

141. H. Vincienne and P. Cliquet, *Extension du Crétacé sup. dans le Sud du Jura; à propos de la brèche de Narlay*, C. R. Soc. géol. France (1948), p. 119.

142. For everything concerning this sector of the Alps, see the work by M. Gignoux and L. Moret (1938) cited note 154, chap. 5.

143. M. Gignoux, *Sur la possibilité de l'extension du Néocomien dans la zone de l'Embrunnais, sur la rive droite de la Durance*, C. R. Acad. Sc. (May 30, 1932); *Sur la présence du Néocomien dans le Briançonnais à l'Argentière (S de Briançon)*, C. R. Soc. géol. France (Nov. 20, 1933). M. Gignoux, L. Moret and D. Schneegans, *Observations géologiques dans le Bassin de la Haute-Durance, entre Gap et la frontière italienne*, Trav. Lab. Géol. Univ. Grenoble, 18 (1934).

144. Work cited note 54, chap. 6.

145. Fossil noted for the first time by L. Moret and D. Schneegans.

146. Nevertheless, together with Messrs. Moret, Schneegans and Renz, we have been able to find the Neocomian with *Aptycus* in the most external units of the Briançonnais zone, at Notre-Dame-des-Neiges, above Briançon, and at the Tête du Grand-Pré, above the Monetier de Briançon.

147. L. Moret and F. Blanchet, *Contribution à l'étude du Crétacé intra-alpin (Alpes occidentales): le problème des "marbres en plaquettes,"* Bull. Soc. géol. France, 4 sér., 24 (1924). F. Blanchet, work cited note 58, chap. 6.

148. E. Raguin, work cited note 126, chap. 7 and *Découverte d'une faune de Foraminifères, très probablement crétacés, dans les calcaires hautement métamorphiques du vallon de Paquier, près de la Grande-Motte (Savoie)*, C. R. Acad. Sc., t. 181 (1925), p. 726. See also F. Ellenberger, work cited note 59, chap. 6.

149. Y. Gubler and H. Schoeller, C. R. Soc. géol. France (1947).

150. For the Upper Cretaceous, see the very detailed and very clear diagram given (p. 216) in H. Bolli, *Zur Stratigraphie der Oberen Kreide in den höheren helvetischen Decken*, Eclogae geol. Helvetiae, 37 (1945); a recent bibliography will be found there.

151. The position of the boundary between the Cretaceous and the Tertiary in these zones has recently been questioned. See for example an article by A. Jeannet, Eclogae

geologicae Helvetiae XVIII, 1923, p. 227. Arnold Heim, Matériaux Carte géol. Suisse, 53rd livraison (1923), p. 1, and L. Rollier, ibid., p. 53, even believed that the presence of nummulites, assilines, and orthophragmines has been proved in beds with Cretaceous inocerames and ammonites. This statement, patently subversive, has since been refuted. See P. Liechti, *Geologische Untersuchung der Dreispitz-Standfluhgruppe und der Flyschregion südlich des Thunersees,* Mitt. Naturf. Ges. in Bern, 1930, Bern (1931).

152. By Arnold Heim, who called this classic locality, "Mont Bifé."

153. B. Tschachtli, *Ueber Flysch und Couches rouges in den Decken der östlichen Prealpes romandes (Simmental-Saanen),* Thèse, Berne (1941): stratigraphy based on foraminifers; the transgressive red beds pass into Tertiary *Flysch.*

154. B. Campana, *Faciès et extension de la nappe de la Simme au Nord-Est de Château d'Oex,* Eclogae geol. Helvetiae, 34 (1941), p. 221.

155. This opinion, long upheld by E. Haug and W. Kilian, now seems to be adopted by many Swiss geologists.

156. O. Weigel, *Stratigraphie und Tektonik des Beckens von Gosau,* Jahrb. geol. Bundesanst., 87, Vienna (1937). K. Leuchs *Die Beziehungen swischen Gosau- und Flyschfazies,* Osterreichische Akad. Wiss., Math. Nat. Kl., Sitz. Ber., Abt. 1 (1947), 156, no. 3–4, p. 167–180. O. Kühn, *Zur Stratigraphie und Tektonik der Gosauschichten,* ibid., p. 200.

157. E. Dittler and O. Kühn, *Ueber den Bauxit von Dreistätten in Niederösterreich,* Verhandl. geol. Bundesanst. (1936), no. 12.

158. O. Kühn, *Ein Danienvorkommen in Niederosterreich,* Mitt. geol. Ges., Vienna, 19 (1926).

159. A. Rodighiero, *Il sistema cretaceo del Veneto occidentale compreso fra l'Adige e il Piave, con speciale riguardo al Neocomiano dei Sette Comuni,* Paleon. ital., 25 (1919).

160. Famous fauna of Turonian rudistids from Col dei Schiosi, in Frioul.

161. E. Passendorfer, *Etude stratigraphique et paléontologique du Crétacé de la série haut-tatrique dans les Tatras,* Trav. Serv. géol. Pologne, vol. 2, fasc. 1, Warsaw (1930).

162. D. Andrusov and J. Koutek, *Le Crétacé sup. à faciès "couches rouges" dans la série des Klippes internes des Carpathes occidentales,* Bull. Serv. géol. Repub. Tschecoslovaque, 3 (1927).

163. G. Macovei and I. Atanasiu, *L'évolution géologique de la Roumanie. Crétacé,* Ann. Inst. géol. Roumanie, 16, 1931, Bucharest (1933). This work contains paleogeographic maps. In the Crimea, very rich Lower Cretaceous faunas with cephalopods have been made classic by the publications of Karakash. The Middle and Upper Cretaceous of this same region have been studied by G. Weber and V. Malychef, Bull. Soc. géol. France (1923).

164. J. Noszky, *Contributions à l'étude des formations crétacées du Bakony septentrional,* Földlani Közlöny, 64, Budapest (1934).

165. J. G. de Weisse, *Les bauxites de l'Europe centrale (province dinarique et Hongrie),* Mém. Soc. vaudoise Sc. nat., no. 58, vol. 9, no. 1 (1948). Geologic map of Bakony and stratigraphic bibliography.

166. It may be said, in fact, that the organic limestone facies is self perpetuating. A country formed exclusively of pure limestone massifs cannot feed detrital sedimentation on the submarine continental platforms which surround it, since its beaches and rivers transport neither clayey muds nor sands. And, in compensation, in these pure waters, reef-building organisms find a constantly favorable milieu, so that limestones will indefinitely succeed limestones.

167. L. Trevisan, *La fauna e i giacimenti del Cenomaniano di facies africano della Sicilia occidentale,* Mem. Istit. geol. Univ. Padova, 12 (1937).

168. The works of Spanish geologists are too numerous to be listed here. We indicate only, as sources of information in French, the following works: R. Douvillé, *La péninsule ibérique, Espagne,* Handb. der regionalen Geol., Heft 7 (1911). L. Mengaud, *Recherches géologiques dans la région contabrique,* Paris, Hermann (1920). M. Dalloni, *Etude géologique des Pyrénées de l'Aragon,* Ann. Fac. Sc. Marseille, XIX (1910) and *op. cit.* note 153, chap. 5. P. Fallot, *op. cit.* note 34, chap. 6.

169. Summary and bibliography in P. Fallot, *Etat de nos connaissances sur la structure des Chaines bétique et subbétique,* Livre jubilaire du Centenaire de la Soc. géol. de France (1930). M. Blumenthal, *Beiträge zur Geologie der betischen Cordilleren beiderseits des Rio Guadalhorce,* Eclogae geol. Helvetiae, 23 (1930).

170. J. O. Carrington Da Costa, *O Neocretacico da Beira-Litoral,* Pub. Mus. Lab. min. geol. Fac. Cienc. Porto, 5 (1937).

171. See especially the reservation made in note 61, chap. 7.

172. P. Fallot and J. R. Bataller, *Itinerario geologico a través del bajo Aragon y del Maestrazgo,* Mem. R. Acad. Ciencias y Artes de Barcelona, 20 (1927).

173. R. Ciry, *Etude géologique d'une partie des provinces de Burgos, Palencia, Léon et Santander,* Thèse Sc. Toulouse (1940), Bull. Soc. Hist. nat. Toulouse, 74 (1939).

174. See the work of Dalloni, cited note 153, chap. 5.

175. P. Fallot even considers that, at the mouth of the Ebro, the transition from the Jurassic to the Cretaceous was made through marine dolomites. Thus, he would have had no emergence between the two systems, in this extreme eastern part of the Aragon gulf.

176. In addition to the works of Savornin, Moret, Glangeaud, etc., cited previously (in particular, note 172, chap. 7), see E. Roch, *Etudes géologiques dans la région méridionale du Maroc occidental,* Notes et Mém. du Serv. des Mines et de la Carte géol. du Maroc (1930); J. Lacoste, *Etudes géologiques dans le Rif méridional,* ibid. (1934); F. Daguin, *Contribution à l'étude géologique de la région prérifaine (Maroc occidental),* ibid. (1927). For the Sahara, see the excellent summary of R. Furon, C. Kilian and N. Menchikoff, cited note 71, chap. 2. Maps of Cretaceous facies of North Africa in the important work of R. Lafitte, *Etude géologique de l'Aurès,* Bull. Serv. Carte géol. Algérie, 2 sér., no. 15 (1939).

177. This is the "Kabylies geanticline" of L. Glangeaud, south of the "deep South Tellian furrow." But farther east, while the former is prolonged by the "Numidian geanticline" the South Tellian trough is prolonged by a "Constantine basin of sedimentation," where, in the Barremian-Cenomanian, numerous shoals existed, above which there was a very abrupt passage to deep-water facies (Djebel Ouach) with very thick, neritic limestone facies (region of Hammam Meskoutine) found in the southern part of central Tunisia. See P. Deleau, *Etude géologique des régions de Jemmapes, Hammam Meskoutine et du col des Oliviers,* Bull. Serv. Carte géol. Algérie, 2 sér., no. 14 (1938). G. Castany, *Les terrains de la Chaîne des Djebels Nara et Touïla (Tunisie centrale),* C. R. Acad. Sc., 223 (1946), p. 684. A. Lambert, *Glissements sous-marins, sédimentation et orogénèse dans la Kabylie des Babors au Crétacé,* Bull. Soc. geol. France, 18 (1948), p. 51.

178. J. Flandrin, *L'Albo-Aptien de la région littorale entre Dellys et Port-Gueydon,* C. R. Soc. géol. France (Feb. 1, 1937). F. Ehrmann and H. Strallen, *Sur la présence du Flysch crétacé inférieur dans la zone axiale de la chaîne calcaire du Djurdjura,* ibid. J. Savornin and P. Deleau, *L'étage valanginien de faciès jurassien sur les hauts-plateaux d'Alger,* C. R. Soc. géol. France (Dec. 7, 1936).

179. See work of R. Lafitte, cited note 176, this chap.

180. The existence of a Saharan Quaternary sea is still hypothetical. A. F. de Lapparent and M. Lelubre, *Interprétation stratigraphique des séries continentales entre Chanet et Bourarhet (Sahara central),* C. R. Acad. Sc., 227 (1948), p. 1106, note, in the lagoonal-marine beds of the upper Nubian sandstone, a pelecypod fauna apparently of Lower Cretaceous age.

181. R. Furon and N. Menchikoff, *Sur l'Eocène et le Crétacé du Tanezrouft (Sahara),* C. R. Soc. géol. France (Apr. 1, 1935).

182. V. Pérébaskine, *Contribution à l'étude géologique du Soudan oriental,* Thèse Sc. Strasbourg (1934).

183. R. Lafitte, *Les faciès de l'Aptien, de l'Albien et du Turonian dans l'Aurès (Algérie),* C. R. Acad. Sc. (Dec. 3, 1934).

184. D. Lafitte, *Les limites stratigraphiques du Sénonien dans l'Aurès oriental (Algérie),* C. R. Acad. Sc. (Dec. 10, 1934).

185. A. Lambert and P. Marie, *Nouvelles observations sur le Sénonien de la zone des Kabylies (Algérie),* C. R. Soc. géol. France (1948), p. 124.

186. One may also consider the provinces of climatic origin: R. Lafitte, *Répartition de la faune néritique au Cénomanien dans le bassin méditerranéen,* C. R. Soc. Biogéogr., 14 année, no. 123.

187. G. Scott, *Etudes stratigraphiques et paléontologiques sur les terrains crétacés du Texas,* Trav. Lab. Géol. Univer. Grenoble, 14 (1927). E. Böse, *Cretaceous Ammonites from Texas and Northern Mexico,* Bur. of Econ. Geol. Univ. of Texas, Bull. 2848, Austin (1927). L. W. Stephenson, etc., "Correlation of the Outcropping Cretaceous Formations of the Atlantic and Gulf Coastal Plain and Trans-Pecos, Texas," Bull. Geol. Soc. Amer. (1942), 53, p. 435, 1 pl.

188. In Colombia, a Barremian with pulchellids belonging to Mediterranean species is also known. J. Royo Y Gomez, *Fosiles del Barremiense colombiano,* Compilacion de los estudios geologicos oficiales en Colombia, t. 6. Serv. geol. nac., Bogota (1945). Appended to this volume will be found a geologic map of Colombia, with explanation. A revision of these famous Colombian faunas by M. Breistroffer is in process.

In Chile and Peru there is found a typical Urgonian with *Requienia ammonia,* etc. See C. H. Fritsche, *Neue Kreidefaunen aus Südamerika,* Neues Jahrb. f. Min., Beilage-Band 50 (1923). Also A. Windhausen, *Lineas generales de la Estratigrafia del Neocomiano en la Cordillera Argentina,* Bol. Acad. Nac. de Ciencias de Cordoba, vol. 23, Buenos Aires (1918), and the work of C. E. Weaver, cited note 192, chap 7.

189. Which did not necessarily extend over the whole North Atlantic.

190. G. C. Martin, *The Mesozoic Stratigraphy of Alaska,* U. S. Geol. Survey, Bull. 776 (1926). This fundamental work contains correlation tables showing relations with other American regions and European stages.

191. F. M. Anderson, "Knoxville-Shasta Succession in California," Bull Geol. Soc. Amer., 44 (1933); *Lower Cretaceous Deposits in California and Oregon,* Geol. Soc. Amer., Spec. paper no. 16, 340 p. 84 pl. (1938).

192. L. W. Stephenson and J. B. Reeside, Jr., "Comparison of Upper Cretaceous Deposits of Gulf Region and Western Interior Region," Bull. Amer. Ass. Petrol. Geol., 22 (1938). J. G. Bartram, "Upper Cretaceous of the Rocky Mountain Area," ibid., 21 (1937). For the Turonian and Senonian, see J. B. Webb and L. G. Hertlein, "Zones in Alberta Shale ("Benton" Group) in Foothills of Southwestern Alberta," ibid. 18 (1934).

193. A rich Senonian fauna, with remarkably well-preserved mollusks was described by Bruce Wade, *The Fauna of the Ripley Formation on Coon Creek, Tennessee,* U. S. Geol. Surv., Prof. Paper 137 (1926).

194. E. Spieker and J. B. Reeside, "Upper Cretaceous Shoreline in Utah," Bull. Geol. Soc. Amer., 37 (1926).

195. E. M. Spieker, *Late Mesozoic and Early Cenozoic History of Central Utah,* U. S. Geol. Surv., Prof. paper no. 205-D (1946).

196. G. Scott, "Age of the Midway Group," Bull. Geol. Soc. Amer., 45 (1934).

197. For more details, see W. D. Matthew, "Fossil Vertebrates and the Cretaceous-Tertiary Problem," Amer. Journ. Sc. (1921); F. Ward, "The Lance Problem in South Dakota," ibid. (1924).

198. For the Asiatic continent, which we have not discussed here, a study of the central continental basins will be found, following Russian, Chinese and American work, in F. K. Morris, "Central Asia in Cretaceous Time," Bull. Geol. Soc. Amer., 47 (1936).

199. See pp. 19 and 488.

Chapter Nine

The Nummulitic or Paleogene

I. Generalities

A. *Definitions and Subdivisions*

It is convenient to combine all the lower Tertiary formations in a single group. This Paleogene[1] or Nummulitic system will be characterized first by the presence of *Nummulites,*[2] almost limited to this period, and its stratigraphic individuality results from its being inclosed between two periods of regression, the effect of which is perceptible over most of Europe. The places where marine sedimentation remained continuous, on the one hand between the Cretaecous and the Paleogene, on the other hand between the Paleogene and the upper Tertiary or Neogene,[3] are in fact extremely rare.

So the individuality of this system is very soon evident, but this is not true of its subdivisions.

The stratigraphy of this Paleogene originates in fact in the Parisian region. At this period, multiple transgressions and secondary regressions followed each other in the Paris Basin and have made possible the definition of as many local stages, each distinguished by its facies, its paleogeography and its fauna. Only toward the end of the Nummulitic did the sea definitely leave the region. But in other countries, it was somewhat different. In northern Germany and Russia, particularly, vast regions were only tardily invaded by the Paleogene seas. The transgressive formations, with which the marine Tertiary begins there, have been designated as Oligocene,[4] while the name of Eocene[5] is restricted to the lower part of the Nummulitic. Thus from Germany comes the idea of an Oligocene sub-system. The Nummulitic will then include two periods, Eocene at the base, Oligocene at the top, a division which would not be so clearly apparent if we knew only the Paris Basin.

B. *Paleogeography*

When once again the sea invaded Europe, following the great regression at the end of the Cretaceous, the continental structure was not altered. There continued, in the north, a great continental area with epicontinental seas, more or less direct appendages of the basin which occupied the North Sea. And south of the zone of Hercynian Massifs of Middle Europe (Brittany, Massif Central, Rhenish and Bohemian Massifs) a great Mediterranean Sea stretched out, as in the Cretaceous, geosynclinal, with deep troughs and cordilleras, always including the location of the Alpine chains, still unformed.

But this mountain-building was to take place in the course of the Nummulitic period, bringing profound changes in the guiding lines of the paleogeography, lines which had prevailed since the Jurassic.

First to be considered are the Pyrenees and the Mountains of Provence (Pyrenees, Provençal Chain), whose final folding and emergence occurred in the Eocene. Since the end of that period they have existed as elevated chains and on their borders the sub-horizontal Oligocene overlies the folded Eocene. Then there is the Alpine Chain proper, whose most important folding took place in the course of the Oligocene. So with the close of the Nummulitic, there came to an end the sort of paleogeographic inversion by which the Tertiary chains, at present the highest of mountains, were formed just at those places which were occupied during the Secondary and Eocene, by the deepest parts of the great Mediterranean. The Neogene seas did no more than encircle these chains, leaving depressions which still surround them today.

In summary, for the study of the Nummulitic in Europe, we are interested in distinguishing three great domains: 1st. the basin of the North Sea and its dependents; 2nd. the zone of the Hercynian Massifs of Middle Europe; 3rd. the vast Mesogean domain.

C. *Provinces*

In the Nummulitic, as in the Cretaceous, the North Sea and the Mediterranean constitute two great faunal reservoirs and thus define two provinces, one northern and the other Mediterranean. To the former belong the Anglo-Parisian Basin and the North Sea with its dependents in Germany, and to the latter, Aquitaine, southern France, and all the Alpine and Mediterranean countries.

These two provinces were separated by the zone of the Hercynian Massifs of Middle Europe, Bohemia, the Rhenish Massifs, and the French Massif Central. West of the latter, there were undoubtedly extensive emerged lands which must have extended over the North Atlantic (North Atlantic continent), of which today only Brittany and the English Primary Massifs survive. For the Nummulitic faunas which we know from the southern Atlantic shore, in Aquitaine, are clearly Mediterranean.

However, some exchanges may have been established temporarily between these two provinces across this emerged Atlantic region, approximately

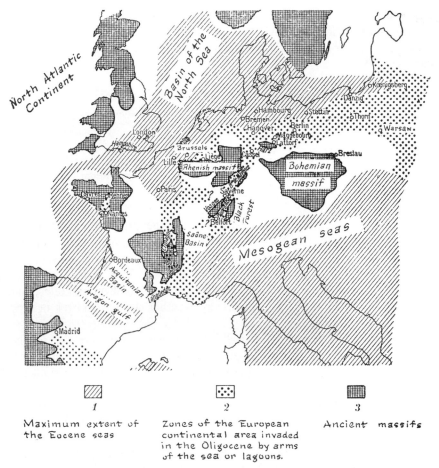

FIG. 109. *Map of the great paleogeographic units of western Europe in the Nummulitic, showing the Oligocene transgression.*

through the present location of the English Channel; we shall return to this later.

D. *The Fauna. Foraminifera*

Here the groups of the nummulitids (nummulites, assilines) and orbitoids (orthophragmines, lepidocyclines) are the fossils most useful in establishing correlation at long distances. Their dispersion center is in the Mediterranean province and they are abundant at all horizons, so that tables of characteristic forms can be established. Confining ourselves to genera, always easy to recognize, we arrive at the following table:[6]

Oligocene............. Small Nummulites.............. Lepidocyclines
Upper Eocene......... Small Nummulites.............. Orthophragmines
Middle Eocene....... Large and small Nummulites...... Orthophragmines, Assilines
Lower Eocene........ Small Nummulites.............. Orthophragmines.

The determination of species can usually be made only by experts. Here, following information furnished by MM. Doncieux and Moret, is the distribution of species of nummulites most frequently referred to (large forms in italics):[7]

Oligocene .... N. vascus-boucheri, N. intermedius-fichteli   ⎱
Upper Eocene .... N. fabianii, N. variolarius-heberti, N. wemmelensis ⎰ N. incrassatus.

Lutetian
  upper.. *N. aturicus-perforatus, N. brongniarti, N.* ⎱
                gizehensis, N. millecaput-complanatus ⎰ *N. contortus-striatus.*
  lower.. *N. laevigatus-lamarcki, N. uroniensis*[8] ⎱
                                                      ⎰ N. murchisoni ⎱
Lower Eocene .... N. planulatus-elegans, N. bolcensis ⎰ N. irregularis ⎰ *N. atacicus.*

The Eocene stratigraphy of the Alps, where other fossils are often lacking, was established, after H. Douvillé and J. Boussac, almost entirely on these tables of nummulites. However, the important thing, on which everyone is agreed, is that the large nummulites[9] essentially characterize the middle Eocene (Lutetian). When there are only faunas of small nummulites, badly preserved, it is sometimes difficult to say whether we have lower or upper Eocene.

The nummulites alone, of these different genera, penetrate the northern province. Still they do so only at certain special epochs and consequently are represented only by a few, rather isolated species, which we shall mention later.[10]

Finally, the very characteristic genus *Orbitolites,* which appears in the Corbières with the Ypresian, becomes abundant in the Paris Basin in the Lutetian.[11]

These large foraminifers are especially valuable for stratigraphers because they penetrate different facies. They are found even in marls or fine-grained limestones of deep-water facies, but their usual associations are more littoral: sandstones and especially nummulite limestones are composed in large part of their tests.

Still more littoral are the alveoline limestones of the Eocene, which, intercalated in brackish or lacustrine beds (Languedoc, Corbières), often mark the first or the last marine influences.

Corals. While in the northern province there are, as at the present time, only isolated corals (ex., *Eupsammia* in the Paris Basin), well developed reefs are found in the Mediterranean province, in Venetia for example (Castelgomberto beds in Vicentin). It is this evidence which leads to the conclusion that our two provinces correspond to climatic zones.

Mollusks and Echinoids. In the formations where the large foraminifers are missing, it is to the echinoids and mollusks that we must turn to find the faunas characteristic of stages. But then it becomes necessary to descend to species, for most of the genera, many of which are still living today, have too great longevity.[12] We cannot, of course, go into such details, for one form does not usually suffice to define a stage. Stages must be based on faunal associations, even though the diversity of these associations, due to the influence of facies, often hides the true chronological relations of the faunas.

We mention particularly *Cerithium*,[13] so abundant everywhere in the littoral or slightly brackish faunas. Boussac was able to distinguish, in the Anglo-Parisian Basin, series of mutations, whose value however has since been questioned. Likewise, J. Roger[14] has shown that species of pectinids can be used to characterize the different stages of the northern Oligocene.

Mammals. Mammals are much more independent of local conditions than marine animals. They are also valuable for establishing correlations between widely separated basins, for the species and even the genera succeed each other in very rapid succession.

In the Nummulitic, and elsewhere in the Tertiary, the mammalian faunas provide the only truly exact criterion for the distinction of stages. Thus they play the same role as the ammonite zones in the Secondary.[15] The following table summarizes the succession of mammalian faunas in Europe, following the classic works of C. Depéret.[16] For each stage, we give the most typical localities, to which we shall refer later.

E. *Limits of the Paleogene*

Lower Limit: It is generally agreed today to leave the Danian stage,[17] which we studied earlier, in the Cretaceous and to begin the Tertiary with the Montian stage, whose representatives in the Paris Basin and in Belgium will be described later.

In fact, while the Danian fauna is still Cretaceous, the Montian fauna is clearly Tertiary. There are no more rudistids or ammonites, and a fauna of cerithids with a decidedly Tertiary stamp appears. In addition, a more or less long lacuna of sedimentation separates the Montian from the Cretaceous. The base of this stage is marked in the Paris Basin by a discontinuity (see later). From the stratigraphic as from the paleontologic viewpoint, the Montian belongs with the Eocene.

Upper Limit: The top of the Paleogene, on the contrary, is a matter of dispute. The Aquitanian stage (type: marine *faluns* [shell beds] of Bazas and Saucats, near Bordeaux)[18] is sometimes classified as Oligocene, sometimes as Miocene. The first opinion is adopted by those who pay special attention to the evolution of mammalian faunas. Indeed, the gray limestones of Agenais, the lacustrine equivalents of the Saucats faluns, contain a mammalian fauna which is only the impoverished Stampian fauna, with no new forms. It is found at St. Gérand-le-Puy (Allier), the typical locality for this Aquitanian fauna.[19]

On the other hand, from the paleogeographic viewpoint, the marine sands which, at Montpellier and near Marseille (Sausset, see p. 500), correspond to the Aquitanian faluns of the Bordelais, mark the cautious beginning of the Miocene transgression in the Rhône valley.

The marine fauna found at these localities (Saucats and Sausset) is quite
isolated and contains peculiar species (ex., the gastropod [20] *Melongena
lainei*) and is thus distinguished from the Miocene faunas, which elsewhere
form a quite homogeneous assemblage (see p. 556).

MARINE STAGES		MAMMALIAN FAUNAS	OCCURRENCES
OLIGOCENE Aquitanian		Impoverished remains of Stampian fauna; typical *Anthracotherium*	St. Gérand-le-Puy (Allier), gray molasse of Lausanne, gray limestone of Agenais.
Stampian	Upper (Chattian)	Large *Anthracotherium* and *Aceratherium* (very abundant), first tapirids	White limestone of Agenais, Gannat (Allier), Lausanne.
	Lower	*Anthracotherium*, last palaeotherids, rhinocerids (*Aceratherium*)	Limagne; Saint Henry clays near Marseille; Céreste (Basse-Alpes); phosphorites of Quercy (in part).
Sannoisian		First *Anthracotherium* and rhinocerids, last *Anoplotherium* and *Xiphodon*	Brie limestone; marls of Pantin, near Paris; Ronzon (Velay).
EOCENE Upper (Priabonian)	Ludian	*Palaeotherium*, *Xiphodon*, *Anoplotherium*	Montmartre gypsum, lignites of Gargas (Vaucluse).
	Ledian	Fauna called Bartonian; last *Lophiodon*, numerous palaeotherids	St. Ouen limestone, near Paris; Robiac (Gard); Castres (Tarn).
Middle = Lutetian		*Propalaeotherium*, *Dichobune*, *Lophiodon parisiense*	Vicinity of Paris, siderolithic of Egerkingen (Switzerland) and of Lissieu (Rhône).
Lower	Ypresian	*Lophiodon*, *Protodichobune* (paridigitate)	Ay and Cuis, near Epernay.
	Landenian a) Sparnacian	*Coryphodon* (amblypod), first imparidigitate (*Hyracotherium*)	Meudon, near Paris; Orsmaël, near Landen (Belgium); Erquelinnes, near Maubeuge (Belgium).
	b) Thanetian	Multituberculates, special creodonts	Cernay, near Rheims.
	Montian	No mammals known in Europe.	

Thus, by its continental facies and its mammalian fauna, the Aquitanian is clearly part of the Oligocene, while through the paleogeography of its marine deposits, it is joined rather to the Miocene. It is naturally necessary to choose between these two opposite points of view and this choice is necessarily arbitrary. Because of the great extent of continental deposits of the Aquitanian in France, and the frequent impossibility of separating them from other Oligocene formations of the same facies,[21] we shall leave the Aquitanian in the Oligocene, while waiting to discuss the marine Aquitanian with the Miocene, when we study the Miocene of Aquitania and the Bouches-du-Rhône.

II. Type Series of Nummulitic Stages in the Paris Basin[22]

In the course of the Nummulitic, a gulf, coming from the North Sea, advanced intermittently and to various distances toward the south into the Paris Basin. In the intervals between these marine phases, and on the edges of the gulf, brackish or lacustrine beds were deposited. These multiple variations of facies have led to the recognition of many successive stages, often having only the value of local episodes, but classic. The marine faunas reflect these variations of facies. They are quite different from each other but it is difficult to discover which of these differences are due to true transformations of the whole group (as by immigration), which merely to changes of facies.

1. Eocene

A. Montian. The question of the Danian, the Montian and the boundary between the Cretaceous and the Tertiary in the Paris Basin, has been the subject of long discussion, perhaps not yet ended.[23]

For a long time, the name Montian has been applied to beds visible in the famous section of Meudon (suburb west of Paris, see Fig. 112), of which the most characteristic is the famous pisolitic limestone.

This name is actually incorrect, for in reality this is a *Lithothamnium* limestone, whose mammillated thalluses have been confused with calcareous concretions or pisolites. And up to the present, this Montian, of which only isolated remnants are known (Meudon, Laversines, near Beauvais, Vertus southeast of Epernay, Vigny south of Reims), appearing in the valley bottoms or abutting against chalk slopes, was attributed to a transgressive sea that remained restricted to fjords (or better, rias), excavated in the chalk. To tell the truth, this picture of the Montian sea seems quite peculiar and very different from those shown by the other marine transgressions in the Paris Basin.

But recently, from the study of numerous wells, R. Soyer[24] has found traces of the Montian in 98 localities. Far from being localized in narrow grooves, the Montian sea was widespread in a large gulf, bounded on the north by the Pays de Bray and Chateau-Thierry and in the south reaching Mantes, Etampes, Montereau and Vertus.

In this sea lived a fauna whose warm character is proved by a flora of green algae.[25] The gastropods have very clear Tertiary affinities; for instance, *Turritella montensis* and *Cerithium inopinatum,* whose types are found at Mons in Belgium. The pelecypods rather show Cretaceous affinities and *Nautilus danicus* of the Danian type has been discovered at Vigny and Vertus by Schoeller. These species with Cretaceous affinities are found everywhere in the beds of Vertus, Vigny and Montereau. So, Chavan[26] proposes to classify them still in the upper Danian and sees there the prolongation of a gulf

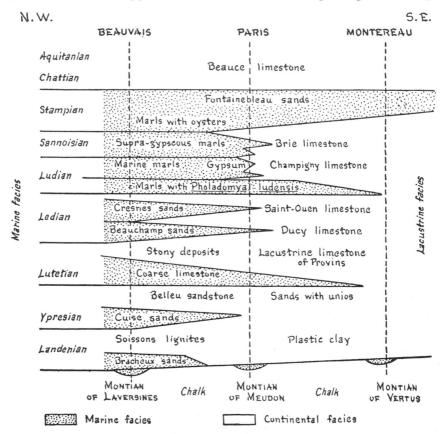

FIG. 110. *Diagram showing the extent of the marine transgressions in the Paris Basin during the Paleogene (partly after M. Leriche).*

coming from Denmark. The other beds, of true Montian age, give evidence, on the contrary, of a transgression coming from the west, through the Channel.

But, in certain of these occurrences called Danian (Vigny), we see in quarry faces that the pisolitic limestone is buried under the top of the Chalk. This relationship may be explained by assuming that *Lithothamnium*[27] pavements filled caverns excavated in the chalk. But according to many Parisian geologists[28] the Montian actually is intercalated in the uppermost part of the Chalk, which here may be Danian.[29]

In addition, F. Ellenberger has recently called attention to the nature of the contact between the Chalk and the pisolitic limestone at Meudon. Munier-Chalmas believed he found there proof of a long period of emergence: the top of the chalk, hard and yellow, is pierced with tubules in which he saw traces of roots of an ancient forest vegetation. Ellenberger remarks that this contact is not emphasized by any trace of continental reworking and he attributes the tubules to perforations due to algae or marine animals. The hard chalk would then correspond only to one of the submarine "hard grounds," swept by currents, of which many examples are known in the Chalk of northern France, and especially in the phosphatized Chalk (further evidence of a regime of currents).[30]

We can reconcile all these apparently contradictory opinions by recognizing that the uppermost Chalk of the Paris Basin is cut by lacunas, but that these do not indicate emergence. After such a lacuna, the beds ascribable to the Danian were deposited locally, and then after another hiatus, the true Montian appeared, with its Tertiary forms. And only after this Montian came the long period of emergence with continental alterations, witnessed by the Meudon conglomerate, made up of flints from the Chalk rearranged at the base of the Landenian.

Thus, the paleontologic boundary between the Cretaceous and the Tertiary, in the Paris Basin, would not exactly coincide with the paleogeographic boundary, which should surprise no one.

B. Landenian. The Transgression of the Bracheux Sands. Following the example of M. Leriche,[31] we shall group under this name, of Belgian origin, the two sub-stages called Thanetian and Sparnacian in the Paris Basin. The Thanetian is the clearly marine lower Landenian and the Sparnacian constitutes the continental or, at most, lagoonal facies of the upper Landenian. It contains no characteristic marine fauna and does not correspond to a marine transgression. The distinction of a Thanetian and a Sparnacian, based on a simple difference of facies, has only local value.[32] In its entirety the Landenian represents a sedimentary cycle (see p. 18) of which the Sparnacian marks the terminal phase of marine regression.

1. *Lower Landenian or Thanetian: Bracheux Sands*.[33] This is the first marine transgression of the Tertiary which has been preserved over wide areas. The whole northern part of the Paris Basin was covered (see Fig. 111) and the transgressive sea stopped only about 30 km. north of Paris.

Over all this area, the Chalk is overlain by the sands of Bracheux, the name of a fossiliferous locality south of Beauvais. The littoral fauna of large and fine shells includes *Cucullaea crassatina, Venericardia pectuncularis,* and *Ostrea bellovacina.* Cyprines and astartes, genera spread at present over all northern seas, were long thought to give a northern stamp to this fauna. But there is a question of species and even of sub-genera different from the present cold forms. On the other hand, fish, calcareous algae, a colonial coral [34] and especially, as we shall see, the flora, suggest a climate which, if not tropical, as Farchad would wish, was at least temperately warm (Chavan, note 96, chap. 8).

In the Bracheux sands, generally, a certain number of paleontologic zones can be empirically distinguished, more or less sharply defined by species of mollusks or echinoids and showing the progressive advance southward of the Thanetian transgression.

On the edge of the gulf, continental formations were deposited of which the most famous examples are seen in the vicinity of Rheims. This is the lacustrine limestone of Rilly with a large left-coiled mollusk characteristic of this epoch, *Physa gigantea*. Calcareous springs have deposited the famous

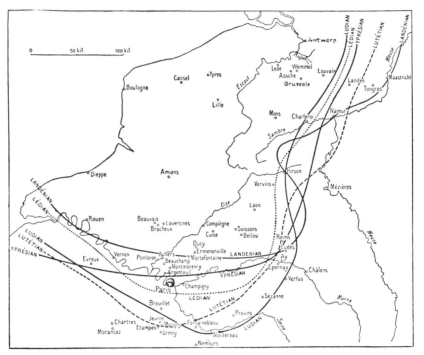

FIG. 111. *Map indicating the limits of the marine transgressions in the Franco-Belgian Basin during the Eocene (after M. Leriche; the Lutetian after A. Abrard).*

The limits indicated correspond to the maximum transgression for each stage; they are, naturally, hypothetical in part, especially for the east and west.

Sézanne travertine on the shore of this lake, with molds of insects, leaves and flowers showing minute details (sassafras, magnolia, ivy, vines). At other places (Mont de Berru, Fig. 113) there are river or lagoonal sands and finally, crowning this Thanetian continental series of Rheims, is the Cernay conglomerate in which appears the oldest Tertiary mammalian fauna known in Europe.

2. *Upper Landenian or Sparnacian: Lignites of Soissons and plastic clay.* In the whole Paris Basin, the sea was transformed into brackish lagoons or freshened swamps, whose deposits spread broadly over the region south of

Paris. Thus, in Paris itself, the Sparnacian lies directly on the chalk or on remnants of the Montian (Fig. 112).

Two facies can be distinguished at this epoch: 1st. north and east of Paris there are rather brackish formations, called Soissons lignites,[35] which at Epernay have furnished the name of the Sparnacian sub-stage. They are clays with beds of lignite and a few beds with marine shells, *Cyrena cuneiformis, Cerithium variabile, Melania inquinata,* and teredos perforating fossil wood; 2nd. at Paris and farther south, the facies seem entirely continental, but the sediments are completely decalcified so that no fossils are found. This is the *plastic clay* proper, with very irregular sandy lentils. Because of the absence of lime, these deposits are more or less refractory: when they are white, without iron salts, the clays are much sought after for the manufacture of faience (Montereau). Toward the south, approaching the Massif Central, the

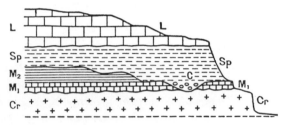

L = Lutetian: coarse limestone.
        Ypresian missing
Sp = Sparnacian: plastic clay (C =
        Meudon conglomerate with
        mammalian remains).
        Thanetian missing.

M_2 = Upper Montian: Meudon
        marls.
M_1 = Lower Montian: Pisolite
        limestone.
        Danian missing.
Cr = Upper Cretaceous:
        Meudon chalk.

FIG. 112. *Section of the Moulineaux hill, at Meudon, near Paris, showing the Montian of Meudon and the lacunas of the lower Eocene at Paris (after Munier-Chalmas, in Haug, simplified).*

proportion of sand increases (L. Bertrand), due to the contributions from the crystalline rocks. There we have the Breuillet arkoses and Nemours conglomerate.

Mammalian remains are present in the Meudon conglomerate, at the base of the plastic clay, and in the Mont de Berru lignites, near Rheims,[36] above the Cernay conglomerate (Figs. 112 and 113).

These sands and refractory clays are again well developed in the south, as far as the chalky plateaus of Yonne. But there, nothing proves that they do not include older zones or more recent ones than the Sparnacian. We shall find in the Rhône Basin a similar, practically contemporaneous facies (see p. 494).

C. Ypresian:[37] Marine Transgression of the Cuise sands. For a second time, marine encroachments spread their sands in the Paris Basin. But this time the transgression went southward [38] beyond the limits of the Thanetian sea so that the Cuise sands (locality between Compiègne and Soissons) are the first to reach the northern outskirts of Paris, being called by early geologists, the Parisian Lower Sands. They are often chosen as the type of the stage, which then becomes the Cuisian, a term synonymous with Ypresian.[39]

The Ypresian fauna, much more than the Thanetian, gives evidence of southern influences, marked by large foraminifers (*Nummulites planulatus-elegans, Alveolina oblunga*) and some mollusks (*Velates schmiedelianus*).[40] Special stress should be laid on the nummulites, whose first appearance in the Paris Basin is here; they have arrived by way of the English Channel (see p. 485).

With the end of the stage, a regression begins, for, near Soissons, a forma-

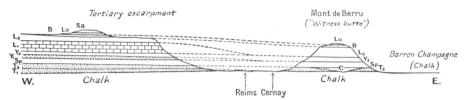

FIG. 113. *Diagrammatic section of the Tertiary escarpment near Rheims, with the "witness butte" of Mont de Berru, showing how the study of facies enables us to reconstruct the position of the ancient shores in the middle Thanetian (the lower Thanetian is missing), in the Ypresian, and in the Lutetian (the lower Lutetian is missing) (after data of C. Depéret and M. Leriche).*

Sa = Sannoisian: Brie limestone, lacustrine.
Lu = Ludian: { Lacustrine marls.
              { Marine marls with *Pholadomya ludensis.*
B = Ledian: Lacustrine marls and limestones.
L_2 = Upper Lutetian: Lagoonal-lacustrine marl-limestones.
L_1 = Middle Lutetian: Marine coarse limestone (*calcaire grossier*).
Y_2 = Upper Ypresian: Sands with unios and lignitic clays.
Y_1 = Lower Ypresian: Cuise sand, marine.
S_p = Sparnacian: Sands and lagoonal-lacustrine lignitic clays.
C = Upper Thanetian: Cernay conglomerate, with mammals.   ⎫
T_2 = Upper Thanetian: Rilly sand, marine; Bracheux horizon.   ⎬ Landenian.
T_1 = Middle Thanetian: Siliceous chalk with *Pholadomya konincki,* ⎭
     marine.

Beds with non-marine facies are left white.

tion of lacustrine sandstone (Belleu sandstone), with impressions of leaves of the camphor tree (*Cinnamomum*), represents the top of the Ypresian.[41]

On the edges of the marine gulf at Ay, near Epernay, a mammalian deposit in the *Unio* sand provides a valuable paleontologic guide, with a fauna having Lutetian affinities.[42]

D. The Lutetian Transgression: Stage of Coarse Limestone (Calcaire grossier). As shown by the Belleu sandstone, there was a retreat of the sea at the end of the Ypresian, so that the marine deposits, which often lie directly over the sands of Cuise, are separated from them by a stratigraphic discontinuity. They are witness of a great transgression, bringing different faunas and facies.

For the first time, the sea clearly goes south of Paris, advancing to points near Fontainebleau and Provins. A decrease in continental, detrital contributions corresponds to this retreat of the shores. The clays and sands are replaced by organic deposits, which have won the stage its name of *Calcaire grossier*. Rock-forming organisms abound and show very marked Mediterranean affinities: large foraminifers (*Nummulites laevigatus-lamarcki, Orbitolites complanatus,* miliolids), echinoids (*Echinanthus, Echinolampas*), and very large mollusks, thick shelled and very ornate (*Venericardia planicosta, Corbis lamellosa, Chama lamellosa, Lucina gigantea, Cerithium giganteum*).

The variations of facies, linked to the vicissitudes of the transgression, render the detailed stratigraphy of the Lutetian very difficult.

According to Abrard,[43] the following paleontologic zones can be distinguished, determined by characteristic fossils:

V. Brackish beds of the upper Lutetian.
IV. Zone of *Orbitolites complanatus*.[44]
III. Zone of *Echinolampas calvimontanus* and *Echinanthus issyavensis*.
II. Zone of *Nummulites laevigatus* (typical).
I. Beds "with two Nummulites": N. *laevigatus* (mut.) and N. *lamarcki*.

Zone I, marking the beginning of the transgression, is usually sandy-glauconitic; but this facies can be found in higher horizons when they are transgressive. Zone II is especially rich in nummulites near Laon and Soissons, that is to say in the northeastern part of the Basin, where these limestones have the expressive name, "coin stones." Zone III, equally calcareous, often ends with banks of "screw-jacks" (internal molds of *Cerithium giganteum*). Zone IV is represented in the outskirts of Paris by miliolid limestone, fine grained and greatly valued as building stone (*banc royal*). On the other hand, at Grignon and Damery (where the lower Lutetian is missing) zones III and IV, transgressive, become sandy and then yield magnificent fossils entirely uncemented, so that they are found in the collections all over the world.

Above, the facies become less clearly marine. At this horizon cerithid limestone is particularly developed. More or less lacustrine episodes are intercalated, such as the "green bank," which crops out at Trocadero, containing palms, *Cyclostoma mumia* and *Planorbis pseudoammonius*. The uppermost part, composed of marly beds with calcareous lentils, cannot be exploited for building: these are the *caillasses* (curdled or clotted stone) of the workers.

South of the domain of the marine Lutetian, here and there, limestones with *Planorbis pseudoammonius* are found, giving evidence of ancient lakes, the two chief ones being those of Provins and Morancez (near Chartres). Some mammalian remains have been found at Passy, Nanterre and Provins.

E. Ledian: Beauchamp Sands and St. Ouen Limestone. After the deposit of the lacustrine or brackish *caillasses,* an aggressive return of the sea marks a complete change of facies. Sands are again substituted for limestones. To this second sandy horizon of the Paris outskirts, early geologists gave the name of Middle Sands. Their best known deposits are found at Beauchamp, near Herblay, between Paris and Pontoise.

But bordering these marine deposits,[45] or alternating with them, are lacustrine intercalations, such as the Ducy limestone, with *Planorbis goniobasis* and *Lophiodon,* and especially the famous St. Ouen limestone (north edge of Paris) where this same *Planorbis* is associated with a large *Limnaea* (*L. longiscata*), characteristic of the stage. These multiple variations of facies have given rise to an essentially local stratigraphy. So the lowest marine horizons, such as the sands of Auvers (near Pontoise),[46] of Beauchamp, Mortefontaine and Ermenonville (northeast of Paris),[47] have long been grouped in a lower or Auversian stage, while above, the St. Ouen[48] limestone and certain marine horizons (sands of Marines, northwest of Pontoise, of Cresnes, etc.) form an upper stage, incorrectly called Bartonian; in fact, the Barton clays, in Britain, are synchronous with our Ludian Stage.

The multiplicity of these local horizons is explained by the instability of ancient shore lines in the course of the Ledian. Thus, near the top of the Auversian, below the Mortefontaine horizon, there may have been an emergence during which the Auversian sands could have been rearranged in cordons of great dunes, then covered with the marine Mortefontaine sands or by lacustrine deposits of the St. Ouen limestone. This emergence would be approximately contemporaneous with the Ducy limestone.[49]

In reality, as Abrard has shown, the marine faunas of these so-called Auversian and Bartonian stages differ only through the facies, which vary from one locality to another. The mutations which Boussac believed he marked between the cerithids of these two horizons, are too subtle by far, especially as the same species of small nummulite (*N. variolarius-heberti*) is found in the upper horizon (Marines, Cresnes) as well as in the lower, to which it was long believed to be confined.

To cut short these complications and errors of nomenclature, we shall, with Abrard, adopt the stage name Ledian, whose type is in Belgium, which will apply everywhere to the zone of *N. variolarius* and its lacustrine equivalents (St. Ouen limestone).[50]

F. Ludian: Stage of Montmartre Gypsum. A change of facies again marks the debut of this stage. The transgressive sea extends to the confines of Champagne, beyond the Ledian sea, and there deposits first the marls with *Pholadomya ludensis,* a very characteristic horizon, cropping out especially at Ludes, near Rheims.[51]

Then the facies[52] are diversified:

a) Northwest of a line running approximately along the course of the Marne from Rheims to Champigny, the gulf, with *Pholadomya ludensis,* was reduced to an inland sea and then somehow disappeared in place, through evaporation, and its salts were precipitated producing the famous Montmartre gypsum, divided into three principal beds or masses, separated by marls with a marine fauna (*Lucina inornata*), showing that the salinity became normal again. Famous from an industrial viewpoint (plaster of Paris), this gypsum is equally important for its richness in vertebrates which provides a most valuable guide deposit. The concentration was sometimes sufficient to produce rock salt, later dissolved, but cubic crystals of which left easily recognizable molds or pseudomorphs. North of the Paris region, there are no more gypsum beds but only, to all appearances, marine marls.

b) Southeast of the Marne, however, stretched a lake in which the Champigny limestone or travertine was deposited. Its contemporaneity with the gypsum, demonstrated by Hebert, has provided one of the first classic examples of lateral variations of facies.

2. *Oligocene*

As we have already said, the idea of an Oligocene group would probably not have arisen if the Paris Basin alone were considered. And in fact, even now, the limits of this group are still disputed.

The gypsiferous marls and fresh water limestones of the Ludian are succeeded, in fact, in the same regions by supragypsiferous marls and lacustrine limestones which do not correspond to well marked changes of regime. But the marine faunas contained in these supragypsiferous marls do not result from evolution of the Eocene faunas in place. They contain new forms, arriving by immigration, and it is natural to relate this event to the great transgression which we shall see characterizing, in other regions, the beginning of the Oligocene. In the same way, mammalian faunas show similar transformations, which lead to leaving the Ludian in the Eocene and making the Oligocene begin with the supragypsiferous marls.

A. Sannoisian: Stage of Supragypsiferous Marls and the Brie Limestone. The type of this stage is taken in the Sannois butte, near Argenteuil (northwest suburb of Paris). The supragypsiferous marls there show the following classic series, from bottom to top:

1st. Blue marls, a salt-marsh formation, almost without fossils, with rare lagoonal crustaceans.

2nd. White marls or Pantin marls, showing a tendency to freshening where *Limnaea* (*L. strigosa*) appears, but marine influences are shown by a few gypsiferous beds.

3rd. Marls with cyrenes, marine, somewhat brackish facies, with *Cyrena convexa* and *Cerithium plicatum*.

4th. Green marls, clearly marine, with *Cytherea incrassata,* providing a good horizon-guide over a broad geographic area.

Southeast of the Marne, that is to say in the regions where the Champigny limestone takes the place of gypsum, these marly facies are in their turn replaced by freshwater limestones, celebrated as the Brie limestone,[53] with *Planorbis cornu.* This limestone, with its siliceous web,[54] becomes, when it has been decalcified by atmospheric action at the surface, a vesicular siliceous rock or millstone, which was formerly quarried for construction because of its light weight. This is the Brie millstone.

B. Stampian: Stage of the Fontainebleau Sands.[55] This stage is very important and easily recognizable everywhere, because of the uniformity of facies. For the last time, the sea spreads over the Paris Basin and spreads very far, especially to the south and east where the position of its shores cannot be exactly determined, situated undoubtedly well beyond the present outcrops.[56]

The stage includes two very constant horizons:

1st. At the base is the oyster marl, containing especially *Ostrea cyathula* and *O. longirostris*.[57] It represents a very important aquifer for all the Oligocene areas of the Paris Basin.

2nd. At the top are the Fontainebleau sands, which are the Upper Sands of early geologists. Their mean thickness is 40 m., but they may reach 75 m. They are usually white and very pure, so that they are exploited for glassmaking and fused quartz, and they are often consolidated into hard sandstones, Fontainebleau sandstones, which make excellent paving stones. They appear in the Forest of Fontainebleau as picturesque rocks where Parisian alpinists practice rock scaling.

Fossils are found only in a few favored spots, isolated in the vicinity of Etampes (Jeurre, Morigny, Pierrefitte, Ormoy), from which the stage name is derived. The fauna (*Pectunculus obovatus, Cytherea splendida, Natica crassatina,* etc.) is entirely different from the Eocene fauna. Taking the variation of facies into account, two paleontologic zones can be distinguished, according to H. Alimen: a lower horizon, with the deposits of Jeurre and Morigny, and an upper horizon of Pierrefitte and Ormoy.[58]

At the end of the Stampian, the sea withdrew and broad expanses of fine sands were left to be dried and reworked by the winds, forming parallel bands of great dunes, separated by swampy water courses where spreading mud and dusty clay were deposited, found today in the form of elongated streaks between the Stampian sands and the Chattian limestone. These water-courses must be analogous, following the ingenious comparison suggested by H. Alimen, to the *bahrs* which today are aligned in the zone between the great marshes of Tchad and the dunes of the Saharan *ergs*. It is the direction of these bands of dunes, long since recorded but not yet explained, which determined the alignment of the zones consolidated into sandstones.

C. Chattian and Aquitanian: Beauce Limestone.   After its great expansion in the epoch of the Fontainebleau sands, the sea definitely left the Paris Basin. The latter is occupied by a great lake (slightly lagoonal) which, instead of continuing to the north as had the earlier marine gulfs or lagoons, was prolonged to the west as far as the Loire. In this lake, freshwater limestones known as Beauce limestones were deposited.

The study of the Beauce alone first led to including all these limestones in a single stage, and they were formerly attributed to the Aquitanian. But a closer comparison with the typical marine formations of Aquitaine (see p. 505) led to the recognition that only the upper part, with *Helix aurelianensis,* was equivalent to the true marine Aquitanian of Aquitaine. The lower part, however, contains the characteristic species *Helix ramondi* which is missing in the upper part. It can be correlated with the marine unit with which the Oligocene ends in the area of Cassel, Germany, which is the type of the Chattian or Casselian (see p. 492) and which is often attached to the Stampian, as an upper element.

The beds of the Beauce limestone being very slightly inclined toward the southwest, the oldest part crops out especially in the northeast (for example

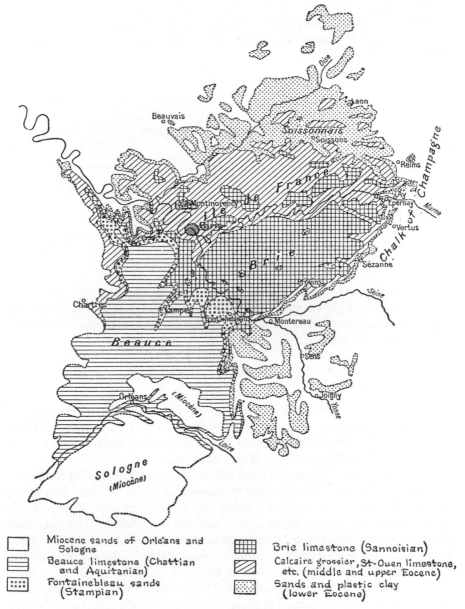

FIG. 114. *Diagrammatic map of the Nummulitic outcrops in the Paris Basin, showing their distribution in natural regions.*

at Etampes). On the contrary, the upper members crop out especially in the region of Orléans[59] (see Fig. 115), so that the stratigraphy of these beds is established in the following way:

Old Aquitanian = ⎰ Upper: Orléans limestone (*H. aurelianensis*) = Aquitanian
Beauce limestone ⎱ Lower: Etampes limestone (*H. ramondi*) = Chattian

Unfortunately, no mammalian faunas are known in the Beauce limestone, to confirm this correlation, which is based only on continental mollusks. Here, this continental Aquitanian seems quite naturally to be part of the Oligocene. (See p. 471.)

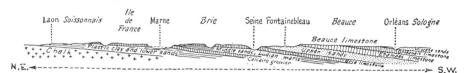

FIG. 115. *Very diagrammatic section across the Paris Basin, showing the structure of the great natural regions (compare with map, Fig. 114).*

N. B.   This section is designed solely to show the distribution of outcrops, not the underlying structure. The different Paleogene formations, which, in order to make the diagram clearer, have been prolonged regularly toward the southwest at depth, in reality thin out and disappear pregressively in that direction, against the edge of the Massif Central.

The Etampes limestone extends somewhat north of Paris, in the form of isolated and decalcified remnants, the Montmorency millstone, formed at the expense of this limestone in the same way that the Brie millstone was formed at the expense of the Brie limestone.

3. *Conclusions: Grouping of Outcrops of the Stages in Natural Regions*

The most resistant formations of this long series of sediments are the Lutetian limestone (*calcaire grossier*), the Sannoisian (Brie limestone) and the Chattian-Aquitanian (Beauce limestone). These limestones form great plateaus, called respectively Ile-de-France, Brie and Beauce.

Approaching the Paris region from the east, that is coming from the barren Champagne, the first Tertiary outcrops appear as a cliff or *côte,* dominating the vast monotonous plain of the Champagne Chalk. The lower Eocene forms the slope and the crest is composed of the *calcaire grossier.* This limestone plays the predominant role in the architecture of the Eocene region of the Paris Basin, or Ile-de-France. Northeast, near Soissons, the covering of *calcaire grossier* is usually removed and the area is underlain by the clayey Sparnacian, making a very wet country. Then, between the Marne and Seine, the *calcaire grossier* disappears gradually under the Middle Sands and the Brie limestone and we have then the Brie plateaus. A zone formed by the Upper Sands, producing soil less suitable for cultivation and thanks to which the immense Fontainebleau Forest is preserved, separates Brie from Beauce, located between the Seine and the Loire. The Beauce limestone produces great expanses of dry land where little except grain cultivation is successful, for ground water is very deep there, and in order to reach it wells have to go as deep as the oyster marls of the lower Stampian.

III. The Other Dependencies of the North Sea Basin

1. *Northern Brittany*

The seas of the Paris Basin never extended very far westward and hardly went beyond the mouth of the Seine.

In fact, all along the eastern edge of the Armorican Massif, the Eocene is represented by scattered blocks of sandstone, unquestionably of continental origin, for only impressions of palm trees similar to the living Sabals have been found in them. They are the sandstones with *Sabalites andegavensis* (= from Anjou).[60] They are of middle or upper Eocene age, for they are directly overlain by lacustrine limestone with *Limnaea longiscata* similar to the Saint-Ouen limestone (Ledian). There are also Ludian lacustrine marls.[61]

But, north of these lakes, marine formations are found, the shelly sands of the cerithid faluns of Cotentin. They are in very small, isolated remnants, lying directly on the Primary or the Secondary at Gourbesville (Manche), for example. The fauna has very clear southern affinities, with *Orbitolites complanatus* and alveolines. These faluns, topped by limestone with *L. longiscata,* are pre-Ledian. Their very rich fauna ties them to the Lutetian.

Bounded on the south by the lacustrine formations of Anjou, this sea of faluns of the Cotentin appears as evidence of a temporary Nummulitic channel, through which a southern fauna reached the Paris Basin.[62] This is also proved by the mineralogic study of the marine sands (Thanetian, Ypresian, Lutetian, Ledian, Stampian) and even of the Parisian sands of the Cretaceous (Albian, Cenomanian). They must have come from the west, carried by currents which swept the Breton coasts, for metamorphic minerals of the Armorican Massif especially are found here. The Sparnacian fluviatile sands, however, contain minerals originating in the Massif Central.[63]

2. *England* [64]

North of the Channel, the English Primary massifs formed the western shore of the old North Sea. But the deposits of this sea do not crop out, in England, as a continuous border. The Weald, an anticlinal region, the extension of the Boulonnais (see p. 412 and Fig. 76), separates two Tertiary basins,[65] the London Basin on the north and the Hampshire Basin to the south, bordered by the Jurassic and Cretaceous band of Portland-Purbeck-Isle of Wight. The history of these two basins during the Eocene was about the same, but the Weald was an emerged area or shoal between them. Moreover, the Oligocene is unknown in the London Basin.

The English Tertiary begins with the transgressive Landenian, which, as in the Paris Basin, shows a clearly marine facies localized especially at the base and in the eastern part of the basins, with continental facies predominating at the top and in the west.

The marine Landenian, or Thanetian, however, is only well developed in the eastern part of the London Basin, where the glauconitic sands of the Thanet peninsula, with *Cyprina morrisi* and *Cucullaea crassatina,* have served as the type for this sub-stage.

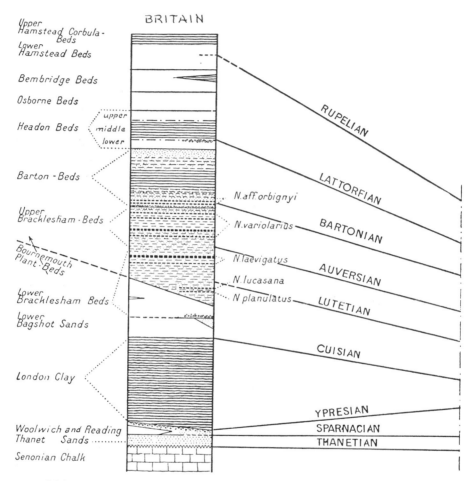

FIG. 116. *Correlation of the Nummulitic stages in Britain, the Paris Basin and Belgium (after A. Wrigley and A. G. Davis, work cited note 69, this chap., somewhat simplified). This figure is an excellent example of correlations carried out in the most extreme detail and translated graphically with much ingenuity.*

N. B. In the nomenclature used in this book, the Auversian and Bartonian are, respectively, the Ledian and the Ludian.

The continental Landenian, comparable to the French Sparnacian, presents two facies, as in the Paris Basin. In the eastern part of the London Basin, that is near the axis of the North Sea, there is the brackish facies of the Woolwich beds (outskirts of London), similar to the clays and lignites of Soissons.

To the west, on the other hand, is the purely continental facies of the Reading beds, equivalent to our plastic clay. In the Hampshire Basin, where marine influences were felt less, the Reading facies predominates.

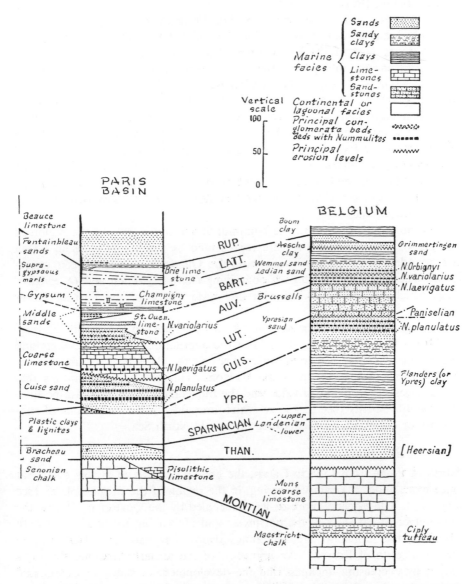

The Ypresian corresponds to the London Clay,[66] which is found in both English basins. The fauna therein is very rich but not identical to that of the Cuise sands because of the difference in facies. The flora has a tropical character emphasized by the abundance of a palm (*Nipa*) living today in the Indo-Malayan region.[67] This was formerly made the type of a Londinian stage, which sometimes included the Sparnacian and Ypresian.[68]

The Lutetian is rather poorly represented in England. It consists of the sands and glauconitic clays with *Nummulites laevigatus,* forming the lower part of the Bracklesham beds (Hampshire),[69] but in the western part of Hampshire, the upper Lutetian becomes continental. Similar facies are found in the London Basin.

The Ledian marks a new transgression, bringing the sea into the western part, which had become continental at the end of the Lutetian. It corresponds to the upper part of the Bracklesham beds, characterized by *Nummulites variolarius* and the mollusks of the Beauchamp sands.

The Ludian is missing in the London Basin, which was definitely emergent at that period. In Hampshire, on the Isle of Wight and at Barton, however, there is a great thickness of clays (Barton clay) with a deep-water fauna, including a very small nummulite, here called *N. prestwichianus,* which did not penetrate the Paris Basin but is found at this horizon in Belgium, where it is called *N. wemmelensis.* This Barton clay cannot be correlated with the sands of Marines and Cresnes (upper Ledian) which contain *N. variolarius,*[70] so that it is incorrect to apply the name Bartonian, still used by British geologists, to these sands.

The more recent stages of the Nummulitic are found only in the region of the Isle of Wight, where they are represented by sands and clays in which the boundary between the Eocene and the Oligocene has long been uncertain.[71] The series ends with beds containing *Ostrea cyathula* and *O. longirostris,* which can be paralleled with the oyster marls of the Parisian lower Stampian.

Thus, great differences of lithologic facies separate the Nummilitic of England from that of the Paris Basin. But the alternations of transgressions and regressions which served to identify stages in the Paris region, are here repeated at almost exactly the same horizons. This clearly demonstrates that these stages have only local value and the movements of the seas are perhaps eustatic movements (see p. 19) to which are added local oscillations of subsidence or elevation, on this border of the old North Sea.

3. Belgium[72]

North of a line from Lille to Calais, the chalky plateaus of Artois disappear once more under a Tertiary covering, in the region of the Belgian plains (see Fig. 117). The Eocene, more or less concealed by the Quaternary, forms the sub-surface of Flanders to the northwest and of Brabant to the southeast. In Flanders, the sediments are sometimes deep-water and very thick, but in Brabant, south of Brussels, the approach of the ancient Ardennes shores is shown by decreasing thickness and the development of sandy or continental facies. Toward the north, the Oligocene appears, forming a wide band from Liége to Antwerp. There the Paleogene disappears to great depth under the thick covering of the Neogene of Campine,[73] from where it is prolonged in the sub-surface of Holland. The maximum depth of the sea must have been at that point, which was the very center of the basin of the North Sea where marine sedimentation was continuous and from which the transgressions advanced into an Anglo-Franco-Belgian gulf on one side and a Holland-

German gulf on the other. But the stratigraphy here can be based only on microforaminiferal faunas brought up by wells.[74] In Belgium then, we shall study only the Paleogene visible in outcrops.

Eocene. In the Montian, the sea must have invaded Belgium much more extensively than in the Paris Basin. At any rate, at Mons, on the northern edge of the Ardennes Massif, are found the beds which are used as the type for the stage. They are soft organic limestones (Cipley *tuffeau,* Mons limestone) with a completely characteristic fauna,[75] already seen in the Paris Basin (*Cerithium inopinatum, Turritella montensis,* etc.). They overlie the Maestrichtian chalk disconformably and are overlain by the Thanetian.

The Landenian has two facies, as in the Paris Basin. Its base, the lower Landenian, is in general marine and transgressive like the Thanetian of the Paris Basin. Its sands or sandy marls (Landen *tuffeau,* near Tirlemont) contain the fossils of the Bracheux sands. The upper part, called fluvio-marine

FIG. 117.   *Diagrammatic map of the principal areas of Tertiary outcrops in Belgium.*

The Oligocene band is ruled. Imagine the Quaternary formations removed, except in the coastal plain, where they are very thick.

Landenian, is actually marine only in the far north (wells of Ostend and Campine). Elsewhere its sands and continental marls recall the Sparnacian facies of the Paris Basin and contain the very interesting deposits of mammals noted on page 472.

The Ypresian[76] is represented by the Flanders clays, up to 100 m. thick, which, at Ypres have been chosen as the stage type, rather unfortunately, for they are very poor in fossils. This facies of the open sea gives way, toward the south, to sandy facies which gradually pass into sands of the Cuise type.[77] In this transition area the Ypres clays (type of the Ypresian) are often overlain by sands with *Nummulites planulatus* (type at Mons-en-Pévèle) which thus represents a Cuisian stage following the Ypresian. Actually as M. Leriche has emphasized,[78] these distinctions are too subtle. The Flanders clay, the London Clay, the sands of Mons-en-Pévèle and Cuise are only facies of a single big stage, the Ypresian.

The Lutetian is hardly represented, except by its basal part, which is called the Bruxellian stage by Belgian geologists. It consists of sands or sandstones in which fossils are much rarer than in the Paris Basin.[79] The rest of the stage seems to have been carried away during the Ledian transgression.

The Ledian is, indeed, very transgressive. *Nummulites variolarius* is abundant in its sands and sandstones, which are developed especially in the vicinity of Lede, type locality of the stage.

The Ludian, here called the Wemmelian (from Wemmel, north of Brussels) is also sandy and contains *Nummulites wemmelensis-orbignyi*.[80] The Wemmel sands are contemporaneous with the sands and clays of Assche, for which the Asschian stage was created.

Oligocene.   The Oligocene transgression spread over broad areas the sandy and clayey Sannoisian sediments, which are very fossiliferous near Tongres. So, the name Tongrian is often used for this stage or even for the whole Oligocene. The upper part, however, corresponds to a regression, for clayey intercalations (exploited in the big tile factories of Tongres) appear with a brackish fauna.

Completely marine facies return with the Stampian. In it are placed the Boom clays, which, mixed with the chalk, make cement in the vicinity of Antwerp. The Rupelian has been named from the Rupel, tributary to the Escaut. In Germany we shall again find this clayey facies which is so great a contrast with the contemporary formation, the Fontainebleau sands.

Finally, the Chattian is unknown in Flanders but its marine sands, south of Liége (Boncelles) spread transgressively even over the first plateaus of the Ardennes. But farther north, it was commonly destroyed by the Neogene transgressions and is scarcely to be found except in wells in Campine.

After the Chattian comes a period of emergence and no formation comparable to the marine Aquitanian of the Mediterranean is found.

4. *The Baltic Domain: North Germany and Denmark*[81]

Between the Finnish-Scandinavian Massif on the north and the Rhenish and Bohemian Massifs to the south, an arm of the North Sea again stretched out over still greater areas.

Eocene.   Where the Danian is present, at the beginning of the gulf in Scania and Denmark, it is overlain by sandy or glauconitic marls belonging to the Montian.[82] These are the only parts of the North Sea domain where sedimentation was almost uninterrupted from the Secondary into the Tertiary. Wells in Denmark have traversed a continuous series of clayey deposits, several hundred meters thick, of which the base belongs to the Danian and the upper part passes without a break into the Oligocene.[83]

However, during all of the Eocene, the sea remained confined to the extreme north of Germany. An interesting occurrence of fossiliferous Ypresian clays has been described by Gripp[84] in the lower valley of the Elbe, between Stade and Cuxhaven. But usually the cloak of Quaternary and Neogene hides everything. Wells reveal great thicknesses of Eocene and Oligocene sands and clays, in which stages can hardly be recognized except by foraminiferal microfaunas, for which Hecht [85] has provided a standard scale. According to K. Staesche,[86] the Eocene alone reaches 800 m. and wells in the Lüneburg heath (Lüneburger Heide) have traversed 1,430 m. of sediments between the Paleocene and the Miocene. Finally, Wetzel [87] has described, near Kiel, an Eocene beginning with a basal conglomerate and glauconitic beds and containing flows and volcanic tuffs, whose location is aligned with the extension of the Rhenish trough.

Thus this North Sea Basin appears, from the beginning of the Tertiary, as a sort of geosyncline or rather a basin of subsidence attracting detrital sedimentation. And as we see it, this subsidence is still continuing at the present time. The Eocene shows a fine example of the contrast between the thick clayey or sandy series of the center of the basin, monotonous, comprehensive series in which it is almost impossible to separate the stages, and the thin beds of quite varied facies, cut by lacunas, rich in fossils like those decribed along the borders of England, in the Ile-de-France and in Belgium. While far to the south, in the constantly emergent regions on the edges of the German Hercynian Massifs, lignites were deposited, the oldest of which yield Eocene *Lophiodon* at Merseburg, in Saxony.[88] The formation of carbonaceous material persists through the Oligocene and Neogene to the peat of the present lakes bordering the Baltic.

Oligocene. On the other hand, with the Oligocene a very important change occurred. The sea overflowed toward the south and east, covered all northern Germany, attacked the Hercynian Massifs and finally spread over all of southern Russia.[89] There it established communication with the Mesogean seas. East of the Urals another arm of the sea, ascending as far as the Arctic Ocean, separated the Finnish-Scandinavian Shield from the Sino-Siberian Continent.

So, while the Eocene is practically negligible in Germany as far as surface geology is concerned, the Oligocene is, on the contrary, very well represented and very fossiliferous. There, as we have said, it shows clean cut individuality. (map, Fig. 109).

a. Beginning in the *Sannoisian,* the sea advanced over the northern part of the Bohemian Massif. This stage is, in fact, represented at Lattorf, near Bernburg in northern Saxony, by greensands which cover the previously mentioned Eocene lignites and which are extremely fossiliferous (10 to 50 m.). So, the name Lattorfian is often preferred to Sannoisian. The only nummulite which reached Germany is found there:[90] *Nummulites germanicus,* known at the same horizon in Belgium. In Eastern Prussia, on the shores of the Baltic, conglomerates with blocks of amber (fossil resin), doubtless produced by the working over of the Eocene lignites, are attributed to this stage.[91]

Toward the southwest, this Lattorfian sea advanced between the Rhenish Massif, Harz and Thuringia. It covered the Gulf of Cassel, where its southern boundaries are marked by lacustrine clays with *Melania* and lignites in the region of Marburg (Hesse), under the marine Stampian.[92] But it did not yet penetrate the Mainz Basin.[93]

b. The *Stampian,* in the sub-surface of northern Germany, follows the Sannoisian in continuity but, toward the south, it is broadly transgressive. The sea very slightly overran the ancient massifs. And especially, a great transgression started from the Gulf of Cassel, circling around the southeast of the Rhenish Massifs on which it nibbled in the Neuwied Basin. Rejoining the Rhine, it spread out widely in the Mainz Basin,[94] the typical region of the German Stampian. Following the Rhenish trough, this arm of the sea extended into Alsace, where, because of its peculiar characteristics, the Oligocene will be studied later (p. 498).

In the regions of northern Germany, where the Sannoisian and Stampian both are present, the boundary between the two stages is often only marked by the faunas. For, near the shores, the sandy facies of the Sannoisian is still prolonged into the base of the Stampian (Magdeburg sands) and is sometimes found at the top (Stettin sands). But most of the stage is normally represented by blue marls with calcareous nodules (called septaria) cemented and veined with calcite. This is the Septarienton, up to 200 m. thick, often called Rupelton, for it is identical to the Boom clays of Belgium. This thick, clayey formation is found in northern Germany (Ratingen clay in the lower Rhine valley) and the gulf of Cassel, as well as in the Mainz Basin. On the edges of this Basin, this clayey facies, very poor in shells (numerous small foraminifers), passes into very fossiliferous sands, known as Meeressand, of which the upper beds (Schleichsande) are the equivalent of the Stettin sands, which in eastern Germany overlie the Septarienton.[95] But these sandy beds (Vallendar-shotter) inaugurating the Oligocene in the Neuwied Basin (where they are overlain, not by the Septarienton, but by the littoral facies of the Arenberg stage), which correspond to the Walsumer Meeressande of the lower Rhine valley, are older than the marine series of the Mainz Basin and thus mark the first position of the Stampian transgression.[96]

c. Finally the Casselian, or better the *Chattian* (Chattes, ancient tribe of the country of Cassel), is represented by fine, glauconitic sands typically developed in the Gulf of Cassel, with a rich fauna characteristic of the stage. Always covering Denmark, the sea did not reach the Oder to the east; to the south, it again outlined a gulf between the Elbe and the Oder.

But in the Mainz Basin, the tendency to emerge is further emphasized. The Septarienton is, in fact, covered there by marls with cyrenes, already a little brackish. It is hard to tell whether they are Stampian or Chattian. In any case, above come the *Cerithium* limestones, surely Chattian, for intercalations of lacustrine limestones (Landschneckenkalk) contain *Helix ramondi*.

d. The Oligocene series ends with *Corbicula* limestones, then *Hydrobia* limestones (formery called Littorinellenkalk), very classic horizons in the Mainz Basin. All these beds are sometimes joined to the lower Miocene. But in addition to containing no trace of a Miocene fauna (Dollfuss),[97] their Oligocene (Aquitanian) age answers a paleogeographic necessity, since the Miocene sea never reached as far as Hesse and could not, thenceforth, reach the Mainz Basin (von Linstow).

IV. The Paleogene in the Zone of the Hercynian Massifs of Middle Europe (Continental Eocene, Lagunal-Marine Oligocene of Subsidence Troughs)

In the immense spaces that separate the gulfs tributary to the North Sea from the Atlantic (Aquitaine) and from the Mediterranean (Alpine sea), the Eocene formations are in general thin, very local and exclusively continental. On the other hand, in certain regions like Limagne, Alsace and the Rhône Basin, the Oligocene gives evidence of marine influences and often accumulates in thicknesses exceeding a thousand meters. These are true troughs of subsidence and their history must be explained.

1. Eocene

The continental sediments of the Eocene have three principal types of facies, each quite different:

1st. The type of siliceous, sandy or refractory clay formations, developed especially in the lower Eocene. These are river or stream deposits, often red, deeply decalcified, which are evidence of weathering of the crystalline massifs, worked over several times by streams, more impoverished with each reworking, and gradually collected in depressions. It is, in short, of the Wealdian type or of the variegated sands and clays of the Neocomian which formed under similar paleogeographic conditions.

2nd. The siderolithic type. On the plateaus of Jurassic or Cretaceous limestones, the *terra rossa,* resulting from the superficial alteration of these limestones, was swept into fissures and is now found in the deposits called siderolithic, for they are red clays with ferruginous concretions. Their geographic or industrial value (iron ores) is very moderate but on the other hand, they are very important from a paleontologic viewpoint, because of the mammalian remains they contain and from a stratigraphic viewpoint because, in sections, they sharply emphasize the lacuna between the Cretaceous and the Tertiary.

3rd. The type of marls or lacustrine limestones. These sediments were mostly formed by precipitation of lime brought in by streams. This facies is especially developed in the middle and upper Eocene. Its appearance perhaps indicates a more humid climate,[98] resulting in persistent flow of freshwater torrents, while in the early Eocene, in a more arid climate, there are only alluvial fans and so stream rather than lacustrine facies.

Let us follow the distribution of these different types in a few regions. This distribution will of course be irregular since they are continental deposits, generally rather thin.

On the border of the Armorican Massif, the *Sabalites* sandstone of Anjou, already studied (p. 485), can be related to the first type, and the overlying Ledian and Ludian lacustrine limestones and marls can be related to the third type.

On the western edge of the Massif Central, a siderolithic deposit composed of red sands and clays has been carefully studied by H. Schoeller.[99] On the north side of the Massif, similar deposits are found which are connected toward the north with the formation of the widely distributed plastic clay (p. 477). Likewise the continental Landenian (p. 476) represents this type on the edge of the Ardennes.[100] Above, Lutetian lacustrine limestones, similar to those so developed in the Lakes of Provins and Chartres (p. 479), form only isolated remnants at Talmay, near Dijon, for example, and at Bouxwiller (Alsace). They are well dated by *Planorbis pseudo-ammonius*. Some were recently found, between the Jurassic and the Oligocene, in drilling the foundations of the great Rhine dam, at Kembs, near Mulhouse,[101] and in Homburg, drilling in the Alsatian potash basin.[102]

The Jura Mountains constitute, as was to be expected, the type region of the siderolithic, called in German-speaking areas Bolus or Huppererde. Mammals are particularly numerous in the Basel district of the Jura Mountains (for example, Egerkingen). A rich Lutetian deposit of this facies also exists in the fissures of the Bajocian limestones of the Lyonais Mont-d'Or at Lissieu (Rhône).

The famous Quercy phosphorites belong to a similar facies, on the southwest border of the Massif Central. These are concretionary deposits filling the fissures or gulfs in the calcareous Causses of Quercy. The phosphate is produced, not by bones of animals fallen into these fissures, as was formerly believed, but rather by the residual alteration of lateritic earth formed from limestone. The mammalian remains show that the filling in, begun sometime in the Ledian, occurred especially during the Oligocene, the age to which most of the species of the celebrated fauna of the phosphorites belong.[103]

In the Rhône Valley, narrow bands of Eocene which crop out at the foot of the first sub-Alpine chains (St. Paul-Trois-Chateaux, Royans) and in the chains themselves (Vercors, Chartreuse and as far as Salève), show a fine development of variegated sands and clays, actively exploited, in Royans especially,[104] for refractory products. Their quartz and flint are doubtless products of the decomposition in place of sandy and flinty limestones of the Upper Cretaceous, while the ultimate source of their flakes of kaolin may have been the Massif Central. A jawbone of *Lophiodon larteti,* the only fossil found in these sands, at Echelles (northwest extremity of Chartreuse), confirms their lower Eocene age.

This facies is prolonged southward into the Apt–Forcalquier or Lower Durance Basin. There it is overlain by Lutetian lacustrine limestones with *Planorbis pseudo-ammonius,* themselves overlain by lacustrine marls in which, at La Débruge, near Gargas (vicinity of Apt), lignite beds have provided a rich mammalian fauna of Ludian age.

In the Alès Basin, a rather reduced lower Eocene is found, similar to that of the Apt Basin. The overlying lacustrine marls and conglomerates represent the Ledian (called Bartonian, up to the present), well dated by the fine deposit of Robiac, near St. Mamert (northwest of Nîmes), with the last *Lophiodon,* grown gigantic (*L. lautricense*). The Ludian is equally easily recognized, thanks to the lacustrine limestones and marls of Euzet-les-Bains, near St-Mamert, with a mammalian fauna.

In the Aix Basin, on the other hand, there is a very different and very interesting Eocene, whose base we have already described in the vicinity of Rognac (p. 431). There, above the bar of Rognac limestones, comes a recur-

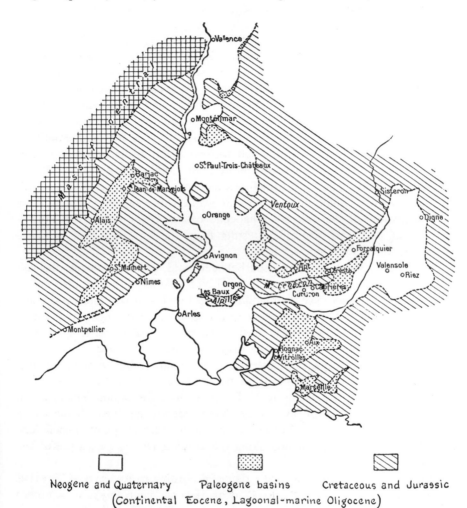

Neogene and Quaternary   Paleogene basins   Cretaceous and Jurassic
(Continental Eocene, Lagoonal-marine Oligocene)

FIG. 118. *Diagrammatic map showing the location of the principal Paleogene basins in the region of the Rhône.*

rence of the red clay facies of the Danian. These are the bright red clays of Vitrolles (Vitrollian). But some intercalations of lacustrine limestone contain *Physa montensis,* a species characteristic of the Mons limestones, so this belongs to the Montian.

This depressed clayey zone is dominated by a last great scarp formed of freshwater limestones including the whole series of stages from Landenian to Lutetian, for *Physa prisca* is found at the base and *Planorbis pseudo-am-monius* at the top. The upper Eocene is missing in the Rognac-Aix district, but lacustrine limestones of that age are known on the north slope of the Alpilles (east of Tarascon).[105]

Thus, the purely lacustrine facies, already established here in the Maes-trichtian, persist throughout the Eocene.

2. *Oligocene*

Important changes took place in middle Europe during the Oligocene and sharply emphasize the individuality of this sub-system. Zones of subsidence were outlined in the Hercynian Massifs and were invaded by marine waters or lagoons. Such are the troughs of the Loire (Forez) and Allier (Limagne) and the Rhenish trough (Alsace). These regions, sinking by degrees as the sediments tended to overload them, produced true "appeals for sedimentation," in which Oligocene deposits, although formed under insignificant depths of water, accumulated in thicknesses of more than 1,000 m., with the result that these zones of subsidence are sometimes incorrectly termed geosynclines. Finally, a very thick Oligocene is also found in the Rhône region, although there the individuality of the different Oligocene basins (Alès Basin, Apt-Forcalquier Basin, Aix and Marseille) results from the localization of outcrops rather than from a tectonic separation.

A. Limagne, Velay.[106]   Enclosed between bold, granite plateaus, the valleys of the Allier, or Limagne, and the Loire (plains of Forez, also called Limagne of the Loire), owe their smiling aspect and their rich and varied husbandry to their Oligocene fill. Farther to the southeast, the Oligocene is found again in the fertile Puy-en-Velay Basin, and to the southwest, it appears at the base of the great Cantal volcano in the vicinity of Aurillac.

The sediment filling the minute (½ km. square), but very interesting, lacustrine basin of Menat, isolated on the ancient platform west of Gannat, is probably Eocene (according to L. Piton, 1940). Bituminous shale, about 100 m. thick, exploited for bone black, has yielded a rich insect fauna and a flora, tropical in character, but presenting a mixture of plant associations which must have been graduated along the mountainous slopes, a useful lesson for paleobotanists.

The *Sannoisian,* paleontologically dated, according to R. Lavocat,[107] exists only in the Velay Basin (famous Ronzon deposit, near Puy), in southern Limagne (Lembron, near Issoire), and in the gulf of Ebreuil which is separated from the Bourbon Limagne west of Gannat. It consists of arkoses, red sands and clays, of quite variable thickness (0 to 250 m.). Banks of lacustrine limestone have yielded a lagoonal fauna, with *Cerithium plicatum, C. margaritaceum, Potamides rhodanicus* and *Melania (Striatella) barjacensis.* The last two species, which are found in the Alès Basin, seem to demonstrate that these first marine influences came from the south, from the Rhône valley, although erosion has destroyed the original continuity of the Tertiary covering of the Cevennes, between Alès and Velay (see Fig. 109).

Then these influences weaken and the *Stampian* develops formidable thicknesses (more than 1,000 m.) of arkoses, marly limestones and lacustrine marls with *Cypris* (a small, freshwater ostracode crustacean). At the base, there are especially arkoses (impregnated with bitumen at Royat, near Clermont), which are only distinguished from Sannoisian arkoses by the mammalian faunas contained in rare beds of lacustrine limestones (Bournoncle, north of Brioude). Then thick white lacustrine marls swarming with impressions of *Cypris* prevail. But, from time to time, green marls with cyrenes, gypsiferous beds, calcareous banks with *Potamides lamarcki*[108] and especially chalk with coccoliths (marine microorganisms discovered by Dangeard), give evidence of marine influences, coming this time from the north, from the transgressive Stampian sea in the Paris Basin.

This Stampian series, explored by oil wells between Clermont and Gannat, reaches its maximum thickness (1,750 m.), not in the center of the Limagne, but near its western border in the vicinity of Riom.

At this period, the first volcanos of Auvergne appeared, exactly on the faults along the edge of the trough of subsidence. There are a few flows (recently discovered by Michel) but particularly sub-lacustrine eruptions, whose products, deposited at the same time as the lacustrine muds, produced curious rocks called *peperites,* whose origin has caused much discussion.

In the upper Stampian or *Chattian,* lacustrine limestones, dated by *Helix ramondi,* predominate. The type comes from Pont-du-Château, east of Clermont, where asphaltic limestones are actively exploited. These limestones are often curiously concretionary (cauliflower limestones) or full of tubes of the caddis worms (caddis flies).[109]

Finally the *Aquitanian*[110] can be clearly distinguished only in the vicinity of St. Gérand-le-Puy, near Vichy, where its limestones, separated from those of the Chattian by a karst surface,[111] are exploited in great quarries. These limestones have yielded the famous mammalian fauna, which defines the type of the stage. *Helix ramondi* is no longer found, only *H. arvernensis,* which however already existed in the Chattian.

B. Alsace. The Rhenish plain in Alsace presents an analogous series, but with much clearer marine influences.

The rare remnants of Oligocene, visible in outcrops on the edges of the basin, are composed of marls and sandstones alternating with thick beds of conglomerate (called coastal conglomerate), whose absolute age is difficult to determine.[112] The information which has led to the establishment of the following series, reaching 2,000 m. thickness, has been obtained from deep drilling for petroleum or potash.

The *Sannoisian,* overlying remnants of the lacustrine Eocene (Bouxwiller limestones, see p. 494), is represented by considerable accumulations (700 m.) of marls in which marine facies with cyrenes alternate with lacustrine facies with *Limnaea* or brackish ones containing gypsum and salt. It is, on a much grander scale, a repetition of the supra-gypsiferous marly facies of the Paris Basin. In this marly complex, called the Péchelbronn beds, are intercalated oil-bearing sands,[113] exploited in the Péchelbronn Basin (north of Strasbourg), and potash beds,[114] developed north of Mulhouse.

F. Quiévreux[115] has very recently discovered, in a clay layer 5 cm. thick intercalated in the midst of one of two potash beds (sylvite, sylvinite and rock salt), a small flora (about 15 species) and a rich insect fauna (some forty genera), whose remarkably well preserved remains must have been windborne into the lifeless, potassic lagoon (comparable to the Dead Sea). By comparison with related living forms, we may deduce a warm temperate (annual median about 18° C.) but not desert climate. Thus the potash beds were possibly deposited in salt lakes fed by streams which had leached the Permo-Trias salts.

But, thirty meters beneath the lower potash bed, there is a guide-horizon, long known as the fossiliferous zone which gives evidence of unquestionably marine influences (fish, *Mytilus, Cyrena,* etc.). The ingression of this Sannoisian sea in Alsace poses an interesting paleogeographic problem, not yet solved.[116] The transgression does not seem to have come by way of the Mainz Basin to the north, nor by the Jura Mountains to the south, since the Sannoisian sea is unknown there. A direct communication with the Paris Basin, by way of the Phalsburg depression, has been suggested (van Werveke). Perhaps more likely would be a connection with the lagoons of the Rhône and Saône (Dollfus). For in this direction, the Oligocene ends against the Jurassic of the Belfort pass, with lagoonal-lacustrine formations (Bourogne system of W. Kilian) lying directly on the Jurassic and probably representing, not the Chattian as was long believed,[117] but the Sannoisian,[118] the rest of the Oligocene having been carried away by erosion.

In any case, in the *Stampian* (see p. 491) the similarity of facies and faunas, as well as the continuity of beds, demonstrates that a single sea extended from the Mainz Basin as far as the vicinity of Belfort, and probably into the Saône valley, in the Swiss Jura.[119] There the Oligocene is preserved in the small basins of Laufen and Delémont and even on the border of the Alps (see note 23, chap. 10).

Thus, in Alsace, marls with foraminifers[120] and shales with fish (*Amphysile*) correspond to the Septarienton. Above, marls and micaceous sandstones containing fish scales (*Meletta* beds), about 500 m. thick, are approximately equivalent to the *Cyrena* marls of the Mainz Basin. The two most characteristic species of this Alsatian Stampian, *Amphysile heinrichi* and *Clupea* (*Meletta*) *longimana,* have lately been found in the lower Stampian of the Canton of Lucerne. These forms have Mediterranean affinities, unknown in the Oligocene of the North Sea, which confirms the existence of direct, marine communication in the Stampian, between Alsace and the Alpine seas, through the Jura Mountains[121] (see Fig. 109).

Toward the Belfort pass, the Stampian marls pass into sandy-clayey coastal facies, very fossiliferous in the Dannemarie quarries near Altkirch,[122] and thus are equivalent to the Meeressande of the Mainz Basin.

Finally, in the *Chattian,* lacustrine marls, then fresh water limestones with *Helix ramondi,* known everywhere on the Baden side of the Rhine (Tullingerkalk), show that marine influences definitely ended. The Mainz facies of cerithid limestone does not go beyond the French frontier on the south.

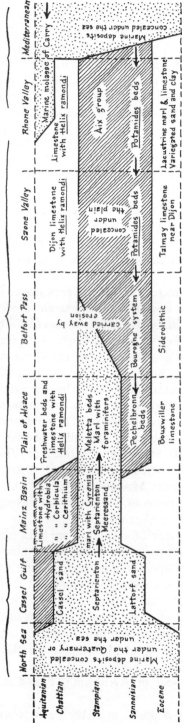

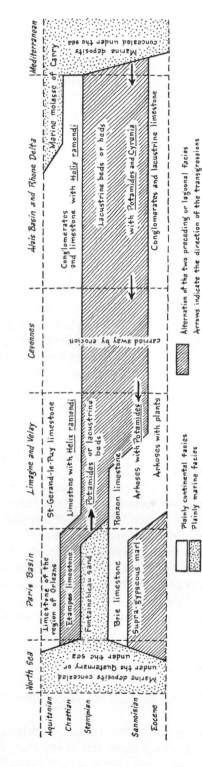

FIG. 119. *Two diagrams showing the transgression of the Oligocene sea or lagoons on the continental zone of middle Europe (compare map, Fig. 109).*

499

C. Rhône region. 1st. *Basin of Alès or Languedoc.* The Oligocene lies on the previously described Eocene, to a thickness exceeding 500 m. The Sannoisian is extremely thick, recalling that of Limagne and even of Alsace, though less marine than the latter. The marine influences are marked by beds with *Potamides, Cyrena* and *Melanoides albigensis.* There are sandstones with *Cinnamomum* (camphor tree) at Célas,[123] very briskly exploited bituminous limestones (asphalts of St. Jean-de-Marvéjols) and even thick beds of lignite (Barjac, Fig. 118).

Finally, in the Stampian and especially the Chattian, continental conglomerates with Cretaceous cobbles develop. The absence of crystalline cobbles shows that the Cevennes, at this period as in the Sannoisian (p. 496), did not stand out.

2nd. *Provençal Basins.* The Basins of Marseille, Aix and Apt-Forcalquier[124] belong to the domain of the Provence folds (Pyrenean-Provençal) which were produced in the upper Eocene. The horizontal Oligocene (except for deformation due to Alpine folding) thus followed a folded, continental Eocene.

As in Languedoc, this Oligocene is characterized by the appearance of marine influences which weaken toward the east in witness whereof are cyrenes (*C. semistriata*) and cerithids (*C. plicatum, Potamides lamarcki*). This Oligocene is especially typical and well studied in the Aix Basin. Extremely thick formations of limestone and marl with gypsiferous beds, called the Aix group by early geologists, are attributed to the Stampian. They are famous for their richness in fine impressions of fish, insects and leaves. This formation, spreading over the three basins, is overlain everywhere by Chattian limestones with *Helix ramondi,* indicating the end of marine influences. The continental facies of yellow and red clays of St. Henry (suburb of Marseille) should be attributed to the Chattian—or to the middle Stampian, according to Viret. These clays, well known for their mammalian fauna, are actively exploited in great quarries located between the railways from Marseille to Aix and Arles, for the manufacture of the small red tiles or *tomettes,* used so much throughout the Midi, and for pipes called Marseille earthenware.[125]

3rd. *Marine Aquitanian of the Mediterranean Littoral.* As we have mentioned before (p. 471), it is convenient to leave in the Oligocene the marine beds which, after the general regression of the Chattian, marked the new arrival of the sea in the vicinity of the present coasts. They consist of marls, sandstones or sands, containing a characteristic fauna (*Melongena lainei, Ostrea aginensis,* etc.) which are the equivalent of the type Aquitanian of the Aquitaine Basin. These deposits are known here only in two regions:

1) On the coastline of the Nerthe Chain, north of Marseille, in the classic localities of Saussel and Rouet de Carry (Fig. 134).[126]

2) In the outskirts of Montpellier (School of Agriculture, Font-Caude quarter).

Between these two regions, Aquitanian deposits probably exist, buried under the littoral plain. But in any case, this Aquitanian sea, on the evidence, hardly went beyond the shores of the present sea.

4th. *Middle Valley of the Rhône.* North of the Apt Basin, the Oligocene crops out especially in the border of the sub-Alpine chains, where we shall study it later. On the right bank of the Rhône, north of the Alès Basin, small remnants are found sheltered against the crystalline rocks of the Massif Central, then around the ridges of the southern Jura. Thus, these variegated marls with layers of lacustrine limestones form the top of the left bank zone of support for the great Génissiat dam on the Rhône upstream from Seyssel. Near Frangy (between Annecy and Seyssel), there are gypsiferous intercalations, calcareous beds with *Potamides lamarcki* (*Helix ramondi* at the top)[127] and beds of bituminous sands from which hydrocarbons have, by lateral migration, impregnated the Urgonian limestones actively exploited as asphalt at Seyssel-Pyrimont.[128]

In the latitude of Lyon, Oligocene outcrops are unknown on the two edges of the Rhône plain, for there the Miocene lies directly over the crystalline rocks at Lyon itself, and over the Jurassic limestones of Ile Crémieu at St. Quentin (p. 562). But between Lyon and St. Quentin, deep wells in search of the extension of the St. Etienne Coal Basin (p. 200) have revealed, under the Miocene, considerable thicknesses (more than 500 m.) of variegated marls, ferruginous conglomerates and lacustrine limestones which undoubtedly, in part, represent the Oligocene.

Farther north, in Bresse, small Oligocene outcrops with *Potamides lamarcki* are known at the edge of the Jura Mountains near Lons-le-Saulnier and in Haute-Saône.[129] H. Vincienne[130] has noted small foraminifers (rotalids) at Coligny, which, if they are not indeed redeposited, give clear witness of marine influences. The great well of Vincelles, near Louhans, in Bresse (note 31, chap. 6) penetrated, beneath 240 m. of Pliocene marls, 420 m. of early Tertiary in which gypsiferous beds certainly correspond to the Oligocene.

Thus, beneath Lower Dauphiné and beneath Bresse, there are perhaps troughs of sedimentation similar to those of Limagne and Alsace, containing lagoonal Oligocene. But this lagoonal-marine regime certainly ended in the Chattian, for at Dijon on one side and Lons-le-Saulnier on the other, lacustrine limestones with *Helix ramondi* are found.

V. The Nummulitic of the French Atlantic Coast

We already know that certain elements of Mediterranean faunas may have reached the Paris Basin through a sort of Nummulitic English Channel. A Nummulitic Atlantic must have existed off the coast of France, a part of the immense Mesogean sea. This Atlantic advanced, in certain regions, well beyond the present coast, forming gulfs of very unequal importance.

A. *The Little Gulfs of Brittany*

The northernmost traces left by the Nummulitic Atlantic along the French coasts were discovered in Morbihan. Milon[131] described, in the Toulven depression south of Quimper, flint-bearing limestones with radiolarians and foraminifers, in formations analogous to the *Sabalite* sandstones (p. 485), which he considered to represent the Eocene. Farther southeast, near Lorient, L. Dangeard [132] described submarine deposits off Gâvres (Fig. 109) composed of nummulitic limestone (Ypresian or Lutetian) whose fauna has very decided Mediterranean affinities (orthophragmines, assilines). Later, the same geologist [133] discovered an outcrop of glauconitic sand with nummulites, probably Ypresian, near Lorient in a cut of the railroad from Port Louis to Hennebont. Finally, a very small deposit of sand with *Nummulites brongniarti* (Lutetian) has been found in the Quiberon Peninsula (Morbihan).[134]

All these facts demonstrate that the Nummulitic Atlantic was nibbling more or less on the southern coast of Brittany.[135]

But the clearest and most extensive traces of an Eocene transgression are seen on the two banks of the Loire estuary. This is the Gulf of the Lower Loire. A rather shallow sea advanced there as far as Saffré (north of Nantes) and its sandy, sometimes calcareous deposits are found in the form of isolated and insignificant remnants, lying directly on the Primary. The most famous are the Bois-Gouët sands, near Saffré, extraordinarily fossiliferous (700 species), with a Lutetian marine fauna.[136] The young stages of pelecypods are exceptionally abundant and F. Bernard has used them for interesting studies on the development of the shell. There is a mixture of Parisian species and others clearly Mediterranean, such as *Nummulites brongniarti* which never penetrated into the domain of the North Sea.

The upper Eocene and Sannoisian are missing or are represented by lacustrine deposits.

Then, in the Stampian, the sea returns in the same region and advances farther, up to Rennes, where it deposits the coarse limestone of Rennes which contains species characteristic of the Fontainebleau sands.[137] Finally the Chattian consists of lagoonal limestones with *Planorbis cornu* and *Potamides lamarcki*.[138]

B. *The Great Gulf of Aquitaine*

An immense nummulitic gulf coming from the Atlantic, covered all of southwest France and, in the Lutetian, brushing the northern edge of the Pyrenees, advanced even into Languedoc.[139] The deposits of the central part of this ancient gulf are generally concealed by the Neogene and Quaternary covering, but those of the borders crop out widely and their study will give a fine example of stratigraphic synthesis.[140]

1. North Shore: Marine Facies of Bordelais.[141] The Nummulitic presents only rather restricted outcrops on the two banks of the Gironde.

The lower Eocene, very poorly known (Landenian?, Ypresian?), is represented only by reworked fossils or fragments of sandstone with *Nummulites planulatus* and *Alveolina oblunga* (vicinity of Royan, on the north bank of the estuary). Wells at Bordeaux[142] have found, under the middle Eocene, sands and sandstones containing *Nummulites guettardi* and *N. globulus,* at the base, Mediterranean forms, and *N. aquitanicus-girondicus* at the top, the ancestral form of *N. laevigatus* of the Paris Basin, here associated with ortho-phragmines and assilines.

The *Lutetian,* however, has well developed outcrops. The limestones of St. Palais (near Royan) and of Blaye (town north of Bordeaux)[143] contain a fine fauna of mollusks and echinoids. They are overlain by the marls with *Ostrea cucullaris* of Plassac, near Blaye. Formerly attributed to the Ledian (because incorrectly credited with *Nummulites variolarius*), these marls still belong to the Lutetian, which ends here with the lacustrine limestones of Plassac, containing *Limnaea logniscata,* but which remains marine at St. Estèphe in Lower Médoc.

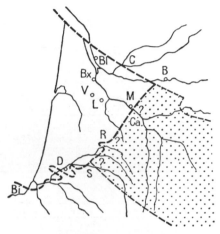

FIG. 120. *Diagrammatic map of the Aquitaine Basin in the Stampian (after F. Daguin, work cited note 144, this chap.).*

Dotted portion covers the domain of the fresh-water Molasse of Agenais. The heavy broken line marks the limit of the marine domain. The small "promontories" jutting into the Stampian sea correspond to sub-Pyrenean anticlines, already outlined in the Stampian, which are still more accentuated after the Oligocene.

Bl = Blaye; Bx = Bordeaux; C = Coutras; B = Bergerac; M =Marmande; L = Landiras; V = Villagrain; Ca = Casteljaloux; R =Roquefort; S = St-Sever; D = Dax; Bi = Biarritz.

Much farther south, Lutetian limestones have been reached by the great well of Abatilles, near Arcachon (see note 149, this chap.) where they contain a completely Mediterranean fauna (orthophragmines, assilines, *Nummulites atacicus, N. perforatus, N. millecaput*) unknown farther north.

The *Ledian* in Lower Médoc is represented by the St. Estèphe clays with *Ostrea bersonensis,* followed by the St. Estèphe limestones with miliolids at the base and echinoids at the top. But southeast, beyond Bordeaux, these marine beds pass into continental sandy-clayey facies of the lower molasse of Fronsadais.

The *Ludian* at St. Estèphe corresponds to a return of clayey facies with *O. bersonensis* and it ends with white marls and soft limestones with *Nummulites incrassatus* and *Orbitolites complanatus.*

In the Abatilles well, the nummulite limestones which represent the upper
Eocene are 110 m. thick.

The *Sannoisian* shows a retreat of the sea. It begins in Médoc with limestones and marls with anomias, followed by marls with cerithids, and it ends
with the lacustrine limestone of Civrac. But to the southeast and at Bordeaux,
the whole stage becomes lacustrine. This is the upper molasse of Fronsadais,

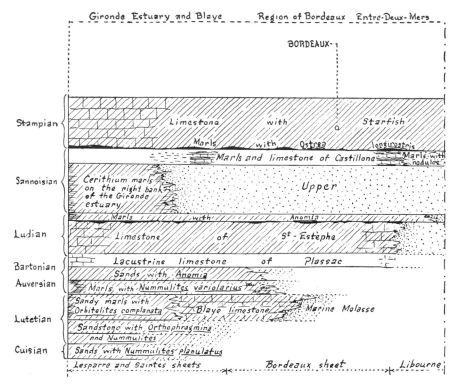

FIG. 121. *Diagrammatic profile showing the correlation of the Nummulitic
formations of the Aquitaine Basin north of the Garonne, from the littoral
Girondin to the confluence of the Lot and the Garonne (after J. Blayac, work
cited Note 140, this chapter; reproduced with the permission of the Soc. géol.
de France).*

overlain by the limestone and marls of Castillon, prolonging the Civrac limestone.

Then in the *Stampian,* which is very important,[144] the marine facies spread
eastward as far as the confluence of the Lot and the Garonne. Beginning with
marls with *Ostrea longirostris,* exactly as in the Paris Basin, the famous starfish limestone follows, containing nummulites characteristic of the Stampian
of the Alps (*N. intermedius-fichteli, N. vascus-boucheri*). This limestone,
forming the framework of the great Entre-Deux-Mers plateau, has been used
extensively for building throughout the Bordeaux region.

The *Chattian,* as almost everywhere, corresponds to a regression. It is missing in the Gironde littoral and only appears farther east, represented by lacustrine beds with *Helix ramondi* and *Limnaea pachygaster.* This is the classic horizon of the Agenais white limestone which extends into the region of Agen.

Finally, the *Aquitanian* marks the beginning of a new transgression, for

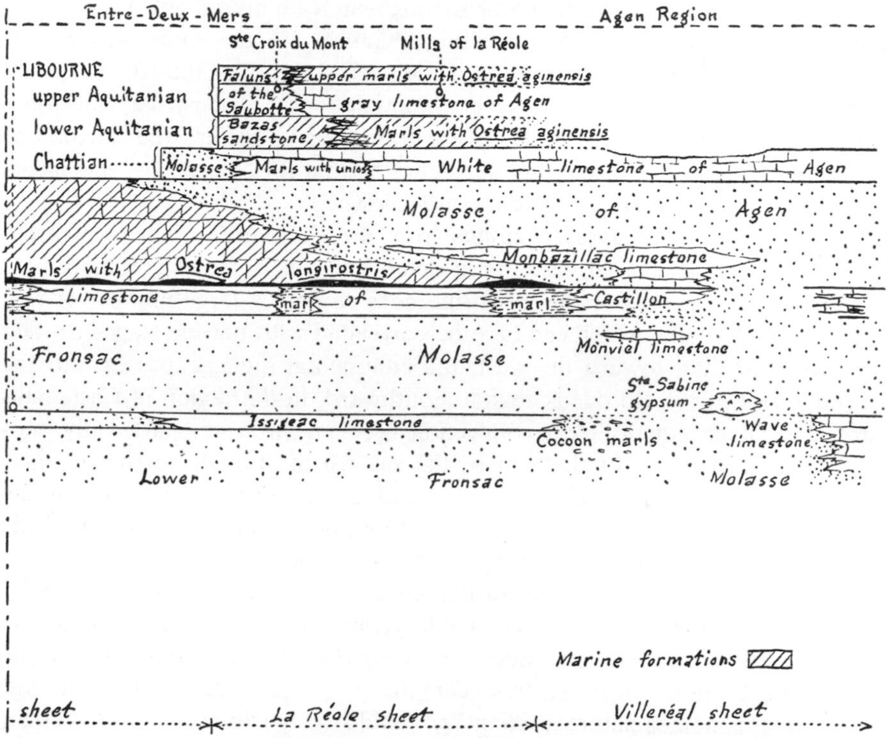

Entre-Deux-Mers — Agen Region

Ste Croix du Mont — Mills of la Réole

LIBOURNE

upper Aquitanian — Faluns of the Saubotte — upper marls with Ostrea aginensis — gray limestone of Agen

lower Aquitanian — Bazas sandstone — Marls with Ostrea aginensis

Chattian — Molasse — Marls with unios — White limestone of Agen

Molasse of Agen

Marls with Ostrea longirostris — Monbazillac limestone

Limestone — marl of — marl — Castillon

Fronsac — Monviel limestone

Ste-Sabine gypsum

Issigeac limestone — Cocoon marls — Wave limestone

Lower — Fronsac — Molasse

Marine formations

sheet — La Réole sheet — Villeréal sheet

here we are in the typical region where this stage shows a rich, marine fauna, with *Melongena lainei,* etc.

The lower Aquitanian, on the left bank of the Garonne, is represented by the *faluns* and sandstones of Bazas (Fig. 98) with amphiopes and scutellas. Between Bordeaux and La Réole, it assumes the rather brackish marine facies of marls with *Ostrea aginensis* (oysters of Agen), which in fact extends as far east as Agen.

The upper Aquitanian is entirely marine only on the left bank of the Garonne. There are the faluns of the Bazas region (Saubotte and Gamachot faluns) and of the vale of Saucats (Lariey faluns). To the east, these marine sands are almost totally replaced by the facies, first brackish, then lacustrine, of the gray limestone of Agen.

2. Continental Facies of the Base of the Gulf: Lacustrine Molasse. All the eastern Aquitaine Basin (see Figs. 88, 98, 123) between the Massif Central (regions of Agen, Bas-Quercy, Albi, Castres) and the edge of the

Pyrenees (region of Toulouse) is filled with continental deposits belonging principally to the Oligocene. There are particularly swamp or quiet-stream deposits, that is to say, marls and sandy clays which have become the more or less marly, calcareous sandstones called molasse. These molasse terrains, ravined and fertile, recall those which we shall describe for the Miocene on the border of the Alps.

Toward the south, coarse conglomeratic facies appear (Palassou conglomerates, see later). The filling of the ancient Nummulitic gulf is produced principally at the expense of the rising Pyrenees, in the same way as the Miocene arms of the sea are invaded by deltas coming from the Alpine Chain. Toward the Massif Central, however, intercalations of lacustrine limestones predominate. But, all these deposits are transgressive toward the north. The more recent deposits conceal the older ones so that no outcrops of this lacustrine molasse older than the Lutetian are known.[145]

A very complex stratigraphy results from the alternation of these different facies,[146] which we cannot describe in detail but which presents considerable paleontologic interest. For the lacustrine beds contain a large number of rich mammalian deposits, which can here be correlated with marine stages. In fact we have seen that, toward the west, the continental molasse passes into the marine series of the Bordeaux region. Southward, in the region of Castelnaudary, there is an equally clear connection between the lower part of the molasse and the deposits of the arm of the sea which, as will be shown later, persisted between the Montagne-Noire and the Pyrenees, until the middle Eocene. So the Aquitaine Basin has an importance equal to that of the Paris Basin for the European stratigraphy of the Nummulitic.

We shall merely mention the formations and most famous occurrences.[147]

The Issel sandstone, near Castelnaudary, has yielded a rich fauna of the upper Lutetian (*Lophiodon isselanum, Propalaeotherium isselanum*). The molasse of Lautrec, near Castres, contains a fauna called Bartonian, but which, in the nomenclature used here, should be attributed to the Ledian stage (*Lophiodon lautricense, Palaeotherium lautricense*). Showing how far the last marine influences are still felt, the Ludian fauna of the Montmartre gypsum is found in the gypsum of Mas-Stes-Puelles, near Castelnaudary. In the Sannoisian, lagoons stretched as far as the region of Albi, where *Melania albigensis* lived. In the Stampian, the Lauraguais molasse, in the region of Toulouse, contains various mammalian deposits and the Agen molasse is lacustrine, but passes laterally into the starfish limestone of Bordeaux.

This Agen molasse is covered, in the region of Agen, by the classic Chattian-Aquitanian series which has been described as the "Agen trilogy," composed of the Agen lacustrine white limestone (Chattian) at the base, then marls with *Ostrea aginensis* (lower Aquitanian) marking the extreme advance of the Aquitanian sea, and finally the gray lacustrine limestone of Agen (upper Aquitanian), crowning the crests and plateaus and overlain by a recurrence of the marine facies with *O. aginensis*. A marly bed intercalated in this gray limestone has yielded the celebrated mammalian fauna of Laugnac (north of Agen), identical to that of St. Gerand-le-Puy.[148] As, on the other hand, in the west these gray limestones pass into the marine upper Aquitanian of the Bordeaux region, we realize that this deposit provides the key to the relation between the marine formations which have been used as the stage type and the continental formations which represent it in middle Europe.

3. A Section on the Southern Shore: Biarritz. Continuously swept clean by the sea, the Biarritz Nummulitic section is the finest of the whole southwest. To the south, lying on the Secondary formations of the Pyrenean border, the Tertiary begins with the upper Lutetian overlying (in discordance?) the Upper Cretaceous. Thus, it is incomplete at the base, proving that the Biarritz region, at that period, marked the southern shore of the ancient gulf.

Then, following the famous Biarritz cliffs northward, we see the whole series of Nummulitic stages up to and including the Stampian, after which

FIG. 122. *Diagrammatic profile of the cliffs of Biarritz, seen from the sea* (*after J. Boussac, in E. Haug*).

Distribution in stages after R. Abrard.

White	= Sands of the Landes, dunes	Quaternary
9	= Gritty marls and sandstone of the Lighthouse	Upper Stampian
8	= Sandy marles of la Chambre d'Amour	Lower Stampian
7	= Rocks of the Villa Eugénie	Upper Sannoisian
6	= Gritty marls and gravel bed of Atalaye and Port-Vieux	Lower Sannoisian
5	= Gray clays of la Perspective Miramar (and of lou Cachaou)	Ludian
4	= Upper marls of the Basque Coast	}Ledian
3	= Lower marls of the Basque Coast with pentacrines	
2	= Beds of the Villa Marbella	}Upper Lutetian
1	= Marl-limestones of the Islet of Gourèpe	

Horizontal scale: about 1/36,000. Height greatly exaggerated.

the cliffs are lost beneath the dunes of Landes and we must go as far as the Gironde to again see the Tertiary along the coast.

This completely marine Lutetian-Stampian series of Biarritz is about 1,500 m. thick. The facies are especially deep-water and marly, the greatest depth being realized apparently in the Ledian, with the pentacrine marls. A succession of numerous fossiliferous horizons, which have been minutely studied and designated by local names, have become classic (Fig. 122); for, because of the richness of the faunas (echinoids, mollusks, nummulites, assilines, orthophragmines), no section is more adequate as a basis of comparison for any geologist who studies the Mediterranean Nummulitic.

4. The Axial Part of the Ancient Gulf: Pyrenean Border. We already know of the existence, in southern Aquitaine, of an Aturian Gulf (see p. 427) at the boundary between the Cretaceous and the Tertiary, in which there is continuous passage from one era to the other through marine facies. This gulf must evidently have ended at the Atlantic somewhere beneath Landes, between Biarritz and Bordeaux. The transgressions which covered the Cretaceous, in the Ypresian at Bordeaux, in the Lutetian at Biarritz, started from its axis.[149] And in fact, northeast and east of Biarritz, we shall find the lower Eocene formations of this ancient gulf; let us travel eastward along it (Figs. 123 and 124).

In the western part, only discontinuous outcrops of the Nummulitic are present, some located (Gaas, Tercis) in Chalosse, the region between Dax

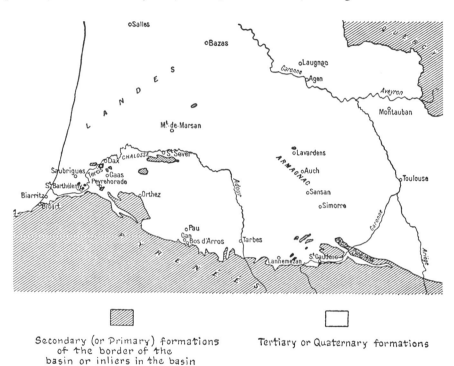

Secondary (or Primary) formations   Tertiary or Quaternary formations
      of the border of the
   basin or inliers in the basin

FIG. 123. *Map showing the classic localities of the southern part of the Aquitaine Basin.*

and St. Sever, others (Gan, Bos d'Arros) south of Pau. These districts are widely cultivated or wooded and with little variety so that the stratigraphy is difficult and uncertain. But H. Douvillé [150] was able to recognize isolated examples of all the Nummulitic stages.

Near Dax, in the Tercis anticline,[151] the series of Cretaceous limestones at the top of a classic Danian with *Nautilus danicus,* ends with banks in which, with this latter fossil, *Micraster tercensis* appears, a fossil usually considered characteristic of the Montian. But, according to J. Cuvillier,[152] a lacuna separates this Cretaceous from a lower Eocene represented by limestone with nummulites, orthophragmines and operculines, which no one would dream of attributing to the Danian or Montian, although it still contains echinoids with Cretaceous affinities and reworked pre-Danian rosalines.[153] However, in the region of Dax, the lower Lutetian with *Nummulites laevigatus* is recognized at St. Barthélemy and Peyrehorade (south of Dax) and it also appears in the Orthez region, with *N. uroniensis*. Finally, at the end of the upper Lutetian, a series similar to that of Biarritz, ending with the fossiliferous beds of Gaas (Stampian), is found in this region of Dax.[154]

South of Pau the Eocene series, which at Biarritz began only with the Lutetian, seems to be complete, including the base. The lower Eocene, very rich in nummulites from the very beginning, is well developed at Gan, where it ends with the celebrated Bos d'Arros beds (upper Landenian?) and the tile beds of Gan (Ypresian?).[155]

So we see the nummulites appearing in abundance at the extreme base of the Tertiary[156] and succeeding each other in a much more continuous way than in the Paris Basin.

Farther east, there is a better section in the small chain of the Petites-Pyrénées, where earlier we described the transition beds from the Cretaceous to the Tertiary (p. 427). The upper Garumnian corresponds to the Montian stage, for in it the most characteristic species of the Mons limestone (*Cerithium inopinatum, Turritella montensis*) are found. Above this unquestionably Tertiary horizon, a few echinoids with Cretaceous affinities again appear (*Ananchytes, Micraster tercensis*), which Leymerie, greatly intrigued, called "a Cretaceous colony" that survived into the Tertiary. That simply shows that the change between the two faunas was not sudden but rather by alternations. A bank with *Operculina heberti* tops the Montian of the Petites-Pyrénées, followed by a Thanetian-Lutetian series which we shall describe.

The Montian sea did not, however, advance farther east than the Petites-Pyrénées.

On the other hand, the whole Thanetian-lower Lutetian series remains marine into Ariège. It is represented by littoral facies, limestones with nummulites, with alveolines, with *Lithothamnium*. Above, beginning with the upper Lutetian, come conglomerates with coarse components, called the Palassou conglomerates (name of a local geologist), formed at the expense of the rising Pyrenees, thus analogous to the Nagelfluh of the Miocene of the Alps (p. 565). These are the last folded beds of the region. The Oligocene, in the form of lacustrine molasse, is always horizontal.

East of the Ariège, we witness the progressive disappearance of marine facies. So in Corbières, the Thanetian-lower Lutetian is represented by alternations of lagoonal, lacustrine and marine facies. Faunas with *Cerithium* as rich as those of the Paris Basin, studied by Doncieux, are found therein. The most purely marine facies is represented by faunas with *Turritella* and nummulites of the lower Lutetian. Then, in Hérault, only the lower Lutetian remains marine. We have seen that in the Rhône region, the whole Eocene is continental. So the Nummulitic Aquitanian gulf was closed toward the east, without the communication with the Nummulitic Mediterranean which we shall find in the Alps.

WEST   EAST

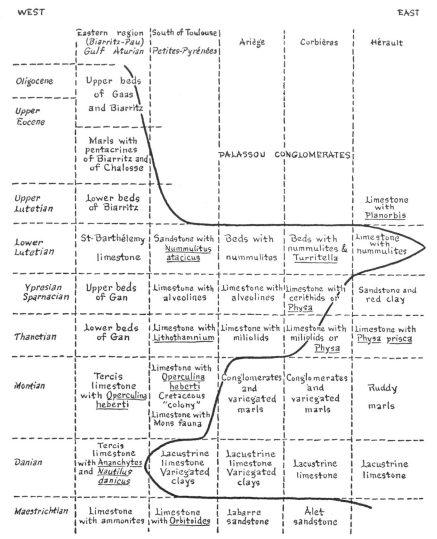

	Eastern region (Biarritz-Pau) Gulf Aturian	South of Toulouse (Petites-Pyrénées)	Ariège	Corbières	Hérault
Oligocene	Upper beds of Gaas and Biarritz				
Upper Eocene					
	Marls with pentacrines of Biarritz and of Chalosse		PALASSOU CONGLOMERATES		
Upper Lutetian	Lower beds of Biarritz				Limestone with Planorbis
Lower Lutetian	St-Barthélemy limestone	Sandstone with Nummulitus atacicus	Beds with nummulites	Beds with nummulites & Turritella	Limestone with nummulites
Ypresian Sparnacian	Upper beds of Gan	Limestone with alveolines	Limestone with alveolines	Limestone with cerithids or Physa	Sandstone and red clay
Thanetian	Lower beds of Gan	Limestone with Lithothamnium	Limestone with miliolids	Limestone with miliolids or Physa	Limestone with Physa prisca
Montian	Tercis limestone with Operculina heberti	Limestone with Operculina heberti / Cretaceous "colony" / Limestone with Mons fauna	Conglomerates and variegated marls	Conglomerates and variegated marls	Ruddy marls
Danian	Tercis limestone with Ananchytes and Nautilus danicus	Lacustrine limestone Variegated clays	Lacustrine limestone Variegated clays	Lacustrine limestone	Lacustrine limestone
Maestrichtian	Limestone with ammonites	Limestone with Orbitoides	Labarre sandstone	Alet sandstone	

FIG. 124. *Diagram showing the extent toward the east of the marine facies in the Nummulitic Gulf in southern Aquitaine.*

The heavy line separates the marine facies (to the left) from the continental facies (to the right).

VI. The Nummulitic Geosyncline in the French Alps[157]

A. *Paleontologic Definition of the Stages*

Molluscan and echinoid faunas can give exact information only in certain regions of the Alpine external zones. In any case, they only bring out general contrasts between the middle Eocene, upper Eocene and Oligocene. In particular, nowhere, either in the French Alps or even in the Swiss Alps are found any faunas indicating the lower Eocene.

So, we must emphasize the recent discovery[158] on the edge of the Austrian Alps, north of Salzburg, of a "Paleocene" with a rich molluscan fauna, incontestibly Thanetian (125 species, including *Cucullaea crassatina,* etc.). In that region a zone of scales[159] is pinched between the Miocene Schlier (p. 567) and the Helvetic zone of the Swiss Alps. Such is the only absolutely certain evidence of a marine early Eocene on the whole north slope of the Alpine Chain.

In fact, usually (always in the whole internal Alpine zone) there are no characteristic fossils other than foraminifers, for which the paleontologic scale indicated on p. 470 is used.

Although, as we shall see, there seems to have been a continuous transition between the Cretaceous and Tertiary in certain regions, in no part of the Alps has a fauna of foraminifers truly characteristic of the lower Eocene been found. Such faunas have recently been noted in the Swiss Alps[160] and even in the Voirons range (ultra-Helvetic nappe) in Haute-Savoie, northeast of Geneva.[161] But they are not accompanied by any molluscan fauna and we may question if their lower Eocene age is absolutely certain.[162]

In any case, the first French Alpine faunas are those called "with large *Nummulites,*" characteristic of the middle Eocene or Lutetian and probably even of the upper Lutetian.

J. Boussac believed he could identify, throughout the Alps, an Auversian stage (p. 480), characterized by the coexistence of a large nummulite (*N. perforatus*) and of *N. striatus* of the upper Eocene. A. F. de Lapparent and M. Mainguy[163] agreed with him in regard to the southern Alps. But in the opinion of other specialists, neither in the Paris Basin (Abrard) nor in the Alps (L. Moret) does this Auversian stage have any individuality, and in the Alps the Auversian of J. Boussac should be included in the Lutetian.

The upper Eocene is very difficult to subdivide. So the Alpine geologists usually make a single stage, the *Priabonian* (Bartonian, *sensu* Abrard), of the two stages, Ledian (Bartonian, *auct.*) and Ludian, which we defined in the Paris basin. In the southern Alps, A. F. de Lapparent and M. Mainguy still say a Bartonian (Ledian) can be distinguished, containing *N. striatus,* and a Ludian in which this species is superceded by *N. bouillei.* On the other hand, when the upper Eocene contains orthophragmines, it is easily distinguished from the Oligocene, but when it contains only small nummulites and no mollusks, the distinction sometimes becomes very delicate (p. 515).

B. *Paleogeographic History*

Reduced to its large features, the history of the Nummulitic of the French Alps, made classic by J. Boussac, can be summarized thus (Figs. 125 and 126):

The marine lower Eocene is missing in the whole external Alpine zone which certainly was emergent at this epoch. Perhaps the sea continued to exist, between the Cretaceous and the Eocene, in certain narrow troughs in the sub-Briançonnais zone and in the zone of the *schistes lustrés* (p. 518).

The middle Eocene, well characterized by its large nummulites, is confined to the eastern part of the Chain both in the internal Alpine zone and in the nappes dependent upon it (Embrunais-Ubaye and Savoy Prealps). In the external zone, the marine Lutetian advances westward, invading two domains widely separated from each other by the region of Pelvoux: 1st, a southern domain, composed of two gulfs stretching south of the Mercantour, the Gulf of Puget-Théniers and that of St. Vallier-Antibes, separated by Cheiron mountain, which was emergent in the Lutetian, according to A. F. de Lapparent;[164] 2nd. a northern or Savoyard [165] domain, spreading over the southern part of the Bauges and the Bornes and over the Sixt Massif, being prolonged into Switzerland in the Wildhorn nappe.

The upper Eocene (Priabonian), represented by beds containing small nummulites and orthophragmines, overlies the middle Eocene in the regions where the Lutetian is present. But it is transgressive toward the west. In the southern area it reaches the Cannes-Gap line but covers neither Dévoluy, Vercors nor Chartreuse. In the latitude of this last massif, back of Belledonne, the most western evidence of a marine Priabonian has just been discovered by R. Barbier[166] at Montvernier, north of St. Jean de Maurienne. It appears there in an unrecognized scale in the Jurassic of the ultra-Dauphinois zone. And, as Barbier has demonstrated, it is likewise in the Priabonian and not the Lutetian, that the thick Nummulitic series of the Aiguilles d'Arves begins, which is also part of the ultra-Dauphinois zone and not of the internal (sub-Briançonnais) zone invaded by the Lutetian sea (here correcting the map, Fig. 125).

Farther north, in the edge of the Savoyard Gulf where the Lutetian sea advanced over the external zone, the Priabonian sea invaded the Bornes massif.

But the end of the Eocene marks the end also of the history of the Alpine geosyncline. The marine Eocene ends everywhere with thick, sandy series, witness of the general filling up of the great Alpine trough. The rising of the internal part of the Alps and the completion of the placement of the great nappes seem clearly to date from the beginning of the Oligocene.

In fact, the Oligocene paleography offers a very different picture from that shown by the Eocene. The purely marine Oligocene sediments, characterized by small nummulites and lepidocyclines (without orthophragmines) are limited to a narrow arm of the sea which extends along the western edge of the two domains. In the southern domain, it reaches the vicinity of Castellane, Barrême, Faucon-Gigors and into Dévoluy. In the Savoyard domain, this Oligocene with nummulites is found in the most external syncline of the Bauges (syncline of the deserts east of Lake Bourget) and at the western edge of the Bornes. But, on the other side, pushed outside of the Alpine Chain which has just appeared, the sea spreads westward, causing lagoons that extend far ahead of the chain, as far as the Massif Central, and into the Saône Basin, the Jura Mountains, the Swiss plain and Alsace. Thus we come again to the Oligocene lagoons already described between Languedoc

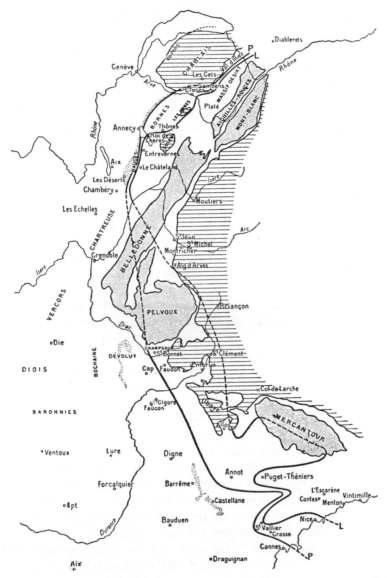

FIG. 125. *Map of the Nummulitic facies in the French Alps (after J. Bous-sac, L. Moret, A. F. de Lapparent).*

In gray: crystalline massifs of the external Alpine zone. Ruled: internal Alpine zone and region of its dependent nappes (Embrunais-Ubaye nappes, Prealpine massifs of Savoy): everywhere marine Lutetian. PP: Western limit of the Priabonian sea. LL: Western limit of the Lutetian sea in the external Alpine zone. Dotted: Oligocene outcrops with nummulites (marking an arm of the peri-Alpine sea).

and Alsace. They can be conceived as forming the external border of a shrinking and dying peri-Alpine sea. Thus, from the Oligocene, the great lines of the present relief are delineated, with an emergent Alpine Chain paralleled by a peri-Alpine depression which is continued in the Miocene.

It is obviously toward this peri-Alpine depression, a wave of subsidence shifting progressively westward, that, in the Oligocene, the nappes of the internal Alpine zone were flowing. Then, in the Miocene, the Swiss Helvetic nappes and the French sub-Alpine folds, domains which were reached, at this period, by the wave of swelling, also progressed toward the exterior of the chain.[167]

It now remains to make a few features of this diagrammatic picture specific by describing the principal facies of the successive stages of the Nummulitic. The stratigraphy becomes, as usual in the Alpine chain, less and less clear as we advance eastward, so we shall begin with the west in our enumeration of the zones of facies.

C. *Facies in the External Zone*

1. Zone of the Oligocene lagoons. This zone is characterized by an entirely continental Eocene, often much reduced or absent and overlain by a lagoonal Oligocene, in which the fossils, cyrenes or potamids, have a brackish stamp. From the lower valley of the Rhône, where it has already been described (Marseille, Aix and Apt–Forcalquier Basins, p. 500) this type extends eastward as far as the borders of Castellane[168] and Barrême, then further north into Baronnies, Diois, Bochaine, Vercors and Chartreuse. Its most extensive outcrops are found along the external border of these sub-Alpine chains, for example, in Vaucluse (Mormoiron gypsums, south of Ventoux) and in Royans, the gulf barely reaching into Vercors. There, over a continental Eocene (variegated clays and sands, described p. 494), a very thick Oligocene developed, especially marly with sandy zones and beds of lacustrine limestones, but in which banks containing cyrenes give evidence of lagoonal influences. The stratigraphy was recently studied in detail by P. R. Giot (work cited note 104, this chap.).

On the edge of the Bauges and the Bornes, the Oligocene borders the molasse Basin of Savoy, from which it extends into the bottom of the Swiss Basin where the Miocene usually conceals the Oligocene. But the latter stage reappears in the edge of the Alps; thus the famous conglomerates of Rigi (Nagelfluh, p. 565) are Oligocene (though without nummulites) and not Miocene as formerly believed.[169] However, the lagoonal Sannoisian and lower Stampian (marls or limestones with cyrenes and potamids) are everywhere overlain by a continental Chattian, composed of limestones with *Helix ramondi,* variegated marls or red conglomerates called red molasse, in the vicinity of Digne and Val d'Illiez (autochthonous sub-basement of the Pre-alps at the Swiss frontier).

2. Zone of the Oligocene with Nummulites. Here the Oligocene, purely marine, is characterized by the presence of small nummulites (*N. vascus, N. intermedius*) and numerous mollusks with Oligocene affinities. Orthophragmines have disappeared. Overlying the continental Eocene, the nummulite sandstones of this narrow peri-Alpine arm of the sea are preserved in the vicinity of Castellane (famous Vit-de-Castellane deposit) and Barrême, then between Faucon and Gigors[170] and lastly in Dévoluy. Their traces are lost in the site of Pelvoux and Belledonne but found again, as we have said before, in the Savoyard domain (classic deposit of Déserts, near Chambéry, containing large naticas).[171] This marine series is almost everywhere overlain by a continental upper Oligocene with red molasse facies.

3. Zone of the Transgressive Priabonian. This is the normal type of the marine Nummulitic in the southern sub-Alpine chains, where it can be observed over wide surfaces. The lower and middle Eocene are missing (or are entirely continental). The Priabonian sometimes begins with a thin complex of marly, even lignitic, beds with very littoral facies, where cerithids swarm (*C. diaboli,* whose type is in the Diablerets Massif, in Switzerland), associated with pelecypods, sometimes corals, and of course the small nummulites characteristic of the stage (*N. incrassatus, N. fabianii, N. striatus*) and orthophragmines. The best known occurrences are those of Faudon[172] and St. Bonnet, near Gap, and of Branchaï (near St. André-des-Alpes) where there are lignites. These *Cerithium diaboli* beds, always very thin (a few meters), are often replaced by conglomerates, especially on the south edge of Pelvoux, where the Nummulitic, more than 1,000 m. thick, is directly transgressive over the crystalline basement.

Above, or usually forming the base of the Nummulitic, comes the very characteristic formation of Priabonian limestones with small nummulites and orthophragmines, reaching nearly 100 m. thickness and indicating bars or beaches. They are overlain by softer sediments, globigerine shales or thick blue marls (fossiliferous only in the Maritime Alps).

Finally, the Nummulitic everywhere is topped by sandy strata, several hundred meters thick, but of a rather variable appearance. Even at Annot and in the region of Allos, they are composed of very thick (several tens of meters) and very hard beds of sometimes coarse sandstones, making mountains of very characteristic form, studded with towers and turrets (Grandes Tours of Lake Allos). But usually, the sandy banks, a few decimeters or meters thick, alternating with shaly beds of the same thickness, form, on the mountain slopes, numerous uniform bands, easily recognizable at any distance. This type is usually designated as the Annot sandstone or Champsaur sandstone in the southern Alps and as the Taveyannaz[173] sandstone in Savoy and Switzerland. These latter usually contain fine volcanic materials, which appear as small, ruddy stains on the dull background of the sandstone. This same facies is found in Champsaur, called *grès mouchetés* (speckled sandstones).

The origin of this volcanic debris has long been discussed,[174] for no trace of vulcanism is known in the Tertiary of the Franco-Swiss Alps. But W. Schroeder[175] recently discovered in the Flysch of the Chablais breccia nappe, at Gets, true submarine lava flows with very characteristic structure (pillow-lavas, variolitic structure) and Vuagnat[176] has just described similar rocks in the speckled sandstones in the vicinity of Gap.

The age of these sandy formations, generally without fossils, has been much discussed. Formerly they were attributed to the Oligocene, solely because of their similarity (?) to the Fontainebleau sandstone. But simultaneously, M. Lugeon and L. Moret [177] called attention to orthophragmines in Switzerland and in Savoy, and farther south in the massif of the Aiguilles d'Arves, R. Barbier[178] has just discovered orthophragmines in the top of that sandy series which overlies the slaty shales exploited at Maurienne.

Thus, north of Pelvoux at the very least, this thick Nummulitic series does not rise as far as the Oligocene. And by analogy the same can be assumed in the southern Alps, for there, as well as in Switzerland, the mention of small, so-called Oligocene nummulites seems by no means to be conclusive.[179]

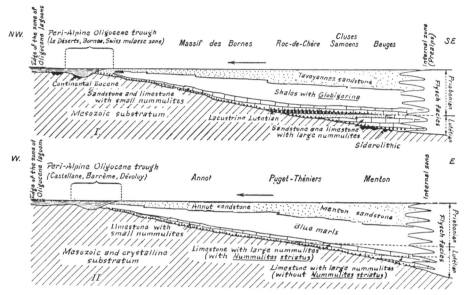

FIG. 126. *Diagrams of the transgressions and facies of the Nummulitic in in the French Alps on the western border of the Alpine Geosyncline (external Alpine zone.)*

I. Northern sub-Alpine chains, or domain of Savoy (after L. Moret).
II. Southern sub-Alpine chains (after J. Boussac and L. Moret).

Arrows indicate the direction of the transgressions.

L. Moret has therefore rightly proposed to give this Nummulitic series of the external Alpine zone the name of the Priabonian trilogy: nummulite limestone—shales or marls—Annot or Taveyannaz sandstone.

4. Zone of the Transgressive Lutetian (in the external zone and autochthon). This zone is distinguished from the preceding only in that, beneath beds with small nummulites, limestones appear containing large nummulites (*N. perforatus,* in particular), showing that the transgression here began with the Lutetian. As we have said, this type is found in a southern domain, south of Mercantour, and in the Savoyard domain.

a. *Southern domain.* In the much more extensive western part of this zone, the limestones with large nummulites (*N. perforatus*) also contain *N. striatus* from the base. Boussac made this his transgressive Auversian stage.

But the mollusk faunas (rich deposits of Escarène and Château de La Paléréa, on the east border of the great Tertiary syncline of Contes) have a definitely Lutetian stamp (Abrard). These limestones, standing erect in imposing bands (ex., that of Entrevaux, notched by the Var above Puget-Théniers, and crowned by the old fortresses of Vauban) form the first part of a trilogy which proceeds with thick Priabonian blue marls with *Serpula spirulaea*[180] and ends with sandstone, here often soft and sandy (Puget-Théniers sandstone, St-Antonin sandstone, south of Puget).

But near the Italian frontier, the base of the limestones with large nummulites no longer contains *N. striatus* and Boussac makes of this his Lutetian (Mortola deposit, between Mentone and Ventimiglia). There also the sandstones that terminate the Priabonian are often very soft and loose (Mentone sandstone) and are hidden under the magnificent pine and chestnut forests.

b. *Savoyard domain.* The Lutetian sandstones with large nummulites are found far to the north in the Alpine external zone; in fact they only appear in the deposits of Châtelard and Entrevernes in the Bauges, of Roc de Chères on the shores of Lake Annecy, of Araches east of Cluses on the Arve, and of Samoëns (Massif of Sixt). But, in this domain, the limestones and sandstones with large nummulites and orthophragmines, representing the base of the Tertiary, are overlain by marly-calcareous beds with *Bulimus*[181] and *Limnaea,* constituting a lacustrine episode at the top of the Lutetian. After this regression, accompanied by erosion, the Priabonian introduces a new marine series which begins with sandstones and marls with lignites (exploited at Entrevernes, in the Bauges, and at Pernan, near Cluses). These consist of beds with *C. diaboli,* also very fossiliferous at the Désert de Platé. Then come the customary Priabonian limestones with small nummulites overlain, as usual, by marls, then the Taveyannaz sandstones.

D. *Internal Alpine Zone: the Flysch*

Here the Nummulitic suddenly assumes very different characters. It is extremely thick and by itself constitutes entire mountainous massifs. Fossils are reduced to very rare nummulites. The tectonics and stratigraphy are completely confused. Black shales and fine sandstones predominate: this is the Flysch.[182] This term typically designates thick black shaly series in which are intercalated thin banks (sometimes centimeters or decimeters thick) of fine-grained, calcareous sandstone, with a brownish patina, or sometimes lentils or nodules of fine pelagic limestone.

So, variations on this theme, many lithologic modifications occur. Where the clayey element predominates, we speak of black Flysch; if the sandstone banks become very thick, it will be a sandy Flysch; when lentils or very thick (several meters or tens of meters) calcareous banks exist, they constitute a calcareous Flysch. In Ubaye and Embrunais, entire mountains are made up of Flysch composed of uniform and very thin (sometimes centimeters) banks of dry calcareous shales, sometimes finely sandy, separated by platy beds, on whose surfaces impressions with very uniform sinuosities (*Helminthoidea labyrinthica*) are sketched, which are regarded as tracks of marine nudibranch mollusks.[183] This is the helminthoid Flysch, lithologically well defined but in which no characteristic fossil has ever been found. Lastly, banks or lenses of micro-breccias, breccias or conglomerates, sometimes with great blocks of crystalline rocks, often appear in this Flysch. When these blocks of rock are very large (several meters or even tens of meters), they are often designated by the German-Swiss term, *Wildflysch*. As M. Lugeon has suggested, much of this Wildflysch surely represents breccias from the collapse of submarine cliffs. This is a cordilleran facies (p. 364); but sometimes it represents rocks tectonically crushed in or between nappes.

Outside the helminthoides, which seem to be quite isolated at the top of the Flysch, and animal tracks or impressions of algae (chondrites?) without significance, the only characteristic fossils are nummulites and especially large nummulites, sometimes accompanied by small species, difficult to determine. But, adding that the occurrences are very localized and the breccias and conglomerates sometimes contain redeposited belemnites and *Inoceramus* fragments, we will understand that even the Tertiary age of some Flysch could be questioned.[184] In fact, in the internal zone, when shaly series without fossils are found, no one would hesitate to attribute them to the Flysch, whose variability is great enough to extend hospitality to the most diverse sediments. We shall also see that certain series formerly attributed to the calcareous Flysch (particularly in the sub-Briançonnais zone) are in reality Jurassic and Cretaceous.[185]

After having dispelled these erroneous interpretations, we know, according to the nummulite faunas, only that the Lutetian (beds with large nummulites) and the Priabonian (beds with orthophragmines and *N. incrassatus*)[186] are surely represented in the series of Tertiary Flysch. This is only natural, since the Nummulitic of the eastern border of the external zone, at the moment when it disappears under the overthrusts of the internal zone, is composed of exactly these two stages. When we add that the sandy Flysch facies, with which the Flysch series often terminates, greatly resembles the sandstones of Annot or Champsaur, we have no reason to believe that the Flysch of the internal zone extends into the Oligocene.

The lower limit of the Flysch is more debated. Crossing the Alps from west to east, the marine Tertiary seems to be extended downward. At first there is only Oligocene, then the Priabonian appears and lastly the Lutetian at the edges of the nappes. Thus we are tempted to assume that farther east, that is, in the internal Alpine zone, the lower Eocene should appear. So, certain geologists (P. Termier, J. Boussac) have agreed that the intra-Alpine Flysch represents a comprehensive series, with continuous passage from the Cretaceous into the Tertiary. Thus, for them, the top of the series of *schistes lustrés* rises into the Eocene.

In reality, such a transition does not certainly exist everywhere, as we shall see, if we review briefly, from south to north, the most remarkable occurrences and facies of this intra-Alpine Flysch.

Note first that in the whole interior of the Briançonnais zone, only a few specimens of nummulites can be cited, reported by F. Blanchet in the breccias of the Escreins Massif, between Guillestre and Saint-Paul-sur-Ubaye. Moreover, it is with no certainty that a few synclinal bands of black shales with sandy banks, between the Briançonnais and the Vanoise, have been attributed to the Tertiary Flysch.

Between Pelvoux and Mercantour, we already know that the great Flysch nappe of Ubaye-Embrunais—which crops out over great areas and constitutes important mountainous massifs—represents the original covering of the Briançonnais Mesozoic, but has moved toward the west. At the contact with this Mesozoic, the series generally begins with very soft, very thick black Flysch, with a zone of outcrop elongated north-south, evidenced by the wide depression of the Vars Pass, between Guillestre and Ubaye. Farther west comes the helminthoid Flysch or its sandy equivalents; that is where the long known St. Clément occurrence of large nummulites is found, on the right bank of the Durance downstream from Guillestre. These Embrunais sandstones represent the equivalent, in the internal zone, of the Champsaur sandstones of the external zone.

Under this Flysch nappe, in the sub-Briançonnais scales, the nummulite occurrences are frequent and the facies varied. The base is often composed of black Flysch or a calcareous Flysch, seeming to follow the marine Upper Cretaceous in continuity, in certain troughs of the Alpine fore-deep (example, Dramonasq trough, in the Morgon Massif, see D. Schneegans).[187] Over the cordilleras which separate these troughs, littoral limestones are found, very rich in large nummulites, transgressive over the coral limestones of the Malm (tabular summits of the Gias de Chamois, of Mourre-Haut, etc., which so strangely dominate the southeastern extremity of the Barcelonnette window; see Y. Gubler-Wahl), or even over the Triassic limestones (Caire fold, Morgon Massif, see D. Schneegans).

North of Pelvoux, the famous Montricher deposit is found in an external unit of the sub-Briançonnais zone, between St. Jean and St. Michel-de-Maurienne. In a lentil of organic white limestones with *Lithothamnium* and remains of pelecypods, were found the first nummulites in the heart of the great Alps, thus proving the existence of Tertiary formations which we would hardly expect to find there. Farther north, as far as the Niélard Massif, south of Moutiers, R. Barbier again describes beds of large nummulites. Still farther, on the right bank of the Isère between Moutiers and Bourg-St-Maurice, he recognizes, as a result of detailed studies by H. Schoeller,[188] that one of the sub-Briançonnais tectonic units, the zone of Tarentaise breccias, corresponding to a "tarine" cordillera, is almost entirely composed of a transgressive Flysch (sometimes lying on the Triassic). This Flysch begins with conglomerates and breccias (difficult to distinguish from neighboring Jurassic breccias), succeeded by several thousand meters of shales and sandstones. But it is a little disturbing that, in spite of long search, Schoeller could find no nummulites there, only chondrites, which are in no way different from those of the Oxfordian shales. This thick Flysch (?) passes into Italy to the south and east of Mont Blanc, then into the Swiss Val Ferret.[189] It finally disappears under the front of the more internal Pennine nappes, in the Sion-Val-Ferret zone.

In the Prealpine Massifs of Savoy (Sulens, Les Annes, Chablais), formed by the piling up of nappes issuing from the ultra-Helvetic (ultra-Dauphinois) and sub-Briançonnais zones, we find Flysch similar to that of these latter zones, recently described by L. Moret.

In a lower nappe (ultra-Helvetic), cropping out especially at the northwest (Les Voirons) and southwest (vicinity of Cluses) borders of the Chablais, the Flysch contains thin banks of calcareous breccias with *Lithothamnium,* orthophragmines, nummulites and assilines, and sometimes assumes the Wildflysch facies, with enormous blocks or plates of Mesozoic limestones.

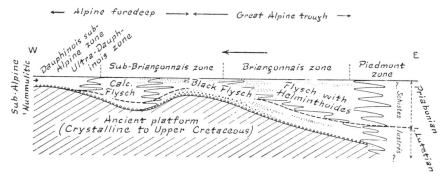

FIG. 127. *Distribution of the Nummulitic facies in the internal zone of the Alpine geosyncline (French Alps) (after L. Moret).*

The arrow indicates the direction of the transgressions; the dots represent the sandy facies in the Flysch.

In a so-called middle nappe (probably still of ultra-Helvetic or ultra-Dauphinois origin), near Cluses and especially at Sulens, the Flysch is characterized by conglomerates analogous to those of the Aiguilles d'Arves, with well rounded crystalline blocks and large nummulites.

The upper nappe of the Annes and of Sulens undoubtedly corresponds to the nappe of the Median Prealps, which constitutes the largest part of the Chablais mountains. There the Flysch is shaly-sandy, but L. Moret has pointed out a Flysch with helminthoids in Chablais, identical to that of the Embrunais.

Finally, in the Chablais breccia nappe, in an otherwise quite commonplace Flysch, the aforementioned volcanic flows are intercalated. At its top appear the enormous blocks of basic volcanic rocks of Gets, formerly considered as debris of the Simme nappe, but in which granitic rocks identical to those of Mont Blanc are also found.

E. *General Conclusions*

There are two striking features in this picture of the Alpine Nummulitic.

First, there is the profound contrast which exists between the Alpine series and the type-series of the Paris Basin. The thicknesses here are measured in hundreds or thousands of meters, no longer tens of meters. The beds are intensely folded, sometimes even metamorphosed, if the upper part of the *schistes lustrés* are recognized as Tertiary. We summarize this assemblage of characteristics under the name of geosynclinal type. This geosynclinal character is accentuated, moreover, as one goes from west to east, in the French Alps. Thus the axis of the Alpine geosyncline in the Nummulitic[190] must be sought in the eastern zones (Briançonnais and *schistes lustrés*). This geosyncline was, however, as in the Jurassic, varied by geanticlines or cordilleras (p. 9) as proved by the thick beds of breccias and conglomerates, which develop in the internal zone.

In the second place, it is evident that the upper Eocene marks the end of this geosynclinal history.[191] The immense thicknesses of sandstone, Annot sandstone, Taveyannaz sandstone and sandy Flysch, forming at that time in the Alpine fore-deep, can only be produced by an already emerged chain. In fact, we now know that the principal folds of the internal zones of the Alps date from the Oligocene. And it is precisely at the moment when the sea was driven from the Alpine domain that it penetrated, on the contrary, at least in the form of lagoons, into the Alpine foreland, into the Rhône Valley, and into Alsace.

From quite another point of view, to find in nature today thick sedimentary accumulations comparable to the intra-Alpine Flysch, detrital, of shallow-water and yet so curiously devoid of life, we have to consider the vast submarine deltas being built on the edge of the continental slopes, by very large, muddy rivers like the Ganges or the Amazon, in muddy waters inhospitable to shellfish. But we must confess that in the Alps there is the question of where to find continental expanses capable of feeding such a sedimentation. For this does not originate, either in the Nummulitic or the Neogene, from vast Hercynian forelands. Neither could we imagine the many small coastal rivers, like the Var or the Tiber, as we see them, in the course of the brief span of Pliocene time, building narrow but very thick[192] fringes of littoral sandy-clayey deposits. But the incessant orogenic rejuvenation of their nourishing chains counterbalances the narrowness of the contributing basins.

VII. The Nummulitic in Italy

A. *The Type-Series of the Vicentin*[193]

Between Vicenza and Verona, a sort of promontory extends southward from the Venetian Alps; it is called the Vicentin (or hills of Vicenza and Verona). These hills lie beyond the geosynclinal zones of the Nummulitic Alpine sea and lack the Flysch facies. The Nummulitic assumes littoral facies, very fossiliferous, but mixed with volcanic products, flows or tuffs. The Vicentin may be said to represent, in the Mediterranean province, the equivalent of the Paris Basin in the northern province. It is a true type-series (*serie-type*), in which the fauna is composed of both mollusks and large foraminifers.

1. The Tertiary in the Vicentin begins with the Spilecco beds (near Bolca), containing *Nummulites spileccensis-bolcensis* and a fauna of mollusks related to that of the Anglo-Parisian Ypresian, so these are generally attributed to the Ypresian by French geologists. But in eastern Friuli, Istria and the environs of Trieste, lacustrine or brackish formations lie above the Cretaceous rudistid limestone and under the Lutetian. These formations end with marine horizons with alveolines, in which the boundary between the Cretaceous and Eocene remains uncertain. Stache called this the Liburnian stage, doubtless including representatives of the Danian, the Montian (containing *Cerithium inopinatum*), and the Landenian. Parona proposes grouping all the Italian lower Eocene under the name Spileccian.

2. The Lutetian, sometimes transgressive over the Senonian (in the Trentino), begins with the Monte Postale horizon, near Bolca. At the base is limestone with *N. atacicus,* next the famous fish beds, containing also the leaves of the Bolca or Monte Postale palms. These rocks are calcareous shales and are overlain by beds with alveolines, *N. laevigatus, N. complanatus, Velates schmiedelianus, Lucina gigantea,* etc. Next comes the San Giovanni Ilarione horizon, made up of basaltic breccias and limestones with *N. perforatus, N. millecaput, N. gizehensis,* assilines, echinoids, *Venericardia planicosta* and a whole fauna of mollusks similar to those of the Parisian Lutetian. Lastly, with Abrard and Douvillé, we still attribute to the upper Lutetian the famous Ronca beds, where Boussac saw a representative of his Auversian. These are limestones containing *N. brongniarti, N. striatus* (rare) and mollusks with Lutetian affinities (*Cerithium giganteum,* etc.), always associated with volcanic tuffs. The middle Eocene ends with a regression, witnessed by the lignitic beds with freshwater mollusks, crocodiles and turtles.

3. The upper Eocene or Priabonian is represented by the beds of Priabona, the type of the stage. The transgression begins with the facies, still somewhat brackish, of the *Cerithium diaboli* beds, an horizon which we learned to recognize in the Alps. Next come limestones and marls[194] with *N. fabianii* and a rich fauna of mollusks; and, lastly, bryozoan marls in which *N. fabianii* persists.

4. The Oligocene, following the upper Eocene, shows, at its base, the Sangonini beds (hills of Marostica, Montecchio maggiore) attributed to the Sannoisian, with *N. intermedius, Pecten arcuatus,* etc. The Stampian is represented by the Castelgomberto beds, famous for their coral reefs, in which, beside numerous warm species and *N. vascus,* characteristic of the Mediterranean province, are found the most classic forms of the Fontainebleau sands, *Pectunculus obovatus, Cytherea splendida, Natica crassatina,* etc. The Lonedo beds (or lower Schio beds), *Lithothamnium* limestones with small nummulites (*N. vascus, N. bouillei*) and lepidocyclines,[195] correspond to the Chattian.

Finally a place by itself should be reserved for the Aquitanian, which has here, for its type, the famous Schio beds (*s. str.*) with large lepidocyclines (*L. elephantina*) and a rich fauna of mollusks and echinoids (*Scutella, Clypeaster*) with Miocene affinities rather than Oligocene. So the Italian geologists put this stage in the Miocene; this is a question which has already been discussed (p. 471).

B. *Peninsular Italy (Apennines)*

1. In all the northern Apennines (beginning in Liguria) and the northern part of the central Apennines (as far as Umbria), the Nummulitic has Flysch facies. Fossils are very rare and the tectonics very complicated.[196] Any stratigraphic synthesis here would be premature, but granting that the Flysch constitutes the whole of this part of the Apennines, we should enumerate its principal formations, which we shall do following the summary presented by Parona.

a. In the northern Apennines, the Tertiary seems to begin with a Lutetian transgressive over the Cretaceous (Serchio valley, north of Pisa), starting with a thin bed of nummulite limestone. This limestone is overlain by a thick shaly-sandy series, ending with compact, calcareous sandstones called *macigno*. This *macigno* forms the highest ridges of the Tuscan Apennines as far as Umbria, mountains with a smooth and monotonous profile. Rare nummulitic occurrences (near Florence) indicate Lutetian[197] overlain by Priabonian. A helminthoid Flysch similar to that described in the French Alps is also attributed to the Priabonian.

The Oligocene of Liguria, transgressive and discordant on the Eocene, is a contrast to all this Flysch. It includes basal conglomerates (well developed in the cliffs of the picturesque Portofino promontory, east of Genoa), fossiliferous clays and sands, and even corallian beds recalling those of the Stampian of the Vicentin. The faunas, quite rich along the Po, have been studied by Rovereto.

Finally, we find the famous formation of the "*scagliose* clay," which plays a big role in all the northern Apennines and which we have already discussed (p. 440). This name is used for the easily weathered clay shales, which break away in great scales and produce gigantic slides known as *frane,* even on slight slopes. Always appearing in very complicated tectonic circumstances, as scales, sheets or injections into other formations, this scagliosa clay very often seems to overlie the Tertiary Flysch. So some Italian geologists (Parona, etc.) make of it the upper Eocene or Oligocene. But it contains (Steinmann) limestone lentils with calpinella, a protozoan characteristic of the Upper Jurassic and Valanginian (p. 357); Cretaceous fossils have been noted in it at different points (Sacco);[198] and slices of basic crystalline rocks or granites (recently studied by Merla) are also intercalated in it.[199] So it is very difficult to see anything but a complex of crushed and laminated Mesozoic formations. For some Italian geologists (Sacco) the superposition of this scagliose clay over the Tertiary Flysch is explained by recumbent folds or scales; for others (Steinmann, Tillmann, Staub and the Dutch school), it is part of an immense nappe (the Ligurides) that, in a sheet 200 kilometers long, has been thrust over the autochthonous Apennines.

b. In the Apennines of Umbria and the Marches, the transition from the Cretaceous to the Eocene seems to be through chalky facies with globigerines, already considered (p. 440) and known as *scaglia*.[200] The red *scaglia,* still Cretaceous, is overlain by gray *scaglia* which, becoming sandier on the Tyrrhenian slope, contains faunas of nummulites (Eocene) and lepidocyclines (Oligocene), recently studied by Principi.[201] This indicates the existence of a land mass at the southwest, on the site of the Tyrrhenian sea, from which came the materials of the sandstone. In fact, the Nummulitic Flysch of the Tyrrhenian coast contains enormous blocks of crystalline rocks at several places (for example, between Rome and Naples), even though ancient rocks of this sort are unknown in the peninsula except in Calabria. The conclusion follows that an immense crystalline massif (the Tyrrhenides) must have existed in the Tertiary, but today is buried under the waters of the Tyrrhenian sea. This massif may have extended as far as Corsica and Sardinia and the Calabrian crystalline massifs may be its remains. Such a mass would have sustained the rich sedimentation of the Apennine Flysch.

2. On the other hand, to the eastward the calcareous facies of the littoral platforms gradually appear in the Nummulitic, at first at the base, then invading the whole series.

This is first manifested in the central Apennines, in the Massifs of Gran Sasso[202] and Majella. On the edges of the latter, Principi [203] describes transition facies between the scagliosa clay type (Upper Cretaceous—base of the middle Eocene) and the calcareous type of the same stages realized in the Majella. He calls these facies the marly scaglia.

But the organic limestone facies developed especially around the great Cretaceous plateaus of the Apulian-Garganian plateau area (Apulia and Monte Gargano). At the two extremities of this domain (Monte Gargano and the Otranto district), there is no longer any Flysch and the whole Nummulitic is represented by rather scanty organic limestones very rich in nummulites. Checchia-Rispoli has described there (and also in Sicily, at Termini-Imerese) curious mixtures of faunas, orbitoids, for example, with Cretaceous affinities associated with Eocene orthophragmines and Oligocene lepidocyclines. These abnormal combinations, which make the classic paleontologic foraminiferal standards useless, have been attributed to reworking and have given rise to much discussion.

In any case, the contrast between the thick folded series of the Apennine Flysch and the thinner, horizontal calcareous Nummulitic of the Apulian-Garganian domain should be given proper emphasis. A similar difference in facies between these two domains was indicated earlier for the Cretaceous (p. 441) and we shall find it again in the Pliocene. This is one more example of the fundamental contrast between the geosynclinal type and the littoral, platform type.

VIII. The Nummulitic in the Iberian Peninsula

Stratigraphic detail is again impossible[204] and we are restricted to indicating in outline the regional distribution of the principal facies. In this manner, the following natural regions can be distinguished (Figs. 104 and 105):

A. *Betic and Sub-Betic Chains*

As in the Alps, the lower Eocene seems to be missing and the best known member is the transgressive Lutetian, represented by limestones or marls with large nummulites, orthophragmines and echinoids. Marls with globigerines, and limestones and sandstones with lepidocyclines,[205] correspond to the Oligocene.

B. *Ebro Basin and Its Borders*

All the huge depression surrounded by the Cantabrian Mountains, the Pyrenees, the coastal chain of Catalonia and the Iberian chain is filled with Tertiary deposits, mostly continental or lagoonal.

1. The Eocene crops out only on the edges of the chains that enclose this depression. Thus, on the northwest slope of the coastal chain of Catalonia, it begins with lower Eocene lacustrine beds (marls and conglomerates). The arrival of the sea corresponds approximately to the base of the lower Lutetian and is marked by alveoline limestones. Then marls with nummulites are equivalent to the upper Lutetian and the Ledian. Finally the Eocene ends with a thick series of conglomerates exactly comparable to the Palassou conglomerates described on the northern slope of the Pyrenees. Here they are called the Montserrat conglomerates, for they compose the jagged crests, northwest of Barcelona, where that famous monastery rises.

In the Catalan Pyrenees,[206] the Eocene border shows the marine facies appearing earlier. Over a continental Landenian, in fact, an Ypresian appears, represented by limestones containing alveolines, assilines, *Nummulites planulatus,* and numerous echinoids. The Lutetian and the Ledian, more marly, also contain fine faunas of nummulites and mollusks. And this Eocene, like that of the northern border of the Pyrenees, also ends with continental conglomerates.

Still farther west, in the Aragon Pyrenees, the lower Eocene also becomes marine. In the Massif of Mont-Perdu, it follows the Danian limestones with operculines.

2. The marine Oligocene is known only in the Cantabrian Mountains, where it is represented by beds with small nummulites and lepidocyclines. Everywhere else the Oligocene is lagoonal or continental; following the Montserrat conglomerates and continued by Miocene beds of the same facies,

its thick formations of marls, sandstones and conglomerates fill up the huge Ebro depression. Its stratigraphy is decipherable only where mammal occurrences are known. This is the case especially in the northeast angle of the Ebro Basin, between the eastern Pyrenees and the coastal chain of Barcelona, as far as the environs of Lerida. Mammalian faunas there, studied by Depéret, Almera and Vidal, permit the recognition of Sannoisian (Ronzon horizon) at Calaf, and Aquitanian (Saint-Gérand horizon) near Martorell in the small, isolated Basin of the Panadès. In recent years, the rich deposits of potassium salts at Cardona, about contemporaneous with those of Alsace,[207] have been discovered in the lagoonal Oligocene of the Province of Lerida.

Thus, the Nummulitic sea came from the northwest to invade a part of the Ebro depression. The Cantabrian Gulf, a tributary of the Atlantic, had its maximum extent in the Ypresian and the Lutetian, like the North Pyrenean Gulf. Possibly it never communicated with the Mediterranean, for no marine Nummulitic is known on that part of the Mediterranean coast.[208]

C. *Surface of the Meseta: Castilian Plateaus*

Beyond a doubt, the greater part of the Meseta must have been covered by Tertiary deposits similar to those which fill the Ebro depression, that is to say, principally by Oligocene and Miocene formations, with continental or lagoonal facies.[209]

But today, these Tertiary deposits are mainly found in two large basins, the northern or Old Castilian, drained by the Douro, and the New Castilian, traversed by the high valley of the Tagus. The stratigraphy of these deposits is still very incompletely known. In general, there is a succession, from bottom to top, of conglomerates, sandstones, marls that are commonly gypsiferous, and lacustrine limestones. But marine Oligocene, with *Potamides lamarcki,* exists near Burgos, Toledo,[210] and Cuenca, and several scattered mammal occurrences indicate the Oligocene or the Miocene.

IX. The Nummulitic in North Africa[211]

A. *Algeria and Tunisia*

Following the classic works of Algerian geologists,[212] E. Haug has presented in his *Traité* a magnificent synthesis of the paleogeography and facies of the Nummulitic in Algeria. We shall follow Haug but also take into account the more recent studies of M. Dalloni, L. Glangeaud and M. Solignac and the new theories of J. Flandrin.

Further, we shall have to use groupings of stages which do not always correspond to the classic subdivisions. We thus distinguish the following stratigraphic units: 1. a lower Eocene, often called Suessonian (note 35, this chap.) by Algerian geologists, which formerly included a part of the Lutetian; 2. a middle Eocene or Lutetian; 3. an upper Nummulitic whose base corresponds to the Priabonian, but the major part of which is Oligocene

(Sannoisian and Stampian); 4. a continental Aquitanian or Aquitano-Burdigalian, represented locally (Dellys) by marine deposits.

We shall study separately the features of the Nummulitic in the following
paleogeographic units, successively from south to north (Figs. 128, 129,
130).

1. The Saharan Basin. We already know that at the end of the Eocene
a shallow sea still stretched over almost all of Tunisia and the southern part
of eastern Algeria, the low Sahara, the Saharan Atlas of the Aurès, the
Némenchas Mountains, and the region of Tébessa. In this Saharan Basin, the
marine lower Eocene follows the marine Upper Cretaceous in continuity.

The transition beds from the Cretaceous to the Tertiary which can be
qualified as Dano-Montian, are very thick black marls, unfortunately containing few fossils.[213] It is convenient to attribute their base, containing
Venericardia beaumonti and Cretaceous oysters (*Ostrea overwegi, O. villei*)

FIG. 128. *Paleogeographic map of Algeria-Tunisia at the end of the lower
Eocene, by J. Flandrin.*

to the Danian, and their top, with *O. multicostata,* a species persisting into
the Eocene, to the Montian.

The lower Eocene is represented by beds with variable facies. In the south,
they are of uncharacteristic siliceous limestones. Farther north, and especially
in the region of Tébessa, Gafsa and Thala, thin beds (up to 10 meters) of
very rich phosphatic limestones are present. These limestones are exploited,
especially near the Algerian-Tunisian frontier in the famous Tunisian phosphate mines (Gafsa). The facies are very littoral and of rough water, in
which fish teeth particularly are found, indicating the existence of shoals
extending into the regions of Batna and Thala (Fig. 128). The phosphatic
facies extend north as far as the Sétif-Souk-Ahras zone, but they become
less rich and cannot be exploited, because a northern, deeper zone is being
approached, the south Tellian trough, to be studied later.

Some beds of white marl and cherty limestone separate the phosphatic
bed, when it is present, from the middle Eocene. In the northern part of the
Saharan Basin (Tébessa region), these beds are limestones with large num-

mulites, characteristic of the Lutetian. The top, a little more marly, contains large gastropods belonging to the genus *Thersitea,* eminently characteristic of North Africa, and also found in Morocco. In the south, the Lutetian becomes lagoonal, represented by variegated, gypiferous limestones and marls. The marine Nummulitic ends with these Lutetian beds in all this vast Saharan Basin.

The Dano-Montian thick black clays form broad landscapes of monotonous ridges, above which the calcareous escarpments of the middle Eocene rise like fortresses (kalaa; for ex., Kalaa es Snam, Fig. 128), above the thin corrugations of the phosphatic beds.

2. The South Tellian Trough. On its western side, the Saharan Basin cannot be followed beyond a line from Bou Saada to Laghouat, west of which no more Eocene outcrops are known (carried away by erosion?). But north of

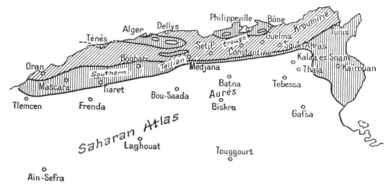

FIG. 129.   *Paleogeographic map of Algeria-Tunisia during the upper Nummulitic (after J. Flandrin).*

In white, emergent area.

Oblique lines, territory invaded by the sea in the upper Priabonian.

Vertical lines, territory invaded by the sea in the Oligocene.

Bou Saada, the northern, deepest part extends westward following a zone approximately at the southern boundary of the Tell, including both the southern part of the folded chains of the Tell and the northern part of the High Plateaus. This is the South Tellian trough of E. Haug and the Algerian geologists.

First is found the prolongation of the lower and middle Eocene of the Saharan Basin, but with deeper-water facies. Above the Dano-Montian marls, the lower Eocene is represented by marly limestones with globigerines and chert, in which there are only traces of the phosphatic horizons of the south. Dareste de la Chavanne discovered at Djebel Bardou, near Souk Ahras, siliceous limestones containing a fairly rich fauna with *Nummulites planulatus* and mollusks with Ypresian affinities. This is the only fine lower Eocene occurrence in all Algeria. The Lutetian also has become of deeper facies. The nummulite limestones are only lentils localized in the southern part of the trough.

Farther north, the lower Lutetian is represented by marly limestones with globigerines, impossible to separate from the lower Eocene. The upper Lutetian corresponds either to very thick marls with shell limestones containing *Ostrea multicostata* and *Thersitea* (departments of Algiers and Constantine) or sandstones and limestones with large *Nummulites gizehensis* (Oran).

Then, toward the end of the Lutetian, an orogenic period occurred. In the south (Sahara) there was simply a rising of the whole area, ending in the emergence of the Saharan Basin. Farther north, in the Saharan Atlas and the High Plateaus, broad undulations were formed in the Jura Mountains style. Still farther north, in the Tellian chains, there was very intense folding, like the Alpine (or Pyrenean), followed by a period of erosion. Moreover, in this region, the northern borders of the South Tellian trough should be found, but the littoral sediments (lower and middle Eocene) of this doubtless very narrow coastal zone have been destroyed by erosion.

Finally, subsequent to this folding, a transgression coming, as we have seen, from the north, brought clayey and sandy sediments of the upper Nummulitic to lie on a varied substratum. The thickness of the sediments increases from south to north, indicating their dependence on a basin of sedimentation situated farther to the north, where we shall study them.

3. The Lutetian Threshold.   As J. Flandrin[214] was the first to elucidate, there was, in fact, all along the northern edge of the South Tellian trough, an east-west zone, varying from 25 to 70 km. in breadth in which no Lutetian is known. Entering Algeria along the coast between Bône and La Calle, the Lutetian threshold touches the sea again south of Ténès and definitely ends in the Sahel of Oran. We are there already in the zone of littoral chains where, as we shall see, folding began well before the Lutetian. Probably these pre-Lutetian movements led here to the emergence of the Lutetian threshold.

4. The Littoral Chains: The Transgressive Lutetian.   Already, with the Lutetian threshold, we reach a very different paleogeographic unit. We have definitely left the domain of the immense littoral platform of the Saharan continent, a platform which we have seen become progressively lower in the South Tellian trough, and we reach an unstable, geosynclinal region, with cordilleras and troughs of sedimentation.

Here the folds were produced well before the Lutetian. The lower Eocene is unknown, as well as the transition beds to the Cretaceous. On an ancient, folded substratum, the Tertiary begins with the transgressive Lutetian, forming here and there quite important outcrops of limestone with large nummulites, overlain by sandstones and conglomerates, passing laterally, in the bottom of the trenches, into shaly marls. But as J. Flandrin has shown, the Lutetian of the littoral chains is very different from that of the South Tellian and particularly the Saharan Basins. There is no longer *Thersitea* or *Ostrea multicostata;* and *Nummulites gizehensis,* so abundant in the southern domain, is here replaced by other species, *N. uroniensis, N. aturicus, N. millecaput,* etc. It may be assumed that these two provinces of the Lutetian seas actually were separated by the Lutetian threshold of J. Flandrin, and that the Lutetian transgression which invaded the littoral chains, instead of coming from the south as has been believed up to date, came from the north, from the Mesogean geosyncline, where troughs (now hidden under the Mediterranean) must have existed, in which the sea persisted during the Upper Cretaceous and lower Eocene.

5. The Transgression of the Upper Nummulitic. The very intense folding which followed the deposition of the upper Lutetian, was succeeded by a period of erosion and by a new transgression which progressively covered the major part of Tunisia, as well as the littoral and Tellian regions of Algeria. In the upper Priabonian (Fig. 129), the sea covered only northern Tunisia and the location of the old Tellian trough. Central Tunisia remained emergent as well as the littoral Kabylies massifs, the chain of Biban and the South Tellian region of the departments of Algiers and Oran. The transgression was sharply accentuated in the Oligocene, submerging central Tunisia, the major

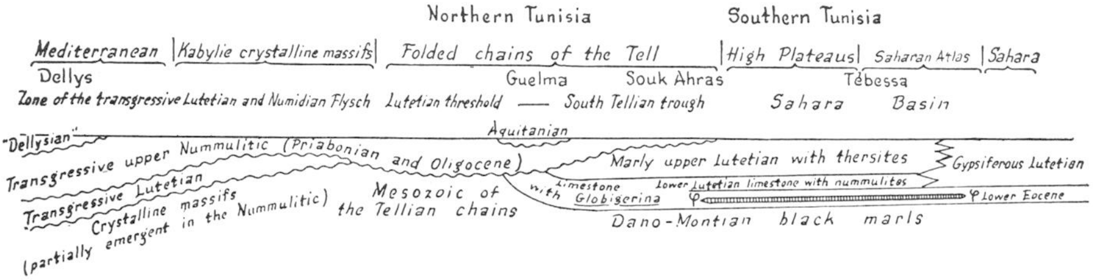

FIG. 130. *Diagram of the facies and the distribution of the stages of the marine Nummulitic in Algeria (after J. Flandrin).*

Wavy lines indicate transgressive and discordant contacts. φφ indicate the phosphatized zone in the Lower Eocene of the Saharan Basin.

part of the littoral Kabylies massifs, the Biban and all the southern border of the Algerian-Oranian Tell.

These transgressive deposits of the upper Nummulitic were formerly classified in a series of local stages (infra- and supra-Nummulitic stages, Medjanian, Numidian, Bogharian, Dellysian) which correspond to facies rather than to well defined stratigraphic horizons. The term Numidian, which is conveniently retained to designate the facies under which the upper Nummulitic is most widely represented in all northern Tunisia and Algeria, applies to a well characterized shaly-sandy series. The base, usually clayey, comparable to the black Flysch of the Alps, begins locally with conglomerates and frequently contains small banks of microbreccias. Its age varies according to the region: Priabonian in Kroumirie and the Tellian regions proper (*N. incrassatus, N. fabianii*), Oligocene on the periphery of the metamorphic Kabylies Massifs (*N. intermedius, N. vascus,* lepidocyclines). Coarse sandstones predominate at the top, in compact, very thick beds as in the sandy Flysch of the Alps. These are the well-known Numidian sandstones. They are generally barren but yield lepidocyclines at some places (Cap Bon, Dj. Morissane near Medjana, region of Tablat), clearly indicating their Oligocene age.

In central Tunisia and the region of Boghari, the upper Nummulitic is represented by alternating fine sandstones with calcareous cement and clayey marls corresponding to shore deposits. They contain an abundant fauna of Oligocene mollusks and echinoids, as well as characteristic foraminifers (*Nummulites intermedius-fichteli* and lepidocyclines).

In the South Tellian chains of Oran the upper Nummulitic, reduced to only the Oligocene, has long been recognized by M. Dalloni,[215] who discovered and described a rich fauna of nummulites, lepidocyclines, echinoids and pelecypods. The sandstone there is frequently glauconitic, more or less coarse, alternating with white marls and containing lentils of very fossiliferous limestone.

Finally, all along the cordillera composed of the Numidian chain and the Djurdjura (*s. lato*) south of the metamorphic Kabylies Massif, the upper Nummulitic is formed of coarsely detrital sediments, conglomerates, breccias, variegated sandstones and sandy marls, which were formerly attributed to the middle Eocene (infra- and supra-Nummulitic stages). These deposits have for some years yielded rich faunas of Oligocene nummulites and lepidocyclines with which numerous Lutetian foraminifers are generally mixed, in consequence of reworking of earlier formations.

6. The Continental Aquitano-Burdigalian. After the Stampian, important folding caused a new complete emergence of Algeria. The newly formed chains were submitted to brisk erosion and the products of erosion accumulated in the continental basins where they produced coarsely detrital red beds (conglomerates, marls and sandy clays), often of considerable thickness. In spite of the absence of conclusive paleontologic evidence, part of this continental formation is logically attributed to the Aquitanian, but in most places the base of the lower Miocene should also be included. These deposits always occur in extremely clear angular discordance above the marine Oligocene, and on the other hand in complete concordance with the first marine members of the Burdigalian. Thus, from a paleographic viewpoint they are attached to the Miocene rather than to the Nummulitic.

In southern Algeria, where the Lutetian is the last known marine stage, the red beds called Aquitanian may include the upper Nummulitic at their base and at their top a more or less important part of the Miocene. This is the Oligo-Miocene of the Algerian geologists, found even in the Sahara.

On the coast of the department of Algiers, in the region of Dellys, marine sediments have been known for a very long time; they overlie in transgression the highest sections of the Numidian, and are covered by the marine Burdigalian. These deposits, for which it is convenient to use the name Dellysian, are devoid of a characteristic fauna. Their stratigraphic position, however, allows them to be considered as the marine equivalent of the red beds of the continental Aquitanian and permits the comparison of the gulf that they outline on the Algerian coast with the gulf of Carry on the Marseille shore.

7. Conclusions. From this study, we recall first the profound contrast between the Nummulitic of the Saharan Basin and that of the Tellian chains. The latter shows a thick Flysch analogous to that of the Alps, while to the

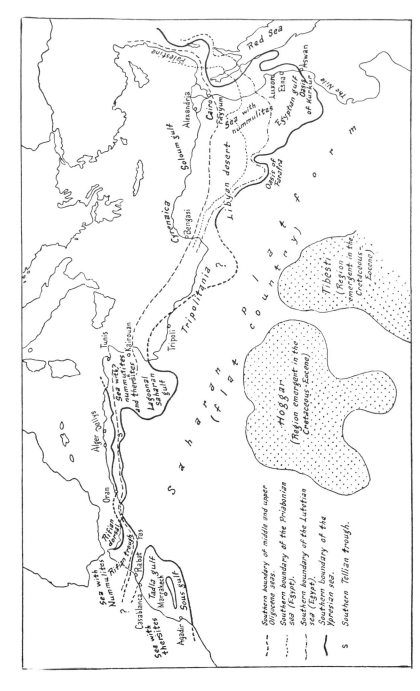

FIG. 131. *Southern border of the Nummulitic Mediterranean (by L. Moret).*

N. B. In the Sahara, the Sous Gulf and southern Egypt, the transition from the Cretaceous to the Eocene is through marine beds; it is not until the Ypresian that the sea withdraws into the Saharan and Sous Gulfs.

Map labels:

Red Sea
Palestine
Soloum gulf
Alexandria
Cairo
Faiyûm
Sea with nummulites
Luxor
Esna
Egyptian gulf
Oasis of Kurkur
Aswan
The Nile
Cyrenaica
Bengasi
Libyan desert
Oasis of Farafra
Tripolitania ?
Tripoli
Saharan country (flat country) form
Tibesti (Region emergent in the Cretaceous-Eocene).
Hoggar (Region emergent in the Cretaceous-Eocene)
Tunis
Kairouan
Sea with nummulites and thersites.
Lagoonal Saharan gulf.
Alger
Dellys
Oran
Rif dorsal
Rifian trough
Fas
Rabat
Casablanca
Tadla gulf
Marrakech
sea with Nummulites
sea with thersites
Sous gulf
Agadir

Legend:
- - - Southern boundary of middle and upper Oligocene seas.
..... Southern boundary of the Priabonian sea (Egypt).
-·-·- Southern boundary of the Lutetian sea (Egypt).
——— Southern boundary of the Ypresian sea.
s   Southern Tellian trough.

532

south, on the contrary, is typical epicontinental sedimentation. On this side are flat and stable coasts, bordered by lagoons, unable to nourish thick accumulations of sediments. Thus the approach of the vast plains of the Saharan continent is shown.

On the other side, the detailed stratigraphy of the Flysch of the Tellian chains allows us to state precisely, even better than in the Alps, the successive phases of their formation and to see how long and complicated was this orogenesis. The South Tellian trough, still on the edge of the Saharan continental platform, is comparable to the Alpine fore-deep, which parallels the Jura Mountains (here, the Saharan Atlas). Farther north, the Tellian chains were built up by successive waves, separated by trenches of sedimentation. The crystalline massifs, emergent and eroded, with a vigorous relief, provided the materials of the Flysch. But we find here no great trenches, comparable to the great Alpine trough, where sediments could descend as far as the zone of metamorphism and from which transgressions originated. They are, farther north, engulfed by the African sea. We see, in the Tell, no more than the external border of a great chain, whose still unfinished history is hidden by the waters of the Mediterranean.

B. *Morocco*

Two very different domains must be distinguished here, a northern or Rifian which lies between the Rifian ridge and the Meseta, and a southern domain.[216]

1. Northern or Nummulite Domain. The axial zone of Nummulitic sedimentation approximately corresponds to the southern edge of the Rif or Pre-Rif. This is the Prerifian trough, possibly a prolongation of the South Tellian trough which we have described in Algeria. Here the sedimentation from the Cretaceous to the upper Oligocene was continuous. There is very thick Flysch, in which the faunas of nummulites, orthophragmines, lepidocyclines and mollusks permit the recognition of the lower, middle and upper Eocene and the Oligocene, ending with an Aquitanian sometimes marine, sometimes continental.

Farther north, on the other hand, comes a zone in which the lower Eocene is probably unknown and the middle Eocene is transgressive. There, in the Rifian domain, the Upper Cretaceous, represented by marl-limestones with rosalines (formerly considered as an Eocene calcareous Flysch), is overlain by a Lutetian Flysch with large nummulites, followed by upper Eocene and Oligocene sandy Flysch.[217] Thus, a series analogous to that in the Algerian Tell, north of the South Tellian trough, is found here.

2. Southern or Phosphate Domain. The seas occupied here two gulfs, at the beginning of the Eocene:

a. North of the Atlas (on the site of the Meseta) is the Gulf of Tadla, separated from the Prerifian trough by an emerged zone corresponding to the northern part of the Meseta. In this gulf, there is everywhere emergence and discontinuity between the Upper Cretaceous and the Tertiary. Note moreover that wherever the upper beds of the Cretaceous (Maestrichtian) were not carried away by Tertiary erosion, they are locally phosphatic. But it is especially at the base of the Eocene that the calcareous-marly or sandy beds are located, extremely rich in phosphates, several meters thick, which are very actively exploited in the celebrated deposits of Oued Zem and El Borouj, southeast of Casablanca. Fossils include numerous fish identical to species of the Belgian Eocene, and *Ostrea multicostata.* This Eocene series, 60 m. thick, ends with a compact bank of limestone with *Thersitea,* a form already seen in southern Algeria.

b. In the Gulf of Sous, are located phosphatized beds still unexploited, first recognized in the region of Agadir, but which L. Moret [218] found on the south slope of the Great Atlas of Marrakech. In this domain, the stratigraphic series is a little different. Beds with *Cardita* cf. *beaumonti,* lucinas, turritellas, and *Glauconia,* with Cretaceous affinities, can be attributed to the upper Maestrichtian-Danian. Then come calcareous or marly beds with carditas and a spantangid echinoid (*Mauritanaster gentili*) indicating the extreme base of the Tertiary (Montian?). Above, a limestone escarpment with *Thersitea* is found, with a fine fauna of silicified mollusks (Landenian?, Ypresian?). And still higher, the phosphatic facies develop. The history of the Paleogene seas in this part of Morocco ends with these beds. For on all the borders of the Atlas, the series of alluvium, conglomerates, and marls, known as Oligo-Miocene, is entirely continental and moreover without fossils.

Finally, we emphasize that in all this southern domain, no nummulite has even been found.

C. *Egypt*

The Egyptian Nummulitic has long been celebrated for its richness in fossils and particularly in nummulites. The most classic sections are those which show the cliffs which dominate the Nile upstream from its delta, and also the slopes or escarpments bordering the depressions (oases) of the Libyan desert. But the distinction of stages has been and is still disputed. We follow here the recent synthesis of Cuvillier[219] (Fig. 131).

1. Danian and Lower Eocene. Recall first that the Upper Cretaceous here shows beds attributed to the Danian, the Esna shales of British geologists, *Blättermergel* of the Germans, paper marls of considerable extent in southern Egypt. They contain *Nautilus danicus* as well as a mixture of forms with Cretaceous affinities (*Ananchytes*) and mollusks with a Tertiary stamp. This Danian has been studied especially in the cliffs of the Nile, at Esna near Luxor and in the oases of Farafra and Kurkur.[220] It is rich in echinoids described by Fourtau.

In the oasis of Farafra, the top of the paper marls already contains the first nummulites (*N. deserti, N. fraasi*) which, moreover, are associated with faunas of Tertiary mollusks. Thus we may see there an approximate equivalent of the Montian.

In fact, according to Faris,[221] there was everywhere in Upper Egypt continuous transition between the Cretaceous and the Eocene, as there was in the South Tellian trough. A lacuna, with an Eocene transgression, appears then only in Lower Egypt. Thus, approaching the present Mediterranean, we reach a zone affected by the recent Mediterranean folding, as we saw in Algeria with the Lutetian threshold and Lutetian transgression coming from the north (Fig. 130).

In Lower Egypt, the age of this transgression, which coincides with the appearance of nummulites in mass, has been carefully studied by Cuvillier. Boussac considers it Lutetian because of the appearance at this moment of *Nummulites atacicus*. But this is not a sufficient argument, for this form is already seen before the Lutetian, for example, at certain points in the Aquitanian Basin (Abrard). So recently Cuvillier has proposed adopting as the base of the Lutetian the beds in which *Orbolites complanatus* appear, accompanied afterwards by the usual fauna of Lutetian large nummulites. If the Lutetian is so defined, Egypt would have a lower Eocene containing the rich fauna formerly described under the stage name Libyan (Zittel) and having affinities with the Ypresian fauna of the Paris Basin. Cuvillier is thus led to date as Ypresian the transgression by which the nummulite sea here covers the Cretaceous platform.[222]

This marine Ypresian is most classic in the hill of Thebes (Djebel Gournah, opposite Luxor), 400 m. high. Here are more or less shaly limestones, in which the tombs of the Valley of Kings were dug. They contain *N. globulus* and a fine fauna of mollusks and echinoids described by Fourtau.

2. Middle Eocene. Cuvillier distinguishes: a) a lower Lutetian, characterized by the appearance of *Orbitolites complanatus,* accompanied by assilines and alveolines, which is the upper Libyan of Zittel; b) an upper Lutetian with a rich fauna of large nummulites, corresponding to the lower part of the Mokattam beds of early authors. In fact, at Djebel Mokattam (a mountain near Cairo), this upper Lutetian, 140 m. thick and transgressive over the Maestrichtian, is made up of compact limestone, forming a scarp. The tombs of the Pharaohs were dug in it and it provided an excellent building material (horizon called "pierre à batir") for all ancient and modern Egypt. The pyramids of Gizeh, near Cairo, have given their name to the giant form *N. gizehensis.* It is accompanied by *N. perforatus, N. uroniensis,* orthophragmines, operculines, assilines, numerous echinoids, corals and mollusks.

3. Upper Eocene. A lower or Ledian period can be distinguished, corresponding to the upper Mokattam beds, with *N. contortus-striatus,* and a Ludian with *N. fabianii,* represented especially in the region of Fayyum, where the upper Eocene is as much as 250 m. thick. The rocks become softer, with marly and clayey intercalations. At the top, there are even beds with gypsum and sand. This is a true estuarine facies, corresponding to the base of the fluvio-marine series of Fayyum. It is from this horizon (top of the Eocene) that the famous genus *Moeritherium* (from Lake Moeris) comes, considered to be an ancestral form of proboscidians.

4. Oligocene. Very recently, a purely marine Oligocene, with mollusks, nummulites and lepidocyclines, was discovered in Lower Egypt, first on the coast west of Alexandria,[223] then 10 km. west of the great Pyramids of Gizeh.[224] But farther south the Oligocene is represented by the upper part of the fluvio-marine series of Fayyum, reaching a thickness of 250 m. In these sands, sandstones and clays, delta of an ancient Nile, have been found the genera *Palaeomastodon, Arsinoitherium,* and several monkeys.

As may be seen, the history of the Nummulitic gulf of Lower Egypt, with its local transgressions and regressions, its multiple variations of facies and the prevalence of the compact limestone of the middle Eocene, represents, on the northern edge of the Saharan Continent, approximately the equivalent of the history of the Paris Basin at the northern border of the Continent of Middle Europe.

X. Paleogene of North America

By the distribution of outcrops as well as by the facies and general character of the faunas, we are led to distinguish five great natural domains in the Nummulitic of North America. Some of these domains, however, follow those recognized in the Cretaceous. They are: 1, the Atlantic coast; 2, the Gulf of Mexico; 3, the Antilles; 4, the Pacific chains; 5, the Central states.

Of these five domains, the first two show a marine Nummulitic of epicontinental type, not folded, deposited on the edge of the North American continental area, that we trace from the Triassic. The fifth corresponds to completely continental deposits of the central part of this area. Lastly, the third and fourth belong to the folded domains of the Tertiary, and the Nummulitic has, principally in California, a rather geosynclinal type, like the Cretaceous of the same region.

A. *Nummulitic of the Atlantic Coast*

As in the Cretaceous, the Paleogene sea only nibbled lightly on the eastern slope of the Appalachians, so that a band of Nummulitic deposits is found in the coastal plain at the foot of these chains. A lacuna, and even a slight discordance, separates them from the Upper Cretaceous. There are marls or littoral sands, generally rich in pelecypods and gastropods, but the faunas are different from those of the Nummulitic in Europe, so that it is difficult to establish a correlation with the European stages.[225]

We note only, in Maryland and South Carolina,[226] the presence of an horizon containing a *Venericardia densata* at least very close to the European *V. planicosta* of the Parisian *calcaire grossier.*[227] So this horizon may be in all probability related to our middle Eocene. But there are no nummulites or orbitoids.

B. *Nummulitic of the Gulf of Mexico*[228]

The outcrops between the Cretaceous and the Neogene and Quaternary plains of the Gulf form a wide band, which, starting from Florida, crosses Alabama, Mississippi,[229] Arkansas and Texas. Here are found, as in Europe, orbitoids and nummulites[230] and the correlation with European stages can be stated precisely.[231]

This Nummulitic has been best studied in Alabama.[232] The Midway group

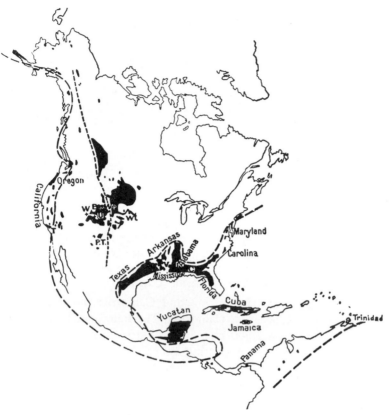

FIG. 132.   *Map of Paleogene outcrops in North America (after Bailey Willis, modified)*.

———— Line marking the maximum advance of the Paleogene seas

Continental formations inside this line:
P, T = Puerco and Torrejon; W = Wasatch; Wr = Wind River; B = Bridger; U = Uinta; Wt = White River.

Marine formations outside this line:
C = Claiborne; J = Jackson; V = Vicksburg; T = Tejon

------- Approximate boundary between the Rocky Mountains and the great plains of the west.

(p. 454) corresponds to the Montian and Thanetian, the Wilcox group to the Ypresian. The middle Eocene is called the Claibornian and contains *Venericardia densata*.[233] The type locality of Claiborne (escarpment along the Alabama River), has provided a very rich fauna of mollusks, studied by M. Cossmann.[234] Above, beds with orthophragmines (Jacksonian stage, from Jackson City), represent the upper Eocene.[235] The first lepidocyclines appear here. Then the Vicksburgian[236] (Vicksburg cliffs on the Mississippi) corresponds to our Oligocene, for it ends with beds containing lepidocyclines associated with small nummulites, beds which are also found in Florida. Thus, the lepidocyclines appear earlier here than in Europe, and the nummulites later

C. *Nummulitic in the Antilles*[237]

We cannot yet determine the exact stratigraphy of this region, but it deserves mention here because of its affinities with the Mediterranean Paleogene. First, different horizons with nummulites are found (appearing here in the lower Jacksonian = Ledian?), also with lepidocyclines and orthophragmines, particularly in Jamaica and Trinidad.[238] And especially, in the latter island, Duncan has described corals identical to Oligocene species of Castelgomberto (Vicentin, p. 522).[239] Thus, it is natural to conclude that a shore zone must have connected the region of the Antilles to the Mediterranean countries. As, on the other hand, the Paleogene faunas of the American Atlantic, without nummulites and without coral reefs, were connected rather, by way of the south shore of the North Atlantic continent, with the Basin of the North Sea, it is reasonable to think, following E. Haug, that these migrations of tropical faunas took place along the southern shores of the Mesogean seas, that is to say, along the African-Brazilian or South Atlantic continent.

D. *Nummulitic of the Pacific Chains*

The Nummulitic is known in Oregon and California but it has been best studied in the Coast Range[240] of California. The Paleogene is there composed of very thick (more than 2,000 m.) littoral marls or sands, sometimes even brackish, containing petroleum-bearing zones. In a certain sense, this is a geosynclinal series, which seems to correspond to the whole of the Eocene.

The middle period, the best known, is called the Tejon formation (from Fort Tejon, north of Los Angeles). It is attributed to the Lutetian as *Venericardia densata* is found in it, as in the Atlantic domain. But there also, there are neither nummulites nor orbitoids. As on the shores of the Appalachians, this is a domain influenced by currents coming from the north which prevented the propagation of the faunas populating the warm seas of Central America (E. Haug).

E. *The Continental Paleogene of the Central States*[241]

Seas coming from the Gulf of Mexico could hardly have reached farther north than the confluence of the Ohio and Mississippi Rivers and those coming from the Pacific did not penetrate into the high plateaus or the Rocky Mountains. So vast stretches of the North American Continent remained constantly emergent. Moreover, the continental deposits—lacustrine, or rather fluviatile (or even eolian, as recently recognized)—could accumulate only in well marked zones where subsidence encouraged sedimentation. This happened in the Rocky Mountains and the bordering plains on the east, for the earth there was less stable than on the Canadian Shield and the primary platform of the central states. Thus there is a series of basins filled to enormous thicknesses with deposits of torrents, rivers and temporary swamps.[242] They are sands, conglomerates and especially clays, which in the desert climate of western America produce the characteristic landscapes of the Bad Lands.

All these formations are sometimes extremely rich in mammalian bones, so that a scale of mammalian faunas can be established, absolutely independent of the American marine faunas. But this scale can be paralleled with the European mammalian faunas and, in that way, with our marine stages. The latter being correlated with the marine fauna of the New World, it is evident that American stratigraphers can thus correlate their continental faunas and their marine stages; a curious example of a singularly indirect method of correlation.

These American continental beds have for us little more than paleontologic interest. So, we shall be restricted to naming the classical stages into which they are divided, indicating their correlation to the European chronology.

Lower Eocene	Puerco stage	—Montian or lower Thanetian (?)
	Torrejon stage	—Upper Thanetian (Cernay fauna, near Rheims)
	Wasatch stage	—Sparnacian
	Lower Wind River stage	—Ypresian

| Middle Eocene | Upper Wind River stage | —lower Lutetian |
| | Lower Bridger stage | —upper Lutetian |

| Upper Eocene | Upper Bridger stage | —Ledian |
| | Uinta stage | —Ludian |

| Oligocene | White River stage | — |

Comparison of American and European forms has established the possibility of exchanges of faunas between the two continents and the interruption of these exchanges, at different periods. Thus, *Neoplagiaulax* of Cernay is found in the Torrejon beds and *Coryphodon* of Meudon in the Wasatch beds. On the other hand, the faunas of the two continents are completely separate in the middle and upper Eocene. And finally, the exchanges must have been resumed in the Oligocene.[243]

REFERENCE NOTES

1. From παλαιος, old, and γενος, birth.

2. The question of Cretaceous nummulites in the Swiss Alps has been studied above (note 151, chap. 8). But in other regions, it is certain that nummulites appear, as rarities, at the top of the Cretaceous. The fact was pointed out for Italy long ago, by H. Douvillé. The most typical case is that of Lavardens in Gers (see Fig. 123), where hippurites and nummulites are contained in a single rocky block: G. Astre, *Etude paléontologique des Nummulites du Crétacé sup. de Cézan-Lavardens* (Gers), Bull. Soc. géol. France, 4 sér. 23 (1924). Arnold Heim, Eclogae Geol. Helvetiae, 19 (1925) has noted nummulites in the Cretaceous of the region of Damas. According to L. Dubertret (*in litt.*) that is because the chalk facies is prolonged there into the lower Eocene with banks of small nummulites; at its top even large Lutetian nummulites appear. A complete bibliography of references to Cretaceous nummulites is found in G. Murgeanu, *Note sur la présence de Nummulites elegans Sow. dans le Sénonien de Dosul Stânei*, Ann. de l'Inst. geol. de Roumanie, 13, 1928, Bucharest (1929). Finally V. Pérébaskine, *La découverte de Nummulites dans le Sénonien de Saint-Marcet*, Bull. Soc. géol. France, 12 (1942) has shown that a nummulite, mentioned as from the Senonian of Haute-Garonne, was actually an amphistegine or a cristellarian (with a bibliography of similar citations).

3. From νεος, new, and γενος, birth.

4. From ολιγος, little, and καινος, recent.

5. From εος, dawn, and καινος, recent.

6. The existence of strata bearing both lepidocyclines and large Eocene foraminifers (nummulites, assilines and orthophragmines) has led some Italian and North African geologists to make the genus *Lepidocyclina* begin with the upper or even middle Eocene. Later works devoted to this question have shown that, at least in the Mediterranean regions, lepidocyclines appear only in the Oligocene and that the Eocene species which accompany them in certain strata had been redeposited. On the other hand we shall note that lepidocyclines persist in the lower Miocene. On these questions see: A. Senn, *Die stratigraphische Verbreitung der tertiären Obitoïden,* Eclogae geol. Helvetiae, 28 (1935); J. Flandrin, *Contribution à l'étude stratigraphique du Nummulitique algérien,* Bull. Serv. Carte géol. Algérie, 2, 18 (1948); H. Gerth, *The Distribution and Evolution of the Larger Foraminifera in the Tertiary Sediments,* Proc. Kon. Akad. Wet., Amsterdam, 38 (1935).

7. See a phylogenetic table in R. Abrard, *Contribution à l'étude de l'évolution des nummulites,* Bull. Soc. géol. France, 4 sér., 28 (1928).

8. Note especially that *N. uroniensis* is sometimes found in the upper Lutetian, for example in Egypt and the Maritime Alps, according to A. F. de Lapparent.

9. The names of which have been written in italics in the foregoing table. It must be noted however that certain forms of the Oligocene group of *N. intermedius* in other regions reach a fairly large size.

10. Excellent summary of these migrations by R. Abrard, *Les migrations des Nummulites vers le Bassin anglo-franco-belge,* C. R. Soc. de Biogéogr., no. 37 (April 20, 1928).

11. R. Abrard, *Sur la répartition stratigraphique d'Orbitolites complanatus,* C. R. Soc. géol. France (Nov. 8, 1943).

12. Nevertheless, A. Chavan, *L'évolution des faunes de Mollusques dans le Nord-Ouest de l'Europe, de la fin du Crétacé à celle de l'Eocène,* Bull. Soc. géol. France, 15 (1945), p. 193, has tried to use the genera (or rather the sub-genera) to characterize stages.

13. R. Charpiat, *Recherches sur l'évolution des Cérithidés tertiaires du Bassin de Paris, etc.,* Thèse Sc., Dijon, 1923, Presses universitaires, Paris (1923).

14. J. Roger, *Quelques caractéristiques essentielles de la fauna de Pectinidés dans le domaine nordique pendant l'Oligocène,* C. R. Soc. géol. France (Dec. 7, 1942).

15. J. Piveteau, *L'apparition des Mammifères,* Mammalia (Mar.-June, 1947), 10.

16. For the lower Eocene, see the important memoir of P. Teilhard de Chardin, *Les Mammifères de l'Eocène inf. de Belgique,* Mém. Musée roy. Hist. nat. Belgique, Mém. no. 36 (1927), and G. Gaylord Simpson, *Census of Paleocene Mammals,* American Mus. Novitiates, no. 848 (1936) which contains a complete list of Thanetian genera (Cernay and Asiatic and American faunas). Later a Paleocene fauna was discovered in Germany, in the Aller valley, in the crevices of Triassic limestones between Walbeck and Weferlingen. It is composed of *Plesiadapis,* arctocyonids, tarsids, birds (*Gastornis* as large as an Ostrich). See K. Weigelt, *Die erste päläozäne Säugetierfauna Deutschlands,* Zeitsch. deutsch. geol. Ges., 92 (1940), p. 199.

17. See note 96, chap. 8.

18. J. W. Durham, "The Type Section of the Aquitanian," Am. Jr. Sc. (May, 1944).

19. The question of the Aquitanian and the evolution of mammalian faunas at the boundary between the Oligocene and the Miocene are discussed in detail by J. Viret, *Les faunes de Mammifères de l'Oligocène sup. de la Limagne bourbonnaise,* Ann. Univ. Lyon, n. s., 1, fasc. 47, Thèse Sc. Lyon (1929), and by J. Hürzeler, *Säugetierpaleontologische Bemerkungen zur Abgrenzung und Unterteilung des Aquitanien,* Eclogae geol. Helvetiae, 38, no. 2 (1945).

20. Revision by S. Venzo, *Melongena dalpiazi n. sp. delle glauconie bellunesi (Cattiano),* Bull. Soc. geol. ital., 55 (1926).

21. These deposits are attributed to the Oligocene on the *Carte géol. de la France,* 1/1,000,000.

22. The most convenient source of documentation is the work of P. Lemoine, cited note 19, chap. 7. For more recent works, consult P. Lemoine, *l'Ile de France*, Mém. Mus. Hist. nat., n. s., t. 5 (1937); M. Leriche, *Les rapports entre les formations tertiaires du bassin belge at du bassin du Paris*, Bull. Soc. belge géol., 47 (1937, 1939); *L'Eocène des bassins parisien et belge*, Bull. Soc. géol. France, 4 sér., 12, 1912, Paris (1915); A. F. de Lapparent, *Excursions géologiques dans le bassin de Paris*, fasc. 1 (1942); fasc. 2 (1946) Hermann et Cie, Paris; R. Furon and R. Soyer, *Catalogue des fossiles tertiaires du bassin de Paris*, 240 p., 32 pl., Lechevallier, Paris (1947).

23. We mention only the last of these numerous recent publications: F. Ellenberger, *Le problème de la craie durcie de Meudon. Bancs-limites et "contacts par racines:" lacune sous-marine ou émersion?* Bull. Soc. géol. France, 17 (1947).

24. R. Soyer, *Recherches sur l'extension du Montien dans le Bassin de Paris*, Bull. Serv. Carte géol. France, no. 213, t. 44, 1943 (published 1944).

25. L. and J. Morellet, *Les Dasycladacées et les Codiacées (algues vertes) du "Calcaire pisolithique,"* C. R. Soc. géol. France (Nov. 4, 1940). The microforaminifers studied by P. Marie, C. R. Soc. géol. France (1947), p. 220, have Lutetian affinities rather than Maestrichtian. R. Lafitte, C. R. Acad. Sc. (June 20, 1938) has listed operculines, large foraminifers essentially Tertiary, in the Montian of Mont-Aimé (near Vertus); but according to P. Marie, Bull. Soc. géol. France, 15 (1945), p. 419, this is actually a new genus, *Lafitteina*, which is also found in Mauritania.

26. A. Chavan, *Rapports entre Danien et calcaire pisolithique*, C. R. Acad. Sc., 226 (1948), p. 1135; *Les caractères de la faune du calcaire de Vigny*, ibid., 228 (1949), p. 494.

27. On the rocky Mediterranean coasts, *Lithothamnium* builds at sea level, against the cliffs, "pavements" which increase slowly in width.

28. H. Alimen, A. F. de Lapparent and G. Lucas, *Observations nouvelles en faveur de l'âge crétacé du calcaire dit pisolithique de Vigny (Seine-et-Oise)*, C. R. Acad. Sc., 227 (1948), p. 1161. An exactly contrary opinion has been expressed by R. Abrard, R. Furon, P. Marie and R. Soyer, ibid., 228 (1949), p. 758.

29. On the contrary, we have said (note 87, chap. 8) that M. Leriche considers that a lacuna represents the Danian and even the Maestrichtian in the Paris Basin.

30. F. Ellenberger, Bull. Soc. géol. France, 17 (1948), p. 255.

31. M. Leriche, *Sur la répartition des faciès lagunaires et fluviatiles du Landénien dans les Bassins belge et parisien*, Bull. Soc. belge Géol., 38 (1929).

32. A. F. de Lapparent, *Une coupe du Sparnacien à Soissons (Aisne)*, Ann. Soc. géol. du Nord, 64 (1939), has described a section illustrating well this intimate connection and even intermingling of the Thanetian and Sparnacian facies. He saw a marine Thanetian with *Ostrea bellovacina* overlying a typical Sparnacian with Soissons facies.

33. H. Farchad, *Etude du Thanétien du Bassin de Paris*, Thèse Sc., Mém. Soc. géol. France, no. 30 (1936). A. Vatan and H. Farchad, *Etude minéralogique des sédiments arénacés du Thanétien (Landénien marin)*, Bull. Soc. géol. France, 6 (1936).

34. L. and J. Morellet, *Découverte d'un Polypier dans le Thanétien du Bassin de Paris; considérations sur la température des eaux du golfe thanétien dans le Bassin de Paris*, C. R. Soc. géol. France (Nov. 19, 1945).

35. From this district comes the stage name "Suessonian," formerly often used to designate all the lower Eocene, while the middle and upper Eocene formed the "Parisian."

36. Local details in A. F. de Lapparent, *Révision de la feuille de Reims au 1/80,000*, Bull. Serv. Carte géol. France, no. 212, t. 44 (1943).

37. To this Belgian term, some French geologists prefer that of Londinian, of English origin (see later).

38. For the eastern limit of this transgression, new information supplied by M. Leriche, *Le terrain wealdien et les terrains tertiaires de l'Ardenne française; l'Ardenne pendant l'ère tertiaire*, Bull. Soc. belge de Géol., 35, 1925, Brussels (1926). This was taken into account in the map, Fig. 111.

39. L. Feugueur, *Etude du Cuisien dans les Vexins français et normands*, Bull. Soc. géol. France, 17 (1947).

40. This fine shell with tropical affinities is known in the Ypresian as far as India and Madagascar. In Vicentin, it still persists in the Oligocene. See R. Abrard, *Extension géographique et stratigraphique de Velates Schmiedelianus,* C. R. Congrès de l'Ass. franç. pour l'Avance. des Sc., Constantine (1927).

41. Revision of this flora by P. H. Fritel, Bull. Soc. géol. France, 4th ser., 24 (1924).

42. H. G. Stehlin, *Ueber die Säugetierfauna der Teredinsande von Epernay und Umgebung,* Eclogae geol. Helvetiae, 33 (1940).

43. R. Abrard, *Le Lutétien du Bassin de Paris,* Thèse Sc., Paris (1925).

44. This fossil, often believed characteristic of zone IV, sometimes appears in zones II and III, according to R. Abrard, C. R. Soc. géol. France (1943), p. 108. That is one more example of the slight value of detailed paleontologic zones formerly believed to be distinguished in this Parisian Tertiary.

45. The detailed outline of these shores of the Ledian gulf, between the Marne and the Aisne, has just been determined by A. F. de Lapparent and J. Morellet, *Etude sur le Bartonien de la partie orientale du Tardenois,* Bull. Soc. géol. France, 12 (1942).

46. A list of 565 species of this type locality of Auvers has been published by L. and J. Morellet, *Nouvelle contribution à l'étude de la faune des sables à Nummulites variolarius d'Auvers-sur-Oise, de Caumont et de Lévignan (Bartonien),* Bull. Mus. Hist. nat., 2 sér., t. 17, no. 5 (1945). For other occurrences, a list of 320 species is found in L. and J. Morellet, *Faune des sables à Nummulites variolarius de Barisseuse, près de St-Vaast-lès-Mello (Oise), et remarques paléontologiques,* Bull. Soc. géol. France, 15 (1945), p. 337.

47. Local details in L. and J. Morellet, *Observations sur les couches à Potamides mixtus (zone d'Ermenonville),* Bull. Soc. géol. France, 4 sér. 25 (1925).

48. *Palaeotherium magnum,* a famous mammal of the Montmartre gypsum, appears at this horizon, where it has been noted even in Paris, at the Gare du Nord, by P. Lemoine and R. Abrard, Bull. Soc. géol. France, 4 sér., 26 (1926).

49. H. Alimen and M. Mercier, *Topographie dunaire au sommet de l'Auversien dans le Tardenois,* C. R. Acad. Sc., 226 (1948), p. 2083.

50. But many Parisian geologists continue to use the term Bartonian, either in a restricted sense, as a synonym of Ledian, or in a broad sense (Ledian-Ludian). On this subject, see L. and J. Morellet, *Les diverses interprétations du terme de Bartonien,* Bull. Soc. géol. France, 10 (1940), and R. Abrard, *Observations à une note de MM. L. et J. Morellet sur le Bartonien et à une Note de M. Denizot sur l'Oligocène,* C. R. Soc. géol. France (Jan. 19, 1942).

51. We see no decisive reason for giving up the term Ludian, sanctioned by custom and leading to no ambiguity, in favor of the Belgian name Wemmelian, as proposed by Abrard.

52. A map of the marly, calcareous and sandy facies in Mlle. S. Perrier, *Contribution à l'étude du Ludien du Bassin de Paris; la faune des marnes à Pholadomya ludensis* Mém. Diplôme Et. sup. Paris (1941).

53. R. Soyer, *L'extension du calcaire de Brie dans le Nord de l'Ile-de-France,* Bull. Mus. nat. Hist. nat., 19, no. 1 (1947).

54. M. Auzel, *Premiers résultats d'une étude des meulières du Bassin de Paris,* Revue géogr. phys. Géol. dynam., 3, fasc. 4 (1930), an entirely petrographic work, concluding that these were originally siliceous limestones and not limestones secondarily silicified.

55. H. Alimen, *Etude sur le Stampien du Bassin de Paris,* Thèse Sc. Paris, 1936; Mém. Soc. géol. France, n. s., no. 14, (1936); an excellent summary by the author, *L'Oligocène marin du Bassin de Paris,* Rév. gén. des Sc., t. 49, no. 4 (1938). G. Denizot, *Le Stampien de la région parisienne et le classement de l'Oligocène,* Bull. Soc. géol. France, 10 (1940). Reviews by H. Alimen, ibid., 11 (1941), by L. and J. Morellet, C. R. Soc. géol. France (Nov. 3, 1941), and by R. Abrard, ibid. (Dec. 1, 1941).

56. According to A. Rivière, *Sur les formations gréseuses du Sud du Bassin parisien,* C. R. Soc. géol. France (May 3, 1943). Remnants of sandstone without fossils give evidence of a marine Stampian.

57. H. Alimen, *Remarques sur la paléobiogéographie de deux espèces oligocènes: "Ostrea longirostris" et "O. cyathula,"* C. R. Soc. Biologie, 18th ann., no. 149-150 (1941).

58. A small nummulite, *N. bezançoni,* was discovered at Jeurre in 1878 (but never found since then). According to H. Douvillé, C. R. Soc. géol. France (April 7, 1924), it represented a local race of the Mediterranean species *N. vascus-boucheri;* it was the last nummulite to penetrate the Paris Basin.

59. G. Denizot, *Les formations continentales de la région orléanaise,* Thèse Sc., Paris (1927); *Les horizons continentaux du Stampien et de l'Aquitanien,* Bull. Soc. géol. France, 4 sér., 29 (1929).

60. P. V. Fritel, *Flore bartonienne des grès à Sabalites,* Bull. Mus. nat. Hist. nat. (1922). The term Bartonian here is synonymous with the Ledian of our classification. The great extent of this sand has been well demonstrated by J. M. Bourdeau, *Recherches sur l'Eocène continental du Massif vendéen,* Bull. Soc. Sc. nat. Ouest de la France, 5 sér., 8, Nantes (1938).

61. G. F. Dollfus, *Etude paléontologique des marnes oligocènes de Thévalle, près Laval,* Bull. Soc. géol. et min. de Bretagne, 2 (1921).

62. J. Bourcart even dredged a typical *Nummulites brongniarti* from the open sea at Roscoff, Bull. Soc. géol. France, 4 sér., 22 (1922), p. 10.

63. A. Vatan, *Etude minéralogique comparée des sédiments arénacés du bassin de Paris,* C. R. Acad. Sc., 205 (1937), p. 70.

64. See the work of L. Dudley Stamp in the Geol. Mag. 58 (1921). This author has given an excellent summary in his work cited note 23, chap. 1.

65. Local details, sections and paleogeographic maps in R. L. Sherlock, *London and Thames Valley,* 2nd edit., British reg. Geol., Geol. Surv. and Mus., London (1947), and in C. P. Chatwin, *The Hampshire Basin and Adjoining Areas,* ibid (1948).

66. L. Morellet, *A propos du "London Clay,"* C. R. Soc. géol. France (Nov. 15, 1937), is inclined to include the London Clay in the Sparnacian, of which it represents a marine facies, as indicated by its mammalian faunas.

67. W. N. Edwards, "The Flora of the London Clay," Proc. Geol. Ass., 47 (1936).

68. This was wrong, for the English Sparnacian, like the French, is only the terminal phase of a sedimentary cycle, the transgressive marine phase being represented by the Thanetian. Thus it is better to group the Thanetian and Sparnacian in a single stage (Landenian).

69. Actually, the extreme base of the lower beds of Bracklesham contain *Nummulites planulatus* and so must be correlated with the Cuise sands. See A. Wrigley and A. G. Davis, "The Occurrence of Nummulites Planulatus in England, with a Revised Correlation of the Strata Containing It," Proc. Geol. Ass., 48 (1937). This important article contains a correlation table, reproduced here, whose conclusions are adopted on the whole, although a little skeptically in regard to exact details, by L. Morellet, *Le problème du synchromisme des assises de l'Eocène inférieur dans les bassins anglais, parisien et belge,* C. R. Soc. géol. France (Nov. 8, 1937).

70. On the other hand, according to Dennis Curry, "The English Bartonian Nummulites," Proc. Geol. Ass., 48 (1937), the form often cited in the Barton Clay under the name *N. variolarius* actually belongs to a new species, *N. rectus.*

71. According to a recent study by Dudley Stamp, the Sannoisian there corresponds to a very distinct sedimentary cycle, between that of the Ludian and the new Stampian transgression.

72. See especially the guide books of the International Geological Congress at Brussels, in 1922.

73. F. Halet, *Coupe des formations tertiaires de la Campine,* Bull. Soc. belge Géol., 33 (1923).

74. A. Ten Dam, *Die stratigraphische Gliederung des niederländischen Paläozäns und Eozäns nach Foraminiferen,* Meded. geol. Stichting ser. C-V, no. 2, Maastricht (1944). *Un coup d'oeil sur la structure du Bassin éocène des Pays-Bas,* C. R. Soc. géol. France (1944), p. 128.

75. E. Vincent, *Etudes sur les Mollusques montiens du poudingue et du tuffeau de Ciply,* Mém. Mus. r. Hist. nat. Belgique, Mém. no. 46 (1930). A. Chavan, work cited note 96, chap. 8.

76. E. Casier, *La faune ichtyologique de l'Yprésien de la Belgique,* Mém. Mus. r. Hist. nat. Belgique, no. 103 (1945).

77. A map showing clearly the distribution of the clayey facies north of Ypres and the sandy facies south of Ypres, in M. Leriche, *L'Yprésien dans le pays compris entre la Sambre et la Meuse,* Bull. Acad. r. Belgique, Cl. Sc. (Dec. 5, 1936).

78. M. Leriche, *Les sables d'Aeltre: leur place dans la classification des assises éocènes du bassin anglo-franco-belge,* Ann. Soc. géol. du Nord, 62 (1937).

79. M. Glibert, *Monographie de la faune malacologique du Bruxellien de Bruxelles,* Mém. Mus. r. Hist. nat. Belgique, no. 53 (1933).

80. M. Glibert, *Faune malacologique des sables de Wemmel,* Mem. Mus. r. Hist. nat. Belgique, no. 78 (1936), no. 85 (1938). M. Leriche, *Les couches du base de Bartonien dans le bassin belge,* Bull. Soc. belge Gèol., 52 (1943). The term Bartonian is used here meaning Ludian.

81. O. von Linstow, *Die Verbreitung der tertiären und diluvialen Meere in Deutschland,* Abh. d. preuss. geol. Landesanst., Heft 87 (1922); paleogeographic maps. A. Bentz, *Tertiär und Diluvium in westphalisch-holländischen Grenzgebiet,* (Zeitschr. deutsch. geol. Ges., 82 (1930). T. Müller, *Das marine Paläozän und Eozän in Norddeutschland und Süd-Skandinavien,* Bornträger, Berlin (1937).

82. See the article by P. Harder cited note 96, chap. 8. J. P. J. Ravn, *Etude sur les Mollusques du Paléocène de Copenhague,* Det. Konigl. Danske Videns Selskab., Biol. Skrif., I, no. 1, Copenhagen (1939).

83. Oedum, *Marint nedre Oligocän i Danmark,* Meded. Dansk. geol. Forening, 9 (1936).

84. K. Gripp, *Ueber das Alttertiär von Hemmoor, ein Beitrag zur Stratigraphie Nordwest-Deutschlands,* 17 Jahresber. Niedersächsischen geol. Ver. Hannover (1924).

85. F. Hecht, *Die Verwertbarkeit der Mikropaläontolgie bei Erdöl-Aufschlussarbeiten im norddeutschen Tertiär und Mesozoikum,* Senckenbergiana, 19, Frankfurt a. M. (1937).

86. K. Staesche, *Die Gliederung des norddeutschen Tertiärs auf Grund von Mikrofossilien,* Jahrb. preuss. geol. Landesanst. f. 1937, 58 (1938). Similar information for the region of Oebisfelde-Fallersleben (Hanover) in H. Hiltermann, *Ein littorales Paläozän in Norddeutschland,* Zeitschr. deutsch. geol. Ges., 93 (1941).

87. W. Wetzel, *Faziesprobleme der mitteleuropäischen Tertiärmeere. 3. Zur Stratigraphie, Sedimentpetrographie und Paläontologie des Alttertiärs von Fehmarn und der Umgegend Kiels,* Zentralbl. f. Min., B (1936).

88. K. Pietsch. *Die Braunkohlen Deutschlands,* Berlin (1925).

89. There, following a Danian sea with *Nautilus danicus,* coming from the west and extending from the Volga to the Urals, an Eocene sea, coming from the north, had brought colder faunas: P. L. Besukov, *Danian Stage of the East European Platform,* Bull. Acad. Sc. URSS., ser. geol. (1936). The Paleogene series is now well known between the Volga and Caucasus, due to its penetration by numerous oil wells, see the guide books of the 17th Inter. Geol. Congress at Moscow (1937). Curious reflections on the European Nummulitic are found in M. T. Lukovic, *The Eocene Molluscan Fauna from the Areas between the Aral Sea and Lake Chalkar and its Importance,* Ann. géol. Péninsule balkanique, 7, 2, Belgrade (1926).

90. A single specimen of *N. laevigatus* was found in a well near Bremen, Wolff, Zeitschr. deutsch. geol. Ges. (1909).

91. K. Andrée, *Der Bernstein und seine Bedeutung in Natur- und Geisteswissenschaften,* etc., 219 p., 51 fig., Gräfe und Unzer, Königsberg i. Preus. (1937).

92. M. Blanckenhorn, *Das Unteroligozän und die Melanientone des mittleren Kurhessen,* Jahrb. preuss. geol. Landesanst. f. 1922, 43 (1923). Farther south, in the Mainz Basin, the Septarienton lies directly over the ancient rocks.

93. A. Steuer, Abhandl. grossherz. hessischen geol. Landesanst., VI, 1 (1912) described a fauna rich in muricides in this basin at Waldböckelheim, near Kreuznach, which he correlated with the Lattorf stage. But, according to the fish fauna, W. Weiler, ibid., VI, 2 (1922), and according to their stratigraphic position (information conveyed by M. W. Wagner), it seems clear that these Waldböchelheim sands are Stampian and belong to the usual *Meeressand* of the Mainz Basin.

94. W. Wenz, *Das Mainzerbecken,* W. Ehrig, Heidelberg (1921). W. Wagner, *Das*

Mainzerbecken, Jahresber. u. Mitt. Oberrheinischen geol. Vereines, n. F., 27 (1938). G. F. Dollfus, Bull. Soc. géol. France (1910), and C. R. Soc. géol. France (Dec. 4, 1922).

95. H. Sindovski, *Sediment und Fauna von Septarienton und Stettiner Sand bei Stettin,* Zentralb. f. Min. B. (1936); *Faziesprobleme der mitteleuropäischen Tertiärmeere. Nr. 1. Pommersches Mitteloligozän,* ibid. (Paleogeographic map).

96. E. Wolk, *Das niederrheinische Mitteloligozän und seine Stellung innerhalb des nordeuropäischen Mitteloligozän,* Zeitschr. deutsch. geol. Ges., 93 (1941); the conclusions of this study have been discussed by W. Klüpfel, *Zur Gliederung und Altersdeutung des Westdeutschen Tertiärs,* ibid., 94 (1942), who believes there was a lacuna representing the middle Oligocene (Stampian) in the Neuwied Basin (?).

97. The Weisenau occurrence has yielded the St. Gérand-le-Puy mammals, typical of the continental Aquitanian, belonging to the top of the Oligocene in the classification adopted here.

98. Perhaps because of the middle Eocene transgressions which caused the maritime climate to predominate over the continental climate.

99. H. Schoeller, *Etudes sur le Sidérolithique du Lot et du Lot-et-Garonne,* Bull. Serv. Carte géol. France, 43, no. 206 (1941).

100. This Landenian is often difficult to distinguish from the Wealdian which has the same facies. See article by M. Leriche, cited note 38, this chap.

101. Buxtorf, Eclogae geol. Helvetiae, 21, no. 2 (1928), p. 325.

102. See p. 16 of Maikovski's work, cited note 114, this chap.

103. B. Gèze, *Contribution à la connaissance des Phosphorites du Quercy,* Bull. Soc. géol. France, 8 (1938). When a rather small cover of lacustrine deposits spread out over the Causses in the vicinity of a gulf, it sealed the fill and thus furnished an upper limit for the age of the fauna: B. Gèze, *Sur les phosphorites du Bas-Languedoc,* ibid., 10 (1940).

104. P. R. Giot, *Contribution à l'étude des terrains tertiaires du Royans (Isère et Drôme),* Trav. Lab. Géol. Univ. Grenoble, 24 (1944).

105. P. de Brun and C. Chatelet, Bull. Soc. géol. France (1923). See also the 2nd edit. of the Avignon sheet of the Carte géol. 1/80,000.

106. Region studied by Ph. Glangeaud and J. Giraud. See also monograph by L. de Launay, Bull. Carte géol. France, no. 147 (1923), and especially one by J. Jung, cited note 33, chap. 1, in which will be found a recent bibliography (up to 1945) which will not be repeated here.

107. R. Lavocat, *Sur l'âge des dépôts lacustres du Bassin de St-Flour et du Bassin de Brioude,* C. R. Acad. Sc., 221 (1945), p. 583.

108. H. Alimen, *Considérations sur l'espèce oligocène* Potamides lamarcki Brongn. *et sur sa répartition en France,* Bull. Soc. géol. France, 18 (1948), p. 97.

109. Insects whose aquatic larvae build themselves tubes or *indusies* with solid particles from the sea bottom on which they live, here with the small shells of hydrobias.

110. See the work by Viret, cited note 19, this chap.

111. The genesis of the phryganid limestone has recently been discussed by J. Hurzeler, *"Karstphänomene" im Phryganidenkalk der Limagne bourbonnaise,* Actes Soc. helvétique Sc. nat. (1941), 121.

112. The relative age of these conglomerates can be estimated, according to an old idea of Bleichers, developed by Kessler, according to the nature of the rock which forms their pebbles. These pebbles are Jurassic for the oldest conglomerates, then Triassic and finally granite, in the most recent conglomerates. For the granite core of the Vosges could not have been laid bare by Oligocene erosion until after its Triassic and Jurassic covering was gone. See note 188, chap. 5.

113. Which are found on the right bank of the Rhine. H. Weber, *Die neuen nordbadischen Erdölbohrungen,* Badische geol. Abh. 7, Karlsruhe (1935). *Eozän und Unteroligozän in den Kraichgauhügeln von Ubstadt und Roth-Malsch südlich Heidelberg,* ibid., 9 (1937).

114. M. Gignoux and C. Hoffmann, *Le Bassin pétrolifère de Péchelbronn, étude géologique,* Bull. Serv. Carte géol. Alsace et Lorraine, 1 (1920). M. Floquet, *Etude sur le gisement de potasse du Haut-Rhin,* Ann. des Mines (1922). W. Wagner, *La géologie des puits des Mines de potasse de la Haute-Alsace,* Mém. Serv. Carte géol. Alsace et Lorraine, no. 1 (1929). *Das Unteroligozän (Sannoisien) im Rheintalgraben unter Berücksichtigung seiner Lagerstätten,* Notizbl. Hessischen geol. Landesanst., Darmstadt, 5, Folge, 19 Heft (1938), with maps and diagrams. V. Maikovski, *Contribution à l'étude paléontologique et stratigraphique de bassin potassique d'Alsace,* Mém. Serv. Carte géol. Alsace et Lorraine, no. 6 (1941). S. Gillet, *La faune oligocène de Péchelbronn,* Bull. Soc. géol. France, 14 (1944). R. Schnaebele, *Monographie géologique du champ pétrolifère de Péchelbronn,* Mém. Serv. Cart. géol. Alsace et Lorraine, no. 7 (1948).

115. F. Quiévreux, *Esquisse du monde vivant sur les rives de la lagune potassique,* Bull. Soc. indus. de Mulhouse (March, 1935).

116. B. Wilser, *Paläogeographische Untersuchungen über das Eozän und Unteroligozän im Oberrheingebiet,* Verh. Naturhist.-Mediz. Ver. zu Heidelberg, n. F., 15 (1923).

117. Which makes probable a lacuna and an emergence in the Sannoisian and Stampian.

118. See L. Meyer, *Etude stratigraphique de terrain oligocène de la Haute-Alsace et du Territoire de Belfort,* Bull. Serv. Carte géol. Alsace et Lorraine, 1, fasc. 3 (1928).

119. Good Paleogene diagrams of northern Switzerland will be found in C. Schmidt, L. Braun, G. Paltzer, M. Muhlberg, P. Christ, F. Jacob, *Die Bohrungen von Buix bei Pruntrut und Allschwill bei Basel,* Beitr. z. Geol. der Schweiz, Geotech. Ser., X Lief. (1924). See especially, E. Baumberger, *Die stampischen Bildungen der Nordschweiz und ihrer Nachbargebiete mit besonderer Berücksichtigung der Molluskenfauna,* Eclogae geol. Helvetiae, 20, no. 4 (1927).

120. These are microforaminifers, used to characterize the horizons in wells. R. Barbier, *Etude micropaléontologique des terrains stampiens du district d'Ohlungen (Bassin de Péchelbronn),* Bull. Serv. Carte géol. Alsace et Lorraine 5 (1938). B. Berndt, *Gliederung und Foraminiferenfauna des Rheintaltertiärs bei Bruchsal,* Mitt. badischen geol. Landesanst., 12 (1938).

121. A. Buxtorf and H. Fröhlicher, *Zur Frage des Zusammenhangs des subalpinen Unter-Stampien-Meeres mit dem Rheintalgraben,* Eclogae geol. Helvetiae, 26, no. 2 (1933). N. Théobald, *Contribution à la Paléontologie du Bassin oligocène du Haut-Rhin et du Territoire de Belfort. Les poissons oligocènes,* Bull. Serv. Carte géol. Alsace et Lorraine, 2, fasc. 2 (1934).

122. S. Gillet and N. Théobald, *Les sables marins de l'Oligocène du Haut-Rhin,* Bull. Serv. Carte géol. Alsace et Lorraine, 3 (1936).

123. N. Théobald, *Les Insectes fossiles de Célas (Gard),* C. R. Acad. Sc. (Jan. 15, 1934).

124. M. Gignoux and L. Moret, *Structure de l'anticlinal de Volx et des Bassins oligocènes de Manosque et de Forcalquier; leurs lignites et leurs roches bitumineuses,* Trav. Lab. Géol. Univ. Grenoble, 15 (1930). J. Goguel, *Révision de la feuille de Forcalquier au 1/80,000,* Bull. Serv. Carte géol. France, no. 190 (1933), with excellent stratigraphic outlines.

125. For more details of the Oligocene of the Aix and Marseille Basins (where it exceeds 1,000 m. thickness), see the publications of Denizot, cited notes 36 and 124, chap. 8.

126. Very detailed descriptions by G. Denizot, Bull. Serv. Carte géol. France, no. 190 (1933), and by F. Catzigras, *L'Aquitanien marin de Carry-le-Rouet,* Impr. Marscillaise, Marseille (1943).

127. M. Gignoux and L. Moret, *L'Oligocène du Bassin du Rhône entre Genève et Seyssel,* Les Etudes rhondaniennes, 15, Lyon (1939). *Sur l'origine des asphaltes du Jura méridional et sur les migrations descendantes des hydrocarbures,* Trav. Lab. Géol. Univ. Grenoble, 14 (1925).

128. J. Viret and J. Hürzeler, *Sur l'âge de la faune de Mammifères de Pyrimont-Challonges,* Bull. Soc. géol. France, 7 (1937).

129. M. Dreyfuss, *Contribution à l'étude de l'Oligocène inf. de la Haute-Saône,* Bull. Soc. géol. France, 4 sér., 26 (1926).

130. H. Vincienne, *Decouverte de Foraminiferes non remaniés dans le calcaire lacustre oligocène de Coligny,* C. R. Soc. géol. France (Apr. 4, 1938).

131. Y. Milon, *Existence d'une formation marine éocène dans la dépression de Toulven (Finistère),* C. R. Acad. Sc. (May 6, 1929).

132. C. R. Acad. Sc., Mar. 24, 1924. See also, by the same author, *Notes sur les blocs de calcaires à Nummulites du polygone de Gâvres (Morbihan),* Bull. Soc. géol. et min. de Bretagne, 5 (1924).

133. C. R. Soc. géol. France (June 8, 1925).

134. S. Durand, *Présence de Lutétien dans la presqu'île de Quiberon (Morbihan),* C. R. Acad. Sc., 223 (1946), p. 1161.

135. R. Abrard, *Les lambeaux éocènes des côtes méridonales de Bretagne,* Bull. Mus. nat. Hist. nat., 2 sér., 13, no. 3 (1941); revision and map of all the Ypresian and Lutetian occurrences.

136. This famous occurrence was added by J. Boussac to his Auversian, an opinion accepted by L. and J. Morellet. We leave it in the upper Lutetian, with R. Abrard, *Comparaison des faunes continentales de Bois-Gouët, du Cotentin et du Bassin de Paris,* Bull. Soc. géol. et min. Bretagne, 8, 1927, Rennes (1930), and *Remarques sur la faune malacologique de l'Eocène de la Loire-inférieure,* C. R. Soc. géol. France (Mar. 2, 1942).

137. M. Cossmann, *Monographie illustrée des mollusques oligocéniques des environs de Rennes,* Jr. de Conch., 64 (1919).

138. R. Milon, C. R. Soc. géol. France (June 16, 1930), noted marine foraminifers in these formations south of Rennes, considered lacustrine up to the present. But it must not be forgotten that these little shells are worked over with the greatest ease. Thus, Italian geologists have described in the fluviatile Quaternary of the Roman coasts, quantities of foraminifers coming from the Pliocene marine marls.

139. It is hardly necessary to remark that this great paleogeographic unit is a heritage from the Cretaceous. The Nummulitic Gulf of Aquitaine descends, in fact, from the Pyrénées-Provençal Gulf, the vicissitudes of which were studied in the Upper Cretaceous.

140. See Fig. 121, borrowed from the memoir of J. Blayac, *Aperçu de la répartition, des faciès et du synchronisme des terrains tertiaires de Bassin de l'Aquitaine au N de la Garonne et jusqu'à Castres,* Liv. jub. du Cent. de la Soc. géol. France (1930). For local descriptions, F. Daguin, *Itinéraires géologiques dans l'Aquitaine occidentale,* Impr. Delmas, Bordeaux (1937). For the paleontology, M. Cossmann, *Synopsis illustré des Mollusques de l'Eocène et de l'Oligocène,* Mém. Soc. géol. France, Paléont., 55 (1921). Especially, F. Daguin, *L'Aquitaine occidentale,* Géologie regionale de la France, vol. 5., Hermann, Paris (1948).

141. A. Fabre, *Description géologique des terrains tertiaires du Médoc et essai sur la structure tectonique du département de la Gironde,* 533 p., 57 fig., 17 pl., Impr. Drouillard, Bordeaux (1939).

142. H. Douvillé, *L'Eocène inférieur en Aquitaine et dans les Pyrénées,* Mem. Serv. Carte géol. France (1919).

143. R. Abrard, *Etude stratigraphique et paléontologique du calcaire de St-Palais et de Blaye,* Bull. Soc. géol. France, 5 sér., 1 (1931).

144. F. Daguin, *Considérations générales sur le Stampien marin du Bassin de l'Aquitaine,* Pub. Univ. Bordeaux, no. 2 (1938).

145. A well at Agen has traversed 280 m. of Oligocene molasse, than 25 m. of continental red clays (lower Oligocene or Eocene?) and finally reached the Jurassic. That clearly demonstrates that the marine Eocene did not reach this region. See L. Mengaud, *Sur quelques sondages profonds dans le Bassin de l'Aquitaine,* Bull. Soc. Hist. nat. Toulouse, 54 (1926).

146. Meticulously studied by Vasseur, Repelin, Blayac.

147. M. Richard, *Contribution à l'étude du Bassin d'Aquitaine; les gisements de Mammifères tertiaires,* Mém. Soc. géol. France, 24 (1946), 380 p., 52 fig.

148. Ch. Depéret has confirmed for me this extremely important fact. This fauna was studied by J. Repelin.

149. In fact, the great well of Abatilles, near Arcachon, which found an artesian horizon in the Lutetian at 465 m. depth, crossed a continuous series of fossiliferous marine beds extending from the Lutetian to the Helvetian. But there are no longer the deep-water, marly facies of Biarritz; therefore this is north of the axis of the trough. See P. Viennot, *Sur le sondage des Abatilles, près d'Arcachon* C. R. Acad. Sc. (July 21, 1924).

150. H. Douvillé and G. O'Gorman, *L'Eocène de Béarn,* Bull. Soc. géol. France, 4th sér., 29 (1929).

151. F. Daguin, *Les rides et les accidents anticlinaux du centre de l'Aquitaine occidentale,* Bull. Serv. Carte géol. France, no. 207, 43 (1941).

152. J. Cuvillier, *Relations du Crétacé et de l'Eocène inf. en Aquitaine méridionale,* C. R. Soc. géol. France (Dec. 3, 1945).

153. Nummulitic horizons of the lower Eocene have also been pointed out in the Chalosse by J. Cuvillier and J. Dupouy-Camet, *Stratigraphie du Crétacé sup. et de l'Eocène inf. dans la Chalosse de Montfort (Landes),* Bull. Soc. géol. France, 16 (1946).

154. Article by F. Daguin, cited note 144, this chap. According to Dollfuss, certain occurrences of the Chalosse, especially that of St. Geours, 15 km. west of Dax, are more recent and represent a marine Chattian, in which the last nummulites are associated with the first lepidocyclines. G. F. Dollfuss, *L'Oligocène sup. marin dans le Bassin de l'Adour,* Bull. Soc. géol. France, 17 (1917).

155. Y. Gubler and J. Pomeyrol, *Nouvelles observations stratigraphiques dans l'Eocène au Sud de Pau (B. P.),* Bull. Soc. géol. France, 16 (1946). They insist upon the Ypresian transgression.

156. See note 2, this chap.

157. M. L. Moret gave me valuable assistance in writing this section.

158. F. Traub, *Geologische und paläontologische Bearbeitung der Kreide und des Tertiärs im östlichen Rupertiwinkel nördlich von Salzburg,* Paläontographica, 88, Abt. A (1938); *Die helvetische Kreide-Eozän-Serie des Haunsberges nördlich von Salzburg,* Zeitschr. deutsch. geol. Ges., 90 (1938).

159. This lower Eocene is represented by sandy marls contained between an equally marly-sandy Cretaceous and a middle Eocene with large nummulites identical to that of the adjacent, classic occurrence of Kressenberg, which itself is prolonged in Switzerland, south of Zurich, by the famous Einsiedeln occurrence, recently restudied by A. Jeannet.

160. W. Leupold, *Zur Stratigraphie der Flyschbildungen zwischen Linth und Rhein,* Eclogae geol. Helvetiae, 30 (1937). P. Arni, *Ueber die Nummuliten und Gliederung des Untereocäns,* ibid. 32 (1939). But these specific determinations are questioned by C. B. M. Caudri, *Beitrag zur Altersbestimmung des Flyches der Niesendecke,* ibid., 30 (1937).

161. J. Pilloud, *Contribution à l'étude stratigraphique des Voirons (Préalpes externes, Haute-Savoie),* Archives Sc. phys. et nat., Geneva, 5 per., 18 (1936).

162. In the vicinity of St. Vallier-de-Thiey, northwest of Grasse (Fig. 125), L. Maurice, C. R. Acad. Sc. (Jan. 28, 1924) collected, in beds overlain by limestones with large nummulites known in the region, a whole faunule of small nummulites which he submitted to H. Douvillé. In accordance with this apparent stratigraphic location, this eminent specialist in Tertiary foraminifers recognized at once a series of species characteristic of the lower Eocene, a stage which he had long been studying in Aquitaine and the Pyrenees. Having noticed that the beds with small nummulites were in their turn overlying a formation of volcanic blocks known as Miocene, I suspect that the Tertiary series must here be reversed tectonically. In fact, A. F. de Lapparent, *Le Nummulitique de St. Vallier-de-Thiey,* Bull. Soc. géol. France, 4 (1934) to whose attention I have referred this unusual lower Eocene, had no trouble in demonstrating that it was actually a matter of the Upper Eocene. This little mischance is very instructive, for it shows how cautious the most conscientious specialists must be in according a precise stratigraphic significance to species of the small nummulites which they determine, espe-

cially when it is a question of unseparated specimens, observable only in thin sections.

163. M. Mainguy, *La transgression nummulitique à l'Ouest du Mercantour,* Bull. Soc. géol. France, 7 (1937).

164. According to J. Boussac, another gulf advanced across the external zone to the vicinity of Allos, where, in the two occurrences of Lauzanier and Noncière, appearing just under the front of the Ubaye nappes, he found a few isolated individuals of *Nummulites perforatus.* But, according to M. Mainguy, these large nummulites are here reworked, in a fauna which otherwise is Priabonian (correcting the map Fig. 125).

165. A general synthesis of the Nummulitic of Savoy, with much new information, in L. Moret, *Géologie du Massif des Bornes et des klippes préalpines des Annes et des Sulens (Haute-Savoie),* Mém. Soc. géol. France, n. s., no. 22 (1934).

166. R. Barbier, C. R. Soc. géol. France (Feb. 7, 1944).

167. M. Gignoux, *Méditations sur la tectonique d'écoulement par gravité,* Trav. Lab. Géol. Univ. Grenoble, 27 (1948).

168. At Bauduen (Var) between Digne and Draguignan, a mandible of a Sparnacian mammal was recently found in the limestones with bythinias overlying the sands and clays of the lower Eocene: P. Teilhard de Chardin and A. F. de Lapparent, *Sur la découverte d'un rongeur du genre* Paramys *dans l'Eocène inf. de Provence,* C. R. Soc. géol. France (Feb. 5, 1931).

169. We come to this question again in connection with the Swiss Miocene. See p. 514 and note 28, chap. 10.

170. This occurrence, a connecting link between Castellane and Dévoluy, was discovered by E. Haug and recently restudied by P. Lory and A. F. de Lapparent, *Remarques sur le Nummulitique du Dévoluy et du Champsaur,* Bull. Soc. géol. France, 7 (1937), p. 359.

171. A rhinocerid characteristic of the Sannoisian, *Acerotherium filholi,* was recently reported by L. Moret, Trav. Lab. Géol. Univ. Grenoble, 24 (1944).

172. With the large natica of Gap, *Natica vapincana,* ancestor of the *N. crassatina* of the Parisian Stampian.

173. From the Taveyannaz Alp, in the Diablerets Massif in Switzerland.

174. De Quervain, *Petrographie und Geologie der Taveyannazgesteine,* Schweizerische Min. Petr. Mitt. (1928).

175. W. Schroeder, *La brèche du Chablais entre Giffre et Dranse et les roches éruptives des Gets,* Archives Sc. phys. et nat., Geneva, 21 (1939). M. Vuagnat, *Les grès de Taveyannaz du Val d'Illiez et leurs rapports avec les roches éruptives des Gets,* Bull. suisse Min. et Pétr. 23 (1923).

176. M. Vuagnat, C. R. Soc. Phys. Hist. nat. Genève, 64, no. 2, pp. 33, 36 & 43.

177. M. Lugeon, *Sur l'âge du grès du Taveyannaz,* Eclogae geol. Helvetiae, 18 (1923). L. Moret, *Sur la découverte d'Orthophragmines dans les grès de Taveyannaz du Massif du Platé (Haute-Savoie), et sur ses consequences,* C. R. Acad. Sc. (Jan. 21, 1924).

178. R. Barbier, *L'âge du Flysch des Aiguilles d'Arves et du grès d'Annot,* C. R. Soc. géol. France (Dec. 20, 1943 and Feb. 7, 1944).

179. S. Deb, *Contribution à l'étude stratigraphique et pétrographique des roches tertiaires des Alpes-Maritimes,* Mém. Soc. géol. France, 36 (1938). L. W. Collet, J. W. Schroeder, E. Pictet, *De l'âge oligocène des calcaires à Nummulites de Barmaz (Parautochtone, région de Champéry, Valais, Suisse),* C. R. Soc. Phys. Hist. nat., Geneva, 63, no. 1 (1946). J. Schroeder and E. Pictet, *De quelques Foraminifères trouvés dans les grès de Taveyannaz et de l'âge de ces derniers,* Archives Sc. phys. et nat., Suppl., 28, Geneva (1946); region of Lake Thun.

180. This small shell, so often cited, actually belongs, not to an annelid, but to a vermetid (gastropod).

181. *Bulimus subcylindricus,* large sinistral form characteristic of the upper Lutetian of Provence (L. Moret). The lacustrine beds extend into the Diablerets Massif, in Switzerland.

182. A term of the German-Swiss dialect, meaning, "terrain which slips."

183. G. Götzinger and H. Becker, *Neue Fährtenstudien im ostalpinen Flysch,* Senckenbergiana, 16 (1934).

184. Remember that farther east the Carpathian Flysch unquestionably includes the Cretaceous and the same is true for the Flysch of the Austrian Alps. See G. Götzinger and H. Becker, *Zur geologischen Gliederung des Wienerwaldflysches,* Jahr. geol. Bundesanst. 82 (1932).

185. M. Gignoux, L. Moret and D. Schneegans, *Le problème du Flysch calcaire dans la région frontale des nappes de l'Embrunais-Ubaye,* Ass. fr. pour l'Avance. des Sc., Congrès de Chambéry (1933); *Observations géologiques dans le Bassin de la Haute-Durance entre Gap et la frontière italienne,* Trav. Lab. Géol. Univ. Grenoble, 18 (1935).

186. L. Moret, *Sur la presence de* Nummulites incrassatus *dans le "Flysch calcaire" des environs d'Orcières (nappe du Flysch de l'Embrunais), et sur la répartition des faciès du Nummulitique dans le géosynclinal alpin,* C. R. Soc. géol. France (Feb. 4, 1934).

187. Very near there, under the front of the Morgon scales, J. Boussac had attributed to his calcareous Flysch, a thick series of calcareous shales in which we now see an Oxfordian-Upper Cretaceous comprehensive series, constituting the ultra-Dauphinois scale of the Batterie du Châtelard. Such uncertainties will surely seem very surprising to stratigraphers of the Parisian Tertiary.

188. H. Schoeller, *La nappe de l'Embrunais au Nord de l'Isère,* Bull. Serv. Carte géol. France, no. 175 (1929).

189. This is, perhaps, the root of the nappe of the Chablais breccia (?).

190. On the relations between the Flysch facies and the tectonics, see the interesting study of E. Kraus, *Ueber den Schweizer Flysch,* Eclogae geol. Helvetiae, 25 (1932).

191. In like manner, the end of the history of the geosyncline of the Hercynian Chain was marked by a Dinantian (Culm) with Flysch facies (Devon, Morvan, Vosges).

192. At Rome, the Pliocene became 900 m. thick (see p. 578).

193. Bibliography up to 1923, in *Trattato di Geologia,* by C. F. Parona. Note especially, R. Fabiani, *Il Paleogene veneto,* Mem. Ist. geol. Univ. Padova, 3 (1915); *Il Terziario del Trentino,* id., 6 (1922); G. Dainelli, *L'Eocene Friulano, Mem. geogr.,* Firenze (1915).

194. This marly facies of the Priabonian, very general in all the Tertiary Chains, is found especially in Hungary. It consists of the Budapest marls with *Clavulina szaboi* (small foraminifer). The Stampian is represented there by 300–500 m. of clays. J. Noszky, *Die Molluskenfauna des Kisceller Tones (Rupelien) aus der Umgebung von Budapest. I Teil, Lamellibranchiata,* Annales Musei nat. hungarici, 32 (1939); *Die Molluskenfauna des oberen Cattiens von Eger in Ungarn,* ibid., 30 (1936), a very interesting study of the relation of this Chattian fauna to the Oligocene and Miocene faunas.

195. A fine paleontologic monograph by S. Venzo, *La fauna cattiano delle glauconie bellunesi,* Mem. Ist. geol. Univ. Padova, 13 (1937), 12 pl.; note the *Pecten praescabriusculus* considered as characteristic (?) of the Rhône upper Burdigalian; *La presenza del Cattiano a Molluschi nel Trevigiano e nel Bassanese,* Bol. Soc. geol. ital., 57 (1938).

196. The recent syntheses by R. Staub, *Zur tektonischen Analyse des Apennins,* Vierteljahreschr. Natur. Ges. in Zurich, 78 (1933) and by P. de Wijkerslooth, *Bau und Entwicklung des Apennins,* Geol. Inst., Amsterdam (1934) are still very hypothetical. The interesting article by R. Teichmüller, *Der Apenninflysch und seine Probleme,* Nachr. Ges. d. Wiss. zu Göttingen, Math.-Phys. Kl., IV, 28 (1932) is much more prudent.

197. T. Lipparini, *Calcare a Nummuliti e Alveoline del Luteziano negli argilloscisti dell'Apennino bolognese,* Boll. Soc. geol. ital., 55 (1936); a very clear picture of parallelisms between the Tertiary series of the different structural units, the autochthon, the Ligurides and the Toscanides.

198. F. Sacco, *Nuovi dati di fatto riguardo l'età degli argilloscisti ofiolitiferi dell' Apennino,* Atti Acad. Sc., Torino, 64 (1928).

199. The most recent study is that by L. Perretti, *I graniti della formazione argilloscistosa ofiolitifera dell'Apennino settentrionale*, Boll. Soc. geol. ital., 53 (1934).

200. O. Renz, *Stratigraphische und mikropalaeontologische Untersuchung der Scaglia (Obere Kreide-Tertiär) im zentralen Apennin*, Eclogae geol. Helvetiae, 29 (1936). The foraminiferal scales given here have been used in many similar works in other regions; diagrams show the distinctions between three facies provinces, northern and southern Umbria and the Abruzzi.

201. We mention only P. Principi, *Intorno alla subdivisione dei terreni del Terziario inferiore e medio dell'Italia centrale*, Boll. Soc. geol. ital., 46 (1927); *I terreni terziari nei Monti Sabini meridionali*, ibid., 53 (1934); *Nuove osservazioni intorno alla presenza dell'Oligocene nell'Italia centrale*, Mem. Soc. geol. ital., 1 (1932); *Intorno all'età della Scaglia cinerea dell'Apennino centrale*, Rendic. R. Accad. Lincei, 17 (1933). This last article contains a very suggestive stratigraphic scheme.

202. P. Principi, *I terreni terziari della conca aquilana*, Boll. Soc. geol. ital., 54 (1935); continuous series from the lower Eocene to the upper Miocene; the Oligocene contains small nummulites, orthophragmines and lepidocyclines all at the same time. Also, same author, *Alcune osservazioni sui terreni terziari del bacino di Sulmona*, ibid., 55 (1936).

203. P. Principi, *Alcune osservazioni sulla Geologica della media valle del Sangro (Abruzzi meridionali)*, Boll. Soc. geol. ital., 57 (1938).

204. The memoir by F. Gomez Llueca, *Los Numulitidos de España*, Museo nac. Ciencias nat., Madrid (1929) unfortunately does not contain any stratigraphic information.

205. A. Robaux, *Sur l'existence de l'Eocène sup. et de l'Oligocène dans la série du Flysch du Sud de la Province de Cadix*, C. R. Acad. Sc. (Feb. 18, 1935).

206. See work by Dalloni, cited note 153, chap. 5.

207. See A. Marin, *Investigaciones en la cuenca potasica de Cataluña*, Bol. Inst. geol. de España, 44 (1923); *La potasa*, ibid., 48 (1926).

208. A curious discovery by G. Astre, *Nummulites remaniées dans la Pliocène de Neffiach en Roussillon*, Bull. Soc. géol. France, 7 (1937), has now proved that there must have been a Nummulitic covering over the Primary axial zone of the eastern Pyrenees. That shows once again how prudent we should be in our paleogeographic reconstructions.

209. Royo y Gomez, *Edad de las formaziones yesiferas del Terciario iberico*, Bol. R. Soc. esp. Hist. nat., 26 (1926); *Tectonica del Terciario continental iberico*, C. R. of the 14th Internat. Geol. Cong. at Madrid (1927). The latter article contains a correlation table of all the continental formations of the Douro, Ebro, Tagus, and other basins.

210. Recently G. Richter and R. Teichmüller, *Die Entwicklung der keltiberischen Ketten*, Abh. Ges. d. Wiss. zu Göttingen, Math.-Phys. Kl., III F., H. 7, Berlin (1933) ask if there was not marine Eocene there.

211. L. Moret and J. Flandrin have very kindly helped me write this section, several paragraphs of which were even literally written by the latter.

212. We refer only to the works of Savornin and L. Glangeaud cited note 172, chap. 7. However a complete bibliography will be found in the Memoir by J. Flandrin, *Contribution à l'étude stratigraphique de Nummulitique algérien*, Thèse Sc., Paris (1948), 340 p., 90 fig., 8 pl., which represents, for North Africa, the equivalent of the Thesis by J. Boussac for the Alpine Nummulitic.

213. Nevertheless, the base of the Eocene, in southeastern Constantine and the region of the Tunisian phosphates, contains a fauna whose age R. Lafitte, *L'Eocène dans l'Aurès oriental*, C. R. Acad. Sc. (Dec. 26, 1934) has shown to be Montian. Moreover, these marls contain an abundant microfauna, similar to that of the Midway in the United States, which characterizes the transition beds between the Cretaceous and the Tertiary.

214. J. Flandrin, *Quelques traits de la paléontologie algérienne à l'Eocène moyen*, C. R. Acad. Sc. (August 5, 1935).

215. M. Dalloni, *Les terrains oligocènes dans l'Ouest de l'Algérie*, Bull. Soc. géol. France, 4 sér., 16 (1916).

216. See works of Daguin, Lacoste, Moret, Roch, previously cited.

217. P. Fallot and L. Doncieux, *L'âge du Flysch de la périphérie de la Chaine calcaire du Rif*, C. R. Acad. Sc. (Jan. 2, 1935). This note contains a small geologic map of the Rif.

218. L. Moret, *Compléments à la stratigraphie de la zone subatlasique méridionale de l'Atlas de Marrakech*, C. R. Soc. géol. France (Dec. 18, 1933).

219. J. Cuvillier, *Révision du Nummulitique égyptien*, Thèse Sc., Paris (1930), Mém. Inst. d'Egypte, 16; we turn to this important work for the bibliography. On the Nummulitic of the Cyrenaica, see articles by G. Stefanini and M. Marchetti in vols. 53 (1934) and 54 (1935) of the Boll. della Soc. geol. ital.

220. J. Cuvillier, *Les Kurkurstufe (sic) dans le désert libyque et leur position stratigraphique*, C. R. Acad. Sc. (Dec. 3, 1934).

221. M. I. Faris, *The Contact of the Cretaceous and Eocene Rocks in the Taramsa-Tukh Area (Quena: Upper Egypt)*, Bull. Inst. Egypte, 28, Cairo (1947).

222. J. Cuvillier, *L'Eocène de la région de Suez et ses rapports avec le Crétacé sup.*, Bull. Soc. géol. France, 11 (1941); *Le passage du Crétacé à l'Eocène dans la région de Suez*, C. R. Acad. Sc. (April 28, 1941).

223. G. Andrew and J. Cuvillier, *Découverte de l'Oligocène marin dans la région de Borg-el-Arab*, C. R. Acad. Sc., Jan. 17 (1938). J. Cuvillier, *Découverte de Lépidocyclines dans l'Oligocène d'Egypte*, ibid. (Feb. 28, 1938); mentions all the marine Oligocene occurrences between Tunisia and Syria.

224. J. Cuvillier, *L'Oligocène du Gebel Khashab (Désert libyque)*, C. R. Acad. Sc. (Feb. 26, 1940.)

225. Monograph on a Jacksonian fauna in L. B. Kellum, *Paleontology and Stratigraphy of the Castle Hayne and Trent Marls in North Carolina*, U. S. Geol. Surv., Prof. Pap. 143 (1926).

226. C. W. Cooke, *Geology of the Coastal Plain of South Carolina*, Bull. U. S. Geol. Sur. (1936).

227. R. Rutsch, *Die stratigraphische Bedeutung der Venericardia planicosta und ihre Verwandten*, Eclogae geol. Helvetiae, 29 (1936). A. Chavan, C. R. Soc. géol. France (May 18, 1936) even concedes that the true *V. planicosta* is found in America.

228. Bibliography and paleogeographic maps in W. Staub, *Zur Entstehungsgeschichte des Golfes von Mexico*, Eclogae geol. Helvetiae (24, 1931).

229. R. E. Grim, *The Eocene Sediments of Mississippi*, Miss. geol. Surv., Bull. 30 (1936).

230. H. Douvillé, *Les couches à Orbitoïdes de l'Amerique du Nord*, C. R. Acad. Sc. (Aug. 12, 1918).

231. M. Leriche has just confirmed this by the study of fish faunas: M. Leriche, *Le synchronisme des formations éocènes marines des deux côtés de l'Atlantique, d'après leurs faunes ichtyologiques*, C. R. Acad. Sc. (April 22, 1940).

232. C. W. Cooke, *Correlation of the Eocene Formations in Mississippi and Alabama*, U. S. Geol. Surv., Prof. Pap. 143 (1926).

233. J. Gardner and E. Bowles, *The Venericardia Planicosta Group in the Gulf Province*, U. S. Geol. Surv., Prof. Pap. 189-F (1939).

234. Mrs. K. van Winkle Palmer, *The Claibornian Scaphopoda, Gastropoda and Dibranchiata Cephalopoda of the Southern United States*, Bull. Amer. Pal., 7, no. 32, 648 p., 90 pl., Ithaca (1937).

235. B. C. Renick, *The Jackson Group and the Catahoula and Oakville Formations in a part of the Texas Gulf Coastal Plain*, Univ. Texas Bull. no. 3619, Austin (1936).

236. C. W. Cooke, *The Correlation of the Vicksburg Group*, U. S. Geol. Surv., Prof. Pap. 133 (1923).

237. H. Douvillé, *Les Orbitoïdes de l'île de la Trinité*, C. R. Acad. Sc. (Aug. 2, 1915 and May 29, 1917). A. Tobler, *Die Jacksonstufe (Priabonien) in Venezuela und Trinidad*, Eclogae geol. Helvetiae, 17 (1922); *Geology of the Republic of Haiti*, Geol. Surv. of Haiti, Port-au-Prince (1924). C. Schuchert, *Historical Geology of the Antillean-Caribbean* Region, 811 p., 16 pl., 107 fig., J. Wiley and Sons, New York (1936). See

especially A. Senn, "Palaeogene of Barbados and its Bearing on History and Structure of Antillean-Caribbean Region" (Bull. Amer. Ass. Petrol. Geol., 24, 1940), with a complete bibliography and stratigraphic diagrams.

238. These large foraminifers are likewise found in the Nummulitic of Panama. On the Tertiary of Ecuador and Peru, a brief synthesis and recent bibliography in M. A. Olsson, *Introduction à la géologie du Nord-Ouest de Pérou et du Sud-Ouest de l'Equateur,* trans. D. Schneegans and J. de Vries, Ann. Off. des Combust. liquides (1939), no. 3.

239. On the same question, see also T. W. Vaughan, "American and European Tertiary Corals," Bull. Geol. Soc. Amer., 35 (1924).

240. B. L. Clark," The Marine Tertiary of the West Coast of the United States; its Sequence, Paleogeography and the Problem of Correlation," Journ. of Geol., 29 (1921). B. L. Clark and H. E. Vokes, "Summary of Marine Eocene Sequence of Western North America," Bull. Geol. Soc. Amer., 47, no. 6 (1936), a synchronism with Europe. The affinities of the faunas of California and of the Paris Basin are so great that the authors suggest migrations of larval forms carried by currents. F. E. Turner, *Stratigraphy and Molluscs of the Eocene of Western Oregon,* Geol. Soc. Amer., Spec. Pap., no. 10 (1938), 130 p., 22 pl. C. E. Weaver, "Correlation of the Marine Cenozoic Formation of Western North America," Bull. Geol. Soc. Amer., 55 (1944).

241. E. H. Wood, etc., "Nomenclature and Correlation of the North America Continental Tertiary," Bull. Geol. Soc. Amer., 52 (1941).

242. And comparable to the Oligocene Basins of the Middle European zone. Glacial(?) Eocene formations have been described in southern Colorado by W. W. Atwood, Journ. of Geol., 25 (1917).

243. For more details, see the classic work of H. F. Osborn, *The Age of Mammals,* New York, Macmillan (1910). We mention also L. Joleaud, *La vie aux temps tertiaires et quaternaires,* Coll. A. Colin, Paris (1924), and the work by Boule and Piveteau (1935) cited note 3, Introduction.

Chapter Ten

The Neogene

I. Generalities

We already know that almost everywhere a very general regression separates the Oligocene from the Neogene. The beginning of the Neogene thus is marked by a transgression, called the Miocene. Then comes a new general regression, followed by a much less important transgression called the Pliocene. Finally a last regression brings us to the beginning of the Quaternary.

Thus, on the whole[1] and for almost all the regions of Europe, the Neogene is divided into two successive sedimentary cycles, the one encased in the other, the older corresponding to the Miocene, the more recent to the Pliocene (Fig. 135).

As in the Nummulitic, these transgressions are dependent on three great marine domains, the North Sea, the Atlantic, and the Mediterranean (Fig. 133).

1st. The Neogene North Sea was never as extensive as that of the Nummulitic. It definitely ended the invasion of the Paris Basin and it did no more than nibble on the English, Belgian, Dutch and German coasts. The fauna inhabiting that sea had a very different character from that of southern Europe, so different that it is almost impossible to establish a precise correlation of deposits with those of the Mediterranean regions. There is, then, a northern province, separated from the Atlantic, at least at certain periods, by an emerged land corresponding approximately to the site of the Pas-du-Calais. So the Neogene of the North Sea Basin will be studied entirely separately.

2nd. The Atlantic pushed gulfs into France in eastern Brittany and in Aquitania. The faunas are not essentially different from those of the Mediterranean, which in fact communicated widely with the Atlantic through southern Spain, under conditions which we shall describe.

3rd. Lastly, the best studied and most interesting Neogene deposits are related to the Mediterranean. We know that the great Alps had already risen by the beginning of the Neogene. The transgressions were thus restricted to the circumference of this chain, in the depressed region which today still follows

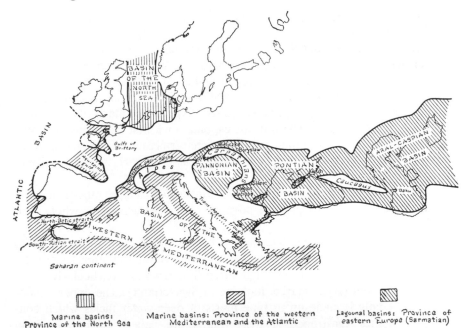

FIG. 133. *Map of marine or lagoonal basins and major faunal provinces in Europe toward the end of the middle Miocene (after E. Haug and A. Andrussov).*

N. B. This sketch, intended only to locate the different basins, is not a paleogeographic map: the heavy lines represent the approximate maximum extent of the Miocene seas in western Europe and the Sarmatian lagoons in eastern Europe.

its outer margin and which we have called the peri-Alpine depression. Moreover, at the beginning of the middle Miocene, all the eastern part of the Neogene Mediterranean was isolated from the rest, and, transformed into an inland sea, acquired a special fauna. This is the Eastern Mediterranean province whose history deserves a chapter to itself.

1. *The Marine Faunas and Mediterranean Stages*

From the beginning of the Neogene, the fauna of the Atlantic and Mediterranean regions appears as the mother-fauna of that in the present-day Mediterranean. Not only living genera but even living species appear in great numbers. So, it is a particularly attractive and instructive study for stratigraphers to follow the transformations which gradually lead us to the present fauna.

Even more than in the Nummulitic, it becomes impossible to give lists of characteristic forms. We shall merely mention the most important. We shall call attention especially to the pectinids,[2] which here play a role of the first order because of their abundance and the stratigraphic significance of many of their species. The same is true for the echinoids.[3] *Clypeaster, Scutella,* and *Echinolampas* are especially abundant in the Miocene in the sandy or organic facies. In the Pliocene, only *Echinolampas* and *Clypeaster* persist, but the latter quit our seas in the upper Pliocene, while *Echinolampas* still survived in the lower Quaternary.

A. Miocene Faunas and Stages.   A first faunal unit is constituted by the Mediterranean Miocene. A series of stages are usually distinguished in it whose definitions are rather stratigraphic and local, related to transgressions or to facies rather than to true transformations of the faunal assemblage.

We agreed to leave the *Aquitanian* stage (type—the faluns of Aquitania, p. 471) in the Oligocene, where it corresponds to a first beginning of transgression. But it contains a certain number of characteristic marine shells, which do not survive the stage, so that by classing it as Oligocene, we give unity to the Miocene fauna.

Thus, the Miocene begins with the *Burdigalian* (type: the Bordeaux faluns), which marks a progressive advance of the sea across the whole peri-Alpine depression.

In the *Vindobonian* (type: Vienna Basin, Austria) local transgressions, to be described later (Lower Dauphiné, intra-Alpine Basin of Vienna) were still occurring. The lower part of this stage, often sandy, is more particularly designated as *Helvetian* (type: marine molasse of Switzerland). The upper Vindobonian frequently is made up of blue marls of deep-water facies which contain pleurotomes (gastropods); these marls are called Tortonian (from Tortona, Piedmont), but this is scarcely more than a facies.

This Miocene sedimentary cycle always ends, in all western Europe and North Africa, with a period of emergence, with which are associated the continental formations designated, incorrectly enough as we shall see, as *Pontian* (from Pont-Euxin, latin name of the Black Sea) and for which we know no certain marine equivalent.[4]

Thus, the series that can be called normal for the Mediterranean Miocene includes the Burdigalian, the Vindobonian and the Pontian. During this whole period, the general character of the marine fauna remains the same.[5] A fairly important number of species are found living in the present Mediterranean, many species are extinct, and lastly a number of forms survive today in warmer waters, either in the Indian seas or especially on the coast of western Africa. For at the beginning of the Miocene the folding of the Alpine Chain cut in two the ancient Mesogean sea, thus suspending communication between the Mediterranean and the Indian Ocean.

We already know that the history of the seas in eastern Europe was very different. Beginning with the upper Vindobonian or Tortonian, it appears that the whole domain of the western Mediterranean was emergent. On the other hand, in the southern part of eastern Europe, where today the Black Sea and the Caspian Sea are located, enormous areas remained under water. This old Eastern Mediterranean, thus isolated from the open seas, was more or less freshened by the contributions of great rivers. The faunas of these lake-seas rapidly changed to the lagoonal or inland-sea type. Thus the normal marine Tortonian is overlain by a *Sarmatian* (from the country of the Sarmates, in southern Russia) containing particular species of cerithids, mactrids, and trochids (*Ervilia*). Above that, the fauna becomes still more Caspian, with large congerias and abnormal species of *Cardium*. This is the true type of the *Pontian* stage, in which the assemblage of the present Caspian fauna already appears.

B. Pliocene Faunas and Stages. Two successive marine faunas correspond to the Pliocene:[6]

1st. That of the early Pliocene differs from the Miocene fauna through the appearance and particularly the disappearance of numerous species. Already the very great majority of living Mediterranean species are found. Added to these are a fair number of extinct forms and others now living only on the western coast of Africa. Thus the marine faunas, and even more clearly, the continental floras prove that the climate at that period was notably warmer than it is today.

This early Pliocene is seen under two principal facies, in which the faunas naturally differ. A clayey facies, or *Plaisancian* (type from Plaisance, northern Italy), is relatively deep-water, quite similar to the Tortonian facies of the Miocene, and like it remarkable for its abundance of large pleurotomes. The other facies is sandy or *Astian* (type from Asti, Piedmont), more littoral, with many large pelecypods. As the two facies are usually superposed, two successive stages are often made of them.

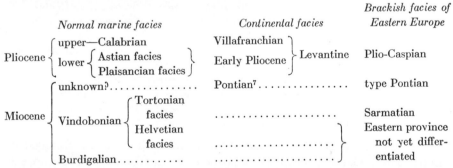

2nd. A second marine fauna corresponds to the upper Pliocene. It is actually almost identical to the present Mediterranean fauna, from which it differs only by the presence of rare extinct species, inherited from the early Pliocene, and by the appearance of a few forms, still very rare, unknown in the early Pliocene and living today in colder seas (for example, *Cyprina islandica*). The stage name *Calabrian* is given to this marine type of the upper Pliocene, as it is especially developed in Italy. But, usually, the upper Pliocene is represented by continental alluvium, called the *Villafranchian* stage (from Villafranca of Asti, Piedmont).

During this time, in the isolated eastern Mediterranean, the fauna continued to develop quite independently. Corresponding to the Pliocene is a stage which can be called *Plio-Caspian,* whose deposits stretch from the Black Sea to the Aral. The fauna, developed in place from the Pontian fauna, seems to be the direct ancestor of that living at present in the Caspian. Finally, on the edge of this eastern Mediterranean were great lakes populated by freshwater shells belonging to peculiar species (carinated paludinas), forming the *Levantine* facies of the Pliocene.

So, finally, the series of stages and facies of the Mediterranean Neogene can be established in the manner indicated in the preceding table.

2. *The Mammalian Faunas*[8]

The best definitions of the stages below result from each containing a special mammalian fauna. According to C. Depéret, the principal characters (for Europe) and the most classic localities are:

Villafranchian[9]	Appearance of the elephant (*E. meridionalis*, the horse (*E. stenonis*) and the ox (*B. etruscus*): last mastodons (*M. arvernensis*), *Rhinoceros etruscus*	St. Prest near Chartres, Villafranca of Asti (Piedmont), Arno Valley (Tuscany), Perrier[10] near Issoire.
Lower Pliocene	*Mastodon arvernensis*, *M. borsoni*, *Rhinoceros leptorhinus*, large antelopes[11]	Montpellier, Bresse, Roussillon.
Pontian[12]	Appearance of *Hipparion*, *Mastodon longirostris*, *M. turricensis*, last *Dinotherium* (*D. giganteum*), *Rhinoceros schleiermacheri*, *Gazella deperdita*	Mt. Luberon (Vaucluse), Eppelsheim (Hesse), Pikermi near Athens.
Vindobonian	*Mastodon angustidens*, *Dinotherium bavaricum*, *Rhinoceros sansaniensis*, last *Anchitherium*, *Dicrocerus elegans*	St. Gaudens (Haute-Garonne), Simorre and Sansan (Gers), La Grive-St. Alban (Isère).
Burdigalian	Appearance of proboscidians, *Mastodon angustidens*, *M. turricensis*, *Dinotherium cuvieri*, *Rhinoceros aurelianensis*, appearance of *Anchitherium* (*A. aurelianense*), *Procervulus aurelianensis*.	Sands of Orléans, La Romieu near Lectoure (Gers).[13]

From the viewpoint of evolution of mammalian faunas, the Burdigalian, Pontian and Villafranchian mark important changes because of the appearance of numerous new forms. That is why German geologists classify the Pontian in the Pliocene, while others (E. Haug) make the Villafranchian the beginning of the Quaternary. The divisions adopted here, however, conform to the stratigraphic relationships of these stages, such as those resulting from the concept of the sedimentary cycle, in the Mediterranean regions, at least, the only ones in which the chronology may be really well defined in every detail.

Notice, moreover, that the chronology of mammalian faunas, like that based on marine faunas, is valuable only within certain geographic limits. Thus, in Abyssinia the coexistence of a *Dinotherium* and an *Elephas* of the *antiquus* group has been demonstrated, though these forms in Europe characterize respectively the Miocene and the Quaternary.[14]

Finally, the idea of the Pontian stage should be clarified. We have already seen that the true type of this stage was defined by deposits in eastern Europe containing a lagoonal fauna. In western Europe, this same name Pontian is applied to wholly continental deposits. The stage is then defined by its mammalian fauna, called the *Hipparion* fauna.

But in the first place, these two definitions do not exactly agree, which is not surprising. The *Hipparion* fauna appears at several places (Provence, p. 564, region of Lyon, p. 564, southern Germany, p. 570, Turkey, p. 591) in the terminal beds of the Vindobonian, defined by its marine or lagoonal faunas. But especially we may ask where are the beds with a normal marine fauna which would be contemporaneous with the Pontian? Long ago, evidences of it were thought to have been found in North Africa (Algeria, Tunisia, Morocco, p. 574), in beds made the type of a Sahelian stage (littoral regions or *sahels* of Algeria and Oran). But, as Lafitte[15] has shown, this stage has no individuality, neither paleontologic nor stratigraphic. The beds called Sahelian, in reality belong, depending on the circumstances, either to the true Miocene (upper Vindobonian) or to the true early Pliocene.

So this term Sahelian should vanish from the list of stages. Then at least the lower part of the continental Pontian containing *Hipparion* might be considered contemporaneous with the upper part of the marine (Tortonian) or brackish (Sarmatian) Vindobonian. As R. Lafitte has suggested, it can also be granted that this Pontian fauna is in part contemporaneous with the base of the marine Pliocene. In fact, the mammalian faunas of that epoch, known in relation to marine beds, are rare and poor. The continental Pontian would thus straddle the Miocene-Pliocene boundary as defined by marine faunas or stratigraphic discontinuities, which is perfectly reasonable (see p. 584, the case of the Bresse Pliocene).

II. The Miocene in the Peri-Alpine Depression

Here we depend upon the classic works of E. Suess and C. Depéret, who have traced with perfect clarity[16] the history of the Miocene between the mouths of the Rhône and the Vienna Basin.

Over the whole stretch of the Alps, from Vienna to the Mediterranean, there was no trace of the sea toward the end of the Oligocene. The mountain range was already established in its main features. Thus the returning Miocene sea respected this chain. It penetrated all along its external border, in the depressions which today make the Rhône Valley, the Swiss Basin and the Bavarian plain. These depressions extended even farther south and eastward than they do today. For the last folding on the external border of the chain incorporated into the Alps a part of the old Miocene depression (sub-Alpine chains in France, front of the Alpine nappes in Switzerland).

In France and Switzerland, the Miocene sediments which filled up this ancient arm of the sea are generally classified as *molasse*. Typically, this word applies, in the popular language of Savoy and French Switzerland, to fine-grained and homogeneous calcareous sandstones, often micaceous or glauconitic, relatively soft, producing a fine building stone easy to exploit and dress. But geologists customarily use the word in a broader sense, as a synonym for

Miocene. Thus we speak of sandy molasse, for sands not cemented into sandstone, of marly molasse when the proportion of clay increases, of calcareous molasse (*tufo calcare* of the Italians, a term recalling the French *tuffeau* of Touraine, p. 419), when the rock becomes organic, full of fragments of shells, corals and bryozoans, and lastly of conglomerates of the molasse (Nagelfluh, p. 565) for the banks of hard conglomerate[17] intercalated in the sandstones.

1. *The Transgression of the Miocene Sea in the Rhône Basin*

Toward the end of the Oligocene, every marine or lagoonal influence had ended on the Provençal or Languedocian shores. For the Chattian everywhere is in a state of lacustrine beds with *Helix ramondi*. Then we saw the sea return in the Aquitanian stage, to nibble lightly on the present coasts at Montpellier and north of Marseille, already suggesting the Miocene transgression (Fig. 134).

1st Stage. Transgression of the lower Burdigalian.   The marine shores extended immediately very far northward and are known as the sands with *Scutella paulensis* (species named after the locality of St. Paul-Trois-Châteaux), containing a few characteristic pectinids (*Pecten paulensis, P. davidi, P. justianus*). At this epoch the sea was widespread in the region of Narbonne, Montpellier, Nîmes and Avignon. It did not reach Marseille, to the east, for the Monts de Provence proper were always respected by the transgression. But to the north, the Rhône Basin extended into Drôme, with the invasion of the Crest Basin, from which the Durance Gulf or Forcalquier Basin branched off.

2nd Stage. The upper Burdigalian transgression.   In the Durance valley, the sea invaded the Digne Basin. It extended very far northward, but instead of following the axis of the Rhône valley, its western shore left this river at Montélimar, leaving emergent Lower Dauphiné, the Lyon district and the southern Jura. It overflowed instead, in a narrow arm of the sea, the region which has since become the northern sub-Alpine chains, and from there extended into Switzerland. In Vercors and Chartreuse, in fact, the Miocene is found in the form of narrow synclines, producing long, rectilinear valleys, grassy and fertile, crowded with hamlets. As always, in these domains of transgression, there are sandy, sandstone or conglomerate facies. The characteristic fossil of this horizon is *Pecten praescabriusculus*.[18]

In the wider southern part of the old gulf, already invaded in the lower Burdigalian, and distant from new shores, there are, on the contrary, very different facies at this horizon. They are organic limestones, known as calcareous molasse and deposited especially in the neighborhood of the Urgonian islands or shoals.[19] Soft enough for exploitation, these rocks can be cut up by saw and then they harden in the air. This is the *pierre du Midi*, actively quarried in the regions of St. Paul-Trois-Château, Beaucaire and the lower Durance. Less massive than the Urgonian limestones and more capriciously carved by erosion, these Miocene limestones outline picturesque silhouettes in many a famous Provençal site (Les Baux). The fauna naturally is that of organic facies: *Lithothamnium,* bryozoans, clypeasters, scutellas, cidarids, and large pectinids.

3rd Stage. The Western Transgression of the Vindobonian. At this moment, the last effort of the marine invasion occurred. The sea invaded Lower Dauphiné and the Lyon district, extending its shores even onto the first slopes

Limit of the Burdigalian   Limit of the Vindobonian
transgression   transgression

FIG. 134. *Map of the Miocene seas in the Rhône basin (after C. Depéret).*

of the Massif Central between Montélimar and Lyon; the whole Rhône valley was then covered.

In the central and southern part of the basin, the facies are of deep and tranquil water, consisting of clayey sands with *Ostrea crassissima*[20] and particularly micaceous marls with *Schizaster,* comparable to the Schlier of Austria (p. 569) which we find at almost the same horizon. The top of the stage is often represented by very fossiliferous blue marls, as at Cabrières d'Aigues

(Vaucluse) where they contain the fauna typical of the Tortonian (*Ancillaria glandiformis,* numerous pleurotomes, and large *Cardita jouanneti*).[21]

In the sub-Alpine chains, the *Pecten praescabriusculus* sandstones are followed by a Vindobonian with facies less coarse at first, composed of marly sands with *Ostrea crassissima.* But especially at the top and toward the east, frequent intercalations of conglomerates witness the proximity of the emerged Alpine chains. The composition of these conglomerates is very different from that of Pliocene or Quaternary alluvium. Crystalline cobbles are very rare, which shows that Belledonne and Pelvoux must still have been concealed beneath their Mesozoic covering. In fact, cobbles of Upper Cretaceous limestones predominate and are associated with cobbles of Jurassic radiolarites and greenstones which could only come from internal Alpine zones, which must formerly have formed important heights feeding the deltas of Miocene coastal rivers.

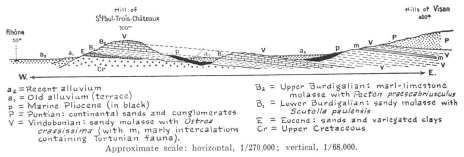

a_2 = Recent alluvium
a_1 = Old alluvium (terrace)
p = Marine Pliocene (in black)
P = Pontian: continental sands and conglomerates
V = Vindobonian: sandy molasse with *Ostrea crassissima* (with m, marly intercalations containing Tortonian fauna).

B_2 = Upper Burdigalian: marl-limestone molasse with *Pecten praescabriusculus*
B_1 = Lower Burdigalian: sandy molasse with *Scutella paulensis*
E = Eocene: sands and variegated clays
Cr = Upper Cretaceous

Approximate scale: horizontal, 1/270,000; vertical, 1/68,000.

FIG. 135. *Somewhat diagrammatic section of the Neogene of the Rhône in the vicinity of St. Paul-Trois-Châteaux (Drôme), showing the Miocene facies in the center of the Rhodanian gulf and the individuality of the Miocene and Pliocene sedimentary cycles (in part after Fontannes and Depéret).*

Finally, in the region of the transgression, Lyon and Lower Dauphiné, there are great thicknesses of yellow crumbly sandstones, containing very few fossils and called the *Terebratulina calathiscus* sands. Thin marly beds are intercalated, containing vestiges of the Tortonian fauna at certain points. This mixture of rock types produces a deeply eroded landscape, with numerous springs, fertile, cut into narrow valleys in which streams flow between steep banks at the bottom of sandy *balmes,* such as the St. Fons *balmes,* dominating the left bank of the Rhône south of Lyon.[22] An occurrence of mammals and birds at La Grive-St-Alban dates these transgressive beds exactly (Fig. 136). It is made up of siderolithic material (p. 493) in the fissures of the Middle Jurassic limestones of the southern end of the island of Crémieu (Fig. 154). This mammalian fauna is clearly Vindobonian.[23] The marine sands overlying it are thus obviously post-Burdigalian. This emphasizes the sharpness of the 3rd stage of our transgression, while the distinction between the 1st and 2nd stages is much less definite.

4th Stage. The filling up of the Rhône Gulf: the continental sediments of

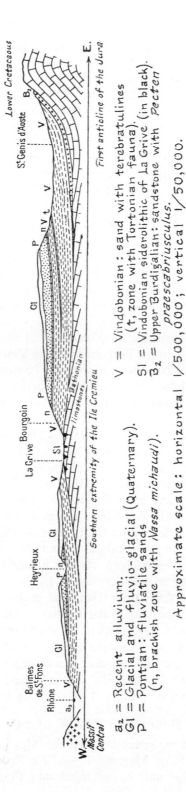

a₂ = Recent alluvium.
Gl = Glacial and fluvio-glacial (Quaternary).
P = Pontian: fluviatile sands
    (n, brackish zone with *Nassa michaudi*).

V = Vindobonian: sand with terebratulines
    (t, zone with Tortonian fauna).
Sl = Vindobonian siderolithic of La Grive (in black).
B₂ = Upper Burdigalian: sandstone with *Pecten praescabriusculus*.

Approximate scale: horizontal 1/500,000; vertical 1/50,000.

FIG. 136. *Semi-diagrammatic section of the Miocene of the Bas-Dauphiné, showing the Vindobonian transgression, dated by the La Grive-St-Alban mammal bed (after data of C. Depéret).*

the Pontian.   But this inundation of the external border of the Alps does not continue and the demand for sedimentation which it made was quickly met by the filling of the Rhône depression. The deltas of the torrents coming down the Alps advanced little by little as far as the Massif Central, and the Miocene accumulation series, whose different vicissitudes we have described, ends with freshwater sands and marls, overlain by an enormously thick covering of continental alluvium, which is called the Pontian.

The end of the marine regime is marked by a final brackish horizon, the *Nassa michaudi* sands of Lower Dauphiné. At higher levels the only fossils found are freshwater shells (*Unio flabellata,* which is found at the same horizon in the Vienna Basin) and especially mammals. The finest deposit of the latter is in the Cucuron red gravels, at the foot of Mont-Luberon, south of Apt. It is called the Mont-Luberon deposit, perhaps the first in which Gaudry studied in detail the *Hipparion* fauna. Sometimes these vast alluvial plains, capping the Miocéne, are still found in the present morphology, in the form of great plateaus not yet destroyed by regressive erosion. Such is the Pontian delta of the Durance, southwest of Digne (Valensoles plateaus, Riez, Fig. 118).[24]

Beginning with the transgressive conglomerates of the Burdigalian sea,[25] continuing with the sands, then the deep marls of the Vindobonian and finally ending with the continental conglomerates of the Pontian, the Miocene accumulation series of the Rhône valley provides a perfect example of the sedimentary cycle, whose local episodes, infinitely varied, nevertheless do not hide the impressive unity.

Now, widening our view, let us try to place this Miocene sedimentary cycle in the history of the Alpine Chain. It then appears to us as one of the last stages in the uniform progression westward of the wave of subsidence, whose advance we have been following since the Eocene. This wave first occupied the site of the great Alps where great thicknesses of Eocene Flysch accumulated. Next, we saw it reach the sub-Alpine chains where the Oligocene peri-Alpine arm of the sea was filled with a thick series of Oligocene marls, sandstones and conglomerates. In the Burdigalian and Helvetian, it reached the external border of the sub-Alpine chain where it caused the accumulation of the molasse of the Miocene sedimentary cycle. In the upper Helvetian, the transgression which submerged Lower Dauphiné under marine sands, then under the marls and conglomerates of the Pontian, marks, in the history of the Miocene, one well-defined stage (and to tell the truth, the only one which is clearly distinguished) in this westward march. Finally, it is only in the Pliocene, at the dawn of the present, that it will begin to gnaw upon the border of the Massif Central, along the Rhône valley, finally determining the great orographic features of the world in which we live.[26]

2. The Molasse Depression North of the Alps

A. The Swiss Basin.   All the space between the Alps and the Jura Mountains is occupied by the Swiss Miocene Basin. We have already described (p. 355) how this tectonic unit is prolonged into France. And from the paleogeographic viewpoint, we have just learned that it was reached by an arm of the Rhône sea in the upper Burdigalian. It is only with this epoch that the marine facies began. On the other hand, the marine series ended here earlier than in France. So the Swiss Miocene is naturally divided into three periods: lower freshwater molasse, marine molasse, and upper freshwater molasse.

In fact, the Miocene is usually composed of fine-grained, micaceous, calcareous sandstone, an easily dressed building stone, but of gray and lustreless tone, which gives Swiss cities their serious and slightly sad aspect. Marly intercalations in it give rise to numerous springs. And this Swiss Basin is in reality a country of verdant hills, much cut up, with deep and abrupt gorges.[27]

There is no longer the slightest trace of freshwater organic facies, for on the bottom of this sea materials coming from the Alps fell in an unceasing rain, increasingly coarser materials nearer the range. In this direction, true marine or lacustrine deltas are found, represented by thick intercalations of conglomerates, becoming thicker toward the Alps. These conglomerates bear the name of *Nagelfluh,* a fairly resistant rock, making great crags: walls (*Fluh*) from which project pebbles resembling nail heads (*Nagel*).

1. *Lower freshwater Molasse.* We already know that the lower part of the thick mass of marls, sandstones and conglomerates composing the Swiss molasse, should be attributed to the Stampian and that it is still marine.[28] The freshwater facies began with the Chattian, easily recognizable at many points by its fauna of mollusks and mammals, of which a typical representative is *Anthracotherium valdense* (animal of the lignites of Vaud Canton) near Lausanne. Above, the gray molasse of Lausanne represents the always lacustrine Aquitanian[29] and lower Burdigalian. In these clayey sandstones of the lower freshwater molasse, A. Bersier[30] has described fine seasonal stratification, revealed by the autumn beds, rich in imprints of leaves. He deduces therefrom that 1 m. of sandstone corresponds to six centuries, which would give about 2½ to 3 million years for the total duration of the Chattian and Aquitanian stages. As for all similar estimates based on speeds of sedimentation, this figure seems much too small if compared to those deduced from phenomena of atomic disintegration (p. 22).

2. *Marine Molasse.* Its base is clearly marked by shelly sandstones (Muschelsandsteine), very rich in pelecypods, *Cardium commune, Pecten subbenedictus* and especially *P. praescabriusculus.* Thus, the arrival of the sea in Switzerland would correspond to the 2nd stage of the Rhône transgression, marked by the same *Pecten.* But recently, A. Bersier[31] has shown that, at the top of the lower, freshwater molasse, there are manifest traces of unquestionable marine influence, such as shark teeth, oyster fragments, and original glauconite[32] (not reworked). As these first marine incursions could not have reached Switzerland at the time of the first French stage, it shows that the distinction of the lower and upper Burdigalian substages, based solely on *Pecten praescabriusculus,* does not perhaps have the mathematical exactness attributed to it by Depéret and his successors.

In any case, the clearly marine regime is followed, after this Burdigalian

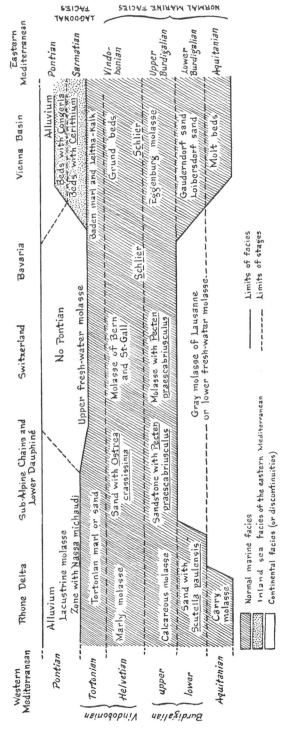

FIG. 137. *Diagram of Miocene facies in the peri-Alpine depression, showing the successive stages of the Miocene transgression, after C. Depéret and E. Suess. In the upper Vindobonian, Switzerland and Bavaria were emergent, breaking the connections between the Western Mediterranean and the eastern domain, which became lagoonal.*

with *P. praescabriusculus,* by the molasse of Berne and St. Gall, containing *Ostrea crassissima* and *Cardita jouanneti,* which has served as type of the Helvetian or lower Vindobonian stage.

3. *Upper freshwaster Molasse.* Already, with the end of the Vindobonian, the marine facies end. In fact, the mammalian fauna of the upper freshwater molasse is composed of Vindobonian, not Pontian, species.[33] To this horizon belongs the famous Oeningen deposit, located on the shores of Lake Constance, celebrated for its insects and rich flora, which indicate a warm, humid climate, similar to that of the Canaries.

B. The Bavarian and Austrian Plains.[34] The molasse here is often concealed under vast stretches of Quaternary alluvial terraces. But the Miocene sea completely covered these great plains. It advanced northward [35] to the edge of the Black Forest and to the eastern end of the Jura plateau (Randen molasse) and reached the first spurs of the ancient Bohemian Massif, just as near Lyon it stretched as far as the French Massif Central.

The succession of facies here is the same as in Switzerland. But beginning east of Munich, in the lower Vindobonian, in place of the sandy molasse with *Ostrea crassissima,* a very thick facies of micaceous blue marls develops, in which fossils indicate a deep sea and are much more rare, as always happens. The most characteristic are two pelecypods with extremely thin shells, *Pecten denudatus* and *Solenomya doderleini* and a nautilus, *Aturia aturi.* This is the *Schlier* (local name of this rock), typical at Ottnang (upper Austria, between Salzburg and Linz).[36] But it must be noted that this Schlier facies may, in the center of the arm of the sea, descend as far as the Burdigalian.

3. *The Miocene of the Vienna Basin: Mediterranean Stages*

It was in the region of Vienna that Suess established for the first time a precise Miocene stratigraphy based on both paleontologic and stratigraphic facts. To understand them it is necessary to know the general structure of the region (Fig. 138).

The Miocene depression which we have been following on the northern edge of the Alps is prolonged to the north of the Carpathians. The part of this depression located opposite the region of contact of these two ranges, facing the Moravian-Czech Massif (southeast side of the Bohemian Massif, Fig. 28), was called by Suess, the extra-Alpine Vienna Basin.

While this depression in France, Switzerland, and Bavaria was closed to the south by the barrier of the Alpine Chain, here the barrier was interrupted at the longitude of Vienna. A transverse collapse separated the Alps from their eastern extension, the Carpathians. To this zone of collapse or sinking, thus located within the domain of the Alpine Chain itself, Suess gave the name of intra-Alpine Vienna Basin. Through it, the extra-Alpine Basin communicated with the vast plains of Hungary or the Pannonian Basin, a dependent of the domain of the Eastern Mediterranean.

The extra-Alpine Basin was occupied by the sea beginning in the Aquitanian and the lower Burdigalian. The sea could not have advanced from the peri-Alpine depression, for that was invaded only in the upper Burdigalian. It must of necessity have come from the east, by the external border of the Carpathians where it connected with the eastern Mediterranean. As for the intra-Alpine Basin, Suess recognized that the sea had penetrated there only in the Helvetian. In reality, as D. Andrusov[37] has recently demonstrated, beginning in the Burdigalian, an east-west arm of the sea must have crossed the northeast end of the Little Carpathians, thus connecting the extra-Alpine Basin with a sea already covering a part of the western Carpathians.

But in particular, at the end of the Helvetian, important orogenic move-

FIG. 138. *Diagrammatic structural map of the Vienna Basin (compare with Fig. 133).*

ments (folds and especially faults) occurred. So, a new sedimentary cycle, the second Mediterranean stage of Suess, begins with formations making, by definition, a Tortonian stage, widely transgressive over the Helvetian or older formations. So, after all, the Vienna geologists have been led to abandon all at once Suess' idea of Mediterranean stages and also the Vindobonian as defined by Depéret and the grouping of the Helvetian and Tortonian. Thus they have adopted (Schaffer) three great divisions: 1st. an Aquitanian-Burdigalian, especially typical in the extra-Alpine Basin where it corresponds to the old First Mediterranean Stage; 2nd. a Helvetian, which is distinguished from the Burdigalian especially by its faunas and its often clayey facies; 3rd. a Tortonian (Second Mediterranean Stage) whose individuality is paleogeographic rather than faunal.[38]

We shall be content now to indicate the most classic occurrences of these different stages.[39]

The Aquitanian-Burdigalian is represented in the extra-Alpine Basin only by a series of very fossiliferous littoral beds, sandy or sandy calcareous. At the base, the Molt beds are generally correlated with the French Aquitanian, followed by the Loibersdorf and Gauderndorf sands, and lastly by the calcareous molasse of Eggenburg, with *Pecten praescabriusculus* and a large rich fauna, studied by Schaffer, which allows the recognition of the equivalent of the upper Burdigalian of the Rhône valley.

The Helvetian begins with the Schlier, a facies we learned to recognize earlier in the peri-Alpine depression. In the intra-Alpine Basin where it marks the beginning of the transgression, it passes at the borders into brackish, lignitic beds with *Cerithium lignitarum*. The stage ends with the famous Grund beds, which can be considered as a shore facies of the top of the Schlier, especially developed in the locality of that name close to the old Bohemian shore. In the Grund fauna, containing *Cardita jouanneti,* appear mollusks with northern affinities, according to Kautsky, which leads to the recognition of direct communication with northern seas by way of Silesia (p. 592).

The Tortonian, well developed in the intra-Alpine Basin, is represented by two principal facies. First is the deep-water facies typical of the Baden marls, reaching 400 m. thickness, with a very rich fauna identical with the Tortona fauna (*Ancillaria glandiformis,* numerous pleurotomes). The second is the facies of the Leitha limestone (*Leithakalk*), developed around the Leitha Massif, which formed an island surrounded by rocky depths, and which is therefore an organic facies with *Lithothamnium,* bryozoans, large ornate pelecypods (spondyles, large pectens) and reef echinoids (clypeasters, *Echinolampas*).

Eastern influences at the end of the Miocene. Beginning with the Tortonian, we have seen that the Swiss and Bavarian depressions were emergent, so that marine communication between the extra-Alpine Basin and the western Mediterranean, through the peri-Alpine arm of the sea, was broken. On the other hand, the region of Vienna was connected with the eastern Mediterranean through the intra-Alpine Basin and the Pannonian Basin. But we shall see that this eastern domain, separated from the west, develops in an entirely independent way, with peculiar faunas (Sarmatian and Pontian stages studied later, see Fig. 144).

Thus, the Miocene series in the Vienna Basin ends with representatives of these two eastern stages. The lower Sarmatian (or Volhynian), up to 200 m. thick, corresponds to beds with *Cerithium* (*Cerithium pictum, C. disjunctum, C. rubiginosum,* etc.) containing the fauna typical of the base of the stage (*Tapes gregaria, Trochus pictus, Ervilia podolica,* etc.). This fauna does not, however, result from evolution of the Tortonian fauna in place but must have come from Romania, via the Pannonian Basin. For only there and in the whole external border of the Carpathians are the Buglow beds found in the upper Tortonian, where the progressive transition of Tortonian and Sarmatian faunas took place (Laskarev).

Then come the beds with large congerias (100 m. thick) accompanied by *Melanopsis*. The base (Slavonian) belongs to the upper Sarmatian and the top (Pannonian), containing different species, must be correlated with the lower part (Meotian) of the Russian Pontian. The whole[40] is topped by sands with a continental fauna (Belvedere deposit of Vienna), with mammals of the Pontian (*Dinotherium giganteum, Hipparion gracile,* etc.).[41]

III. The Miocene in the Western Mediterranean

1. *Italy*

Most of Italy was still covered by the Miocene seas, so that instead of filling isolated basins, the Miocene formations spread out in a great sheet, between the last beds of the Apennine Flysch and the Pliocene formations of the low hills and plains. They are in general loose sediments, marls, sands, sandstones or conglomerates.

A. Classic Localities of the Northern Slope of the Apennines.[42]   The Burdigalian usually begins with conglomerates and sandstones which, in the Turin hills, discordantly overlie the upper Eocene and contain lepidocyclines studied by Prever. Above are generally found more blue marls with pteropods of deep-water facies, abounding with small fragile shells of these pelagic mollusks but with few other fossils. This is the *Langhian* of Italian geologists (from the hills of Langhe, on the north slope of the Ligurian Apennines). Species of the Austrian Schlier (*Solenomya doderleini, Aturia aturi*) are found in it, so that it may quite as well be called lower Helvetian. Near the Apennines, this deep-water facies passes laterally, as in Austria, into littoral facies of organic limestones (example, Rosignano stone, near Casale Monferrato).

The upper Helvetian in the hills of the Superga, which overlook Turin, is represented by conglomerates and very fossiliferous sandstones (*Cardita jouanneti,* and miogypsines, though there are no more lepidocyclines). Boulders of *pietri verdi* are found there, doubtless originating in the Alps (serpentine gravels of the Superga).

The Tortonian has its type in the region of Tortona, on the north slope of the Ligurian Appennines, east of Alessandria (Stazzano, Sant'Agata dei fossili). It is composed of blue marls, abounding with large pleurotomes and other fossils of the marls of Baden and Cabrières d'Aigues.[43]

Finally, the Miocene ends with a thick series of lagoonal or continental beds, evidences of a general regression of the sea, which ended the Miocene sedimentary cycle.

First there are brackish beds with gypsum and sulphur (doubtless produced by the reduction of gypsum by hydrocarbon-bearing materials which impregnate the sediments). This *formazione gessososolfifera* developed in Romagna,

Calabria and Sicily, can be compared to the Sarmatian of eastern Europe. In fact, it contains (in Sicily, for example) peculiar mollusks which characterize this stage, *Mactra podolica, Ervilia podolica*. Above comes a continental Pontian (tripolite, with diatoms, clays with small congerias) and the whole complex is called *Messinian* by Italian geologists.

B. Central Apennines. Here the lower and middle Miocene generally retain the sandstone-shale facies comparable to the Flysch, so that differentiation from the Nummulitic often becomes difficult (see recent works by Principi, note 202, chap. 9). East of Rome and as far as the Sabine Mountains, there is continuous sedimentation between the Oligocene and the Miocene, but in southern Latium, nearing the ancient Tyrrhenian continent, a lacuna appears and the transgressive Miocene loses the calcareous facies and becomes detrital, clayey-sandy.[44] Finally, as in the Nummulitic, the Apennine facies may be contrasted with an Apulian-Gargano type, represented by organic limestones in the plateau region of Apulia. Thus, in the country of Otranto, the *pietra leccese* (Burdigalian) has provided the town of Lecce with a material easy to carve, comparable to our calcareous molasse. From it came the flowering of architectural ornamentation which earned for Lecce the name of "Florence of Rococo."

C. Southern Italy and Sicily. Similar facies are found in these areas, where they played a great role in antiquity. The tombs and the quarry-prisons of Syracuse were dug in the calcareous molasse or *tufi*. But the upper Miocene is particularly developed. The gypsiferous-sulphurous formation which supplies the sulphur mines of Romagna, is found again in the Sicilian sulphur mines, and even in North Africa. And the hydrocarbons, which caused the reduction of the gypsum, sometimes impregnate the limestones in proportions sufficient to make them exploitable as asphalts (Ragusa, southwest of Syracuse).

2. *Spain and Morocco: Miocene at the Gates of the Mediterranean*

In all of northern Spain, especially in the huge basin of the Ebro, the Miocene is represented only by continental formations.[45] The sea no more than touched upon the Mediterranean coasts, where it invaded the small Panadès Basin (see Fig. 105) near Barcelona in the Catalan coastal chain.

The ancient Meseta Massif also remained emergent. There the steppe-like plateaus of New Castile (Tertiary basin of the Straits) and of Old Castile (Tertiary basin of the Douro), are filled, at the centers, with continental Miocene while on their borders are the Eocene and Oligocene outcrops described earlier (p. 526).[46]

So, it is necessary to go south of the Meseta to find traces of the arm of the sea which, in the Miocene, must of necessity have connected the Mediterranean and the Atlantic.

South of the Meseta, there is first the vast depression through which the Quadalquivir flows and which is filled with Neogene formations. It is called the North Betic depression. Then come ranges folded in the Tertiary and

composed of Secondary and Tertiary formations, known as the sub-Betic
Ranges. Farther south, thick masses of crystalline schists appear (comprising the range of the Sierra Nevada, for example), remains of an ancient
massif, likewise folded in the Tertiary. Similar rocks form the Moroccan
Rif and to this ensemble is given the name Betic-Rifian Massif. Finally, still
farther south, comes a new depression filled with Neogene deposits and
bounded on the south by the Moroccan Meseta, the Middle Atlas and the
Oran tablelands, which we call the South Rifian depression. It is there, over
the Taza threshold, that the great route of communication between Algeria
and Morocco passes.

But the study of the Neogene of the North-Betic depression seems to show
that communication must have existed there between the Mediterranean and
Atlantic during most of the Miocene. For the Burdigalian and Helvetian are
found in the Guadalquivir valley, in the Granada Basin, in all the synclinal
basins of the sub-Betic chains as far as the Mediterranean between Valencia
and Cartagena,[47] and finally in the Balearic Islands.[48] But this connection[49]
must have been closed at the end of the Vindobonian, as proved by the continental conglomerates which terminate the Vindobonian in the vicinity of
Granada[50] and as also indicated by the gypsiferous-sulphurous formations
of Lorca near Murcia.[51]

The South Rifian depression was also certainly open up to the very end
of the Miocene. It is, in fact, filled with Miocene marine sediments, which
constitute, according to Lacoste,[52] a single sedimentary cycle, beginning with
a lower Burdigalian containing myogypsines and continuing with the sandy
or marly Vindobonian, containing Helvetian or Tortonian faunas. At the
top are marly-sandy beds, very fossiliferous at Dar Bel Hamri of the Rharb
(western part of the South Rifian depression), the extension of which through
the whole length of the South Rifian strait was recognized by Lacoste. The
age of this Dar Bel Hamri fauna has been much debated. Besides a large
number of species common to the Tortonian and Plaisancian, it contains
Ancillaria glandiformis, a typically Miocene form.[53] So some paleontologists[54]
have assigned it to the Sahelian of Algeria and Tunisia, a stage which we
are led to give up as badly defined.

We conclude then that these beds of Dar Bel Hamri are still connected
paleontologically to the Tortonian. In the same way, stratigraphically, they
mark the top of the marine series of the sedimentary cycle of this South
Rifian Miocene, which ends with lagoonal beds, gypsiferous or lignitic, indicating the definite closing of the South Rifian strait.[55] The latter remained
open then perhaps a little longer than the North Betic strait.

In any case, at the beginning of the Pliocene, these two straits were certainly closed, for the marine Pliocene does not cross their thresholds. And
there remains no open thoroughfare except that of the Strait of Gibraltar,
on whose shores (Tétouan in Morocco, Malaga and Almeria in Spain)
Pliocene sediments are, in fact, found, deposited by a sea widely invading
a dislocated and collapsed Betic-Rifian Massif.

3. *Algeria and Tunisia*

The marine Miocene, in its entirely, is well characterized in Algeria and Tunisia.[56] Pre-Miocene folding had already occurred in the Tellian Atlas, so that Miocene outcrops are found scattered in numerous basins, which correspond to depressions in the present orography. They are separated by emerged massifs, which later became more elevated mountains. In the Mountains of Batna, marine Miocene is found at altitudes of more than 1,500 m. This very thick Miocene (more than 1,000 m. in Oran) is itself folded.

A very complicated paleogeography results, which we shall not describe in detail. We can say in brief that the Miocene seas partially covered the zone of the Tellian Atlas, encroaching to the south on the zone of the High Plateaus (Fig. 107). The extreme southern limit of the advance of these seas (Fig. 128) passes close to Tlemcen, then between Tiaret and Frenda, circling on the north the Mountains of Bou-Saada to go back toward Biskra and thus enter the Aurès. There the sea covered part of the Saharan Atlas and possibly even penetrated into the Sahara. Farther east, all the northern part of eastern Algeria, that is the region of Constantine-Guelma and the Kroumirie, was emergent and the arm of the sea passed southward through Aïn-Beïda and Souk-Arras to spread out over central Tunisia.

The detailed stratigraphy of the Miocene is still rather confused, because of the absence of mammalian occurrences, which alone would be capable of providing precise guides.

The only marine deposit comparable to the Aquitanian is the Dellysian (p. 531). The transgression begins with the Burdigalian, starting with littoral, sandy facies, with characteristic echinoids and pectens (*Pecten praescabriusculus*). Then come great thicknesses of hard, gray marls, containing *Aturia aturi* and other fossils of the Schlier facies. To this assemblage, found in all North Africa, Algerian geologists give the name Cartennian.[57] The base is surely Burdigalian and the top, identical with the Schlier, can be attributed to the upper Burdigalian or to the Helvetian.

Above there are frequently conglomerates and even discordances(?). So, at many places in Algeria and Tunisia, geologists describe the Vindobonian as a sedimentary cycle distinct from that of the lower Miocene and often transgressive over pre-Miocene formations. Quite varied facies make up this Vindobonian: conglomerates and sandstones with *Ostrea crassissima*,[58] marls called Helvetian, generally containing few fossils and often confused with marls of the Cretaceous or Nummulitic, *Lithothamnium* limestones called Tortonian, similar to the Leitha limestone. This Vindobonian sometimes ends with lignite beds (Cap Bon in Tunisia, Marceau between Algiers and Ténès) and lagoonal beds with *Cerithium lignitarum* or finally with alluvium containing *Hipparion* and red clay with land shells.[59]

But in the littoral region (Sahel) east of Oran and in the lower valley of the Chélif (Dahra hills), the top of the Miocene presents its most interesting peculiarities. There, Tortonian marls and sands are overlain by chalky white marls (Ravin Blanc, slashed in the cliffs east of the port of Oran), containing chert, pectinids and *Ostrea cochlear,* a smooth, deep-water oyster still living in the Mediterranean. There are also *Lithothamnium* limestone, beds of diatomite, and especially magnificent impressions of fish. In the Dahra, these terminal Miocene deposits contain beds with gypsum and hydrocarbon seepages. On the whole, this complex[60] is quite analogous to the gypsiferous-sulphurous formation and the diatomite of the Messinian of Sicily. It is considered one of the type sections of the Sahelian stage.

Let us point out lastly that, in Kabylie, there were, during the Miocene, volcanic outbursts and even intrusion of granitic or dioritic, deep crystalline rocks, recently studied by L. Glangeaud.

The question of the Sahelian. The Sahelian stage was originated in 1858 by A. Pomel, in applying the theories of Elie de Beaumont on directions of folding, to the region of Algiers. He took as type, first the marls of the Sahel (littoral region) of Algiers, then the beds of the Sahel of Oran.

Actually, the Sahel marls of Algiers were quickly recognized as unquestionably Pliocene (Plaisancian). But, in the vicinity of Oran (valley of the Chélif, Dahra, deposits of Carnot and El Bordj), the marly-sandy beds containing a fauna of marine mollusks, called intermediate between those of the Tortonian and the Plaisancian, continued to be attributed to the Sahelian stage. C. Depéret confirmed the latter opinion and the name Sahelian was thenceforth established in the stratigraphic nomenclature and considered as the marine equivalent of the Pontian, defined by its *Hipparion* fauna. Later, equivalents of the Sahelian were believed to be found in Tunisia (Solignac) and Morocco (see above).

The question was recently reopened by R. Lafitte.[61] A new study of the stratigraphic conditions and the faunas of the Sahelian of Algeria led him to conclude that in reality it was everywhere Tortonian, making up a part of the Miocene sedimentary cycle and separated by a discordance, or at least a discontinuity, from the Pliocene in these regions. In Tunisia, however, the so-called Sahelian described by Solignac and Stchepinski [62] is Pliocene.

Thus, the beds attributed to the Sahelian in no way differ, either in facies or faunas, from either the Tortonian or the Plaisancian. The name could be preserved, as a facies name, for the upper members of the Miocene in the region of Oran, which are the same type as the gypsiferous-sulphurous formation of Sicily. It would then become about the equivalent of the Messinian of Italian geologists. But it would thus be changed from the original meaning given it by Pomel, Brives, Solignac, Depéret, etc., which runs the risk of introducing confusion. Better, eliminate Sahelian from stratigraphic nomenclature, as proposed (p. 559).

IV. The Miocene of the French Atlantic Regions

The Miocene Atlantic advanced transgressively over two different regions in France: Eastern Brittany and the Lower Loire, and the Gulf of Aquitaine.[63]

1. *The Gulf of Aquitaine*

The central part of this great gulf, hidden under Quaternary formations, displays no Miocene outcrops. These are restricted to three zones.

A. The North Shores. The Miocene seas do not seem to have passed beyond the course of the Garonne on the northeast and all the occurrences are found on the left bank (Fig. 98). The outcrops are very isolated, limited to the bottoms of a few ravines cut into the covering of recent deposits. The facies are almost entirely sands with shell remains, or the Aquitaine faluns, so that stratigraphy here is a thankless task. The richness in fossils, on the other hand, is such that it has been chosen as the type for the Aquitanian and Burdigalian stages.

A continuous Aquitanian-Burdigalian series occurs in the valley of Saucats ravine. Beginning with the Lariey faluns, which are classified as Oligocene (Aquitanian), it continues with the Burdigalian faluns (*Pecten burdigalensis, P. beudanti*, etc.) of Peloux, then of Pont-Pourquey. Very near, at Léognan, the base of the Burdigalian is sandy, forming the Léognan molasse, overlain by the Coquillat faluns.

Finally, the Helvetian, the last exposed member, is represented by the faluns of Salles, with *Cardita jouanneti, Pecten besseri, P. latissimus,* etc. At this point, the northeast shore follows an almost straight line from Bordeaux to Lectoure, so that the gulf must end at a point between Agen and Auch.

B. The South Shores (Fig. 123). On the southeast side, the ancient shore, starting from Lectoure,[64] ends between Pau and Orthez. Thus the Chalosse was covered, but usually the Miocene sands there have been decalcified and reddened and no longer contain fossils. These are the tawny sands of the Chalosse, whose age has been much discussed. But there are also fine fossiliferous deposits in that region, especially in the vicinity of Dax. Here are found an Aquitanian and a Burdigalian containing the last lepidocyclines. Also attributable to the Burdigalian are the blue marls with pleurotomes of Saubrigues (between Bayonne and Dax), celebrated for the wealth of fossils, up to the present attributed to the Tortonian.[65] Finally the Helvetian is visible at Mont-de-Marsan.

C. The Continental Deposits at the Head of the Gulf. These deposits continue the Oligocene facies studied earlier. Thus, in the Agen region, against the Massif Central, there are especially fine-grained sediments, chalky marls (Burdigalian) and lacustrine limestones containing *Helix larteti* (Helvetian). To the east, however, where the continental Miocene extends as far as Toulouse, and to the south, in Armagnac, the formations are more detrital, like the Armagnac molasse, in which, however, calcareous banks sometimes remain (region of Auch). Finally, along the edge of the Pyrenees, between Pau and St. Gaudens, coarser, gravel facies appear as usual. The alluvial conglomerates which, topping the Miocene alluvial series, form the plateaus of Lannemezan,[66] are sometimes attributed to the Pontian. They are the remains of an immense alluvial fan that descended from the Pyrenees and are comparable to the Pontian deltas of Alpine rivers (Durance, for example, p. 564).

As in the Oligocene, fine mammal deposits succeed each other. The La Romieu occurrence, near Lectoure, is of Burdigalian age.[67] The three successive faunas of Sansan, Simorre,[68] and St. Gaudens belong to the Vindobonian, customarily attributed respectively to the Helvetian, Tortonian and Sarmatian. Finally, at the foot of the Pyrenees, the Orignac lignites contain the Pontian fauna.

2. *The Breton Gulfs*

East of the Armorican Massif, between the Cotentin and the Lower Loire,[69] traces of two successive and independent marine invasions are found. They have two faunas and two distinct paleogeographies. These invasions covered only the lower part of the country. The ancient shores in general follow the curves of the 100 to 140 m. contours. However, the outlines of these ancient gulfs, as they have been reconstructed by Dollfus (Fig. 139), are based in particular on the extent of present outcrops and consequently remain very hypothetical.[70]

A. "Falunian" or Vindobonian Gulf.   Starting from the vicinity of the Cotentin, the first marine invasion covered the environs of Rennes and Angers, extending as far as Tours, Blois and Chinon. It deposited shelly sands, reduced today to the state of small isolated remnants, long known as the faluns of Touraine and Anjou. Their fauna, very rich, shows them to be attributable to the middle Miocene or Vindobonian. This is the Falunian stage of local geologists.[71]

B. "Redonian" Gulf.   In this new invasion the sea hardly goes beyond Angers, but on the other hand, it covers the region of Nantes and Lower Loire, transforming the Armorican peninsula into an island. The calcareous sands then formed gullied the Vindobonian faluns and, in the vicinity of Rennes, contain a very rich fauna, with 50% of living species, in which existing forms appear (*Pecten maximus, P. jacobaeus,* etc.), unknown in the classic Miocene. So, we may conclude that this transgression belongs to a very recent Miocene. It is the Redonian stage (type at Rennes) of local geologists.[72]

C. Continental Formations East of the Gulfs.[73]   During these transgressions, the Paris Basin, remaining emerged, received the alluvium of streams descending from the Massif Central, constituting the sands of Orléans, and sands and clays of Sologne. These formations are usually completely decalcified and thus represent, in the Miocene, the equivalent of the Eocene variegated sands and clays and plastic clay, the lower Cretaceous streaked sands and clays, and the Wealdian, etc.

The Orléans sands, relatively less decalcified, still produce fertile soil. They are especially interesting for their mammalian fauna, which make this formation a good type of the Burdigalian stage.[74] The Sologne sands and clays, more recent (Vindobonian), on the contrary form the vast solitudes of this forest or swampy region (Fig. 114).

This same alluvial formation, dated by the Burdigalian occurrence of Givreuil (near Moulins), is found in the northern part of the Limagnes of the Allier and the Loire. These Bourbonnais sands, forming an almost continuous sheet from the confines of Auvergne to those of Nevers, must formerly have been continuous with the sands of Orléans and Sologne.

FIG. 139. *Map of the Breton gulfs in the Miocene (after G. F. Dollfus).*

These materials derived from the Massif Central are still found in isolated outcrops on the tops of the plateaus as far as the environs of Paris, where they are called "granitic" sands as contrasted to the beach sands of the Eocene and Oligocene.

V. The Mediterranean Pliocene

No other stratigraphic unit is as clean-cut as the Mediterranean Pliocene.[75] For, following the great regression at the end of the Miocene, the Pliocene formations always lie in discontinuity over the older formations. In addition, the end of the period is always marked by a retreat of the sea. Enclosed thus between a transgression and a regression, the Pliocene corresponds to a sedimentary cycle, to a depositional series followed by a period of erosion which inaugurates the Quaternary.

However, save for rare local exceptions (external border of the Romanian Carpathians, north slope of the Apennines), the Pliocene sediments have hardly been disturbed, save for movements of the whole mass or faulting, but no folding. So, in a single region, the old shore lines can be followed with geographic continuity. Granting that the Pliocene transgression began with a sea whose level was below that of the present sea,[76] it will suffice, to give a clear synthetic idea of the Pliocene in a given region, to know the maximum altitude reached by the transgressive sea.[77] This altitude will be the same as the top of the Pliocene fill (Fig. 142).

As to the importance, often underestimated, of these recent fills, the following figures will give an idea. A test well, located in Rome itself, remained in the marine Pliocene from 52 to 925 m. depth.[78] There are 1,400 m. of Plaisancian near Carpaneto, in the Po plain, and 1,600 m. of Pliocene in the Pannonian Basin (Hungary). At Rawalpinki, on the edge of the Himalayas, the Pliocene and early Quaternary reach 5,000 m., and to that must be added, nearby, 1,000 m. of late Quaternary (alluvium of the Ganges). In California, the marine Pliocene is 3,000 to 4,000 m. thick in the Los Angeles Basin and 6,000 m. in the Ventura and San Joaquin Basins.

1. *Subdivisions and Facies*

When, as is usually the case, the sedimentation has been fed particularly by terrigenous, detrital materials, a uniform succession of facies is found almost everywhere. Above a usually thin basal conglomerate come thick blue marls of deep-water facies. Then, as the fill from the land progressively increases, the sediments become coarser: yellow sands with a more littoral fauna. And finally the coastal plains are reached, so that the series ends with conglomerates, marine at first, then entirely continental.

Three stage names have been created for these facies, which are found always in the same order in many regions: the blue marls form the *Plaisancian,* the yellow sands the *Astian,* and the continental alluvium the *Villafranchian.*

Examining the history of the faunas (p. 557), on the other hand, it will be seen there is, in reality, reason to distinguish only two subdivisions in the Pliocene, subdivisions defined either according to marine faunas or to mammalian faunas: a lower, or early, Pliocene, in which the faunas typical of Plaisance and Asti correspond only to two facies, and an upper Pliocene, usually represented by the continental or Villafranchian facies, though a marine facies, called *Calabrian,* is also known in almost all of Italy (and perhaps in Syria and Rhodes).

Finally, in the regions where the Pliocene sea surrounded small islands or bathed flat, calcareous coasts, without rivers or terrigenous materials, there are, as in the Miocene, sediments formed solely of remains of organisms, calcareous molasse (*tufi* of the Italian geologists). These facies are especially developed around the calcareous islands of Apulia and Monte Gargano, in particular at the base of the Pliocene. For contrast with the Plaisancian and Astian facies, these organic, calcareous facies should be called *Materin,* a name created by Mayer-Eymar for the *tufi* of Matera and Gravina (Apulia, Fig. 143), first attributed by him to a stage intermediate between the Miocene and Plaisancian. Similar molasse or calcareous sandstones are found around the islands of the Tuscan Pliocene archipelago (Fig. 141), on the northern edge of the Pliocene peninsula of Maures-Esterel (Biot molasse), around the island of Bouzaréah north of Algiers (Mustapha molasse), and at the foot of the calcareous mountains of the northern coast of Sicily.[79]

2. The Pliocene in Italy

The Italian peninsula is the classic land of the Pliocene. The Pliocene sea, indeed, almost entirely covered it, except for the Apennine Mountains. So, the sub-Apennine hills which border the range, especially on the slope toward the Po and the Adriatic, are entirely composed of Pliocene, which early geologists, for that reason called the sub-Apennine formation.

Against the mountains, first comes an initial zone, composed of Plaisancian marls which give a countryside of rounded hills, with dry soil, covered with extensive farming, sometimes cut by deeply eroded ravines (*calanchi*). Then, a second zone made up of yellow sands, containing beds alternately more clayey or more sandy, which produces a soil impregnated with water and

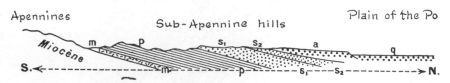

FIG. 140. *Diagrammatic section of the Pliocene in the region of Plaisance, Italy.*

q = Quaternary alluvium of the Po plain
a = Villafranchian alluvium ⎫ Upper
s_2 = Upper yellow sands with *Cyprina islandica* (Calabrian) ⎬ Pliocene
s_1 = Lower yellow sands with Astian fauna ⎫ Lower
p = Blue marls with Plaisancian fauna ⎬ Pliocene
m = Conglomerates or lagoonal marls of the Messinian   Pontian

allows very rich and varied farming. Finally, the Villafranchian alluvium crowns plateaus inclined toward the plains, at the edges of which it is difficult to distinguish the Pliocene alluvium from that of the Quaternary terraces (Fig. 140).

The boundary between the early Pliocene and the upper Pliocene is purely paleontologic. It is placed, in the depositional series, at an altitude increasing toward the northwest. Thus, in the country of Asti (southeast of Turin), all the upper Pliocene is composed of Villafranchian continental alluvium. But in the vicinity of Plaisance, beds with a Calabrian fauna appear near the top of the yellow sands.[80] All along the Adriatic, all the yellow sands and often even the top of the blue marls must be attributed to the Calabrian. This is quite natural, since the continental fill of this ancient gulf of the Po must have progressed from west to east.[81]

At the same time, the maximum altitude reached by the Pliocene transgression seems to increase to the south. Near 400 to 500 m. in the northern part of the Apennine range, it reached 1,000 m. in Calabria and Sicily.

On the northern coast of the great Island, the rich Altavilla occurrence (east of Palermo) presents a completely typical Astian facies. And the base of Etna is composed of "sub-Etnean" clays. But south of Syracuse, where the Neogene rests upon the great calcareous plateaus of the southeastern part of the Island and where the Miocene showed *tufi* similar to those of the Apulian-Garganian domain, organic facies with brachiopods and corals are

FIG. 141. *Paleogeographic map of Italy in the Pliocene (after a map of F. Succo,* Boll. d. R. Soc. geogr. italiana, 1919).

N. B.   Later, some marine Pliocene was discovered in Sardinia.

found in the upper Pliocene. According to Trevisan,[82] the Calabrian there was transgressive and independent of the early Pliocene, contrary to the usual rule, which is not surprising in this volcanic region, where the movements of the earth must have been particularly intense and disorderly.

During this period, intra-Apennine depressions existed in the very interior of the Apennine Range (Fig. 141), saved from marine invasion by rapid continental deposition, so that the Pliocene is there entirely fluviatile or

FIG. 142. *Theoretical section showing the distribution of facies in the early and late Pliocene, between Rome and the Apennine Chain (after the works of Roman geologists).*

The vertical is much exaggerated in relation to the horizontal. The volcanic tuffs overlying the Pliocene are not shown.

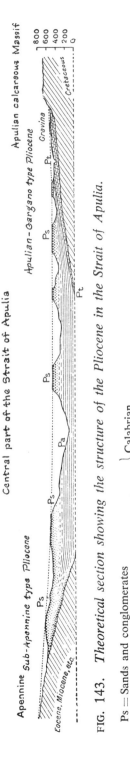

FIG. 143. *Theoretical section showing the structure of the Pliocene in the Strait of Apulia.*

Ps = Sands and conglomerates   {upper} Calabrian
Pa = Sandy clays and plastic clays   {lower} Early Pliocene

Pt = Calcareous molasse (tufa)
Dashed line indicates the top of the Pliocene fill.
Approximate scale: Horizontal 1/300,000; vertical 1/80,000.

Showing the contrast between an Apulian-Garganian type, in which the thickness is greatly reduced while at the same time organic calcareous molasse (*matérin faciès*) appears at the base, and the sub-Apennine type, characterized by enormous thicknesses of sand and conglomerate.

582

lacustrine. Mammalian fossils are found there, especially abundant in the upper Pliocene (celebrated Villafranchian deposits of the Arno Valley, above Florence).

On the Tyrrhenian slope, the Pliocene border is less continuous. For long distances on the coasts, no traces of marine Pliocene are seen, which leads to the belief in the existence of an emerged land (or Tyrrhenides, p. 524) at this epoch, perhaps connected with Corsica and Sardinia,[83] with Maures and Esterel, which was submerged in the Quaternary. East of this Tyrrhenides are found the fine Calabrian deposits of Monte Mario near Rome (Fig. 142) and of Vallebiaja near Leghorn.[84]

3. *Pliocene of the French Mediterranean Coasts*

The Pliocene here forms scarcely more than gulfs, corresponding to the mouths of the present great valleys.

The small gulfs of the Ligurian Riviera are succeeded by those of the French Côte d'Azur. The most important is that of Nice, filled with gravels of the Pliocene Var (Pliocene delta of the Var) which, overlying Plaisancian clays, rise more than 600 m., sometimes faulted and trimmed off along the north shore of the former gulf, thus bearing witness to the persistence of Alpine folding. On the southwest border, however, against the tabular region of the Jurassic calcareous plateaus north of Antibes, organic facies reappear: the Biot molasse with brachiopods and amphistegines.

Still farther west, in the Argens gulf, between Maures and Esterel, a clayey Pliocene is found, never more than 100 m. in altitude.[85]

Next, all along the shore of Maures, as far as Marseille, there is no trace of the Pliocene.

It reappears in the Rhône valley, where the sea insinuated itself in a narrow gulf or *rias,* wrongly called a Pliocene fjord, which has been minutely reconstructed by Fontannes. It was evidently an ancient valley, excavated in the Miocene hills during the Mio-Pliocene regression, then invaded by the sea which ascended as far as 20 km. south of Lyon, pushing fingers into the tributary valleys, especially on the left bank (Fig. 135). Thus the Durance valley was invaded as far as the foot of the Luberon, that of the Drôme as far as Crest, that of the Isère as far as Châteauneuf, where the Pliocene marls have been reached by the foundations of the hydroelectric plant of Beaumont-Monteux.

In these quiet waters, the Plaisancian facies especially develops, with *Ostrea cochlear, Venus multilamella, Nassa semistriata,* species which are still living on the muddy bottom of the present Mediterranean. Its blue clays hold captive sheets of underground water, feeding some of the artesian wells near Carpentras and Visan,[86] thus facilitating the culture of early vegetables.

Near the shores, especially at the beginning and the end of the period, there were brackish facies with potamids, lacustrine beds (marls with *Helix* and lignites of Hauterive, Drôme) or fluviatile beds (sands of Lens-Lestang, Drôme). Finally, this series of Pliocene fill ends with Villafranchian alluvium, which toward the east covers the Lower Dauphiné plateaus, cut in the Miocene molasse. Profoundly altered, reduced to a clayey surface with quartzite pebbles, this old alluvium forms the soil of the *Terres-Froides,* abandoned to thin, swampy forests (plateaus of Chambaran and Bonnevaux, Fig. 154).

During this period, the Pliocene gulf, north of Lyon, ended in a vast lacustrine basin which can be compared to the freshwater gulfs in Bothnia and Finland in which the Baltic Sea ends today. It is called the Bressan Lake, extending from the Massif Central to the Jura Mountains and the Jura side of the Morvano-Vosgian threshold. In this great basin of subsidence (comparable to the intra-Apennine depressions) which occupied all the lower valley of the Saône, enormous thicknesses of lacustrine clays (Bresse marls) accumulated, in which are found paladines which recall, in less developed form, those of the Levantine Pliocene lakes (p. 591). However, at certain places at least, the base of these marls, visible at the bottom of ravines cut into the southern edge of the plateau of the Dombes, still contains a fauna of pelecypods (*Unio*) and of mammals with Pontian affinities.[87] In the upper part, lignite beds[88] are developed, formed by the debris of a forest vegetation, doubtless brought by streams descending from the Jura Mountains: wood from pines, *Sequoia* and *Taxodium distichum* (or *mexicanum*), forms with North American affinities, also found in the Neogene lignites of Northern Germany.

On the right bank of the Rhône, at Théziers (Gard), opposite Avignon, the curious and too little known site of the Fournès troughs shows the only French countryside which can give an idea of the sub-Apennine Plaisancian, with its *calanchi.*

In Languedoc, the old Pliocene shores follow along the foot of the Cretaceous wastelands north of Nîmes, at about 150 to 200 m. altitude, as far as Montpellier, where yellow sands with an Astian fauna contain one of the finest mammalian assemblages known for the early Pliocene.

Finally, after an interruption corresponding to the Massif of Corbières, the beautiful Pliocene Gulf of the Roussillon is outlined, in which a Plaisancian and an Astian contain an equally famous mammalian fauna, whose study inaugurated the scientific career of C. Depéret.[89]

4. *Pliocene of the Iberian Coasts*

In the north, a very fine marine Pliocene is known in the Gulf of Ampourdan (near Rosas), symmetrical with the Roussillon, across the Pyrenean chain of the Albères, and also in the Gulf of Llobregat, at Barcelona. The Pliocene sea likewise advanced into the lower valley of the Ebro. But farther south, the marine Pliocene seems to be missing in the sub-Betic zone facing the Balearics, as well as in the islands themselves. Perhaps there was an emerged land. At any rate, the great gulf ascending the valley of the Guadalquivir from the Atlantic was certainly not connected with the Mediterranean (p. 571). On the other hand, the Pliocene sea sent several gulfs (Vera, Almeria, Malaga) into the southern slope of the Betic chain,[90] showing that the central part of the Betic-Rifian Massif was submerged, making way for a Strait of Gibraltar, wider than today.

And in fact, on the Portugese coast north of the Tagus, a very fossiliferous Atlantic Pliocene is found, the fauna of which differs in no way from that of the Mediterranean Pliocene.

5. *The Pliocene of French North Africa*

A. Morocco. We already know that the Strait of Gibraltar was open in the Pliocene. The Mediterranean was nibbling on the Moroccan coast, cutting into it the little Tetuan Gulf.

Farther south, a North-Moroccan Atlantic Gulf was closed off in the South Rifian depression. Between Safi and Magazan, the Pliocene is no longer found along the coast, only in the interior, in Doukkala. This led Yovano-vitch to claim the existence of a strait of Doukkala but Gigout [91] has shown that the Pliocene on the coastal plateau was removed by erosion and that this never was a strait closed on the Atlantic side, another example of the caution which should be used in attempting paleogeographic reconstructions.

B. Algeria. A great gulf corresponds to the Sahel of Oran and the lower valley of the Chélif. Its deposits, stratigraphically independent of those of the upper Miocene of the same region (Dalloni), are composed of the usual succession of blue marls with Plaisancian facies, yellow sands called Astian and Villafranchian alluvium. The whole series is folded into anticlines with dips up to 45° (Lafitte, see note 146, chap. 11). Another gulf corresponds to the Sahel of Algiers, extending eastward into the Kabylie Massif, as far as the Tizi-Ouzou Basin, of which Dalloni[92] has recently made a paleo-geographic map. Here the blue marls in the vicinity of Algiers had been attributed to the Sahelian.[93] Dalloni has shown that they contain a typical Plaisancian fauna. But, as is frequently true in the Mediterranean Pliocene, the most fossiliferous horizon is found in the transition beds between the marls and yellow sands. The fauna here described by Lamothe and Dautzen-berg is one of the richest known for this stage and moreover differs in no way from the Italian faunas.

Finally, as in France, the Pliocene deposition ends with Villafranchian alluvium. The marine Calabrian is unknown up to the present time.

C. Tunisia. The Cap Bon anticline, with a Nummulitic and Miocene core, is encircled with a border of marine Pliocene, described as Sahelian by Stchepinski (p. 574). Farther north, near Bizerte, R. Lafitte and E. Dumon[94] have just described a complete Pliocene series, folded like that of Oran, and topped by alluvium with a Villafranchian fauna.

VI. The Pliocene in Western and Central France

1. *The Marine Pliocene of Brittany*

In the whole stretch of French coastline between Belgium and Spain, it is only on the border of the Armorican Massif that paleontologically dated marine Pliocene is known. Even here the faunas are rather poor.

Later we shall study the shelly sands or Crags, deposited on the English coast by a Pliocene Channel. On the French coast, this sea left only two witnesses: 1st. marls cropping out at Bosq d'Aubigny, containing *Nassa prismatica* and *N. conglobata,* extinct species well known in the Pliocene; these marls were deposited in a gulf which must have opened out on the coast east of the Cotentin, south of Carentan. 2nd. On the west coast of this peninsula, at Blainville-sur-Mer, west of Coutances, Quaternary sands contain redeposited shells with a brown patina like that on specimens from the Crags of England. There is even a large, ridged *Pectunculus* with American affinities, unknown at Bosq d'Aubigny, which can be explained by assuming that this ancient gulf of Blainville opened toward the west,[95] toward the Atlantic.

This Pliocene Atlantic pushed a gulf into the Lower Loire where it deposited sands and clays with marine fossils at St. Jean-la-Poterie, near Redon.[96] In this region, the formation of the "red sands of Brittany" also was long attributed to a continental Pliocene, developed especially in the Lower Loire, up to an altitude of 96 m. Y. Milon[97] has established, in fact, the existence of glauconite, a mineral which is never formed in continental deposits and may be considered as a "characteristic fossil" of marine facies. So these red sands probably represent ancient marine, glauconitic sands, decalcified and oxidized (like the Diestian of Belgium) and the Pliocene seas were probably more extensive than had been believed.

2. *The Great Pliocene Volcanoes of the Massif Central*

We mention these volcanoes briefly here, as an example of the stratigraphic history of a volcanic massif.[98]

The oldest manifestations of Tertiary vulcanism in the Massif Central surely go back to the Oligocene in the Limagne (p. 497). And the first well-dated lava flows of Mont-Dore are of Pontian age. At the base of the great volcano the lava flows are associated with plant-bearing tuffs of this age (Bourboule deposit). Alluvium and sands with flints containing the Pontian fauna with *Hipparion gracile* date the oldest flows of Cantal (Puy-Courny deposit, near Aurillac), of Velay and the Coirons plateau west of Montélimar (deposit of Aubignas, near Privas).

But it was principally during the lower Pliocene that the great volcanic piles of Cantal and Mont-Dore were erected. Before being attacked by Quaternary erosion these must have been comparable to Mount Etna today. The mud and lava flows of Cantal, reaching 1,000 m. thickness, descended the sides of this cone, covering ash containing lower Pliocene plants and insects. The massifs of Mézenc and Mégal in Velay also date from this period, for they are anterior to the alluvial deposits of the *Mastodon* sands (*M. arvernensis, M. cuvieri*) known around the Puy. And the great eruptions of Cantal and Mont-Dore ended in the upper Pliocene, as shown by the alluvium and mud flows which, descending from Mont-Dore, contain a rich Villafranchian mammalian fauna in the famous Perrier deposit (near Issoire, note 10, this chap.). In the upper Pliocene also, huge basaltic flows were discharged, issuing, no doubt, from a large number of vents, extending all around Cantal, Mont-Dore (Limagne), between these two massifs (Planèze) and in the Cézallier. Deeply gashed by Quaternary erosion, they are known as plateau basalts and thus form, in the Massif Central, the equivalent of the Villafranchian alluvial plateaus described on the border of the Alps in Lower Dauphiné.

We know, however, that these eruptions continued in the Quaternary in the Chaîne des Puys and in Velay and its dependents.

VII. The Neogene of Eastern Europe

1. *Lower and Middle Miocene of Normal Type*

In the whole immense eastern domain (Fig. 133), the lower Miocene (Burdigalian), though often poorly understood, still has a normal type with faunas identical to those of the western Mediterranean. We shall not dwell on it.

This is also true for the lower Vindobonian, where facies, similar to those described farther west, are found. Thus, there are organic facies at this period on the border of the Russian platform along old flat coasts that were poor in continental materials. These facies contain limestones with bryozoans and *Lithothamnium,* similar to the Leitha limestone. On the other hand along the Carpathians, as along the Alps, terrigenous facies predominate. There the Burdigalian is represented by conglomerates transgressive over previously folded formations, followed by very thick Vindobonian marls, dated by the Schlier fauna, but often having lagoonal facies. The Miocene itself is much folded.

So in Galicia, on the border of the Polish Carpathians, thick beds of rock salt (salt deposits of Bochnia, and Wieliczka, Fig. 133) and potassium salts (Stebnyk, Kalysz) are found above the Burdigalian conglomerates (of Sloboda Rungurska). These deposits of a dying Miocene sea (E. Suess) are called the saliferous formation. It has recently been established that beneath the conglomerates, there are also salt beds, assignable to an "Aquitanian."

These two lagoonal horizons are found at the foot of the Romanian Carpathians but here the best developed salt-bearing horizon (salt deposits of Slanic, etc.) is located beneath the Burdigalian conglomerates (here called Pietrician). This is the salt-massif formation or Cornu beds, attributed, without decisive proof, to the Aquitanian.

Moreover, here we are in the region of the oil fields of Poland (Boryslaw) and Romania, where oil-bearing horizons are found from the Eocene Carpathian Flysch up to the Pliocene of the Romanian sub-Carpathians. But despite the research needed for the exploitation, the tectonics are so complicated that the stratigraphy of this sub-Carpathian Miocene is very difficult.[99]

Finally, in the immense eastern plains, appear the overlying deposits of an upper Miocene of eastern type. A complete succession may be seen in the Kerch peninsula (Crimea), for example.

2. *Upper Miocene and Pliocene of the Eastern Type*

Beginning with the Vindobonian, the seas covering eastern Mediterranean regions, east of the Carpathians and Balkans, become separated from the western Mediterranean. In the great inland sea created by this isolation, the biological conditions (especially the salinity) developed separately and special faunas were differentiated, becoming the eastern type of the Neogene.

The lacustrine or marine basins which today represent the remains of this inland sea are Lake Balaton in Hungary, the Black Sea, the Caspian and the Aral Sea. But study of the faunas and distribution of Neogene deposits[100] leads to the distinction of a certain number of basins in this inland sea, which were either separated or connected according to the epoch. From west to east, these basins are:

1st. A western or *Pannonian Basin:* Lake Balaton is the only present survivor of this basin. It is included between the arc of the Carpathians and the Balkan Mountains. Its northwest extremity is none other than the intra-Alpine Vienna Basin, described earlier. At its southeast extremity it communicated, through the Danube Valley at the Iron Gates, with the Dacian Basin, the first of the three following basins called eastern, and which were united, at certain periods, in a vast Pontian Basin (Fig. 133).

2nd. *The Dacian Basin.* This extended principally over the lower valley of the Danube, the external border of the Romanian Carpathians and the Bessarabian plains as far as the vicinity of Odessa, Cherson and the Crimean Mountains. Thus the Black Sea is its present remnant. The ancient Massif of Dobrogea formed an island in it.

3rd. *The Euxine Basin.* This included the eastern part of the Black Sea and the Sea of Azov. Its deposits are found especially in the region of Kerch and at the end of the Black Sea (Batum, Kuban).

4th. *The Caspian (or Aral-Caspian) Basin.* This basin stretched northward far beyond the present Caspian (as far as Saratov and Samara) and eastward as far as the Aral Sea, at certain periods.

A brief description of the evolution of faunas in these different basins will give a magnificent example of stratigraphic methods.[101] Follow this explanation on the diagram in Fig. 144.

A. Sarmatian.[102] This stage may be considered as the approximate equivalent of the upper Vindobonian of the normal type.[103] The fauna is still marine, though of an inland sea. Pelecypods, gastropods and bryozoans are very abundant, to the exclusion of almost all other groups of animals. In addition, the species, although represented by an enormous number of individuals, have little variety. Along with a few brackish forms sparsely represented everywhere in the normal Miocene (for example, *Cerithium pictum, C. rubiginosum*), are found peculiar types, such as *Ervilia podolica, Mactra caspia, Tapes gregaria,* etc. This double character, wealth of individuals but poverty of species, is completely characteristic of the impoverished faunas of inland seas (pp. 215, 279). So a kind of residue of the normal Vindobonian fauna must be seen in the Sarmatian fauna, a residue selected

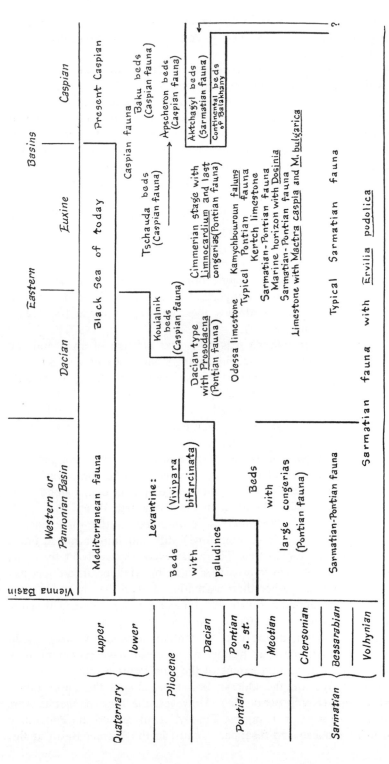

FIG. 144. *Diagrammatic chart showing the succession of stages and faunas in the eastern European province, in the upper Miocene and in the Pliocene. (After an analogous chart by N. Andrussov, simplified and completed.)*

N. B. The heavy lines indicate the divisions between the various basins, in which different faunas develop. For the Quaternary, the very complicated details of the marine invasions and the faunal migrations are not shown.

589

by the special biologic conditions of the inland sea, in which certain forms, preadapted to these conditions (Cuénot), could survive and rapidly evolve in this isolated medium.

1st. In the lower Sarmatian (*Volhynian*) our four basins were connected. The fauna is that of the *Cerithium* beds of the Vienna Basin, with *Ervilia podolica, Mactra podolica, Trochus pictus, Tapes gregaria,* etc.

2nd. In the middle Sarmatian (*Bessarabian*), the Pannonian basin was isolated. In the three eastern basins, interconnected, the fauna acquired its maximum richness, with organic calcareous facies. Thus, in Bessarabia, the type region, there are limestones with *Nubecularia novorossica;* at Kerch and in the Taman, bryozoan reefs.[104] On the other hand, in the isolated Pannonian Basin, the salinity diminished during this period. There are sometimes freshwater deposits, sometimes beds in which the Pontian *Congeria* fauna, to be taken up immediately, begins to appear (in the Vienna Basin especially).

3rd. In the upper Sarmatian (*Chersonian,* from Cherson or Kherson, east of Odessa) the inland sea fauna became impoverished in the three eastern basins. Pontian transitional forms appear. In the still isolated Pannonian Basin, at this moment, there was already the true Pontian fauna (beds with large congerias of the Vienna Basin).

B. Pontian.   The Pontian fauna was no longer a fauna of an inland salt sea, as was the Sarmatian, but a freshened lagoonal fauna of a "lake-sea," as Russian geologists say. However, as we shall see, this fauna is directly related to that of the present Caspian.

Poverty of species is still accentuated. The most characteristic elements are the large species of *Congeria* and innumerable, quite varied examples of *Cardium,* all sprung, no doubt, from *Cardium edule,* living since the Miocene in the small lagoons of our western seas, but which, becoming king of this immense Pontian-Caspian domain, expanded in multiple variations (reduction of the hinge, thinning of the shell, development of the siphon).[105] Large congerias are especially abundant in the Pannonian Basin.

1st. The lower Pontian (*Meotian*) is represented in the three eastern basins by deposits (example, Kerch limestone) still containing a mixed fauna with Sarmato-Pontian characteristics. There are even, especially at the base, some purely marine forms (*Dosinia exoleta,* a living Mediterranean species) with affinities Vindobonian rather than Sarmatian. But in the always isolated and more freshened Pannonian Basin, the typical Pontian fauna with large congerias, which appeared in the Chersonian, naturally persists.[106]

2nd. On the other hand, in the middle Pontian (*Pontian, s. str.*) conditions became uniform in the four basins, which must have communicated. This was the period of maximum extent of the true Pontian fauna. The type formations of the stage are the Odessa limestones[107] and the lower faluns of Kamych-Bouroun (Kerch peninsula). However, the large congerias were more abundant in the west, in Hungary. Finally, at this period the Pannonian Basin began to be reduced and disappear. Thus, in the Vienna Basin at this moment there were only purely lacustrine beds with paludines, with the Belvedere *Hipparion* fauna (p. 570).

3rd. The upper Pontian (*Dacian*) corresponds to a period of regression. In the Pannonian domain only freshwater lakes remained in which were deposited beds with unios and paludines, ending with a characteristic horizon containing *Paludina* (*Vivipara*) *bifarcinata*.[108] As for the three eastern basins, there was no longer intercommunication, for each of them contained special faunas. In the Dacian Basin, there are beds with large cardiids (*Prosodacna*) and *Vivipara* (the horizon with *V. bifarcinata* is found here), and *Congeria*, which, on the border of the Romanian Carpathians, constitute the semi-lacustrine type of the stage. In the Euxine Basin, the fauna, sometimes taken as type for a Cimmerian stage, is very close to that of the present Caspian, with *Limnocardium* and *Congeria*. In the Caspian domain, however, above the thick continental oil-bearing series of the Balakhany beds, a very different fauna is found, that of the Aktchagyl beds, discovered by Andrussov. Very curiously, these show marine affinities (*Cardium, Mactra* close to *caspia, Potamides*) and resemble the Sarmatian fauna. We do not know, however, any region where the Sarmatian fauna could have persisted during the Pontian *s. str.* to thus reappear in the beds of Aktchagyl.

C. Pliocene. At this time, the unity of the great Euxine-Caspian lake-sea was reestablished. Its sediments are the type, called Plio-Caspian, of the eastern Pliocene. Faunas of the Caspian type are found in the Euxine domain (Kouialnik beds, near Odessa, at the base, and at the top, Tschauda beds of Cape Tschauda, on the south shore of the Kerch peninsula) as well as in the Caspian domain (at the base, Apsheron beds, at the top, Baku beds, the latter sometimes being classified as Quaternary).

During this period there were only freshwater lakes in the western part of the Dacian basin, from Bessarabia as far as the Romanian Carpathians and throughout the Pannonian Basin. This is the Levantine facies of the Pliocene.

This Levantine fauna is very different from the contemporaneous Caspian fauna, for it includes only freshwater species, unios, dreissensias, and particularly paludines. Especially well known is the classic example of the evolutionary series of paludines studied by Neumayr, beginning with smooth forms and culminating in twisted and ornamented forms.

The Levantine formations are deposited in three principal lacustrine regions: 1) a Pannonian lake, covering the Hungarian plains, having started in the Dacian, as we have seen, where the classic *Paludina* beds of Slavonia are found; 2) a Dacian lake, separated from the former by the curve of the Carpathians near the Iron Gates and covering the plains of the lower Danube, differentiated after the Dacian and corresponding to the *Paludina* beds of Romania; 3) an Aegean lake, corresponding to the Sea of Marmara and a good part of the Aegean Sea of today (Adrianople, Greece, Island of Kos).[109]

These lakes have disappeared today. Through the Dardanelles, opened in the Quaternary, the waters of the Mediterranean invaded the domain of the Aegean and the Black Sea, bringing the normal Mediterranean fauna, which replaced the Levantine and Caspian faunas. The latter exists only in the Caspian and Aral Seas which have, up to date, escaped the Mediterranean invasion.[110] As for the Levantine fauna, its descendants are found in Lake Baikal [111] and as far as the lakes and streams of Yunnan. Thus the migrations of these marine, brackish or lacustrine populations are shown by a veritable flight toward the east.

VIII. The Neogene of the North Sea Basin

The Neogene formations of the North Sea region[112] are extremely difficult to synchronize with the Mediterranean types. This is first because this is a different faunal province. Thus, the pectinids, so frequent in the Mediterranean Miocene, are almost absent, as are the cerithids. The single northern *Cerithium* is *C. lignitarum* of Bolderberg (Belgian Miocene). Second, the outcrop conditions are much less favorable. Natural sections are rare (cliffs of Essex, Suffolk and the Island of Sylt). Usually, we are reduced to limited observations derived from wells or excavations, for the Quaternary formations cover almost everything.

The Neogene facies, moreover, are extremely monotonous, always sands, more or less clayey or glauconitic.

1. *The Miocene Seas*

A. Lower Miocene. An important regression took place between the Oligocene and Miocene, so that the lower Miocene does not crop out in England, Belgium or Holland,[113] but only in Denmark, Schleswig-Holstein and the region of Hamburg. These outcrops are composed of fossiliferous sands and sandstones, some tens of meters thick, constituting the Vierländer stage of German geologists.[114] A part of the blocks of shelly sandstone scattered by ancient glaciers and known as Holsteinergestein (Holstein stone) comes from this formation.

The fauna still includes 60% of Oligocene species, of northern stamp, and a very small number of species existing in the Aquitanian-Burdigalian of Aquitaine, but without relatives in the German upper Oligocene. Finally, there are some forms which do not appear in the Mediterranean province until the middle Miocene. On the whole, Kautsky correlates the Vierländer stage with the French Burdigalian, not the Aquitanian. Communication with the Miocene Bordeaux basin was apparently made north of Scotland, for northeast of the Orkneys, in the North Sea, there are deposits which can be attributed, through their fauna, to the lower Miocene.

B. Middle Miocene. An important transgression took place west of the Elbe River. The sea invaded northern Hanover, reaching Bremen and Osnabrück. According to Kautsky, it must even have communicated, through Posen and Silesia, with the peri-Alpine sea.[115] This would explain the appearance of numerous forms with northern affinities in the Vienna Basin in the middle Miocene (p. 569). In any case, the sea spread over Holland and eastern Campine, where recent wells have passed through fossiliferous, glauconitic sands. This is the horizon called Hemmoor stage[116] in Germany and it passes laterally into compact clays without fossils (Hamburg clay). It is enclosed between two beds of sand containing lignite, indicating regressions, isolating this stage in relation to the lower and upper Miocene. In Belgium, a long-known outcrop exists at Bolderberg near Hasselt.[117] It has served as type for the *Bolderian* stage of the Belgians.

Many shells (22%) appear, known from the Burdigalian in Aquitaine but missing in the German lower Miocene. The faunas, studied by Kautsky, contain 129 species common to the Helvetian of Touraine. Thus a communication at this period, between the Atlantic and the North Sea, via the English Channel, may be assumed. It is precisely from this Miocene Channel that the "Falunian" transgression of Cotentin started (p. 576).

C. Upper Miocene. Compared to the Tortonian by Kautsky, this stage is represented in Germany (Hamburg-Lübeck region) and Schleswig-Holstein by a fossiliferous horizon called "Dingden-Reinbeck stage," in which most of the forms with southern affinities disappear, and by the lower part of the micaceous clays (Glimmerton) in which the northern stamp is accentuated. Astartes and certain fusids, which persisted in the northern Pliocene seas, began to develop. It is often considered that the region of Bremen and Hanover was emergent then (this is the hypothesis set forth in Fig. 145). Kautsky believes, however, that the upper Miocene is represented everywhere in the vicinity of Bremen by non-fossiliferous micaceous clays overlying the middle Miocene. In the island of Sylt, these clays are visible in the cliffs of Morsum and K. Gripp recently discovered there a tooth of *Hipparion* showing that they rise as high as the Pontian.

In any case, the sea was transgressive over western Campine. It reached the outskirts of Antwerp, where very fossiliferous, glauconitic sands directly overlie the Stampian clays of Boom. This is the *Anversian* stage of the Belgians, ending with a bed of molds of *Pectunculus pilosus* (a still living pelecypod).

2. The Pliocene Seas

The island of Sylt seems to be the only spot in Denmark or Germany where the Pliocene crops out. For, above the micaceous clays, the Neogene series continues with limonitic sandstone which can be attributed to the base of the Pliocene. But recently some early Pliocene was discovered in a well southeast of Tönder (northern Schleswig), at 80 m. depth.[118] On the other hand, Belgium and England were broadly invaded at this epoch.

A. Belgium. In fact, an important transgression covered Flanders and Brabant. On the surfaces of the Flemish hills and as far as south of Brussels, there are oxidized and decalcified sands, without fossils, the type of the

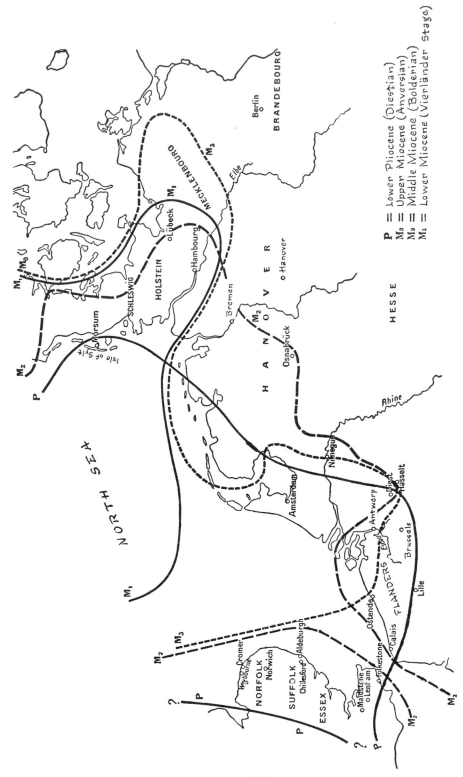

FIG. 145. *Map showing the boundaries (very hypothetical) of the North Sea in the Neogene (in part after Gripp, von Linstow and Tesch, 1942).*

P = Lower Pliocene (Diestian)
M₃ = Upper Miocene (Anversian)
M₂ = Middle Miocene (Bolderian)
M₁ = Lower Miocene (Vierländer Stage)

Diestian (from Diest). But, at Antwerp, buried under more recent sediments, these sands remain glauconitic and rich in very well preserved shells, especially *Terebratula perforata* (an extinct species) at the base, *Isocardia cor* (a living species) at the top.

Then the sea withdrew. The last marine beds deposited in Belgium are confined to the Campine. The debris produced in digging the Antwerp basins shows extraordinarily fossiliferous glauconitic sands beneath the Quaternary. This is the *Scaldisian* (from Escaut) whose uppermost beds assume a very littoral facies (Poederlian). Villafranchian mammals, providing a valuable guide, are found in it. The Neogene ends with the thick series of sands and clays of Campine, fluviatile or estuarine deposits, whose thicknesses increase proportionally toward the northeast. In Holland, they pass partially into marine beds (Amstelian, from Amstel River of Amsterdam). This Amstelian is no longer northern in character, but it is overlain transgressively by the *Icenian,* which reached the Holland-Belgian frontier and which, through its northern-arctic fauna, is equivalent to the Crags of Chillesford and Weybourne in England.[119]

B. England. It seems clear that Britain must have been entirely emergent until the Anversian.[120] Thus the folds of the Weald, of the Isle of Wight, etc. (p. 485) apparently were formed during the Miocene.

The oldest Neogene deposits known have, in fact, a Diestian fauna. There are the *Lenham beds* or coarse sands, found in isolated outcrops on the surface of the North Downs between Folkestone and Maidstone. Shells with a southern stamp are quite abundant, so a communication with the Atlantic at the beginning of the Pliocene may be assumed, perhaps by way of the northern part of the Weald. In fact, at St. Erth, at the foot of the Land's End peninsula, deposits of ancient beaches of about this period are known, containing southern species, some of which are unknown elsewhere in Britain. These are evidences of a Pliocene Channel, traces of which we have already found in Brittany (p. 586).

This warm character of the fauna persists, though weakening, in the Coralline *Crag* (crag = shelly sand), cropping out near Aldeburgh (Suffolk). Abundant bryozoans are found there, formerly taken for corals, from which the sands were named.

On the other hand, in the overlying Red Crag, which crops out over wide surfaces in Suffolk, the warm species have completely disappeared and only cold forms remain. Probably the connections with the Atlantic were suspended.

This English Pliocene series[121] finally concludes with the fluvio-marine Crag of Norwich, very extensive in Suffolk north of Aldeburgh and in Norfolk between Norwich and the sea. This is the Icenian stage of British geologists. In fact, new northern forms appear, due perhaps to the chilling at the end of the Pliocene, a phenomenon comparable to that explained in the Mediterranean Calabrian. Indeed the Norwich Crag contains a Villafranchian mammalian fauna, as do the Chillesford beds and the Weybourne Crag, which follow, with marine mollusks showing arctic affinities.

3. *The Neogene Lignites of Northern Germany*[122]

Beyond low coasts with changing contours, under the mild and humid climate, vast lakes or lagoons of fresh water and immense estuaries stretched out, here and there, over the plains of northern Germany. This must have been a landscape similar to that shown today by the coastal plains of the lower Mississippi, with their swamps or swampy forests (p. 163).

The remains of these Neogene forests, buried under sands and muds, are found in the form of lignites. The analogy with the swampy forests is complete to the same forest species: *Taxodium distichum* (bald cypress) and *Sequoia,* with their roots still in place and trunks overturned after the death of the tree.[123] These lignite beds, sometimes 100 m. thick and exploitable in open pits, form part of Germany's wealth. They extend into Pomerania, Brandenburg, Saxony, Silesia, and the low plains of the lower Rhine. Through Hesse, the region of Vogelsberg where they are associated with important volcanic formations, and Wetterau, they extend into the Mainz Basin, thus following the same route as the Oligocene sea.

As shown by the faunas of freshwater mollusks and mammals (in particular the famous Pontian occurrence of Eppelsheim, in the Mainz Basin) these lignite formations are distributed through all the stages of the Tertiary. They begin, as we have said (p. 491) with the Eocene and continue during the Oligocene (note 92, chap. 9). The largest part are of Miocene age, the period in which we have seen them mingled with the marine deposits of the North Sea, and some are of upper Pliocene age. Doubtless it was the chilling at the end of the Pliocene which killed the forests. Certain mollusks[124] belong to special faunas of eastern type. They reached that far, no doubt, by passing from lake to lake through the Vienna Basin and Württemberg. But to them also, less fortunate than their companions who reached the Orient (p. 592), the chilling at the end of the Pliocene was fatal.

REFERENCE NOTES

1. For we would not say that the movements of the seas were *exactly* contemporaneous everywhere, which would be to adopt the eustatic theory *a priori* (p. 19).

2. C. Depéret and F. Roman, *Monographie des Pectinidés néogènes de l'Europe et des régions voisines,* Mém. Soc. géol. France, no. 26 and n. s., no. 10; followed by J. Roger, *Le genre Chlamys dans les formations néogènes de l'Europe. Conclusions générales sur la répartition géographique et stratigraphique des Pectinidés du Tertiaire récent,* ibid., 17 (1938–39). F. Kautsky, *Die biostratigraphische Bedeutung der Pectiniden des niederösterreichischen Miozäns,* Ann. Natur.-hist. Mus., Vienna, 42 (1928).

3. Cf. G. Cottreau, *Les Echinidés du Bassin méditerranéen, époque néogène,* Thèse Sc., Paris (1913); Ann. Inst. Océanogr., VI, 3.

4. Remember that all the geologists of central and eastern Europe classify the Pontian in the Pliocene. It is a question of choice. See later, p. 559, a discussion of the Sahelian stage.

5. To such a point that many Italian geologists (De Stefani) consider these stages only as paleogeographic episodes or as local facies, whose interest lies especially in that they are often found in the same successive order. So it seems a bit daring to wish to

find everywhere (North Africa, Spain, etc.) precisely the Burdigalian, Helvetian and Tortonian stages defined in Aquitania, Italy and Austria, relying on a few pectinids. The essential thing is to establish local stratigraphies first and to generalize from them with caution.

6. See M. Gignoux, *Les formations marines pliocènes et quaternaires de l'Italie du Sud et de la Sicile*, Thèse Sc., Lyon (1913); Ann. Univ. Lyon, 1, 36); *Le Pliocène et le Quaternaire marins dans la Méditerranée occidentale*, C. R. Internat. Geol. Congress in Belgium, Brussels (1922).

7. Strictly speaking, a new name should be created. The old name Pannonian (from the Pannonian Basin, Hungary) is at present used in the restricted sense of lower Pontian (Meotian).

8. For the Pliocene (and Quaternary) floras, an excellent general statement, with bibliography, in G. Depape, *Le monde des plantes à l'apparition de l'homme en Europe occidentale (flores récentes de France, d'Angleterre, des Pays-Bas)*, Ann. Soc. Sc. de Bruxelles, 48 (1928), ser. B, pp. 39–102.

9. For the upper part of the Villafranchian, in which Mastodons are no longer found, the sub-stage name St. Prestian (from St. Prest) has been proposed.

10. New data by Stehlin, Dangeard, and Michel-Lévy on this famous deposit are included in P. Bout, *Observations géologiques sur le plateau de Perrier*, Bull. Soc. Hist. nat. d'Auvergne (July, 1933), and A. Viret, *Observations relatives à l'âge des sables pliocènes de Perrier*, Bull. Soc. Hist. nat. Toulouse, 65 (1933). See recent restatement in the memoir by J. Jung, cited note 33, chap. 1.

11. Actually, these "large antelopes" (*Palaeoryx*) of Roussillon are nearer the Bovidae. Arambourg and Piveteau, Soc. géol. France (May 27, 1929) made the type for a new genus *Parabos*.

12. The most recent work on the Pontian faunas is that of Arambourg and Piveteau, *Les Vertébrés du Pontien de Salonique*, Ann. de Paléon., 18 (1929).

13. F. Roman and J. Viret, *La faune de Mammifères du Burdigalien de la Romieu (Gers)*, Mém. Soc. géol. France, n. s., Mém. no. 21 (1934).

14. C. Arambourg, *Le Dinotherium des gisements de l'Omo (Abyssinie)*, Bull. Soc. géol. France, 5 sér. 4 (1934).

15. R. Laffitte, *Sur l'étage Sahélien Pomel*, Bull. Soc. Hist. nat. Afrique de N., meeting of Feb. 14 (1948). I wish to thank this obliging colleague for his useful information.

16. Perhaps with even too much clearness and precision. We shall in fact see that sometimes detailed stratigraphic sections are definite only with respect to facies, or to species of pectinids thought characteristic of paleontologic zones, but clearly connected only to facies. For the Rhône Burdigalian in particular, it is a little like the Parisian Bartonian or Stampian, in which it must be recognized that the multiple paleontologic horizons of the first stratigraphers have no true individuality. So we cannot unreservedly subscribe to the detailed paleogeographic reconstructions described by C. Combaluzier, *Le Miocène de la Basse-Provence*, Bull. Serv. Carte géol. France, no. 182 (1932).

17. Very often with *impressionné* cobbles. See L. Moret, *Précis de Géologie*, p. 181, 183. A recent bibliography on this curious problem (and the not less curious one of stylolites) is presented by P. Macar, *Sur des "cailloux impressionnés" de quartzite trouvés dans le poudingue burnotien à Wéris*, Bull. Soc. belge Geol., 61 (1937–38).

18. Nevertheless, we have seen this *Pecten* appearing in Italy (p. 523) beginning with the Chattian. So, it may be questioned whether the pectinid standards established by Depéret have a very general value. Likewise, the hard sandstone-limestone facies generally considered characteristic of the Burdigalian does not have an unquestionable value for the stage. Thus the Miocene basin of Carpentras (Vaucluse) is girdled by a border of "Burdigalian" sandstone or limestone, for there, the Miocene shores were rocky, composed of Urgonian limestones; in the center of the basin, on the contrary, a substratum composed of Oligocene marls appears in places and on the Avignon sheet the base of the Miocene, there sandy-clayey, is attributed to a transgressive "Vindobonian." We are thus led to this obviously paradoxical conclusion of a transgression which reaches the edges of a basin before invading its center. See p. 550, Note 195.

19. Islands or calcareous coasts, supplying few detrital materials, will perhaps be surrounded by organic, calcareous bottom deposits. That is a general observation which

we have already expressed in saying that "calcareous facies attract each other," see note 166, chap. 8.

20. This species is generally considered characteristic of the Vindobonian. Nevertheless, identical large oysters are known in the Nummulitic of Algiers.

21. A *Hipparion* has recently been found in these marls by G. Denizot, *La Crau, la Camargue et l'Etang de Berre, l^re partie*, Trav. Lab. Geol. Univ. Aix-Marseille, 2 (1939).

22. M. Julien, *Révision de la faune vindobonienne de Saint-Fons*, Trav. Lab. Géol. Fac. Sc., Lyon (1940), fasc. 38, mém. 31. J. Viret, *Sur la coexistence des Equidés Anchitherium et Hipparion en Europe occidentale*, Bull. Soc. géol. France, 15 (1945), has just pointed out there, at the top of the sands with terebratulines, *Hipparion* and *Tragocerus amaltheus*, mammals generally considered characteristic of the Pontian, in which *Anchitherium* does not survive. Thus here would be the transition between the Vindobonian and Pontian faunas.

23. Recent revision of this fauna by E. Ennouchi, *Contribution à l'étude de la faune tortonienne de la Grive St-Alban (Isère)*, Thèse Sc., Paris (1930).

24. There is agreement on the Pontian age of the materials underlying these plateaus. But recently G. Denizot, *Note sur l'extension des cailloutis pliocènes dans le Sud-Est de la France*, Bull. Soc. géol. France, 4 (1934) and A. F. de Lapparent, C. R. Soc. géol. France (Feb. 4, 1935) have maintained that the alluvium of their summits and consequently their topographic form, dates only from the upper Pliocene. However, Goguel, ibid. (Dec. 4, 1933) continues to attribute the whole mass of the alluvium to the Pontian.

25. The arrival of the sea is very frequently indicated by deposits of glauconite covering the pebbles of the conglomerate. This is the classic horizon, known in the Rhône as the "conglomerate with green pebbles," an horizon very convenient as a marker, but whose age varies from one region to another, since it marks the beginning of the transgression.

26. Seen from this angle and on the scale of space and time in which the hardest rocks act like viscous fluids, the uniform progress of this wave of the earth's crust recalls the movement of the iridescence that we can see on a soap bubble and which also results from superficial flow over a fluid surface.

27. The two terms, Swiss Basin or Swiss Plateau, though often used, are thus incorrect. The German Swiss use the term *Mittelland* which is hardly translatable into French.

28. We have mentioned (pp. 514 and 564) this important new concept of a lower marine molasse of Stampian age. So the famous *Nagelfluh* of Rigi belongs to the Oligocene. On this subject, see E. Baumberger, *Zur Tektonik und Altersbestimmung der Molasse am schweizerischen Alpennordrand*, Eclogae geol. Helvetiae, 24 (1931), and the *Guide géologique de la Suisse*, published on the occasion of the fiftieth anniversary of the Soc. géol. suisse (1934).

29. A fauna of freshwater mollusks characteristic of the true Aquitanian (not Chattian) was noted for the first time in the Swiss molasse by E. Baumberger, *Ueber eine aquitanische Molluskenfauna vom Untern Buchberg (Ob. Zürichersee)*, Eclogae geol. Helvetiae, 20 (1927).

30. A. Bersier, *Critérium de durée dans l'Oligocène vaudois*, Bull. Soc. vaudoise Sc. nat., 59 (1936).

31. A. Bersier, *La forme de la transgression burdigalienne dans la région vaudoise*, C. R. Soc. géol. France (Mar. 30, 1936).

32. On this question of glauconite, see H. Renz, *Die subalpine Molasse zwischen Aare und Rhein*, Eclogae geol. Helvetiae, 30 (1937); *Zur Geologie der östlichen St. Gallisch appenzellischen Molasse*, Jahrb. St. Gallischen Naturw. Ges., 69 (1937–1938).

33. *Hipparion*, long unknown in Switzerland, was recently found by Stehlin, but outside the molasse region, in the strips of Pontian alluvium in the vicinity of Basel. On the other hand, H. Tobien, *Ueber Hipparion-Reste aus der Obermiozänen Süsswassermolasse Südwestdeutschlands*, Zeitschr. deutsch. geol. Ges., 90 (1938) found *Hipparion* near Immendingen on the Danube, in an horizon corresponding to the upper beds of Oeningen.

34. Bibliography in the article by Kautsky, cited note 112, this chap., containing information about different recent works on the European Miocene.

35. On the position of the northern shores of the Miocene seas, see H. Kiderlen, *Beiträge zur Stratigraphie und Paläogeographie des süddeutschen Tertiärs*, Neues Jahrb. f. Min., Beilage-Band 66, Abt. B (1931). A. Roll, *Beobachtungen längs der Küste des burdigalen Meeres auf der Schwäbischen Alb*, Zeitschr. deutsch. geol. Ges., 90 (1938). E. Heisenhut, *Geologische Untersuchungen im Bereich des burdigalen Kliffs zwischen Harthausen und Ingstetten (Schwäbische Alb)*, Neues Jahrb. f. Min., Abhandl., Abt. B, 87 (1942).

36. I. Meznerics, *Die Schlierbildungen des mittelsteirischen Beckens*, Mitt. naturwiss. Ver. f. Steiermark, 73, Graz (1936).

37. D. Andrusov, *Karpathen-Miozän und Wiener Becken*, Petroleum, 34, Jahrg., no. 27, Vienna (1938). In the intra-Alpine Basin, certain Helvetian clayey series with Schlier facies were incorrectly attributed to the Nummulitic (for example, the Flysch of Unin).

38. R. Sieber, *Neue Beiträge zur Stratigraphie und Faunengeschichte des österreichischen Jungtertiärs; I. Das niederösterreichische Mittelmiozän*, Petroleum, 33, Jahrg., no. 13 and 18 (1937), insists on the importance of the break between the Burdigalian and Helvetian, while between the Helvetian and the Tortonian there are only differences in facies. This shows that it would be better to adopt the French stages than the Mediterranean stages of E. Suess.

39. F. Kautsky, *Die Bivalven des niederösterreichischen Miozäns (Taxodonta und Veneridae)*, Verh. geol. Bundesanst., Vienna (1932). O. Kühn, *Neue Burdigalausbildung bei Horn*, Sitzungsber, Akad. Wiss. Wien, Math.-nat. Kl., I, 145 (1936). A. Boni, *Studi comparativi fra il Neogene del bacino di Vienna e quello del bacino piemontese-ligure; I, Sabbie e argille a Gaindorf*, Boll. Soc. geol. ital., 56 (1937).

40. A detailed stratigraphy of the beds with congerias in the Vienna Basin, and elsewhere in the whole Pannonian domain, is given in K. Friedl, *Ueber die Gliederung der pannonischen Sedimente des Wiener Beckens*, Mitt. geol. Ges. in Wien, 24, 1931, Vienna (1932).

41. This occurrence, known as Belvedere gravels, is classic. But, as Schaffer has shown, these gravels are Quaternary and gully the Pontian sands from which the mammalian bones actually are derived. See C. Depéret, Bull. Soc. géol. France (1903), p. 631.

42. On the very interesting Miocene of Venetia not discussed here, see R. Fabiani, *Il Terziario del Trentino*, Mem. Ist. geol. Univ. Padova, 6 (1922); G. Stefanini, *Il Neogene veneto*, ibid., 3, 1915) and S. Venzo, *Il Neogene del Trentino, del Veronese e del Bresciano*, Mem. Mus. Storia nat. Venezia tridentina, II, 2, Trento (1934).

43. E. Montanaro, *Studi monografici sulla malacologia modenese, I, I Molluschi tortoniani di Montegibbio*, Paleontographia italica, 35 (1935).

44. P. Principi, *Osservazioni sui terreni terziari del Lazio meridionale*, Boll. Soc. geol. ital., 57 (1938).

45. However Royo y Gomez attributed lagoonal beds with gypsum and potamids to the upper Miocene. See Royo y Gomez, *El Mioceno continental iberico y su fauna malacologica*, Com. de investigaciones pal. y prehist., Mem. no. 30, Madrid (1922); *Notes sur la Géologie de la Péninsule ibérique*, Bull. Soc. géol. France, 4 sér., 25 (1925).

46. A very suggestive description of these regions, with fine photographs, is given by E. Hernandez-Pacheco, *Geologia y Paleontologia del Mioceno de Palencia*, Com. de investig., Mem. no. 5, Madrid (1915).

47. M. Gignoux and P. Fallot, *Contribution à la connaissance des terrains néogènes et quaternaires marins sur les côtes méditerranéennes d'Espagne*, C. R. Internat. geol. Congress in Spain, Madrid (1927).

48. P. Fallot, *Etude géologique de la Sierra de Majorque*, Thèse Sc., Paris (1922).

49. Blumenthal, recalling previous observations of de Orueta, has recently observed that, traversing the Betic Massif itself, an arm of the sea must have existed at least through the Burdigalian, occupying the transverse valley of the Guadalhorce River. See

M. Blumenthal, *Beiträge zur Geologie der betischen Cordilleren beiderseits des Rio Guadalhorce,* Eclogae geol. Helvetiae, 23 (1930).

50. P. Viennot, *Observations géologiques dans la région de Grenade,* Livre jubilaire du Centenaire de la Soc. géol. France (1930).

51. P. Fallot, *Note préliminaire sur les formations néogènes des zones subbétique et bétique selon la transversale de Caravaca (Province de Murcie),* Mem. R. Soc. española de Hist. nat., 15, Madrid (1929).

52. The most recent works on the Moroccan Miocene are summarized by Lacoste, see note 176, chap. 8.

53. G. Lecointre and J. Roger, *La faune de Dar Bel Hamri (Maroc) est d'âge pliocène ancien,* Bull. Mus. Hist. nat., 2 sér., 15 (1943). Actually these authors consider *A. glandiformis* here to be redeposited.

54. J. Bourcart, G. Zbyszewski and A. Chavan, *La faune de Cacela en Algarve (Portugal),* Com. Serv. geol. Portugal (1940), 21. This fauna, called Tortonian, is compared with the fauna called Sahelian of Dar Bel Hamri; an attempt at the Portuguese Miocene stratigraphy and comparison with Andalusia and North Africa. A. Chavan, *Etude complémentaire de la faune de Dar Bel Hamri,* Bull. Soc. géol. France, 14 (1944).

55. South of this strait, in Morocco, are continental formations extending into southern Algeria and Tunisia, which have been attributed to an Oligo-Miocene. At certain places, they contain Pontian mammalian faunas. See G. Choubert, *Note préliminaire sur le Pontien au Maroc,* Bull. Soc. géol. France, 15 (1945).

56. In addition to general works previously cited, see M. Dalloni, *Recherches sur la période néogène dans l'Algérie occidentale,* Bull. Soc. géol. France, 4 sér., 15 (1915).

57. From Cartenna, latin name of Ténès, on the coast between Oran and Algiers.

58. This species is found, however, as early as the base of the Cartennian and hence is not very characteristic. So, we may question whether all this Algerian stratigraphy is really well founded.

59. A rich mammalian deposit in the Pontian of Oran has recently been discovered by M. Suess, C. R. Ac. Sc. (May 30, 1932).

60. Much information on this upper Miocene series of Oran in the fine memoir by C. Arambourg, *Les Poissons fossiles d'Oran,* Matér. Carte géol. Algérie, 1 sér., no. 6 (1927).

61. Work cited note 15, this chap.

62. V. Stchepinski, *Contribution à l'étude de Sahélien de Tunisie,* Mém. Soc. géol. France, Mém. no. 37 (1938).

63. M. Cossman and A. Peyrot, *Conchologie, néogénique de l'Aquitaine,* Actes de la Soc. linnéenne de Bordeaux, 1–6 (1909–1932). J. Repelin, *Le Bassin d'Aquitaine à l'époque helvétienne: le golfe marin* (with paleogeographic map), C. R. Acad. Sc. (Mar. 12, 1928); id.: *les formations continentales,* ibid. (Mar. 26, 1928).

64. G. Astre, *Les relations des sables de la mer helvétienne et de la molasse de l'Armagnac dans le Lectourois,* Bull. Soc. Hist. nat. Toulouse, 53 (1925).

65. A. Magne and M. Vigneaux, *Les gisements de Saubrigues et de St-Jean-de-Marsac,* C. R. Soc. géol. France (1948), p. 293. But Saubrigues seems rather Vindobonian.

66. The last publication on the disputed age (Miocene, Pliocene) of these conglomerates is by G. Denizot, Bull. Carte géol. France, no. 140 (1920) who, following M. Boule, attributes them to the Pliocene.

67. F. Roman and J. Viret, *Le Miocène continental de l'Armagnac et le gisement burdigalien de la Romieu (Gers),* Livre jubilaire du Centenaire de la Soc. géol. France (1930) and work cited note 13, this chap.

68. L. Mestre, *La place stratigraphique de Sansan et Simorre,* Bull. Soc. Hist. nat. Toulouse, 67 (1935).

69. G. Denizot, *Les sables de la Basse-Loire,* Bull. Soc. géol. et min. de Bretagne, 5 (1924).

70. C. Barrois, Ann. Soc. géol. du Nord, 55 (1930) has rightly pointed out that the Breton Miocene outcrops are aligned by, and dropped down between, faults. Thus it is incorrect to try to find ancient gulfs there.

71. G. Lecointre, *La Touraine,* Paris, Hermann (1947), Vol. IV of the *Géologie régionale de la France,* 250 p., 49 fig., 4 pl. G. F. Dollfuss and Ph. Dautzenberg, *Conchyliologie du Miocène moyen du Bassin de la Loire,* Mém. Soc. géol. France, mém. no. 27.

72. J. Roger and S. Freneix, *Remarques sur les faunes de Foraminifères du Redonien,* Bull. Soc. géol. France, 16 (1946), emphasizing the affinities of these faunas with those of the Nordic Pliocene, even propose classifying this Redonian in the Pliocene.

73. See works by G. Denizot cited note 59, chap. 9.

74. L. Mayet, *Etude des Mammifères miocènes des sables de l'Orléanais et des faluns de la Touraine,* Ann. Univ. Lyon, 1, 24 (1908).

75. M. Gignoux, note 6, this chap.

76. A recent well on the Roman coast, near Mt. Circeo, found the base of the Pliocene only at the depth—277, Novarese, Boll. R. Uff. geol. ital., 55 (1930).

77. Of course, here the question is only of relative movements. To simplify the language, we have supposed the sea to be mobile and the continents fixed, but, if preferred, the inverse supposition can be made.

78. R. Signorini, Boll. Soc. geol. ital., 58 (1939), fasc. 2–3, p. LX.

79. F. Cipolla, *Il Pliocene di Lascari,* Giorn. Sc. nat. econom. Palermo, 34 (1924–26).

80. M. Gignoux, *Il Pliocene di Castellarquato,* Boll. Soc. geol. ital., 42 (1924).

81. M. Gignoux, *L'étage Calabrien (Pliocène sup. marin) sur le versant Nort-Est de l'Apennin, entre le Monte Gargano et Plaisance,* Bull. Soc. géol. France, 4 sér., 14 (1915). G. Ruggieri, *Il Calabriano e il Siciliano nella valle del Santerno (Imola),* Giorn. di Geol., ser. 2a, 17, Bologna (1944). F. Guatani, *Revisione delle faune dei lembi pliocenici della Prealpi lombarde,* Ist. geol. Milano, ser. P, no. 39 (1944). R. Zuffardi-Comerci, *I depositi marini pliocenici subalpini del Piemonte considerati in rapporto ai movimenti epirogenetici postpliocenici,* Atti R. Accad. Sc. Torino, 70 (1934–1935). S. Venzo (work cited note 42, this chap.) mentions the marine Calabrian at Castanedolo, near Verona.

82. L. Trevisan, *Problemi relativi all'epirogenesi e all'eustatismo nel Pliocene e Pleistocene della Sicilia,* Atti. Soc. toscana Sc. nat., Mem., 51, Pisa (1942).

83. Marine Pliocene, not indicated on the map, Fig. 141, was recently discovered on the eastern coast of Sardinia, at Orosei: Fossa-Mancini, *La trasgressione pliocenica nella Sardegna orientale,* Boll. R. Uff. geol. ital., 51 (1926).

84. C. Socin, *Nota preliminare sulla fauna malacologica di Vallebiaja (Colline pisane),* Atti. Soc. toscana Sc. nat., Mem., 49, Pisa (1941).

85. On these regions, see L. Lutaud, note 167, chap. 5.

86. Many of these wells are fed by aquifers in the Miocene. See M. Gignoux, *Forage artésiens et rivages pliocènes sur la rive gauche du Rhône entre Carpentras et Valréas,* Les Etudes rhodaniennes, 5, Lyon (1929).

87. J. Viret, *Note préliminaire sur la formation bressane de Mollon (Ain) et sur de nouvelles faunes de Vertébrés et d'Invertébrés qui s'y rencontrent,* C. R. Soc. géol. France (1937), p. 7.

88. G. Mazenot, *Les lignites bressans; le bassin lignitifère de Chaumergy,* Pub. Bur. Recher. géol. et géophys., no. 1, Paris (1945).

89. J. Bourcart, *Etude des sédiments pliocènes et quaternaires du Roussillon,* Bull. Serv. Carte géol. France, 45 (1945), no. 218.

90. See article by M. Gignoux and P. Fallot, note 47, this chap.

91. M. Gigout, *Compléments sur le Pliocène des Doukkala et du Sahel (Maroc occidental),* C. R. Soc. géol. France (1947), p. 88.

92. Dalloni, *Le Pliocène du Sahel oriental et de la Kabylie,* Bull. Soc. Hist. nat. de l'Afrique du N, 24 (1933).

93. The Sahelian reported by Ehrmann in the region of Bougie must also correspond to a small Pliocene gulf.

94. R. Lafitte and E. Dumon, *Plissements pliocènes et mouvements quaternaires en Tunisie,* C. R. Acad. Sc., 227 (1948), p. 138.

95. A. Chavan and J. Coatmen, *Etude paléontologique et stratigraphique du hâvre de Blainville-sur-Mer (Calvados)*, Bull. Soc. géol. France, 13 (1943).

96. G. Denizot, *Les sables de la Basse-Loire*, Bull. Soc. géol. et min. de Bretagne, 5 (1924).

97. Y. Milon, *Présence de la glauconie dans les sables pliocènes de Bretagne*, C. R. Acad. Sc. (Dec. 2, 1929). M. Gautier and A. Guilcher, *Contribution à l'étude du Pliocène breton* C. R. Soc. géol. France (1947), p. 40.

98. In J. Jung's fine memoir, cited note 33, chap. 1, will be found an excellent study of the great Pliocene volcanoes of Cantal (map p. 221 and section p. 222) and of Mont-Dore (map p. 191 and section p. 205) with a table of general correlations (p. 250).

99. See especially the *Guide des Excursions de l'Association pour l'avancement de la Géologie des Carpates. Réunion à Bucarest* (1927).

100. The maximum thicknesses (sometimes several hundred meters for each sub-stage) seem to be reached in areas of geosynclinal or rather fore-deep character, which border the folded chains of the Carpathians and Caucasus.

101. According to the posthumous memoir of N. Andrussov, *Le Pliocène de la Russie méridionale d'après les recherches récentes*, Mém. Soc. roy. Sc. de Bohème, Prague (1927) and Mlle. S. Gillet, *Essai du synchronisme du Miocène supérieur et du Pliocène dans l'Europe centrale et orientale*, Bull. Soc. géol. France, 5 sér., 3 (1933). See also A. Keller, *Le Néogène de l'Europe orientale d'après les travaux récents*, Revue de Géogr. phys. et de Géol. dynam., 6 (1933) and especially E. Jekelius, *Das Pliozän und die Sarmatische Stufe im mittleren Donaubecken*, Ann. Inst. géol. Roumanie, 222 (1943), pp. 195–398. I have not yet been able to study the latter work, very important but difficult to read, with no maps or tables. I wish to thank Mlle. S. Gillet for her kind help in editing these paragraphs.

102. I. Simionescu and I. Z. Barbu, *La faune sarmatienne de Roumanie*, Mém. Inst. géol. Roumanie, 3 (1940), 194 p., 11 pl., 163 fig.

103. Near Istanbul, *Hipparion,* characteristic of the Pontian, was discovered in beds with *Mactra bulgarica*, thus belonging to the upper Sarmatian (Chersonian): E. Chaput and S. Gillet, *Les faunes de Mollusques des terrains à Hipparion gracile de Küçük Çekmace près Istambul (Turquie)*, Bull. Soc. géol. France 8 (1938).

104. Magnificent photographs of these bryozoan reefs were published by N. Andrussov, *Die fossilen Bryozoenriffe der Halbinseln Kertsch und Taman,* published by the author, Kiev (1909–12).

105. Mlle. S. Gillet, *Variations des Cardiidés dans le Bassin dacique*, Bibl. de l'Inst. fran. des Hautes-Etudes en Roumanie, III, sér. sc., Libr. E. Leroux, Paris (1930); *Les Limnocardiidés des couches à Congéries de Roumanie*, Mem. Inst. géol. Roumanie, 4 (1943); *Lamellibranches dulcicoles; les Limnocardiidés*, Rev. sc., no. 3258 (Oct. 1946).

106. L. Strausz, *Das Pannon des mittleren Westungarns*, Ann. Hist. nat. Mus. nat. Ungarici, 35 (1942).

107. N. Macarovici, *L'âge des calcaires d'Odessa*, Bull. Sec. Sc. Acad. roumaine, 27, no. 7 (1945), maintains that these limestones are of lower Pontian age (Meotian).

108. B. Prashad, *Recent and Fossil Viviparidae. A Study in Distribution, Evolution and Palaeogeography*, Mem. Indian Mus., 8, no. 4, Calcutta (1928).

109. For the marine Pliocene of Greece, which we shall not discuss, a list of occurrences known up to now will be found in a Note by Kténas, C. R. Acad. Sc. (Mar. 21, 1927). Note in passing that, according to S. Gillet, *Sur la présence d'éléments caspiques dans la faune quaternaire de Corinthe*, C. R. Soc. géol. France (1938), p. 163, at a given time in the Quaternary (Tyrrhenian) there was communication, traversing the Aegean continent and the Dardanelles, between the Corinth Sea and the Sea of Marmara, then a dependent of the Caspian domain.

110. Some remains of Caspian faunas still live in the "limans" of the Lower Danube and the Sea of Azov, where biological conditions are similar to those of the ancient Plio-Caspian lagoons. These "limans" are, in fact, sounds whose waters are sometimes freshened by floods of the Danube, sometimes saline from the contributions of the Black Sea. See J. Borcea, *Faune survivante de type Caspien dans les limans d'eau douce de Roumanie*, Ann. Sc. Univ. Jassy, 13, fasc. 1–2 (1924), fasc. 3–4 (1926).

111. The present fauna of Lake Baikal is derived from the freshwater faunas of the

Tertiary. Certain Tertiary forms have persisted as relics, others have evolved and, by convergence, resemble marine forms, which could lead to the belief in marine origin. See H. Johansen, *Der Baikalsee, Physiogeographischer und biogeographischer Ueberblick*, Mitt. geogr. Ges. München, 18 (1925).

112. Bibliographies will be found in Leriche, Livret-Guide Internat. Géol. Congress, Belgium (1922); in Briquet, Bull. Soc. belge de Géol. (1922); in von Linstow Abh. d. Preuss. geol. Landesanst. (1922); in Harmer (Paleon. Soc., since 1913); and especially in F. Kautsky, *Die boreale und mediterrane Provinz des europäischen Miocäns und ihre Beziehungen zu den gleichaltrigen Ablagerungen Amerikas*, Mitt. geol. Ges. in Vienna, 18 (1925) and R. Tavernier, *Le Néogène de la Belgique*, Bull. Soc. belge Géol., 52 (1943), with paleogeographic maps and table of stratigraphic correlations (p. 26) between Belgium, Britain and Germany.

113. Where, reached by deep wells, the different Miocene stages can be identified according to their microforaminiferal faunas. A. Ten Dam and T. Reinhold, *Die stratighaphische Gliederung des niederländischen Oligo-Miozäns nach Foraminiferen*, Meded. Geol. Stichting, ser. C, 5, no. 2 (1942). P. Tesch, *L'origine du sous-sol des Pays-Bas*, Tijdschr. Aardr. Gen., 45, Leyden (1938); *De Nordzee van historisch-geologisch Standpunkt*, Meded. S'Rikks geol. Dienst, ser. A, no. 9 (1942). W. A. E. van de Geyn, *Das Tertiär der Niederlände mit besonderer Berücksichtigung der Selachierfauna*, Leidsche geol. Meded., 9 (1937); a table giving the thickness of all the Tertiary stages in Holland; the ichthyologic determinations were discussed by M. Leriche, Ann. Soc. géol. Belgique, 62 (1938) and 63 (1940).

114. This stage and those following were named after localities in the Hamburg-Bremen region, see map, Fig. 145.

115. This hypothesis was not shown on the maps, Figs. 133 and 145. In fact, this communication remains hypothetical. Certain authors, von Linstow, von Bubnoff, *Geologie von Europa*, II, 2 (1935) believe evidence is found in the marine clay of Xions, thought to be Miocene. But F. Berger, *Zur Altersbestimmung des ostdeutschen Braunkohlentertiärs; II, Die "Xionser Meerestone,"* Zentralbl. f. Min., Abt. B (1941), no. 9, recalls that there is an error there and that these clays were long ago known to be Jurassic.

116. F. Kautsky, *Das Miocän von Hemmoor und Basbeck-Osten*, Abh. preuss. geol. Landesanst., n. F., H. 97 (1925).

117. Study of the Bolderberg section was recently undertaken by F. Halet, Bull. Soc. belge Géol., 33 (1923). M. Glibert, *Faune malacologique du Miocène de la Belgique. I. Les Pélécypodes*, Mém. Mus. r. Hist. nat. Belgique, no. 103 (1945).

118. H. Odum, *En forekomst af marint Pliocaen ved Tönder*, Med. Dansk geol. Foren., 8 (1934). H. L. Heck, *Zur Verbreitung des Pliozäns in Schleswig-Holstein*, Zeitschr. deutsch. Geol. Ges., 87 (1935). S. Thiele, *Die Stratigraphie und Paläogeographie des Jungtertiärs in Schleswig-Holstein*, Neues Jahrb. f. Min., Abt. B (1941), 85, p. 1–143, 8 pl.

119. See work of A. Ten Dam and T. Reinhold, cited note 113, this chap., with paleogeographic maps from the Scaldisian to the Icenian.

120. Nevertheless, the Pliocene Crags of Norfolk and Suffolk contain, at their base, molds of Miocene fossils in rolled stones called Boxstones, showing that the Miocene seas must have touched the English coast.

121. S. W. Wooldridge, "The Pliocene History of the London Basin," Proc. Geol. Ass., 38 (1927).

122. See work by K. Pietsch, cited note 88, chap. 9.

123. Nevertheless, this classic interpretation should be modified, according to W. Gothan, *Neue Ansichten über die Bildung von Braunkohlenflözen*, Ber. d. deutsch. botan. Ges. (1924). For this author, the *Taxodium* of the lignites would be, not *T. distichum* of the swamps, but rather *T. mexicanum* of the mountainous forests of California, where it accompanies *Sequoia sempervirens*. Thus the lignites would be formed from the material of dry forests (?). See also, R. Kräusel, Centralbl. f. Min., B, no. 5 (1925). The same *Taxodium* is found in the Pliocene lignites of Bresse (see p. 584).

124. *Hydrobia slavonica, Prososthenia, Congeria kayseri*. See. W. Wenz, work cited note 94, chap. 9. K. Fischer and W. Wenz, *Die Prososthenienschichten von Frankfurt a. M. bis Praunheim und ihre Fauna*, Arch. f. Molluskenkunde, 57 (1925).

Chapter Eleven

The Quaternary

I. Special Character of Quaternary Stratigraphy

The Quaternary era deserves to be distinguished from the Tertiary only because of two great new developments: first, the appearance (at least in the present state of our knowledge) of Man and relics of his industry and, second, the development of great glaciers, covering a large part of the classic regions we have studied, in Europe and North America.[1]

The development of these glaciers was not due to purely local causes, for they were produced at the same time in Europe, America and more generally over the whole globe. It can hardly be explained except by a general and simultaneous chilling of the two hemispheres, which everywhere lowered the limit of the eternal snows. The Quaternary glaciers may therefore be represented as exaggerations of present glaciers, originating, like the latter, in mountain ranges of sufficient elevation. So the altitude and latitude of these ranges will give, *a priori,* an idea of the relative dimensions of the glaciers which they nourished, taking into account the local climatic peculiarities.[2]

In Europe, we shall first study the old glaciers issuing from the Scandinavian mountains. Crossing the North Sea and the Baltic, they advanced into eastern Britain and covered a large part of northern Germany, Poland, and Russia. In the other European massifs, we shall discuss only the ancient glaciers of the Alps, the only ones which left their nurturing mountains to spread widely over the neighboring plains.[3]

In central Asia, the Himalaya and other nearby high massifs were the seat of great glaciations comparable to those of the Alps.[4] In North America, an immense ice cap, similar to that which in Europe descended from the Scandinavian Mountains, advanced southward beyond the Great Lakes.[5] In the southern hemisphere, the American Pacific cordilleras show traces of old glaciations analogous to those of the Alps.[6] A vast sheet of ice emanated from Patagonia, covering all the southern part of the continent. Finally, beneath the equator, the Massif of Killimanjaro also shows evidence of an important glaciation.

Everyone agrees, then, in assuming a general chilling of the globe, whose causes must be sought in extraplanetary phenomena.

Thus, of late years, certain specialists on the Quaternary have adopted as a basis for their syntheses, the theory of Milankovitch, who, after theoretical studies on the phenomenon of the procession of the equinoxes, believed he could establish a curve indicating the variations of solar radiation (and consequently of the temperature at the earth's surface) during the whole Quaternary era.[7] But, as F. Nölke[8] has rightly remarked, this theory seems to geologists very difficult to accept; for, extending Milankovitch's curve beyond the Quaternary, we should be forced to concede periodic returns of glaciation in the course of all geologic history, especially in the Neogene. Seeking another explanation, Nölke assumes that, during the Quaternary, the solar system traversed zones of dust or of dark clouds in interstellar space. According to astronomers, such an hypothesis would not be at all improbable. But, this recourse to a *Deus ex machina* does little more than push back the problem. With A. Penck,[9] the outstanding student of Quaternary glaciations, we are forced to confess our ignorance and modestly assemble objective observations which may give a solid basis for future explanations.

In any case, all the Quaternary stratigraphy, its delimitation as well as its subdivisions, is governed by the history of these two great facts, the history of the ancient glaciers and the story of prehistoric man. This stratigraphy thus acquires a very special character. Human industries provide a chronological scale for which there was obviously no equivalent in earlier epochs. In addition, the development of glaciers occurred more than once. There were several cold, glacial epochs, separated by interglacial epochs, in the course of which the climate sometimes became warmer than it is at present. These different vicissitudes led, in the classic regions to be studied, to important migrations of animal and plant populations, which will greatly complicate the history of faunas and floras, that is to say, our paleontologic scales.

Finally, the relief forms built up during the Quaternary by the different geologic phenomena have often remained very fresh and unaltered. Their study will provide a valuable means of reconstructing these phenomena and establishing their chronology.

Geologists of the Quaternary should thoroughly understand, even in its details, the present geographic distribution of animals and plants. They should, moreover, be prehistorians, morphologists (physio-geographers) and even pedologists.[10] Thus the stratigraphy of the Quaternary becomes so different from normal stratigraphy that geologists who have studied it in Europe felt the need of forming an International Association for the Study of the European Quaternary,[11] though no one would think of forming a similar organization for the study of the Rhaetian or the Oligocene.

Nothing emphasizes better than this the special character of the methods that are used in the study of the Quaternary. The most novel methods for geologists are the morphologic ones.

II. Morphologic Methods

Among the land forms are *erosion forms,* whose study is more especially the province of geographers. But knowledge of *accumulation forms* is also indispensable to geologists, for it allows them to reconstruct the history of the geologic phenomena which produced these forms, and consequently the history of the sediments themselves. Every accumulation being shown by deposition, these are then the forms of depositional surfaces which we shall study.

1. *Surfaces of River Deposition: Terraces*

A river which fills up its valley constructs an alluvial plain. This is an almost horizontal surface, with a slight slope downstream, whose breadth is determined by the removal of the rocky side slopes. It is built up in the course of successive meanderings of the river, meanderings which lead it to flow successively over every point of its alluvial plain. Thus, when we see a very broad alluvial plain, we must be careful not to conclude that the river was formerly as wide as its plain. It is this false idea, more or less explicitly formulated, which formerly led to the conclusions that streams of the Quaternary were much more important than present rivers, which gave rise to the old idea of the diluvial period, leaving its trace in the nomenclature. In many foreign countries, the word Diluvium is still used synonymously with Quaternary.[12]

Now if deposition, in a given part of a stream course, stopped for any reason (rising of the earth, lowering of base level at the stream mouth, modification of its rate of flow, etc.) this river will begin to dig into its bed, entrenching itself in previously deposited alluvium. The surface of the banks, rising, for example, 35 meters above the new stream bed, will constitute a terrace, in this case called a 35 m. terrace.[13]

Let us suppose, finally, that after having entrenched its bed, the river begins to fill it up again. Two alternatives may occur: a) either the new fill will rise higher than the first, and then the previously formed terrace T will be buried beneath a new alluvial plain and will disappear, or, b) the new fill will stop below the level of terrace T and its alluvial plain may, in its turn, be transformed by a later entrenchment into another terrace T', lower than T. And so on (see left part of Fig. 147).[14]

Thus, however complicated may be the vicissitudes in the excavating and filling by a river, we finally see the different stages of its history, at a given point in its course, translated in the topography by a succession of terraces, rising in tiers at a given point, the highest being the oldest. There is, thus, the illusion of a succession of fills of progressively decreasing altitude up to the present time. In reality, there is no reason why these altitudes should have decreased regularly, which would give to the present period the value of a singular point in the history of these valleys; but, automatically, all the fills which escaped this law of regular diminution were buried beneath later fills.

2. Surfaces of Glacial and Fluvioglacial Deposition

The regions where sediments were deposited by ancient glaciers, however, have a very irregular topography, which, as a whole, is described as a *morainal topography*. Lines of ridges, or *vallums,* are found more or less continuous for long distances: surface moraines, terminal or lateral according to their position in relation to the contours of the ancient glacial front, which may be reestablished at each stage. Ground moraines, on the other hand, deposited beneath the glacier itself and not along its edges will generally have an extremely chaotic topography. However, morainal accumulations are often identified in the form of elongated mounds parallel to the direction of movement of the ice, called drumlins, comparable to the strips or bars of sand and gravel shaped by currents on the very bottom of the bed of a great river. Such drumlins, formed by the ground moraine, are seen in great numbers in the plains of northern Germany, constructed at the time of the last extension of the ancient Scandinavian glaciers. Others are found, on a much smaller scale, in the domain of the final Alpine glaciation, especially in the basins of the Reuss River and Lakes Constance and Zurich.

Study of the great ice cap (Inlandeis), which today covers Greenland, has shown that the flow of melt water, in the terminal part of the glacier, takes place not on top of the glacier, but beneath it, the waters uniting in a few strong, sub-glacial torrents. Some of these torrents may have had an obstructed outlet. These tunnel-valleys (Tunneltäler) are then filled with torrential alluvium, and after the melting of the obstructing ice, these alluvial fills are found in the form of longitudinal ribbons, more or less sinuous, which, although alluvial, rise above the surrounding plains. They are called eskers (or *Oser* or *Äsar;* singular *Os*), and examples are found in the Baltic countries and Ireland.[15] If, however, the subglacial stream continues without fill until the disappearance of the glacier, its location will then be evidenced by a longitudinal gutter, the bottom of which, however, may present irregular counter-slopes, since the sub-glacial flow takes place under pressure and consequently is not subject to the usual laws of free surface flow. In the plains of northern Germany, there are gutter valleys (Rinnentäler), often marked by occasional lakes (Rinnenseen).[16] On the east coast of Jutland and Schleswig (Fig. 150), many of the ancient valleys in which subglacial streams ran from east to west, were invaded in the east, near the present coast, by the Baltic Sea. They became elongated gulfs, called Föhrden, which should not be confused with Norwegian fjords, which represent ancient glacial valleys (not sub-glacial stream valleys), excavated in the rock in place.

Finally, when blocks of ice, more or less lenticular in form, were abandoned in place by the retreating glacier,[17] in regions which escaped later fills, their location, after complete melting, is indicated by more or less circular, enclosed depressions, often with very abrupt borders. These are called cuvettes or kettle lakes (Kesselseen) if they are large, Sölle (*das Söll, die Sölle,* the word for them in northern Germany) if they are small (sometimes about 10 m.).[18]

Subglacial streams, rising under the ice (a phenomenon observed at the

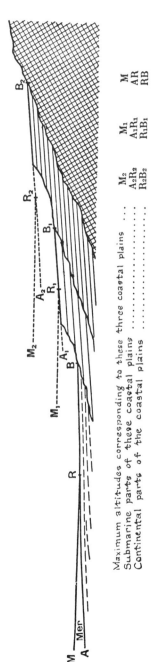

Maximum altitudes corresponding to these three coastal plains ....
Submarine parts of these coastal plains ....
Continental parts of the coastal plains ....

M	M$_1$	M$_2$
AR	A$_1$R$_1$	A$_2$R$_2$
RB	R$_1$B$_1$	R$_2$B$_2$

FIG. 146. *Theoretical diagram showing three successive terraced coastal plains.*

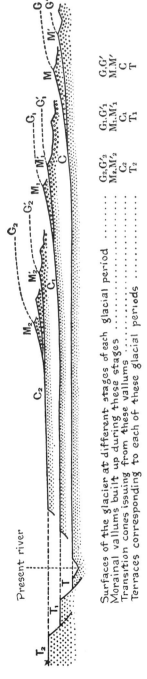

Present river

Surfaces of the glacier at different stages of each glacial period ....
Morainal vallums built up during these stages ....
Transition cones issuing from these vallums ....
Terraces corresponding to each of the glacial periods ....

G,G′	G$_1$,G′$_1$	G$_2$,G′$_2$
M,M′	M$_1$,M′$_1$	M$_2$,M′$_2$
C	C$_1$	C$_2$
T	T$_1$	T$_2$

FIG. 147. *Theoretical diagram showing three terraced fluvioglacial complexes.*

terminus of the great glaciers of Iceland and Alaska) gush out to the surface around ice caps and divide into a multitude of secondary, changing branches, which deposit sands spreading out fanwise on the glacier borders. These sandy *outwash plains,* beautiful examples of which are seen today in Iceland, are designated by the Icelandic term Sander (or Sandr). Thus, in the morainal regions of northern Germany, gutter valleys (Tunneltäler) are often seen to end at the head of an outwash plain, when they reach the crossing of ancient terminal moraines. Downstream, the surface of the outwash plain joins, of course, with the old alluvial plain of a great river, that is to say, a terrace.

In valley glaciers of the Alpine type these phenomena obviously will not be found. Only glacial torrents are found, emerging from terminal moraines, building up, in front of these moraines, transition cones, which join downstream with an alluvial plain. The assemblage of these terminal moraines (behind which lies the depression formerly occupied by the glacier, the terminal depression or Zungenbecken), the transition cone, and the terrace which prolongs it, has been called a *fluvio-glacial system,* in the language of the Alpine geologists.

In summary, every time an ice front was stationary a sufficiently long time, the study of the surface forms, supported by observation of the lithologic constitution of the sediments, allows the definition of a glacial stage, with its intraglacial forms (central depression, drumlins, eskers, gutter valleys, Föhrden, Sölle, etc.), its bordering deposits (terminal and lateral moraines) and its periglacial formations (outwash plain, transition cones, terraces, etc.). The reconstruction of these different stages, in every country invaded by ancient glaciers, will thus be the first task of the geologist of the Quaternary (Fig. 147).

Let us note, however, that when a glacier advances beyond the limits of an earlier stage, the topographic forms originating in that stage will be destroyed by erosion or buried under later fill [19] and it will usually be impossible to find them. So in fact, the only stages we can reconstruct precisely will perforce be the progressively decreasing stages, the stages of retreat, graduated between a maximum glaciation and the present minimum. But it must be remembered that actually the history of a glacier may be infinitely more complex. Stratigraphic observations provide multiple proofs of this. It is only in consequence of a veritable selection that we have the illusion of a series of progressively decreasing series of stages. We repeat here the same statement already made in reference to river terraces.

3. *Depositional Surfaces along Ancient Shores: Coastal Plains*

The ancient marine shores are somewhat the same. They too have left morphological evidence, the ancient coastal plains.[20] Along a coast which is nowhere too abrupt, a surface sloping slightly toward the open sea tends to rise, composed, in its emerged portion, of littoral strands, lagoonal fills, alluvium of coastal rivers or floods; in its submerged parts, of beach sands spread by currents and waves. We call the surface of this assemblage of sediments, half marine and half continental, a coastal plain (Fig. 146).

If the sea level rises,[21] the old coastal plains are destroyed or buried beneath more recent ones. If, on the contrary, sea level is lowered, the old coastal plain exists in the form of a marine terrace overlooking new shores. Thus the history of ancient shores will be inscribed in the morphology in a series of tiered, marine terraces, with continually decreasing altitudes. But, like river terraces, this so-called law of regular diminution will be only an appearance and an illusion by which geologists are too often taken in.

4. *Application of Morphologic Methods to the Chronology of the Quaternary*

It is significant to point out first that the stratigraphy of the Quaternary imposes a task much more difficult and more ambitious than for previous periods. It is no longer a question of reconstructing the large features of the paleogeography, of knowing when a region was emergent, occupied by lakes,

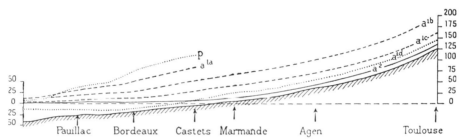

FIG. 148. *Profile of the terraces of the Garonne between Toulouse and mouth of the Gironde (after A. Fabre, work cited note 143, this chap.; between Marmande and Toulouse, after J. E. Chaput).*

Oblique ruling—Bed rock.
a^2 = Recent alluvium (main bed of the Garonne).
a^{1d} = Terrace of 15 m. between Toulouse and Agen, which, between Castets and Marmande, has yielded *Elephas antiquus* (recent mutation) and *E. primigenius* (early mutation).
a^{1c} = Terrace of 30 m. between Toulouse and Agen.
a^{1b} = Terrace of 50 m. between Toulouse and Agen.
a^{1a} = Terrace of 75 m. at Castets, which has yielded *E. antiquus* (early mutation) between Bordeaux and Pauillac.
p = Pliocene alluvium: the top has yielded *E. meridionalis* var. *cromerensis* near the present coast line.

The terraces decrease in height and approach each other as they near the sea, which indicates deformation of the continental bedrock.

lagoons or more or less deep seas. We wish, in the Quaternary, to know if a certain remnant of sand, yielding bones or dressed flints in a quarry, is older or more recent than certain others, visible in another quarry; if a certain layer of loess or till is below or above a similar layer visible several kilometers or tens of kilometers distant. The facies are both too similar on the whole and too locally variable in detail to give us useful guidemarks. In addition, paleontologic scales, supplied by the succession of faunas, floras and human industries, are, as we have seen, confused by multiple and repeated migrations.

And it is precisely to attack all these new difficulties that we are led to use morphologic methods, imperfect and inexact as they are.

Indeed, we see that the study of a given fluvio-glacial system often permits the correlation of a glacial stage with a river terrace, that is to say, with a period of the history of a great valley, with its sediments, its fauna, its flora, its human industries. We can often follow a terrace over a certain length of the valley.

In addition, approaching ancient shores, we shall often see terraces joined to ancient coastal plains. Thus we shall have means of correlating continental faunas with marine faunas.

Finally, if we can follow continuously a system of terraces all along a river valley and see them united, on the one hand with moraines, on the other with ancient shores, the whole problem of correlation is solved.

To de Lamothe and Depéret belongs the great honor of having called attention to the relationship of fluvial terraces and ancient shores and to the assistance drawn therefrom for the chronology of continental and marine Quaternary deposits.

Unfortunately and contrary to expectation, it is extremely difficult to follow fluviatile terraces continuously from the region of moraines as far as former marine shores. For these different terraces are frequently interrupted. Differences in altitude separating them are often slight (5 to 15 m.) and in the strips in which they exist, their relative altitudes above rivers may be increased or decreased by local causes (alluvium in sharp descent from tributaries, rill deposits descending from side slopes, later erosion, etc.).

Finally and especially, we have no reason to believe that the deformation characteristic of the earth's crust suddenly ceased at the dawn of Quaternary time; we even have many proofs of the contrary. But the altimetric measurements of Depéret and de Lamothe, certainly very meticulous,[22] were conducted with the preconceived idea that the continents had remained stable. So, for them, the tiers of terraces in the great river valleys which they studied (Rhône, Rhine, Moselle, Danube, Isser in Algeria, etc.) were due only to variations of the base level, that is the general sea level, thus to what we have called (p. 19) eustatic movements.

Believing they recognized, in all these great valleys, terraces rising in tiers at constant relative altitudes of 15 m., 30 m., 60 m., 100 m., they deduced therefrom that the terraces must correspond to former maxima of marine levels at successive elevations of 15, 30, 60, 100 m., levels which they endeavored to find over the whole earth. Still more unfortunately, they gave the name of geologic stages to these levels, as Tyrrhenian, Monastirian, Milazzian, Sicilian, corresponding, for them, to so many (more or less well) defined glacial periods in the Alps, under the names of Wurmian, Rissian, Mindelian, Günzian. And such is the power of words, even to scientific minds, that many geologists continue to use these terms and to assume corresponding levels as guiding lines for their observations.[23]

But, if the history of Quaternary times has taught us anything, it is that, assuming the continents to be stable, the maxima of marine levels must necessarily correspond to the minima of glaciations, that is to say, to the interglacial periods. It is evident, in fact, that when the glaciers have melted, their melting waters, returning to the oceans, must have raised the general level of the latter. Inversely, the glacial maxima should correspond, other things equal, to the minima of the general sea level. Precise reckonings are obviously difficult, for they assume knowledge of the cubic total of ice which, at the moment of the maximum of glaciation in the two hemispheres, was elevated above the general sea level. Thus, starting with a warm period, in which no Arctic or Antarctic glacial sheets existed, and ending at the period of the greatest glaciation of the Quaternary, the general sea level should be lowered, according to Penck, by 40 m. (1922 computation), or by 200 m. (1933 computation).[24] W. Ramsay proposed the figure 300 m. and G. Dubois, about 180 m.[25]

This analysis suffices by itself to destroy the basic concept of levels of Depéret and de Lamothe and it is astonishing to see geologists still refer to it.

It remains true, nonetheless, that locally morphologic methods often allow us to establish, in the same region, the rigorous chronologic classification of marine or continental formations which would be impossible to distinguish otherwise. When, on the slope of a valley, we see a strip of alluvium (a^1) 35 m. above a river, we can affirm with complete certainty, that this alluvium is previous to that (a^2) which, below the first, has served to form the base of a terrace of 20 m.[26] The same is true for marine formations. And morainal vallums, still intact, left by a glacier 200 km. distant from the massif of its origin, will for a certainty be more recent than those left 300 km. distant from the same massif. When a terrace is insinuated in an erosion valley cutting through moraines, it is obviously more recent than these moraines, etc.

Morphology can, then, be a valuable guide. We need merely to point out that the chronology of the Mediterranean marine faunas was established by this method.[27]

III. Lithologic Characteristics of Certain Quaternary Deposits (Glacial or Interglacial Deposits; Loess)

1. Distinctive Character of Glacial Deposits

In textbooks, the distinction between moraines (non-stratified, with angular blocks and striated boulders) and alluvium (stratified, with rounded cobbles) seems very clear and easy. In practice, it is far from being so.

The striated boulders remain the most distinctive features of a morainal deposit, but these are present only if the moraine contains rocks of unequal hardness. Look then especially for striae on the polished surfaces of calcareous rocks. In vain would they be sought in the purely granitic moraines of the ancient Vosgian glaciers. The angular form is preserved only in the upper part of glaciers, so that quarries in the moraines of the peri-Alpine plains usually show only rounded stones and have an alluvial appearance. Only the great erratic blocks, if there are any, will remain angular.

Finally and especially, the deposits left on the sides or the bottom of a glacier are not all true moraines. The study of the great living glaciers of Alaska, in particular, which give us a good idea of what the Alpine glaciers of the Quaternary must have been, is very instructive on this subject. They are frequently bordered by marginal streams accumulating thick alluvium. And when we find such marginal or periglacial alluvium on the flanks of Alpine valleys, often at great heights, it does not necessarily mean that the valley had been abandoned by glaciers and that an interglacial period is indicated. In the same way, sometimes quite extensive lakes can exist for a more or less long period on the edge of a glacier, especially at the opening of lateral valleys, when the tributary glacier has not yet reached or joined the principal glacier. In these marginal lakes, fine and well stratified lacustrine clays accumulate. Furthermore, the principal glacier may float on a sub-glacial lake, in which case it drops blocks or boulders in these glacial-lacustrine clays which are found scattered and isolated in the stratified clays of purely lacustrine appearance, which nevertheless are not necessarily interglacial, preglacial, or postglacial. Such is the case of the Wurmian clayey moraines, more than 100 m. thick, which we find in the Rhône valley between Lake Geneva and Seyssel, and in the Drac valley south of Grenoble. As for the pre-Wurmian clays cropping out at Eybens near Grenoble and those which fill the great terminal basin of the Isère glacier between Grenoble and Moirans, they are probably at least in part truly interglacial and comparable to those which are actually being deposited in Lake Geneva or in the Italian lakes.[28]

Thus, quite frequently, the glacial or interglacial age of a Quaternary alluvium or lacustrine clay can only be definitely determined if faunal or floral remains are found, testifying to a cold or warm climate.

2. *Residual Blocks*

When an alluvium or moraine containing great blocks has been completely removed during a period of erosion, it often happens that the currents, in the course of this period, were never violent enough to carry away these blocks. Then they are found, as residual blocks, buried at the base of a new alluvial series. This observation often permits the determination of the original extent of moraines which have disappeared, or the separation of superposed alluvial series of different ages.

Thus, along the Rhône, between Geneva and the Fort-l'Ecluse pass, through which the river flows from the Lake Geneva basin, the boundary of the pre-Wurmian old alluvium and postglacial terrace alluvium, deposits which are very difficult to distinguish, is often marked, according to Genevan geologists, by a bed of "cannon-balls." In this bed, enclosed in the base of postglacial alluvium, are found residual blocks, resulting from the destruction of Wurmian moraines, which the postglacial river could not remove.

Similarly, in the alluvial terraces of the Isère across from St. Lattier (below St. Marcellin) and of the Durance downstream from the Sisteron pass, great Alpine blocks give evidence of the farthest advances of the old glaciers (F. Bourdier).

3. *Seasonal Stratification (Varves)*

In arctic or glacial climates, there is an enormous difference between the sedimentation of summer and that of winter. In winter, the surface water remains constantly frozen and alluvial transport is completely arrested. Lakes and seas which border the glacial sheets (for example, the Baltic Sea bordering the Scandinavian glacier) were covered by an ice-pack under which, in still water, only the finest, clayey sediment was transported and deposited. In summer, on the contrary, waves or currents dispersed to far distances the sands brought by melting torrents. Thus the marine or lacustrine deposits reveal a very clear succession of winter beds, of very fine, dark colored clay, separated by more or less sandy summer beds, of lighter appearance. These successive layers (or *varves,* to use a Scandinavian folk word) were first noticed by the Swedish geologist De Geer[29] in the Quaternary clays of the Baltic. They allowed him to estimate in years the duration of "postglacial" time in Sweden and Finland, and later, in North America.

In less arctic climates, the contrast between winter and summer is not so abrupt. Especially, in spring and autumn, there will be alternations of frost and thaw, of rain and drought, and these vicissitudes are apparent in the sedimentation by elementary varves, evident in a detailed analysis. Nevertheless, seen from a distance, a quarry face will still allow the distinction of the alternations of annual zones, alternately darker and lighter, by reason of the predominance of clayey, winter facies in the former and sandy, summer facies in the latter.[30]

Thus this varve structure can be observed in very different climates under conditions which admit of sufficiently marked seasonal contrasts.

One example is furnished by M. Schwartzbach's[31] study of lacustrine clays in Northern Germany, which are a little older than the greatest glaciation, that is, dating from the time when the corresponding period of abnormal cold was nearly ended. There, the elementary varves are from .2 to 1 mm. thick and the seasonal beds are marked by light, sandy, summer zones 5 or 6 (sometimes 10) cm. thick, separated by thin, dark, clayey, winter zones, with 6 m. of clay corresponding to 100 or 120 years. According to F. Bourdier, the pre-Wurmian clays (partially interglacial) of Eybens, near Grenoble, with a total thickness of at least 60 m., show annual zones with a thickness of the order of a decimeter, while the elementary varves are a few millimeters or up to 1 cm. thick.

Finally, notice that according to L. W. Collet and his collaborators,[32] clays now being deposited in Lake Geneva show seasonal beds thicker and more evident as one nears the delta of the Rhône in this lake.

4. *Loess and Old Soils*

In great regions of Europe, particularly in northern France, on the west and northern borders of the Alps, and in the plains of Germany and eastern Europe, the soil is composed of a very special rock, loess[33] (called *ergeron* in northern France). It can be described as a kind of calcareous dust, of light yellow color, very permeable, neither clayey nor plastic, friable in the fingers but nevertheless coherent in outcrops, sometimes forming vertical walls several meters or tens of meters high. Sunken roads with steep banks are a characteristic feature of the loess countries. These characteristics, combined with a total lack of stratification, make the loess easy to distinguish from simple clayey sediments formed by weathering or streams.

In fact, it is immediately recognized that loess cannot have been formed under the present climatic conditions in the countries where it is found. Quite on the contrary, its upper surface, where it has not been unceasingly worn away by erosion, is always found more or less deeply altered. The rock becomes reddish from oxidation and hydration of iron salts. It loses its calcium in solution and in return develops colloidal, clayey minerals which make it plastic and less permeable. It is said to be rubefied, transformed into *lehm*[34] or lehmified. And the dissolved calcium is deposited in the lower part of the altered zone where it forms concretions, known as loess dolls (Loesskindel), correspondingly larger as the alteration was more prolonged.

Inversely, it can be assumed that under certain climatic regimes of long periods of intense evaporation, the circulation of water through the loess became ascending rather than descending, producing superficial beds cemented by deposits of carbonate of lime, forming the calcareous crusts well known in certain very dry, Mediterranean regions (North Africa, southern Spain). Such perhaps is the origin of the "hard loess" described by early geologists of Lyon, containing, at St. Vallier south of Vienne, a very rich deposit of mammals of very old appearance, now being studied by J. Viret and F. Bourdier (article cited note 126, this chap.).[35]

We must add that loess appears like a mantle, covering all relief forms indiscriminately. It is as thick on hills and especially along lee slopes, as in the bottoms of depressions.

This description shows why geologists are unanimous, after some discussion, now ended, in considering loess as an eolian formation. It is an accumulation of dust, windborn, as seen today in steppe regions. The fact that, under the present climatic conditions in western Europe, loess is not stable, but is transformed into rubefied, decalcified, clayey lehm, shows that this very peculiar rock must have been formed in arid climates.[36] The thickest accumulations of loess known (several hundred meters) are those of the steppes of central Asia, where loess covers a wide band extending from the Caspian Sea to the region of Peiping and there, under these climatic conditions, loess still continues to accumulate.

However, dust transported by the wind cannot be retained and fixed except in regions where the soil is covered by a more or less continuous carpet of grassy vegetation. And exactly so, typical loess is always traversed by a web of fine small channels, more or less filled with calcareous deposits, traces of roots of the grass of the ancient steppe. This regular fabric of tubules which stands out in white against the yellow background of loess, provides the most convenient practical characteristic to distinguish true loess, not worked over, from stream-deposited lehms or *limons*. We may add that the fauna of loess mollusks is composed of species (*Helix hispida, Succinea oblunga, Pupa muscorum,* etc.) which still live in somewhat damp prairies.

The place of origin of this dust, however, must necessarily be sought in regions deprived of vegetation, with bare soil. This is true of the deserts of central Asia, around which extend the steppes with loess.[37] This was also true in the Quaternary in Europe. At the edges of the glaciers, vast stretches of sand and fluvio-glacial muds, not yet taken over by vegetation, were swept by winds.[38] Thus, loess is not necessarily linked to the neighborhood of glaciers, but the latter created periglacial countrysides favorable to its formation. Loess is, above all, a rock of climatic origin, a steppe facies.[39] The mammalian fauna which it contains shows this too, for example, reindeer, musk oxen and especially numerous rodents of the steppes or even tundras (different hares, gophers, lemmings, marmots, jerboas, *Lagomys,* etc.).

In France, loess is especially thick in Alsace and the vicinity of Lyon[40] (up to 20 m. and more) but it is also found several meters thick in all the rest of the country, especially in the Paris Basin[41] and Normandy. In central Europe it covers the region contained between the domains of the last Alpine glaciation on one side and of the northern European glaciation on the other. Thus, in the Quaternary the zone of the present central Asian steppes extended across western Europe to the Atlantic shores. On the other hand, no loess, or almost none, is found in Spain, Italy or in general in the countries which today have the Mediterranean climate. This is because, in these regions, the chilling in the Quaternary was not enough to establish a steppe or tundra regime, but only to produce relatively humid forests.

Age of the loess; old soils. It has long been known that the formation of loess was not uninterrupted. In many regions where thick series of loess are shown cut by very clear vertical sections, one or several rubefied zones are distinguished, similar to that seen now at the upper surface of the loess. These rubefied zones were formed under climatic conditions more or less similar to those of the present day, that is, during periods when the arid climate of the cold steppes gave way to a mild and humid climate. Then loess stopped accumulating and its upper surface, often designated as an old soil, altered more and more deeply. Thus each bed of unaltered, homogeneous, true loess corresponds to a cold period, therefore to a glacial period,[42] and each old soil to a warmer, more humid period or interglacial period. Theoretically, the traces of all the glacial and interglacial periods should be inscribed in the series of loess. But practically, if we consider that the accumulation of loess is itself irregular, dependent on winds and local topography, and also that the surface of the loess, from the time it ceases to accumulate, may be subject to gullying and erosion, we can easily understand the improbability of sections

where all the details of the vicissitudes of Quaternary climates will be regis-
tered. Nevertheless, this is the directing idea which should guide the study of
loess.

And indeed, both in France and in Germany, at many places, old loess
has been distinguished, deeply and often completely altered, which is attributed to old glacial periods and is separated by a long interglacial period from
a recent loess, much less deeply altered, whose formation was contemporaneous with a later glaciation (called Wurmian in the Alps, Vistulan in northern
Germany). Thus, in Germany, the principal loess domain (old and recent)
extends first over the areas which escaped the northern European glaciation
and also (recent loess only) over the moraines of the early glaciation called
Saale, but not over those of the Vistula glaciation. Similarly, on the edge
of the Alps, recent loess covers the high terraces and old moraines (Rissian),
but not the low terraces or recent moraines (Wurmian). This rule is not,
however, absolute, for the accumulation or alteration of the loess may have
depended on local conditions.

So it is not surprising that one cannot always correlate the old soils, which
locally subdivide the old loess or the recent loess. As examples of detailed
sections in a series of loess, note that of Achenheim, near Strasbourg, described later (p. 621) and those in the vicinity of Belgrade, where Laskarev[43]
distinguished four successive old soils in a series of loess more than 30 m.
thick, overlying fluviatile clays of the early Quaternary with *Corbicula
fluminalis* (p. 622).

Finally, let us add that these phenomena of superficial alteration are not
peculiar to loess. They are the phenomena which produce soil at the expense
of any underlying rock. The chemical composition and physical structure of
a soil depend, not only on the parent rock, but also on the climate, the plant
covering, and the eolian additions which are always more or less present,
although their importance is generally misjudged. These last three factors,
regional, not strictly local, tend to make uniform, over vast areas, the nature
of soils which, despite the variety of their parent rocks, evolve slowly toward
the clearly defined climatic types.

This science of soils or Pedology, was founded and developed especially by
Russian savants in the great plains of their country where various climatic
zones follow each other. Thus, from the climate, pedologists can deduce the
nature of the soil. And inversely, former climates can be reconstructed by
study of former soils, either buried and therefore called "sealed" as we have
seen in the loess, or remaining exposed to superficial alteration, so that their
upper parts develop according to present climatic conditions.

Such studies, to which we shall refer later (p. 644) have been little more
than outlined in France, but they will certainly provide a valuable means of
correlation of Quaternary sediments, for they call upon sound climatic scales,
as valuable as paleontologic scales, over geographically extensive domains.
We have seen examples in the most remote geologic periods (climates of the
Torridonian, Devonian, Carboniferous, Permo-Triassic, etc.). Indeed, certain
types of ancient soils (alluvium with black spots, fissured loess, red beds,

etc.), long recognized by local prehistorians (for example, Commont in the Somme), are found to be identical in the most diverse regions (Somme, Dordogne, Alsace, outskirts of Paris, Rhône Basin).[44]

IV. Quaternary Faunas and Floras

1. *Marine Faunas*

We already know that in the three great domains of the Atlantic, North Sea and Mediterranean, the only ones to be studied here, the living faunas of these seas already existed in their general features, at the end of the Pliocene. The Quaternary faunas, in relation to the latter, show only insignificant differences, appreciable only when arranged in particularly rich collections.

A. Atlantic.   We know almost nothing about variations which may have affected the marine faunas in the Quaternary. At any rate, the very rare occurrences of marine Quaternary on the French coasts have, up to now, shown no species different from those living in the nearby ocean.[45]

B. North Sea.   Here, on the contrary, and especially in the tributary Baltic Sea, vicissitudes have been many. Extinct forms are very rare and are reduced to varieties (for example, *Tapes aureus,* var. *eemiensis,* which is found in Holland, Germany and Denmark). But immigrant forms are numerous. They sometimes show northern influences (called boreal and even arctic faunas), sometimes southern (called Lusitanean faunas). Because of changes of climate and consequent vicissitudes in the development of glaciers, these successive faunas have a very complicated history which will be described at the same time as that of the great north European glaciers in these regions.

C. Mediterranean.   The history of the Mediterranean Quaternary faunas constitutes a separate chapter in the chronology of the Quaternary, a chapter which we are, for the moment, unable to synchronize with accuracy with the history of the great glaciers.

As we said earlier, marine deposits here seem connected with successively lower and lower shore lines in each region. In establishing to which depositional series (corresponding to a given shoreline) certain fossiliferous deposits belong, they can be classified chronologically in relation to neighboring occurrences.

Studies so conducted, without any hypothesis, have led to distinguishing three steps in the history of Mediterranean faunas. Conforming to the usage followed for previous epochs, stage names can be adopted for the periods characterized by these steps.[46]

1. *Sicilian Stage* (of Doderlein).   Its fauna is closely related to that of the upper Pliocene of the same regions (Calabrian). It is distinguished by the disappearance of some extinct forms which had persisted in the Calabrian (especially *Flabellipecten*). On the other hand, some quite rare extinct forms are still found (*Plicatula mytilina, Nucula placentina, Arcopagia ventricosa, Dentalium rectum,* etc.). Still more important are the cold forms, living today

only in the North Atlantic (*Cyprina islandica, Mya truncata, Buccinum undatum, Trichotropis borealis,* etc.) some of which had already appeared in the Calabrian.

The type occurrence of this stage is found in the Gulf of Palermo, where, in a sea 80 to 100 m. higher than the present, sediments of varied facies were deposited: deep water clays of Ficarazzi and tufas or organic, calcareous molasse at the foot of the calcareous cliffs of Monte Pellegrino.[47]

On the west coast of Calabria in the Gulf of Squillace, a rather typical cold fauna has been discovered [48] in the sands and clays also corresponding to an old shoreline at about 80–100 m., which I formerly attributed to the Sicilian without any paleontologic proof. I collected *Cyprina islandica* in similar conditions at Gallipoli (near Otranto, Italy) and it has long been known in the *panchina* (calcareous tufa) of Leghorn, where the position of the shoreline cannot be determined. In Sardinia, a submarine deposit at two m. depth, with *C. islandica* and *Modiola modiolus* (large shell of northern seas) was discovered by A. C. Blanc.[49] Finally, along French coasts, no cold fauna is known except in dredgings made by Pruvot in the open sea at Cap Creus, at 100–200 m. depth, bringing up a large number of northern shells.[50]

No cold fauna has ever been discovered on the African coasts, but it seems that different deposits of the eastern Mediterranean (especially at Rhodes)[51] can be related to the Sicilian.

In all, the very great rarity of these deposits containing a cold fauna, which contrasts with the large number of occurrences containing a warm fauna in the Tyrrhenian (see later), and the fact that certain occurrences are at present buried beneath the sea, inclines us to believe that the general level of the Mediterranean in the Sicilian stage was lower than at present, and thus that this stage corresponds to a glacial period. But that is a very daring deduction. In the same way, the presence of species of northern seas seems an insufficient argument to attempt the correlation of this Sicilian (or the Calabrian) with one of the glacial periods. For it must not be forgotten that the bulk of the fauna remains identical to that of the present Mediterranean. On the other hand, correlation is possible with continental faunas, for, in the Sicilian, *Elephas meridionalis* has been replaced by *Elephas antiquus,* which was contemporaneous with the Sicilian of Palermo. As we shall see, that suffices to classify the Sicilian, by definition, in the Quaternary and not in the upper Pliocene.

2. *Tyrrhenian Stage* (Issel).[52] The role of extinct species is now ended. One may now cite only *Tapes dianae,* a form related to *Tapes eemiensis* of the northern Quaternary. On the other hand, a few Senegalian species appear in great numbers: *Strombus bubonius, Conus guinaicus, Mytilus senegalensis, Tritonidea viverrata, Natica lactea,* etc.[53] The richest occurrences are those of Tarento,[54] Ravagnese (near Reggio Calabria), Monastir (Tunisia, work cited note 180, chap. 7) and the vicinity of Nice and Mentone.[55] A fauna with *Strombus* is found in Spain, near Vera, and in the Balearics. And the number of these occurrences, distributed over all the Mediterranean coasts (Algeria, Roman coast, Tuscany, Sardinia, Corsica, Isle of Cos, etc.)[56] in-

creases constantly. The Tyrrhenian fauna always retains the same characters and is therefore a true, well defined, paleontologic stage.

It is certain, as shown by observations made by Boule at the Grotte du Prince, near Mentone, that *Elephas antiquus* was still living during and after the deposit of the beds with *Strombus*. Studies of Blanc at the Romanelli Grotto (near Otranto)[57] also seem to confirm this. On the other hand, mammalian faunas called cold (mammoth, large penguin of the Romanelli Grotto) seem everywhere later than the *Strombus* fauna. The warm faunas of the Tyrrhenian still belong, in the mammalian chronology, to an early Quaternary. The Quaternary of Palermo has yielded dwarf elephants of the *antiquus* group (*E. melitensis, E. falconeri, E. manidriensis*) *Hyaena crocuta, Hippopotamus amphibius, H. pentlandi* and plants (*Laurus canariensis, Persea indica*) which are now living in the Canaries and at Madiera.[58]

Let us add that the sea levels for these Tyrrhenian faunas are generally rather low, between 0 and 35 m. But there are exceptions, especially near Reggio in Calabria, where the shore lines attain 100 m. and on the Isthmus of Corinth, up to 350 m., according to Depéret.[59] In these seismic regions, it is not surprising to find very recent movements of the earth. On this subject, we recall the classic example of the temple of Serapis, in the volcanic district of Pozzuoli near Naples, a temple submerged, then emerged since Roman times. But elsewhere the great number and the wide distribution of these deposits with a warm fauna lead to the belief that the general level of the Mediterranean in the Tyrrhenian was higher than it is today[60] and therefore that this stage corresponds to an interglacial period; but which one?

3. *The Living Fauna.* It results from the simple disappearance of warm forms which characterized the Tyrrhenian fauna. But of course, when we find occurrences in which no characteristic species exist, we cannot thereby assert that they are pre-Sicilian or post-Tyrrhenian. Such deposits with a commonplace fauna allow no conclusion as to their age. This is unfortunately too often the case.[61]

2. *Continental Faunas*

The *mammals* have provided a chronology, however often obscured by multiple migrations. Three successive mammalian faunas can be distinguished.

A. Early Fauna, called warm. This essentially is characterized by *Elephas antiquus* whose appearance marks the beginning of the Quaternary, *Elephas meridionalis* being characteristic of the upper Pliocene.[62] The usual companion of the *E. antiquus* is *Rhinoceros mercki,* also an extinct form. More rare is *Hippopotamus major,* closely related to the living *H. amphibius* and clearly accenting the warm character of this fauna.

B. A Cold Fauna. The most typical elements of this fauna are *Elephas primigenius* (mammoth)[63] and the wooly rhinoceros (*R. tichorhinus* = rhinoceros with separated nostrils), both forms extinct. Sometimes the musk ox (*Ovibos moschatus*) of arctic regions (Greenland and North America) is added, as well as the reindeer (*Rangifer tarandus*) and, especially, numerous rodents, still living either in the tundras (*Lepus variabilis* or snow hare, *Myodes torquatus* or lemming) or in the steppes (gophers, *Alactaga* or jerboa, whistling hare or *Lagomys,* marmot or *Arctomys marmotta, A. bobac*).

The reindeer especially seem to remain abundant very late, in our region, so that sometimes an age of reindeer is distinguished, perhaps incorrectly, including small arctic rodents and musk ox, an age which would immediately precede the living or temperate fauna.

Driven from our regions by the first glacial chilling, the warm fauna of the beginning of the Quaternary returned again, at one or several times, during interglacial periods, so an alternation of two faunas is sometimes seen. But usually the history of these migrations can only be reconstructed indirectly and uncertainly. Nevertheless, in a few deposits, a succession of several different faunas in vertical superposition in the same section has been found, as for example, in the section of the famous loess pits of Achenheim and Hangenbieten, in the outskirts of Strasbourg.

There, the alluvium and loess cut by vertical walls up to 35 m. high, where the patient research of Wernert [64] has yielded collections of bones and dressed flints, show the following succession from bottom to top:

1. Rhenish limons and sands, with a mollusk fauna of interglacial character, cervids, *Hippopotamus, Rhinoceros etruscus*(?); thus a warm fauna.

2. Gravels of Vosgian origin and old, sandy loess, with a cold fauna (reindeer, mammoth).

3. Early loess, with several surfaces of alteration, indicating interruptions in the deposit of loess (old soils). The base contains a warm fauna, with *Elephas antiquus, Rhinoceros mercki, Felis spelaeus, Hyaena spelaea.* At the top a cold fauna is developed, with reindeer, mammoth, marmot and a rich industry of the upper Acheulean.

4. Recent loess, containing a cold malacologic fauna, with mammals of the cold steppes (mammoth, reindeer) and a Mousterian industry.

No other Quaternary section shows so complete a succession of cold and warm faunas, thus demonstrating directly the importance of migrations due to climatic changes.

The deposits in caves sometimes have allowed similar reconstructions, one example being the celebrated Grimaldi caves, near Mentone, in Italian territory but very near the French frontier. Boule has described there the following succession from bottom to top:[65]

1. Marine beds with *Strombus bubonius* (Tyrrhenian fauna).

2. Lower debris with Paleolithic hearths, industry of the Mousterian type and a warm fauna of land mollusks (*Glandina antiqua*) and mammals (*Elephas antiquus, Rhinoceros mercki, Hippopotamus major, Hyaena spelaea,* etc., etc.).

3. Upper debris with hearths and tombs of Aurignacian men and a cold fauna (reindeer, ibex).

Finally and more generally, along with the species just mentioned as having a very clear climatic significance, there are many others, more ordinary, indicating relatively temperate forests or steppes, such as horses, deer, elk, aurochs (*Bos primigenius*), bison (*B. priscus*), lion, cave bear, etc.

Among the *birds,* one of the most curious discoveries is that of the arctic penguin (*Alca impennis*), extinct in the arctic seas for two centuries and found by Blanc[66] in the Romanelli Grotto of Otranto. This bird, unable to fly, reached there by swimming the Straits of Gibraltar. And Miss Bate recently discovered remains of this penguin in a cave at Gibraltar, thus verifying Blanc's ingenious conjecture. In conjunction with the mammoth,[67] this animal demonstrates that the chilling of the Glacial epoch was undoubtedly felt as far as southern Italy.

Lastly, among the fresh water *mollusks* utilized in stratigraphy, we list only the paludines and *Corbicula fluminalis,* a pelecypod which is still living in the streams of the eastern Mediterranean, thus in a relatively warm climate. It is also found "preglacial" in Holland (Tegelen clays), in Germany in the "early interglacial" (Mindel-Riss) and at Belgrade[68] in gravels probably of the same age, at the base of the loess series. In the two latter deposits, *Corbicula* is accompanied by *Paludina* (*Vivipara*) *diluviana,*[69] a very characteristic, extinct form which, according to Laskarev, developed in place from the paludines of the Levantine lakes, while *P. glacialis* characterizes the "preglacial" of Dutch geologists and *P. duboisi* is characteristic of the "recent interglacial" stage of northern Germany.

3. The Floras[70]

Their climatic significance is very clear and they make possible the reconstruction, even in detail, of the changes due to glacial and interglacial stages. Their impressions are very frequent, either in tufa,[71] or fine sand or clay, or finally in interglacial peat. In recent years, the systematic determination of seeds and pollen that are found in abundance in clay or peat has greatly increased the accuracy of our knowledge of the evolution of forest plants by the establishment of pollen diagrams showing the relative abundance of certain species.[72]

In central and northern Europe, the following floral groups are so distinguished:

1. A flora of the tundras or *Dryas* flora, characterized by *Dryas octopetala* (Alpine tea) of high mountains and present polar regions, *Salix polaris, Betula nana,* etc.

2. A flora of the steppes, with grasses and mosses in which pines and birches (*Betula alba*) begin to appear.

3. A flora of the forests, with the Norway pine (*Picea excelsa*), oaks and beeches (*Fagus sylvatica*), etc.

In many northern European Quaternary interglacial deposits a succession from bottom to top, covering several meters, is seen as follows: *Dryas,* pines, oaks, beeches, pines, *Dryas,* thus inscribing the floral history of the interglacial episode, boxed by two glacial periods.

Sometimes there is evidence that, during certain interglacial periods, the climate was warmer than it is today, as plants are frequently found in interglacial deposits which today live only much farther south, like box (*Buxus sempervirens*), *Taxus baccata, Trapa natans, Vitis vinifera,* and especially *Brasenia purpurea* (water lilies), *Dulichium spathaceum* (grass) and *Rhododendron ponticum,* which today are restricted to the Pontic region or Asia. We find *Trapa* and *Brasenia* even in an interglacial deposit in Esthonia.

The return of the warm species of the beginning of the Quaternary, driven away by glacial chilling, was apparently much complicated by the Alpine and Mediterranean chains, oriented E-W. In America, on the other hand, where the mountainous massifs range from north to south, this return was easier. So the present flora of North America contains, in contrast to the European floras of the same climate, many more warm species, heritages of the Tertiary, returning after the glacial epoch (*Magnolia, Taxodium, Liriodendron,* etc.).

V. History of Human Industries[73]

Of the two great periods into which Prehistory is divided, that of trimmed stone (Paleolithic) and that of polished stone (Neolithic), it is the former, the oldest, which is of most interest to geologists.

Two periods can be distinguished in the Paleolithic, each subdivided into a certain number of stages, the most classic of which are:

1. *Early Paleolithic*

This era begins with the *Chellean* (from Chelles, on the Marne, east of Paris).[74] Here the predominant implement, called *coup-de-poing* or better amygdaloid, is shaped like an almond, pointed at one end, rounded at the other, retouched on the two faces by successive strokes, so that the transverse section is biconvex and the edges are sinuous when looked at from the side. Usually vestiges of the original surface of the rock or raw flint show on the lateral faces.

Next comes the *Acheulean* (from the old limons of St. Acheul, near Amiens). The *coups-de-poing* are now skillfully retouched so that the sinuosities of the sharp edges have disappeared. Usually retouching has completely removed the original surface of the flint.

Finally the *Mousterian* (from Moustier, between Perigueux and St. Yrieix) is characterized by implements made from a splinter of flint, retouched on but one face, in the form of a spearhead or scraper.

2. *Late Paleolithic*

The number of stages distinguished here, principally following the shape of spears made of bone, increases constantly. The most classic are:

At the base, the *Aurignacian* (from Aurignac, north of St. Gaudens, Haute-Garonne), in which the beginning of the late Paleolithic is marked by the first appearance of bone implements and more skillfully dressed flint (blades).

The *Solutrean* (from Solutré, near Mâcon) is characterized by very fine flints in the form of "laurel leaves," very wide and thin, with very regular contours. They are the finest specimens of the art of dressed stone.

Lastly, in the *Magdalenian* (from the cave of La Madeleine, in Dordogne), the flint blades are very abundant and often worked up into knives. The bone industry develops exuberantly, thus preparing for the Neolithic. It is also the great era of prehistoric art (sketches, painting, sculpture).

VI. The North-European Quaternary

The Scandinavian mountains, which today still contain great glaciers, during the Quaternary were the source of a gigantic glacial sheet, comparable to that now covering Greenland. Ice then covered the present domain of the Baltic and extended over a large part of Russia and Poland and over all of northern Germany. There the southward movement was stopped by the first slopes of the massifs of central Europe (Harz and Riesengebirge). The latter also nourished local glaciers which were never sufficiently developed to join the Scandinavian glacier. But to the west the latter covered the North Sea and all the eastern part of Britain. There its ice pushed westward the ice of the local glaciers originating in the mountains of Scotland and Wales.

1. *The Front Line Reached by the Scandinavian Glaciers*

The most easily reconstructed feature of the history of the great Scandinavian glacier is that of its maximum extent. This is marked everywhere by erratic blocks, brought from Scandinavia or Finland, whose extent stakes out the extreme front of the glacial advance (Figs. 149, 150).

As we have seen, the local Scottish and Welsh glaciers prevented the Scandinavian glacier from covering all of Britain, but it certainly reached into Yorkshire where Norwegian rocks are found.[75] Then, passing through London, the front of the glacier crossed the channel and reached the mouth of the Rhine. Most of Holland and all the plains of northern Germany were covered by glacial and fluvio-glacial deposits attaining an average thickness of about 100 m. On the northern edge of the Harz, erratic blocks are still found at an altitude of 400 m., that is to say 130 m. above the surrounding plains. On the northern edge of the Riesengebirge, these Scandinavian blocks reach an altitude of 580 m. These figures give an idea of the thickness of the ice mass, which certainly exceeded 2,000 m. in its source region in Scandinavia and must have still been 1,000 m. thick on the south shore of the Baltic. Reaching the Russian plains,[76] the ice could reach out freely toward the south and extended two great lobes along the Dnieper and the Don. Next, it turned back toward the north and reached the northern end of the Urals, which even farther south maintained local glaciers.[77] Contrary to earlier theory, most of Siberia was glaciated, except the central part. There were numerous small centers of glaciation, from which ice spread in every direction.[78]

FIG. 149. *Map of the successive limits of the Scandinavian glacier (after De Geer, Wahnschaffe, Woldstedt, etc.).*

In gray = Existing glaciers.
In black = Mountainous massifs more than 500 m. high.
    I = Limit of the maximum extent (external moraines).
  III = Limit of the internal moraines (third glaciation, called the Vistula).
    F = Great Scandinavian moraines and the *Salpausselkä* of Finland: beginning of the "end-glacial" epoch of the Scandinavian geologists.
    P = Beginning of the post-glacial epoch: the Scandinavian glacier is divided into two sections issuing from two centers in which actual glaciers still exist.

2. Morphologic Studies: Glacial Stages, External and Internal Moraines

In the interior of this great ring, morainal topography is everywhere the rule. And study of this topography alone permits the reconstruction, as mentioned earlier, of a whole series of successive glacial stages, marking the periods of glacial retreat. This study has been carried very far. Numerous belts of frontal moraines have long been recognized, distinguished, and followed for greater or lesser distances; then outwash plains, tunnel valleys, and the like have often been found corresponding to some of these stages. But uncertainties still exist. A certain succession of morainal arcs, even if very clear in a long sector, is found to be interrupted at its wings and no one knows to which series of arcs of the following sector it should be joined. And it is especially difficult to make a choice in the succession of stages: which are the most important; which should be selected to mark the great periods of the history of the glacier? This is often a matter of personal opinion, which explains why there has been and still is uncertainty concerning the extent of certain stages and especially concerning their relative importance.

Finally, it might be thought that the line of maximum extent of the ice would determine a precise boundary, this maximum being simultaneous everywhere. We should then have the complete and certain line of at least one stage, corresponding to the maximum glaciation. But detailed studies have shown that this is not without some doubt, since the glacier returned several times in the same region, after its greatest extension, stopping sometimes beyond, sometimes within its previous boundaries.

Nevertheless, in the plains of northern Germany, morphologic observations long ago established two very distinct regions, even on small-scale topographic maps.

a. To the north, a region where glacial relief has remained very fresh. Morainal vallums form long, continuous bands; glacial lakes, outwash plains, etc. are well preserved. The different stationary glacial fronts are relatively easy to reconstruct. In front of each the water from the melting glacier, joined to rivers descending from the Hercynian massifs of southern Germany, united in gigantic streams (Urströme = original rivers) which paralleled these fronts, flowing in a general SE-NW direction, to enter the North Sea between Schleswig and Holland, not into the Baltic (then still buried beneath ice) as rivers of these regions do today. Thus a great valley (Urstromtal) corresponds to each glacial front and these Urstromtäler are still used, in successive segments, by the present rivers, which explains the winding courses of these rivers (Fig. 150).

One is thus tempted to consider this whole region as having been covered by a recent glaciation, followed by successive retreats. This is the domain of the last glaciation (called Vistula glaciation) or of internal moraines.

b. Outside this domain, on the other hand, extends an area where the glacial topography has been almost entirely effaced, either by erosion, or rather (according to Gripp) by the phenomena of solifluction during the final glaciation.[79] This is the domain of external moraines, in which we shall attempt later to define two early glaciations.

Such is the first great division, and to tell the truth, the only clear one, which appears immediately in the morphology. And even the boundary between these two domains is sometimes a little uncertain (see later the discussion of the Warthe stage).

3. Stratigraphic Superpositions: Interglacial Deposits

But the study of forms alone tells nothing of what happened between two stages. So some German geologists, knowing their country very well (for example, Geinitz) have held the opinion that the withdrawals separating two successive stages were very unimportant and there was no proof of the existence of several glacial periods. These monoglacialists believed the glacier had one maximum and was stationary with small oscillations in detail, then began to retreat spasmodically and the climate did not become similar to the present until after this retreat, in post-glacial times.

This opinion can be refuted only by referring to the evidence of deep wells sunk in the region of Berlin. The question being important, for this is the single, decisive proof we have of the reality of the interglacial periods, it seems useful to reproduce the section of one of these wells, Rüdersdorf well III (near Berlin), according to Wahnschaffe:

> 0–5 m.—Sands and superficial alluvial deposits.
> 5–22 m.—Recent moraines.
> 22–27 m.—Interglacial sands, called Rixdorf (with mammoth).
> 27–35 m.—Middle moraines.
> 35–65 m.—Sands.
> 65–81 m.—Interglacial clays (with a bed containing *Paludina diluviana*).
> 81–136 m.—Sands and banded clays (Bändertone, varves).
> 136–178 m.—Lower moraines.

These two interglacial periods do not correspond merely to local incidents.

The *Paludina* bed, always several meters thick, with an abundant fauna, was found in several wells in the vicinity of Berlin, located between –7 and –20 m., and always in the same relative position to the moraines enclosing it. Its fauna, studied by Schmierer, includes *Bithynia tentaculata, Valvata piscinalis, Dreissensia polymorpha.* There are some nenuphars (water lilies) (*Nuphar luteum*) and not a single form that could indicate a climate colder than today's. This is the lower interglacial period. Therefore, glaciers must have retreated very far northward, for in Esthonia[80] recently, between two moraines, a peaty interglacial deposit was discovered which probably dates from the same period, with two essentially southern plants, *Brasenia purpurea* and *Trapa natans.*

As for the upper interglacial, called the Rixdorf, it has long been known in the quarries of Rixdorf (now Neukölln) near Berlin, where, under 2 to 5 m. of upper moraines, 10 m. of sand (containing bones at the top), overlie 4 m. of lower moraines. Similar sands are found at Koenigsberg in Prussia and in the vicinity of Poznan (Posen). The fauna of this horizon has caused some discussion: the mammoth and its usual companions (*Rhinoceros tichorhinus, Ovibos moschatus,* reindeer) are associated there with warm forms (*Elephas antiquus, Rhinoceros mercki, Cervus elaphus,* lion, etc.) and in addition, at the same level as the sand, there is peat representing its equivalent, southeast of Berlin for example, containing a flora warmer than that of the present day (*Ilex aquifolium*). This is then a true interglacial period and the cold fauna is explained by recognizing that it is a little more recent and dates from the end of that interglacial period.

So most north European geologists now recognize the existence of three glacial periods separated by two interglacial epochs. But uncertainty arises as to the positions of the glacial fronts corresponding to the three glaciations determined by stratigraphic superposition in the Berlin area. For the upper moraines, whose continuity in outcrop is obviously easier to follow, the face can very probably be recognized in the Brandenburg phase. The frontal moraines of this phase, very clear between the Elbe and the Warthe, mark the extreme advance of the last glaciation (to be described later under the name Vistula glaciation), 50 km. southwest of Berlin. But as to the middle and lower moraines, it must be admitted that there is no very solid argument for connecting them respectively, as is usually done, with the Saale and the Elster glaciations defined (more or less clearly) according to morphology.

4. *Chronologic Description of North-European Quaternary Formations*

A. Preglacial. Only continental formations seem to date from this epoch, of which three examples follow:

1. *The Cromer forest bed.* This celebrated deposit is found on the English coast at Cromer (Fig. 145). It is an estuarine formation containing pieces of fossil wood, from which it derives its name. It is stratigraphically superposed on the Pliocene Crag described earlier (p. 595) and below the oldest moraines known in Britain. It is believed to have been deposited by a river coming from Holland, comparable to the Rhine of today, at a time when the British Isles were connected to the continent. The flora is composed of living species indicating a climate similar to that of the present time. The fauna is very curious. It includes upper Pliocene forms (*Elephas meridionalis, Rhinoceros etruscus, Equus stenonis*), then warm species of the early Quaternary (*Elephas trogontherii, Hippopotamus*) and finally, perhaps, cold forms (*Ovibos moschatus?, Gulo luscus?*). In any event, in the upper beds (Arctic freshwater beds) the flora becomes polar and the section terminates with moraines. This may be considered a transition from the Pliocene to the Quaternary during the course of which a chilling was felt, evidence perhaps of a glacial period older(?) than the classic north European glaciations. British geologists consider that it is a question of upper Pliocene strata already containing the first beginning of the Quaternary fauna.

2. An analogous fauna, sometimes attributed to the Villafranchian, with 22 mammalian species (*Hippopotamus, Equus stenonis, Elephas antiquus, Rhinoceros etruscus,* etc.) is found in the *Tegelen clays*[81] in the lower Rhine valley. These are considered to be earlier than the oldest moraines, and reach 100 m. thickness. This is the horizon with *Paludina* (*Vivipara*) *glacialis* of the Dutch geologists, also containing *Corbicula fluminalis,* a rather warm form. In Belgium, it is represented by the *Campine clays,*[82] likewise exploited as pottery clay, whose base is Pliocene.

3. Finally, similar faunal associations are found in the old *alluvium of Süssenborn*[83] which, 5 km. east of Weimar, forms a high terrace of 50–70 m. Archaic forms are found there (*Epimachairodus, Trogontherium cuvieri, Rhinoceros etruscus, Elephas trogontherii*) and also reindeer and musk ox, which show chilling. It must be noted that this alluvium contains no northern cobbles. It is therefore certainly prior to the oldest Scandinavian glaciation.

B. First Glaciation or Elster Glaciation. The Elster is a river passing by Leipzig and it is there that this glaciation has been defined. One sees old alluvium overlain by banded clays (with varves, see p. 614) and then a moraine. There, in Saxony, as also in Thuringia and the vicinity of the Weser, this glaciation advanced farthest. Elsewhere it seems to remain behind the front of the second glaciation.

C. First Interglacial. From this epoch date the Berlin beds with paludines which we discussed earlier. At this moment, the Baltic Sea must no longer have existed. But farther west, a marine gulf advanced into the

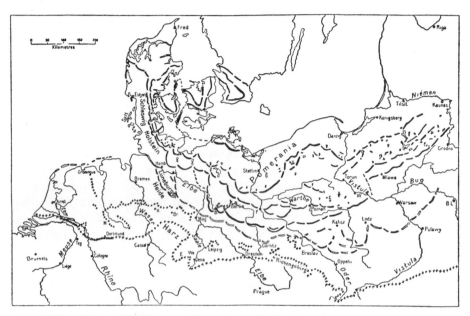

FIG. 150. *Map of the varied stages of the Scandinavian glacier on the southern shores of the Baltic (after Woldstedt).*

Heavy black lines..... Morainal ridges (*vallums*) of the Vistula glaciation (with its successive stages: Brandenburg, Poznan, and Pomeranian).
Double lines......... Morainal ridges of the Warthe stage.
Black dots........... Morainal ridges of the Saale glaciation.
Crosses .... Southern limit of erratic blocks.

B—Brandenburg; BL—Brest-Litovsk; Br—Brunswick; E—Erfurt; F—Frankfurt-am-Oder; Fred—Frederikshavn; H—Hanover; Hamb—Hamburg; L—Lauenburg; M—Munster; Mag—Magdeburg; Teg—Tegelen; W—Wloclasek; We—Weimar.

region of Hamburg and Lauenburg (southeast of Hamburg) where numerous wells have traversed a marine clay, with a fauna close to that of the present day. This is Penck's Holstein Sea.[84] To the north, the Esbjerg marine clays with *Yoldia* and *Tellina* cropping out near the Danish coast north of the Island of Sylt,[85] are classified in the same epoch. They contain *Portlandia* (*Yoldia*) *arctica,* an arctic form localized at the base, and *Tellina calcarea,* a form simply northern.

Toward the southwest, in Westphalia, on the other hand, there is a continental interglacial, intercalated between two moraines, which, in the vicinity of Münster,[86] has yielded *Corbicula fluminalis,* which appeared earlier in the Dutch preglacial. Here it is curiously associated with *Elephas primigenius.* Also, not far away in the Ruhr district, there are beds containing seeds of several immigrant species[87] which perhaps should also be joined with this same old interglacial.

D. Second Glaciation or Saale Glaciation. This has been defined in the vicinity of the Saale, west of Leipzig, but the most external moraines of the lower Rhine valley, where it advanced beyond the preceding glaciation, are also classified here. The great moraines of the *Warthe phase,* which extend from the valley of the Bug, northwest of Brest-Litovsk, into the Lüneburg Heath (*Lüneburger Heide,* south of Hamburg) are generally considered as a transitory advance associated with the Saale glaciation.[88] The glacial topography is less fresh than in the domain of internal moraines, but the thick continuous covering of loess, which cloaks the true external moraines, is no longer found.

E. The Second or Eemian Interglacial. The most interesting deposits are the peat or lake deposits (muds with diatoms, tripoli, exploited as kieselgur) which have been studied [89] in western Jutland and the Lüneburg Heath. These peats show two beds with a warm temperate flora (*Brasenia, Dulichium, Trapa*) separated by a subarctic flora (*Betula nana*), demonstrating that momentarily a chilling occurred during this period, without the glaciers advancing beyond Scandinavia.

After much discussion, the marine deposits of the *Eemian stage*[90] named after the valley of the Eem, south of the Zuider Zee, are also attributed to the second interglacial. They are clays or clayey sands containing a fauna well characterized by an extinct variety, *Tapes eemiensis,* and Lusitanean [Portuguese] species. No specifically northern form has been found in it. The deposits of this age are very widespread, extending from the Belgian frontier into eastern Prussia and giving evidence of the advance of a true Baltic Sea during this interglacial epoch. This Eemian is connected to the previous period by the momentary chilling just mentioned. Contrarily, it is to the upper part of the interglacial epoch, following this chilling, that the celebrated marine series of Skaerumhede is attributed, found in a well west of Frederikshavn (northeast extremity of Jutland). There, under 57 m. of the last glacial material, is a zone with *Portlandia arctica* (40 m.) with arctic species, next a zone with *Abra nitida* (8 m.) without Lusitanean forms. Finally at the base is a zone with *Turritella terebra* (74 m.) with 22 Lusitanean species. This series of marine formations, 122 m. thick, showing a warm, interglacial fauna which becomes progressively colder at the approach of the last glaciation, is certainly one of the most interesting in all of northern Europe.[91]

Finally, south of this Quaternary Baltic, continental interglacial formations are deposited, such as the Rixdorf sands which we have already mentioned, and also the famous tufas (travertines) of Taubach and Ehringsdorf, near Weimar, situated beneath a bed of loess. The lower part contains a warm flora (*Thuya occidentalis,* etc.) with *Elephas antiquus, Rhinoceros mercki* and human remains of the Neanderthal race.[92]

F. Third or Vistula Glaciation.   Three succesive phases are distinguished, beginning with the oldest (follow on map, Fig. 150), called: 1. The *Brandenburg phase,* very clear between the Elbe and the Warthe, where it forms the external front of the last glaciation. 2. The *Frankfurt-am-Oder phase,*

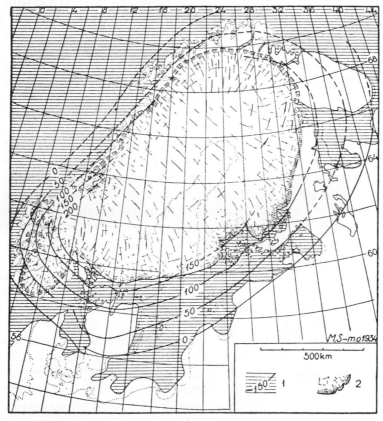

FIG. 151.   *Map of the* Yoldia *sea, by Matti Sauramo (1934).*

1 = Isobases of the *Yoldia* sea, that is to say lines joining all the points where the old shores of this sea are found today at the same altitudes (0, 50, 100, 150 meters, etc.).
2 = Front of the ice cap.

also called the Poznan (Posen) phase or external Baltic moraines. Extending from northeast of Berlin, toward the northeast, this constitutes the front of the third glaciation. In these two phases, the forms of the frontal moraines are a little blunted, but the outwash plains on the other hand are remarkably well preserved and outline the southern limit of the lake country which extends northward to the coast. 3. The *Pomeranian phase* or internal Baltic moraines. There the forms of the frontal moraines are preserved in all their freshness.

G. Postglacial Times. The moraines of the Pomeranian phase mark the last epoch when the Scandinavian glacier occupied all the area of the present Baltic Sea and reached its southern shores. Next, for geologists of central Europe, the postglacial period begins.[93]

The southern part of the Baltic, abandoned by the ice, was first transformed into a lake, while the glacial front retreated and remained stationary long enough to build an imposing trail of moraines, which in a general E-W direction, traversed the southern part of Finland (where its reliefs are called Salpausselkä) and central Sweden where they describe an arc between the regions of Stockholm and Oslo (Fig. 149).

Then the withdrawing ice allowed this Baltic lake to communicate with the North Sea, through a broad open strait across southern Sweden. The Baltic was then occupied by the *Yoldia sea* (with *Y. arctica*). Its deposits can easily be studied in Finland and Sweden, for they are found today, as we shall see, elevated well above the present sea level. These deposits are banded clays, called varve clays, which we studied earlier (p. 614).

The thickness of a varve varies from .2 to 3 cm., and each of them corresponds, in principle, to a year. Thus, examining a section of a clay pit, we may learn in exactly how many years the beds were deposited. The relation of one pit to another is established by comparing the peculiarities (for example, relative variations of thickness of a series of varves) which are found identical in both pits. Finally, it will be seen that each varve could be formed only in front of the face of the glacier in the sea. The oldest varves stop progressively as one goes northward. In summary, the study of varves is believed to allow the establishment of the chronology, in years, of the successive glacial fronts. So, according to DeGeer, founder of this method, the Yoldia sea dates from about 8,000 B. C.

Next, after this clearly marine phase, uplift interrupted communication with the North Sea. The Baltic was transformed into a freshwater lake, the *Ancylus lake* (with *A. fluviatilis*, a small gastropod very frequent in freshwater lakes today). That happened about 6,000 to 7,000 B. C. At that time the glaciers had already withdrawn into the Scandinavian mountains (Fig. 152).

Then a transgression took place both on the coast of Flanders (Flandrian transgression) and in the Baltic domain. The Ancylus lake was transformed into a *Littorina sea* (with *L. littorea*, a species very abundant on French coasts), saltier than the present Baltic Sea, and the faunas and floras indicate a warmer climate than today's.

Finally, after the Age of Bronze, the marine faunas left the freshened depths of the Baltic gulfs and were replaced by the lacustrine fauna with *Limnaea*. But in the course of historic time, a clearly marine species, *Mya arenaria*, has again penetrated the Baltic.

The history of the eastern Mediterranean domain during the Neogene (p. 587) has already given us an earlier example of the vicissitudes of faunas of inland seas, but this history of the Quaternary Baltic can be followed in much greater detail.

If the Baltic region lends itself so well to the study of these old marine
or lacustrine formations it is because, unlike what happened on the French
coast for example, the whole Finnish-Scandinavian domain was uplifted after
the disappearance of the glaciers. The amounts of these uplifts can be read
on the maps, Figs. 151, 152, 153. As may be seen, they are greatest in the

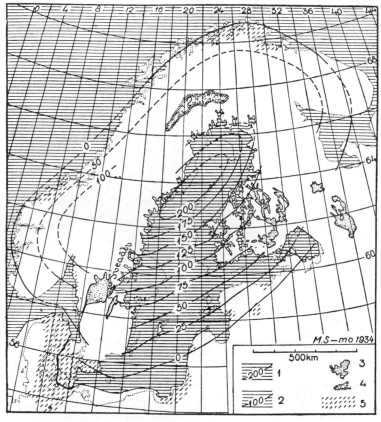

FIG. 152. *Map of the* Ancylus *lake at the moment of its greatest extent, by*
Matti Sauramo (*1934*).

  1 = Isobases of the *Ancylus* lake.
  2 = Isobases of the North Sea at the same epoch.
  3 = Small interior lakes.
  4 = Residue of the ice cap.
  5 = Regions inhabited by prehistoric man at this epoch.

region which must have corresponded approximately to the center of gravity
of the ice sheet. We are therefore justified in believing that under the excess
weight of this sheet, the continental mass of the old Shield gave way momentarily, then it was progressively uplifted by degrees as the ice melted,
but with a certain delay since this uplift still continues. Thus stratigraphic
studies have here made possible the accurate retracing of the history of the
deformation of the earth's crust (p. 651).

However, in addition to these local isostatic deformations,[94] we know that there were also general eustatic movements (p. 19) in the level of the oceans: regressions during glacial periods, transgressions during interglacial periods (p. 612).

Studying, on the ground, the deformations of old post-glacial shorelines in Finland and Sweden, M. Sauramo tried to separate, in these changes, the

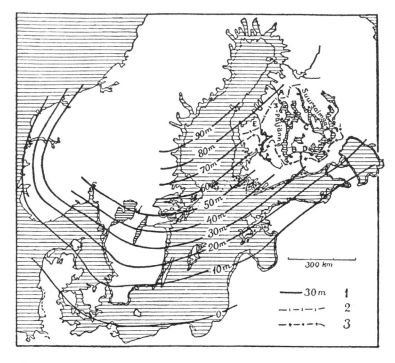

1 = Isobases of this sea
2 = The present watershed in Finland
3 = The same at the period of maximum extent of the Littorina sea
A = Contours of the old Lake Paijanne before this maximum
B = The same after this maximum
C = Contours of old Lake Saimaa slightly before this maximum
D = The same at the moment of this maximum
E = Contours of old Lake Näsijärvi, at about the moment of this maximum

FIG. 153. *Map of the* Littorina *sea, at the moment of its maximum extent* (*about 4,000 B. C.*), *by Matti Sauramo* (*1929*).

part due to the local isostatic uplift and that due to general eustatic movements of the seas.[95] He estimates that, at the epoch of the Yoldia sea, the general level of the oceans must have been 80 m. lower than the present sea level and 60 m. lower at the epoch of the Ancylus lake, while at the time of the Littorina sea, the oceans were a few meters above their present level. These high figures lead therefore to values close to those of Ramsay, Penck (1933), and Dubois, mentioned on p. 612.

VII. History of Alpine Glaciations[96]

1. *Generalities*

The history of the Alpine glaciations is very similar to that of the north European glaciers, with the same obscurities.

A. External Limit of the Glaciations. As in the north, the feature that is easiest to reconstruct is that of the maximum extent of the ancient glaciers, for this extent is marked by the external limit of erratic blocks of Alpine origin and by morainal deposits, that is to say by what was formerly called the erratic formation or diluvial formation.

So it may be affirmed that, in the southern Alps, the glaciers of the Roya, the Var and its tributaries (Vésubie and Tinée) were restricted to the domain of the high mountains.[97] The same is true for the glaciers of the Verdon and the Bléone (a river which flows by Digne). The old glacier of the Durance[98] descended much lower, as far as Sisteron (p. 614). But, even at the moment of maximum extent, these southern glaciers always remained in glacial valleys, of the Alpine type, comparable to the present glaciers of the Himalaya, for example.

The glaciers of the Rhône and Isère, on the other hand, better nourished in a colder climate, spread widely over the Alpine piedmont. The glacial currents issuing from their two valleys, joined in Lower Dauphiné in a vast sheet of ice comparable to those formed today by the Alaskan glaciers (piedmont glacier type) at the base of the mountains. The front of this ice sheet turned from the edge of the Alps southwest of Grenoble to cover the first slopes of the Massif Central at Lyon and passed through Bourg. From there, it followed the edge of the Jura Mountains between Bourg and Lons-le-Saunier. The highest ridges of the Jura, covered with local glaciers, formed a barrier to the Alpine glaciers, which covered the Swiss plateau, with only the molasse summit of Napf (1,408 m.) emerging, between Berne and Lucerne. The ice at the edge of the Jura reached a height at certain points of nearly 1,400 m. (at Chasseron). The snow line was about 1,000 m., so that a slight modification of climate and consequently of this line, would suffice to vary in enormous proportions, the surface of alimentation and consequently the size of the glacier.

The ice sheets could therefore surmount the low passes of the Jura range, so that beyond that chain they outlined a great advance to the latitude of Pontarlier.[99] The common front of the glaciers of the Aar, the Reuss and the Rhine, joined to terminate a little south of Basel. From that point, it passed near Schaffhausen, then advanced to join the front of the glaciers of the Danube tributaries, which reached points south of Ulm and Munich. Thus almost the whole Bavarian plain was covered.

On the Italian slope, the glaciers remained separated from each other and did not pass beyond the mouths of the great Alpine valleys in the plain of the Po. There they built magnificent amphitheatres of frontal moraines, encircling lakes which occupy the terminal depressions.[100]

B. Distinction of Different Glacial Epochs.   Behind this line of the maximum extent of the ice, naturally come series of morainal arcs, each of which can be used to define a "phase" which corresponds either to the prolonged stillstand of a glacier in the course of its retreat or rather to a relative maximum, to a more or less important glacial growth.[101]

It is difficult to know what happened between two phases of growth. We have shown previously (p. 613) that the deposition of fluviatile alluvium or lacustrine muds did not necessarily prove that the glacier had retreated far upstream. Such formations are not necessarily interglacial or even interphase.

In order to classify the phases inscribed in the morphology, and to appreciate their importance, it is often necessary to resort to indirect means.

1. *The Relation between Moraines and Terraces.*   In the neighborhood of the Alps, terraces were quite certainly strictly dependent on glacial fluctuations. As Penck and Brückner have very well said, going up any one of the great valleys descending from the Alps, the old moraines begin to appear by degrees as the terraces disappear. Morainal landscapes succeed terrace landscapes.[102] Thus it is often possible to find fluvio-glacial complexes, as we have defined them (p. 607). Then as many glacial periods can be distinguished as there are terraces (and moraines connected with them). Successive terraces necessarily being encased one within another, the glacial periods so defined will be separated by periods of erosion (Fig. 147)[103] and they will also be of progressively diminishing extent. Therefore, remembering what was said earlier (p. 609) we are not sure to find evidence of every glacial advance. In addition, we cannot estimate the importance of the glacial decreases separating our glacial "periods," nor the climatic changes.

2. *The Degree of Alteration of Moraines.*   This alteration (and eventually that of terraces) is shown either by decomposition of the rocks making up the fluvio-glacial deposits or by disappearance of their topographic forms.

From this point of view, when one includes in a single survey, as did Penck and Brückner, the assemblage of morainal vallums which cover the domain of Alpine glaciations, one perceives that two great divisions can be quite clearly distinguished, as in northern Germany.

a. The most external morainal arcs are already considerably modified in topographic form by erosion and their materials profoundly altered. The crystalline rocks have become friable, the calcareous cobbles, half dissolved, are sometimes represented only by a skeleton with a siliceous web. The iron minerals tend to pass into a state of hydrated oxides which give a characteristic yellow or red color to their alteration products (rubefaction or *ferrétisation*). We call these old or external moraines, connected with the high terraces which have the same characters.

b. The most internal moraines, on the contrary, are distinguished by their sharp topography and fresh materials. Rubefaction has acted only on a relatively thin, superficial layer. These are the recent or internal moraines and the low terraces.

3. *The Covering of Loess.* If it is concluded, as we have done (p. 615), that true loess is produced only during true glacial periods, determined by their cold dry climates, it follows that the formation of loess must have ended with the beginning of the last glacial retreat, caused by the definite ending of climatic conditions which led to the glacial advances. And in fact, as was stated for northern Germany, loess covers the old moraines and high terraces and is never found, or almost never, on the recent moraines and low terraces.

4. *Interglacial Deposits.* These deposits are of necessity much more localized and less extensive than in the realm of the north European glaciation. They do exist, however, and the most typical of them are:

a. The Hötting breccia, near Innsbruck. There, intercalated between two moraines, breccias of old debris and tufas deposited by springs are found. These tufas contain numerous impressions of *Rhododendron ponticum,* a plant relegated today to Pontic [Black Sea] regions, of box (*Buxus sempervirens*) and wild vine (*Vitis vinifera*),[104] which are no longer living at Innsbruck. So this flora indicates a climate warmer than the present climate of the region, and consequently smaller glaciers than those of today.

b. Beds with *Rhododendron ponticum* are also found on the Italian slope at Re, in the Val Vigezzo (near Ossola).[105]

c. The laminated coals (Schieferkohlen) of Switzerland [106] are lignites deposited between two moraines. In the vicinity of Zurich (Dürnten)[107] they have yielded a flora composed of species living in the region, with *Brasenia purpurea* (p. 623) in addition and a fauna of warm character (*Elephas antiquus, Rhinoceros mercki, Ursus spelaeus,* etc.) without reindeer or mammoths. Similar lignites, non-fossiliferous, are found near Geneva (Bâthie Wood) and Chambéry (Voglans lignites, with *Buxus sempervirens?*).

All these occurrences are found in the realm of internal moraines, and even 100 km. behind the ancient glacial fronts. So, as in northern Germany, it is almost impossible to know with certainty to which of the glacial fronts belong the moraines which enclose the interglacial formations just described.

So we should not be surprised if the distinction and reconstruction of different glacial periods in the Alps still remain very uncertain. It may be said that the different geologists who have studied different Alpine regions, or the same region successively, almost never reach the same conclusions. The single distinction that is fairly clear is that between the internal and external moraines, long ago emphasized by Penck and Brückner.

2. *Bavarian and Swabian Alps*

This is the region where Penck and Brückner started their classic syntheses of Alpine glaciation. These authors distinguished four glacial periods here, which they called, after the names of rivers of the region, Günz, Mindel, Riss (external moraines) and Würm (internal moraines).[108] In addition, they named the Achen fluctuation, a period of regression following the Würm maximum, and followed by phases of retreat called Bühl, Gschnitz, and Daun.

The Günz and Mindel glaciations were prior to the great excavations of the valleys, so that the fluvio-glacial gravel resulting from them, reduced to small remnants, without clear topographic forms, are always found on elevated plateaus. These are the *Deckenschotter* (cover gravels or plateau gravels). In general (but not always), the Riss advanced farthest and can be called the great glaciation.

We shall not insist on describing these regions, too far removed from France, and shall be satisfied to note that geologists, who have studied them after Penck and Brückner, reach slightly different conclusions. Thus Wehrli [109] recognizes only two great glaciations, while Eberl and Knauer[110] distinguish a very large number of glacial phases.

As for the famous Hötting breccia, near Innsbruck, the most famous interglacial deposit of the Alps (p. 637), there is much uncertainty concerning its age. Penck first considered it to belong to the last interglacial (between the Riss and the Würm), next as post-Würmian (inter-phase), and finally[111] attributed it to an old interglacial (between the Mindel and the Riss). The most recent study is that of H. Katschthaler[112] who, thanks to the construction of a new highway, reconstructed the history of the region in this way: first glaciation; deposition of the breccia; erosion, second glaciation, erosion; deposition of alluvium, erosion; third glaciation, erosion. The author does not commit himself, however, on the correlation of these three glaciations with the classic glacial stages of Penck and Brückner.

3. *The Rhine Basin and its Tributaries*

A. The Region of Moraines in the Swiss Alps. Here, the two most recent syntheses are those of Albert Heim and P. Beck.[113] Their conclusions, however, differ on many points, as we shall see.

1. The first question is to distinguish the fluvio-glacial deposits antecedent to the great excavation of valleys. These are the *Deckenschotter* recognized earlier in this region by Penck and Brückner, with the two glaciations called Günz and Mindel, difficult to separate. These formations are, in fact, reduced to insignificant remnants on the plateaus. There is no connection between the alluvium and the moraines, which appear superposed or juxtaposed.

Between Aare and Glatt, the Günzian moraines go little farther than the internal moraines (Würmian). Northwest of Lake Constance, they remain conspicuously behind the latter, but in the Schussen-Iller region, they mark the extreme limit of glacial advance. The altitude of the Günzian reaches 940 m. at Albis (a hill near Zurich), where its alluvium, covering the bottom moraines, overlooks Lake Zurich from a height of 500 m. At Basel, the Günzian Deckenschotter are found from 360 m. to perhaps 110 m. above the Rhine.

As for the Deckenschotter called Mindelian, they appear lower than the preceding, 110 m. lower at Schienberg, near Zurich, and 55 m. lower near Basel. The extent of the Mindelian glaciers differed little from that of the Günzian glaciers.

2. Next, during a long period, the great excavation of valleys occurred. It was followed by an important accumulation of alluvium which, differing from the Deckenschotter, reached even the bottoms of old valleys, sometimes coinciding, sometimes not, with present valleys (Rinnenschotter = gorge gravels, so differing from Deckenschotter). Heim gives the name *Hochterrassenschotter* or high terrace gravels to these thick alluvial masses, which never overlie moraines, although, covered by moraines which gully them, they do not constitute true, morphologic terraces (see note 13, this chap.).

3. Then, over these fill formations and gullying them, a great glaciation advanced, called Riss by Beck and *grösste Vergletscherung* by Heim.[114] These are the external moraines of Penck and Brückner (Riss) which mark the extreme limit of glacial advances near Basel. In the interior of the Alps, on the valley slopes, the old lateral moraines of this glaciation were destroyed by erosion. Only isolated erratic blocks remain, situated a little above the moraines of the following glaciation. At approximately the same time, the Swiss lakes began to develop, from "increasing glacial excavation." Heim believes, however, that these deep depressions are evidence of a general subsidence of 150 to 200 m. affecting the whole border of the Alps.

4. Then a great interglacial period arrived. According to Heim, and this opinion seems entirely reasonable, the laminated lignites, which we have already discussed, were formed at that time in the vicinity of Zurich (classic Dürnten deposit). Beck, however, considers these lignites as preceding his Riss (grösste Vergletscherung of Heim) and he parallels them with the Cromer Forest bed and the bank of paludines at Berlin.

Finally, this interglacial period perhaps dates the curious prehistoric deposit of the Wildkirchli cave, at 1,500 m. altitude in the Säntis massif (southeast of Zurich). Remains of several thousand skeletons of *Ursus spelaeus* are found, and dressed flints, apparently Mousterian. This industry of ancient stamp has led to attributing to this deposit an age prior to that of the last retreat of the ice (which is everywhere accompanied by Magdalenian populations) and to attach it to the Riss-Würm interglacial epoch. It would then be a striking proof of the retreat of glaciers during this period.[115]

5. Finally, comes the advance of the last glaciation, that of the external moraines, which corresponds, for everyone, to the Würm of Penck and Brückner. The Rhine glacier did not extend beyond Schaffhausen. Its front united with that of the Reuss glacier, but that of the Aar remained separate, ending 40 km. northeast of Bern. And the Aar-Rhône glacier no longer crossed the Jura.

The topographic forms produced by this glaciation and its stages of retreat have retained remarkable freshness, in the whole Swiss plateau, with its drumlins and especially its successive arcs of frontal and lateral moraines, which encircle the terminal depressions occupied by lakes. There, as in northern

Germany, the history of the stages of retreat of the glaciers is clearly read in the topography.

B. Alluvial Terraces of the Middle Rhine Valley. This is a very difficult study and has led to no complete and definitive synthesis. For, contrary to the theoretical ideas of Depéret and De Lamothe, there is no reason, quite the contrary, to believe that, far from the Alps, all the terraces correspond to glacial maxima and follow each other clear to the sea always maintaining the same relative altitudes. In fact, as the works of Quiring and A. Briquet [116] have well demonstrated, the Rhenish terraces were deformed by local movements of the earth and even by faults (Wernert, note 64, this chap.).[117] However, the great thickness of the alluvium in the Rhenish trough, in contrast to the slight thickness in the Rhine gorge through the Rhenish Schiefergebirge between Bingen and Bonn, forces the recognition that subsidence must have occurred here in the course of the Quaternary.[118]

Having discussed the loess of Alsace (p. 621) we shall confine ourselves to mentioning a few mammalian occurrences in the alluvium.

First comes the celebrated *Mosbach* deposit, near Wiesbaden, in the Mainz Basin, at the foot of the Taunus. Its lower part is Pliocene (*Elephas meridionalis, Mastodon arvernensis,* etc.). But the upper part, containing *Elephas antiquus,* corresponds to the Rhenish high terrace, covered by old and recent loess, well developed near Strasbourg (Hangenbieten terrace) and on the Baden bank where it is part of the group of Bergsträssen terraces. This terrace disappears downstream from Bonn and is probably older than the Saale glaciation (Riss).[119] Likewise, the classic deposit of *Mauer,*[120] near Heidelberg, is composed of alluvium of a terrace 30 m. above the Neckar which has yielded, with a fauna of *Elephas antiquus,* the famous jawbone of *Homo heidelbergensis.*

On the other hand, the low terrace (Talwegterrasse) of the Lower Rhine was contemporaneous with the Saale glaciation and Rissian moraines. According to Mordziol, "it is the only Rhenish terrace which may be in direct relation with the Scandinavian and Alpine moraines." Thus, it would demonstrate that the Saale glaciation was contemporary with the Alpine Riss (or grösste Vergletscherung).

4. Rhône and Isère Basins: French Alps

The French districts where glaciations have been best studied correspond to the domain of maximum extent of the old Rhône and Isère glaciers. We shall describe their history in detail, by way of example.[121]

At the points where the valleys emerge from the sub-Alpine chains and the southern Jura, masses of ice were wide-spread over the plains of the Rhône and of the Saône, whose substratum is Miocene and Pliocene. This platform of Neogene formations was, and still is, slashed by three great depressions descending from the Alps, in which terraces are very clear (Fig. 154).

The first, south of the Isère valley, follows approximately the boundary of the sub-Alpine chains and Miocene hills of Lower Dauphiné. Next is the abandoned valley of Bièvre-Valloire, inclosed between the Miocene plateaus (with Pliocene cover) of Chambaran on the south and Bonnevaux on the north. This depression is not traversed today by any notable stream but it served as an important overflow bed, originating in former times from the junction region of the Isère and Rhône glaciers. Its terraces have remained remarkably continuous. Finally the third depression corresponds to the great valley of the Rhône upstream from Lyon, between the last Miocene hills of Lower Dauphiné and the edge of the Dombes plateau with its Pliocene platform.

A. **The Moraines and Terraces of Bièvre-Valloire.** In this abandoned valley, which has escaped recent erosion, topographic forms have remained sharpest [122] and easiest to interpret. Here will be found the key to the French Alpine Quaternary.

The very bottom of this long depression is formed by an alluvial sheet, not cut by any stream, which, approaching the Rhône at St. Rambert d'Albon, ends in an erosion embankment overlooking, from a height of about 15 m., the present alluvial plain of the river. Above, the low terrace of 15 m. joins a system of frontal moraines whose vallums cover a threshold with a Miocene base. These are the moraines of Rives, corresponding to the Würm maximum. On the southeast slope of this Rives sill,[123] the Isère glacier in process of diminution deposited successive bands of lateral moraines, which represent so many stages of Würm retreat. The melting torrents, not able to flow directly toward the Rhône through Bièvre-Valloire, joined the lower Isère, depositing narrow pipings of marginal alluvium along the moraines, a tiny reproduction of the Urstromtäler which bordered the front of the Scandinavian glacier (Fig. 155).

All of this first assemblage, the Würmian terrace (or 15 m. terrace) of Bièvre-Valloire, the Rives moraines and stages of retreat with their alluvium, is composed of gravels which have remained very fresh, generally gray in color. The superficial rubefied zone does not exceed a few decimeters and it has no covering of loess. There the characters of internal moraines are shown the best of any place in the Alps.

The most striking feature of the morphology of Bièvre-Valloire is a transverse band of external moraines, marking the front of a glacial still-stand, which can be called Riss. These are the moraines of Faramans and Beaufort. The Würm alluvial plain of the valley bottom crosses this barrier through a narrow opening, which separates the two wide sectors of Bièvre, above, and Valloire, below. But through this neck or opening also passes a piping of high terrace which, in the Bièvre, joins the intermediate moraines with very subdued form, in the region of Côte-St-André. This Côte-St-André phase can still be attributed to the Riss, as a stage of retreat.[124] In Valloire, another high terrace (the Beaurepaire terrace) is found which, hardly distinct from the preceding one, joins the Faramans-Beaufort moraines above, marking the Rissian maximum, and proceeds downstream as far as the vicinity of St. Rambert where it overlooks the Rhône from a height of about 30 m.[125]

This whole Rissian complex, maximum moraines, moraines of retreat and high terraces, carries a cover of loess and yellow loess-like limons. The usual

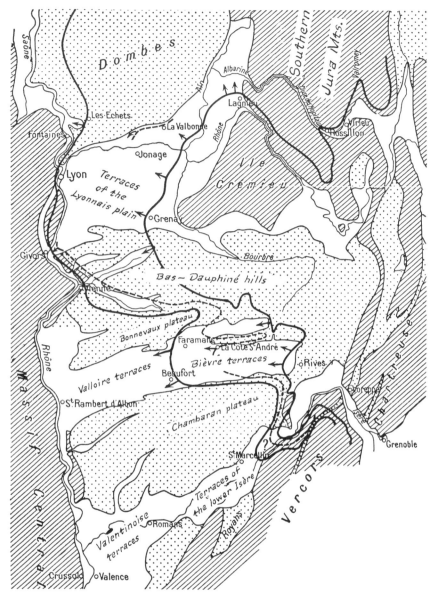

FIG. 154. *Structural map of the region of fluvio-glacial terraces and frontal moraines of the old Rhône-Isère glacier (in part after C. Depéret and W. Kilian, Lyon and Grenoble sheets of the* Carte géol. de France *1/80,000).*

Ruled lines: Mountainous or hilly country on a base composed of Secondary formations (Jura, sub-Alpine chains) or ancient formations (Massif Central).

Dotted area: Hilly country on a base composed of Miocene formations (Bas-Dauphiné) or Pliocene formations (Dombes), more or less concealed under moraines.

White area: Depressions filled with Recent alluvium, fluvio-glacial terraces, transition cones or moraines.

Heavy lines: Correspond respectively to the maximum advances of the external moraines (Rissian) and the internal moraines (Wurmian).

Heavy, broken line: Indicates the intermediary moraines (retreat of the Riss), quite clearly distinguished in the region of Bièvre (La Côte St-André phase), and probably found at the south edge of the Dombes (region of Valbonne).

Arrows: Mark the locations of the transition cones.

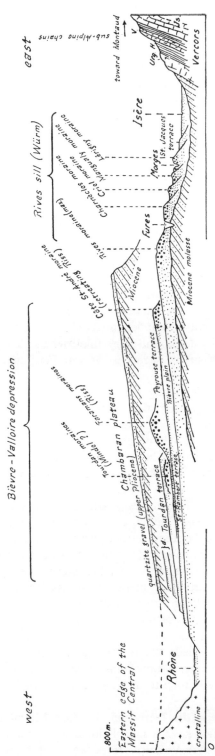

FIG. 155. *Fluvio-glacial formations of Bas-Dauphiné.* (*Reproduced from M. Gignoux and L. Moret, Géologie dauphinoise, Arthaud, Paris-Grenoble 1944, with modifications based on new data by F. Bourdier*).

In the foreground, section passing through the abandoned valley of Bièvre-Valloire and the sill of Rives, between the present valley of the Rhône at St-Rambert d'Albon and the alluvial plain of the Isère downstream from Grenoble, and extending into the terminal basin of the ancient Würm glacier.

In the background, successive profiles of morainal fronts and terraces rising in tiers above the bottom of the Bièvre-Valloire.

At *d* (Deckenschotter of Penck and Brückner), old Quaternary or Upper Pliocene terraces. On one of these is found the hardened loess of St. Vallier with a Villafranchian fauna (see note 126, this chap.).

color of the whole mass of alluvium and moraines, as seen in cuts in the gravels, is yellowish, no longer gray.

Finally, in Valloire, the high Rissian terrace of Beaurepaire is in its turn, dominated from a height of 25 to 30 m. by the terrace of Tourdan (hamlet north of Beaurepaire). Penck calls this Deckenschotter. F. Bourdier could see, on its edges and in a few ravines which cut through it, that its base was composed of typical moraines, with striated pebbles and erratic blocks packed in a compact, clayey cement, the top of which is buried beneath the alluvium of the terrace.

This curious complex where the moraines appear buried beneath alluvial fill and where the classic theory of a fluvio-glacial system no longer applies, indicates a more external glacial advance than the Faramans moraines (10 km. upstream) and is separated from the Rissian period by a long inter-glacial epoch with a warm climate. The whole complex underwent a pro-found and prolonged alteration, probably evidence of a very warm climate, for it ended with the formation of clay with a very bright reddish violet color, comparable to that of the siderolithic and variegated sands and clays of the Eocene (in these ravines, certain places are called *Terres-rouges* [red earth]). It can, at least by definition, be called Mindelian. Its alluvium extends as far as the Rhône and is covered by loess and very thick lehms [loess poor in calcium], in which old loess[126] surely seems to appear beneath the recent loess.

So, we can distinguish three glacial stages in Bièvre-Valloire, Mindel, Riss and Würm, separated by two interglacial stages, Mindel-Riss and Riss-Würm, the latter seemingly characterized by a climate little different from our own. It will be noted that this history of Alpine glaciation harmonizes very well with that of the Scandinavian glaciations in northern Germany.[127]

Moreover, the influence of this Mindel-Riss interglacial climate can be followed even in the old alluvium of the lower Isère, at the point where it reaches the Rhône near Valence. The highest terraces overlooking this city on the north and south (terraces of Foullouse and La Léore) show intense rubefaction similar to that of the Tourdan terrace. And curiously, this altera-tion even affects the summit of a molasse ridge which, at Châteauneuf d'Isère, was uplifted above the old alluvial plains during this interglacial period. The red earth of this epoch, formed at the expense of molasse in place (sandy Helvetian) and exceptionally well preserved here, is sufficiently thick and decalcified to support the exploitation of refractory products.[128]

Moreover, these Mindelian formations, up to the present time, have not been recognized with certainty outside the regions just described. However, they should be sought in the complexes now lumped under the name of Ris-sian. So, in the following, we are limited to distinguishing external (Riss) and internal (Würm) moraines.[129]

B. External Moraines between the Isère and the Jura Mountains. No-where do these external moraines have a morphologic individuality as clear as at Faramans-Beaufort in Bièvre-Valloire. Here we shall be satisfied to recognize the maximum extent of the Alpine glaciers by following the distribution of their erratic blocks.

In the lower Isère, river erosion has left no trace of frontal moraines. Residual Alpine blocks, observed by F. Bourdier opposite St. Lattier, seem to demonstrate that the Isère glacier advanced that far.

Farther north, it must have submerged the eastern extremity of the Chambaran plateau, which, at Parménie (787 m.), is strewn with erratic blocks. Then a lobe advanced into Bièvre as far as the Faramans-Beaufort moraines. Curving around the eastern end of the Bonnevaux plateau, the glacial front ran along the Rhône between Vienne and Givors.

There it crossed the Rhône and then the Saône at Vaise above Lyon. So that the Rissian Rhône, enlarged by the Saône which was thrust westward by the glacier, passed west of Lyon in an old valley[130] which today is filled with the alluvium of the high terrace (dominating the Rhône from about 60 m.) and is used for the route of the new railway from Lyon-Vaise to Givors, avoiding crossing the great city. The famous Fourvières and Croix-Rousse hills, cradle of the Rhône capital, thus bear, on their granite base, Alpine erratic blocks which formerly posed the problem of the Diluvium[131] to geologists of Lyon.

On the left bank of the Saône the glacier reached nearly to Bourg. So it covered all the Dombes plateau which, carpeted with greatly eroded old moraines, has an undulating surface, covered with ponds and forests, in contrast to the great monotonous plains of the non-glaciated Bresse.

However, before the arrival of the glaciers, but following the great excavation of the valleys, an important fluvial fill occurred, at least in the region of Lyon. Often, indeed, consolidated preglacial alluvium[132] appears under the moraines, along the southern (or *costière*) edge of the Dombes plateau or against the first slopes of the Massif Central. Early Lyon geologists called it alluvium of progression, deposited during glacial advance. At any rate, it is gullied by glacial deposits which cover the slopes composed of this alluvium. As is evident, this relationship is very reminiscent of those Heim described between his Hochterrassenschotter and his grösste Vergletscherung.[133]

C. Internal Moraines of the Würmian Maximum at the Outlets of Alpine Valleys. Indistinct in the lower Isère, the Würmian front is, on the contrary, admirably outlined at the entrance to the Bièvre through the Rives moraines, where the bottom alluvium of the Bièvre-Valloire makes its exit. The tributary valley of Nantoin-Commelle also opens into Bièvre; its alluvium is derived from a very small amphitheatre of frontal moraines closing the swampy central depression of Lac (now exploited for peat), crossed by the Lyon-Grenoble railroad between the stations of Chabons and Grand-Lemps.

Next, after a sinuous course across the Lower Dauphiné hills, the Würmian front is found in the beautiful frontal moraines of Grenay, which join downstream with a low terrace reaching the gates of Lyon (Villeurbanne terrace) where it overlooks the Rhône from a height of about 15 m. At that point, the Lyon geologists for the first time conceived the idea of a fluvio-glacial system.

Upstream is excavated the vast terminal depression of the peaty swamps of the Bourbre, at the southwest end of the Ile Crémieu.

Farther north, forcing the Bourbre to deviate northward to join the Rhône, the frontal moraines of the Würmian maximum are directed toward Lagnieu. There, a magnificent morainal amphitheatre was constructed by the glacier which debouched from the Rhône defile between the Ile Crémieu and the Jura. For the Würmian glacier no longer crossed this chain through the Hôpitaux pass; it closed the opening of this pass where it built thick lateral moraines in the region of Rossillon (note 18, this chap.).

Still farther north, the glacial front twisted back as a gulf into the lower part of Valromey, then returned to follow, on the right bank of the Rhône, the Grand-Colombier chain. From there, lateral moraines succeed each other on the flank of the Jura, bordering the great terminal basin of Lake Geneva, passing into Switzerland. At the Würmian maximum, the Rhône glacier was still joined to that of the Aar which ended 40 km. northeast of Bern, but henceforth remained separated from the Rhine glacier, which did not extend beyond Schaffhausen.

D. Interglacial Deposits in the Interior of the Alps and Jura-like Chains of Savoy.[134]   In the umbilicus of Grenoble, in Grésivaudan and the depressions (Lake Bourget) which, between the Jura and sub-Alpine chains, extend between the Jurassian links of Savoy as far as the Geneva basin, the old Rhône-Isère glacier covered all the mountainous slopes with a more or less continuous carpet of moraines, up to an altitude of about 1,100 to 1,200 m. This limit is recognized as approximately marking the Würmian maximum. Above, only isolated erratic blocks are found, sole evidence of older (Riss) moraines, almost entirely carried away by erosion.

But, a little above the valley floors and cropping out under the Würmian glaciation, from place to place, old alluvium or lignitic lacustrine clays are seen, much of which can be considered as pre-Würmian interglacial material. However, to be sure of it, one must be able to assert that the moraines overlying them surely date from the maximum of the Würmian glaciation and not simply from a stage of retreat, in which case, it would be a matter of not truly interglacial deposits but simply interphase (or even periglacial, see p. 613). This has aroused much discussion.

Finally, still more rarely, small remnants of old moraines are found under the interglacial deposits, remains of the Riss locally preserved and in some way sealed under the post-Rissian fill.

We shall describe a few examples:[135]

South of Grenoble, on the edge of Belledonne, a large quarry allows the convenient study of the Eybens clays, exploited for the manufacture of hollow tiles. The clays are 60 m. thick at the minimum. These clays contain varves (p. 614) and are perhaps partly periglacial or subglacial; at any rate they were certainly covered by Würmian glaciation which, on the slope of Belledonne, built up a great band of lateral moraines about 1,200 m. high. So they can be classified as interglacial, although they have yielded only plant or mollusk remains without stratigraphic significance.

Farther south, in the valley of the Drac, clayey Würmian moraines (p. 613) cover old alluvium, which can also be attributed to a Riss-Würm interglacial stage. In fact, on the right bank of the Drac near Pont-de-Claix, under the alluvium at the base of the morainal plateau of Champagnier, are found outcrops of old moraines which can be attributed to the Riss.[136]

But above all, at the northern end of the Grésivaudan in the Chambéry pass, old alluvium is widely developed under the Würmian glaciation, consisting of sand at the base, followed by lignitic clays. These are the famous lignites of Voglans and La-Motte-Servolex, exploited on both edges of the Chambéry-Lake Bourget depression. In it, tree trunks are reduced to very thin sheets (a few centimeters) which proves a great age and considerable weight which can hardly be that of Würmian ice and moraines. The structure, quite like that of the laminated lignite around Zurich, whose interglacial age is demonstrated paleontologically (p. 637), seems to prove that this represents a true Riss-Würm interglacial stage and not late marginal deposits dating from a phase of retreat of the Würm, as R. Blanchard suggested.[137]

In fact, an analogous occurrence between these interglacial deposits of Chambéry and Zurich is provided by the well-known lignites of the La Bathie Woods (southern outskirts of Geneva) cropping out at the base of the Würmian glaciation of the Geneva basin. And at the downstream end of this basin, at the entrance of the Rhône gorge at Fort-l'Ecluse (Pont Carnot) beneath alluvium and clayey sand undoubtedly comparable to the Geneva old pre-Würmian alluvium, appears a ridge of very compact, morainal clay, of a very different, ancient appearance from that of the Würmian clayey moraines. It is probably Rissian. In fact Geneva geologists find ancient moraines under their interglacial, both in wells around Geneva and even in outcrops on the edge of the lake at Hermance.[138]

Finally, in Chablais,[139] the famous conglomerates of the Dranse regularly form the floor of the Würmian moraines. They are completely comparable to the old alluvium of the Drac and are probably interglacial. Remnants of old Rissian moraines are sometimes preserved at their base.

So, curiously, if in the region of morainal fronts beyond the Alps, the distinction of several glacial periods can be based only on morphologic and pedologic arguments, it is only far in the interior of Alpine valleys that we find interglacial deposits supporting truly stratigraphic arguments. But it is very difficult, as in northern Germany, to understand the relation of these interglacial stages to the moraines surrounding them and especially to the different morainal fronts.

This should not surprise us. For, at present, in the course of the interglacial stage in which we are living, lacustrine muds are accumulating especially in the great intra-Alpine depressions of Geneva and Lake Bourget. In these muds the geologists of the future will be able to find the most characteristic witnesses of this present interglacial stage.

NORTHERN EUROPE	ALPINE REGIONS	HUMAN INDUSTRIES	MAMMALIAN FAUNAS	MEDITERRANEAN FAUNAS
Postglacial times { Littorina Sea / Ancylus Lake / Yoldia Sea / Baltic Lake }	Phases of retreat of the Würm	Age of Bronze / Neolithic / Magdalenian / Solutrean / Aurignacean	Age of Reindeer	Ordinary (Recent) faunas
Retreat of ice				
Vistula glaciation — { Recent loess; internal moraines, low terraces } — Würm glaciation		Mousterian	Cold fauna with mammoth	
2nd Interglacial { Marine deposits of Skaerumhede (North Jutland) and Eemian stage }	Continental deposits of Rixdorf (near Berlin) and of Taubach (near Weimar) / Lignites of regions of Zurich, Geneva, Chambery; Eybens clays, near Grenoble		Warm fauna with *Elephas antiquus*	
Saale glaciation — { Old loess; external moraines; high terraces } — Riss glaciation		Acheulean(?)	Cold fauna?	
1st Interglacial { Marine deposits of Esbjerg (North Jutland) and of the Holstein Sea }	*Paludina* bed of Berlin / Hötting breccia(?) Hochterrassenschotter of Switz. "Preglacial" alluvium of Lyon. Red earth of Valloire	Chellean?	Warm fauna?	Warm faunas of the Tyrrhenian?
	Elster glaciation — Very old loess — Mindel glaciation		Cold fauna?	Cold faunas of the Sicilian?
"Preglacial" wholly continental deposits: Clays of Tegelen and Campine, Gravels of Süssenborn	↑ Deckenschotter ↓ Gunz glaciation? St-Vallier loess		Fauna with *Elephas antiquus*	
Cromer Forest Bed				
Upper Pliocene (Villafranchian)			Fauna with *Elephas meridionalis*	Cold faunas of the Calabrian

Table indicating very hypothetical correlation of the principal Quaternary sediments listed here (following Boule, Woldstedt, etc.)

648

VIII. Conclusions

As we said in the beginning, the correlation of the different Quaternary formations is still far from being established with any certainty. Each specialist in one of the chronologic scales which can be used for this purpose too often has a too exclusive confidence in his method. In short, a stratigraphic synthesis of the Quaternary is, for its author, one of the numerous possible ways of relating and grouping, without too much inconsistency, the detailed observations which he deemed most interesting, many of which are often devoid of all stratigraphic significance. So solutions of problems thus posed are many and varied.

Among the different solutions, the preceding table (p. 648) has no claim other than presenting a sort of mean.

Actually the study of the Quaternary of each region should be undertaken for its own sake, making provisional use of local divisions. Nothing is more dangerous than to try to find everywhere and at any price, stages established elsewhere, on other scales.

In particular, too many geologists and even prehistorians are led astray by the "theory of levels" of Depéret and De Lamothe, which gives them, without the necessity of special knowledge, too simple and too clear a framework, in which it is always possible to insert every observation. But this theory, as we have seen, is basically invalidated by a radically false idea of the relationship between glaciations and sea levels. Even many of those who knew enough to free themselves from this whole rigid eustatism (and I myself was one of them) often retained an unconscious and deceptive obsession.

However, the great interest of Quaternary geology is precisely that of comparisons between truly geologic phenomena, that is to say, the orogeneses and deformations of the earth's crust, geographic phenomena or the results of external dynamics, erosion and sedimentation, and finally biologic phenomena, which have transformed, through evolution, and mingled, by migrations, animal, plant and human populations. All these different phenomena are unfolded in very different chronologic scales. To understand them, we must adapt ourselves to these different scales and understand the relations between them. Study of the Quaternary gives us this opportunity.

Varved sediments of the northern European and North American Quaternary have allowed us, by their seasonal stratification, to extend our chronologic history back into prehistoric times, and have given us an idea of the number of years that have elapsed since the Scandinavian glacier freed the Gulf of Finland.

The study of oceanic sedimentation, still scarcely touched, already seems to reveal, not annual, seasonal beds, but infinitely longer climatic periods.

In the great depths of the tropical Atlantic,[140] it was possible to try to distinguish pelagic deposits with a warm fauna, characterized by *Globorotalia menardii* d'Orb. and a cold fauna without *G. menardii* but containing *Globi-*

gerina bulloides d'Orb. and *G. inflata* d'Orb. Below a superficial bed (no. 1) with a warm fauna (postglacial) is found a bed with a cold fauna (no. 2, Würmian glaciation) and lastly another warm bed (no. 3, Riss-Würm interglacial epoch). The thickness of these beds is obviously variable at different points of sounding and also with the lithologic nature of the deposits. Assuming, with Schott, that the deposit of bed no. 1 took 20,000 years, the rate of sedimentation of this bed was found to be, in centimeters per 1,000 years:

Blue mud (6 samples)	from .9 to 3.3	Average: 1.78
Mud with *Globigerina* (8 samples)	from .53 to 2.13	Average: 1.2
Red clay (7 samples)	from .5 to 1.33	Average: .86

According to the same author, the rate is about twice as much for bed no. 2, which can be explained by recognizing that terrigenous contributions increase during glacial periods. Thus, climatic epochs, like those of the glacial epochs, are shown by beds whose thicknesses are of the order of a decimeter. But we have seen that many pelagic sediments of different ages (Alpine Jurassic and Cretaceous, for example) display similar regular alternations of more clayey or more calcareous layers, whose thickness, of the order of a decimeter, shows that they cannot be annual beds. Perhaps they belong to climatic periods of a duration similar to that of the Quaternary glacial periods and are explained, for example, by a modification of the regime of currents or of the temperature of the water.

So, a decimeter per 10,000 years at the bottom of the Atlantic, a decimeter per ten years in the Quaternary Baltic (p. 632), a decimeter per year in the glacial lake of Eybens (p. 614), these are the values, whose order of size varies from 1 to 10,000, and for which study of the Quaternary has permitted us to evaluate the rates of sedimentation. We see then how difficult it is to estimate, in a given region, the duration of geologic stages according to the thickness of the sediments representing them.

The importance of erosion is no less variable. When we survey the Breton moors, the plateaus of the Ardennes or the Saharan hammadas, our view covers immense areas over which the covering of Jurassic, Cretaceous and Tertiary sediments must never have exceeded a few hundred, perhaps tens of meters. And since those distant epochs, within these narrow bounds of altitude, surfaces shaped by marine abrasion or continental peneplanation have succeeded each other.

On the other hand, reaching the edge of the French Alps, we see in the plateaus of Lower Dauphiné Pliocene surfaces rising rapidly to neighboring ridges 1,000 m. high. There they are suddenly interrupted, for their prolongation would pass into the air above the highest summits of the region.[141] So, when we are at the bottom of the Arve valley, at St. Gervais (700 m.), at the foot of Mt-Blanc (4,810 m.), we must remind ourselves that this gigantic gorge, 4,000 m. deep, is entirely the work of Quaternary erosion. This does not mean, however, that the Alpine summits were ever much higher than today, for the "wave of intumescence" of the French Alps puffed up slowly enough that erosion had time to destroy the crests of the highest regions as they were being elevated.

And so the study of the Quaternary incites us to analyze more closely the mechanisms of these slow deformations of the earth's crust, to which geologists give the name of epeirogenic movements. Only lately have we learned to recognize their importance even during these recent epochs. These have warped the river terraces of our great valleys. Baulig and Denizot [142] have demonstrated that Rhône terraces sink and plunge beneath the sea upon reaching the Crau [Rhône delta]. According to Fabre[143] the same is true of terraces of the Garonne in Médoc. As Major Stevens[144] recently reported, "the surface of the Norwich Crag (boundary of the Pliocene and Quaternary) today is found above sea level in England, while in Holland, a surface of the same age is found 400 m. below"; that is, nevertheless, a region considered stable, where an epicontinental sea spread over the domain of the old North Atlantic continent.

It was formerly believed that these epeirogenic movements progressed, in the course of geologic time, with majestic slowness and tranquil rhythms, as opposed to orogenic movements proper, whose classification as tempestuous[145] or cataclysmic was granted. Actually the reverse is true, if we wish to reserve the name orogenic movements for deep deformations of hard rocks which produce folded structures.

No parts of the Quaternary formations have had time to acquire such structures. We see them deformed, inclined in their entirety, but never folded internally.[146]

But there again, by an unforeseen detour, the geology of the Quaternary permits us to define and even to translate into mathematical language, the mechanics of these flows.

We recall that the Finnish-Scandinavian Shield, depressed under the weight of the Quaternary glacial sheet, has risen since the melting of the ice in postglacial times.[147] The southern end of the area thus raised passes visibly through Leningrad, the Gulf of Riga, the southern point of Scania and the northern extremity of Jutland. Starting there, the amount of the uplift increases toward the north and reaches its maximum today (275 m.) near the western shores of the Gulf of Bothnia. As we have said earlier, this uplift is not yet ended. It proceeds with a speed which diminishes with time and increases as one leaves the southern edge (.4 m. per century near Helsinki) and approaches the center of the ancient glaciation, that is, the regions formerly most depressed (maximum 1 m. per century at the head of the Gulf of Bothnia). We know here, at least by the order of size, the radius of the depressed area (about 1,000 km.), the maximum amount of the uplift, perhaps about 100 m. in 10,000 years, and finally the average density of the rocks involved (about 2.8). So there, it is a matter of a phenomenon of deformation of the earth's crust, of which we know all the numerical characteristics, of length, mass and time. This slow deformation is not concerned with elasticity nor the rigidity of the rocks (which interfere only in rapid deformation), but only the capacity to flow without rupture, that is, the viscosity. Like all properties of a material, this viscosity is expressed as a function of length, mass and time. So the study of the deformation of the Scandinavian Shield permits geophysicists to calculate the mean viscosity of the rocks (very old and very hard) which make up this shield. This viscosity is of the order of 10^{22} poises.[148]

We can then, with M. King Hubbert, start with these data and calculate, according to the mathematical laws of flow of fluids, the rate at which, under the weight of superposed sediments only, the bed at the base of a rocky cliff 400 m. high would flow. In ten years, this bed would elongate one millionth, and in a million years, one tenth.

Thus a million years becomes the unit of time of the chronological scale we must use to see, under the action of gravity alone, the hardest rocks flow and fold, and the thrust nappes of the great folded chains advance, in short to comprehend the phenomena of the internal dynamics of the earth's crust. On this scale, the phenomena of external dynamics, which develop on the superficial part of this crust, seem like the play of lightning, simple and fugitive scratches which have no relation to the deep and infinitely slow flow of the rock masses.[149]

Finnish, Swedish and North American geologists, who, meticulously and patiently, counted the varves of their clays, followed the morainal arcs in front of the ancient Scandinavian glacier and the Canadian ice sheet, and measured the heights of the littoral fringes of the ancient Baltic and the ancient American Great Lakes, most assuredly do not question that this thankless task produces clearer and more exact ideas concerning the mechanisms of orogenesis than do all the great practitioners of Alpine tectonics. Such is one of the triumphant and unexpected successes of Quaternary geology.

Finally, we now ask what this geology has taught us about the evolution of living creatures, on the continents or in the seas. When we survey the whole assemblage of marine faunas, we find difficulty in distinguishing most of the genera and even many of the species from the Neogene on from their living representatives. A few species have been transformed or disappeared but on the other hand many have migrated and these warm or cold migrants especially have provided our characteristic fossils, since the Miocene. In particular, if I may be permitted to recall personal memories, nothing is more striking than to collect on the old Calabrian shores of southern Italy, sometimes uplifted to an altitude of 1,000 m., hundreds of shells which hardly differ at all from those of the present Mediterranean. In the Calabrian, Sicilian, and Tyrrhenian, the faunas of this old Mediterranean, though contained in beds affected by important earth movements, have undergone only modifications of very subtle nuances, only appreciable because we know the recent faunas to the most minute detail. These nuances would be considered completely negligible in the case of Jurassic or Cretaceous faunas. So, the great paleogeographic events are expressed by migrations rather than by evolution. And in the oldest epochs, the sudden faunal changes, attributed by D'Orbigny to so many successive creations, and those which allow modern paleontologists to define zones and hemerae seem surely due to migrations, not to evolution in place. So, for the time and places where we live, the paleontologists of the future will doubtless adopt as stratigraphic guides a "zone of Doryphore" or a "zone of *Elodea canadensis.*"

In the faunas and continental floras, the role of migrations is still more marked and their rhythm more rapid. Imagine the multiple successions of alternations of cold and warm faunas, since the Pliocene, on French soil; remember the strange *Dinotherium,* which suddenly appeared in the Miocene, so curiously isolated from the environment of the other proboscidians, and which was still living in Africa during the Quaternary (p. 558). This incessant mixing up of animal populations makes the distinction of phylogenetic branches almost indecipherable. To reconstruct the branches, it is quite necessary to admit that comparative anatomy brings more clarity than the stratigraphic succession, so cut up and discontinuous in continental facies.

Thus, since the Primary, it is the sea which has provided bases for our chronology: it is in marine waters that the most regular rhythm has been beating, more universal and slower than the longest hours marked on the dial of our geologic stages; on this continuous and profound background the play of continental life has only embroidered rapid, capricious and often imperceptible variations.

And indeed it is in the depths of the waters that almost all the stratigraphic series which we have described were built up: torrential waters spreading over the deserts and accumulating there prodigiously thick sediments, lagoonal waters or coastal plains in process of sinking, marine waters dispersing afar the muds and sands, and nourishing the submarine prairies of the continental shelves.

We have left to petrographers and experts in tectonics the task of following the recrystallization, folding and metamorphism of the rocks whose genesis we have described. For it is Pluto who rules in the dark depths of the earth's crust, where resounds the harsh rhythm of the hammers of the Niebelungs, forerunners of our modern petrographers. But it is Neptune, god of the waves, whose scepter rules stratigraphy: it is the voices of the waters we have heard rising from the depths of the mountains. And inasmuch as we quoted a clear and precise Mediterranean idea at the beginning of this work, to guide us in reporting observed facts, allow us now to extend these facts using mysterious

R. WAGNER, *Rheingold, IV.*

Nordic symbols which only musical language can interpret. We shall then hear the somber chant of the Earth, the theme of the Nornes, daughters of Hertha, repeating first in a modulated, minor key, then in descending scale, this theme of the waters which, taken up by the daughters of the Rhine in their songs, rises joyously and ripples in the light.

So, the chanting of the waters, which cradled the birth of mountains, also shrouds their destruction. And it is upon the ruins of these successive worlds whose history we have traced—Valhallas born in the depths of the sea and returning thereto, "machines to create Gods" *—that, during the course of the ages, has been erected the immortal reign of the Spirit.

REFERENCE NOTES

1. As reference works on the Quaternary, in addition to the classic textbooks, consult: W. B. Wright, *The Quaternary Ice Age,* London (1914), an extremely charming book to read; H. F. Osborn and Chester A. Reeds, *Old and New Standards of Pleistocene Division in Relation to the Prehistory of Man in Europe,* Bull. Geol. Soc. Amer., 33 (1922); A. P. Coleman, *Ice Ages; Recent and Ancient,* New York (1926), dealing more particularly with North America; A. Mochi, *I sincronismi tra glaciazioni, faune e indus-trie quaternarie,* Archivio per l'Antropologia e l'Etnologia, 57, Florence (1927); P. Woldstedt, *Das Eiszeitalter, Grundlinien eine Geologie des Diluviums,* Stuttgart, Enke (1929), a work containing an excellent restatement of the North European Quaternary, which has largely inspired this work; E. Antevs, *Maps of the Pleistocene Glaciations,* Bull. Geol. Soc. Amer., 40 (1929); R. A. Daly, *The Changing World of the Ice Age,* Yale Univ. Press, New Haven, Conn. (1934).

2. Very recently Joukowski and Gagnebin have shown how, in order to appreciate the relative development in a single period of old glaciers of two neighboring valleys, the extent and altitude of their basins of alimentation must be compared. That is a very interesting method of synchronizing the glacial stages recognized in these two valleys.

3. The mountains of Scotland and Ireland also had their local glaciers, which joined the Scandinavian glacier: J. Kaye Charlesworth, "A Tentative Reconstruction of the Quaternary Ice-sheets in the Region of the North Sea," Proc. R. Irish Acad. 40, sec. B., no. 4 (1931). "Some Observations on the Glaciation of North-East Ireland," Ibid., 45 (1939). For the ancient glaciers of the French Massif Central, see the memoir of J. Jung, cited note 33, chap. 1. The glaciers of the Vosges just managed to reach the edge of these mountains, A. Nordon, *Etude des formes glaciaires et des dépôts glaciaires et fluvio-glaciaires du Bassin de la Haute-Moselle,* Bull. Soc. géol. France, 5 sér., 1 (1931), like those of the Black Forest (Théobald). Neither the Ardennes nor the Rhenish Schiefergebirge could feed glaciers. But the Harz, the Bohemian Forest, and the Ries-engebirge were glaciated. In the Jura, local glaciers were able to resist the attack of the great sheet of ice descending from the Alps. On the Carpathian glaciers, articles by Gadomka, Pawlowski and Klimaszewski will be found in the C. R. of the 3rd Inter. Conference on the Quaternary in Vienna (1938). In Bulgaria, the highest massifs of the Balkan chains exceed the limits of perpetual snow by 700 m., A. Annaheim, *Die Eiszeit im Rila-Gebirge, Bulgarien,* Petermanns Mitt., 85 (1939). Information on the ancient glaciers of the Caucasus will be found in the Guide Books of the Intern. Con-gress of Geol. at Moscow (1937). For the Apennines, see K. Suter, *Les glaciations quaternaires de l'Apennin central,* Revue Géogr. alpine, 28, Grenoble (1940). The gla-ciers of the Pyrenees, H. Alimen, C. R. Acad. Sc., 227 (1948), p. 140, stopped at the outlet of the mountains and those of the Spanish ranges (especially the Sierra Nevada) remained confined near the summits.

4. See the volume by Dainelli, *Studi sul Glaciale,* in the great work cited note 213, chap. 5.

* Translator's note: The author quotes here the celebrated phrase of the spiritual philosopher Bergson: "l'univers est un machine à faire des dieux."

5. R. F. Flint, *The Pleistocene Epoch and Glacial Geology*, J. Wiley, New York (1947).

6. J. Bruggen, *Zur Glazialgeologie der Chilischen Anden*, Geol. Rundschau, 20 (1929).

7. M. Milankovitch, *Astronomische Mittel zur Erforschung der erdegeschichtliche Klimate*, Handbuch der Geophysik, Lief. 3, IX, Berlin (1938). This theory was adopted, *a priori*, by Soergel in Germany, Beck in Switzerland, Choubert in Morocco, etc. Such a method can be dangerous, for it leads to unconscious distortion of the interpretation of observed facts, forcing them to tally with theories not sufficiently justified. Nothing stirs the imagination more than the study of the Quaternary. Thus, F. Heritsch, Geol. Rundschau, 32 (1941), p. 379, analyzing a work by the meteorologist, A. Wagner, seems to agree (p. 382) with the latter that, during the Middle Ages, the Alpine glaciers had almost completely disappeared and that vineyards were then cultivated in England and Normandy.

8. F. Nolke, *Zum Problem der Eiszeiten*, Zeitschr. deutsch. geol. Ges., 93 (1941).

9. A. Penck, *Die Ursachen der Eiszeit*, Sitzungsber. preuss. Akad. Wiss., 6 (1928); *Die Strahlungskurve und die astronomische Zeitrechnung*, Zeitschr. Ges. f. Erdkunde, Berlin (1938). Numerous articles on these questions in Band 34, H. 7–8 (1944), entitled *Diluvial-Geologie und Klima* of the Geol. Rundschau.

10. Pedology is the study of ancient soils (p. 616).

11. An association referred to earlier, p. 42.

12. The early theories on the origin of glacial deposits, formerly attributed to gigantic torrents of running water, also contributed to the birth of this idea of Diluvium.

13. The name terrace, designating a topographic form, should be reserved for the surface of the fill and not applied to the entire mass of alluvium as is sometimes done by foreign geologists. When this surface has been destroyed by later erosion, the word terrace obviously has no meaning. It is the source of frequent ambiguities.

14. See the meticulous analyses made by L. de Lamothe, on the subject of false terraces and by J. E. Chaput on polygenetic terraces. de Lamothe, *Les anciennes nappes alluviales de la Vallée du Rhône en aval de Lyon*, Bull. Soc. géol. France (1921). J. E. Chaput, *Recherches sur les terrasses alluviales de la Seine entre la Manche et Montereau*, Bull. Serv. Carte géol. France, no. 153 (1924); *L'origine des terrasses de la Garonne*, Bull. Soc. géol. France (1924), and especially *Recherches sur l'évolution des terrasses de l'Aquitaine*, Bull. Soc. Hist. nat. Toulouse, 56 (1927).

15. Authors writing in English use the term *eskers,* and the term *kames* when the glacial cavity, filled with alluvium, has a circular or irregular form, rather than ribbon-like.

16. The small Lake of St-André-le-Gaz (Isère), which is found about the middle of the map (Fig. 154), under the letter D of the word Dauphiné, may be a discharge-channel lake.

17. The phenomena due to *dead ice* were the subject of a very suggestive study by S. A. Andersen, "The Waning of the Last Continental Glacier in Denmark as Illustrated by Varved Clay and Eskers," Jour. of Geol., 39, Chicago (1931).

18. Craterlike basins similar to the Sölle have been pointed out, by M. Gignoux and P. Combaz, in the lateral moraines between Rossillon and Virieu (Fig. 154). They were formed there by the dead branch of the Würmian Rhône glacier which left the opening of the Hopitaux pass. E. Gagnebin (note 139, this chap.) has compared these little basins (tubs = marmites in local dialect) which dot the surface of the Würmian ground moraines above Thonon, to Sölle. But probably many of these pot-holes are due to collapses in the Triassic gypsum lying beneath the moraines.

19. Like all physical agents, rivers, winds, seas (compare with statement note 32, Intro.), a glacier destroys or builds. It respects nothing.

20. A. C. Blanc, *Lo Studio stratigrafico di pianure costiere*, Boll. Soc. geol. ital., 54 (1935).

21. We might just as well say: "if the continent is lowered"; because, for the moment, we are considering the result of the *relative* movements of the land and the sea.

22. We must not forget that the latter had an early mathematical training and only tardily became a naturalist.

23. Thus, some years ago, a young geographer confidently found in Corsica not only the Alpine glacial stages of Günz, Mindel, Riss, Würm, Bühl, Gschnitz and Daun, but also the terraces and corresponding old marine shores. And very recently, certain geologists or prehistorians, correlating the "pluvial periods" of Morocco and Portugal with the glacial periods of the Alps (which is by no means proven), have believed they could synchronize the prehistoric stations of these countries with the ancient beaches classified according to the levels of Depéret and de Lamothe.

24. A. Penck, *Eustatische Bewegungen des Meeresspiegels während der Eiszeit,* Geogr. Zeitschr., 39 (1933).

25. G. Dubois, *Essais statistiques sur les états glaciaires quaternaires et les états correspondants du niveau marin,* Ann. de Géogr., 40 (1931).

26. Of course, one must be sure that the terrace of 20 m. is not an erosion terrace modeled in the course of erosion of the mass of the a^1 alluvium, or as is sometimes said, that the a^2 alluvium is well encased in the a^1 alluvium. This is often difficult to recognize.

27. On the contrary, the scales of human industries and of mammalian faunas were obtained in part by using the ordinary stratigraphic methods, based on the superposition of deposits, as for example, in the filling of grottos, caverns or recesses in the rocks.

28. A recent well completed in the alluvial plain 4 km. south of Grenoble, passed through 400 m. of clays (thus descending to 175 m. subsea) without reaching rock, M. Gignoux, C. R. Soc. géol. France (1944), p. 77. Remember that Lake Bourget is 145 m. deep, Lake Geneva, 319 m. and Lake Como, 414 m. In the basin of Sallanches-sur-l'Arvre, a well dug in 1948, to the right of La-Roche-sur-Foron, went through 50 m. of compact clays, etc.

29. His last work is a real geologic Treatise on varves: G. de Geer, *Geochronologia suecica principles,* Kungl. svenska Vet. Akad. Handling, 3. ser., 18, Stockholm (1940), no. 6, 360 p., 53 pl., 65 fig., Atlas 37 pl. A brief and clear summary in E. Brückner, *Geologische Untersuchungen über die Dauer der Postglazialzeit in Schweden, in Finnland und in Nordamerika,* Zeitschr. f. Gletscherkunde, 12 (1921).

30. These elementary varves have sometimes been confused with seasonal beds giving rise to errors committed, for example, in Denmark (see article by Andersen, cited note 17, this chap.). Likewise A. P. Coleman, "Long Range Correlation of Varves," Jour. of Geol., 37, Chicago (1929) has corrected proposed correlations between European and American glaciations.

31. M. Schwartzbach, *Das diluviale Klima während des Höchstandes einer Vereisung, ermittelt aus den Tageswarwen der Bändertone,* Zeitschr. deutsch. geol. Ges., 92 (1940). The qualification, daily varves (Tagewarwen), used by the author, truly seems far too definite.

32. See L. W. Collet, article cited note 44, chap. 1. Another example in E. M. Kindle, "Sedimentation in a Glacial Lake," Jour. of Geol., 38, Chicago (1930).

33. See W. Soergel, *Löss, Eiszeiten und paläolithische Kulturen,* Jena (1919); *Das Eiszeitalter,* Jena (1938); and especially the study by Vera Malycheff, *Le Loess,* in course of publication since 1929 in the Revue de Géogr. phys. et de Géol. dynamique; these contain abundant documentation on all European deposits. On the origin of the word loess, see H. Quiring, *Herkunft, Aussprache und Schreibung des Wortes "Löss,"* Zeitschr. deutsch. geol. Ges., 88 (1936).

34. In northern France, altered loess is known as *terre à briques.* For true, pure loess, not clayey, cannot be used for the manufacture of bricks. In North America, clayey rocks resulting from alteration of loess have been studied especially under the name *gumbotil.*

35. In these cases of ascending circulations, the oxidation of the mass of loess progresses from bottom to top. Perhaps for that reason, much old loess is uniformly altered throughout, from the bottom.

36. On the formation and alteration of loess in relation to climates, see especially F. Münichsdorfer, *Der Löss als Bodenbildung,* Geol. Rundschau, 17 (1926).

37. This same contrast between regions of aeolian accumulation and erosion is found in present deserts in tropical zones between rocky (hamada) or alluvial (reg) regions and dune regions (ergs): the hamadas and regs nourish the ergs.

38. As seen today in the border of Greenland's ice sheet. W. H. Hobbs, "Loess, Pebble Bands and Boulders from Glacial Outwash of the Greenland Continental Glacier," Jour. of Geol., 39 (1931).

39. Of course, there is no reason why this loess facies should be peculiar to the Quaternary. For example, we mentioned the probable existence of ancient loess in Devonian Old Red Sandstone (see p. 113). There, too, this facies appeared related to steppe or sub-desertic conditions. True loess has also been shown in the continental red sandstones of the Upper Cretaceous of Buenos Aires, cf. W. Schiller, Geol. Rundschau, 12, p. 364 (1922). Likewise in the Karroo beds (Permo-Triassic) of South Africa, in the Upper Cretaceous of Mongolia, etc.

40. See Tang-Yuet Suen, Le loess de la vallée du Rhône, Thèse Lettres, Lyon (1934).

41. The loess of the Paris vicinity was studied by V. Agafonoff and M. Malycheff, Le loess et les autres limons du plateau de Villejuif, Bull. Soc. géol. France, 4 sér., 29 (1929).

42. Formerly, Penck and Brückner (work cited note 96, this chap.) considered western and central European loess as dating interglacial periods. This opinion is universally abandoned today.

43. V. Laskarev, Sur le loess des environs de Belgrade, Ann. géol. de la Péninsule balkanique, 7 (1922) and 8 (1924). Interesting photographs.

44. See article by F. Bourdier (1947) cited note 121, this chap.

45. On the coasts of Calvados, at Saint-Come de Fresné, L. Guillaume, C. R. Soc. géol. France (1932), p. 119, described glauconitic sands with Modiola modiolus, a northern species, which has now disappeared from the Channel.

46. See M. Gignoux, works cited note 6, chap. 10.

47. E. Tamajo, Il piano Siciliano e le sue relazioni paleontologiche col Calabriano in base allo studio di un nuovo giacimento del bacino di Palermo, Boll. Soc. geol. ital., 56 (1937). M. Gignoux, Monographie, au point de vue des faciès et de la bathymétrie, de deux gisements quaternaires italiens, Palerme et Tarente, C. R. Congrès Soc. savantes à Grenoble en 1913, p. 13, Paris (1914).

48. G. Ruggieri, Terrazzi quaternari e faune siciliane nel golfo di Squillace, Giorn. di Geol., s. 2, 15, Bologna (1941).

49. A. C. Blanc, Giacimento sottomarino a "Cyprina islandica L." nel golfo di Terranova Pausania (Sardegna), Rendic. R. Acad. naz. d. Lincei, Cl. Sc. fis. e nat., 22, ser. 6 (1936).

50. Later dredging was done by J. Bourcart, C. R. Acad. Sc. 224 (1947), p. 1175.

51. We refer only to recent paleontologic studies by A. Bevilacqua, Studi sulla fauna fossile marina pliocenica e quaternaria dell'Isola di Rodi (Egeo), Atti. Soc. Sc. nat. Milano, 67 (1928), and by G. Vecchi, Studi sulla fauna fossile marina pliocenica e quaternaria dell'Isola di Cos (Egeo), Boll. Soc. geol. ital., 52 (1934). In this island of Cos, the Tyrrhenian is surely represented. It would be extremely interesting to study the stratigraphy of these regions.

52. General information in A. C. Blanc and E. Tongiorgi, Appunti di Ecologia quaternaria. Il Tirreniano, Boll. Comit. glaciologico ital., 18 (1938), and in G. Denizot, Observations sur le Quaternaire moyen de la Méditerranée occidentale et sur la signification du terme de Monastirien, Bull. Soc. géol. France, 5 (1935).

53. G. Checchia-Rispoli, Appunti di echinologia fossile siciliana, Boll. Soc. Geol. ital., 57 (1938), found, in the Tyrrhenian beds with Strombus of the Isle of Favignana, Echinolampas hoffmanni, an echinoid genus which was believed to be extinct in our seas after the Sicilian. But the question may be raised whether it did not come from Sicilian beds existing there beneath the Tyrrhenian.

54. See M. Gignoux, work cited note 47, this chap.

55. P. Leonardi, I Molluschi pleistocenici della Barma grande, "I Balzi Rossi," parte II, Fauna; Ist. ital. di Pal. umana, Florence (1935), a particularly interesting monograph.

56. A. C. Blanc, Una spiaggia pleistocenica a Strombus bubonius presso Palidoro (Roma). E. Maury, Sur une terrasse marine de la côte Sud-Ouest de la Corse, C. R. Soc. géol. France (1937), p. 188; a terrace of 10–15 m. with a large Senegalian Conus (C. testudinarius) between Ajaccio and Bonifacio. A. Chavan, Sur un dépot pléistocène

à Cardium près de Gruissan, Aude, ibid. (Feb. 5, 1945) reported a large mussel with Senegalian affinities (*Mytilus perna* L. = *afer* Gmel.) in a low coastal deposit near those where Doncieux collected *Tapes dianae* (see Narbonne sheet, 1/80,000). R. Lafitte, *Plissements post-pliocènes et mouvements quaternaires dans l'Algérie occidentale,* C. R. Acad. Sc., 215 (1942), p. 372.

57. References in a general work by R. Vaufrey, *Le Paléolithique italien,* Archives Inst. Paléont. humaine, no. 3 (1928).

58. T. de Stefani, *L'evoluzione biologica e geografica della Sicilia dall' inizio del Quaternario ad oggi,* Il Naturalisto Sicil., ser. 3, ann. 3, Palermo (1946).

59. C. Depéret, C. R. Acad. Sc. (Feb. 10, Mar. 3, April 7, 1913).

60. As G. Lecointre has sensibly remarked, it is obviously strange that the Senegalian *Strombus* (*S. bubonius*) has never been found on the Moroccan coasts, the connecting link between Senegal and the Mediterranean. Must we believe that these coasts have everywhere subsided since the Tyrrhenian?

61. So it is that the quite rich Milazzo deposit on the northeast coast of Sicily, although it may have been deposited in a sea about 60 m. above the present sea, contains no characteristic species. It is thus unjustifiable to select it, as has been done, for the type of a Milazzian stage, a term originated by C. Depéret but which should be deleted from stratigraphic nomenclature. I am in a good position to speak of this, for I am the only geologist who had occasion to show this Milazzo deposit to Depéret. The same is true for Depéret's Monastirian, whose fauna is in no way different from that of the Tyrrhenian. As for the term Normannian, proposed by L. Dangeard, *Sur la définition d'un étage Normannien,* C. R. Soc. géol. France (May 18, 1936) "to replace the Monastirian" and to designate certain Quaternary formations of the Norman coasts, it has no paleontologic basis either and can have only a purely local significance.

62. Remember that many foreign and some French (E. Haug) geologists still attribute to the Quaternary, by definition, the fauna with *E. meridionalis.* It seems more natural to leave it (with M. Boule and C. Depéret) in the Pliocene, for in many Mediterranean countries (France, Italy) this fauna appears at the top of the Pliocene sedimentary cycle (Villafranchian = Calabrian).

63. C. Arambourg, *L'Elephas recki* Dietrich; *sa position systématique et ses affinités,* Bull. Soc. géol. France, 12 (1942). Here will be found (p. 87) a table summarizing the author's ideas on the phylogeny of Pliocene and Quaternary elephants and the origin of *E. primigenius, africanus, indicus.*

64. P. Wernert, *La station paléolithique d'Achenheim dans le cadre des formations pléistocènes de la vallée du Rhin,* Bull. Ass. philomathique Alsace et Lorraine, 8, 4 (1937); Revue Géogr. phys. et Géol. dynam., 11 (1938), showing a fault affecting the old loess with an offset of 6 and perhaps 14 m. Much information on the Alsatian loess in the thesis by J. Franc de Ferrière, *Contribution à l'étude de la Géologie et de la Pédologie des formations quaternaires de la Plaine d'Alsace,* Impr. alsac., Strasbourg (1937).

65. See also the monograph cited note 55, this chap.

66. G. A. Blanc, *Sulla presenza di Alca impennis Linn, nella formazione pleistocenica superiore di Grotta Romanelli in Terra d'Otranto,* Arch. per l'Antropol. e l'Etnolog., 58, Florence (1927).

67. R. Vaufrey, *Le Mammouth et le Rhinocéros à narines cloisonnées en Italie méridionale,* Bull. Soc. géol. France, 4 sér., 27 (1927).

68. V. Laskarev, *Troisième Note sur le Quaternaire des environs de Beograd,* Ann. géol. Péninsule balkanique, 15 (1938).

69. D. Geyer, *Paludina diluviana, eine ökologische und geologische Untersuchung,* Jahrb. preuss, geol. Landesanst., A (1931), 52.

70. A history of French floras in the Quaternary was published by J. Braun-Blanquet, Ann. Soc. linn. Lyon, 68 (1921). See also, by the same author, *L'Origine et le développement des flores dans le Massif central,* Librairie Lhomme (Paris). Finally, remember the article by Depape cited note 8, chap. 10.

71. We mention only the celebrated tufas of La Celle-sous-Moret, between Melun and Montereau, whose base is 15 m. and whose top is 30 m. above the Seine. They have yielded a warm flora, including the fig, the Judas tree (*Cercis siliquastrum*), and box-

wood. They contain Acheulean flints and are overlain by limons with Mousterian flints.

72. K. Faegri, *Heterodokse tanken om pollenanalysen,* Geol. Fören., Stockholm, 69, 55–56 (1947), criticizes the value of pollen analyses.

73. The most recent discoveries of fossil men are summarized by L. Moret, *Manuel de Paléontologie animale,* 2nd edit. (1948). See also the excellent little volume by C. Arambourg, *La Genèse de l'Humanité,* Presses univ., Paris (1943).

74. H. Breuil, *Le gisement de Chelles; ses phénomènes, ses industries,* Quartär, Band 2, Berlin (1939). Flints of the Chellean type being found, even at Chelles, worked over in the more recent gravels, H. Breuil proposed replacing the term Chellean by that of Abbevillian (from Abbeville, on the Somme).

75. On the Ice Age of the British Isles, which we do not discuss, see the article of J. Kaye Charlesworth (1931), cited note 3, this chap.

76. S. von Bubnoff, *Das Quartär in Russland* (Geol. Rundschau, 21, 1930). H. Spreitzer, *Die Eiszeitforschung in der Sowjetunion,* Quartär, 3, Berlin (1941). V. I. Gromov, *Les principaux résultats de l'étude du Quaternaire depuis 25 ans en U.R.S.S.,* Bull. Acad. Sc. U.R.S.S., Geol. (1943), 3, in Russian with English summary.

77. A. A. Kolokolov and K. A. Lvov, *Traces de glaciations dans l'Oural méridional,* Bull. Soc. géogr. U.R.S.S. (1945), 77, in Russian.

78. P. D. Krynine, *Pleistocene Glaciation of Siberia,* Amer. Journ. of Sc., 5th ser., 34, no. 203 (1937).

79. In the present polar regions, the eternally frozen subsoil constitutes an impermeable substratum, at slight depth (called "tjale" in Scandinavian countries), which prevents the surface water from infiltrating (swampy plains = tundras). During the summer, this surface earth thus impregnated with water becomes, when it is horizontal, the seat of rising, turbulent currents (*Brodelböden* = bubbling soil), the mechanics of which are still obscure, but which in any case give rise to very peculiar structures (polygonal soils, found in our high mountains, see M. Gignoux, Trav. Lab. Géol. Univ. Grenoble, 20 1936). When inclined, the whole mass of earth flows like fluid lava. This is *solifluction,* a simple exaggeration of the general and slower phenomenon of "creeping of ground" which happens even in our climate. Milon, Dangeard, Bigot, Breuil, etc., have attributed to solifluction certain peculiarities of the structure of Quaternary deposits in our regions (Normandy, for example). And lately Dutch geologists especially (Edelman) have studied the phenomena of "cryoturbation" due to freezing of soils.

80. P. W. Thomson, *Die Klima- und Waldentwicklung des von K. Orviku entdeckten Interglazials von Ringen (Röngu) bei Dorpat (Tartu), Estland,* Zeitschr. deutsch. geol. Ges., 93 (1941).

81. A. Schreuder, *The Tegelen Fauna, with a Description of New Remains of its Rare Components,* Arch. neerland. Zool. (1945), 7.

82. R. Tavernier, *L'âge des argiles de la Campine,* Bull. Soc. belge Géol. (1942), 51.

83. W. Soergel, *Unter welchen klimatischen Verhältnissen lebten zur Bildungszeit der altdiluvialen Kiese von Süssenborn* Rangifer, Ovibos und Elephas trogontherii *im Mittel- und Norddeutschland?* Zeitschr. deutsch. geol. Ges., 91 (1939), p. 828.

84. H. O. Grahle, *Die Ablagerungen der Holstein-See (Mar. Intergl. I), ihre Verbreitung, Fossilführung und Schichtenfolge in Schleswig-Holstein,* Abhandl. preuss. geol. Landesanst., n. F., H. 172 (1936); paleogeographic map.

85. K. D. Jorgensen, *Marint Pliocaen (?) ved Esbjerg,* Medd. dansk geol. Foren. (1944), 10, no. 4.

86. H. Wehrli, *Interglaziale und vor-saaleeiszeitliche Ablagerungen in der Münsterschen Bucht,* Zeitschr. deutsch. geol. Ges., 93 (1941).

87. R. Kräusel, *Pflanzenreste aus den diluvialen Ablagerungen in Ruhr-Emscher-Lippe-Gebiete,* Verhandl. Naturhist. Ver. Rheinlande und Westphalens, 95, A. Geol. Abt., Bonn (1937).

88. This is at least the opinion of Wollstedt. Others, on the contrary, see there an independent glaciation. H. Neumann, *Die Gliederung des Diluviums des Altmoränenlandschaft Schleswig-Holsteins und der südlich angrenzenden Gebiete,* Schriften geol. Inst. Univ. Kiel (1933).

89. K. Jessen and V. Milthers, *Stratigraphical and Paleontological Studies of Inter-*

glacial Fresh-water Deposits in Jutland and Northwest Germany, Danmarks geol. Undersögelse, 2 Raekke, Nr. 48 (1928); numerous examples of "pollen diagrams."

90. V. Nordmann, *La position stratigraphique des dépôts d'Eem,* Danmarks geol. Undersögelse, 2 Raekke, Nr. 47 (1928). For everything concerning the Danish Quaternary, see the general work cited note 74, chap. 8.

91. V. Zans, *Das letzinterglaziale Portlandia-Meer des Baltikums,* Bull. Comm. géol. Finlande, no. 115 (1936).

92. It is likewise from this interglacial that a skull of *Homo steinheimensis* dates, found in 1933 in a gravel quarry at Steinheim a. d. Murr, presenting more advanced characteristics than those of the Neanderthal race, although it is doubtless older. In fact, molars of *Elephas antiquus* have been found at 1 to 20 m. above the skull. F. Berckheimer, *Der Urmenschenschädel aus den zwischeneiszeitlichen Fluss-Schottern von Steinheim an der Murr,* Forschungen und Forschritte, 12, Jahrg., no. 28, Berlin (1936).

93. For Scandinavian geologists, on the contrary, the Postglacial naturally commences later (see legend of Fig. 149). The fundamental work is by Matti Sauramo, *The Quaternary Geology of Finland,* Bull. Comm. geol. Finlande, no. 86 (1929). We have borrowed Fig. 153 from it. Note that G. Dubois has applied the old name Flandrian to the whole period following the Brandenburg stage. A full bibliography will be found in his *Tableau de l'Europe flandrienne,* Livre jub. du Centenaire de la Soc. géol. France (1930).

94. These upheavals enter into the category of movements called isostatic. In fact, isostasy is the obvious law according to which the weight per unit of surface of the earth's crust down to a surface of equilibrium (or of isostatic compensation), which certainly exists at an unknown depth, must always remain the same. An excess of ice on a given portion of the crust thus destroys this isostatic equilibrium which is then progressively reestablished by isostatic movements, with a delay due to the viscosity of the fluids constituting the bottom of the crust.

95. See M. Sauramo, *Der Anteil der eustatischen Komponente an den Niveauverschiebungen in Fennoskandia,* Fennia, 50, no. 10, Helsinki (1928); *Zur spätquartären Geschichte der Ostsee, vorläufige Mitteilung,* Soc. geol. Finlande, no. 8 (1934); Figs. 151 and 152 are borrowed from the latter article, with the kind permission of the author; *The Mode of the Land Upheaval in Fennoscandia During Late-Quaternary Time,* ibid., no. 13 (1939); *Kvartärgeologische studien i östra Fennoskandia,* Geol. Fören. Förenhandl. (1942), 64.

96. The fundamental work always remains that by Penck and Brückner, *Die Alpen im Eiszeitalter.* Translations of the chapters relative to the French Alps have appeared in the Trav. Lab. Géol. Univ. Grenoble, t. 8 and 9. Under the auspices of the International Association for the Study of the Quaternary, *Literatur zur alpinen Eiszeitforschung* was published in the Zeitschr. f. Gletscherkunde.

97. E. De Martonne, *L'ancien delta du Var et les vallées des Alpes-Maritimes,* Ann. de Géogr., 32 (1923).

98. David Martin, *Les glaciers quaternaires des bassins de la Durance et du Var,* Bull. Soc. d'études des Hautes-Alpes, Gap (1926). R. Blanchard, *Les phases du glacier de la Durance à Sisteron,* Revue de Géogr. alpine, 16, Grenoble (1928).

99. M. Piroutet, *Les différentes phases glaciaires dans le Jura salinois,* Bull. Soc. géol. France, 4 sér., 25 (1925).

100. V. Norarese, *Il Quaternario in Val d'Aosta e nelle valli del Canavese,* Boll. R. Comit. geol. d'Italia, 42 (1911), 44 (1913–14), 45 (1916); *Gli apparati morenici wurmiani del Lago Maggiore e del Lago d'Orta,* id., 52 (1927). S. Venzo, *Rilevamento geomorfologico dell' apparato morenico dell' Adda di Lecco,* Atti Soc. ital. Sc. Nat., 7 (1948). G. Nangeroni, *Studi recenti sul morenico quaternario delle Alpi italiane,* Atti XIV Cong. geogr. ital., p. 146; a summary of recent studies up to and including 1947.

101. Observation of present glaciers shows that none is actually stable: their whole existence is passed in growth and decrease.

102. Example: contrasts between the valley of the Durance below and above Sisteron, between the valley of the Isère below and above the region of St-Marcellin-Rovon, etc.

103. This is valid, of course, only in regions near glacial fronts. In the downstream parts of the great river valleys, the terraces correspond, on the contrary, to the maxima

of the old sea levels, thus (p. 612) to interglacial periods. Up to the present, it has not been possible to establish, for any large valley, a complete synthesis showing the relations between the systems of glacial terraces upstream and marine terraces downstream.

104. J. Murr, *Neue Ubersicht über die fossile Flora der Höttinger Breccie*, Jahrb. geol. Bundesanst., 76 (1926). H. Gams, *Die Flora der Höttinger Breccie*, Führer zu den Quartärexkursion in Österreich, 2, Teil, Vienna (1936).

105. V. Novarese, *L'età delle filliti di Rè in Val Vigezzo (Ossola)*, Atti R. Accad. Sc. Torino (June 12, 1927). This author considers these deposits as simply "inter-stage," post-Würmian.

106. *Die diluvialen Schieferkohlen der Schweiz*, Monograph by several authors, Beitr. geol. Karte d. Schweiz, geotechnische Ser., 8 Lief. (1923).

107. See also W. U. Guyan and H. Stauber, *Die zwischeneiszeitlichen Kalktuffe von Flurlingen (Kt. Zürich)*, Eclogae geol. Helvetiae, 34 (1941).

108. These are names of tributaries of the Danube (near Ulm) which cross the plateaus formed by ancient terraces. The alphabetic order of the names reproduces the order of age of the glacial periods.

109. H. Wehrli, *Monographie der interglazialen Ablagerungen im Bereich der nördlichen Ostalpen zwischen Rhein und Salzach*, Jahrb. geol. Bundesanst. 78, Vienna (1928).

110. B. Eberl, *Zur Gliederung und Zeitrechnung des alpinen Glazials*, Zeitschr. deutsch. geol. Ges., 80 (1928). J. Knauer, *Glazialgeologische Ergebnisse aus dem Isargletschergebiet*, ibid.

111. A. Penck, *Die Höttinger Breccie und die Inntalterrasse nördlich Innsbruck*, Abhandl. preuss. Akad. Wiss., 1920, Berlin (1921).

112. H. Katschthaler, *Neue Beobachtungen im Gelände der Höttinger Breccie*, Jahrb. geol. Bundesanst., 80 (1930).

113. Albert Heim, *Geologie der Schweiz*, I, Leipzig (1919). P. Beck, *Ueber das schweizerische und europäische Pliozän und Pleistozän*, Eclogae geol. Helvetiae, 26 (1933). The same author presented a summary in the *Guide géologique de la Suisse* (work cited note 62, chap. 6); finally, in his *Studien über das Quartärklima im Lichte astronomischer Berechnungen (Schluss)*, Eclogae geol. Helvetiae, 31 (1938), the author, who adopts the "climatic curve of Milankovitch" (p. 605), as a basis of his syntheses, has greatly modified his earlier ideas, certain of which were obviously subversive (Günzian and Mindelian considered as prior to the marine Pliocene of the Rhône valley and the plain of the Po).

114. For these moraines gully the *Hochterrassenschotter* while the Riss of Penck is connected, in the fluvio-glacial systems, with the high terrace of this author.

115. More recently, the Drachenloch cave, 2400 m. above Vättis northwest of Coire (Grisons), has also provided a Mousterian industry. See E. Bächler, *Das Drachenloch ob Vättis im Taminatal und seine Bedeutung als paläontologische Fundstätte*, Bull. Soc. Sc. nat. de St-Gall, 57 (1921). Also, in the French Alps, the cave of the Eugles, 1200 m. above St-Laurent-du-Pont (Chartreuse), yielded flints to H. Müller which were deemed Mousterian by A. Breuil and F. Bourdier.

116. A. Briquet, *Le Quaternaire de l'Alsace*, Bull. Soc. géol. France, 30 (1930).

117. P. Macar, *Sur une faille affectant la terrasse principale de la Meuse à Lanaye*, Bull. Soc. géol. Belgique, 70 (1946–1947), p. B. 25, recently described a fault (post-Rissian?) with 6 m. offset.

118. N. Théobald, *Carte de la base des formations alluviales dans le Sud du fossé rhénan*, Mém. Serv. Carte géol. Alsace et Lorraine, no. 9 (1948).

119. C. Mordziol, *Beiträge zur "Fluvialstratigraphie." 3. Hochterrasse und Talwegterrasse im Rahmen des Diluvialphänomens*, Senckenbergiana, 21, Frankfurt a. M. (1939).

120. L. Rüger, *Ein Lebensbild von Mauer*, Badische geol. Abhandl., Jahrg. 3 (1931).

121. According to C. Depéret, *L'histoire fluviale et glaciaire de la vallée du Rhône aux environs de Lyon*, C. R. Acad. Sc. (Oct. 6, 1913). W. Kilian and M. Gignoux, *Les formations filluvio-glaciaires du Bas-Dauphiné*, Bull. Carte géol. France, no. 129 (1911); *Les fronts glaciaires et les terrasses entre Lyon et la vallée de l'Isère*, Ann. Univ. Gre-

noble, 28 (1916). See also the Lyon, 2nd edit., and Grenoble, 3rd edit., sheets of the *Carte géol. de France,* 1/80,000 and the work by F. Roman cited note 146, chap. 5. More recent works (especially by J. B. Martin) are mentioned by G. Denizot, *Observations sur la glaciation quaternaire et les terrasses de la région lyonnaise,* Bull. Soc. géol. France, 5 sér., 3 (1933), who develops rather different ideas from those of his predecessors. In what follows, we are largely inspired particularly by the recent works of F. Bourdier, who has modified our early ideas on many important points: F. Bourdier, *Nouvelles observations sur l'extension des anciens glaciers dans la basse vallée de l'Isère,* C. R. Acad. Sc. (Jan. 25, 1937); *Les moraines du Würm, du Riss, et du Mindel en Bas-Dauphiné, leurs caractères distinctifs et leurs corrélations probables avec certains dépôts à industrie humaine,* ibid., 208 (1939), p. 530; *Les caractères distinctifs de chaque glaciation alpine d'après les couvertures de loess et les sols d'altération,* in "La Géologie des terrains recents dans l'W de l'Europe," Extraordinary session of the Belgian Societies of Geology, Sept. 19–26, 1946, Brussels (1947).

122. Even more clear, in the opinion of foreign visitors, than the type regions of Bavaria where the Riss and the Würm were defined.

123. First studied by W. Kilian, then by R. Blanchard, *Le seuil de Rives,* Zeitschr. f. Gletscherkunde, 6, Berlin (1912).

124. From every point of view, it is comparable to the Warthe phase, described in Northern Germany.

125. The relationships and the nomenclature of terraces and moraines indicated here follow the interpretations of F. Bourdier and are also close to those of Penck and Brückner; but they are very different from the solutions proposed by W. Kilian and M. Gignoux and inscribed on the latest editions of the Grenoble and St-Etienne sheets, 1/80,000. That shows that even in typical regions, the interpretation of surface forms often remains very uncertain.

126. At St. Vallier, south of Vienne, some hardened loess (p. 615) contains a magnificent deposit of Villafranchian mammals (*Mastodon arvenensis, Elephas, Equus, Leptobos, Machairodus,* etc.) discovered by L. Doncieux (St-Etienne sheet, 1/80,000) and recently excavated by F. Bourdier and J. Viret, C. R. Acad. Sc., 227 (1948), p. 684. If loess is considered to be truly characteristic of glacial periods, here would be proof that the oldest glaciations began in the latest Pliocene, if we leave the Villafranchian in the Pliocene.

127. This distinction of Mindel altered to bright red, Riss altered to brown or yellow and Würm remaining grey, is found, feature for feature, in the morainal amphitheatre of Adda (Lake Como), sections of which, completely analogous to those of Bièvre-Valloire, have recently been published by Venzo (work cited note 100, this chap.).

128. These refractory earths, which here are very close to the exploited Eocene earths in the vicinity of Vercors, are surely post-Miocene at Châteauneuf d'Isère.

129. Here, just as in Switzerland, in the frontal region, no clearly interglacial formation separating the external from the internal moraines is known. Penck and Brückner cited as such a bed of loess at Jons, near Jonage, east of Lyon, intercalated between two moraines. In fact, at that time, they considered loess to be an interglacial deposit; but since then, it is generally agreed that loess was deposited during glacial periods. An intercalation of loess thus indicates only a slight oscillation of the glacial front.

130. Comparable to an Urstromtal of northern Germany.

131. One of these blocks called the *Gros Caillou* [large stone], 2 to 3 m. in diameter, preserved in the gardens of the Red Cross, is composed of Triassic quartzite originating in the internal Alpine zones, thus from upper Valais.

132. In these conglomerates on the banks of the Saône south of Lyon (Quai des Etroits), is excavated the famous "cave of J. J. Rousseau," the setting for a romantic nocturnal dream inspiring a page which has become classic.

133. Through similarity to the "intermediary moraines" (La Côte-St-André phase) distinguished in Bièvre by W. Kilian and M. Gignoux, C. Depéret believed he could also identify in the plains near Lyon, traces of a pre-Würmian glacial still-stand, dating from a time when the glacier no longer surmounted the Dombes plateau. To this glacial period he first gave the name Neoriss. Later, he qualified it as Riss, his former Riss having become his Mindel. Such is the nomenclature adopted on the 2nd edition of the Lyon

sheet, 1/80,000. Today, Lyon geologists unanimously agree that it is truly impossible to distinguish frontal moraines there. They are, rather, drumlins of the Rissian glacier.

134. P. Lory attributed some of these deposits to an interphase period, posterior to the Würm maximum and previous to a phase of contraction of the Würm, which he called Eybens phase and which Kilian called Neowürmian. See W. Kilian, *Contribution à l'histoire de la vallée du Rhône, à l'époque pléistocène. Le défilé du Fort-de-l'Ecluse (Ain)*, Zeitschr. f. Gletscherkunde, 6, Berlin (1911); *Sur les "seuils de débordement" glaciaires et sur une phase importante dans la succession des oscillations glaciaires dans les Alpes françaises*, Bull. Soc. géol. France, 4th sér., 11 (1911).

135. For the whole Grenoble-Chambéry region, see the *Géologie dauphinoise* by M. Gignoux and L. Moret. The Quaternary is studied there in detail as objectively as possible. In particular, references will be found to the numerous publications of P. Lory.

136. However, some geologists (P. Lory) consider that the whole series of Champagnier dates from a stage of retreat of the Würm. The lower moraine could thus be early Würmian.

137. See M. Gignoux and F. Bourdier, C. R. Acad. Sc., 204, pp. 212 and 310.

138. Recent works by J. Favre, E. Joukowsky and H. Lagotala are mentioned in A. Jayet, *Sur la présence de terrains glaciaires anciens et interglaciaires dans la partie Nord du Canton de Genève*, Eclogae geol. Helvetiae, 22 (1929).

139. Region studied by Charles Jacob, W. Kilian, then by E. Gagnebin, *Les terrains quaternaires des environs de Thonon (Haute-Savoie)*, Eclogae geol. Helvetiae, 26 (1933).

140. C. W. Correns, *Die Sedimente des aequatorialen Atlantischen Ozeans; Wissenschaftliche Ergebnisse der deutschen Atlantischen Expedition auf dem Forschungs- und Vermessungsschiff "Meteor," 1925–1927*, De Gruyter and Co., Berlin and Leipzig (1935–37). W. Schott, *Ueber die Sedimentationsgeschwindigkeit rezenter Tiefseesedimente*, Geol. Rundschau, 29 (1938). von Bubnoff, *Rythmen, Zyklen and Zeitrechnung in der Geologie*, ibid., 35, 1 (1947). I cannot yet use the very important results obtained from the submarine cores of Swedish oceanographers. See H. Petersson, Geogr. Journ., CX, 4–6 (Dec. 1947).

141. Thus it is quite incorrect, it seems to me, for certain geographers to try to find Pliocene erosion surfaces some hundreds of meters above the bottoms of our intra-Alpine valleys.

142. Work cited note 21, chap. 10.

143. A. Fabre, *Les terrains de revêtement du Médoc*, Bordeaux, Impr. Drouillard (1939).

144. C. Stevens, *Considérations sur l'origine de la mer flamande*, Ann. Soc. géol. Belgique, 62 (1938–1939). In comparison with movements of similar amplitude, we see how slight becomes the importance of the "eustatic" episode which the "Flandrian transgression" represents (note 93, this chap.).

145. M. Lugeon, *Trois tempêtes orogéniques; la Dent de Morcles*, Livre jub. Soc. géol. France (1930).

146. R. Lafitte, *Plissements pliocènes et mouvements quaternaires dans l'Algérie occidentale*, C. R. Acad. Sc., 215 (1942), p. 372, and article cited note 94, chap. 10.

147. The history of the Canadian Shield during the glacial period was identical with that of the Scandinavian Shield. There also the whole northern part of the North American Continent was depressed under the weight of the glacial ice sheet, then rose and has continued to rise since this sheet began to melt. During the last glacial period (called Wisconsin), the Great Lakes were barred toward the north by the glacial front, along which stretched great lacustrine areas, Lakes Algonquin and Nipissing. Traces of their old shores rise progressively to the north, where they are found at a maximum altitude of 1,500 ft. above Hudson Bay. This upheaval, not yet ended, is shown, between the northern and southern extremities of Lake Michigan, a distance of perhaps 100 miles, by a change in relative elevation of 1 foot in 100 years, a change which, at the southern end of Hudson Bay, reaches 6 feet per century.

This parallelism in the history of the Quaternary of Northern Europe and America constitutes a truly impressive proof of the explanations based on glacial overloading and unloading in these two regions.

148. The *poise* is the c.g.s. unit of viscosity. To evaluate these ideas, let us recall the magnitudes of the viscosity (variable with temperature and pressure) of a few substances: water, 10^{-2}; lubricating oil, 1; honey, 40; asphalt, 10^7.

149. See the studies by Blondel and de Maillet and Pavans de Ceccaty, mentioned in M. Gignoux, *Méditations sur la théorie de l'écoulement par gravité*, Trav. Lab. Géol. Univ. Grenoble, 27 (1948) and especially M. King Hubbert, *Strength of the Earth*, Bull. Amer. Ass. Pet. Geol. 29, no. 11 (1945), a very clear and suggestive study to which we have had recourse in writing these lines. The very interesting tests of experimental tectonics on a reduced model carried out by D. Griggs, "A Theory of Mountain Building," Amer. Journ. Sc., 237, no. 9 (1939) are summarized in the classic textbook of A. Holmes, *Principles of Physical Geology*, Nelson, London (1947) and in M. Gignoux, *La tectonique d'écoulement par gravité et la structure des Alpes*, Bull. Soc. géol. France, 5, 18 (1949), p. 739.

Index

The Index is necessarily limited to the listing of geographic names, stages, formations, some stratigraphic and other geologic terms, and some large biologic units (such as fish and fusulinids).

For some countries, such as France and the United States, all references are distributed among smaller units, such as Ardennes, Alsace, and Appalachians. For other countries, such as Italy and Spain, some references are listed under these heads but others are to be found under smaller units, such as Apennines, Apulia, or Meseta.

General terms, such as facies or lacuna, are mostly represented by references to the Introduction only.

Boldface numbers refer to pages where names appear on Maps or in other Figures.